Key

ECUADOR

PACIFIC OCEAN

COLOMBIA

PERU

ESMERALDAS

CARCHI

IMBABURA

SUCUMBIOS

PICHINCHA

NAPO

COTOPAXI

TUNGURAHUA

PASTAZA

BOLIVAR

LOS RIOS

CHIMBORAZO

MORONA SANTIAGO

GUAYAS

CANAR

AZUAY

EL ORO

LOJA

ZAMORA CHINCHIPE

MANABI

Cordillera de Chindul

Cordillera de Condorcillo

Cordillera del Condor

Cordillera de Cutucu

Cayambe

Pichincha

Antisana

Cotopaxi

Sumaco

Chimborazo

Altar

Sangay

Isla Puna

N

Altitude (meters)

300   600   1200   2000   3000+

The Birds of
Ecuador

VOLUME II

The Birds of
Ecuador

A FIELD GUIDE

Robert S. Ridgely
and
Paul J. Greenfield

With the collaboration of
Paul Coopmans

In association with
The Academy of Natural Sciences

CHRISTOPHER HELM
LONDON

Published 2001 by Christopher Helm, an imprint of A & C Black Ltd.,
37 Soho Square, London W1D 3QZ

Copyright © 2001 by Robert S. Ridgely and Paul J. Greenfield

ISBN 0-7136-6117-8

A CIP catalogue record for this book is available from the British Library

Printed in Hong Kong

10 9 8 7 6 5 4 3 2 1

Contents

Foreword

For many decades world tourism has treated the tiny Andean country of Ecuador as a staging site for the ultimate ecotourism destination, the Galápagos Islands, some 800 km off the Ecuador coast in the Pacific Ocean. Yes, the wild remote beauty and tame wildlife in a natural laboratory of evolution guaranteed a remarkable experience. After all, the finches and mockingbirds, giant tortoises and marine iguanas, as well as other creatures had inspired Charles Darwin, and all those who were privileged to follow him to the Enchanted Isles.

Mainland Ecuador, however, awaited serious world attention. Astride the equator, this amazing little country embraces diverse habitats from the dry Pacific coast to the towering volcanoes of the Andes to the great forests of the Amazon basin. In just 283,000 sq km, hundreds of bird species beckoned, most of them little known, perhaps some even yet to be discovered. We all could manage the fascinating, but minimal, avifauna of the Galápagos. But the birds of mainland Ecuador posed a daunting challenge indeed.

More than twenty years ago, Bob Ridgely and Paul Greenfield began the process of modern exploration and discovery on the Ecuadorian mainland. Frank Chapman and others had cracked the shell and peeked inside. But it was Ridgely, Greenfield, and their colleagues who mastered the new avifauna, secret after secret. They found new birds in accessible sites thought to be well known. Year after year they documented poorly known bird faunas in the remote corners of Ecuador, corners that were gradually becoming more accessible (some of them). Their work, supported by the Academy of Natural Sciences in Philadelphia (where Ridgely worked with me in the Ornithology Department), the Museo de Ciencias Naturales in Quito, and the John D. and Catherine T. MacArthur Foundation, had several goals, one of the most important of which was to produce a well-illustrated field guide to Ecuador's birds. The hope—and I think it is justified—was that this would attract the attention of world birders and ecotourists to the untapped riches found in mainland Ecuador. The ultimate purpose was broader and grander: the conservation of the extraordinary diversity of Ecuador and beyond.

In 1984 I had the privilege of joining Bob Ridgely and Paul Greenfield on a punishing expedition to the biologically unknown Cordillera de Cutucú in southeastern Ecuador. Ridgely and Greenfield alone knew bird vocalizations well enough to pick out that one that was slightly different, and whose author would usually turn out to be a rarity. Day after day, there and elsewhere, they—together with others, notably Mark Robbins, then also at the Academy (and, justifiably, a collaborator on Volume I of this book)—made ornithological history with the rediscovery of long-lost or hardly known birds. Elsewhere they even found some totally new ones. *The Birds of Ecuador* is the grand result of this expedition, and of many others. The two volumes are landmark works in that they graduate our scientific knowledge to new heights. They are also landmarks in that at last the door to full public appreciation of Ecuador's avifauna is open.

Finally, this wonderful new book challenges us to protect what we know. No more excuses. Conservation is born first of discovery and wonder, then of understanding, and finally of action. Thank you, Bob Ridgely and Paul Greenfield, for persevering and sharing with us your profound knowledge of and—it shows—love for the birds of Ecuador. Now we have the tool we need to ensure their future.

Frank B. Gill
National Audubon Society

Preface

More than twenty years ago, in July 1978, RSR—together with a friend from Yale University, David Wilcove—was conducting research in Ecuador on the status of certain rare parrot species. We had assistance during that trip from several people in the U.S. State Department and Peace Corps, and one of them chanced to mention that a young American artist, interested in birds and married to a Guayaquileña, had just moved to Quito. People interested in birds were a rarity in those days, so I called him, and shortly we were out looking for birds in the mountains west of the city and then at Tinalandia. The artist was, of course, PJG. And from our very first meeting, it seems we were discussing the possibility of together "doing" a book on the birds of Ecuador.

Naive were we; little did we know what we were getting ourselves into! But you are holding in your hands the result of our collaborative effort—which was aided, of course, by the efforts of many others. At the outset, it is fair now to admit, we did not comprehend just how little we knew. In part it was that realization, and that we would have to make extraordinary efforts over the years to fill in the gaps of knowledge, that delayed completion of *The Birds of Ecuador*. Some despaired of our ever finishing, and indeed at times it seemed to us too that we would never reach that point, that it would continue to recede into the future as RSR continued to revise and update text and PJG to fine-tune his paintings. By 1998, however, it was clear that we were approaching the end, and a superhuman effort that extended over many months put us over the top.

The Birds of Ecuador represents the culmination of our two-decade research effort investigating Ecuador's avifauna. Of course there is much yet to be learned—and avifaunas are never static anyway—so it is our fervent desire that this ongoing period of active field work will continue. In particular we hope that the gradually increasing number of Ecuadorian nationals conducting research or simply going out to observe and enjoy birds will continue to increase. We hope *The Birds of Ecuador* itself will contribute to this burgeoning interest.

It is our even more fervent hope that our book's release will stimulate efforts to protect Ecuador's birdlife. Both of us feel incredibly fortunate to have seen as much as we have; it is still a wonderful world out there! Nothing would please us more than to know that through the active participation of both Ecuadorians and interested parties from abroad, Ecuador's avifauna continued to prosper. To this end, we encourage all readers and users of *The Birds of Ecuador* to support the activities of the numerous nongovernmental conservation organizations that have sprung up over the past few decades. Most of these—notable among them Fundación Jatun Sacha, Fundación Maquipucuna, and Arcoiris—are broadly based, but we would be remiss not to mention the two that explicitly focus on birds and the threats they face: Fundación Ornitológica del Ecuador (CECIA) and Fundación Jocotoco. We actively work with and support both organizations, and we strongly encourage anyone with an interest in Ecuador's birds to do so as well. Both of us look forward to working with you.

Robert S. Ridgely
Ornithology Department
Academy of Natural Sciences
1900 Benjamin Franklin Pkwy
Philadelphia, PA 19103
USA

Paul J. Greenfield
Urbanización El Bosque
2da Etapa, Calle 6, Lote 161
Edificio El Parque
Quito
Ecuador

CECIA can be contacted at:
La Tierra 203 y los Shyris
P.O. Box 17-17-906
Quito
Ecuador

Fundación Jocotoco can be contacted through:

Dr. Robert S. Ridgely   or
(address above)

Dr. Nigel Simpson
Honeysuckle Cottage
Tidenham Chase
Nr. Chepstow, Gwent
NP6 7JW United Kingdom

Acknowledgments

Any book such as ours inevitably is the result of the efforts of many individuals and organizations. Our desire here is to express our heartfelt gratitude to everyone who has been involved in what has doubtless at times seemed a never-ending process.

In particular the debt we owe to our two collaborators is immeasurable. Mark B. Robbins, formerly collection manager of the Department of Ornithology at the Academy of Natural Sciences of Philadelphia (ANSP), is surely the finest expedition organizer anywhere, and we all benefited from his logistical know-how, but it was for his skill in preparing field specimens, and enthusiasm for teaching others the minutiae of that art, that he will perhaps be longest remembered. His assistance in the preparation of the initial drafts of Volume I's text was substantial, and especially involved making correct subspecific diagnoses. Paul Coopmans is a relative newcomer to the Ecuadorian ornithological scene, but in the mid- and late 1990s he probably spent more time in the field than anyone else. In the past decade Paul has developed a particular interest in bird vocalizations, to the point where the breadth of his knowledge on the subject is perhaps unrivaled. Paul has directed his careful eye to the texts of both volumes, in Volume I sharing his many personal observations and helping to keep RSR abreast of ornithological developments in Ecuador, and in Volume II concentrating on accurately transcribing a representative range of vocalizations for each species.

Financial assistance came from various quarters, and we are grateful to all. First and foremost, we thank the John D. and Catherine T. MacArthur Foundation for its generous support of our field investigations throughout Ecuador in the early 1990s. The MacArthur funding permitted us to vastly accelerate our efforts to learn as much as we could about Ecuador's rich avifauna. Little did the foundation realize—nor did we—that almost another decade would be needed for our efforts to reach fruition, and we can only hope that the wait was worth it. Those funds were channeled through the ANSP, a marvelous institution where RSR has been privileged to be on staff for more than fifteen years; a more congenial "home" could not be imagined, and PJG too enjoyed its hospitality during his frequent working visits. We are also grateful to our host institution in Ecuador, the Museo Ecuatoriano de Ciencias Naturales (MECN) in Quito, whose staffing and infrastructure improved markedly during our period of most extensive collaboration and which was always of great assistance in permitting and other logistical details during our work in Ecuador.

Various individuals also helped keep us (particularly PJG) financially afloat through some lean years. PJG acknowledges his special gratitude to Evelyn Fowles who volunteered her time, energy, and enthusiasm and, together with Christine Bush and RSR, organized a fund-raising drive on PJG's behalf through the ANSP. Numerous persons, too many to mention every one, participated in this campaign, and we are grateful to all of them for the confidence they extended to us and hope they enjoy what they now have in front of them. The following individuals made especially important contributions to this fund: Wallace Dayton, Daisy Ford, Evelyn Fowles, William Greenfield, Kit Hansen and Stephen Greenfield, Dr. Norman Mellor, in memory of Cdr. Gregory Peirce, and Dr. and Mrs. Howard E. Wilson. We would like to single out Tom Butler, who was an early supporter of our project and made several significant financial contributions, and Jim and Jean Macaleer, who participated in a major way toward the end.

The only way to become really familiar with an avifauna is to study it intensively in the field as well as in the lab or studio. The recent upsurge in birding tours to Ecuador, a development in which both of us played a major role, has provided us with a previously unparalleled opportunity to get into the field on a regular basis. Both of us have benefited substantially from this frequent and repeated exposure to Ecuador's birds, having led numerous trips to various parts of the country for more than twenty years, especially under the auspices of Victor Emanuel Nature Tours. RSR has also worked with Wings and PJG with several other companies, among them Wilderness Adventure, Voyagers, Ornitholidays, Princeton Nature Tours, New Jersey Audubon Society, and Neblina Forest. To all these companies, and to the individuals who participated in the trips themselves, we can only extend a humble thanks and express the hope that we will see you again in Ecuador.

A few of our trips, especially those of RSR, were privately financed by individuals willing to endure the rigors of serious expedition travel. These individuals include Ken Berlin, Hugh Braswell, Nigel Simpson, Rod Thompson, Marc Weinberger, and Minturn Wright. The Catherwood Foundation underwrote the ANSP's initial exploratory trip to Ecuador, our arduous trek to the previously unexplored upper slopes of the Cordillera de Cutucú in 1984. We are grateful to one and all and trust that the stories you have been able to relate have more than compensated for any of the difficulties we encountered.

Other field work has been sponsored by commercial companies in Ecuador, including Ecuambiente (with Maria Eugenia Puente and Jorge Aguilera) and Transturi and Metropolitan Touring (and Raul Garcia and the late Pedro Proaño), and we are grateful for the opportunities provided. The owners of several private properties, notably SierrAzul (= Hacienda Aragon) in Napo and Hacienda La Libertad in Cañar, also encouraged our research visits to the areas they hold dear.

A major thrust of the ANSP's work in Ecuador has been to assemble a comprehensive working collection of modern, full-data study skins of Ecuadorian birds, the collection that both of us ultimately depended on for our work on *The Birds of Ecuador*. Assembling such a collection is not a simple task, and many individuals played crucial roles in its success. Apart from the aforementioned Mark Robbins, foremost among these was Francisco Sornoza, who was for many years our in-country project coordinator. Young and inexperienced at the start, "Pancho" quickly matured as he took on increasingly heavy loads of responsibility, gradually learned Ecuador's birds, and also learned a little English; we remain immensely grateful to him for his herculean efforts. Throughout this period we worked in close concert with the MECN in Quito. That institution, and in particular its directors, Miguel Moreno and Fausto Sarmiento, always proved a willing partner and was especially helpful in working through the intricacies of the governmental permitting process. MECN staff members participated in all of our expeditions, and we greatly appreciate the efforts of Marco Jácome, Juan Carlos Matheus, and the late Juan José Espinosa. Col. Paul Scharf of the U.S. Marine Corps enabled us to visit several remote Ecuadorian military camps and participated in several trips. William Phillips facilitated our visits to SierrAzul. Other individuals who participated in trips and expeditions, and all of whom made valuable contributions to their success, include David Agro, David Brewer, Christine Bush, Angelo Capparella, Tristan Davis, Peter English, Frank Gill, Skip Glenn, Steve Greenfield, Steve Holt, Rick Huber, Niels Krabbe, Jackson Loomis, Todd Mark, Terry Maxwell, Bob Peck, Tracy Pedersen, Gary Rosenberg, Tom Schulenberg, Fred and Jodie Sheldon, Beth Slikas, Fernando Sornoza, Doug Wechsler, and Andrew Whittaker.

Much of the actual work on *The Birds of Ecuador* was accomplished at the ANSP, and a more stimulating place to write and paint can hardly be imagined. Here we benefitted not only from the Academy's marvelous collection of study skins but also its superb library and the most comprehensive collection of bird photographs ever assembled (Visual Resources for Ornithology [VIREO]). The following individuals materially abetted our efforts in one way or another at the Academy: David Agro, Louis Bevier, Christine Bush, Sally Conyne, Frank Gill, and Mark Robbins. Over the past several years PJG's brother, Steve Greenfield, has been especially helpful in work on the distribution maps, as has Sally Conyne. Through it all we remain especially grateful to Frank Gill, for much of this period chair of the Ornithology Department and who for many years abetted and encouraged RSR's ongoing research on Ecuadorian birds, quietly enduring the many delays in our completion of the task.

Both of us, but especially RSR, have spent substantial periods of time at other institutions, especially the American Museum of Natural History in New York, or have communicated with individuals at those museums concerning Ecuadorian material in their care. At the American Museum of Natural History, John Bull, Bud Lanyon, Mary LeCroy, François Vuilleumier, and the late John Farrand were especially helpful. We also thank Steve Cardiff, John O'Neill, and Van Remsen at the Louisiana State University Museum of Zoology in Baton Rouge; Lloyd Kiff and Manuel Marín at the Western Foundation for Vertebrate

Zoology in California; Ken Parkes at the Carnegie Museum in Pittsburgh; Raymond Paynter, Jr., at the Museum of Comparative Zoology in Cambridge, Massachusetts; and Tom Schulenberg and Melvin Traylor at the Field Museum of Natural History in Chicago.

During the last several decades many other individuals have investigated one or more aspects of Ecuadorian ornithology. As word got out that we were preparing *The Birds of Ecuador*, all freely shared their questions and newly acquired information with us, thus creating what became truly a communal effort. Although our gratitude goes out to all, we here name the more important of those individuals, mainly those who have not been mentioned previously in some capacity and each of whom has had significant input into this book: John Arvin, Dusty Becker, Bob Behrstock, Karl Berg, Brinley Best, Rob Bleiweiss, Bonnie Bochan, Greg Budney, Chris Canaday, Juan Manuel Carrión, Mario Cohn-Haft, Peter English, Jon Fjeldså, Ben Haase, Steve Hilty, Steve Howell, Olaf Jahn, Ralph Jones, Lou Jost, Guy Kirwan, Raymond Lévêque, Bernabé López-Lanús, Jane Lyons, Mitch Lysinger, Felix Man Ging, Manuel Marín, John Moore, Lelis Navarrete, Jonas Nilsson, Fernando Ortiz-Crespo, David Pearson, David Peerman, Michael Poulsen, Rick Prum, Carsten Rahbek, Jan Rasmussen, Giovanni Rivadeneira, Gary Rosenberg, John Rowlett, Rose Ann Rowlett, Paul Salaman, Paul Scharf, Fred Sibley, Francisco Sornoza, Dan and Erika Tallman, David Wege, Bret Whitney, Andrew Whittaker, Rob Williams, David Wolf, and the late Tom Davis and Ted Parker. We should especially like to single out Niels Krabbe, who put at our disposal his vast knowledge of Andean birds, and Paul Van Gasse, whose meticulous critical reading and proofing of Volume I were invaluable. Lastly, the all-important copyediting phase of the work was ably executed by Elizabeth Pierson, whose meticulous eye managed to pick up inconsistencies that crept into the text, not to mention some outright slipups; RSR's gratitude for her patient assistance is substantial indeed. Despite our—and our helpers—best efforts, however, inevitably a few inconsistencies and misstatements will remain, errors of omission and commission for which we take full responsibility (but please tell us about them!).

As with all other aspects of this opus, the illustrations have not been produced in a vacuum. Although the brush—actually, hundreds of brushes!—was ultimately wielded only by PJG over these twenty years, the plates could not have been painted without much help and consultation. The two of us worked together closely during their planning and execution, and PJG good-naturedly undertook all the corrections that RSR could spot (no matter how minor or subtle). The late Gustavo Orcés shared his knowledge with PJG when he first arrived in Quito, and both Bill Davis and later Paul Scharf were PJG's most frequent field companions for several years during this "learning process." Many individuals looked over the plates while they were in various stages of production and offered helpful comments; among them were Jon Fjeldså, Niels Krabbe, Mark Robbins, John Rowlett, Rose Ann Rowlett, Tom Schulenberg, and Guy Tudor. Louis Bevier shared his knowledge of plumage and posture details for certain boreal migrants and pelagics. Bill Clark, John Dunning, Arthur Panzer, Doug Wechsler, and the entire VIREO team made their photographs available. Tracy Pedersen, a talented artist in her own right, graciously agreed to paint a species that was inadvertently left off the plates (we won't reveal which it was). PJG's brother Steve was always a help, and PJG's wife, Martha, assisted in cleaning up the plates.

PJG's deepest gratitude extends to Eva and Felix Hirschberg and especially Lenore Greenfield for their encouragement, help, and support; their presence was always an inspiration. Of special importance were Jorge and Martha de Kalil, whose hospitality, generosity, and love helped make PJG's life in Ecuador so special; they are missed. To William Greenfield—who will never see the fruits of this labor—PJG expresses his love and appreciation for his endless and all-encompassing positivity.

RSR was introduced to the natural world by his parents, Beverly and Barbara Ridgely, and he remains truly grateful for their forbearance, and encouragement, as he commenced his career as an ornithologist and conservationist. It may not have been financially rewarding, but the many other, less tangible rewards have more than made up for it.

Lastly, we both express our gratitude to and love for our wives, Martha Greenfield and Peg Ridgely, whose forbearance during this process has been nothing short of a marvel. Martha unselfishly awaited PJG's return from innumerable field and work trips and put up with all the years of "bird talk." Peg has been the very model of a wife and partner to RSR and has learned to put up with (and even enjoy!) all those late dinners. Neither of us could have done this without you, and our gratitude will never end.

The Birds of
Ecuador

VOLUME II

Plan of the Book

An all-too-frequent complaint directed at the authors and illustrators of Neotropical bird books is that "the book is too big—I'd have to hire a porter to carry it around." Essentially these critics want it both ways. They want everything illustrated, and they want the detail and distribution maps necessary to enable them to sort through the superabundance of birds. At the same time they want the book to be a manageable size—and to be cheap too! Something has to give: there simply are too many birds in most Neotropical countries to make this possible, and the complexities are too vast for simplification to be an option.

We wrestled with this conundrum for years before devising a simple but relatively novel solution: write two books! And that is what we have done, with one volume intended primarily for field use and the other for your library (or hotel room or even car). The books are designed to be used together, following precisely the same family and species sequence.

Volume I includes information on the distribution and status of each species in Ecuador, thoroughly referenced and placed in a historical context when necessary. If a species is deemed at risk, its conservation status in Ecuador is discussed. Then follows a taxonomic discussion in which species-level and subspecific systematics issues are presented, together with possible alternate treatments and our rationale for adopting the approach we did. Subspecies are evaluated in terms of their validity, and each taxon's distribution in Ecuador is given. In addition, we address the contentious issue of English names. Lastly, we give the species' worldside, extra-Ecuador distribution.

This leaves for Volume II all matters explicitly pertaining to identification: the 96 plates, each with a facing page, and following these the individual species accounts. Each account includes a description of the species; sections on similar species, habits, and voice; and a map of that species' distribution in Ecuador.

We recognize that presenting information in such a way inevitably means repeating some things and that this takes up valuable space. We have attempted to minimize this, however, and hope that the result has more advantages than disadvantages. We also recognize that neither volume is "small" in the sense that a book dealing with the birds of a relatively species-poor area in the temperate zone can be. But really the glory of the tropics *is* its diversity: revel in it,

1

marvel at it, and have fun trying to figure it all out. We find few other activities to be as thoroughly engrossing.

Volume II: Field Guide

This volume has been designed strictly as a field guide and conveys only information thought to be useful for identification purposes. It is also designed to be used in close conjunction with Volume I, in which extensive background information concerning each species' abundance, distribution, taxonomy, conservation status, and overall world range is given.

Note that most of the introductory chapters for *The Birds of Ecuador* are placed only at the beginning of Volume I. What is presented here is first, in this chapter, an explanation of how Volume II is organized and designed to be used. Following this is a chapter aimed particularly at beginning birders—though we hope more experienced birders will also encounter some points of interest. The plates and main text of the field guide immediately follow the two introductory chapters.

Plates

PJG prepared all of the artwork for the field guide. With the exception of two species that were recorded after the plates were finished (Band-tailed Gull and Bicolored Antpitta), and the introduced Rock Pigeon, all of the nearly 1600 bird species occurring in mainland Ecuador are illustrated. As much as feasible, the same sequence of families and species is followed in both the plates and the main text, but a few compromises have been made in order to place a sufficient number of similarly sized species on individual plates. On the last plate, Plate 96, we depict a mixture of species discovered in Ecuador subsequent to the completion of the plates where those species should have gone; numerous other species have been squeezed in at the appropriate spot on the other plates.

We have depicted as much plumage variation as seemed appropriate. Males (♂♂) and females (♀♀) are shown where there is significant sexual dimorphism. For rare migrants or vagrants (e.g., certain *Larus* gulls), we have opted not to include all plumages, but all species are covered by at least one illustration. Where significant racial variation (involving relatively obvious visual differences) occurs within Ecuador, we include illustrations of two or, more rarely, three subspecies.

All primary figures on an individual plate are drawn to the same scale. Flying birds typically are depicted as insets, usually at a smaller scale.

The figures are based on our field experience in Ecuador and elsewhere in the Neotropics; this knowledge proved especially important in relation to posture, shape, and soft-part coloration. Specimens—especially those housed in the collections of the Academy of Natural Sciences of Philadelphia (ANSP), the American Museum of Natural History in New York, and the Museo Ecuatoriano de Ciencias Naturales in Quito—were of crucial importance, and indeed our work could not have proceeded without them. Photographs—especially those archived in the Visual Resources for Ornithology (VIREO) collection at the ANSP—proved to be vital for several difficult groups. Other specialized references were also sometimes consulted for certain details.

Despite our diligence, we are sure that a few details have been incorrectly shown. If this is the case, we would certainly appreciate hearing about it. But do be aware that individual variation in bird plumages does occur, and that this variation could cause the bird you are looking at to not perfectly match its illustration. Birds in fresh plumage usually appear neat, brightly colored, and boldly patterned, whereas those in worn plumage tend to appear faded in color and less distinct in pattern (and often have obviously frayed and abraded tails). Our bias has been, wherever faced with making a choice, to depict birds in relatively fresh plumage.

Accompanying notes, placed on the page facing each plate, give a brief synopsis of each genus with more than one species, and a very brief summary of each illustrated species' distribution in Ecuador, habitat, and distinguishing characteristics. Generally there is no room for interspecific comparisons. When two or more subspecies are shown, this is indicated by naming the subspecies involved, employing the following symbols for the part of Ecuador where each subspecies occurs:

E = eastern lowlands, or east slope of the Andes;

W = western lowlands, or west slope of the Andes;

N = northern Ecuador (usually in the Andes; if the northern part of the western or eastern lowlands, this is usually indicated by NW or NE);

S = southern Ecuador (usually in the Andes; if the southern part of the western or eastern lowlands, this is usually indicated by SW or SE);

H = highlands;

L = lowlands; and

J = juvenile.

In some instances these symbols are used in relation to each other; for example, for the Gray-and-gold Warbler (*Basileuterus fraseri*) the nominate race ("S") occurs south of the race *ochraceicrista* ("N"). Such symbols are not used if only one taxon is illustrated, and the subspecies then is not named. Birds in **breeding plumage** are noted by the symbol "B" and those in **nonbreeding plumage** by the symbol "NB."

Main Text

RSR is the author of the entire text, and it is on him that responsibility for errors of commission and omission that may have crept in must be placed—though he has done his utmost to keep these to a minimum! During the course of this text's preparation, it has benefitted especially from the comments of collaborator Paul Coopmans, to whom gratitude is hereby expressed. PJG also played a role, especially as he and RSR worked together in crafting the text for the facing pages for the 96 plates. Note that the cutoff date for the inclusion of new information in all of the text occurred in the first half of 1999, with a few exceptions having been made for particularly significant discoveries and clarifications.

The sequence of orders, families, genera, and species is precisely the same in this volume as it is in Volume I. Introductions to all of Ecuador's bird families and to all genera with more than one species in Ecuador are presented in this volume. Following the family name, the number of species in that family occurring in Ecuador is given. Included in these introductions are generalizations about the family or genus's general distribution, habitat requirements, appearance, and behavior. General descriptions of their nests are included (but not, with a few exceptions, for individual species).

If the species in a family or genus do not exhibit sexual variation in plumage, this is noted in that family or genus introduction, in boldface, with a comment such as "Sexes alike." If this is noted for a family, it can be assumed that this is the case for all species in that family; if for a genus, then for all species in that genus. Either way, it is not repeated for each species; thus, if in a species account there is no such notation, it can be assumed that there is no sexual variation. For genera in which some species vary and others do not, this is noted under the appropriate species account.

Information on each species is presented in the same sequence. Inevitably, though, some species present more complexities than others, and those accounts are longer. We have tended to treat species that occur in Ecuador only as vagrants somewhat less thoroughly; thus, for example, a few gulls that occur only as casual vagrants, and which in fact have very complex plumage sequences, are described only generally, with the assumption that the interested reader will, if necessary, refer to other references for additional detail.

Each species is introduced by its *English, scientific, and Spanish name*. These are all bracketed if the status of that species is hypothetical in Ecuador (see the discussion on hypothetical species under "Abundance Terms" in the chapter "Plan of the Book" in Volume I). Also included in the species heading is the number of the plate on which that species is depicted, followed by a number in parentheses; the latter number refers to the species' position on the plate and is designed to speed one's transfer between the main text and plate (and a plate's facing page). Thus the Gray-headed Kite (*Leptodon cayanensis*)—figured on Plate 11(2)—is the second species illustrated on Plate 11.

Each species account begins with that bird's *overall length*, from the tip of its bill to the tip of its tail, as it is laid out on its back in what is intended to be a "natural" position. In fact these lengths are taken from museum specimens, so are to some extent not "natural," and they should therefore be taken as an approximation of a bird's length in life (which itself varies, depending on posture). Every effort has been made, however, to make length comparisons between similar, related species meaningful and accurate; thus if the length of one tyrannulet is slightly shorter than another, that difference should be real. Lengths are given in both centimeters (cm) and inches ("), with a range given especially if there is sexual dimorphism in size. An additional bill-length measurement is given for all species of hummingbirds (for which bills are such an important identification feature) and for a few other species for which it is significant. A tail measurement is given for species in which the tail is unusually elongated.

The initial sentence in each species account provides an abbreviated *abundance, habitat, and range statement*. (The abundance terms used are defined in Volume I in the chapter "Plan of the Book," and the habitat terms are described in the Volume I chapter "Geography, Climate, and Vegetation.") For particularly *striking or unusual species*, that aspect is also mentioned; here, as elsewhere, distinctive characteristics are highlighted by being placed in italics. This is followed by, for *migrants*, a summary of the period when that species is present in Ecuador.

Next in each species account comes, when needed, a sentence summarizing *alternate taxonomic and nomenclatural options* that differ from the names and taxonomy we employ. Again, these issues are explored much more fully in the appropriate species accounts in Volume I.

A description of the *color of a species' soft parts*—its eye (iris), bill, and legs—follows. For the most part these can be assumed to be black or—in the case of the iris—dark brown if they are not specifically mentioned, but these features can be important identification marks and thus are sometimes highlighted by being put in italics.

The *basic description of a bird's plumage* comes next (unlike the sections that follow, however, it is not labeled as such). Following convention, if the species is sexually dimorphic, the male ($\male$) is described first as its plumage usually is the more distinctive; that of the female ($\female$) follows, often presented in relation to that of the male in order to economize on space. If the sexes are alike but there are age-related plumage differences, we describe the adult first. We use the terms "breeding" and "nonbreeding" plumages for species that have different plumages at different times of the year—these rather than the terms "alternate" and "basic," sometimes used, as the former seem clearer and more generally understandable. The plumage that is seen more often in Ecuador is described first, with—as in sexual dimorphism—the second often presented in relation to the first. For birds frequently seen in flight, descriptions of the species' opened wing and spread tail are given. Other age-related plumage stages ("juvenile," "immature") are described next, as necessary, and again in relation to previously described plumages if this can be done clearly.

The description itself typically proceeds from the head of the bird back down its upperparts, ending with the wings and tail. The underparts are described next, starting with the throat and proceeding back to the crissum. As much detail is given as seemed necessary, but we should emphasize that these were not written as feather-by-feather descriptions—many unimportant (indeed potentially confusing) details have purposely been omitted. Distinguishing characteristics are highlighted by placing them in italics.

Some knowledge of a bird's topography is needed, and indeed knowing the

Figure 1

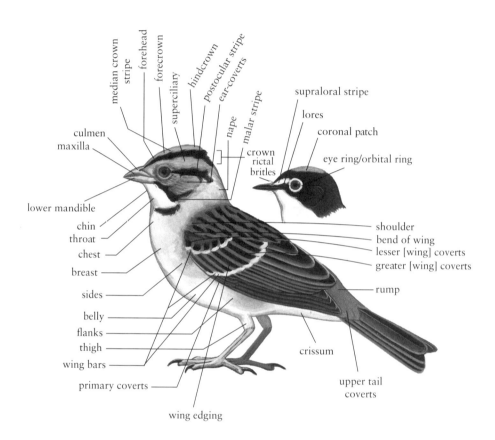

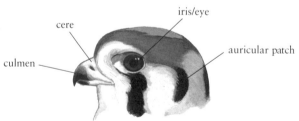

Figure 2

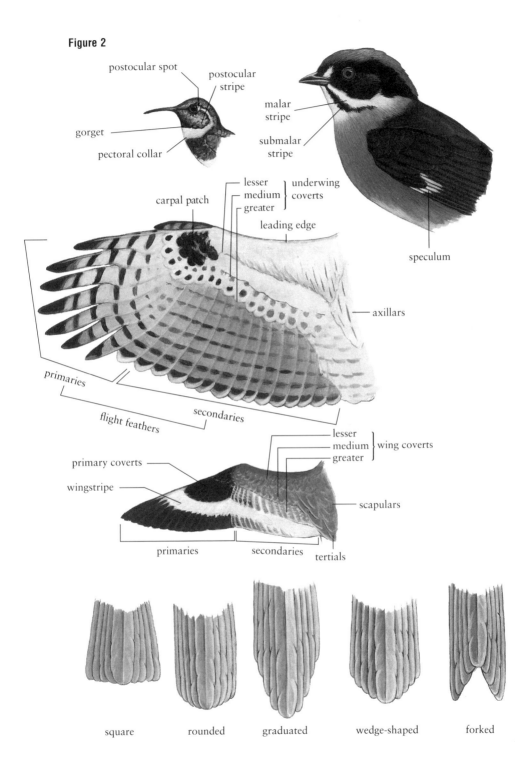

postocular spot

postocular stripe

gorget

pectoral collar

malar stripe

submalar stripe

speculum

lesser
medium } underwing coverts
greater

carpal patch

leading edge

axillars

primaries

secondaries

flight feathers

lesser
medium } wing coverts
greater

primary coverts

wingstripe

scapulars

primaries

secondaries

tertials

square

rounded

graduated

wedge-shaped

forked

difference between primaries and secondaries, and greater wing-coverts and lesser wing-coverts, is nearly essential. Please refer to Figures 1 and 2, which highlight the more important terms we use in this book.

When important subspecific variation occurs within Ecuador, the most widespread or most numerous subspecies in Ecuador is the one described first, followed by comments on ancillary subspecies, these usually given in comparison with the race originally described. We generally do not refer to a subspecies by name, rather referring to it by describing its geographic range in Ecuador. (As always, their actual names and more details can be found by referring to the species account in Volume I.) If no subspecies are mentioned, it can be inferred that important geographical variation does not occur in Ecuador.

Occasionally, when two species are closely similar, or when one is much rarer or more range-restricted than another, we may simply compare the second species directly to the first, avoiding the necessity of repeating what amounts to virtually the same description. This is never, however, done for more than two species at a time, for doing so then requires the reader to make complex, three-way comparisons.

In the *"Similar species"* section, comparisons are made between the species under discussion and those most likely to be confused with it. If the species is so distinctive as to not require such a comparison (i.e., it is unmistakable or close to it), then this section is omitted. Likewise, if a basic description has been built off a previous species (as in the case of a rare species being described directly off a much more numerous one), this section also may be eliminated. Only similar species that are sympatric (i.e., occur together) are compared; species that are similar but occur on either side of the Andes, for instance, are so indicated, with no further discussion. In the case of pairs of species that are similar and require complex discussion, often this is discussed only once, generally under the species that is rarer; under the more common species, reference is made to the fact that the discussion exists in the other species account.

In the *"Habits"* section a basic summary of the species' behavior as it relates to identification is presented. Topics that are stressed include whether a species is gregarious or not (many are typically seen only singly or in pairs, whereas others occur in groups of their own species); whether it tends to occur in mixed-species flocks or not; how and when it forages; its manner of flight; any particular mannerisms that may be distinctive; and so on. For many species, particularly those found in humid forests, the microhabitat it may favor is of crucial importance, and this is always mentioned.

Lastly, in the *"Voice"* section an attempt is made to describe and transcribe the major vocalizations of all species for which voice is deemed important and for which we have information, and to put those vocalizations into a behavioral context. (In some instances, information on voice is included only at the family/genus level.) This, we admit, is easier said than done. There are many complications. The songs of many species vary individually and geographically, and some have alternate songs. Various other vocalizations, given in contexts other than that of a primary song (one given by the male in order to defend a territory and attract a mate), are also given; these are typically termed "calls" and can be given in order to maintain contact between members of a pair, in agonistic encounters, and so on. In general we have emphasized primary songs (or "territorial calls") in the species accounts, as these tend to be the most distinctive and thus the most useful from the standpoint of identification.

Accurately describing bird vocalizations by putting them into words is difficult. Everyone hears sounds differently, and interpreting them so the transcriptions are intelligible to others is difficult at best. All we can say is that we have attempted to be consistent in our approach, and in the qualitative and descriptive terms we use, most of which are standard in such exercises. For the most part our descriptions are derived from our own experience and/or our own tape-recordings (many of which are, or will be, archived at the Library of Natural Sounds at the Cornell Laboratory of Ornithology). When they are not, this is so indicated, with reference to another published source, to another individual's tape-recording (e.g., "L. Navarrete recording"), or simply to another individual. In general we have attempted to convey pitch either through words (e.g., "high" or "rising") or through the choice of vowels used; thus in the sequence *i*, *e*, *a*, *o*, and *u*, each vowel conveys a slightly lower pitch than the previous one. The quality of the sound produced is generally conveyed by the choice of consonants used; thus a hard sound is presented with a *k*, a buzzy sound by a *z*, and so on. An accent on a vowel indicates that that note (or syllable) is emphasized, or the same idea may be conveyed by an exclamation point or, occasionally, the use of capital letters. A few mnemonics have been provided where we or others could devise one; these are especially helpful for certain well-enunciated vocalizations, less so for others.

Our collaborator Paul Coopmans played a major role in improving and expanding upon RSR's original voice transcriptions, clarifying many and adding new vocalizations from his vast storehouse of knowledge on the subject. In instances where the voice contribution is substantially his, this is so indicated.

We emphasize that although our voice descriptions are as accurate and evocative of bird vocalizations as we can make them, nothing can equal actually hearing the birds vocalize. Fortunately this is becoming more feasible, with many excellent tape-recordings and CDs covering many Ecuadorian bird species now available commercially; paramount among these are the series produced by John Moore and his coauthors, with more in the pipeline.

To conserve space, we give each species' overall world distribution only in Volume I, to which reference should be made.

References

References are included throughout the species accounts in Volume I; they are generally not referred to, however, in Volume II. References that are cited repeatedly or that were used extensively during the preparation of Volume I are given in full in the bibliography at the end of that volume. References in Volume II have been kept to a minimum, in order to make for easier reading. The bibliography at the end of this volume thus includes only those references actually cited in Volume II, as well as selected references that pertain specifically to field identification. We encourage you to consult the bibliography in Volume I for a more complete list of references.

Maps

A distribution map has been created for each species occurring in Ecuador. Every effort has been made to ensure the accuracy of these maps, within the constraints of their format. These maps are not perfect; they depict the generalized range of each species. Not only do distributions change through time, but also there are inherent limitations in attempting to depict broad-scale distribution patterns on a small-scale map. Obviously one cannot attempt to show abundance levels. Further, one cannot really depict patchy distributions, patterns inherent in a species being restricted, for example, to arid intermontane valleys or microhabitats that are found only locally. Even attempting to show elevational ranges in a region as topographically complex as Ecuador is nearly impossible. The best one can hope to do is to interpret and approximate reality, and to recognize that there are limitations to this format.

Despite their limitations, we nonetheless feel that the maps do portray with a reasonable degree of accuracy each species' current distribution in Ecuador; more details concerning most species can be found in the species accounts in Volume I. We have endeavored to keep these maps as up to date as possible, but inevitably a few recent records and revised interpretations may not be adequately or accurately depicted; if there is a discrepancy, the text in Volume I, which has always been updated, should be taken as correct.

Each resident species' generalized range is depicted through a shading pattern. Migrants are depicted as occurring within a solid line (with no shading), boreal migrants open from the north, austral migrants open from the south. Isolated records are shown as individual dots; these may represent merely vagrants or, occasionally, sites for a species that are thought to be isolated from the rest of that species' range. For a few rare species, specific localities are depicted *within* their overall range. The two stars on the map represent the cities of Quito (in the north) and Guayaquil (in the southwest); the two irregular north-south lines are the 1000-m contour lines on either side of the Andes; and the two irregular east-west lines are the Río Napo (in the north) and the Río Pastaza (in the south). A synopsis of each species' elevation range is given adjacent to its map.

We certainly recognize that species distributions change through time and that new discoveries are constantly going to be made. Thus some of these maps will inevitably be outdated the moment they are published. We welcome comments from readers suggesting any updates or corrections we might make.

Beginning With Birds

We recognize that this field guide will not be easy for a beginning birder or budding scientist to use. The complexities are simply too great, the avian diversity in Ecuador too overwhelming. All we can say is persevere, and recognize that all proficient birders and ornithologists have at some point endured going through this stage—often without a book like the one you are now holding!

Perhaps the ideal way to begin is to have a mentor, someone more experienced with birds who can gradually introduce to you the tricks of the trade, such that gradually accumulated bits of knowledge begin to come together into a more comprehensive whole. But even finding such a person can be hard. If you are on your own, don't despair; be patient, and try to work out the more common birds around you. Use those as the basis for expanding your knowledge.

Virtually no equipment is needed for starting to watch birds. No even binoculars; as a boy, RSR went birding for several years without them, thereby learning to use his ingenuity to approach birds and to coax them in close. (Further, plenty of country people are knowledgeable of the birds around them, even if they've never seen—much less owned—a pair of binoculars.) However, you will soon learn that a good pair of binoculars will add immeasurable pleasure to your efforts. If possible, purchase a good pair of 7- or 8-power binoculars; that number refers to the magnification, in this case revealing that the image you will see is seven or eight times larger than you see it with your naked eyes. The second number (e.g., in 8×42) is also important, for it refers to the diameter (in millimeters) of the objective (outer) lens and thus to how much light the lens admits; dividing the first number into the second reveals how much light-gathering capacity your binoculars have. You want as much as possible, for the more light there is, the brighter the image you see. Also, be aware that the more rugged and moisture-proof your binoculars are, the better; and that the closer your binoculars will focus, the better (RSR likes his present pair, which will focus on his toes!). All these factors contribute to cost, but in the long run the value you receive is worth it.

The diversity of birds in Ecuador is tremendous, and this diversity can be confusing and even overwhelming. The hardest part is getting started and learning to recognize some of the basic groups or families of birds. In 25 years of leading birding tours, both of us have noted that the greatest difficulty novice birders have is placing the bird they are looking at in its correct family, or in the case of a large family (e.g., the tyrant flycatchers), in its correct "group." How does one do this? Well, one looks for clues, concentrating on generalized points such as *overall size, shape,* and *coloration* (don't worry about details just yet), *bill shape* (this is surprisingly important), *what the bird is doing* (If perched, is it moving around or holding still? What is its posture? Etc.), and *where it is* (Is it, for example, in forest? If so, where in the forest, how high above the ground?). *If you misjudge which family a bird belongs to, you don't have a chance of identifying it correctly.*

In this chapter we present a simplified summary of the major families of Ecuadorian birds—not all families, omitting the ones you are unlikely to see at first and also many coastal birds—together with some basic tips on how to recognize them. For now we ignore any consideration of bird vocalizations, which are in fact of vital importance for bird recognition but simply bewilder many novice birders. Simple, diagrammatic illustrations of representative common species are included. We of course realize that some families are easier to recognize than others; everyone knows what a duck looks like, but what about some of a duck's near look-alikes from other families, such as grebes, cormorants, or coots? The descriptions below an end with a reference to the color plate(s) on which all the species of that particular group or family are depicted (note that different groups or families may overlap on the same plate[s]).

Tinamous. Chunky, rotund, vaguely chicken-like terrestrial birds with small heads, long necks, and often droopy beaks. Walk on forest floor, where very hard to see. Beautiful, quavering songs are often heard. Plate 1.

Grebes. Small, duck-like birds that swim on freshwater ponds and lakes. Plumage often fluffy. Dive frequently and for long periods, and can sink beneath surface. Plate 8.

Cormorants. Large, vaguely duck-like black birds with long and slender bills that swim and dive in water, or perch nearby (wings sometimes outstretched). Young birds paler below. Gregarious. Plate 4.

Pelicans. Very large coastal birds with unmistakable pouch on underside of bill. Plunge-dive for fish; perch with neck in an S shape. Often in flocks. Plate 4.

Ducks. Shape at least vaguely similar to familiar domestic ducks, but wary behavior in the wild very different. Can occur in flocks; strong, fast flight. Plate 8.

Herons. Slender, long-legged, and long-billed birds that usually stand in or near water; most are large, and many are at least partially white. Plates 5–7.

Vultures. Common large birds, black with featherless heads, that eat carrion and garbage. Often soar high. Plate 9.

Kites, Eagles, and Hawks. Predatory birds with hooked bills and powerful talons to capture live prey (which can—depending on the species—be mammals, birds, lizards, large insects, etc.). Plumage variable, brown, gray, and black predominating; many species are hard to identify. Eagles are very large (and rare), kites more slender and delicate. Some are conspicuous, perching in the open; others are secretive in forest. Some species soar high in sky, but most are rarely above treetops. Plates 9–16.

Falcons and Caracaras. Generally similar to previous family; most species also predatory, but a few eat carrion. Many are easily seen open-country birds. Plates 15–17.

Curassows, Guans, and Chachalacas. Large, vaguely turkey-like birds found in forests; clad in various shades of brown, a few in black. Much hunted, therefore usually shy and hard to see. Plate 18.

Rails, Gallinules, and Coots. Secretive birds of marshes, wet grassy areas, and mangroves. Most have fairly long, slightly decurved bills (shorter in "crakes," which are small rails). Some gallinules and coots swim, rather duck-like. Plates 20–21.

Jacanas. Distinctive marsh inhabitants with amazingly long toes. Walk on floating vegetation. Yellow on wings conspicuous in flight. Plate 20.

Sandpipers. Large group of strong-flying migratory shorebirds from North America—some snipes are resident—that feed in or at edge of shallow water (fresh and salt), most common along coast. Plumage differences subtle; bills usually long and slender. Plates 22–25.

Plovers and Lapwings. Another shorebird group, with shorter and thicker bills than preceding. Occur in much the same sort of places; about half are migratory from North America. Lapwings are larger and fancier looking. Plates 22–23.

Gulls and Terns. Fairly large, mainly white or pale gray waterbirds found mainly along coast and on rivers. Gulls are heavier bodied with thicker bills; terns have slender, often colored bills, and tails are often forked. Many are boreal migrants. Plates 26–27.

Pigeons and Doves. Well-known family with small, rounded heads and slender bills; the domestic pigeon is typically shaped. Pigeons tend to be large, doves small. Most are some shade of brown, often with distinctive wing and tail markings. Some are arboreal in forests, but most are mainly terrestrial, either in open country or inside forest. Plates 28–29.

Parrots and Macaws. Well-known family with colorful plumage, strongly hooked bills, and dextrous feet; body size varies markedly. All are colorful, with green predominating in most species. Mainly occur in forest or woodland, at varying elevations; fast, strong flight, often in groups. Loud raucous or chattering calls, given especially when flying. Some species are very popular in captivity. Plates 30–32.

Cuckoos and Anis. Cuckoos are slender, secretive birds with long graduated tails found in forest and woodland; anis, clad in black, are much more obvious in open country. Plates 33–34.

Owls. Mainly nocturnal predatory birds with large heads, soft fluffy plumage, and very keen hearing; talons very strong. Size varies markedly. Feed mainly on large insects and small mammals. Many species are secretive, heard more than seen. Plates 35–36.

Nightjars and Nighthawks. Nocturnal, insectivorous birds best known from their vocalizations; feed from on or near ground. Variegated, cryptic patterns, sometimes with white in wings and tail. Nighthawks have more pointed wings and are more arboreal than nightjars. Plates 37–39.

Swifts. The most aerial of birds, drably plumaged swifts fly fast and high on stiff, bowed wings. Feet are so tiny birds can perch only on vertical surfaces. Bills very small but open wide; insectivorous. Superficially similar swallows and martins have looser flight style and often perch on wires (swifts never perch in open). Plate 40.

Hummingbirds. Unmistakable. Small to tiny birds with slender bill and minute feet, males often very colorful and sometimes iridescent or ornamented (head plumes, lengthened tail feathers, etc.). Wingbeats so fast that wings themselves can't be seen, flight very rapid and maneuverable. Come to flowers for nectar but also eat small insects. Widespread and conspicuous, especially in Andes; some in forest but many others in open terrain. Plates 41–46.

Trogons and Quetzals. Distinctive group of colorful, forest-inhabiting birds, sluggish and often hard to spot, but frequently vocal; perch erectly. Quetzals are larger than trogons and have elongated wing- and tail-coverts. Plates 47–48.

Kingfishers. Fish-eating birds with long, powerful bills. Found near freshwater, mainly in lowlands. Plate 49.

Motmots. Large birds of forest and woodland understory, colorful but surprisingly inconspicuous. Most species have rackets at tips of long tails. Plate 49.

Jacamars. Fairly small birds, some highly iridescent, with long pointed bills used to capture insects such as bees and butterflies. Found mainly in Amazonian lowland forests. Plate 50.

Puffbirds. Stolid, chunky birds found mainly in lowland forests, some in canopy, others in lower growth. Browns and grays predominate. Nunbirds are excitable and social birds, gray with colorful bills. Plate 51.

Barbets. Colorful relatives of toucans, but smaller. Arboreal in lowland and montane forests. Plate 50.

Toucans. Unmistakable and colorful, fairly large to large birds with unique outsized bills. Arboreal in lowland and montane forests, some species, in groups. Plate 52.

Woodpeckers and Piculets. Distinctive group of birds that perch vertically on treetrunks, using stiffened tail feathers as support. Cf. browner woodcreepers (which always have rufous tails). Vary in size, some small (piculets), others large and powerful; many sport a crest. Plates 48, 53–54.

Ovenbirds. This family and all of the following families comprise the passerine birds, many of which have more elaborate and melodic songs than the previous groups. Ovenbirds comprise a diverse group of mostly brown to rufous birds found in habitats varying from paramo to humid forest to desert scrub. Most, including the multitude of small spinetails, foliage-gleaners (which are larger), treehunters, and leaftossers, are obscure birds, not likely to be noticed unless especially sought out. A few, such as cinclodes and horneros, are bolder, often foraging in open. Unlike woodcreepers, most ovenbirds do not creep up trunks and along branches. Plates 56–59.

Woodcreepers. Brown, often streaked passerines with rufous wings and tail. Creep up trunks and out branches, using stiffened tail feathers for support. Bills long, usually with small hook at tip. Differ from woodpeckers and piculets in coloration, more slender shape, and longer tails. Most range in forest and are not often in the open. Plates 54–55.

Typical Antbirds. A varied and difficult group, found primarily in lowland forests where most skulk in lower growth. A few range in Andes, but almost none occurs in open. All manage to be hard to see. Males typically grayer or blacker than the browner or more rufous females, but there is much variation between species. Some accompany mixed flocks, others are more sedentary. Only a few actually follow army ants (hence, the name "antbird"); none habitually eats ants. Some groups (e.g., antwren, antvireo, antshrike) are named after their fancied resemblance to other, sometimes extralimital bird groupings. Plates 60–63.

Antpittas and Antthrushes. Mainly terrestrial antbirds found almost entirely inside lowland or montane forest. Most are very hard to see. Clad in hues of brown, rufous, and gray; sexes alike. Some have very long legs. Plates 64–65.

Tapaculos. Confusing group of obscure and skulking small birds found primarily in montane forest undergrowth. Most are gray and show little pattern. Plate 66.

Tyrant Flycatchers. Ecuador's most difficult and diverse bird family, found everywhere from high paramo to lowland forest and desert scrub. Many are obscure, olive and yellow with wing-bars, often quite small, and some closely similar to each other; most flycatchers are best left to more experienced observers, though you should gradually learn to recognize the more numerous and distinctive species. A few, however, are much more identifiable and conspicuous, tending to perch vertically in the open and sallying into air after insects. Plates 67–75.

Cotingas. Another diverse group, hard to generalize about. Mostly found in lowland forests, some ranging in Andes. Few cotingas are very conspicuous, but all are worth searching out, being some of Ecuador's most colorful or bizarrely ornamented birds. "True" cotingas (especially genus *Cotinga*) are uncommon canopy birds with dove-like rounded heads. Males of some species gather in leks to sing and display. Plates 76–77.

Manakins. Small, round, short-tailed frugivorous birds found inside forest, mainly in lowlands. Inconspicuous, though males of many species are colorful and may have fancy displays. Plate 78.

Jays. Fairly large, long-tailed, colorfully patterned birds (blue usually predominates) ranging in forest and woodland. Social, and often noisy. Plate 49.

Vireos. Plain, mainly olive arboreal birds found widely in forest and woodland, especially in lowlands. Thicker bills (hooked in peppershrikes and shrike-vireos), less active than warblers; greenlets are smaller. Persistent, repetitive songs. Plate 81.

Thrushes. Simply patterned and colored midsized passerines, varying from black to various shades of brown. Many have yellow or orange bill, legs, and eye-ring. Some are bold and familiar, others shy forest denizens. Most are good songsters. Plate 82.

Swallows and Martins. Insectivorous birds often seen in flight over open country or around water; very gregarious. Martins are large, heavy-bodied swallows. Often perch on wires; some nest around buildings. Swifts (which see) are superficially similar but have stiffer, more swept-back wings and never perch in open. Plate 79.

Wrens. Small, mainly brown or brownish and white birds, usually with dark wing and tail barring, found in shrubbery and forest/woodland undergrowth (often skulking). A few larger species are arboreal. Occur in pairs or (at most) small groups. Plate 80.

Warblers. Small, active insectivorous passerines, about half of species arboreal and half in undergrowth; some are very like certain smaller tanagers, others can resemble vireos. Bills slender. Many species are migratory from North America, others (mainly genus *Basileuterus*) are resident. Often accompany mixed flocks. Plate 83.

Tanagers. Small to (only a few) midsized passerines with variable but typically quite stout bills found throughout Ecuador, mainly in forest and woodland. Some are more familiar, coming out into clearings. Many species are colorful and boldy patterned, but some Andean genera are dull and olive. Many accompany mixed flocks. Most eat fruit, some also insects. Plates 84–90.

Cardinaline Finches. Variable group of midsized passerines, usually with heavy swollen bills. Range in a wide variety of habitats, saltators mainly in cleared areas. Eat mainly fruit and seeds. Most have attractive melodic songs. Plate 91.

Emberizine Finches. Another varied group of small (usually) to midsized passerines, almost all with heavy conical bills adapted for eating seeds. Most are sombrely hued in blues, grays, browns, and blacks; males often duller and/or streakier than females. Range in a variety of habitats, most in open grassy or shrubby terrain, virtually none in lowland forests. Plates 91–93.

Orioles and Blackbirds. Another varied group, most characterized by black or mainly black plumage and rather long, pointed bills. Occur throughout Ecuador, most species in lowlands. Many are gregarious, oropendolas and caciques nesting colonially (with conspicuous long, bag-shaped nests). Plates 94–95.

Siskins. Well-defined group of small finches with stubby conical bills and yellow flashes in wings. Mainly in Andes. Plate 91.

Familiarize yourself with these examples and compare them with the illustrations of other members of their family. Try hard to master the basic groups and families, and the differences between them, always remembering that some of the larger and more diverse families will be much harder than the others. Recognizing a trogon should soon be easy, but telling certain warblers from certain tanagers is not (in fact, as new information comes to light, some species have been switched between families!).

At this point you are ready to graduate to the species level and will need to refer repeatedly to the field guide. The cardinal rule is: *learn to recognize the more common species, with all of their variations, first*, for you will see many more of them than you ever will rare or out-of-range species. Once you know the common birds, you will be in a far better position to pick out the bird that's different. But be certain, don't guess, and try to be able to document why it is that scarcer or out-of-range species (and not something that's numerous).

Always be aware that the vast majority of Ecuadorian birds are residents and are unlikely to be found outside their stated habitats or ranges (for details of these, you will need to refer to the species accounts in Volume I). For example, if a species is stated to occur only in the eastern lowlands, it is extremely unlikely ever to be found in the western lowlands. And if a species is stated to occur only on the west slope of the Andes, its chances of occurring on the east slope are vanishingly small. Andean species are very unlikely ever to be found in the lowlands, and vice versa. But surprising discoveries continue to be made, and bird ranges and abundances do change over time, so if you are confident of an unusual sighting, let someone with more experience know—but be prepared to be rigorously interrogated for details!

Species known to be migrants or wanderers to Ecuador have, almost by definition, a far greater chance of occurring in unexpected places. These are the species most likely to be found outside their stated ranges. We now know the general distribution patterns of migratory birds in Ecuador, but more is certainly left to be learned. So always be on the alert.

As you learn more and more about Ecuadorian birds, your interests may gradually expand beyond just identifying birds by sight. In particular you may wish to start learning to recognize birds by sound, which for most people is a far more difficult proposition. Doing so requires patience and practice, and a reasonably good musical ear, but it can be done, and it will greatly increase the pleasure you receive from looking for birds. It will also mean you will succeed in finding many more birds! Many Ecuadorian birds, including a high proportion of those found in forests of all types, are relatively skulking and hard to see. You will record vastly more of these reclusive species once you learn to recognize them by sound as well as sight.

The process of learning to identify birds by voice is much the same as in learning to recognize birds by their appearance: start with the more common, or more vocal, birds and learn those well. Then when you hear something different, you have a better chance of recognizing it as such and you can track down that sound. An increasing number of commercially available tapes and CDs reproducing the vocalizations of an ever-growing number of Ecuadorian birds now exists, and it is bound to grow. But as always, the best way to learn is through trial and error, on your own, one species at a time, gradually; that way you stand a better chance of really remembering what you learn.

Basically you can make of your study of birds whatever you wish. It can be a solitary pursuit, or a social one, whichever you prefer, though there will always be others sharing your interest and willing to help. You can move into bird photography, or make your own recordings, or get into serious scientific or conservation work. The rewards and pleasures birding brings are surely greater the deeper you delve into it. We envy those of you only now choosing to start out on this path, or to move farther along it, and can only affirm that it is a journey worth taking. We would love to hear from you, hear of your successes (and frustrations!), learn of your discoveries. But most important, enjoy and protect the extraordinary bounty that is Ecuador's birdlife.

Species Accounts

Tinamiformes
Tinamous: Tinamidae (16)

A primitive group, tinamous range only in the Neotropics, where they inhabit forest and woodland, the two *Nothoprocta* in more open terrain. **Sexes are usually alike.** Tinamous are *cryptically colored in various shades of brown, gray, and rufous.* They are *terrestrial*, and most do not fly well, preferring to walk deliberately on the ground, usually within cover; they can run rapidly. Tinamous are shy, usually freezing when danger becomes apparent; as a result, even the larger species can persist in areas where other "gamebirds" (e.g., cracids) have been shot out. All are *heard much more frequently than seen*, and their presence in an area is best indicated by their characteristic, often beautiful, vocalizations. Most eat fleshy fruits that have fallen to the ground. They nest on the ground, with males incubating and caring for fledged young. Their beautiful eggs have a glazed, almost enamel-like surface, typically intense blue, turquoise, or green, sometimes olive or even deep brown.

Tinamus Tinamous

Large to fairly large tinamous found inside humid forest in the lowlands and foothills. Shy and infrequently seen, with notably loud and beautiful vocalizations, often given at night. Terrestrial by day, *Tinamus* roost on a regularly used, fairly thick low branch or liana to which they fly up at dusk; there they rest on their legs, gripping the branch with the rough rear part of the tarsus. Nests are usually placed within the confines of buttressed roots.

Gray Tinamou, *Tinamus tao*
Tinamú Gris   Plate 1(1)

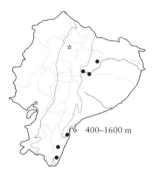

43–46 cm (17–18"). A *large* and *rare* tinamou of *foothill and lower subtropical forests on e. slope.* Iris brown; bill black above, yellowish below; legs grayish blue. *Crown and neck blackish* with *freckled black-and-white throat and stripe from eye down neck.* Otherwise *dark olivaceous gray above with blackish barring and vermiculations.* Below grayish brown, paler on belly, throughout with black vermiculations; crissum rufescent. **Similar species:** Great Tinamou (which is only slightly smaller) much browner overall; Greats in east have rufous (not blackish) crown and neck and show little or no neck stripe (quite prominent in Gray). **Habits:** Poorly known in Ecuador, with only a few recent records; a rarely seen and shy denizen of deep, remote forests. Behavior appears similar to that of much more numerous Great. **Voice:** ♂'s song (N. Krabbe recording, from Loreto road) an abrupt, single hooting note, "hooooo," with quality of better-known Great Tinamou but lower pitched, followed by pair of shorter and slightly lower-pitched "hoo" notes; it is unknown whether latter notes are given by same bird or its mate. Song is repeated at long intervals (10 or more seconds).

Great Tinamou, *Tinamus major*

Tinamú Grande   Plate 1(2)

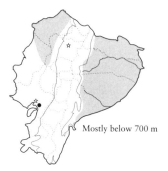

Mostly below 700 m

38–43 cm (15–17″). *Widespread on ground inside humid forest in lowlands of east and northwest*, in east mainly in terra firme; a few range up into foothills. Iris brown; bill blackish above, grayish below; legs bluish gray. In **east** *crown and neck rufous*; otherwise *olive brown above* with scattered blackish bars. Throat whitish; underparts grayish brown, paler on belly, with dark vermiculations, flanks and crissum barred dusky. In **northwest** similar but crown darker and browner and showing *slight crest*, upperparts more rufescent. **Similar species:** White-throated Tinamou considerably smaller, has blackish crown, and shows considerable buff spotting on wings (the last not shown at all by Great). Cf. also Gray Tinamou (even larger, and distinctly darker and grayer overall). Undulated Tinamou considerably smaller and paler and more grayish below. *In w. lowlands, no other tinamou is nearly as large.* **Habits:** Heard far more often than seen. Sometimes a surprised bird will sedately walk away and then freeze, in the hope you haven't noticed it, but more often an approached bird suddenly flushes with a great clap of wings. Great Tinamous favor forest with a fairly open understory and where undisturbed can be moderately numerous. Feed mostly on fruits and seeds, obtained while walking on forest floor. **Voice:** ♂'s haunting song, one of the most beautiful Neotropical bird sounds, consists of up to 7 tremulous whistled notes, the first set sometimes repeated, the second note slightly higher pitched but then sliding down, "whoo, who-o-o-o-or." At times the last "who-o-o-or" note is given alone, or it may be given in a series of up to about 6 notes that gradually become stronger. Singing can occur at any time, day or night, but is most frequent around dawn and dusk. Flushed birds sometimes give a chippering as they fly off.

White-throated Tinamou, *Tinamus guttatus*

Tinamú Goliblanco   Plate 1(3)

To 400 m

33–36 cm (13–14″). On ground inside *terra firme forest in lowlands of east*. Iris brown; bill black above, dusky-yellow below; legs dull grayish olive. Crown blackish, face and sides of neck freckled buff and blackish; otherwise rufescent brown above with scattered blackish bars; *wing-coverts and inner flight feathers distinctly spotted with buff*. *Throat white*; underparts grayish brown, lower flanks and crissum barred dusky. **Similar species:** Considerably smaller than Great Tinamou, with which east of Andes it shares the dim forest floor; Greats there have rufous crown and show no spotting on wings. White-throated is larger than any of the forest-dwelling *Crypturellus*; Variegated and Bartlett's Tinamous are both obviously barred above. **Habits:** Similar to Great Tinamou. On rare occasions the two species can be found together feeding on fallen fruit. They are frequently heard singing in the same area. **Voice:** Distinctive mournful song a pair of low-pitched hollow notes, the second (given after a pause of 1–2 seconds) distinctly upslurred, "hooo . . . hoo-a." As with other forest tinamous, it is given especially around dawn and dusk.

Nothocercus Tinamous

Fairly large, quite rufescent tinamous that range *inside Andean forests*. Even more than other tinamous, *Nothocercus* are heard much more often than seen.

Highland Tinamou, *Nothocercus bonapartei*
Tinamú Serrano   Plate 1(4)

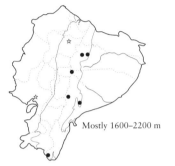

Mostly 1600–2200 m

2300–3400 m

35.5–38 cm (14–15″). Scarce on ground inside *subtropical forest on e. slope*. Iris brown; bill dark gray above, pale brown below; legs brownish gray. *Crown and neck blackish*; above otherwise dark rufous brown with blackish barring and vermiculations, and buff barring on wings. *Throat tawny-ochraceous*; chest rich rufous brown *becoming paler and more cinnamon-buff on breast and belly*, some dusky barring on lower flanks and thighs. **Similar species:** Tawny-breasted Tinamou occurs at higher elevations and differs in having obviously rufescent crown and contrasting white throat; the two species differ strikingly in voice too. At lower edge of range (overlap?), cf. Great Tinamou. **Habits:** Poorly known and infrequently seen, perhaps occurring at relatively low densities even where conditions are favorable. Basically solitary, walking on ground inside forest, hardly ever emerging from cover though occasionally one is glimpsed scurrying down a trail. **Voice:** Far-carrying song a long-continued repetition of a simple, somewhat nasal phrase. "ko-á, ko-á, ko-á, ko-á . . ." that can go on for 30 or more seconds.

Tawny-breasted Tinamou, *Nothocercus julius*
Tinamú Pechileonado   Plate 1(5)

35.5–38 cm (14–15″). Scarce on ground inside *temperate forest on e. slope* and on w.

slope as far south as w. Cotopaxi. Iris brown; bill blackish above, bluish gray below; legs gray. *Crown and neck rufescent*; above otherwise rufous brown with blackish barring and vermiculations, and buff barring on wings. *Throat white*; chest olivaceous brown *becoming bright cinnamon-rufous on breast and belly*, some dusky barring on lower flanks and thighs. **Similar species:** Highland Tinamou occurs at lower elevations and has blackish crown (not rufescent), tawny-ochraceous throat (not white), and less richly colored underparts. **Habits:** Behavior much like Highland Tinamou; Tawny-breasted is equally infrequently seen. On rare occasions, especially early in morning, one may emerge to feed in small fields at edge of forest. **Voice:** Far-carrying song a very distinctive fast and rhythmic series of almost chanting notes ("trree-er tree-er tree-er tree-er . . ."), a little faster than 1 note/second; this may continue for a minute or more, but then bird signals approaching end by inserting a shorter and lower-pitched phrase ("tru-tru-tru-trreeu") before adding a few more "tree-er" phrases and fading off. Calling birds are easily overlooked as they stand perfectly still, even remaining motionless if you approach.

Crypturellus Tinamous

Small to midsized tinamous occurring widely in most forested or wooded habitats, with diversity greatest in e. lowland forests; two species (Berlepsch's and Pale-browed) are restricted to the west, and one (Tataupa) occurs only in the Zumba region. In color and pattern they range from being very dark and uniform (Cinereous and Berlepsch's) to quite boldly patterned (notably Variegated). Like other tinamous, *Crypturellus* are heard much more often than seen, their attractive vocalizations being among the characteristic sounds of lowland forests.

Cinereous Tinamou, *Crypturellus cinereus*
Tinamú Cinéreo   Plate 1(6)

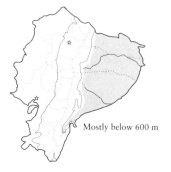

Mostly below 600 m

30–30.5 cm (11³/₄–12″). Fairly common on ground *inside várzea forest and woodland, and along watercourses in terra firme, in lowlands of east.* Iris dusky-orange; bill blackish above, gray below; legs grayish. *Uniform sooty brown,* slightly paler below, sides of neck and throat with some fine whitish streaks. **Similar species:** Berlepsch's Tinamou occurs only west of Andes. Smaller Undulated Tinamou is paler, especially below, with white throat contrasting sharply with gray and brown breast. **Habits:** Much like other *Crypturellus* tinamous, but seems even more difficult to see than most, in part because of especially dense and tangled habitats it favors. Most apt to be seen when crossing a trail or little-used road, especially in early morning. Unlike Undulated Tinamou, rarely seems to emerge from forest cover. **Voice:** Frequently heard song a clear ringing whistle on one pitch, "puuuu," lasting just under 1 second and repeated at intervals of 3–5 seconds, sometimes continuing for long periods. Sunbittern's whistle (less often heard) is somewhat similar.

Berlepsch's Tinamou, *Crypturellus berlepschi*
Tinamú de Berlepsch   Plate 1(7)

28 cm (11″). *Scarce* on ground inside humid forest and woodland in *lowlands of far northwest (mainly Esmeraldas).* Formerly considered conspecific with Cinereous Tinamou. *Iris yellow-orange;* bill blackish above, dull orange-red below; legs dark

Mostly below 300 m

reddish brown. *Uniform sooty black,* slightly blacker on foreparts. **Similar species:** In its limited range virtually unmistakable; Little Tinamou is smaller and much browner and more rufescent generally. Cinereous Tinamou occurs only east of Andes. **Habits:** Poorly known but presumably differs little from other forest-inhabiting tinamous. Birds seen have been walking alone inside forest, sometimes near streams. **Voice:** Song a short and high-pitched (unusually so for a tinamou) piercing whistle, "teeeee" (O. Jahn recording, and P. Mena Valenzuela).

Little Tinamou, *Crypturellus soui*
Tinamú Chico   Plate 1(8)

To 1200 m

21.5–23 cm (8¹/₂–9″). A *small, plain* tinamou found widely in lowlands, *favoring secondary habitats* of various types including woodland, overgrown clearings and plantations, and forest openings. Iris brown; bill black above, pale greenish to horn below; legs olive. *Crown blackish,* sides of head grayish; *otherwise rich rufous brown above. Throat whitish,* chest brown; *lower underparts rich ochraceous-rufous.* Some individuals are more blackish above and duller below;

♀♀ average brighter. **Similar species:** In many areas the most numerous and frequently heard tinamous as, unlike so many others, it is not confined to tall forest. In the west, dark individuals can easily be confused with rarer and blacker Berlepsch's Tinamou. Looks most like rare Brown Tinamou, though that species is larger with gray throat (not white) and dark flank barring. **Habits:** Extremely furtive and hard to see even where, by voice, you know it is numerous. Almost exclusively terrestrial, tending to remain in dense thickets and rarely in open for long; it either freezes or, more often, scurries away upon approach. **Voice:** Primary song a series of clear, tremulous whistles, each slightly higher pitched than previous one; it gradually increases in volume and then ends abruptly. Also gives a slurred call that rises and falls, "pee-ee-ee yer-r-r," as well as phrases that may resemble those of Great Tinamou but never are as loud, resonant, or low pitched as that species'.

Brown Tinamou, *Crypturellus obsoletus*
Tinamú Pardo   Plate 1(10)

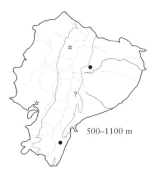

25.5 cm (10"). *Rare and local* on ground inside humid forest in *foothills on e. slope.* Crown dusky, sides of head grayish; otherwise rich rufous brown above. *Throat gray; underparts rich rufous, lower flanks and crissum barred blackish.* **Similar species:** Likely to be confused only with smaller Little Tinamou, which is found in secondary habitats and has, most notably, a whitish (not distinctly gray) throat and shows no barring on flanks. **Habits:** Hardly known in Ecuador. Elsewhere much like other forest tinamous, and at least equally hard to see. **Voice:** In Peru gives a 3-noted, rather harsh series of

whistles, "trreenh, trreenh, trenh?" Song in Ecuador still not certainly known.

Undulated Tinamou, *Crypturellus undulatus*
Tinamú Ondulado   Plate 1(11)

25.5–26.5 cm (10–10½"). *Common* on ground in *várzea and riparian forest and woodland (even some larger river islands) and in adjacent clearings in lowlands of east.* Iris pale brown; bill black above, yellowish below; tarsus olive gray. Crown dusky; otherwise dull brown above with fine blackish vermiculations, wing-coverts and inner flight feathers with scattered buff bars. *Throat white*, chest brown; *remaining underparts pale grayish* with faint brown vermiculations, median belly whiter, lower belly with some brown barring. **Similar species:** Cinereous Tinamou larger and much darker generally. Little Tinamou smaller and rich rufous below (not mostly gray). **Habits:** Shy and inconspicuous but somewhat easier to see than many other tinamous as it favors riparian areas with little or even no understory, such as areas recently exposed by falling water levels. Also comes out into cleared areas more often, but is still heard far more often than seen. **Voice:** Frequently heard voice a distinctive series of 3–4 whistled notes with characteristic cadence, "whooh, whoh-hoah?"

Variegated Tinamou, *Crypturellus variegatus*
Tinamú Abigarrado   Plate 1(13)
25.5–26.5 cm (10–10½"). A handsome, *boldly patterned* tinamou found on ground inside *terra firme forest in lowlands of east.* Iris brown; bill black, base of lower mandible yellowish; legs dull olive-gray. *Crown and sides of head black*; throat

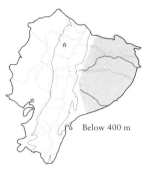

Below 400 m

white; *neck, upper back, and entire breast bright rufous*, becoming paler buffy whitish on median belly, with flanks and crissum obscurely barred dusky. *Upperparts otherwise blackish, boldly barred with cinnamon-rufous.* **Similar species:** Combination of conspicuously barred upperparts and rufous breast distinctive. Somewhat smaller Bartlett's Tinamou inhabits same terra firme forests, and also has barred upperparts, but differs in its duller brownish gray upper back and breast. **Habits:** Though regularly heard, notably shy and only infrequently seen. Foraging birds walk alone on forest floor, crouching and freezing when sensing danger. **Voice:** Distinctive song a single long mournful whistle followed, after a long pause of up to 4–5 seconds, by a rather fast and ascending series of up to 9 shorter and modulated upslurred whistles.

Bartlett's Tinamou, *Crypturellus bartletti*
Tinamú de Bartlett   Plate 1(12)

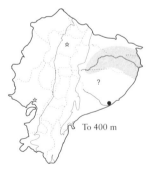

To 400 m

23–24 cm (9–9½"). Uncommon on ground *inside terra firme forest in lowlands of east.* Iris brown; bill black above, brown below with greenish yellow at base; legs yellowish

olive. *Crown and sides of head sooty black; neck and upper back sooty brown; upperparts otherwise blackish, boldly banded with buff or olive brown.* Throat white; *upper breast grayish brown*, becoming brown on lower breast; belly paler, buff to creamy white, with some dusky barring on lower flanks and crissum. **Similar species:** Variegated Tinamou is more brightly colored with obviously rufous (not sooty and brown) neck and breast. Other deep-forest tinamous are not boldly banded above. **Habits:** Similar to Variegated, and equally infrequently seen. **Voice:** Distinctive and memorable song a series of whistled notes that commences with several pure notes (each recalling whistle of Cinereous Tinamou, but louder and more penetrating) given at long intervals (5–8 seconds); it then proceeds into a faster and rising series of shorter whistled notes that gradually rise in pitch and are given with ever-shorter intervals.

Pale-browed Tinamou
Crypturellus transfasciatus
Tinamú Cejiblanco   Plate 1(14)

Mostly below 800 m, locally to 1600 m in Loja

25.5 cm (10"). Not uncommon on ground *inside deciduous woodland and forest in lowlands of southwest*, locally ranging out into regenerating scrub (but never in true desert). In w. Loja also ranges up into lower subtropics. Iris brown to olive brown; bill blackish above, whitish to pale yellowish below; *legs pale orange.* The only Ecuadorian *Crypturellus* showing sexual dimorphism. ♂ crown brownish dusky with *conspicuous whitish superciliary*; otherwise grayish to rufescent brown above, lower back and rump narrowly barred with black; wing-coverts barred and tipped buff. Throat white; *sides* of neck and breast pale grayish; belly whitish to buffy whitish, flanks and crissum barred blackish. ♀ differs in having *wing-coverts, inner flight feathers, and middle of back to rump boldly banded blackish and rufous to buff*. **Similar species:** Only other *Crypturellus* in this species' range is the very different Little Tinamou (with no brow, rich rufous underparts, no barring above, etc.). Cf. also Andean Tinamou. **Habits:** Behavior similar to other *Crypturellus* tinamous. Like them, Pale-browed is usually very difficult to see; sometimes one will call almost at your feet yet somehow remain invisible. **Voice:** Distinctive song an abrupt, loud, ringing "ooo-eeé?" or "ooo-íng" with liquid quality. Vocalizes primarily during rainy season.

Tataupa Tinamou, *Crypturellus tataupa*
Tinamú Tataupá   Plate 1(9)

650–950 m

23 cm (9"). A *small* tinamou found only in *semideciduous woodland and scrub near Zumba in Río Marañón drainage of far southeast*. Iris pale brown; bill gray, dull purplish red basally; *legs dull purplish red. Head, neck, and breast gray*, throat whitish. Above otherwise unmarked rufescent brown; lower underparts pale grayish, palest on median belly, with some blackish scaling on lower flanks. **Similar species:** Little Tinamou also occurs in scrub and regenerating woodland around Zumba; it is similarly sized but very different in plumage (being mainly rich rufous, not gray), leg color, and voice. **Habits:** Similar to other *Crypturellus* though a little easier to see than most. **Voice:** Song very different from that of any other Ecuadorian tinamou; consists of a short descending series of gravelly notes, the first longer and slightly rising in pitch, remainder faster

and shorter, e.g., "drreeyp? dreey-dri-dri-dri-dri-dru."

Nothoprocta Tinamous
Intricately patterned tinamous ranging in more open habitats than other Ecuadorian tinamous, both *Nothoprocta* favor semiopen grassy areas at higher elevations. They have *decurved bills* and *obvious yellow legs*. *Nothoprocta* fly more strongly than the other Ecuadorian tinamous, and they are more apt to flush and fly off considerable distances.

Andean Tinamou, *Nothoprocta pentlandii*
Tinamú Andino   Plate 1(15)

1000–2300 m

25.5–26.5 cm (10–10½"). *Montane scrub and adjacent grassy clearings and fields in highlands of Loja and adjacent Azuay and El Oro*. Iris yellowish to pale brown; *slender decurved bill* black above, dull pinkish below; *legs pale yellow*. Above brown with whitish streaking, grayish mottling, and rufescent barring; wings more barred with buff. Throat grayish, *breast gray with large buff spots*; lower underparts pale buffy ochraceous. **Similar species:** Curve-billed Tinamou is much more rufescent below (with no gray on breast and more deeply colored on belly); it occurs above Andean (basically in or near paramo) and is not known to range as far southwest. Cf. Rufous-bellied Seedsnipe. **Habits:** Despite being found in more semiopen habitats than most other Ecuadorian tinamous, Andean is nonetheless a hard bird to see, one occasionally being glimpsed as it crosses a road or trial. Generally keeps to tall grassy or scrubby cover. **Voice:** High-pitched, whistled call an abrupt and shrill "pii-eeng!"; usually given at quite long intervals, hence hard to locate.

Curve-billed Tinamou, *Nothoprocta curvirostris*
Tinamú Piquicurvo   Plate 1(16)

28–29 cm (11–11½″). *Local in shrubby paramo grassland and woodland patches,* also ranging down into adjacent agricultural fields. Iris brown; *slender decurved bill* black, lower mandible yellowish flesh basally; *legs pale yellow.* Above dark brown with whitish streaking and dense rufescent vermiculations; wings more barred with buff, *flight feathers extensively rufous-barred* (*obvious in flight*). Throat buffy whitish; *remaining underparts tawny-buff,* chest with some dark spots and whitish streaks. **Similar species:** The only tinamou at all likely to be seen in paramo, though it rarely strays far from woodland or scrub. **Habits:** Hard to see except when accidentally flushed; in early morning sometimes feeds at edge of roads or trails. **Voice:** Call a series of 3 whistled notes, the first lower pitched, given every 5 seconds (Fjeldså and Krabbe 1990).

Podicipediformes
Grebes: Podicipedidae (3)
Small aquatic birds with short tails, grebes are adept swimmers that come to land only to nest; the nests are no more than floating platforms anchored to aquatic vegetation. Their legs are set far to the rear of the body—grebes are incapable of walking—and their toes are lobed. Grebes range mainly on freshwater lakes and ponds and are only infrequently seen in flight. **Sexes are alike.**

Least Grebe, *Tachybaptus dominicus*
Zambullidor Menor   Plate 8(1)
21.5–23 cm (8½–9″). A *small* grebe, *widespread and locally common on ponds and*

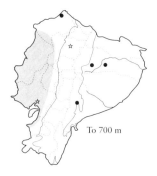

To 700 m

lakes in lowlands of west, but very rare in east. Formerly placed in genus *Podiceps. Iris golden yellow; slender bill black tipped pale gray* (often looks slightly upturned); legs blackish. **Adult** has *blackish crown, slaty gray face and neck* (with black throat when breeding). Above otherwise blackish; below grayish, more brown on flanks, also some cinnamon-brown on breast. **In flight** shows broad white stripe on flight feathers. **Juvenile** similar but eye less bright, base of lower mandible paler; throat whitish. Very young birds may retain some whitish head striping. **Similar species:** Pied-billed Grebe, which often occurs with this species, is larger and browner overall with *much heavier and pale bill.* **Habits:** Usually occurs in pairs or small groups on quiet, more or less secluded ponds and lakes, most often where there is at least some fringing woodland. Nesting pairs may move onto quite small (sometimes remarkably so) and ephemeral ponds, departing when water levels drop. Downy young are often carried on parents' backs. Nonbreeders may gather in quite large aggregations on lakes and reservoirs that retain water when many other areas are devoid of it. Dives for food, aquatic insects and small fish; can slowly sink from sight, not making a ripple. **Voice:** Usually quiet, but breeding birds give soft purring calls and a descending churring somewhat like certain *Laterallus* crakes.

Pied-billed Grebe, *Podilymbus podiceps*
Zambullidor Piquipinto   Plate 8(2)
28–33 cm (11–13″). *Widespread and locally common on ponds and lakes in lowlands of west,* also locally on *lakes in highlands of north.* Iris brownish, eye-ring whitish; *notably thick bill chalky whitish to pale grayish,* with *conspicuous black ring when*

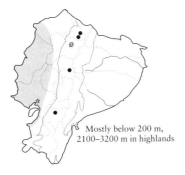

Mostly below 200 m,
2100–3200 m in highlands

breeding; legs blackish. **Adult** *mostly grayish brown*, darker and browner above, paler below with gray face and neck and *black throat*; median breast, belly, and crissum white. **In flight** wings dark. **Nonbreeding adult and juvenile** have head and neck more cinnamon brown with throat whitish. Very young birds may retain some whitish head striping. **Similar species:** No other Ecuadorian grebe has such a heavy bill; Least Grebe is smaller with much finer bill, yellow eye, etc. Cf. juvenile Common Gallinule and various of the smaller ducks. **Habits:** Much like Least Grebe though somewhat more sedentary and even less likely to fly; favors deeper and more open water, though the two species often occur together. **Voice:** Breeding birds give a series of hollow notes, e.g., "cuk-cuk-cuk-cuk, cow, cow, cow"; also various whinnies.

Silvery Grebe, *Podiceps occipitalis*
Zambullidor Plateado   Plate 8(3)

29–30½ cm (11½–12″). A mainly gray and white grebe, now *uncommon and very local on lakes in paramo and n. part of central valley*; no longer present at many of its earlier

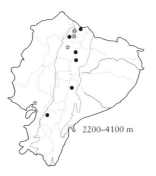

2200–4100 m

haunts. Iris red; *short pointed bill blackish*; legs blackish. **Adult** has crown gray and hindneck black, with *tuft of buffy gray feathers on ear-coverts*. Otherwise dark gray above; *underparts snowy white*, some gray on flanks. **In flight** shows white patch on secondaries. **Nonbreeding adult and juvenile** similar but lacking head plumes. **Similar species:** Not likely confused in its Ecuadorian range; shining white foreneck and thin bill distinctive. **Habits:** As noted above, this species is now very local in Ecuador, though it can be quite numerous on the few lakes where it yet survives. Rather gregarious, swimming on open water, often with rearparts held high out of water, exposing much white. Feeds mainly by picking at insects on water's surface, diving less than other grebes. Nesting is usually colonial.

Spenisciformes
Penguins: Spheniscidae (1)
Flightless seabirds with *"flipperlike"* wings, penguins have streamlined bodies, short stiff tails, and webbed feet. Penguins are uniformly and densely feathered—they lack the feather tracts of most other birds—and this provides insulation and waterproofing. **Sexes are alike.**

Humboldt Penguin, *Spheniscus humboldti*
Pingüino de Humboldt   Plate 4(12)

65–70 cm (25½–27½″). *A casual wanderer to coast of s. Ecuador*. An unmistakable black-and-white seabird that walks erectly but is mainly at home swimming in coastal waters. Iris brown; heavy bill black with *extensive fleshy pink at base*; legs blackish. *Essentially black above and white below*; a white band arches up around black face and chin to forehead, and a *prominent black band arches up sides and across chest*. **Habits:** All Ecuadorian records of this globally rare penguin are of dead or dying (dispersing?) birds found on beaches; some may have been brought to Ecuador by sailors or fishermen. Elsewhere Humboldt Penguins are gregarious birds that nest in small colonies on offshore islands.

Procellariiformes
Albatrosses: Diomedeidae (2)

Very large, long- and narrow-winged seabirds found primarily in southern oceans, a few ranging in the North Pacific and one (Waved) nesting mainly on the Galápagos. Albatrosses are highly pelagic when not breeding. Their bills are long and heavy with external tubular nostrils used for the secretion of excess salt. Both species were formerly placed in the genus *Diomedea*. **Sexes are alike.**

Waved Albatross, *Phoebastria irrorata*
Albatros de Galápagos   Plate 2(1)

86.5–91.5 cm (34–36″). A *scarce visitant to offshore waters*, mainly or entirely in south; a few breed on *Isla de la Plata*. Also called Galápagos Albatross. *Huge. Heavy long bill yellow to orange-yellow* tipped olive; legs grayish to bluish gray. *Head, neck, and breast white* with *crown and hindneck tinged buffy yellow*; upperparts dark brown with narrow wavy white vermiculations on upper back and rump; tail dusky. *Lower underparts white with narrow wavy dusky vermiculations*. **In flight** shows white primary flash; underwing dusky brown with underwing-coverts white vermiculated dusky. **Similar species:** *The only albatross regularly occurring in Ecuadorian waters*, where therefore

easily recognized by huge size. **Habits:** Basically pelagic. In mainland Ecuadorian waters usually occurs alone, sailing effortlessly and scaling low over water on stiff outstretched wings, flapping only occasionally (more frequently in light winds). Also often loafs on water's surface, head and neck held high. Does not seem to be attracted to ships. Feeds mainly on squid and fish. Nests in loose colonies, pairs mating for life, each pair's single egg laid directly on ground; elaborate courtship dancing precedes egg-laying. **Voice:** Courting pairs utter nasal calls, "ayah-uh."

Black-browed Albatross
Thalassarche melanophris
Albatros Ojeroso   Plate 2(2)

81–86.5 cm (32–34″). A *casual vagrant* to offshore waters in south. *Bill rich yellow tipped orange* (grayish horn tipped blackish in juveniles); legs bluish gray. **Adult** has *head, neck, and entire underparts white with black smudge around eye*. Upperparts brownish black with contrasting white rump and gray tail. **Juvenile** similar but with partial dusky collar on foreneck. **In flight** underwing white broadly margined blackish. **Similar species:** Not likely confused; cf. even larger Waved Albatross and Kelp Gull. **Habits:** Similar to Waved Albatross though much more apt to be attracted to ships, and feeding inshore more often.

Shearwaters and Petrels:
Procellariidae (9)

Midsized to fairly large seabirds that, like albatrosses, have external tubular nostrils that are fused on top of the bill. Mainly pelagic, they come ashore only to nest on islands, many species in burrows; none breeds in mainland Ecuadorian waters, and many appear to occur here only as vagrants. Many species have a stiff-winged gliding-and-sailing flight similar to that of the albatrosses though not quite as masterful. They are vocal only on their nesting grounds, and voice is thus not described here. **Sexes are alike.**

[Southern Fulmar, *Fulmarus glacialoides*
Fulmar Sureño] Plate 2(3)

46–49.5 cm (18–19½″). An attractive *pale* seabird, only a *casual vagrant* to offshore waters in south. Also called Antarctic Fulmar. *Heavy bill mainly pinkish* with blackish tip; legs also pinkish. *Head, neck, and underparts white*; *upperparts pale pearly gray*. **In flight** shows mainly pale pearly gray upperwing with variable amount of black and a white flash in primaries; underwing mostly white. **Similar species:** Really does not resemble any other seabird; it is vaguely gull-like, though its stiff-winged flight style is very different. **Habits:** Flies with stiff, somewhat bowed wings low over water, wings sometimes appearing actually to slice waves. Often accompanies larger numbers of Pintado Petrels, though less likely to follow ships for extended periods of time.

Pintado Petrel, *Daption capense*
Petrel Pintado Plate 2(4)

38–40.5 cm (15–16″). An unmistakable, *boldly pied* seabird that is an *irregular visitant* to offshore waters in south. Also called Cape Petrel. Bill and legs black. *Above sooty blackish, back and rump white with conspicuous black chevrons and spots*; broad tail-tip blackish. Throat sooty blackish; *remaining underparts white*. **In flight** has mainly black-

ish upperwing *with two large, prominent white patches* (one on inner primaries, other on inner wing-coverts and secondaries), underwing white with black border. **Similar species:** Not likely confused, no other seabird found in Ecuadorian waters being as boldly patterned. **Habits:** In areas where it occurs regularly, can be one of most numerous seabirds, tending to occur in scattered loose flocks and often attracted to ships. Often ranges into inshore waters, sometimes even following fishing boats into harbors. Feeds mainly by pecking quickly at objects on water's surface, sometimes at night.

Dark-rumped Petrel, *Pterodroma phaeopygia*
Petrel Lomioscuro Plate 2(5)

43 cm (17″). A *rare visitant* from its Galápagos breeding grounds to offshore waters in south. *Thick stubby bill black*; feet mostly pinkish flesh. *Above uniform sooty brown to blackish* aside from *contrasting white forehead*, blackest on head; tail rather long and wedge-shaped. Below entirely white. Some individuals show white at sides of rump. **In flight** upperwing uniform blackish, underwing white broadly margined with black and

with *black diagonal bar across coverts.* **Similar species:** No other Ecuadorian seabird shows conspicuous contrasting white forehead of this dashing petrel. **Habits:** Typical flight fast with long glides and much banking in wide arcs, but with little flapping, especially under windy conditions; in strong winds banks up steeply, then glides steeply back down. Usually seen singly; rarely associates with other seabirds. Feeds mainly by picking objects from water's surface.

Procellaria Petrels

Large, heavy-bodied seabirds with *stout, pale bills.* Only one species (Parkinson's) occurs regularly in Ecuador.

[White-chinned Petrel
Procellaria aequinoctialis
Petrel Barbiblanco]   Plate 2(6)

53.5–56 cm (21–22″). *Accidental* well off coast of Santa Elena Peninsula. *Stout ivory-colored bill* with black lines; legs black. A *large and heavily built* seabird, *uniform sooty brown*, usually with *small white patch on chin* (inconspicuous in field). **Similar species:** Resembles more numerous Parkinson's Petrel but is considerably larger and not so black, with entirely pale bill (no dark tip). **Habits:** Similar to Parkinson's Petrel. Flight powerful and steady, gliding for long periods on outstretched wings provided there is sufficient wind. Frequently attracted to ships.

Parkinson's Petrel, *Procellaria parkinsoni*
Petrel de Parkinson   Plate 2(7)

46–47 cm (18–18½″). A *regular and locally not uncommon* visitor to offshore waters in south, in recent years mainly recorded from off Santa Elena Peninsula where it appears to

be present in all months (though perhaps most numerous during austral winter). Also called Black Petrel. Stout greenish ivory to whitish bill with black lines and *blackish tip*; legs black. *Uniform sooty blackish.* In flight primaries from below may show silvery flash. **Similar species:** Considerably larger and heavier than Sooty Shearwater, which is grayer in overall plumage tone and has more slender and black bill. Cf. also much rarer White-chinned Petrel. **Habits:** In Ecuadorian waters regularly occurs in small groups that may loaf on water's surface for protracted periods, often congregating around fishing boats. Glides with little flapping if winds are adequate, but flight otherwise rather labored, with heavy and slow wingstrokes. Apparently feeds primarily at night.

Puffinus Shearwaters

Rather slender seabirds with long pointed wings that typically are held stiffly as they glide and sail low over the water's surface, hardly flapping at all if there is sufficient wind. Only two species (Pink-footed and Sooty) are regular in Ecuadorian waters.

Pink-footed Shearwater, *Puffinus creatopus*
Pardela Patirrosada   Plate 2(8)

46–48 cm (18–19″). A *large* shearwater with *bicolored plumage*, regular though never very numerous offshore. *Bill dull pink with dark tip*; legs pink. Blackish to grayish brown above; *below white* with variable amount of dusky scaling and mottling. **In flight** shows uniform dark upperwing, underwing whitish with some dusky mottling. **Similar species:** Only other large and bicolored (dark above, white below) shearwater known to occur in mainland Ecuadorian waters is much rarer Buller's. **Habits:** Similar to Sooty Shearwater, though flight heavier with long glides interspersed by brief bouts of labored flapping; often occurs with more numerous Sooty. Sometimes attracted to fishing boats, but more often seen as the odd individual just flying past.

Buller's Shearwater, *Puffinus bulleri*
Pardela de Buller   Plate 2(9)

43–46 cm (17–18″). *Accidental* (one w. Guayas specimen). Formerly called Gray-backed Shearwater. Rather slender bill black; legs dull pink. *Crown blackish* blending into *gray back and rump*, with lower back more blackish; tail black. *Underparts pure white.* **In flight** shows *striking blackish M-pattern on upperwing* with *dark primaries and (especially) coverts contrasting with whitish secondaries and outer secondary-coverts*; *underwing white.* **Similar species:** So strongly patterned that it is unlikely to be confused with any other shearwater or petrel known to occur in Ecuador. **Habits:** Much as in other shearwaters, with graceful and buoyant flight.

Sooty Shearwater, *Puffinus griseus*
Pardela Sombría   Plate 2(10)

43–46 cm (17–18″). *The most numerous shearwater in Ecuadorian waters* (oc-

casionally seen even from shore), seemingly occurring in varying numbers year-round. Rather slender bill black; legs blackish and gray. *Sooty brownish gray*, darkest on head and upperparts. **In flight** shows *relatively narrow pointed wings*, and *underwing usually shows silvery white flash on coverts.* **Similar species:** The only all-dark-bodied shearwater found in Ecuador; body looks cigar-shaped. Cf. larger Parkinson's Petrel (with heavier whitish bill, etc.). **Habits:** Flight strong and powerful, with wingbeats often fast; regularly banks from side to side, exposing the silvery underwing. Also glides purposefully low over waves, flapping very little. When conditions are calmer, Sooties are often seen swimming on surface, regularly in groups and sometimes with other seabirds.

[Audubon's Shearwater, *Puffinus lherminieri*
Pardela de Audubon]   Plate 2(11)

29–30.5 cm (11½–12″). *Apparently a casual visitant to offshore waters*, perhaps mainly in warmer water of north. A *small*, "*black-and-white*" shearwater. Bill blackish; legs flesh to dusky. *Above, including crown to below eyes,*

blackish to very dark brown. Below contrastingly white, with dusky mottling on flanks and black crissum. **Similar species:** Notably smaller than other Ecuadorian shearwaters, and not as strong a flier. **Habits:** Flight rapid and fluttery or even "sloppy," often not long sustained, usually consisting of 5–10 shallow flaps interspersed by a short glide. In many areas (e.g., the Galápagos) quite gregarious, and often approaches boats, circling them and then settling on water. Often feeds in small groups together with flocks of terns, swimming and making short thrusts into water.

Storm-Petrels: Hydrobatidae (10)

Small to very small seabirds found widely across the oceans of the world; no storm-petrel breeds in mainland Ecuadorian waters, though several do breed on the Galápagos. A number of species seem to be rare here, though the rarity of some may more be the result of a relative lack of pelagic field work rather than actual small numbers. Storm-petrels have generally dark plumage, often accented by a white "rump" patch; many are hard to identify. They are vocal only while nesting, and voices are not described here. **Sexes are alike.**

Oceanites Storm-Petrels

Storm-petrels with comparatively long legs, long enough for the feet to extend past their square tails in flight.

Wilson's Storm-Petrel, *Oceanites oceanicus*
Paíño de Wilson   Plate 3(1)

17–19 cm (6¾–7½"). Apparently a *very rare austral winter visitant* to offshore waters in

south (overlooked?). Bill and long legs black, with *yellow on webs of feet* sometimes visible as birds patter on water's surface, and feet protruding beyond tail. Sooty black with *rounded white band on uppertail-coverts that extends around to lower flanks*, sometimes with a little white on crissum; *tail square.* **In flight** shows pale greater coverts, rather rounded wings. **Similar species:** Smaller but equally long-legged White-vented Storm-Petrel shows considerable white on median belly and pale area on underwing (latter lacking in Wilson's). **Habits:** Flight somewhat swallow-like, tending to be steady and direct with rather shallow fluttery wingbeats and little gliding. Often gather around ships, sometimes following them for protracted periods. Feeding birds hover low while pattering loosely dangled feet on water's surface, wings held in a V above back, then bound to a new spot and repeat process.

White-vented Storm-Petrel, *Oceanites gracilis*
Paíño Grácil   Plate 3(2)

15–16 cm (6–6¼"). Apparently a *rare visitant* to coastal and offshore waters in south. Also called Elliot's Storm-Petrel. Bill and *long legs* with *yellow webs on feet* as in Wilson's Storm-Petrel. White-vented resembles larger Wilson's Storm-Petrel, differing in having a *variable but usually considerable amount of white on median belly* and *pale area on underwing* (Wilson's underwing dark). Wilson's is apparently the rarer of the two in Ecuadorian waters. **Habits:** Similar to Wilson's Storm-Petrel, though White-vented is more apt to occur inshore, sometimes even entering harbors; at times can even be seen from land.

White-faced Storm-Petrel
Pelagodroma marina
Paíño Cariblanco   Plate 3(10)

21 cm (8¼″). Apparently a *casual* visitant to far offshore waters. Bill and long legs black. Distinctively patterned, with *dark gray crown and ear-coverts contrasting with white forehead and superciliary*; above otherwise brownish gray, narrow nuchal collar and *rump paler pure gray*, slightly forked tail blackish. *Below white*. In flight shows pale upper wing-bar, extensively white underwing. **Similar species:** Hornby's Storm-Petrel, also boldly patterned for a storm-petrel and with white underparts, differs in having deeply forked tail, gray chest-band, and no white superciliary. Otherwise easily recognized. **Habits:** Normal flight erratic with much veering and banking, wingstrokes often jerky. Rarely follows ships. When feeding intersperses short glides with pauses, then throws its feet forward, appearing almost to bounce from spot to spot.

Oceanodroma Storm-Petrels
Most storm-petrels belong to this rather variable and difficult genus. Some *Oceanodroma* are—aside from their pale greater coverts—entirely dark, whereas others have a white "rump" band of varying extent. Species identification can be tricky, but flight styles—though varying to some extent with wind conditions—are often species-specific.

Least Storm-Petrel, *Oceanodroma microsoma*
Paíño Menudo   Plate 3(3)
14–15 cm (5½–6″). An irregular boreal winter visitant (Dec.–Feb.) to offshore waters. Bill and legs black. *Easily the small-*

est storm-petrel, with rather long narrow pointed wings and *moderately short wedge-shaped tail*. Uniform sooty blackish. In flight shows only a weakly marked pale upper wing-bar. **Similar species:** Black and Markham's Storm-Petrels are much larger; other storm-petrels in Ecuador have at least some white in plumage (either on rump or underparts). Wedge-shaped effect of Least's short tail can be hard to see in field, when it can appear more rounded. **Habits:** Flight fast and direct, low over water with deep wingbeats and little gliding except in stronger winds. Flight more erratic when feeding, pattering along surface.

Wedge-rumped Storm-Petrel
Oceanodroma tethys
Paíño Danzarín   Plate 3(4)

15–16.5 cm (6–6½″). A fairly common visitant to offshore waters of south (northward as well?); recorded only May–Oct. Also called Galápagos Storm-Petrel. Bill and legs black. Sooty blackish with *large and long triangular white patch on uppertail-coverts* that extends down to lower flanks and sides of crissum; tail notched. **In flight** has rather long and narrow wings, pale upper wing-bar. **Similar species:** Wedge-rumped's white patch on its hind-end is so extensive the bird can often look almost white-tailed, rendering it easily identified. Only other white-rumped, dark storm-petrel known from Ecuadorian waters is very rare Band-rumped. **Habits:** Flight usually fast and steady with deep wingstrokes interspersed by occasional glides; when feeding, birds have a more bounding flight, dropping down to water with legs dangling. In calm conditions, Wedge-rumpeds—like most other storm-petrels—are sometimes encountered swimming, often in small groups.

[Band-rumped Storm-Petrel
Oceanodroma castro
Paíño Lomibandeado]   Plate 3(5)

20–21.5 cm (8–8¹/₂″). Apparently a *casual* visitant to offshore waters of south. Also called Madeiran, or Harcourt's, Storm-Petrel. Bill and legs black. Sooty blackish with *sharply defined but narrow white band across uppertail-coverts* that extends down to sides of crissum; tail notched. **In flight** shows less prominent pale upper wing-bar than many other storm-petrels. **Similar species:** Much more numerous Wedge-rumped Storm-Petrel has white "rump" patch larger and more triangle- or wedge-shaped. **Habits:** A highly pelagic storm-petrel, with strong steady flight, banking from side to side and often (especially when winds are strong) even gliding, shearwater-like.

Markham's Storm-Petrel
Oceanodroma markhami
Paíño de Markham   Plate 3(8)

21.5–23 cm (8¹/₂–9″). Apparently an uncommon visitant to offshore waters of south,

perhaps occurring mainly during austral winter (Dec.–Feb.); status uncertain because of difficulty of separation from Black Storm-Petrel. Has been called Sooty Storm-Petrel. Bill and legs black. *Uniform sooty brown; long tail deeply forked.* **In flight** shows extensive and prominent pale upper wing-bar. **Similar species:** Closely resembles Black Storm-Petrel, so much so that most large, all-dark storm-petrels seen off Ecuador cannot be identified to species. Black is slightly blacker above, has slightly more deeply forked tail, and its pale upper wing-bar does not quite extend to front of wing (but all of these characters are hard to discern in field). In the hand, Markham's bill is longer and legs shorter. In life the two species are perhaps best separated by flight characteristics (see below), but even these can vary depending on wind conditions, so caution is advised. **Habits:** Flight controlled, generally with shallow fast wingbeats and frequent gliding periods.

Black Storm-Petrel, *Oceanodroma melania*
Paíño Negro   Plate 3(7)

21.5–23 cm (8¹/₂–9″). Apparently a fairly common visitant to offshore waters, perhaps present year-round (in varying numbers?). Bill and rather long legs black. *Sooty blackish above, sooty brown below*; long tail quite deeply forked. **In flight** shows extensive and prominent pale upper wing-bar that does not quite reach leading edge of wing. **Similar species:** Closely resembles Markham's Storm-Petrel; see discussion under that species. **Habits:** Similar to Markham's Storm-Petrel. Black's flight tends to be languid and graceful—it often recalls a Black Tern—with deep wingstrokes, wings often reaching well

above horizontal; both species can engage in bouts of gliding, but Markham's wingstrokes are almost invariably shallower and more "fluttery."

[Ashy Storm-Petrel, *Oceanodroma homochroa*
Paíño Cinéreo]   Plate 3(6)

18–19 cm (7–7½"). Apparently a *casual* boreal winter visitor to offshore waters. Bill and legs black. Resembles Black and Markham's Storm-Petrels but smaller and with different flight style. Paler and grayer overall, especially on underwing. **Similar species:** Cf. also considerably smaller Least Storm-Petrel. **Habits:** Flight usually steady and direct, low over water, with quite fluttery, shallow wingbeats that barely rise above horizontal; generally glides very little.

Hornby's Storm-Petrel, *Oceanodroma hornbyi*
Paíño de Hornby   Plate 3(9)

22 cm (8¾"). Apparently an *irregular* visitor to offshore waters in south. Also called Ringed Storm-Petrel. Bill and legs black. *Crown and sides of head blackish, contrasting with white forehead, throat, and narrow*

nuchal collar; above brownish gray, paler on uppertail-coverts; *rather deeply forked tail* blackish. *Underparts white, chest crossed by gray band*. **In flight** shows whitish upper wing-bar. **Similar species:** A distinctively patterned storm-petrel, to be confused only with even rarer White-faced (which lacks chestband, has square tail, etc.). **Habits:** Normal flight rather erratic, coursing low over water, a few rather deep wingstrokes interspersed by a glide; periodically pauses to hover over water, legs dangling. Seems not to be especially attracted to boats.

Pelecaniformes
Tropicbirds: Phaethontidae (1)

Spectacular mainly aerial seabirds found on tropical seas, nesting locally on often remote islands. **Sexes are alike.**

Red-billed Tropicbird, *Phaethon aethereus*
Rabijunco Piquirrojo   Plate 4(1)

43–48 cm (17–19"), excluding *adult's extremely long tail streamers* (another 46–53 cm, 18–21"). Small numbers breed on *Isla de la Plata*; a few occur offshore elsewhere, but always at very low densities. A beautiful *gleaming white* seabird with *heavy blood red bill.* **Adult** white with *black eye-stripe* and *narrow black barring on back, rump, and inner upperwing-coverts.* **In flight** shows black outer primaries. **Juvenile** differs in its dull yellow bill and lack of tail streamers; its *black eye-stripes converge around nape,* and black-tipped tail. **Similar species:** Unmistakable. Juvenile could carelessly be mistaken for a Royal Tern. **Habits:** Pelagic away from nesting islands. Usually wary and solitary when at sea, flying purposefully and rapidly (somewhat falcon-like) well above water; often appears out of nowhere, then disappears just as quickly. On rare occasions an individual is located while swimming, long tail streamers cocked out of water; these birds may allow a closer approach. More apt to be seen around its breeding islands, where birds favor cliffs and can be seen in spectacular display flights (often, curiously, a trio of birds is involved); nests are hidden on ledges and cliff recesses. Feeds by plunge-diving for fish and squid. **Voice:** Typically silent, but courting birds give a tern-like guttural "tk-tk-tk-tk-tcheeeeeer."

Frigatebirds: Fregatidae (2)
Very large, mainly black seabirds found in tropical oceans, frigatebirds have the greatest wingspan-to-body-weight ratio of any birds, enabling them to fly almost effortlessly for very long periods.

Magnificent Frigatebird, *Fregata magnificens*
Fragata Magnífica   Plate 4(13)

96.5–106.5 cm (38–42″). *Numerous and widespread along entire coast,* also regularly occurring a short distance up larger rivers

(e.g., Río Guayas). A *very large* seabird with *extremely long, narrow, crooked wings* and *long deeply forked tail* (latter often folded so as to appear pointed). *Long hooked bill* grayish; feet blackish. ♂ has blackish orbital ring. Its plumage is entirely lustrous black, with purple and green sheens on upperparts; *large distensible red throat-pouch is inflated in display* (but otherwise is inconspicuous). ♀ has blue orbital ring. Its plumage is mainly black, but with *sides of neck and entire breast contrastingly white,* some whitish scaling on axillars, and pale brownish band on upperwing-coverts. **Juvenile** has *entire head white* and *more extensive white on underparts* (at some stages showing a black "wedge" protruding onto sides of chest). **Similar species:** Unmistakable along Ecuadorian coast, aside from vagrant Great Frigatebird (which see). **Habits:** Very conspicuous, congregating in large numbers at roosting sites on islands and in mangroves; also sometimes roosts on ships' rigging and masts. Otherwise supremely aerial, floating effortlessly and almost motionlessly for long periods, sometimes soaring very high, almost out of sight. When birds flap at all, wingbeats are very deep. Feeding birds congregate around fishing boats, or around fishermen unloading catches, competing for scraps with pelicans. Also eat fish and refuse, obtaining these by swooping low over water and grabbing with bills; but they cannot swim and do not land on surface. They are best known for kleptoparasitic habits in which they harry other seabirds—especially boobies, terns, and gulls—in an attempt to force them to disgorge their gainfully obtained food. **Voice:** Foraging birds mostly silent, but nesting birds utter a variety of clacking noises and wheezy screams and chatters.

[Great Frigatebird, *Fregata minor*
Fragata Grande]   Plate 4(14)

89–96.5 cm (35–38″). An *accidental* wanderer to coast of w. Guayas, with only one (May) sighting. Resembles much more numerous Magnificent Frigatebird. ♂ differs in its *pinkish red feet* (not blackish), *pale brownish band on upperwing-coverts* (lacking in all but a tiny minority of Magnificents), and pale grayish scaling on axillars. ♀ differs in its *red orbital ring* (not blue),

gray throat (not black), and all-black under-wing (with no whitish scaling). **Juvenile** differs in its *cinnamon head, throat, and mid-chest*; head gradually becomes whiter, throat and chest retaining cinnamon color longer. **Habits:** As in Magnificent Frigatebird.

Boobies and Gannets: Sulidae (5)

Large seabirds with *long pointed wings, tapered tails*, and *strong pointed bills* that are found widely in tropical oceans (gannets only occur in temperate oceans). They are boldly patterned in white and black or brown, immatures duller; bill and legs are often brightly colored. Boobies nest colonially on islands; they feed on fish obtained in often-spectacular plunge dives. **Sexes are alike.**

Blue-footed Booby, *Sula nebouxii*
Piquero Patiazul   Plate 4(2)

76–84 cm (30–33″). *Fairly common and widespread along entire coast, especially where rocky*; nests only very locally. Iris pale yellow; bill and facial skin dull bluish to greenish gray; *legs bright enamel blue*. **Adult** has *head and neck whitish finely streaked dark brown*; upperparts otherwise dark

brown with *white patch on upper back*, white scaling on back and scapulars, and *white patch on rump*. **Immature** differs in its dark iris, duller blue legs, and solidly brown head and neck (with no streaking). **In flight** shows dark underwing with large white axillar patch and two stripes on coverts. **Similar species:** Considerably rarer Peruvian Booby never has such bright blue feet and has profuse small white spots on wing-coverts (wings plain in Blue-footed). Adult Peruvians are much whiter on head and neck (with no dark streaking), whereas immatures are dingier and more uniformly brown-streaked above (*lacking* white upperback patch). Cf. also immature of very rare Brown Booby. **Habits:** A coastal booby, rarely venturing much beyond sight of land. Gregarious, roosting on rocky islets and shorelines (less often on rigging of ships), fanning out to feed though often foraging in small groups. Feeds by plunge-diving, often angling sharply down into water. Nests in colonies on open ground on islands, courting pairs engaging in marvelous foot-stomping displays. **Voice:** Quiet away from breeding grounds, where nesting birds give a variety of whistles and brays.

Peruvian Booby, *Sula variegata*
Piquero Peruano   Plate 4(5)

71–76 cm (28–30″). An *irregular and irruptive visitant* to coast of south; on rare occasions (during El Niño warm-water events) fair numbers may be present, but in most years there are none. Iris pale yellow; bill and facial skin bluish gray to blackish; legs bluish gray. **Adult** has *snowy white head, neck, and underparts* contrasting with dark brown upperparts, back and rump scaled white, and uppertail-coverts white; *wing-coverts finely*

spotted with white. **Immature** differs in having head, neck, and underparts finely streaked dark brown, and back shows less white scaling. **Similar species:** Much more numerous (and resident) Blue-footed Booby always shows dark streaking on head and neck; it never looks gleaming white like adult Peruvian. Younger birds of the two species are more similar, but note Blue-footed's white back patch (Peruvian is more dingy and uniform above) and lack of wing-covert spotting. **Habits:** Similar to Blue-footed Booby, and often consorts with that species in Ecuadorian waters. Peruvian Boobies are locally phenomenally numerous along Peru coast—though their numbers are now sadly much reduced from earlier years.

Nazca Booby, *Sula granti*
Piquero de Nazca   Plate 4(4)

79–86.5 cm (31–34″). A *fairly common breeder on Isla de la Plata*, dispersing over oceanic waters to feed, rarely or never far south of Santa Elena Peninsula. Only recently specifically separated from Masked Booby (*S. dactylatra*). Iris yellow; *bill orange*, facial skin blackish; legs gray. Striking **adult** *snowy white* with *black flight feathers and greater wing-coverts* and *black tail*. **Immature** very different, with dusky yellowish bill, *dark grayish brown above and on throat*, with *whitish nuchal collar*; white below. **Similar species:** Adult unmistakable, though cf. much rarer white-morph Red-footed Booby. Young birds are more confusing and resemble similarly sized Blue-footed Booby, though Nazca never shows streaking on its solidly dark head and neck. **Habits:** Pelagic when away from its nesting islands, and rarely seen from land, unlike Blue-footed Booby not even

returning to land to roost (it sleeps while standing on driftwood or swimming). Flight powerful and steady, usually quite low over water. Feeds by plunge-diving, feeding especially on flying fish. Nests in fairly dense colonies on open barren ground. **Voice:** Basically silent away from nesting grounds, where birds give various whistled calls.

[Brown Booby, *Sula leucogaster*
Piquero Pardo]   Plate 4(3)

66–73.5 cm (26–29″). Uncertain, perhaps a very rare visitant to tropical waters off Esmeraldas. Bill and legs greenish to yellow; iris brown. **Adult** *mainly dark brown* with *sharply contrasting white breast, belly, and crissum*; underwing-coverts also white. ♂ has whitish forecrown lacking in ♀. **Immature** *mostly dark grayish brown*, but *already with a shadow of adult's pattern* (breast and belly flecked white, paler than the dark chest); *underwing-coverts contrastingly white*. **Similar species:** Adult should be easily recognized. Immatures could be confused with immature Red-footed Boobies (before these acquire red feet), but note especially their whitish-tipped tail (tail all dark in Brown) and contrast between dark underwing and pale underparts (reverse of that seen in Brown). **Habits:** Less pelagic than Nazca Booby but more so than Blue-footed. Flight strong, often scaling low over water much like a very large shearwater.

Red-footed Booby, *Sula sula*
Piquero Patirrojo   Plate 4(6)

66–73.5 cm (26–29″). *Breeds in small numbers on Isla de la Plata*, dispersing over oceanic waters to feed (seen occasionally as far south as off Santa Elena Peninsula). Poly-

Mostly below 800 m

morphic; *mainly the* **brown morph** *has been noted in mainland Ecuadorian waters. Bill pale blue, facial skin pale blue and pink; legs bright red*; iris brown. **Adult** *brown overall* with head, neck, and underparts typically paler than upperparts; *tail tipped whitish.* In flight *underwing-coverts dark*, contrasting with comparatively pale body. **Immature** similar but with grayish bill and legs. **White morph** (a few have been reported, though greatly outnumbered) *white*, with buffy yellow wash on crown and hindneck; flight feathers (except for inner secondaries) contrastingly black; tail blackish narrowly tipped white. **Similar species:** The only booby with red legs and feet, though these can be hard to see except on perched birds. Cf. very rare Brown Booby. **Habits:** Similar to other boobies, though Red-footed places its nest in shrubs and low trees, not on ground.

Cormorants and Shags: Phalacrocoracidae (2)

Aquatic birds with long slender necks and fairly long tails, most cormorants and shags range on salt water along coasts, a few also occurring inland. They dive for small fish. Sexes are alike.

Neotropic Cormorant
Phalacrocorax brasilianus
Cormorán Neotropical   Plate 4(9)

63.5–68.5 cm (25–27″). *Widespread and locally common along rivers and on ponds and lakes in lowlands of west*, but *markedly less numerous and more local in east*; few records from highlands, where only a wanderer. Formerly called Olivaceous Cormorant and named *P. olivaceus. Blackish bill long and slender, hooked at tip*; gular pouch and

facial skin dull yellow to orange (brighter when breeding), outlined by narrow line of white feathers; legs black. **Breeding adult** *black*, somewhat browner above, with a few white filoplumes on head and even neck; non-breeders duller black, lacking facial plumes and with less noticeable white border to facial skin. **Immature** grayish to dusky brown above, paler grayish brown below; **juvenile** almost white below and on sides of head and neck. **Similar species:** Not likely confused; *the only cormorant normally seen in Ecuador* (along south coast, cf. rare Guanay). Anhinga has longer and more pointed daggerlike bill, longer and thinner neck and tail, silvery white on wings, etc. When swimming, cormorant looks vaguely duck-like (cf. especially Muscovy Duck). **Habits:** Notably gregarious, occurring almost anywhere that fish swim, and seems markedly nomadic. Swims low in water, often with just head and neck protruding, bill tilted up at a jaunty angle; when feeding dives frequently. As plumage is not waterproof, cormorants are often seen perched on snags or trees, often with wings outstretched to dry. Flight strong and steady, often high, with neck held slightly kinked; birds sometimes fly in V formation.

Guanay Shag, *Phalacrocorax bougainvillii*
Cormorán Guanero   Plate 4(10)

68.5–73.5 cm (27–29″). An irregular, *irruptive* visitant to coastal waters, mainly in south; *in most years none are present at all.* Often called Guanay Cormorant. Long narrow bill yellowish to grayish, *facial skin bright red*; legs dull pink. **Adult** has upperparts and neck glossy black, *contrasting with snowy white underparts* (small throat patch also white). **Immature** browner above, less pure white below. **Similar species:**

82.5–89 cm (32½–35″). Uncommon and local along rivers and around freshwater lakes and ponds in lowlands. *Distinctive shape*, with *small head, very long slender neck*, and *long fan-shaped tail. Sharply pointed bill* yellow to orange, culmen duskier; facial skin bluish (brighter when breeding); legs yellowish. ♂ *glossy black* with contrasting *lesser and median upperwing-coverts silvery white edged black, greater upperwing-coverts silvery white*; tail narrowly tipped brown. Breeding birds have scattered white filoplumes on head and neck. ♀ similar but *head, neck, and chest grayish buff.* **Immature** like ♀ but with reduced white on wing. **Similar species:** Cf. Neotropic Cormorant. **Habits:** Less gregarious than Neotropic Cormorant; Anhinga is most often seen perched in trees or bushes along water's edge, often with wings outstretched to dry its feathers. Though its flight, deep wingstrokes interspersed with short glides, often seems more labored than a cormorant's, the Anhinga is capable of sustained high soaring on outstretched wings and broadly fanned tail. Swims low in water, moving ahead sinuously, often only head and neck protruding, snakelike. Dives or simply submerges when foraging for food, skewering small fish with bill, bringing them to surface before swallowing.

With their whitish underparts, younger Neotropic Cormorants can look vaguely like Guanay Shags, but they never show such a sharp black-white contrast; Guanay's profile is rather different (especially apparent in flight), with longer and thinner bill, considerably longer and more slender neck, and shorter tail, resulting in more streamlined (less "dumpy") appearance. **Habits:** In its normal range, a strictly coastal and intensely gregarious cormorant that can occur in staggeringly large aggregations, particularly on and near its nesting islands off Peru. Guanays in Ecuador occur only as vagrants or dispersive residents fleeing the temporary unavailability of their normal food source, anchovies, caused by temporary warming of Humboldt Current waters (the El Niño phenomenon).

Darters: Anhingidae (1)

Cormorant-like, darters have *more pointed daggerlike bills* and *longer, more fan-shaped tails*. They are found exclusively on freshwater.

Pelicans: Pelecanidae (2)

Very large, fish-eating birds, conspicuous and familiar along Ecuadorian coasts, and characterized most notably by their *distensible pouch under the lower mandible.* **Sexes are alike.**

Anhinga, *Anhinga anhinga*
Aninga   Plate 4(11)

Brown Pelican, *Pelecanus occidentalis*
Pelícano Pardo   Plate 4(7)

Mostly below 400 m

117–132 cm (46–52"). A *very large, heavily built* coastal bird, well known and unmistakable aside from next species (which is even bigger). *Bill very long*, grayish with whiter base and more orange tip, with *flexible pouch underneath* (bill and pouch redder when breeding); iris pale, often bluish; short legs dusky. **Adult** has *head and stripe down neck white*, crown often tinged buff, and a tuft on hindneck; hindneck chestnut, *otherwise silvery gray above*, feathers edged darker, with blackish flight feathers. *Below dark brown*. Neck white in **nonbreeders**. **Immature** much less patterned, *mainly brownish with whiter belly*. **Similar species:** Cf. Peruvian Pelican. **Habits:** Highly gregarious, pelicans are conspicuous along most Ecuadorian coasts, though they breed only on remote Isla Santa Clara. Though they may gather in large aggregations at roosts (on rocks, also in trees such as mangroves), foraging birds most often range in smaller groups. Pelicans fly with a characteristic few flaps and a sail, often scaling low over water but also sometimes soaring to great heights. Perched or flying, the head is drawn back so as to rest on neck. Feeds by plunge-diving after fish, extending neck just before hitting water's surface; prey is swallowed immediately—*not* carried in pouch—unless it is robbed by gulls or frigatebirds.

Peruvian Pelican, *Pelecanus thagus*
Pelícano Peruano   Plate 4(8)

137–152 cm (54–60"). A *huge* pelican found locally on *sw. coasts, dwarfing Brown Pelican* (obvious when together). Peruvian differs further from Brown Pelican—with which formerly considered conspecific—in *more brightly colored bill* (especially when breeding, when blue and red can be quite vivid;

despite not breeding in Ecuador, many individuals seen in Ecuador do show bill colors) and *extensive white on upperwing-coverts* (contrasting noticeably in flight, and also often apparent on birds at rest). Even younger Peruvians usually show a contrasting pale panel on upperwing not seen in Browns. **Habits:** Similar to Brown Pelican, the two species sometimes loafing together, notably at the Ecuasal lagoons. Peruvians seem to dive less than Browns, rather obtaining much of their food by scooping fish from surface and by gathering around fishing boats. Whereas Browns are rare beyond sight of land, Peruvians often feed well offshore.

Anseriformes
Screamers: Anhimidae (1)
Very large, goose-like birds found locally around water in the lowlands. Screamers are unusual in lacking feather tracts. They are considered excellent eating and as a result have declined markedly in most areas. Pairs are highly territorial, mating for life; the nest is a platform of sticks and other vegetative material anchored to vegetation in shallow water. **Sexes are alike.**

Horned Screamer, *Anhima cornuta*
Gritador Unicornio   Plate 7(10)

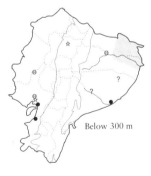

Below 300 m

84–91.5 cm (33–36"). An unmistakable *huge* and ungainly bird found locally in *more remote marshy areas, lake margins, and on islands in rivers in lowlands of east*; in west now very local, basically confined to Manglares-Churute Ecol. Reserve. Iris golden yellow; short hooked bill dusky; thick heavy legs grayish. Both sexes have a *long, slender "horn"* springing from forehead; both also have a sharply pointed spur protruding from bend of wing. *Mainly glossy black with feathers of crown and foreneck broadly edged silvery whitish*; belly white. *Large patch of silvery white on wing-coverts* is conspicuous in flight, but often not too evident on perched birds. **In flight** wings long and broad, with underwing-coverts white. **Habits:** Usually found in pairs that stand around on grassy areas or sandbars near but usually not in water; in the few areas where they remain numerous, can be more social. In most areas quite wary, flushing ponderously at considerable distances, struggling to become airborne, often then alighting atop a distant shrub or tree. Entirely herbivorous, grazing on leaves and roots of various aquatic plants. Sometimes soars high above ground, then almost looking like a huge vulture. **Voice:** Very vocal (though it doesn't "scream"), with extremely powerful voice that can be heard from at least several kilometers away. Call an unmistakable, and unforgettable, deep and throaty "guu-uulp, güü," usually uttered by perched birds, rarely in flight.

Ducks, Geese, and Swans: Anatidae (16)

A familiar and diverse group of water-loving birds (often termed "waterfowl"), ducks—only one "goose" (and no swan) is found in Ecuador—do not form an especially prominent part of the Ecuadorian avifauna. All are swimming birds with webbed feet and have dense, waterproofed plumage with a downy underlying layer.

Dendrocygna Whistling-Ducks

Two fairly large, gregarious ducks—named for their whistled calls—found in marshy areas in the lowlands, mainly in the west. Both are distinctive gangly-looking waterfowl with long thin necks and long legs. **Sexes are alike.**

Fulvous Whistling-Duck, *Dendrocygna bicolor*

Pato Silbador Canelo   Plate 8(4)

48–53.5 cm (19–21″). Locally common in freshwater marshes and ponds, sometimes out onto rice fields, in *lowlands of west*. Iris brown; bill and long legs bluish gray. *Head, neck, and underparts tawny-fulvous* with diagonal whitish furrows on sides of neck and *creamy whitish tips to elongated flank feathers (forming effect of a stripe*

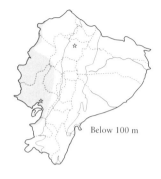

Below 100 m

down sides); crissum creamy white. Above blackish, feathers broadly edged tawny giving barred effect. **In flight** *wings look essentially dark*, with lesser- and median-coverts chestnut, greater-coverts and flight feathers black; *white "ring" on uppertail-coverts* is conspicuous. **Similar species:** Not likely confused. Cf. juvenile Black-bellied Whistling-Duck, whose pattern can be quite subdued though it always shows bold white wingstripe, etc. **Habits:** Favors open marshy vegetation, usually standing at edge of water and not swimming all that often. Frequently active at night, and sometimes then heard calling overhead. Regularly occurs in flocks, up to thousands of birds together, sometimes consorting with Black-bellieds. Rarely or never perches in trees. Fulvous Whistling-Ducks in flight have distinctive "drooping" silhouette with head angled downward and long legs dangling below tail. **Voice:** Call a rather shrill whistle, "ki-wheeah," most often given in flight.

Black-bellied Whistling-Duck
Dendrocygna autumnalis

Pato Silbador Ventrinegro   Plate 8(5)

Mostly below 200 m

46–51 cm (18–20″). Locally common in freshwater marshes and ponds, sometimes out onto rice fields and in mangroves, in *lowlands of west*; also a few wanderers to lowlands of northeast. Iris brown; *bill and legs pinkish red*. Head and neck gray with crown and stripe down hindneck rufous brown; lower neck and chest tawny-brown, becoming grayish on upper breast; *lower breast and belly black*, crissum mottled with white. Above mostly rufous brown, wing-coverts whitish, tail black. In flight shows *broad and conspicuous white wingstripe*. Juvenile similar but with gray bill and legs, washed-out plumage though adult's pattern already discernible, especially the gray face, black belly, and white wingstripe. Similar species: Not likely confused. Similarly shaped Fulvous Whistling-Duck lacks white in wing, never shows black belly, etc. Habits: Similar to Fulvous Whistling-Duck though in Ecuador the Black-bellied seems never to assemble in such huge flocks as Fulvous. Black-bellied does, however, freely perch in trees, especially on dead branches (though also locally in mangroves), and usually nests in tree cavities. "Droopy" shape in flight is similar, as are its partially nocturnal habits. Voice: Call consists of high-pitched whistles, e.g., "wi-chi-tee" or "wit-chee, wit-chee-chee."

Orinoco Goose, *Neochen jubata*
Ganso del Orinoco   Plate 8(18)

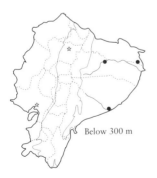

Below 300 m

56–63.5 cm (22–25″). A *large, goose-like* waterbird, now *very rare and local on sandbars along major rivers in lowlands of east*, though remaining *more numerous in Río Pastaza drainage near Peruvian border*. Iris brown; bill black above, red below; *legs*

reddish pink. Sexes alike, though ♀ smaller. *Head, heavy neck, and breast pale grayish buff*, neck feathers often ruffled, with *contrasting rufous belly*. Back, rump, and tail black with purplish gloss, crissum white. *Wings mostly dark green* with *broad white band across secondaries* conspicuous in flight. Juvenile similar but duller and more washed-out. Similar species: Essentially unmistakable, there being no other goose-like bird found on river sandbars. Habits: Usually found in well-dispersed pairs (sometimes small family groups) that walk on sandbars and around associated lagoons with an elegant upright carriage. Unlike most other waterfowl, ♂♂ engage in no courtship display, but rather may vigorously fight with ♂♂ other before pairing up with a ♀. They seem not to associate with other waterfowl. Mainly herbivorous, grazing on short grass. Nests in tree cavities. Voice: Both sexes utter distinctive nasal honking, "unnhh?"; also a high-pitched whistled note.

Muscovy Duck, *Cairina moschata*
Pato Real   Plate 8(17)

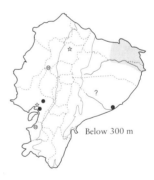

Below 300 m

♂ 76–84 cm (30–33″), ♀ 71–76 cm (28–30″). *Now very local on forest-fringed rivers and lakes in lowlands of east* (most numerous in Río Pastaza drainage near Peruvian border), a few also perhaps still persisting in lowlands of southwest. Iris brown; bill pinkish with black mottling, ♂ with mainly red caruncles at base of bill and blackish facial skin; legs blackish. ♂ substantially larger than ♀; *mainly glossy greenish black*, with slight expressive bushy crest. In flight shows *large area of white on wing-coverts* (usually hidden at rest), smaller area on axillars. Older birds gradually acquire more white. ♀ similar, but lacking crest and generally showing less white (older birds have more). **Juveniles** dark brown to blackish, with no gloss; white on wing reduced or (more often) entirely absent. Note that domesticated Muscovy Ducks—which are frequent throughout much of lowland Ecuador and often wander far from houses—almost always show scattered white feathers in body plumage, a pattern never seen in truly wild birds. **Similar species:** Nearly unmistakable, though in a quick look a juvenile can be mistaken for Neotropic Cormorant. Cf. the rare Comb Duck. **Habits:** In contrast to their ungainly domesticated brethren, wild Muscovies are elegant and alert ducks, often very wary and flying heavily but strongly. They rarely associate with other waterfowl. Graze on short grass, also dabbling in shallow water. Perch freely in trees (sometimes high above ground), and on branches protruding from water; where numerous groups gather to roost in trees. Nest in tree cavities. Sadly, because of heavy hunting pressure, seeing a flock of wild Muscovies in Ecuador is becoming increasingly hard to do. **Voice:** Surprisingly quiet, but occasionally utters soft hisses and quacks.

Comb Duck, *Sarkidiornis melanotos*
Pato Crestudo   Plate 8(19)

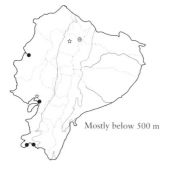

Mostly below 500 m

♂ 68.5–71 cm (27–28″), ♀ 53.5–56 cm (21–22″). *Rare and very local along rivers and in adjacent marshes and rice fields in lowlands of s. Loja*, a few wanderers elsewhere. Iris dark brown; bill black, ♂ *with large fleshy knob protruding from upper mandible* (smaller when not breeding); legs blackish. ♂ has *head, neck, and underparts white* with *black speckling on head and neck* and narrow black line on crown and hind-

neck; sides and flanks broadly blackish, crissum tinged yellowish buff. Upperparts black glossed green and purple. **In flight** *wings entirely dark*. ♀ substantially smaller than ♂; resembles ♂ but sides only mottled pale grayish and with no buff on crissum. **Similar species:** Muscovy Duck is similarly sized but lacks white on head, neck, and underparts. Cf. also Neotropic Cormorant. **Habits:** Birds seen in Ecuador have mainly been resting on sand or gravel bars in rivers, flying out to adjacent marshy areas and rice fields to feed. Somewhat active at night, and generally wary. They sometimes perch in trees. Small groups sometimes consort with flocks of whistling-ducks. Nests in tree hollows, less often on ground.

Torrent Duck, *Merganetta armata*
Pato Torrentero   Plate 8(16)

700–3200 m

38–42 cm (15–16½″). An attractive, slender duck with *long stiff tail*, widespread but inconspicuous *along swift-flowing rocky rivers and streams in highlands*. Iris brown; *narrow bill and legs bright coral red*. Both sexes have short spur protruding from bend of wing. ♂ has *head and neck mostly white* with *black atop crown and down hindneck*, also a *conspicuous black stripe extending back from eye and down sides of neck*. Otherwise grayish to brown above with blackish and buff streaking, rump densely vermiculated gray and white; below whitish variably streaked with gray. **In flight** shows small green speculum (hard to see) bordered narrowly with white. ♀ very different: *bluish gray above*, back and wing-coverts black-streaked, rump as in ♂. *Face and entire underparts orange-cinnamon*. **Similar species:** Unmistakable. No other duck occurs in the raging torrents this species favors. **Habits:** Usually occurs in pairs, and apparently sedentary. Most easily seen while resting on boulders out in turbulent water; much harder to spot when swimming in turbulent water. The streamlined Torrent Duck's swimming ability is legendary; it can swim and dive in almost unimaginably swift-flowing currents, though where possible it does take advantage of eddies behind boulders. Feeds mainly on aquatic invertebrates, mainly insect larvae and molluscs, obtained while diving and also while picking and probing among rocks; may also take some fish. Surprised birds may take flight, but remain low over water, and strictly follow watercourses. **Voice:** Usually silent, and in any case would be hard to hear over a swift-flowing river's roar.

Anas Teals and Pintails
"Typical" ducks found in a variety of aquatic habitats, mainly in freshwater where they feed by tipping or dabbling in shallows (only rarely diving). Some species are highly gregarious. The three resident species are more or less monomorphic, but the three boreal migrant species show marked sexual dimorphism, with males losing their colorful and boldly patterned nuptial plumage when they go into what is termed an "eclipse" plumage in which they resemble females. All species have a distinct speculum, an area of contrasting color on the secondaries that shows prominently in flight. Flight is strong and direct, and birds are capable of springing up directly from the water (with no preliminary pattering along the surface, unlike the pochards and "stifftails").

Andean Teal, *Anas andium*
Cerceta Andina   Plate 8(6)

Mostly 3000–4000 m

40.5–43 cm (16–17″). A *plain* ("hen-plumaged"), *small and compact* duck found on *ponds and lakes in paramo, a few slightly lower*. Formerly often considered conspecific with Speckled Teal (*A. flavirostris*), found farther south in South America. Iris brown; *bill dark gray, blackish on culmen*; legs dusky. **Sexes alike.** *Head and neck densely speckled dusky and whitish (looks dark)*; above otherwise dusky, feathers with paler edgings; rump and tail dusky. Below buffy whitish, breast speckled with black. **In flight** wings with *dark green speculum bordered by buff stripes*. **Similar species:** Similarly sized ♀ Blue-winged Teal is paler and buffier brown generally (not so grayish), and in flight shows conspicuous pale blue wing-coverts. Yellow-billed Pintail is larger with a pointed tail, obvious yellow on bill; it is paler brown generally. **Habits:** Usually in pairs or small groups, often resting on lakeshores or along small nearby streams. Feeds on both invertebrates and aquatic plants, obtained mainly while walking along water's edge. **Voice:** Gives a fast "kree-krik" and a low-pitched quacking.

White-cheeked Pintail, *Anas bahamensis*
Anade Cariblanco   Plate 8(7)

44–47 cm (17¼–18½″). Local on *ponds and lagoons (both fresh and saltwater, including shrimp ponds) along coast, most numerous on Santa Elena Peninsula*. Bill bluish to olive gray with *conspicuous area of bright coral red on basal half of maxilla* (smaller in ♀); legs dusky. ♂ with *face, throat, and foreneck snowy white contrasting sharply with brown crown and hindneck*; otherwise blackish above, feathers broadly edged tawny-buff; *pointed tail buffy whitish*. Below buff boldly spotted with black. **In flight** wings with green speculum bordered broadly by cinnamon. ♀ similar but duller, especially on head, and with shorter tail. **Similar species:** Should not be confused; no other Ecuadorian duck has red on bill or prominent white on face. **Habits:** This lovely duck usually occurs in small groups which swim lightly and elegantly on water's surface; they also regularly loaf on muddy or sandy shorelines. In some areas, notably at a few sites on outer Santa Elena Peninsula, White-cheeked Pintails gather in large flocks, at least when not breeding. They dabble and tip up for food.

Yellow-billed Pintail, *Anas georgica*
Anade Piquiamarillo   Plate 8(8)

Mostly 2200–4000 m

48–56 cm (19–22″). A *slim, long-necked* duck, local on *ponds and lakes in paramo* and (in small numbers) also in central and interandean valleys. Iris brown; *bill bright yellow* with leaden gray tip and black culmen; legs dusky. ♂ mainly *pale buffy brown*, darker above with feathers edged buff; *long pointed tail* dusky-brown. Sides of head, neck, and throat finely speckled dusky; chest brown, underparts whitish, throughout vaguely spotted brown. **In flight** wings with black speculum bordered by buff. ♀ similar but smaller, and with duller and browner speculum. **Similar species:** Andean Teal smaller, shorter-tailed, and darker overall (especially on head); its bill is dark (not yellow). **Habits:** Similar to other *Anas* ducks, often consorting with Andean Teal; in Ecuador generally not in large flocks. Tips up for food, also walks forward in shallows straining water through bill. **Voice:** Gives a

semimusical "trrr" similar to that of other pintails.

Blue-winged Teal, *Anas discors*
Cerceta Aliazul   Plate 8(10)

To at least 3200 m

35.5–40.5 cm (14–16″). A *locally common boreal migrant to lakes, ponds, and marshes in lowlands of west*, also some in highlands, but only a few reports from lowlands of east; mostly Oct.–Apr. Iris brown; bill black (♂) or gray (♀); legs yellow to orange-yellow. ♂ has *head and neck blue-gray* with black crown and *broad white crescent in front of eye*; above otherwise blackish, feathers narrowly edged buff; rump and tail dusky. Buffy brown below densely spotted with black, crissum black. **In flight** wings with *extensive pale blue on wing-coverts* (sometimes visible at rest) and green speculum. ♀ **and eclipse ♂** mainly dusky-brown above, paler on face with dark crown and eye-stripe and *whitish spot at base of bill*. Buffy whitish below with dusky-brown spotting, especially on breast. *Wing-coverts as in ♂*, but speculum darker. **Similar species:** Attractive ♂ in full plumage easily recognized; it molts into this plumage by Nov.–Dec. This species' pale blue wing-coverts, though visible mainly in flight, are unique among regularly occurring Ecuadorian ducks (though patterns of much rarer ♀ Cinnamon Teal [extirpated?] and ♀ Northern Shoveler are similar). **Habits:** Usually occurs in only small groups, and migrants can turn up in odd places (often where resident ducks are not present); by middle of northern winter, Blue-winged Teal usually have congregated in zones of favorable habitat, sometimes in flocks of hundreds or even thousands. Feed primarily by dabbling and head-dipping in shallow water.

Cinnamon Teal, *Anas cyanoptera*
Cerceta Colorada   Plate 8(11)

2500–2800 m

35.5–40.5 cm (14–16″). *No recent confirmed Ecuadorian records.* Formerly resident on highland lakes in far north, and also a (rare?) boreal migrant to same area (Dec.–Apr.). Iris yellow-orange or red; slightly spatulate bill black (♂) or gray (♀); legs yellow to orange-yellow. ♂ *mostly bright chestnut*, darker and browner on crown and upperparts; crissum black. Extirpated resident race differed from northern migrants in being somewhat more deeply colored below, with variable amount of black spotting on breast and belly. In flight wings with *extensive pale blue on wing-coverts* (sometimes visible at rest) and green speculum. ♀ closely resembles ♀ Blue-winged Teal, differing slightly in its more uniform and buffer face, *without* whitish spot in front of bill often so prominent in Blue-wings (though often showing a whitish eye-ring). **Similar species:** ♂ virtually unmistakable in full plumage. In other plumages Cinnamon and Blue-winged Teals are often not safely distinguished. Cf. also ♂ Andean and Masked Ducks (also mainly rufous-chestnut, but very differently shaped with black on head, etc.). **Habits:** Similar to Blue-winged Teal, with which any vagrant Cinnamon Teal would be expected to consort. Should especially be searched for after Dec., when ♂♂ have molted into full plumage.

[Northern Shoveler, *Anas clypeata*
Pato Cuchara Norteño]   Plate 8(9)
43–50.5 cm (17–20″). An *accidental* boreal vagrant to shallow lakes and lagoons in w. Guayas. Iris yellow (♂) or brown (♀); *oversized spatulate bill* blackish (♂) or orange with blackish culmen (♀); legs reddish

orange. ♂ has *head and neck dark glossy green*, contrasting with *white chest*, contrasting in turn with *rufous-chestnut breast and belly*, with white area on lower flanks. Above blackish, elongated scapulars edged white; tail whitish. In flight wings with *extensive pale grayish blue on wing-coverts* (sometimes visible at rest), green speculum bordered with white in front and behind. ♀ mottled brown and buffy-brown overall (upperparts darker); *wings as in ♂ but wing-coverts more grayish.* **Molting immature** ♂ like dull-plumaged full ♂, but often with vague whitish crescent in front of eye (recalling ♂ Blue-winged Teal). **Similar species:** Obviously spatulate bill unique among Ecuadorian waterfowl. **Habits:** Sole Ecuadorian record involved a ♂ and ♀ associating with other waterfowl; elsewhere shoveler often consorts with Blue-winged Teal.

Southern Pochard, *Netta erythrophthalma*
Porrón Sureño   Plate 8(13)

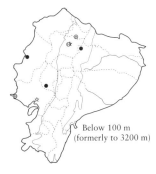

Below 100 m
(formerly to 3200 m)

46–48 cm (18–19″). *Very rare and local* on freshwater ponds, lakes, and marshes in *lowlands of southwest* in Manabí, Los Ríos, and Guayas, with recent records mainly from

Manabí; formerly also in highlands of north. Iris red (♂) or brown (♀); bill bluish gray with black tip; legs gray. *Very dark-looking ♂ has head, neck, and breast glossy blackish chestnut*; otherwise dark brown, more rufescent on sides. In flight wings show *conspicuous white stripe on flight feathers.* ♀ *mainly brown* (not as dark as ♂) with *striking white facial pattern* (foreface, throat, and stripe arching up behind cheeks to behind eye all white). Wings as in ♂. **Similar species:** No other duck is as dark overall as ♂ of this species; face pattern of ♀ unique. At a great distance, flashing white wingstripe might bring to mind a Black-bellied Whistling-Duck, though the two species are utterly different in profile (pochard being compact in build with much shorter neck and legs). **Habits:** Not well known in Ecuador, mainly because numbers now are so reduced. Elsewhere flocks are regularly seen on open bodies of water such as reservoirs (and indeed in 1950s they were found in such a situation on Santa Elena Peninsula), but in Ecuador pairs and small groups have all been on shallow ponds or in marshy areas. Feeds both by diving and by dabbling on surface of shallow water. Flight swift and direct, birds taking off after pattering along surface.

Lesser Scaup, *Aythya affinis*
Porrón Menor   Plate 8(12)

2800 m

38–43 cm (15–17″). An *accidental* boreal winter vagrant to highlands of north (1 old record from what is now Quito). Iris yellow; bill bluish gray with black tip; legs grayish. ♂ has *head and neck black with purplish sheen*, crown peaking to rear; *chest black. Above pale gray* (finely vermiculated) with black rump; breast and belly white. In flight wings shows *conspicuous white stripe on sec-*

ondaries. ♀ brown overall, darker above, with *well-defined white patch around base of bill*; belly white. Wings as in ♂. **Similar species:** Cf. Southern Pochard. **Habits:** Favors moderately deep water, diving for food (aquatic plants and invertebrates).

Oxyura and *Nomonyx* Ducks
Small, compact ducks with *stiff tails* (sometimes held erect), found locally on freshwater ponds and lakes. The legs are placed far back on the body, and unlike other ducks they rarely rest at water's edge. The genus *Nomonyx* was recently separated from *Oxyura.*

Andean Ruddy-Duck, *Oxyura ferruginea*
Pato Rojizo Andino   Plate 8(14)

2100–4000 m

40.5–43 cm (16–17″). *Local on deeper lakes in central valley and paramo.* Formerly often considered conspecific with Northern Ruddy-Duck (*O. jamaicensis*) of North America and West Indies. A chunky, heavy-set duck with short thick neck and *stiff tail often held cocked out of water.* Iris brown; *bill bright pale blue* (breeding ♂, duller at other times) or blackish (♀); legs dusky. **Breeding** ♂ has *head, upper neck, and upper throat black*, with a few white feathers on chin; *otherwise mainly bright rufous-chestnut*, belly grayer with black markings. In flight wings dark. **Nonbreeding** ♂ duller and browner. ♀ has *blackish head*, cheeks sometimes showing vague whitish horizontal stripe; *dusky above* with dark vermiculations. Throat whitish, chest brownish, lower underparts grayish with dusky markings. Wings as in ♂. **Similar species:** ♂ distinctive, especially when breeding, but even when not it shows enough rufous-chestnut to be readily recognized. ♀ drab and dark, but really resembles no other

Ecuadorian duck, especially in its dumpy shape. Cf. Masked Duck of w. lowlands (smaller, etc.). **Habits:** Usually seen swimming in loose groups on open water, often on lakes with extensive reedbeds (where it nests). Flies relatively little, typically low over water. In both sexes tail is often spread and cocked at acute angle. Displaying ♂♂, often in small groups, inflate necks and beat bills against chest. **Voice:** Displaying ♂♂ give an odd nasal "raah" preceded by several "tic" notes.

Masked Duck, *Nomonyx dominicus*
Pato Enmascarado   Plate 8(15)

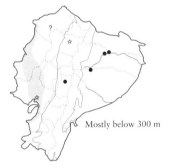

Mostly below 300 m

33–35.5 cm (13–14″). *Local and secretive on marshy, overgrown ponds in lowlands of west*, also a few records from east and in highlands. A chunky, heavy-set duck with short thick neck and *stiff tail usually held near surface of water, only occasionally cocked*. Iris brown with (♂) narrow blue eye-ring; *bill bright blue* (♂) or bluish gray to dusky-gray (♀); legs gray. **Breeding** ♂ has *black face and crown* contrasting with *rufous-chestnut nape, neck, and chest*; *upperparts otherwise rufous-chestnut spotted with black*; tail black. Breast and belly buffy whitish. **In flight** wings with *square white patch on secondaries*. ♀ **and nonbreeding** ♂ lack rufous-chestnut; crown blackish, *face buff crossed by two prominent blackish horizontal stripes*; above blackish spotted with buff; tail blackish. Below tawny-buff, whiter on midbelly, breast spotted blackish. **Similar species:** ♂ Andean Ruddy-Duck occurs only in highlands (though Masked Ducks wander, and have even occurred on highland lakes). Andean superficially resembles ♂ Masked but is larger with more extensive black on

neck and no spotting on upperparts. ♀ Andean Ruddy-Duck is darker and more uniform, lacking ♀ Masked's pale face crossed by pair of blackish stripes. **Habits:** An elusive and skulking duck, favoring ponds (sometimes surprisingly small) with abundant emergent and floating vegetation, where it swims low in water and usually is hard to spot; early and late in day sometimes more in open. Does not associate with other ducks. Feeds mainly by diving; also can simply sink beneath surface, grebe-like.

Phoenocopteriformes
Flamingos: Phoenicopteridae (1)
Lovely but gangly birds, flamingos have apparently only recently begun to appear in Ecuador. The Chilean is the most numerous of the four flamingo species found in South America.

Chilean Flamingo, *Phoenicopterus chilensis*
Flamenco Chileno   Plate 7(9)

99–109 cm (39–43″). An unmistakable, *large* and *mainly pink* wading bird, now a local and year-round visitant to *saltwater lagoons and mudflats along sw. coast*, most regular and numerous at Ecuasal lagoons on Santa Elena Peninsula. Iris pale yellow; *bent-downward ("broken-nose") bill whitish at base, black at tip; very long legs mainly yellowish gray with contrasting red "knees" and feet*. **Sexes alike. Adult** *mainly pale pink*, most deeply colored on long neck and chest; *wing-coverts and tertials pinkish red*. **In flight** wing-coverts (both above and below) pinkish red contrasting with black primaries and secondaries. **Juvenile** *considerably whiter*, even pale grayish, with pale pink mainly on wings.

Habits: Typically seen wading in shallow water, often in groups. Feeds on various aquatic invertebrates, obtained by filtering water using specially adapted bill and tongue; feeding birds often hold neck underwater while walking ahead. Though they have to run considerable distances to take flight, once airborne flamingos fly strongly with powerful deep wingstrokes, long neck and legs outstretched. **Voice:** Usually quiet in Ecuador, though low honking calls are sometimes heard; when breeding, much noisier.

Ciconiiformes
Herons, Bitterns, and Egrets: Ardeidae (20)

Long-necked and long-legged wading birds with pointed and straight bills. They vary markedly in size from the diminutive *Ixobrychus* bitterns to the impressively large *Ardea* herons. The soft-part colors of many herons and egrets become more intense during a brief period at the onset of the breeding season, and a few species are also then adorned with various ornamental plumes (in some called "aigrettes"). Virtually all members of this family fly with their necks retracted in an S shape and their legs outstretched. They feed mainly on fish and small vertebrates obtained in shallow water and mud; a few, notably the Cattle Egret, forage primarily on open dry ground. Nests are platforms, often quite flimsy, made of sticks and placed in trees or bushes; some species are colonial, others solitary. The Boat-billed Heron was formerly classified in its own monotypic family. **Sexes usually are alike.**

Pinnated Bittern, *Botaurus pinnatus*
Mirasol Neotropical   Plate 7(8)

Below 50 m

63.5–76 cm (25–30″). A large, *cryptically colored* heron, *local in extensive marshes (especially reedbeds) and adjacent wet pastures and rice fields in lowlands of southwest.* Iris yellow, loral skin yellowish; long stout bill yellowish with dusky tip and culmen; legs yellowish olive. Crown dark brownish, face grayish, and *sides of neck buff narrowly barred blackish; above rich buff striped and barred with blackish*; tail blackish. Throat white, *foreneck and underparts buffy whitish coarsely streaked with pale brown.* **Similar species:** Virtually unmistakable in its Ecuadorian range, where there are no other large bitterns and where Rufescent Tiger-Heron is nearly if not totally extirpated. Should the tiger-heron ever be relocated in west, juvenile could be distinguished from bittern by broadly banded upperparts (especially across wings), its markings being not nearly as intricate as in bittern. Immature night-herons are smaller and more grayish with streaking on upperparts, etc. **Habits:** Hard to see, tending to remain in marshy cover though in low-light conditions may hunt more in open; also sometimes seen in flight low over reeds. Usually solitary, primarily hunting by slowly stalking prey. When alarmed, or spotted in open, usually freezes, sometimes crouching and retracting neck, at other times stretching neck skyward; can also "sink" down, virtually disappearing into fairly short grass. **Voice:** Unknown in Ecuador. In Costa Rica breeding ♂ ♂ give a booming "poonk" or "poonkoo," often at dusk or night (Stiles and Skutch 1989).

Ixobrychus Bitterns
Very small and *inconspicuous* herons that skulk in luxuriant marshy vegetation.

Least Bittern, *Ixobrychus exilis*
Mirasol Menor   Plate 5(5)

28–30.5 cm (11–12″). A *boldly patterned* and attractive *small* bittern, *scarce and local in marshy vegetation fringing oxbow lakes in lowlands of northeast, and in freshwater marshes in lowlands of southwest*; vagrants in Quito area. Iris pale yellow, loral skin yellow-green (red when breeding); bill yellow-orange with dusky culmen (brighter when breeding); legs yellow (orange when breeding). ♂ has *black crown* contrasting

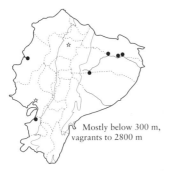

Mostly below 300 m, vagrants to 2800 m

300 m

with *ochraceous buff to rufous face and sides of neck* and *rich rufous nape and upper back*. *Upperparts otherwise black* with thin white stripe down either side of back; *wing-coverts ochraceous-buff, greater-coverts and tertials rufous*, both contrasting with black primaries and secondaries **in flight**. ♀ similarly patterned but *black replaced by dark brown*, sides of neck grayer, and underparts lightly streaked with brown. **Similar species:** Cf. accidental Stripe-backed Bittern and immature Zigzag Heron. Striated Heron larger and stockier and has all-dark wings. Otherwise this pretty, pint-sized bittern is hard to confuse. **Habits:** A secretive small heron that climbs about in reeds and other marshy vegetation, feeding by stalking. When spotted in open, often freezes with neck outstretched. Flushed birds fly low over reeds with dangling legs, then pitch back into cover, usually disappearing. **Voice:** Distinctive call of birds in Napo a low-pitched, hollow "wohh" repeated steadily at several-second intervals (very different from call of N. Am. birds). It is not known whether western birds sound the same, or indeed if they are resident (conceivably they could be boreal migrants).

**[Stripe-backed Bittern, *Ixobrychus involucris*
Mirasol Dorsiestriado]** Plate 5(6)

32–34 cm (12½–13½"). An *accidental* vagrant to marshy vegetation around oxbow lakes in lowlands of northeast (La Selva). **Adult** resembles smaller and darker Least Bittern, differing most notably in *grayish buff face, sides of neck, and nape* with only a narrow black coronal stripe, and *conspicuous ochraceous-buff striping on back*. **Juvenile** similar but buffier on face and sides of neck, and more streaked below.

Habits: Much as in Least Bittern; equally hard to see.

Zigzag Heron, *Zebrilus undulatus*
Garcilla Cebra Plate 5(4)

Below 300 m

30.5–33 cm (12–13"). *Local in undergrowth along sluggish streams and around edge of oxbow lakes in várzea forest in lowlands of east.* Until recently thought to be very rare, but now known just to be inconspicuous. Iris yellow; bill black above, dark brown to horn below; legs dull yellowish, browner to rear. **Adult** *looks very dark in field. Mostly blackish above with wavy narrow buff barring, shaggy crest blacker*; tail and flight feathers black. Below buffy whitish *densely vermiculated and chevroned with blackish*. **Juvenile** differs in having *rufous-chestnut forecrown, face, and sides of neck*; below pale buff with sparse blackish streaking and vermiculations. **Similar species:** Should not be confused, though it does occur in areas where the larger and stockier—and much easier to see—Striated Heron is found. **Habits:** Difficult to see unless calling. Zigzag Herons are solitary birds that tend to remain in heavy cover, unlike most other herons hardly ever coming out into open. Foraging birds stand on ground adjacent to water, less often on low branches. When nervous they flick tail sideways like a tiger-heron. **Voice:** Call a far-carrying (though not terribly loud) and hollow-sounding "hhoow-oo" with almost a grunting quality; it is steadily repeated at intervals of 4–6 seconds, often for long periods. Calling birds usually vocalize from low perches inside forest or woodland, at times some distance from water; they call primarily at dusk and often continue long into night.

Tigrisoma Tiger-Herons

Heavy-set, thick-necked herons with *short legs.* Younger examples of both species are boldly banded buff and black; the group name of "tiger-heron" is derived from the vaguely tiger-like plumage of these birds.

Rufescent Tiger-Heron, *Tigrisoma lineatum*
Garza Tigre Castaña   Plate 7(6)

Mostly below 500 m

66–76 cm (26–30"). Widespread but never very numerous in *swampy and várzea forest along lakes and streams in lowlands of east*; a few may persist locally in marshy areas of west. Less conspicuous in Ecuador than in many other parts of its wide range. Iris yellow to hazel, bare skin around gape yellow; bill dusky, yellowish at base; legs olive. **Adult** has *head and neck rich rufous-chestnut*; upperparts dusky-brown very finely vermiculated buff. Throat and foreneck white with dark median stripe on foreneck; lower underparts buff. **Juvenile** very different: *head and neck rufous-cinnamon with prominent black chevrons*; dark brown above boldly spotted buff and cinnamon, with *very bold buff banding across wings*; tail

blackish with four narrow white bands. Throat white, underparts pale buff with dark bars and chevrons. Requires at least 4 years to attain adult plumage, gradually acquiring rufous on head and neck and losing barring and spotting. **Similar species:** Adult distinctive with extensive rufous on head and neck. Younger birds are also readily recognized in most of their Ecuadorian range (though cf. Pinnated Bittern in west). However, in foothills they can occur with Fasciated Tiger-Heron, which is confusingly similar in its earlier plumage stages. Usually the two cannot then be distinguished, but note Fasciated's somewhat shorter and heavier bill and its tail with only three white bands (not four). **Habits:** Usually solitary, often standing motionless and with hunched neck for long periods at water's edge, awaiting prey. Sometimes follows very small streams inside extensive forest, and rarely fully in open; often active at night. At times notably stolid, allowing close approach, but at other times wary and flushing quickly. Perches freely in trees. **Voice:** Seems to vocalize mainly at night, giving a fast series of groaning notes, "honh-honh-honh-honh ...," often ending in a more protracted phrase, "honnhhh-hh."

Fasciated Tiger-Heron, *Tigrisoma fasciatum*
Garza Tigre Barreteada   Plate 7(7)

Mostly 600–2200 m

61–66 cm (24–26"). *Scarce and local along fast-flowing rocky rivers and larger streams in foothills and subtropics on both slopes* ranging at elevations above those of Rufescent Tiger-Heron. Iris and bare skin around gape yellow; bill dusky, yellower at base; legs dusky. **Adult** has *black crown* and *slaty gray face*; *sides of neck slaty black finely barred* *with buff*; upperparts blackish brown very finely vermiculated buff. Throat and foreneck white with dark median stripe on foreneck; lower underparts tawny-buff. **Juvenile** and various intermediate stages essentially identical to Rufescent Tiger-Herons of comparable ages, but in the hand Fasciated can be seen to have only 3 narrow white tail bands (vs. 4 in Rufescent), and its bill is slightly shorter and heavier with more arched culmen. **Similar species:** Adult and subadult Rufescent Tiger-Herons have rufous heads and necks, increasingly obvious as they age. For the most part the two tiger-herons segregate by range and habitat. **Habits:** Usually seen standing on boulders out in turbulent water, also on gravel bars. Generally wary.

Ardea Herons and Egrets

Large and stately, members of the genus *Ardea* range widely in all but polar latitudes. Although *Ardea* tend to feed more solitarily than the more gregarious *Egretta*, members of both genera are often found together and even sometimes nest in mixed colonies.

Cocoi Heron, *Ardea cocoi*
Garzón Cocoi   Plate 7(2)

To 400 m

104–127 cm (41–50″). *A large and long-necked heron found widely around both fresh and salt water in lowlands of east and southwest*; most numerous in and near mangroves along sw. coast. Formerly often called White-necked Heron. Iris yellow; facial skin pale greenish (bluer when breeding); heavy bill yellow to orange with dusky ridge (deeper orange when breeding); legs greenish. **Adult** has *black crown and nape extending down to just below eyes*, with black occipital plumes when breeding; *neck and breast*

white with a few black streaks on foreneck and long plumes on breast; *otherwise bluish gray above* with white plumes springing from scapulars; tail black. Bend of wings extensively black, closed wing otherwise mainly gray. *Belly black*, with *contrasting white thighs*. **In flight** shows much white on forepart of wing. **Juvenile** much less patterned, essentially grayish throughout, lacking all plumes; thighs already white. **Similar species:** Cf. much rarer migratory Great Blue Heron. Otherwise not likely confused: *the only large, boldly black-and-white patterned heron in Ecuador*. **Habits:** Generally forages solitarily, standing and waiting for prey in shallow water or at edge, also slowly stalking it. Gathers in groups where feeding conditions are favorable, as at pools that have been left isolated by receding water levels. Flight slow and steady on deep wingbeats. Nests in small groups, sometimes with or adjacent to colonies of other herons but more often apart. **Voice:** Usually quiet, though disturbed birds often utter a complaining "kwawk" or "kwaak" as they flush.

Great Blue Heron, *Ardea herodias*
Garzón Azulado   Plate 7(1)

To 2200 m

104–127 cm (41–50″). *A casual vagrant to w. and n. Ecuador*, most or all birds presumed to be derived from northern populations. *Resembles much more numerous Cocoi Heron in shape and comportment*. Iris yellow; bill yellow with dusky culmen; legs dusky to olive. **Adult** differs from Cocoi mainly in having *top of crown white* (only sides of crown are black); *neck and sides of chest buffy grayish* (not pure white); more streaked lower underparts (not contrastingly black); and *rufous thighs* (not white). **In flight** shows much less white on upperwing. **Juvenile** duller and more similar to juvenile Cocoi, though Great Blue is more brownish gray overall, showing rufescent thighs (not whitish) from an early age. **Habits:** As in Cocoi Heron.

Great Egret, *Ardea alba*
Garceta Grande   Plate 7(3)

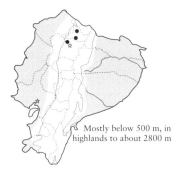

Mostly below 500 m, in highlands to about 2800 m

91.5–99 cm (36–39"). *Widespread near both fresh and salt water in lowlands*, a few records from highland lakes; most numerous near sw. coast. Formerly separated in genus *Casmerodius*. Iris yellow; *bill bright yellow*, loral skin yellow-green (brighter when breeding); *legs black*. **Adult** *entirely white*, with long filmy aigrettes springing from back and foreneck when breeding. **Juvenile** similar but yellow bill tipped dusky. **Similar species:** This large and strikingly long-necked heron can only be confused with smaller Snowy Egret (which also differs in its black bill and yellow feet) and immature Little Blue Heron (with bicolored bill, greenish legs). **Habits:** Similar in feeding behavior to Cocoi Heron, but Great Egret differs in its more gregarious habits: it regularly gathers in sizable flocks (even flocks of hundreds in southwest). Nests in colonies, often together with other herons. **Voice:** Usually quiet, but gives a low-pitched throaty "ahhrrr," especially just after being startled or flushed.

Egretta Egrets and Herons
A diverse group of midsized herons, some *Egretta* are white, whereas others are mainly or entirely dark blue-gray; they are *most numerous on or near the coast*, especially in the southwest. Nests are placed in trees in colonies, sometimes of substantial size, often several species together. Although mainly silent (and voices are thus not described below), members of this genus occasionally give gruff, hoarse squawks.

Snowy Egret, *Egretta thula*
Garceta Nívea   Plate 6(1)

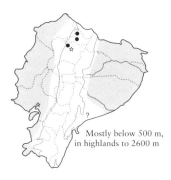

Mostly below 500 m, in highlands to 2600 m

53.5–63.5 cm (21–25"). *Widespread near both fresh and salt water in lowlands*, a few also occurring around highland lakes in north. Most numerous by far near sw. coast, breeding locally. Iris yellow, loral skin yellow (brighter, almost orange, when breeding); *slender bill black*; *legs black with bright yellow feet* (the "golden slippers"), yellow sometimes extending up rear part of legs. **Adult** *all white*, with graceful filmy aigrettes springing from crown, back, and chest when breeding. **Juvenile** similar, but bill can be yellowish and extensive greenish yellow may extend up rear part of legs. **Similar species:** Great Egret much larger with proportionately longer neck and bright yellow bill. More likely to be confused with immature Little Blue Heron, which differs in its bicolored and stouter bill, entirely greenish yellow legs. **Habits:** An elegant and lovely egret that tends to feed more actively than many other herons and egrets, dancing and prancing about gracefully. Sometimes stirs up shallow water with feet in an effort to startle prey into attempting to flee.

Little Blue Heron, *Egretta caerulea*
Garceta Azul   Plate 6(2)

56–66 cm (22–26"). *Most numerous around both fresh and salt water in lowlands of southwest*, less so northward mainly along coast; *boreal migrants* occur along rivers in

Mostly below 600 m,
in highlands to 2800 m

lowlands of northeast, and around highland lakes in north (in west as well?). Formerly separated in genus *Florida*. Iris yellow, loral skin dull greenish (bluer when breeding); *fairly heavy bill bluish gray with outer third to half black*; *legs greenish gray to greenish yellow*. **Adult** *dark slaty blue-gray* with somewhat contrasting *reddish maroon head and neck*; when breeding, head and neck become brighter and elongated plumes spring from crown, chest, and back. **Immature** very different, *all white* aside from inconspicuous dusky tips to outer primaries. Birds about a year old that are molting into adult plumage can look white *irregularly splotched with slaty*, giving pied appearance. **Similar species:** Compare white immatures to slimmer, more elegantly shaped Snowy Egret. All-dark adult Little Blue should not be confused, but cf. Tricolored Heron. **Habits:** A fairly active feeder, though less agile and graceful than Snowy Egret; also often stands motionless, waiting for unsuspecting prey to approach. Individuals are more apt to turn up along flowing rivers and around isolated ponds than are most other larger herons. Unlike other herons, Little Blue often flies with neck at least partially outstretched, especially soon after taking off.

Tricolored Heron, *Egretta tricolor*
Garceta Tricolor   Plate 6(3)

58.5–68.5 cm (23–27″). *Quite strictly coastal in Ecuador*, rarely venturing inland; most numerous in Guayas and El Oro, much smaller numbers occurring northward. Formerly separated in genus *Hydranassa*. A slender heron with *long and very thin neck*. Iris red, loral skin yellowish (violet when breeding); *long slender bill* yellowish with

dark culmen and tip (bluish when breeding); legs greenish yellow (redder when breeding). **Adult** *mostly slaty blue-gray; white rump and uppertail-coverts* (visible mainly in flight, then obvious). Throat and front of neck white with narrow median stripe of rufous; *belly contrastingly white*. Birds in breeding plumage have long white occipital plumes and creamy-buff plumes springing from back. **Juvenile** like adult but with grayish crown, *cinnamon-rufous face and neck*, broad rufous edging on wing-coverts. **Similar species:** Adult Little Blue Heron stockier and entirely dark. **Habits:** Tends to be an active feeder, often running and prancing across mud and through shallow water; sometimes stealthily attempts to sneak up on prey, then often wading up to belly.

Cattle Egret, *Bubulcus ibis*
Garceta Bueyera   Plate 6(8)

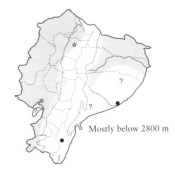

Mostly below 2800 m

47–52 cm (18½–20½″). A fairly small *stocky heron, very common in semiopen country in more humid lowlands of southwest*, less numerous northward; in e. lowlands and n. highlands (where scarce) apparently occurs mainly as a boreal migrant. Known to breed only in west. A relatively recent (1960s) arrival in Ecuador. *Much more apt to be found away from water than other Ecuadorian herons.* Iris yellow, loral skin yellowish; *stout and fairly short bill* yellow (more orange, even reddish, when breeding); legs olive yellowish to greenish (more reddish when breeding). Entirely white; breeding-plumage birds acquire *prominent buff plumes on crown, back, and chest* (a trace of this color is retained by some adults when they are not breeding). **Similar species:** Cf. Snowy Egret and immature Little Blue Heron, both of which are larger and differ in bill coloration, etc. Cattle Egret has heavy jowl, imparting a distinctive look quite different from slim-faced appearance of other similar herons. **Habits:** Highly gregarious, especially at roosts, from which flocks fan out in all directions to feed in open country. True to its name, often feeds with cattle, pursuing insects flushed by the animals, often perching on cows themselves. Also forages in other semiopen areas, favoring plowed fields but regular along roadsides, especially where garbage or bananas have been dumped. Unless cattle are present, however, generally does not frequent marshy areas.

Butorides Herons

Small, chunky herons with shaggy crests and short legs. Another *Butorides* species is endemic to the Galápagos Islands.

Striated Heron, *Butorides striatus*
Garcilla Estriada   Plate 5(2)

38–43 cm (15–17″). *Widespread and generally numerous in a variety of freshwater habitats in lowlands*—along rivers, around ponds and lakes, in marshes and rice fields, etc.—with smaller numbers in saltwater habitats

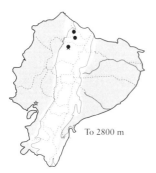

To 2800 m

(especially in *mangroves*) and up into central valley, at least in north. Iris yellow (more orange when breeding), loral skin yellow; bill blackish with yellow at base of mandible (all black when breeding); *rather short legs yellowish* (*reddish orange* when breeding). **Adult** has *crown and shaggy erectile crest black*; otherwise greenish black above, wing-coverts edged buff, tail black. *Sides of head, neck, and chest gray*, with white brown-bordered stripe from throat down middle of foreneck; lower underparts grayish. **Juvenile** like adult but crown streaked rufous, browner upperparts, whitish underparts striped with brown. **Similar species:** Only likely confusion is with rare boreal migrant Green Heron, which see. In e. lowlands cf. also Zigzag Heron. **Habits:** Normally more or less solitary, though in some areas this species is so numerous that it appears to be in small flocks. Generally hunts by standing or crouching on a perch just out of water, not actually wading. When nervous often flicks tail sideways and elevates shaggy crest. Usually nests alone, at most in small groups; generally not with other herons. **Voice:** Flushed birds often flush with a characteristic abrupt and complaining "kyow!"; also has other clucking calls.

Green Heron, *Butorides virescens*
Garcilla Verde   Plate 5(1)

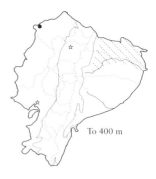

To 400 m

38–43 cm (15–17″). *A very rare boreal migrant* (Dec.–Mar.) to edge of forested streams, lakeshores, and mangroves in lowlands of north. Resembles much more numerous Striated Heron (with which Green has sometimes been considered conspecific, as Green-backed Heron). **Adult** differs in its *maroon-chestnut sides of head, neck, and chest.* **Juvenile** probably indistinguishable from juvenile Striated, though tending to be browner on sides of head, neck, and chest. **Habits and Voice:** As in Striated Heron.

Agami Heron, *Agamia agami*
Garza Agamí   Plate 6(4)

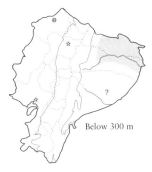

Below 300 m

63.5–71 cm (25–28″). *Rare and inconspicuous along forested margins of lakes and streams and in várzea forest in lowlands of northeast*; an old record from Esmeraldas. Formerly often called Chestnut-bellied Heron. A beautiful, *multicolored* heron with *exceptionally long and slender bill* and *long thin neck*. Iris orange to yellow, bare facial skin grayish green to olive; bill black, yellowish below at base; rather short legs olive to yellowish. **Adult** has crown and hindneck black with silvery gray occipital plumes (longer when breeding); *sides of neck chestnut with short curved silvery gray plumes springing from lower neck*; throat and median stripe down foreneck white, with brown streak down center. *Upperparts (including tail) dark glossy green. Lower underparts rich dark chestnut.* **Juvenile** brown above and on neck, with blackish crown and hindneck and white throat; lower underparts whitish, coarsely streaked dark brown. **Similar species:** Beautifully colored adult unmistakable. Even dull-plumaged younger birds are not likely confused with other herons on account of thin, rapier-like bill. **Habits:** A solitary and shy heron that favors thick, almost impenetrable vegetation in swampy areas; almost never feeds in the open and is apparently quite active at night. Hunts by waiting motionless and spearing fish. Disturbed birds sometimes flush up and land on an exposed branch, but more often they sneak back into cover and freeze, thereby hoping to remain undetected. Else-

where known to nest in small colonies, sometimes in association with other herons. **Voice:** Usually quiet, but has been heard to give a low-pitched guttural croaking (J. Moore recording).

Capped Heron, *Pilherodius pileatus*
Garza Pileada   Plate 5(3)

Below 400 m

53.5–58.5 cm (21–23″). Uncommon but fairly conspicuous along larger rivers and at edge of swampy areas in *lowlands of east*. Unmistakable. Iris brown; *bill and facial skin cobalt blue* (more intense when breeding), sometimes tipped pale purplish; legs bluish gray. **Adult** has *black crown* with long white occipital plumes (exceptionally so when breeding), a bit of white on forecrown; *head, neck, and breast pale creamy buff* (deeper when breeding). Above otherwise very pale pearly gray; lower underparts white. **Juvenile** similar but lacking occipital plumes and with some grayish crown streaking. **Similar species:** None of the egrets or white herons has any black on crown, and none shows bright blue on bill and face. Chunky shape of flying birds recalls Black-crowned Night-Heron. **Habits:** More or less solitary (sometimes 2–3 birds loosely associating), feeding on muddy or grassy shorelines. Appears to forage mainly by standing quietly and spearing prey, less often stalking. Flies with very shallow wingbeats. **Voice:** Generally silent, but an occasional short croak has been reported.

Nycticorax, Nyctanassa Night-Herons
Fairly large, compactly built herons found mainly near the southwest coast, both night-herons have a distinctly different, *brownish juvenal plumage* in which the two species

resemble each other. The genus *Nyctanassa* is often merged into *Nycticorax*.

Black-crowned Night-Heron
Nycticorax nycticorax
Garza Nocturna Coroninegra   Plate 6(6)

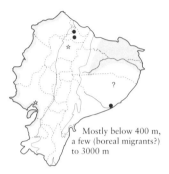

Mostly below 400 m, a few (boreal migrants?) to 3000 m

56–61 cm (22–24″). A stocky heron with short neck, rather local in *both fresh and salt-water situations* in lowlands of west (mainly Manabí southward) and northeast; a few may persist around highland lakes in north. Iris red, with loral skin olive (blackish when breeding); stout bill black; legs yellow (redder when breeding). **Adult** has *crown, nape, and back glossy black* with two long white occipital plumes (even longer when breeding) and narrow white forehead; lower face, sides of neck, and entire underparts whitish. *Wings and tail pale gray.* **Juvenile** very different with yellowish iris, *lower mandible mostly dull greenish yellow. Above dark brown with prominent buff to whitish streaking and large spots on wing-coverts*; below whitish streaked with grayish brown. **Subadult** already shows at least an echo of adult's pattern but is generally browner. **Similar species:** Adult nearly unmistakable, though cf. Boat-billed Heron. Juvenile easily confused with juvenile Yellow-crowned Night-Heron (*but recall that Yellow-crowned only occurs along coast*). Yellow-crowned differs in its rangier shape with longer legs projecting beyond tail in flight (those of Black-crowned barely protrude); its even thicker bill is black, and it is grayer above with finer pale streaking and spotting. Cf. also Pinnated Bittern. **Habits:** True to its name, this species is active primarily at night, at dusk flying out from its roost to feed. Feeds more by day when nesting. Roosts are situated in shady leafy sites where disturbance is unlikely; sometimes other herons are present as well. Hunched neck gives this species a characteristic slumped posture. **Voice:** Has a distinctive abrupt "quok" or "wok" call, given especially in flight but also when disturbed.

Yellow-crowned Night-Heron
Nyctanassa violacea
Garza Nocturna Cangrejera   Plate 6(7)

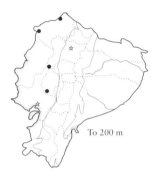

To 200 m

56–61 cm (22–24″). *Local in mangroves and on tidal flats along coast in southwest*, but scarce in Esmeraldas; very rare away from coast. Iris orange-brown (red when breeding), with loral skin yellowish (green when breeding); *very stout bill black*; legs yellow (more reddish orange when breeding). **Adult** has *head black with contrasting creamy white crown and broad white stripe on lower face*, and long black and white occipital plumes (even longer when breeding); *neck and entire underparts uniform gray.* Above dusky brown, feathers broadly edged brownish gray. **Juvenile** very different, with blackish crown streaked buff, face and neck streaked buff and brown; *upperparts dark grayish brown with short buff streaks and spots*, wing-coverts narrowly edged whitish. Below buff heavily streaked dark brown. **Similar species:** Adult easily recognized. Juvenile resembles juvenile Black-crowned Night-Heron, which see. **Habits:** Mainly nocturnal, but more often active by day than Black-crowned Night-Heron, standing on mudflats and gravelly beaches. Almost always roosts in mangroves, sometimes substantial numbers together. Diet mainly crabs. **Voice:** Less vocal than Black-crowned Night-Heron; Yellow-crowned's flight call a slightly higher-pitched and more nasal "kwak" or "kwek."

Boat-billed Heron, *Cochlearius cochlearius*
Garza Cucharón   Plate 6(5)

To 400 m

48–53.5 cm (19–21″). A stocky, *nocturnal* heron with an *exceptionally broad and heavy bill*. Inconspicuous around ponds, lakes, and forested streams and rivers in *lowlands of east*; only a few old records from west. Iris brown, loral skin grayish; bill black above, yellowish below (all black when breeding); legs olive to yellowish. **Adult** has *crown, long and wide crest* (even more ample when breeding), *and back black* with forehead white; *otherwise pale pearly gray above. Face, sides of neck, and breast white*; median lower underparts rufous-buff, with sides and flanks black. **Juvenile** similar but crest shorter and washed with cinnamon above, buff on breast. **Similar species:** Only possible confusion is with vaguely similar adult Black-crowned Night-Heron, but bill entirely different, etc. **Habits:** Roosts by day in thick foliage near water, there easily overlooked though not overly wary and reluctant to flush; usually in groups, sometimes in association with other herons (though more often apart). At or soon after dusk disperses to feed, usually solitarily; unlike night-herons, Boat-billed never seems to feed by day. Feeds at edge of shallow water, mainly obtaining food in a manner not dissimilar from that of other herons (despite its strikingly divergent bill); Boat-billeds also apparently scoop and sift muddy water. **Voice:** Usually silent. Flushed birds give a low-pitched "qua" or "kwa" in flight (vaguely like quacking of a duck); roosting birds may give a low clucking and they also bill clap.

Ibises and Spoonbills: Threskiornithidae (7)

Large, long-legged wading birds with *characteristic bill shapes*: long and decurved in the ibises, broad and spatulate in the spoonbill. A cosmopolitan group, in Ecuador they range mainly near water in the lowlands; *most species here are scarce* (only the White and Green being at all frequent). **Sexes are alike.** Ibises and spoonbills feed mainly on crustaceans and small fish, obtained primarily by probing in mud and shallow water; one species (Black-faced Ibis) is more terrestrial.

Black-faced Ibis, *Theristicus melanopis*
Bandurria Carinegra   Plate 5(12)

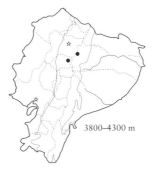

3800–4300 m

71–76 cm (28–30″). A *large* and *strikingly patterned* ibis, *now sadly rare and local in paramo and vicinity of lakes around Volcanes Antisana and Cotopaxi*. Formerly often considered conspecific with Buff-necked Ibis (*T. caudatus*) of S. Am. lowlands. Iris red to reddish brown, with bare black ocular area and stripe on sides of chin; long decurved bill blackish; *legs salmon pink*. Unmistakable. **Adult** has *buff head, neck, and breast*, deepest on crown and palest on throat; *otherwise brownish gray above, paler on wings*; tail black. Brownish gray crescent below front of wings; lower breast buffy whitish, belly and crissum black. **In flight** shows black flight feathers. **Juvenile** similar but duller and with dusky streaks on head, neck, and underparts, most pronounced on crown and foreneck. **Habits:** Black-faced Ibis is conspicuous in the few places where it still occurs. It ranges in pairs or small flocks, foraging mainly on dry ground, walking on short grass and probing soil for grubs, worms, frogs, etc. Rather wary, doubtless in part because in many areas it is still hunted. Flies strongly, sometimes at great heights. Apparently nests semicolonially in reedbeds. **Voice:** Rather noisy, especially when flying. Call a far-carrying—often the birds can be heard long before they are seen—metallic "tur-túrt," characteristically doubled.

Green Ibis, *Mesembrinibis cayennensis*
Ibis Verde   Plate 5(11)

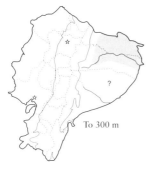

56–58.5 cm (22–23″). *Uncommon along forest-fringed lakes, ponds, and streams and in swampy várzea forest in lowlands of east.* Iris gray, bare facial skin dark green; *long decurved bill and rather short legs green* (in some individuals quite bright, almost turquoise). **Adult** *mostly very dark bronzy green*, blacker on breast and belly, with short bushy crest (usually not too apparent, but sometimes ruffled) and *some shiny green feathers on nape and hindneck.* **Juvenile** similar but duller and blacker overall, lacking shiny green. **Similar species:** Not likely confused in its Ecuadorian range, *where the only normally occurring dark ibis.* Cf. very rare Bare-faced Ibis. **Habits:** Rather an inconspicuous ibis that usually forages solitarily, at most in pairs, probing in muddy or grassy areas along shores of rivers and lakes; also perches freely in trees. Ranges in the open mainly at dawn and dusk, and appears to be primarily crepuscular (also apparently active through night). Flight decidedly jerky, limpkin-like, with stiff quick wingstrokes. **Voice:** Loud and easily recognized call a mellow rolling "koro-koro-koro-koro" or "klu-klu-klu-klu," usually given in flight.

Bare-faced Ibis, *Phimosus infuscatus*
Ibis Caripelado   Plate 5(9)

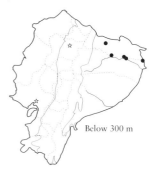

48–51 cm (19–20″). *A very rare visitant* to sandbars and grassy areas along larger rivers in *lowlands of northeast.* Has been called Whispering Ibis. Iris brown, *with conspicuous bare area on foreface red; long and slender decurved bill reddish brown*, often tipped darker; rather short legs pinkish red. **Adult** *entirely bronzy greenish black*, duller on underparts. **Juvenile** similar, but duller with less bronze and bill blackish. **Similar species:** Green Ibis has green facial skin, and legs (never with any sign of red). **Habits:** In Ecuador almost invariably seen as the odd individual, standing alone on a sandbar or in nearby marshy terrain. Elsewhere notably gregarious, feeding mainly by probing into damp or wet ground in marshes, pastures, and lake edges. Flight strong, with steady fast wingbeats; often flies high overhead when moving between feeding grounds or to and from its roosts. **Voice:** Normally silent.

Eudocimus Ibises
Beautiful ibises with *distinctive black-tipped primaries.*

White Ibis, *Eudocimus albus*
Ibis Blanco   Plate 5(7)

56–61 cm (22–24″). *Locally common in mangroves and tidal flats along coast*, smaller numbers occurring inland in adjacent marshes; *most numerous in Guayas and El Oro.* Iris bluish white; *facial skin, long decurved bill, and legs pinkish red* (more intense when breeding, when even has a small extended gular patch; tip of bill may become blackish); ♂'s bill longer. **Adult** unmistakable, *all white* with *black tips to outer primaries* (normally visible only in flight).

Juvenile has pinkish bill with darker tip, grayish iris; head and neck whitish streaked with dusky; above dark brown with *contrasting white rump and uppertail-coverts* (normally visible only in flight, then very conspicuous); underparts white. **Similar species:** Striking adult is obvious. Younger, mainly brown individuals differ from other ibises in their contrasting white rumps and underparts; cf. very rare Glossy Ibis. No overlap with Scarlet Ibis. **Habits:** A gregarious ibis, often occurring in good-sized flocks, feeding by probing into mud and shallow water, also picking food from surface. Flight graceful and controlled, with neck and legs held extended; relatively shallow wingbeats are interspersed with short glides on slightly bowed wings, and also often circles on set wings. **Voice:** Usually silent; occasionally emits soft honks and grunts.

[Scarlet Ibis, *Eudocimus ruber*
Ibis Escarlata]   Plate 5(8)

56–61 cm (22–24″). A casual vagrant to lakeshores and riverbanks in lowlands of northeast. Iris brown; *facial skin, long decurved bill, and legs pinkish red* (more

Below 300 m

intense when breeding), but bill of some individuals entirely blackish; ♂'s bill longer. **Adult** unmistakable, *entirely vivid scarlet* with *black tips to outer primaries* (normally visible only in flight); a few birds are paler and more orangey. **Juvenile** identical to juvenile White Ibis; gradually a few red feathers start to appear, revealing bird's identity. **Habits:** As in White Ibis; in Ecuador most likely to occur alone. Adult Scarlets are even more spectacular and especially in flight they present a breathtaking spectacle.

[Glossy Ibis, *Plegadis falcinellus*
Ibis Morito]   Plate 5(10)

Below 50 m

56–61 cm (22–24″). A casual vagrant to freshwater marshes and adjacent rice fields in lowlands of southwest. Iris brown, loral skin slaty with narrow bluish white edges both above and below; *long decurved bill* and legs grayish, but bill often pinker. **Nonbreeding adult** has *head, neck, and underparts dark grayish brown,* head and neck with narrow whitish streaking. *Upperparts dark metallic bronzy green.* **Breeding adult** (a plumage unlikely to be seen in Ecuador) has *head, neck, and underparts chestnut,* with more iridescence on upperparts. **Similar species:** *The only all-dark ibis ever recorded from w. Ecuador* (the other two found in east, Green and Bare-faced, are both exceedingly unlikely in west). Cf. immature White Ibis (with white underparts and rump). **Habits:** Often wades in fairly deep water, probing into mud. Flies with long neck and legs outstretched.

Roseate Spoonbill, *Ajaia ajaja*
Espátula Rosada   Plate 5(13)

*71–79 cm (28–31″). A spectacular and unmistakable *pink* wading bird with *long flat*

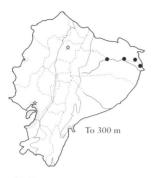

To 300 m

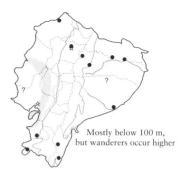

Mostly below 100 m,
but wanderers occur higher

spatulate bill found *locally in mangroves, tidal flats, and nearby marshy areas in lowlands of southwest*; most numerous in Guayas. A few also occur along rivers in east. Iris orange to red; bill grayish to pinkish; legs mainly pink to red. **Adult** has *unfeathered head grayish to pale greenish with black band on nape. Otherwise mostly pink* except for white neck and upper back; reddest on lesser upperwing-coverts and underwing-coverts (especially evident in flight); some buff on sides of chest; tail orange. **Immature** with feathered head and much whiter overall, though it already has pink tail and underwing-coverts; it gradually becomes pinker with age, requiring 3 years to acquire adult plumage. **Similar species:** Not likely confused, but cf. Chilean Flamingo (larger with much longer neck and legs, very different bill). **Habits:** Quite gregarious. Feeds by wading into shallow water and sweeping bill from side to side. Especially lovely in flight when it flies with neck held stiffly outstretched, interspersing wingbeats with brief glides. **Voice:** Usually silent; rarely gives soft grunts.

Storks: Ciconiidae (2)

Found mainly in the Old World tropics; three species occur in America. Storks are large to very large wading birds with long legs, heavy bills; plumage mainly or entirely white. **Sexes are alike.**

Wood Stork, *Mycteria americana*
Cigüeña Americana   Plate 7(4)

89–101.5 cm (35–40″). A *very large, mainly white* stork, *local and nomadic around freshwater ponds and marshes in lowlands of southwest*; wandering individuals or groups sometimes occur elsewhere, generally just while flying overhead. Iris brown; blackish *bill long and heavy, somewhat decurved*; legs dusky to grayish with pink feet. **Adult** has *unfeathered head and neck mostly dark gray*, with paler forecrown and black nape band. *Otherwise white* with *contrasting black flight feathers* (mainly hidden except in flight). **Immature** dingier generally, with partially feathered head and neck. **Similar species:** Not likely confused. White Ibis adult much smaller with red bill and facial area, black only on wing tips. Soaring birds have a flight pattern not dissimilar from King Vulture's. **Habits:** Gregarious, regularly congregating in flocks where feeding conditions are favorable, and often with herons and egrets. Somewhat ungainly in appearance on the ground or when perched in a tree, Wood Storks are powerful and graceful fliers, capable of soaring to great heights on outstretched wings, neck and long legs held outstretched. **Voice:** Mainly quiet away from nesting colonies, but does emit various grunting calls.

Jabiru, *Jabiru mycteria*
Jabirú   Plate 7(5)

127–150 cm (50–59″). *A casual vagrant to sandbars, river margins, and adjacent open areas in lowlands of northeast. A huge* stork with a *massive upswept bill*. Iris dark brown; bill and legs black. Unmistakable. **Adult** has *unfeathered head and neck black with broad red band around base of neck* (sometimes appearing "swollen") and small tuft of white feathers on nape. *Otherwise pure white*. **Immature** dingier generally, with red on neck duller and scattered brownish feathers. **Similar species:** Hardly to be confused, the gigantic Jabiru is—together with Andean Condor—the largest bird in Ecuador. Though big, the Wood Stork is much smaller

Below 300 m

Mostly 2000–4000 m

with black flight feathers, and its drooped bill shape is very different. **Habits:** Less gregarious than Wood Stork; in their normal range Jabirus typically occur in pairs that stride across grassy areas or in shallow water, striking at prey (fish, frogs, snakes, even young caiman) with their powerful bills. When not breeding, may gather in flocks. Though take-off is labored, once airborne Jabirus are strong fliers and can soar (vulture-like) effortlessly, sometimes very high.

American Vultures: Cathartidae (5)

Large, superficially hawk- or eagle-like birds with broad wings highly suitable for extended periods of soaring. Their *heads and upper necks are featherless* (and often brightly colored), apparently so that these areas do not become soiled as the birds rip into carcasses; virtually all of their food is carrion. Bills are hooked for tearing into flesh, but the *feet are relatively weak* and not suitable for carrying food. Except in the huge Andean Condor—one of the largest flying birds in the world—**sexes are alike.** "Nests" are almost nonexistent, eggs simply being laid on the ground in a secluded spot, often in a hollow in a tree or bank. American vultures and condors defecate on their legs, one point—of many others, most of them anatomical—of similarity to the Storks (Ciconiidae), which present evidence now indicates the American Vulture family is more closely related to than it is to the superficially similar Kites, Eagles, Hawks, and Osprey (Accipitridae).

Andean Condor, *Vultur gryphus*
Cóndor Andino   Plate 9(1)

102–127 cm (40–50″). A *huge* soaring bird of *open and more remote highlands*, especially

paramo. Despite being the national bird, sadly now *scarce and declining in Ecuador.* Iris dark brown; bill dull yellowish; legs blackish. **Adult** ♂ has *bare head and neck wrinkled and dull reddish* with *large comb on forehead* and extensible large dewlap under throat; head of ♀ *blacker,* lacking comb and dewlap. *Mainly black* with *fluffy white ruff on neck; flight feathers* (except outer primaries) *extensively silvery white,* especially conspicuous in flight but also showing on closed wing. **Juvenile** browner, and lacking adult's white neck ruff and white on wing; it acquires adult features gradually, requiring at least 4–5 years to do so. **Similar species:** Nothing really similar because of its great size. Turkey Vulture much smaller, and instead of flying steadily, it tilts in a shallow dihedral on narrower wings; the difference is apparent even at great distances. **Habits:** Now seen singly or in at most small groups, though in former years it probably gathered in flocks at carcasses. Condors feed entirely on carrion, located through their keen vision; on rare occasions they take some live prey (e.g., recently born animals), and as a result they still suffer from persecution, mainly poisoning, at the hand of rural residents. Given proper conditions, condors are capable of effortlessly soaring and sailing to great heights, flying steadily on broad flat wings with primaries outstretched; at other times, probably especially when searching for food, they may cruise closer to ground. They nest and roost on remote and inaccessible cliffs. **Voice:** Nearly silent; birds at nest and in agonistic encounters at carcasses occasionally hiss.

King Vulture, *Sarcoramphus papa*
Gallinazo Rey   Plate 9(2)

Mostly below 500 m

71–81 cm (28–32″). A *spectacular*, *large* vulture of lowland forests, widespread in east but now rare and local in west. Iris white to straw yellow, eye-ring red; *caruncles on base of bill reddish and orange, tip of bill red*; legs whitish to pale gray. Unmistakable **adult** *mostly white* with *head and upper neck bare and multicolored*, head dark purplish gray with folds of whitish skin, neck mostly orange; *large ruff around lower neck dusky. Flight feathers, rump, and short tail contrastingly black*. **In flight** long and very broad wings held flat. **Juvenile** *sooty gray* with colors of bare head and neck already partially indicated (as is pale eye); it acquires adult features gradually, in 4 or more years. **Similar species:** Adult could only be confused—at a great distance—with Wood Stork (which has a similar flight pattern, but not much else). Juvenile King Vulture could be confused with Turkey Vulture, though even on younger Kings generally some whitish mottling is apparent, at least on underwing-coverts; flight style of the two species very different, with Turkey Vulture tilting from side to side with wings held in a dihedral (in King, wings are held steady, flat, and outstretched). Cf. also Black Vulture. **Habits:** Usually seen solitarily or in pairs, circling high in sky on broad flat wings, not associating with lesser species of vultures for very long—though, because Kings lack a sense of smell, they depend on Turkeys and Greater Yellow-headeds for locating food. Strongly dominant over other vultures at carcasses. Unlike other vultures, Kings are rarely seen perched, and hardly ever rest on open branches.

Black Vulture, *Coragyps atratus*
Gallinazo Negro   Plate 9(5)

Mostly below 2000 m, a few to 3000 m

56–63.5 cm (22–25″). *Widespread, common, and conspicuous in lowlands* (though less so where forest remains extensive), smaller numbers up into highlands (where mainly around towns and cities). Iris dark brown; bill blackish with pale horn tip; legs blackish. **All ages** have *bare head and neck dark gray*; plumage dull black. **In flight** shows broad and fairly long wings, *short tail*; *outer primaries have whitish patch at their base*, conspicuous both from above and below. **Similar species:** Juvenile King Vulture much larger and from an early age shows white mottling on underwing-coverts and underparts. Great Black-Hawk has a similar flight profile (broad wings, short tail), but its larger, feathered head and neck protrude more, and it has prominent white in tail (and lacks white in primaries). **Habits:** A familiar bird in many areas, and one of the few large birds in Ecuador clearly to have benefitted from humans' omnipresence. Often becomes tame around towns and settlements, frequently roosting in large congregations in trees, feeding on refuse as well as carrion (also eats some live food), hopping and even running with considerable agility on ground. Unlike *Cathartes* vultures, which it dominates at food sources, has no sense of smell. In typical flight its shallow, stiff, and fast wingbeats are interspersed with short bouts of sailing, but it is also capable of soaring to great heights.

Cathartes Vultures

Vultures with *relatively long wings and tails*, the wings characteristically not held flat when soaring but rather *tilted up in a distinct dihedral*.

Turkey Vulture, *Cathartes aura*
Gallinazo Cabecirrojo   Plate 9(4)

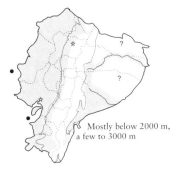

Mostly below 2000 m, a few to 3000 m

66–76 cm (26–30″). *Common and widespread in lowlands and lower montane areas in west* (including coast and offshore islands), but *much less numerous in east*, where largely confined to areas near Andes. Iris grayish; bill whitish; legs reddish. **Adult in west** has *warty bare head and upper neck reddish*; plumage brownish black, wing-coverts edged brown. **In flight** wings long and fairly broad, tail fairly long; pale brownish shafts on outer primaries show from above, *underside of flight feathers silvery gray contrasting with black coverts*. **Juvenile** similar but head blackish and bill dusky, brown edging on feathers of upperparts more distinct. **Coastal adult** has head brighter red, and brown feather edging on upperparts more distinct. (especially on coverts) so broad as to look generally brownish. **Adult in east** similar but with *several whitish or pale grayish bands across back of head*, contrasting with the red. **Similar species:** Greater Yellow-headed Vulture (only in east) larger and blacker, with differently colored head (mainly yellow) and inner primaries distinctly darker than the silvery of other flight feathers. **Habits:** Familiar in west, frequently seen in its distinctive tilting flight with long wings held in a marked dihedral, rarely flapping; often soars quite high. Apparently eats only

carrion, located through its keen sense of smell, and capable of locating food hidden beneath forest canopy; Black and King Vultures, which cannot smell, watch for the descent of Turkey Vultures.

Greater Yellow-headed Vulture
Cathartes melambrotus
Gallinazo Cabeciamarillo Mayor   Plate 9(3)

Mostly below 800 m, a few to 1300 m

74–81 cm (29–32″). In and over humid forest in *lowlands and foothills of east*. Iris dark brown; bill pinkish; legs reddish. **Adult** has *bare warty head and upper neck multicolored, mainly rich yellow but with blue on crown and orange or reddish on nape*; plumage black, somewhat glossy across mantle. **In flight** wings long and broad; *whitish shafts on outer primaries show from above, underside of most flight feathers silvery gray, but those of inner primaries contrastingly blackish*. **Juvenile** similar but with blackish head, dusky bill. **Similar species:** Overlaps only marginally with Turkey Vulture, which is smaller, not so black, and has mainly reddish head; their underwing patterns also differ. **Habits:** A bird of humid forest, seen in only small numbers at most localities; in good weather, however, it becomes conspicuous as it begins to soar low over forest around 9:00 A.M. Flight steadier than Turkey Vulture's, with less tilting from side to side, on wings that are held flatter (showing less dihedral). Roosting birds may perch in open on dead snags, also inside forest. Most food is obtained through uncanny skill at locating carrion, even under thick canopy.

Falconiformes
Kites, Eagles, Hawks, and Osprey:
Accipitridae (48)

A large family of diurnal birds of prey ("raptors"), found virtually throughout the world and in a wide variety of habitats; they are well represented in Ecuador, though many species are distinctly uncommon and inconspicuous. Most have loud and often distinctive vocalizations. Raptors are characterized by their strongly hooked bills and strong feet with sharp talons, well adapted for killing and carrying prey. Although many species are opportunistic feeders on a variety of prey items, others have more specialized habits, with certain species preying on birds, aerial insects, snails, or snakes and lizards, and two species even specializing in fish. Nests are (often flimsy) twig platforms, usually lined with a sprig or two of green leaves, generally well hidden in a tree.

All members of this family have a soft horny plate, often brightly colored, that is called a cere and overlays the maxilla (falcons also have this); often the loral and orbital regions are unfeathered and also sometimes brightly colored. Unless otherwise indicated, the **sexes are alike** in plumage (though, complicating matters, some species are dimorphic); however, *males are always smaller than females, sometimes notably so*. In many species there is a distinctly different immature plumage; some species require several years to complete the progression from juvenal through immature to adult plumage. These complexities often result in identification problems, and on the whole the diurnal raptors, especially in flight, are not easy to tell apart.

Osprey, *Pandion haliaetus*

Aguila Pescadora   Plate 9(6)

54–58.5 cm (21¼–23″). A unique *fish-eating* hawk, *wide-ranging near water*; does not breed in Ecuador, but prebreeders are present year-round, and an occasional young bird or pair has been known to build a "practice" nest in the Neotropics (not so far reported in Ecuador). Heavily scaled talons, rough soles, and a reversible hind toe assist in grasping slippery, wriggling prey. Short crest. Iris yellow; cere and legs bluish gray. *Head and underparts white*, with some dark streaking

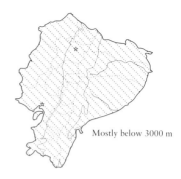

Mostly below 3000 m

on crown and (especially in ♀♀) chest. *Dark brown eye-stripe* extends back to nape, continuing onto *dark brown upperparts*; tail barred grayish and dark brown, tipped white, paler and grayer from below. **Immature** similar but upperparts paler, feathers with buffy whitish edging. **In flight** shows long and rather narrow wings *held distinctively "crooked"*; from below wings look pale, with white underwing-coverts contrasting with *black carpal patch*. **Similar species:** Nearly unmistakable, with distinctive silhouette, plumage, and behavior. **Habits:** Often perches on bare branches near water, from there launching out to fish. Circles over water, hunting mainly while hovering, rather ponderously, often at considerable heights. Plunges in feet-first, then struggles to become airborne. In normal flight glides on set wings, with deep, deliberate wingstrokes; also soars, sometimes quite high. Usually solitary—and apparently territorial on its winter quarters—though several birds may congregate around especially productive water. **Voice:** Often quite noisy, giving a variety of yelping or piping calls, perhaps most frequent being an upward-inflected "cleeyp" (sometimes in series).

Gray-headed Kite, *Leptodon cayanensis*

Elanio Cabecigris   Plate 11(2)

46–53.5 cm (18–21″). Widespread in humid forest and borders in lowlands, now rather scarce and local in west. Iris dark brown; cere, orbital area, and legs bluish gray. **Adult** has *pale pearly gray head* contrasting with *slaty black upperparts* and *white underparts*; tail black with two narrow pale gray bands and whitish tip, bands wider and whiter from below. **In flight** shows fairly long, broad, and

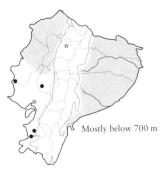

Mostly below 700 m

Hook-billed Kite, *Chondrohierax uncinatus*
Elanio Piquiganchudo   Plate 11(1)

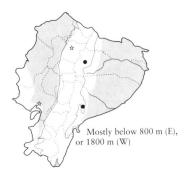

Mostly below 800 m (E), or 1800 m (W)

rounded wings and long tail; from below with *black underwing-coverts*, flight feathers barred grayish white and blackish, the *dark wings contrasting strongly with white underparts*. **Immatures** dimorphic; cere, orbital area, and legs always yellowish. **Light morph** has *head, neck, and underparts white* with small black crown patch; upperparts dark brown. **Dark morph** has blackish brown head, blackish-streaked underparts (some birds almost solidly dark across chest, others with throat white except for dark median stripe). **In flight** from below, underwing-coverts white in both morphs. **Similar species:** Adult nearly unmistakable, *often looking curiously small-headed*. Light-morph immature resembles Black-and-white Hawk-Eagle but has yellow (not orange) cere, pale (not black) lores, and browner upperparts; kite's underwing is darker (not so predominantly white), and it lacks hawk-eagle's white leading edge. Compare dark morph to immature Gray Hawk and even immature Double-toothed Kite. **Habits:** Ranges mainly in forest canopy, regularly perching on open branches in early morning but otherwise remaining within cover. Soars freely, often quite high, especially when displaying; distinctive display flight involves a steep climb out of a steady glide, rapid flapping, then a sudden downward glide with wings held upward. Broad diet includes insects, snakes, lizards, and birds, all procured primarily in canopy (not from ground). **Voice:** Regularly gives a loud, excited-sounding, nasal cackling "keh-keh-keh-keh-keh-keh" (sometimes up to 30–40 "keh"s), usually from a perch but sometimes in flight. Perched birds occasionally give a loud, nasal "nyeeeeeiyáw!" (P. Coopmans).

38–43 cm (15–17″). *Rare and rather local* in humid forest and woodland in lowlands, also ranging up very locally into subtropics. *Complex plumage varition.* Iris whitish, with *bare crescent above eye orange-yellow*; *heavy and strongly hooked bill* black with *greenish cere and facial skin*; legs yellow-orange. **Light-morph adult ♂** *slaty gray to slaty black above*; tail black with narrow whitish basal band, broader gray distal band, and whitish tip, both bands broad and white from below. *Below gray to slaty gray*, usually with *at least some whitish or pale buff barring* (but barring sometimes nearly absent). **In flight** shows *broad and rounded wings that are held somewhat forward and are narrow at base*, mainly grayish with whiter primaries boldly barred blackish. **Light-morph adult ♀** mainly dark brown above with gray face and *prominent rufous nuchal collar*; tail as in ♂. *Below coarsely barred rufous brown and creamy whitish*. **In flight** shows rufous-barred underwing-coverts. Relatively scarce **dark-morph adult** (sexes alike) *more or less uniform brownish black*, including underwing, with tail bands as in light morph. **Light-morph immature** (sexes alike) brown above with *blackish crown* and *creamy white nuchal collar, sides of neck, and underparts*, the last with variable amount of coarse dusky barring (can be extensive); tail with three gray bands, narrower than in adult. **Dark-morph immature** (sexes alike) much like dark adult, but tail bands narrower. **Similar species:** The variation is confusing. Often this rare kite is best recognized by structural characters such as its bill shape, greenish facial skin, and unique patch above eye (the last often surprisingly easy to see, and in concert with bill imparting an odd visage). The "oval" wing shape of flying birds also can be helpful (but cf. especially Roadside Hawk). Pale-morph adults, the most often seen, are relatively easy; the "capped" look of pale-morph juveniles also helps. **Habits:** Sluggish and often approachable, remaining perched for long periods without moving much while searching for its primary prey, land snails (it also eats small lizards and frogs). Soars regularly, though usually not for too long or very high. **Voice:** Not very vocal, but perched birds occasionally give a fast chattered "weh-keh-eh-eh-eheheheh," first ascending and then descending, lasting about a second.

Swallow-tailed Kite, *Elanoides forficatus*
Elanio Tijereta   Plate 10(1)

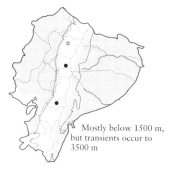

Mostly below 1500 m, but transients occur to 3500 m

56–61 cm (22–24"). A *beautiful and graceful* raptor with long pointed wings and *characteristic very long and deeply forked tail.* Widespread and conspicuous in and above canopy and borders of humid forest and montane forest and woodland. *Unmistakable.* Iris red; cere and legs bluish gray. *Head, neck, and underparts snowy white* contrasting with *black upperparts, wings, and tail.* Depending on race (and plumage freshness), at close range the back and upperwing-coverts can be seen to be glossed with blue or green. **In flight** underwing-coverts white, contrasting strongly with blackish flight feathers. **Similar species:** Distant flying bird could carelessly be mistaken for a frigatebird. **Habits:** Seen in flight far more often than perched, when it usually huddles inconspicuously in forest canopy (only rarely in open, unlike the Plumbeous Kite which it so often accompanies). Flight graceful and buoyant,

with deep slow wingstrokes and long periods of easy gliding and soaring; sometimes rises very high into sky. Rather gregarious, with flocks of up to 50–100 birds having been observed (but more often only 5–10), especially in foothills on w. slope. Feeds on insects, captured both in air and snatched while flying just above canopy, and on frogs, lizards, and snakes. Occasionally swoops down to drink water on wing. **Voice:** Usually quiet, but gives various shrill piping calls and whistles, mainly in flight and apparently especially while breeding.

Pearl Kite, *Gampsonyx swainsonii*
Elanio Perla   Plate 10(7)

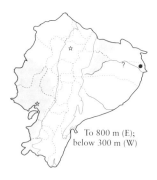

To 800 m (E); below 300 m (W)

23–26 cm (9–10¼"). A *small*, falcon-like kite, uncommon and local in *arid scrub and agricultural terrain in lowlands of southwest*; also now slowly spreading and increasing in *cleared areas in lowlands of northeast.* Iris carmine; bill black; legs yellowish. ♂ *slaty blackish above* with *forehead and cheeks creamy buff* and narrow white nuchal collar edged with rufous; tail square, gray above, paler below. *White below* with blackish patch on sides of chest and *rufous sides, flanks, and thighs.* ♀ like ♂, but slightly browner above. **In flight** wings pointed, underwing pale with *narrow white trailing edge.* **Similar species:** Not likely confused—no other falcon-like raptor is so white—this attractive small kite does resemble American Kestrel in shape, behavior, and even habitat; the kestrel is barred above, more or less streaked below, and longer tailed. **Habits:** Usually conspicuous, perching in open on a wire or atop a low tree, scanning surroundings for prey. Often rather tame. Catches mainly lizards, captured after a short dive to ground. **Voice:** Not very vocal, but a high-pitched scolding has been heard (Hilty and Brown 1986).

White-tailed Kite, *Elanus leucurus*
Elanio Coliblanco   Plate 10(4)

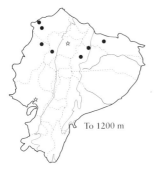

To 1200 m

38–40.5 cm (15–16″). *Rare and local* in pastures *and other open areas* mainly in lowlands of northwest and northeast; first found in Ecuador only in 1984, and may increase. Formerly sometimes called Black-shouldered Kite, *E. caeruleus*. Iris red; cere and legs yellow. **Adult** has *head, neck, and underparts snowy white* with small black patch in front of eye; back pale pearly gray, wings with *large black area on lesser- and median-coverts. Rather long tail pure white.* **In flight** wings rather long and pointed, underwing white with black patch on primary-coverts, primaries dusky. **Juvenile** resembles adult but has brownish eye, dark brown streaking on crown and nape, mainly brown back, and pale gray tail. **Similar species:** This lovely kite is unlikely to be confused. Similarly shaped Plumbeous and Mississippi Kites are much grayer; they favor less open terrain and do not hover as this species so characteristically does. **Habits:** A very conspicuous raptor that has benefitted from the expansion of agriculture into formerly forested and wooded terrain, though it has been slow to increase in Ecuador. Usually perches in open, and seems most active in early morning and late afternoon. Flight easy and graceful with deep wingstrokes, the wings held in a shallow dihedral while gliding. Hunts primarily while hovering with body held at an angle of about 45°, diving to ground after its primary prey, small rodents. **Voice:** Usually silent.

Rostrhamus Kites
Chunky, *snail-eating* kites with *specialized slender and very sharply hooked bills.* Both species are found in the lowlands, the Snail Kite in marshes, the Slender-billed more forest-based and only in the east.

Snail Kite, *Rostrhamus sociabilis*
Elanio Caracolero   Plate 10(5)

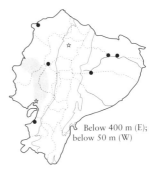

Below 400 m (E); below 50 m (W)

40.5–45 cm (16–17¾″). Locally fairly common (but decreasing) in *freshwater marshes and adjacent rice fields and canals* in lowlands of southwest; very local around a few lakes in lowlands of northeast. Iris red; *bill slender and very sharply hooked,* with *cere, lores, and orbital ring orange-red* (yellower in ♀♀, grayer in juveniles); *legs orange-red.* **Adult** ♂ *uniform slaty black; uppertail-coverts, basal half of tail, and crissum contrastingly white,* tail narrowly tipped whitish. **Adult** ♀ blackish brown above with buffy whitish forehead and superciliary; *tail as in* ♂. Throat buffy whitish; *underparts heavily mottled and streaked creamy buff and dark brown.* **Immature** resembles ♀ but browner above and more obviously streaked below. **In flight** wings broad and rounded; ♂'s underside blackish with whitish in primaries, ♀ and immature's browner and more mottled with whitish flight feathers (whitest in primaries). **Similar species:** Behavior of this conspicuous, marsh-loving kite is normally diagnostic, though soaring birds in the east must be distinguished from Slender-billed Kite, which never shows any white in its noticeably short tail. Immatures of both *Buteogallus* black-hawks have prominent tail barring. Dark-morph Hook-billed Kite has very different soft-part coloration. Cf. also immature Harris's Hawk.

Habits: Notably sociable, concentrating in groups of dozens of birds where feeding conditions are optimal. Formerly numbers were much larger in the southwest. Roosts and even nests communally. Perches low and in open, often on fence posts or ground, even on wires. Flight surprisingly agile, quartering slowly low over water and marsh on somewhat bowed wings, searching for *Pomacea* snails that comprise most of its diet; crabs and turtles are eaten when snails are in short supply. Having snatched the snail with its talon, the kite flies to a regularly used feeding perch where it uses bill to pry snail out of shell. Sometimes scans for snails from low perches. Snail Kites seem to have a propensity to wander, with the odd bird showing up in unexpected sites; they may regularly shift sites in response to fluctuating water levels. **Voice:** Usually quiet, though perched birds give a throaty rasping "kahhrrrr."

Slender-billed Kite, *Rostrhamus hamatus*
Elanio Piquigarfio   Plate 10(6)

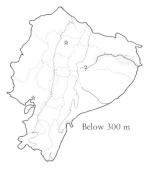

Below 300 m

37.5–40.5 cm (14³/₄–16″). Scarce and local in *várzea and swampy forest* in lowlands of northeast, *almost entirely near Río Napo.* Formerly placed in genus *Helicolestes. Iris yellowish white; bill slender and very sharply hooked*, with *cere, lores, and orbital ring orange-red*; legs orange-red. **Adult** *uniform slaty gray*, with primaries and *short tail black.* **Immature** similar but with a little vague whitish barring on underparts, whitish tipping on wing-coverts, and *tail with two narrow white bands and white tip.* **In flight** has *notably short, broad, and rounded wings,* with underside blackish; tail so short it barely protrudes past wings, almost recalling a Black Vulture. **Similar species:** Adult ♂ Snail

Kite differs in having obvious white at base of tail and red iris. Slender-billed is more likely to be confused with Slate-colored Hawk (also gray, with pale iris, orange at base of bill), but that species has somewhat longer tail crossed by a single broad white tail-band, also less sharply hooked bill. **Habits:** A sluggish, forest-based hawk that usually perches within cover and is easily overlooked. Does soar regularly, sometimes even in small groups, but usually not for very long. Apparently feeds almost exclusively on *Pomacea* snails, captured after a short flight from a low perch. **Voice:** Distinctive call a loud, slurred, nasal "kyeeeahhhh," given both while perched and during soaring flight; Roadside Hawk's call is somewhat similar.

Harpagus Kites
Relatively sluggish, forest-based kites with *dark throat stripes* and maxilla with *two notches.*

Double-toothed Kite, *Harpagus bidentatus*
Elanio Bidentado   Plate 10(8)

Mostly below 1800 m

31.5–35.5 cm (12¹/₂–14″). An *Accipiter*-like kite found in canopy and borders of humid forest in lowlands of east and northwest, also ranging up into subtropical forest on both slopes; most numerous in northwest. Iris orange to amber; cere and lores greenish yellow; legs yellow. In **west, adult** ♂ has *head bluish gray, remainder of upperparts more slaty gray,* sometimes with whitish mottling on scapulars; rather long tail blackish with three narrow whitish bands and tip (bands grayer from below). Throat white *divided by dusky median stripe*; chest mixed rufous and gray (usually quite solid), *lower underparts evenly barred gray and white* with *crissum white.* **Adult** ♀ similar above, but *underparts* with considerably more rufous, typically almost solid across breast and with rufous (not gray) belly barring. In **east**, both sexes (especially ♀♀) almost solidly rufous below with little or no barring (♂♂ may show some on belly). **In flight** wings fairly long and rounded, with underside mainly white (contrasting with dark body); fluffy white feathers of crissum also often conspicuous. **Immature** dark brown above, often with whitish mottling on scapulars; tail as in adult. Whitish to pale buff below, sparsely to rather heavily and coarsely streaked with dark brown; median throat marked as in adult. **Similar species:** Resembles an Accipiter when flying, though wings are longer and tail less apt to be spread; white crissum feathers more conspicuous than they ever are in an Accipiter. Cf. immature Broad-winged Hawk (larger, lacking median throat stripe but with a malar stripe). **Habits:** Usually seen perched quietly in midlevels and subcanopy, regularly at borders, often allowing close approach. Hunts for lizards and large insects, and well known for regularly accompanying troops of monkeys, capturing prey they disturb while moving through trees. Soars regularly, and often quite high, but usually not for long periods; display flight consists of a series of steep dives ending with a looping recovery. **Voice:** Rather quiet, but perched birds give several high-pitched, thin, whistled calls (actually quite flycatcher-like), e.g., "wheeey-whit, pii, wheeey-whit!"

[Rufous-thighed Kite, *Harpagus diodon*
Elanio Muslirrufo] Plate 10(9)

31.5–35.5 cm (12½–14″). Known only from two 1979 sightings at Limoncocha in lowlands of east. Iris orange; cere and lores

300 m

greenish yellow; legs yellow. **Adult** uniform slaty gray above; rather long tail blackish with three narrow whitish bands and tip (bands grayer from below). Throat whitish divided by dusky median stripe; underparts pale gray fading to white on crissum, with thighs contrastingly rufous. **Immature** resembles immature Double-toothed Kite, like that species already with median throat stripe, but already shows rufous thighs. **Similar species:** Adult's plumage is strikingly reminiscent of adult Bicolored Hawk, but it lacks "capped" look of that species (with rounder head and less fierce-looking visage); the hawk also, of course, never shows a median throat stripe. **Habits:** Not well known, but apparently resembles Double-toothed Kite. It is possible that the Ecuador records refer to austral migrants that wandered far from their usual range.

Ictinia Kites
Predominantly gray kites with long pointed wings that are highly aerial over humid forests, capturing insects on the wing.

Plumbeous Kite, *Ictinia plumbea*
Elanio Plomizo Plate 10(2)

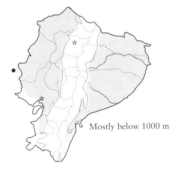

Mostly below 1000 m

34.5–37 cm (13½–14½″). Widespread and conspicuous in and above canopy of humid forest and woodland in lowlands and foothills; more numerous in east, in west now mainly in Esmeraldas. Iris red; cere gray; short legs orange-red to yellow-orange. **Adult** leaden gray, slightly paler on head and darker on back; wings blackish, with inner webs of outer primaries rufous (usually hidden on perched birds); tail blackish, showing two white bands from below (usually not apparent from above). **In flight** wings long and *pointed* (though primaries are spread when soaring, resulting in more rounded aspect), with *rufous flash in primaries usually obvious*. **Juvenile** has whitish head heavily streaked blackish; above slaty black, feathers edged paler. Below whitish coarsely streaked dark gray. Primaries have little or no rufous. Apparently quickly molts into adult plumage. **Similar species:** Cf. much rarer Mississippi Kite. Otherwise Plumbeous Kite is readily known on the basis of its gray coloration and long wings; on perched birds, *wings extend well beyond tip of tail*, imparting a unique silhouette. Note, however, that wings in juveniles are notably shorter, such that perched individuals can be confused with various other young raptors having streaked underparts. Flying birds can look vaguely falconlike. **Habits:** Spends much of day in flight, gracefully soaring and gliding in open air, often high above ground. Mainly subsists on insects captured in flight, sometimes also snatching them from canopy. Often rather gregarious, regularly associating with other raptors when flying. Perched birds often rest on high limbs or snags. **Voice:** Rather quiet. Flying birds give a thin "ye-kuw" (S. Davis recording).

[Mississippi Kite, *Ictinia mississippiensis* Elanio de Mississippi]

Plate 10(3)

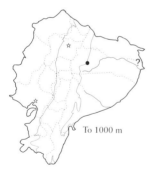

To 1000 m

35.5–38 cm (14–15"). Apparently a *casual transient*, with a few Apr. sightings from lowlands and foothills of east; perhaps overlooked. Iris red; cere gray; legs yellow. **Adult** has *whitish to pale gray head* contrasting with gray upperparts; *pale gray secondaries show as prominent band on closed wing*, primaries black; fairly long tail black. **In flight**

wings long and pointed, with *contrasting pale secondaries*. **Juvenile** much like juvenile of far more numerous Plumbeous Kite but *streaking below reddish brown*. **Similar species:** Adult Mississippi Kite differs from Plumbeous in lacking rufous flash in primaries (it has contrastingly pale secondaries instead) and in having distinctly paler head (uniform in Plumbeous); on perched birds the proportionately longer tail should be evident (such that wings barely extend its tip, unlike Plumbeous). **Habits:** Similar to Plumbeous Kite. The few birds seen in Ecuador have been in small, migrating flocks that were passing overhead.

Cinereous Harrier, *Circus cinereus*
Aguilucho Cinéreo

Plate 11(3)

Mostly 3000–4000 m

43–49.5 cm (17–19½"). Scarce and local in *paramo and grassy agricultural areas in highlands* south to Chimborazo. Iris yellow; cere olive yellow; legs orange-yellow. Usually seen in low, tilting flight with *wings held in a shallow dihedral*; *contrasting white rump* then conspicuous. Owl-like facial disk apparent at close range. Elegant **adult** ♂ *pearly gray above somewhat mottled with brownish*; tail brownish gray with four dusky bands and tip. Throat and chest gray; *remaining underparts whitish barred with rufous*. **In flight** wings quite long, underside mainly whitish, outer primaries blackish. **Adult** ♀ browner above, often with whitish brow and some streaking on nape and foreneck, and with coarser rufous barring below; underwing-coverts barred rufous, flight feathers banded with blackish. **Immature** even darker and browner above than ♀, often showing paler brow and irregular nuchal collar; foreneck dark brown, underparts buff coarsely streaked dark brown. **Similar species:** No other harrier is known to occur in Ecuador, hence this species can be readily recognized on basis of generic and behavioral characters. **Habits:** Normally seen in coursing flight low over grasslands, peering downward and listening for prey (rodents and small birds), occasionally dropping down and disappearing into grass. Not often seen perched. **Voice:** Usually quiet. Courting ♂♂ give various cackling calls, mainly in flight.

Accipiter Hawks
A distinctive group of bird-eating hawks whose *rather short and rounded wings* and *long, squared-off tails* assist them in maneuvering through dense cover when pursuing prey. **Sexes are alike**, but males are markedly smaller than females, especially in the Tiny, Bicolored, and Gray-bellied Hawks. *Accipiter* are found widely but sparsely in forests.

Plain-breasted Hawk, *Accipiter ventralis*
Azor Pechillano   Plate 15(3)

Mostly 1700–3500 m

28–33 cm (11–13″). Widespread in *subtropical and temperate* forest and woodland, and adjacent clearings and agricultural land; seems relatively tolerant of habitat disturbance. Sometimes considered conspecific with Sharp-shinned Hawk (*A. striatus*) of North America. *Highly polymorphic*. Iris, cere and orbital skin, and legs yellow. **Typical morph** plumbeous gray above; tail blackish with 3–4 gray bands. *White below*, variably marked or shaded with rufous and faintly barred with dusky, but always with *contrasting rufous thighs*. **Pale morph** similar but more bluish gray above and *pure white below* except for *rufous thighs*. **Dark morph** *uniform slaty gray to blackish* becoming

rufous on belly and thighs; one ANSP specimen is uniform black except for gray tail banding and white banding on underside of flight feathers. **In flight** wings fairly short and rounded, underwing-coverts whitish with flight feathers boldly banded whitish and dusky. **Immature** browner above, feathers edged rufous; white below with brown streaking, *already with rufous thighs*. Some individuals are more solidly brown below. **Similar species:** By far the most frequently seen *Accipiter* in the highlands. Cf. much rarer Semicollared Hawk, also Bicolored Hawk. Double-toothed Kite can also look similar, but in flight note its "fluffy" white crissum feathers. **Habits:** A bold and rapacious raptor whose habits remain surprisingly poorly known. Has been seen chasing small birds which it usually hunts during a short dive from a concealed perch. Also sometimes rests on exposed, open branches. Soars regularly, sometimes quite high. **Voice:** Perched birds occasionally give a high-pitched piping, "kee-kee-kee-kee," slower paced than most *Accipiter* (J. Moore recording).

Semicollared Hawk, *Accipiter collaris*
Azor Semicollarejo   Plate 15(2)

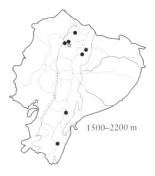

1500–2200 m

24–26.5 cm (9½–10½″). *Very rare and local* in *subtropical* forest and adjacent clearings on both slopes. A small but heavily built *Accipiter*. Iris, cere and orbital skin, and legs yellow. **Adult** has *black crown and nape* and *partial* but usually quite prominent *white nuchal collar*; otherwise brownish black above; tail blackish with four dark gray bands that often are hard to discern. Throat white; *remaining underparts white coarsely barred with brown*. In flight wings fairly short and rounded, underwing-coverts white with blackish markings. **Juvenile/immature** plumages poorly understood, but most are brown above (blacker on crown) with *nuchal collar rufous*; barring below likewise rufous. Some birds are evidently more rufous above with cinnamon nuchal collar and are barred tawny-rufous and brown below. **Similar species:** Tiny Hawk much more finely barred below and never shows nuchal collar; it inhabits lowland forest with little or no overlap with this montane species. Plain-breasted Hawk never shows barring below. **Habits:** Poorly known. Semicollared would seem to be the Tiny Hawk's "upper-elevation replacement," but behavior so far as known seems just as reminiscent of Plain-breasted Hawk. Semicollared occasionally takes prominent perches, and unlike Tiny it appears to soar on a fairly regular basis. **Voice:** Unknown.

Tiny Hawk, *Accipiter superciliosus*
Azor Chico   Plate 15(1)

Mostly below 900 m

20.5–28 cm (8–11″; ♂♂ much smaller than ♀♀). *Rare* (doubtless somewhat overlooked) in humid forest and borders of lowlands of east and west. Iris red; cere and orbital skin yellow; legs orange. **Adult ♂** slaty gray to blackish above, blackest on crown; tail blackish with 3–4 dark gray bands (hardly contrasting). White below, *narrowly barred with dark gray* except on throat. **Adult ♀** very similar, perhaps marginally browner above and buffier below. **Immature** dimorphic. **Normal morph** grayish brown above with darker crown, tail banded brown and grayish brown; *buff below barred with rufous*. **Rufous morph** *rufous brown above* with darker crown, tail banded rufous and blackish; *buff below barred with rufous*. **Similar species:** Aptly named, this "pint-

sized" but fierce little *Accipiter* can generally be identified on basis of size alone. Semicollared Hawk of subtropics comparably small (though more heavily built) but much more coarsely barred below. Cf. adult Barred and Lined Forest-Falcons (larger, with dark chests, etc.). **Habits:** An infrequently seen little hawk that ambushes birds from perches in subcanopy or understory; occasionally, in early morning, one will perch in the open to sun itself. Seems rarely or never to soar. **Voice:** Usually quiet, only rarely giving a weak "kree-kree-kree" call.

Bicolored Hawk, *Accipiter bicolor*
Azor Bicolor   Plate 15(4)

To about 2500 m

33–46 cm (13–18″, ♂♂ much smaller than ♀♀). *Rare* in humid and deciduous forest and borders in lowlands, ranging up well into subtropics on both slopes. Iris yellow to amber; cere and orbital skin dull yellow; legs yellow. **Adult ♂** has crown and nape blackish, otherwise slaty gray above; tail blackish with 2–3 dark gray bands (hardly contrasting). *Below pale gray* with *contrasting rufous thighs*, crissum white. **Adult ♀** similar but slightly browner above, and substantially darker gray below. **Immature** dark brown above with blacker crown; *partial nuchal collar and underparts creamy buff to white* (rarely deeper buff); tail bands usually paler and more contrasting than adult's. **Similar species:** Two-toned gray adults with their contrasting rufous thighs are not difficult to identify, but cf. even rarer Gray-bellied Hawk (and Rufous-thighed Kite). Immature most likely mistaken for a forest-falcon, in particular Buckley's or a small ♂ Collared, though both of these show a conspicuous dark crescent on pale ear-coverts, have longer legs and more graduated tails. **Habits:** A sneaky and inconspicuous hawk; rarely seen though it can be very bold, indeed at times almost fearless of humans. Perches quietly on semiconcealed branches, from there dashing off in pursuit of small or medium-sized birds; less likely to perch in open than Tiny Hawk. Rarely or never soars. **Voice:** Usually quiet, but territorial birds give a loud cackling "keh-keh-keh-keh . . . ."

Gray-bellied Hawk, *Accipiter poliogaster*
Azor Ventrigris   Plate 15(5)

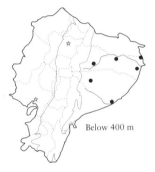

Below 400 m

38–51 cm (15–20"). A *rare* and little-known, *large* (especially ♀♀) *Accipiter* of humid forest and borders in *lowlands of east.* Iris, cere and orbital skin, and legs yellow. **Adult** *above slaty blackish, blacker on crown* with sides of head blackish or gray; tail blackish with three gray bands and white tip. *Below mostly pale gray,* whiter on throat and pure white on crissum. **Immature** very different, bearing remarkable resemblance to adult Ornate Hawk-Eagle: brownish black above, blackest on crown with *contrasting rufous-chestnut cheeks, partial nuchal collar, and sides of chest;* tail as in adult. White below with black malar streak; *sides, flanks, and thighs with coarse black barring.* **Similar species:** Adult resembles adult ♂ Bicolored Hawk (and there is overlap in size); Bicolored's gray below is deeper, and Gray-bellied never shows rufous thighs (these can, however, be obscure and hard to see in Bicolored). Adult also can be confused with adult Slaty-backed Forest-Falcon, though that species lacks Gray-bellied's "capped" appearance; the forest-falcon's legs are shorter, tail more graduated, and underparts whiter (either creamy or with at most a slight

gray tinge). Adult Ornate Hawk-Eagle differs from immature Gray-bellied in its much larger size, pointed crest, and feathered legs. **Habits:** Not well known, but behavior does not seem to differ appreciably from Bicolored Hawk, though Gray-bellied seems more apt to perch in open. It is not known to soar. **Voice:** Unknown.

Crane Hawk, *Geranospiza caerulescens*
Gavilán Zancón   Plate 16(1)

Below 400 m

46.5–51 cm (18¼–20"). A *lanky, very long-legged, small-headed* raptor; scarce in humid forest and borders in lowlands of east, and mainly in deciduous forest and borders in lowlands of southwest. Iris red to orange; cere gray; *legs orange-red to salmon pink.* **Adult** *gray* with variable amount (usually very little) of whitish barring on belly and thighs; *long tail* black with two broad white bands and white tip. **In flight** wings rather long and rounded, underwing gray with whitish vermiculations on coverts and *conspicuous white band across primaries.* **Immature** similar but with more whitish barring below, often some on face and throat as well; some individuals show some tawny-buff below, especially on lower belly and crissum, and pale tail bands can be buff on their underside. **Similar species:** Distinctive shape, brightly colored legs, and dark face of this gray raptor are usually enough to identify perched individuals; flying birds are readily known through the unique white primary band. **Habits:** Usually encountered singly, often foraging actively and sometimes clumsily on branches and even trunks of trees, probing into crevices, epiphytes, and even bird nests with its long legs; often flaps wings furiously to maintain balance. Soars and sails regularly, though usually not for too long. **Voice:** Infrequently gives a whistled "wheeeoo" or "kweeeoo."

Leucopternis Hawks

A rather diverse group of *Buteo*-like hawks found in humid forests, especially in the lowlands. *Leucopternis* have broad wings and relatively broad tails, and gray and white predominate in their relatively simple plumage patterns. There are two distinctly different groups: four species (Slate-colored, Plumbeous, Semiplumbeous, and Black-faced) are unobtrusive, fairly small raptors found inside forest, and these rarely or never soar; the other three (White, Gray-backed, and Barred) are larger and more conspicuous species that soar regularly.

Slate-colored Hawk, *Leucopternis schistacea*
Gavilán Pizarroso   Plate 12(6)

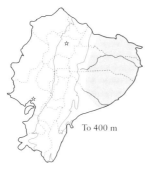

To 400 m

40.5–46 cm (16–18″). Scarce inside humid forest in *lowlands of east*. Iris yellow; *cere and facial skin orange-red*; legs also reddish orange. **Adult** *uniform plumbeous gray*, slightly blacker on head; tail black with *single broad white median band* and narrow white tip. **Juvenile** similar but with some whitish barring on lower belly and thighs; sometimes an extra whitish band near base of tail. **Similar species:** Slender-billed Kite has more slender and sharply decurved bill and lacks white in its shorter tail. Plumbeous Hawk occurs only west of Andes. **Habits:** Usually found singly, most often perching at mid-levels on a large horizontal branch, frequently along edge of forested rivers; often quite unsuspicious. Drops down to ground for its prey, typically snakes and frogs. Rarely or never soars, though occasionally flies

through or just over canopy. **Voice:** Most frequent call a loud slurred whistle, "kyeeeeee!" Also gives a fast and long-continued "kikikikikikikiki . . ." lasting about 5 seconds (P. Coopmans).

Plumbeous Hawk, *Leucopternis plumbea*
Gavilán Plomizo   Plate 12(5)

To 1700 m

35.5–38 cm (14–15″). Scarce inside humid forest in *lowlands and foothills of northwest*, ranging up into lower subtropics. Iris red; *cere and base of bill orange*; legs orange. **Adult** *uniform dark slaty gray*, blacker on wings; tail black *with single narrow white band*. Underwing-coverts white. **Juvenile** similar but with variable amount of whitish barring on lower flanks and (especially) thighs; in some birds a second white tail-band shows. **Similar species:** No other basically gray hawk found on Pacific slope has the bright orange cere and legs of this deep-forest raptor. **Habits:** Found singly, usually perching inside forest at varying heights; occasionally rests on a high exposed branch in early morning. Rarely or never soars. **Voice:** Not very vocal, but perched birds occasionally give a descending drawn-out "wheeeeeu."

Semiplumbeous Hawk
Leucopternis semiplumbea
Gavilán Semiplomizo   Plate 12(4)

33–35.5 cm (13–14″). Scarce inside humid forest and borders in *lowlands and foothills of northwest*. Iris yellow; *cere and base of bill orange*; legs orange. **Adult** *gray above*, blacker on wings; tail black crossed by single narrow white band. *Below entirely white*. Underwing-coverts white. **Juvenile** similar but head and neck somewhat streaked

To 600 m

whitish; underparts tinged buff and with sparse blackish streaking. **Similar species:** This chunky but small hawk is unlikely to be confused in its limited Ecuadorian range. No vaguely similar gray-and-white hawk has comparably bright orange soft parts. **Habits:** Similar to Plumbeous Hawk but more apt to occur at forest edge; likewise does not soar. **Voice:** Not very vocal, but does give a rather high-pitched, drawn-out, and whistled "ki-weeeeeeeh," sometimes repeated a few times in succession.

Black-faced Hawk, *Leucopternis melanops*
Gavilán Carinegro   Plate 12(3)

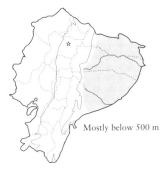

Mostly below 500 m

37–42 cm (14½–16½"). Scarce inside humid forest, mainly terra firme, in *lowlands of east.* Iris brown; *cere and base of bill orange-red*; *legs yellow-orange.* **Adult** has *head, neck, upper back, and underparts white*; crown, sides of neck, and upper back streaked black, and with black lores and triangular area behind eye. Upperparts otherwise black, wing-coverts and scapulars boldly spotted with white; tail black *with single white median band and narrow white tip.* Under-wing-coverts white. **Juvenile** similar but has

white areas tinged buff, and reduced streaking on head and neck. **Similar species:** Likely confused only with larger White Hawk (the two species can occur together in same terra firme forests); aside from size, White Hawk differs in its gray (not orange) cere, black spots (not streaks) on upper back, and black tail with broad white terminal band (not a median band and almost no tipping). **Habits:** Similar to Plumbeous Hawk, typically remaining inside forest, perching at various levels; generally inconspicuous, not often perching in open. Eats reptiles and nestling birds. **Voice:** Rather quiet, occasionally giving a fairly high-pitched, slurred, and semiwhistled "keee-u" call, sometimes repeated every 5–7 seconds.

White Hawk, *Leucopternis albicollis*
Gavilán Blanco   Plate 12(1)

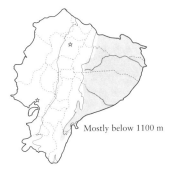

Mostly below 1100 m

43–49½ cm (17–19½"). Scarce and seemingly local in hilly terra firme forest in *lowlands and foothills of east.* Iris brown; *cere gray*; legs yellow. **Adult** has *head, neck, upper back, and underparts white*; upper back spotted black and with gray lores. Upperparts otherwise black, wing-coverts and scapulars fringed white; ample tail mainly black from above with *broad terminal band white, from below white with wide black subterminal band.* **In flight** wings very broad and rather rounded, *underwing mainly white.* **Juvenile** similar but with some dusky streaking on head, especially crown. **Similar species:** Black-faced Hawk smaller and has orange cere, crown to upper back more prominently streaked than ever seen in White, and different tail pattern; unlike White Hawk, it never soars. **Habits:** A beautiful but often lethargic forest hawk that regularly perches in open at forest edge, quietly surveying its surroundings. Unlike the previous four *Leucopternis*, White Hawk soars freely, often circling quite high with its wings held flat and tail widely fanned. Feeds mainly on reptiles, also on small mammals and large insects, etc. **Voice:** Often gives a loud, husky scream, "shrreeeyr," both while soaring and when perched.

Gray-backed Hawk, *Leucopternis occidentalis*
Gavilán Dorsigris   Plate 12(2)

Mostly below 1300 m

46–52 cm (18–20½"). *Scarce and local* in semihumid, humid, and montane forest and borders in *lowlands and subtropics of west.* Iris brown; cere and base of bill bluish gray; legs pale yellow. **Adult** dark gray above, *head and neck with prominent white streaking; tail white* with *broad black subterminal band. White below.* **In flight** wings very broad and rather rounded, with underwing mainly white. **Juvenile** similar but slightly browner above, some birds with a little black streaking on sides of chest. **Similar species:** Not likely confused in its range, where the only other *Leucopternis* are the much smaller Plumbeous and Semiplumbeous and very different Barred Hawks. ♂ Variable Hawk (typically entirely gray above) lacks streaking on head and nape; in flight from below it has somewhat similar pattern, though Variable's wings are not as ample. **Habits:** Similar to White Hawk, though perched birds seem even more apt to be very confiding, regularly allowing a remarkably close approach. Graceful wheeling flight is similar. **Voice:** Vocalizes primarily in flight, a loud husky scream ("shreeeyr") similar to White Hawk's; often given several times in quick succession.

Barred Hawk, *Leucopternis princeps*
Gavilán Barreteado   Plate 12(7)

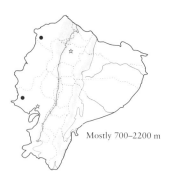

Mostly 700–2200 m

52–61 cm (20½–24"). A large and heavily built hawk found locally in *foothills and subtropics on both slopes.* Iris brown; cere and base of bill pale yellow; legs yellow. **Adult** has *upperparts and throat and chest blackish slate; breast and belly contrastingly white, evenly and narrowly barred with black;* rather short tail black with narrow median white band. **In flight** wings very broad and rather rounded, underwing whitish with blackish barring on flight feathers. **Juvenile** similar but wing-coverts edged whitish. **Similar species:** Combination of this impressive raptor's large size and dark plumage contrasting with pale lower underparts unique. The barring is not, however, prominent at any distance. Cf. even larger Black-chested Buzzard-Eagle (short-tailed, grayer above; the two species rarely if ever occur together). Back-lit birds can look gray below; then cf. Solitary Eagle. **Habits:** Rarely seen perched, this handsome hawk is most often noted on sunny mornings when 1–2 birds take to the skies and proclaim their presence with loud calling; occasionally up to 3–4 birds fly together. At such times they may also engage in spectacular display flights in which they make steep looping dives and sometimes even lock talons, briefly tumbling earthward. **Voice:** Calls include a loud hawk-eagle-like "wheey-aaar" or "wheeeuw," sometimes repeated or followed by a fast series of "weep" notes.

Buteogallus Hawks and Black-Hawks
A trio of raptors characterized by their relatively broad wings, short tails, and rather

long legs. The Savanna Hawk differs strikingly in its rufous plumage.

Savanna Hawk, *Buteogallus meridionalis*
Gavilán Sabanero   Plate 11(4)

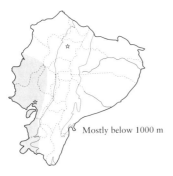

Mostly below 1000 m

53.5–61 cm (21–24″). A *large, long-legged, mainly rufescent* hawk, relatively numerous in *semiopen and agricultural areas of southwest*, ranging up into cleared subtropics of Loja. Formerly placed in genus *Heterospizias*. Iris brownish to hazel; cere and long legs yellow. **Adult** has *mostly dull cinnamon-rufous* underparts with fine black barring, back variably mixed with gray. *Wings mainly rufous*; rather short tail black with narrow median band and tip white. **In flight** wings very long and broad, *underside mainly rufous*, flight feathers tipped black. **Immature** very different, sooty brown above with buffy whitish forehead and superciliary and with *some buff to rufous on wing-coverts and scapulars*; tail blackish with narrow pale buff banding. Below deep buff heavily streaked and mottled with dusky. **Similar species:** Handsome rufescent adult unlikely to be confused. Younger birds could be mistaken for immature black-hawks (because of habitat considerations, Great most likely) though neither shows the rufous present on Savannas even at an early age; cf. also young Harris's Hawk. **Habits:** A conspicuous hawk of open terrain, often seen perched on a low post or tree (even wires), sometimes also on ground; in Río Guayas basin regular near water. Feeds on a variety of prey, including small mammals, birds, frogs, reptiles, and even large insects. Soars freely on broad flat wings, sometimes ascending to considerable heights. **Voice:** Usually silent, but occasionally gives a drawn-out and fairly high-pitched "keeeeuu," most often in flight.

Common Black-Hawk, *Buteogallus anthracinus*
Gavilán Negro Cangrejero   Plate 11(5)

42–47 cm (16½–18½″). *Scarce in mangroves along coast from e. Guayas to El Oro* (possibly northward? only formerly?). Sometimes separated as a distinct species, Mangrove Black-Hawk (*B. subtilis*). Iris dark brown; cere and facial area pale yellow; legs yellow. **Adult** *slaty black*, often with some pale barring on lower flanks and thighs; wings usually with some rufous mottling at base of secondaries. *Rather short tail* black with single broad white median band and narrow white tip. **In flight** *wings very broad and rounded, underwing mainly dark* though may show buff area at base of secondaries and inner primaries. **Immature** has *face pale buff with contrasting dark brown eye-stripe and malar streak*; otherwise dark brown above with some creamy streaking, especially on back, scapulars and wing-coverts with some buff mottling; tail grayish buff above with 4–7 dusky bars (outer one wider), below paler with 5–8 narrow blackish bars. Below creamy to rich buff with coarse dark streaking, often blotched on breast, thighs more barred. Underwing buff with dark markings, usually with whitish area in primaries. **Similar species:** Identification of this hawk usually straightforward as it is found *exclusively in or immediately adjacent to mangrove forests*, and *no other similar raptor occurs with it in Ecuador*. Great Black-Hawk larger with proportionately longer legs and tail, such that on perched birds the wings do not reach end of tail (in Mangrove they are about same length). Adult Greats have a different tail pattern that shows much more white. **Habits:** Strictly confined to mangroves, feeding primarily on crabs that are captured from a low perch, sometimes while standing or walking on mud or mangrove roots. Often quite unsuspicious. Soars freely, sometimes in pairs. **Voice:** Most frequent call a series of loud ringing whistled ("spinking") notes that somewhat recall Osprey.

ians, fish, even crabs. In the east sometimes stands on muddy banks of rivers and on sandbars. Soars regularly, sometimes ascending very high. **Voice:** Most frequently heard call a drawn-out, high-pitched scream, "kueeeeeeeeeeeee!," lasting 2–3 seconds, given both while perched and in flight. Also gives a fast "kukukukukukukukukukú" (J. Moore recording).

Great Black-Hawk, *Buteogallus urubitinga*
Gavilán Negro Mayor   Plate 11(6)

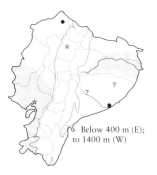

Below 400 m (E);
to 1400 m (W)

Solitary Eagle, *Harpyhaliaetus solitarius*
Aguila Solitaria   Plate 11(8)

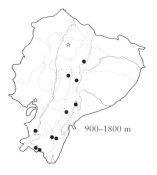

900–1800 m

53.5–61 cm (21–24"). Rather uncommon in lowlands, local and scarce in west; in east primarily near water, in southwest often up into lower subtropics. Iris brown; cere and facial area yellow; *rather long legs* yellow. **Adult** *uniform slaty black. Basal half of tail white, terminal half black* with narrow white tip. **In flight** wings broad and rounded, *underwing blackish and showing little pattern* (sometimes some white at base of primaries). **Immature** has buff face with *dark brown eye-stripe and malar streak*; otherwise dark brown above with buff and rufous streaking and mottling; tail longer than adult's, grayish with 5–8 blackish bars (outer one wider), below paler with 5–7 narrow bars. Below creamy to rather rich buff, coarsely streaked with dark brown, thighs densely barred. **Similar species:** In all plumages resembles Common Black-Hawk, which see; that species is confined to mangroves, in which Great is not known to occur. The rare Solitary Eagle is even more massive but has an obviously short tail; its adult is distinctly gray, not black; *it occurs only in montane areas* (not in lowlands). **Habits:** A powerful raptor that eats a variety of prey ranging from birds and small mammals to amphib-

68–73.5 cm (27–29"). A *very large, rare, and local* eagle of montane forest in *foothills and subtropics*. Iris dark; cere and base of *massive bill* yellow; *thick legs* yellow. **Adult** *uniform slaty blue-gray to slaty gray*; slight bushy crest is rarely apparent. *Short tail* blackish with single broad white median band and narrow white tip. **In flight** wings very long and broad, underside uniformly dark. **Immature** dark brown above with *buff face* and *dark brown postocular stripe extending down sides of neck to chest*, which is *almost solid brown*. Below buff streaked and mottled with dark brown, *thighs entirely brown*. Tail grayish brown with ill-defined dark subterminal band (*but little barring*). **Similar species:** This huge and imposing eagle is likely to be confused only with more numerous Great Black-Hawk, with which it can occur locally (at least in southwest), and with which it is frequently confused; recall that *eagle does not occur in lowlands*. Black-hawk's tail is proportionately longer; eagle's is so short that in flight it often appears barely to protrude beyond wings. Adult black-hawk is, true to its name, really black—whereas the eagle is distinctly gray (though it can look very dark until seen against a dark background or in good light). Immature best distinguished by relative size and bulk. **Habits:** Usually seen while soaring majestically over Andean slopes and valleys, often in pairs, generally taking to air in midmorning when it is sunny. Rarely seen perched, then typically atop a large tree. **Voice:** Flight call a series of short, far-carrying whistled notes, "klee-klee-klee-klee-klee"; also a very short "kyi!," a "kuuy-eeee?," and a more drawn-out "kyuuuuuu" (P. Coopmans).

Harris's Hawk, *Parabuteo unicinctus*
Gavilán Alicastaño   Plate 16(2)

To 2900 m

48–53.5 cm (19–21"). *Agricultural lands and deciduous scrub and woodland in lowlands of west* (in southwest also higher), also locally in intermontane valleys of north. Sometimes called Bay-winged Hawk. Cere, lores, and legs yellow. **Adult** *mostly blackish to sooty brown* with *contrasting rufous wing-coverts and thighs*; crissum white. *Uppertail-coverts and base of rather long tail white*, terminal half of tail black, narrow tip white. **In flight** wings fairly long and narrow, underwing-coverts rufous and flight feathers blackish. **Immature** brown with extensive buff to whitish streaking and mottling, especially below; *already shows rufous on wing-coverts* (though often paler), thighs more barred. Tail pattern as in adult though *somewhat less clear-cut. Underwing-coverts already show at least some rufous*, flight feathers paler than in adult. **Similar species:** Adult's rufous patterning distinctive, but it can look all dark except in good light; the rufous is more obscure in younger birds, but generally is still apparent. Wings longer and narrower

than in any *Buteo.* Cf. larger and more rufescent Savanna Hawk and ♀/immature Snail Kite (with more hooked bill, etc.). **Habits:** Often perches in open, even on ground, sometimes several individuals together (elsewhere it is known to hunt cooperatively; in Ecuador?). Eats small mammals as well as birds, capturing them in fast low flight or in a short stoop from a perch. Soars freely, sometimes quite high in sky. **Voice:** Usually quiet. Occasionally gives a descending "krreeaarrh."

Black-collared Hawk, *Busarellus nigricollis*
Gavilán de Ciénega   Plate 11(7)

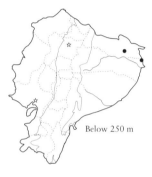

Below 250 m

46–51 cm (18–20"). An unmistakable *large, mainly rufous* raptor found in small numbers *in lowlands of far northeast* where it occurs in *marshy areas and near water.* Iris brown; bill blackish; legs pale flesh to bluish. **Adult** *bright rufous above* with *contrasting whitish head and throat*, nape and back sparsely streaked black; short tail blackish with narrow rufous bands near base and narrow whitish tip. *Below bright cinnamon-rufous* with *black crescent across chest.* **In flight** *wings very broad* and rounded, *mostly cinnamon-rufous with contrasting black primaries and trailing edge to secondaries.* **Juvenile** much duller, though *already showing contrasting pale head and dark brown collar*; above dark brown mottled and barred with rufous, below pale buff mottled and streaked with dark brown. **Similar species:** Unique in its limited Ecuadorian range. **Habits:** Usually perches quite low, pouncing on fish in shallow water or in aquatic vegetation, its spiny soles aiding in grasping prey. Often quite unsuspicious, allowing a close approach. Though often sluggish, Black-collareds are also powerful flyers, and can soar to great heights on their broad wings. **Voice:** Not very vocal, but perched birds give a low, raspy "reh-h-h-h."

Black-chested Buzzard-Eagle
Geranoaetus melanoleucus
Aguila Pechinegra   Plate 14(7)

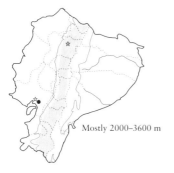

Mostly 2000–3600 m

62–68.5 cm (24½–27″). An impressive, *large* raptor found in *semiopen terrain in highlands*, regular up into *paramo*. Iris brown to amber; cere and base of bill pale yellow; legs yellow. **Adult** nearly unmistakable, with *strikingly short wedge-shaped tail* that barely protrudes past tail in flight. *Upperparts as well as throat slaty gray*, becoming black on chest; *lower underparts contrastingly white* with fine wavy dusky barring. *Shoulders pale gray vermiculated black*; tail gray, essentially unmarked. **In flight** wings long and broad, especially toward base; underwing-coverts whitish, flight feathers grayer. **Immature** dusky brown above, without gray shoulders; whitish to buff below, heavily streaked brown, and *often with belly contrastingly dark*; *tail considerably longer than in adult* (imparting a more "normal" silhouette). **Similar species:** Immature most likely confused with immature Variable Hawk (which also is basically brown and coarsely streaked to variable extent), but eagle is larger and more heavily built with different flight profile (wings broader, tail shorter). **Habits:** A powerful bird of prey that takes mostly small mammals. In Ecuador most often seen in flight, regularly in pairs, gliding effortlessly along cliffs and ridges on flat or slightly raised wings. Usually perches on rocks or ground. **Voice:** Not very vocal, but occasionally flying birds give a surprisingly high-pitched (weak for size of bird),

broken "ku-keéu" and a faster, more singing "kukukukuku."

Buteo Hawks
A rather large group of "typical" midsized hawks—called "buzzards" in the Old World—with broad and rounded wings that are adapted for *frequent soaring*; most soar a great deal, with two species (Short-tailed and White-throated) rarely being seen perched. *Buteo* prey mainly on small mammals but also pursue birds (Short-tailed and White-throated specializing in the latter). Several species are dimorphic, the well-named Variable Hawk notably so.

Gray Hawk, *Buteo nitidus*
Gavilán Gris   Plate 13(1)

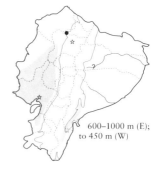

600–1000 m (E); to 450 m (W)

40.5–45 cm (16–17¾″). *Deciduous woodland, forest borders, and clearings in lowlands of west*; scarce along base of Andes in southeast. Sometimes placed in genus *Asturina*; Mid. Am. birds have sometimes been treated as a separate species (*B. plagiatus*), in which case S. Am. birds are called Gray-lined Hawk. Iris dark brown; cere pale yellow; legs yellow. **Adult** *gray above, paler pearly gray on head and neck*, with wavy darker gray barring throughout; tail black with two white bands and narrow tip, underside dark gray with white bands. White below *with narrow dense dark gray barring* except on throat. **In flight** wings whitish with faint gray spotting and barring. **Immature** dark brown above, *face contrastingly paler buff with dark brown eye-stripe and malar streak*, often with whitish at base of tail; tail blackish with 3–4 gray bands, underside pale grayish with dusky barring relatively indistinct. Below whitish to creamy buff with dark brown spotting and streaking, *thighs often barred brown.* **Similar species:** Attractive adult easy to recognize, but cf. duller and browner Roadside Hawk. Immature resembles young of several other hawks, notably Broad-winged (mainly montane in Ecuador). Broad-winged has less strongly marked facial pattern (generally with no dark eye-stripe), less white at base of tail, dark spotting or streaking (not barring) on thighs, more prominent dark trailing edge to wing, and darker and more contrasting dark tail banding with broader subterminal band. **Habits:** Favors areas where forest has been fragmented, perching at varying heights though most often high. Hunts a wide variety of prey, usually attacking from a perch. Soars, though usually not for very long or too high. **Voice:** Gives a series of high-pitched, clear, whistled phrases "wuu-yeéuw, wuu-yeéuw, wuu-yeéuw . . ." (up to 6–7 in total), usually from a perch in canopy. Call an abrupt, clear "keeeuw" (P. Coopmans).

species: Roadside Hawk is an important species to learn to recognize, for it will be seen often. No other similar raptor shares the prominent rufous in primaries, though this color is usually hidden on perched birds; prominent orange-yellow on cere is also unique among Ecuadorian *Buteo.* Cf. especially Gray and Broad-winged Hawks. **Habits:** Usually common and conspicuous, though in extensively forested areas scarcer and confined to borders, especially along rivers. Often perches in open, and—for a raptor—can be rather confiding, allowing close approach. Perched birds often swivel tail sideways. Usually flies with shallow stiff wingbeats interspersed with short glides. Does not soar often or very high except in display, in which it may circle up a long way though rarely or never fanning tail. **Voice:** One of the more vocal raptors. Perched birds often give a high-pitched nasal, complaining scream, "rreeeeah," whereas in flight (less often from perch) birds give a fast series of many nasal "reh" notes.

Roadside Hawk, *Buteo magnirostris*
Gavilán Campestre   Plate 13(2)

Mostly below 1600 m, smaller numbers higher

White-rumped Hawk, *Buteo leucorrhous*
Gavilán Lomiblanco   Plate 13(6)

Mostly 2000–3200 m

33–38 cm (13–15"). *Widespread and often common and conspicuous in clearings and forest borders in lowlands and subtropics of east and west,* in many areas (though not southwest) one of the most frequently seen raptors. Iris and legs yellow; *cere orange-yellow.* **Adult** *above gray to brownish gray,* somewhat paler on throat and chest; *breast and belly barred whitish and dull grayish rufous.* Tail broadly banded dull gray and blackish. **In flight** has underwing barred grayish with *rufous in primaries* (evident both from above and below, especially from above). **Juvenile** similar but browner. **Similar**

33–38 cm (13–15"). *Scarce in subtropical and especially temperate forest and borders on both slopes.* Iris yellow; cere yellow, base of lower mandible grayish; legs yellow-orange. **Adult** *black* with *white rump* (hard to see when perched), *white crissum,* and partially rufous thighs. Tail blackish with single ashy band, two more prominent white bands from below. **In flight** has *white underwing-coverts* that contrast strongly with black body and gray-and-white banded flight feathers. **Immature** blackish above with some rufous streaking on head and upper back, *rump white.* Below tawny-rufous with coarse blackish streaking, throat whiter and flanks blacker. **Similar species:** This rather small, mainly black raptor is distinctive, especially in flight when its white rump and underwing-coverts can be conspicuous. Perched birds can look *Accipiter*-like (but note White-rumped's different tail pattern). Immature blacker above than other similar montane hawks. **Habits:** Like certain other *Buteo* (e.g., Short-tailed, White-throated), seen most often in flight, soaring and sailing over mountain forests. **Voice:** Call a high-pitched squeal, "squeeeuh," sometimes extended in a short tremolo, "squeeeuh-uh-uhuh."

Broad-winged Hawk, *Buteo platypterus*
Gavilán Aludo   Plate 13(3)

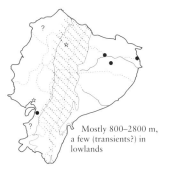

Mostly 800–2800 m, a few (transients?) in lowlands

38–43 cm (15–17″). An uncommon boreal migrant to *borders of foothill and subtropical forest and woodland and adjacent clearings*, occasionally elsewhere; recorded mostly Oct.–early Apr. Iris amber to brownish; cere and legs yellow. **Adult** dark brown to grayish brown above with dark brown malar streak and some paler mottling on wing-coverts and scapulars; tail blackish with two broad whitish bands and narrow whitish tip, *underside with single broad white band*. Whitish below *coarsely mottled and barred grayish rufous to rufous*. Rare **dark morph** never reported from Ecuador. **In flight** wings relatively pointed for a *Buteo*, with *underside mainly whitish*, flight feathers with broad dark trailing edge. **Immature** dark brown above with whitish superciliary and *prominent blackish malar streak*; tail grayish brown with 4–5 narrow dark brown bands, underside pale grayish with 4–5 narrow dark bands with broader subterminal band. Below whitish sparsely streaked, spotted, and barred

with brown. **Similar species:** Smaller and grayer Roadside Hawk shows distinctive rufous in primaries. Immature resembles immature Gray Hawk, but latter shows prominent dark eye-stripe, white at base of tail, less obvious dark trailing edge on wing, and less distinct undertail pattern. Cf. also immature Double-toothed Kite. **Habits:** Often seen perched at forest edge, regularly in open; sometimes quite tame. Soars frequently. Usually hunts from a perch, feeding on a wide variety of prey. The great migratory flocks of Broad-winged Hawks seen in Middle America as far south as Panama have never been reported in Ecuador, evidently because only small numbers get so far south. The vast majority of birds reaching Ecuador are adults. **Voice:** Often-heard call a shrill, piercing high-pitched "p-teeeeeee," given both while perched and in flight, by both adults and young birds.

Short-tailed Hawk, *Buteo brachyurus*
Gavilán Colicorto   Plate 13(4)

Mostly below 1600 m

39.5–43 cm (15½–17″). *Widespread* in semi-open areas and forest and woodland borders in lowlands and subtropics of east and west. *Almost invariably seen in flight* (perched birds are almost always hidden in leafy canopy). Iris brown; cere yellow with base of bill grayish; legs yellow. **Pale-morph adult** (which predominates in Ecuador) *blackish brown above*, this color *extending down onto sides of head and neck and imparting obvious hooded effect*; forehead usually whitish; tail grayish brown with 4–5 indistinct dark bars, underside pale grayish with 3–4 indistinct darker bars. *Below white.* **In flight** *underwing mainly white*, some dark barring on flight feathers and primaries tipped black. **Dark-morph adult** *entirely* *sooty black* aside from whitish forehead; tail as in pale morph. **In flight** *blackish underwing-coverts* contrast with whitish flight feathers. **Pale-morph juvenile** as in adult but head streaked buff to whitish, sides with quite extensive dark streaking. **Dark-morph juvenile** as in adult but underparts and underwing-coverts variably marked with buff to whitish. **Similar species:** Pale morph readily known by its dark "hood," a character not shared by any other similar raptor; note also its white underwing and lack of obvious tail-banding. Dark morph can be more difficult, and is especially likely to be confused with Zone-tailed Hawk; Zone-tailed has comparatively long and narrow wings, flies in a distinct dihedral, and tail shows more obvious white banding. In highlands, also cf. scarce White-throated Hawk (at best limited overlap with Short-tailed). **Habits:** As noted above, almost invariably seen in flight, often soaring high with other raptors and vultures. Preys mostly on birds, mainly obtained in a fast descending stoop. **Voice:** Usually silent, but occasionally gives a high-pitched whistle, "kleeeeu."

White-throated Hawk, *Buteo albigula*
Gavilán Goliblanco   Plate 13(5)

Mostly 2200–3200 m

39.5–43 cm (15½–17"). *Rare* in *temperate* forest and woodland and adjacent semiopen areas, possibly only an austral migrant to Ecuador. Iris brown; cere and legs yellow. **Adult** blackish brown above, *sides of head and neck more rufous-chestnut and imparting obvious hooded effect*; tail grayish brown with 4–5 indistinct dark bars, underside pale grayish with 3–4 indistinct darker bars. *Below white* with usually sparse brown streaking across breast (*most solid on sides*)

and down flanks; *thighs barred rufous and white*, usually looking contrastingly darker. **In flight** underwing whitish with faint dark markings. **Juvenile** similar to adult but buffier below and on underwing-coverts. **Similar species:** Most closely resembles pale-morph Short-tailed Hawk (which is equally "white-throated"). That species is shorter-tailed, blacker above and cleaner white below, lacks rufous and brown markings on underparts, and never shows thigh barring. Cf. also immature Broad-winged Hawk. **Habits:** Similar to Short-tailed Hawk, though White-throated seems to soar less. **Voice:** Calls near nest in Argentina a loud, whining, querulous "squee-geé."

Swainson's Hawk, *Buteo swainsoni*
Gavilán de Swainson   Plate 13(7)

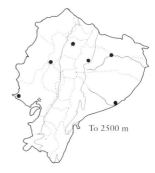

To 2500 m

48–56 cm (19–22"). A *very rare* boreal migrant, with a few scattered records of the odd individual bird. *Plumage variable*. Iris brown; cere and legs yellow. **Light-morph adult** dark brown above with some *white on uppertail-coverts*; tail dark gray with 6–8 blackish bars, underside pale grayish with 4–6 faint dusky bars and wider subterminal band. *Throat white* contrasting with *brown band across chest*; lower underparts whitish sometimes with brown barring on sides and flanks. **In flight** wings rather long, *underwing-coverts creamy white* contrasting with dark gray flight feathers. Scarcer **dark-morph adult** dark brown throughout, with some buff barring on lower belly and crissum and *white on uppertail-coverts* as in light morph. Intermediates occur. **Immature** has buff face with dark eye-stripe and malar streak; otherwise dark brown above with white on uppertail-coverts; tail quite uniform. Buff below with variable amount of dark spotting and blotching (more in dark morph). **Similar species:** Light-morph adults predominate in overall population (and are relatively easy to recognize), but immatures may be more apt to be seen in Ecuador, especially on southward passage. These can be very confusing, but note the *absence* of obvious tail pattern; white on base of uppertail is an additional helpful mark. Swainson's often flies in a slight dihedral. Cf. especially immature of broader-winged Variable Hawk. **Habits:** Favors open country, but migrants overfly any type of terrain.

Zone-tailed Hawk, *Buteo albonotatus*
Gavilán Colifajeado   Plate 13(8)

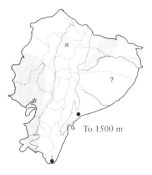

To 1500 m

47–56 cm (18¹⁄₂–22″). *Scarce and local* in forest and woodland borders as well as cleared areas in lowlands of southwest and along e. base of Andes, ranging locally up into lower subtropics. *In flight bears superficial but striking resemblance to Turkey Vulture.* Iris brown; cere and legs bright yellow. **Adult** *uniform dark slaty gray to blackish*; *rather long and narrow tail* blackish with two inconspicuous gray bands and narrow white tip, *underside with 2–3 white bands.* **In flight** wings relatively long and narrow, *distinctly two-toned* with *black underwing-coverts contrasting with paler flight feathers.* **Juvenile** as in adult but with variable amount of white flecking; upperside of tail grayish brown with 5–7 dark bars, underside pale gray with 4–7 dark bars. **Similar species:** Larger and blacker Turkey Vulture flies with the same tilting dihedral and shows much the same two-toned effect on underwing; it differs, however, in its small naked head and lack of tail-banding. Dark-morph Short-tailed Hawk has more typical

Buteo proportions (in flight wings shorter and broader), shows much less distinct tail-banding. Zone-taileds are not often seen perched, and separation from other dark raptors can be difficult when they are; especially cf. larger and heavier Great Black-Hawk. **Habits:** Usually seen in flight, tilting and with wings held in a marked dihedral; often flies fairly low, and may accompany larger numbers of Turkey Vultures. Zone-tailed thus appears truly to mimic the vulture, presumably thereby fooling potential prey into not seeking cover. Eats birds, small mammals, and lizards. **Voice:** Not very vocal; perched birds occasionally give a rough scream, "reeeeah."

Variable Hawk, *Buteo polyosoma*
Gavilán Variable   Plate 12(8)

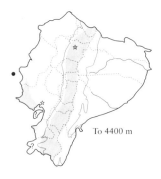

To 4400 m

46–61 cm (18–24″). Well named, this *exceptionally variable* hawk ranges widely in semi-open areas, mainly in highlands and regularly up into paramo, but occurs lower in south (especially Loja and El Oro), and also locally on coast of w. Guayas. It comprises what was formerly considered two species, Red-backed Hawk (*B. polyosoma*) and Puna Hawk (*B. poecilochrous*); the latter was thought to be a large, high-elevation taxon ranging primarily above treeline. Iris brown or hazel; cere greenish yellow; legs yellow. Sexes tend to differ in plumage as adults, with ♂♂ usually being gray-backed and ♀♀ usually rufous-backed. All adults have *tail strikingly white with a little dusky barring and prominent black subterminal band.* **Pale-morph ♂** *gray above* and *white below*; flight feathers blackish. **Pale-morph ♀** similar but with *rufous back.* **Dark morph** (either sex) *entirely slaty gray*; these are most numerous at higher elevations. **Rufous-morph** birds tend to be ♀♀ and may have *rufous both on back and breast* with lower underparts gray-barred, or rufous on back as well as most of underparts. Other variants occur. In **flight** wings long, underside variable but coverts usually solid (either whitish, blackish, or rufous), flight feathers with fine dark barring. **Immature** also variable: typically dark brown above, sometimes with rufous on back; below buff, streaked brown on throat and chest, and barred on lower underparts (brown streaking and barring sometimes so dense that underparts are almost solidly dark); tail pale grayish with narrow blackish barring. **Similar species:** Plumage variation shown by this species is confusing, but it is much simpler now that only one species is recognized; separating what were formerly called Red-backed and Puna Hawks was a nightmare. White-throated Hawk is smaller and has dark hood contrasting with white underparts that show only sparse streaking and contrasting barred thighs. Cf. also Gray-backed Hawk. **Habits:** This handsome hawk often perches in the open, frequently on rocks and also on poles. Hunts mainly in flight, often while hovering (rather heavily in calm conditions, much more gracefully when windy, at times then almost "hanging" stationary). **Voice:** Not terribly vocal, but occasionally gives a "keeeyow" or "kee-kee-kee" call.

Crested Eagle, *Morphnus guianensis*
Aguila Crestada   Plate 14(1)

71–84 cm (28–33″). *Very rare* in humid forest (mainly in extensive areas of terra firme) in *lowlands of east*, with a few records also from northwest. *Very large*, almost as big as Harpy Eagle but more slightly built, with *broad tail*

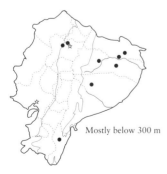

Mostly below 300 m

proportionately longer. Long erectile, single-pointed crest. Iris brown; heavy bill and lores blackish; legs yellow. **Light-morph adult** has *head and chest pale ashy to brownish gray*, with crest black; upperparts blackish with wing-coverts fringed whitish; tail boldly banded black and pale gray. Underparts white with some fine cinnamon barring, especially on thighs. **In flight** wings broad and rounded with *underwing-coverts white*, flight feathers white boldly barred blackish. **Dark-morph adult** (rarer) like pale morph above, but *blacker generally*, with little or no pale fringing on coverts; chest blackish, *underparts boldly banded black and white*. Intermediates occur. *Immature* plumages vary, and adult plumage not acquired for 3 years: *head, neck, and underparts white* (foreparts gradually becoming grayer), *wing-coverts (especially) and back with conspicuous whitish marbling*, tail at first with more narrow banding. **Similar species:** Liable to be confused with even larger Harpy Eagle though the Harpy is substantially more heavily built with broader wings and shorter tail, much thicker legs. Adult Harpies are relatively easy, but younger birds of the two are easily confused (especially ♀ Cresteds vs. ♂ Harpies); note Harpy's bifurcated crest and black on underwing-coverts. Also cf. the *Spizaetus* hawk-eagles. **Habits:** Surprisingly secretive for such a large bird, generally remaining in canopy; occasionally rests in open at forest edge (which Harpy hardly ever does). Occasionally circles above forest canopy, or sails across valleys. Feeds on small to midsized mammals (even small monkeys), snakes, some birds. **Voice:** Call a loud hawk-eagle-like scream, "wheyr-wheyr-wheyr-wheyr-wheyr-whéyr-br" (J. Moore recording).

Harpy Eagle, *Harpia harpyja*
Aguila Harpía   Plate 14(2)

89–99 cm (35–39″). A *huge* and *powerful* eagle that occurs *at low densities* in humid forest (especially extensive terra firme) in *lowlands of east* and (only formerly?) in northwest. Very heavily built, with *massive bill, legs, and talons. Long erectile, double-pointed crest.* Iris amber to pale grayish; bill and lores blackish; legs yellow. **Adult** has *head and neck pale gray* with crest blackish;

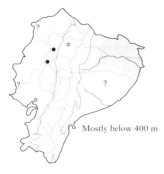

Mostly below 400 m

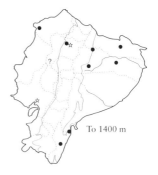

To 1400 m

upperparts blackish; broad and fairly long tail boldly banded black and pale gray. *Broad band across chest black*, contrasting with white underparts; *thighs boldly barred black*. **In flight** wings very broad and rounded, *underwing-coverts white with conspicuous black bar*, *black axillars*, flight feathers white with black barring. Immature plumages vary, requiring 4 years to attain adult plumage: *head (even crest), neck, and underparts white, coverts and back very pale gray* (gradually becoming darker); tail at first with more narrow banding; underwing-coverts at first lack the black. *Traces of adult's black chest-band appear quite early.* **Similar species:** So big that confusion is improbable except with the somewhat smaller and slighter Crested Eagle; for distinctions see under that species. **Habits:** Often considered the world's most powerful bird of prey, Harpy is—given its huge size—remarkably inconspicuous. It mainly remains inside forest, though one occasionally perches in the open at forest edge (especially when drying off after a rain) or crosses an open area such as a river. The harpy rarely or never soars and is almost never seen above canopy level. Feeds on various midsized mammals (including large monkeys and sloths) and larger birds; if prey is too heavy, it may be dismembered on the spot. **Voice:** Infrequently gives a whistled "wheeeee" or "wheeee-wheeea."

Black-and-white Hawk-Eagle
Spizastur melanoleucus
Aguila Azor Blanquinegro   Plate 14(6)

53.5–61 cm (21–24″). *Rare and local* in humid forest and adjacent clearings in lowlands and lower subtropics, mainly in east. Short bushy crest. Iris yellow; *cere bright orange* contrasting sharply with *black lores and bill*; feet yellow. **Adult** has *snowy white head, neck, and underparts* with *short crest black*; *upperparts otherwise contrastingly black*. Tail blackish with three gray bands and narrow whitish tip, underside whitish with 3–4 dark bars, subterminal band widest. **In flight** wings broad and relatively long, *underside mainly white* with only faint dark barring on flight feathers; *also shows prominent white leading edge to inner wing*. **Juvenile** similar but slightly browner above. **Similar species:** Immature Ornate Hawk-Eagle somewhat similar but has long pointed crest, only dusky lores (whereas black lores of Black-and-white are remarkably conspicuous), shows bold black barring on flanks and especially thighs; in flight its wings are proportionately shorter and tail longer, and Ornate lacks Black-and-white's white leading edge to wing. Immature light-morph Gray-headed Kite superficially similar but lacks orange and black on face. **Habits:** This stunning raptor, which seems to be unusually scarce in Ecuador, is most often seen in graceful soaring or gliding flight and only rarely perches in open. It hunts mainly from the wing, stooping swiftly down on unsuspecting prey (primarily birds), but also waits in ambush from a partially hidden perch. **Voice:** Not very vocal. Call in Mexico a series of accelerating piping notes recalling Ornate Hawk-Eagle, "whee whi-whi-whi-whi-wheé-eer" (Howell and Webb 1995).

Spizaetus Hawk-Eagles
Spectacular large eagles with *notable crests* and *tarsi feathered to the toes*. They range in humid lowland and foothill forests, and except in territorial display are suprisingly inconspicuous.

Black Hawk-Eagle, *Spizaetus tyrannus*
Aguila Azor Negro   Plate 14(4)

Ornate Hawk-Eagle, *Spizaetus ornatus*
Aguila Azor Adornado   Plate 14(5)

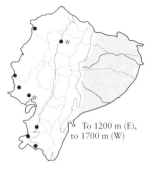

To 1200 m (E),
to 1700 m (W)

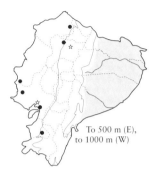

To 500 m (E),
to 1000 m (W)

58.5–66 cm (23–26″). Uncommon in humid forest in lowlands and foothills of east and west, in west now very scarce and found primarily in foothills. *Erectile bushy crest.* Iris golden yellow; cere and lores grayish; feet yellow. **Adult** *black*, crest basally white (sometimes easy to see), flanks and (especially) *thighs coarsely barred white. Long tail* banded black and dusky-gray, *underside more boldly banded black and paler gray.* **In flight** wings long, broad, and rounded, with *underwing-coverts black, flight feathers boldly banded black and white.* **Immature** rather different and variable, at first with creamy white superciliary, crown and sides of head mottled black and white; above otherwise blackish brown, below mixed buff and blackish (streaked on chest, barred lower down, especially on thighs); underwing-coverts more marked with white. As they age, gradually become blacker. **Similar species:** Most often seen in flight; *no other blackish raptor has such conspicuous banding on underside of wings.* Cf. Ornate Hawk-Eagle; some Hook-billed Kites have somewhat similar flight patterns. **Habits:** A powerful raptor that hunts many birds (up to the size of macaws) and some midsized mammals, usually stooping on them from a perch inside or at edge of forest. Not often seen except while soaring, which it does regularly, especially during sunny mornings; it then draws attention with its loud calling. **Voice:** Soaring birds call frequently, a far-carrying whistle, "wheep, wheep, whee-teeeeer," with distinctive long final drawn-out note somewhat higher-pitched (this note can be given alone).

58.5–68 cm (23–26¾″). A *beautifully patterned* hawk-eagle, rare in humid forest in lowlands of east and west, in west also ranging up into foothills. *Long erectile pointed crest,* in perched birds often held straight up. Iris golden yellow; cere greenish yellow, lores grayish olive; feet yellow. **Adult** has *black crown and crest; face, sides of neck, upper back, and side of chest rich rufous* bordered below by bold black malar stripe; upperparts otherwise brownish black. Long tail boldly banded black and gray, underside whiter with narrower black bands. Below white with *breast, belly, and thighs boldly barred with black.* **In flight** wings broad and rounded, *mostly whitish* with flight feathers banded blackish. **Immature** has *head, neck, and underparts white,* already with black crest and *blackish spotting on flanks and barring on thighs;* upperparts browner. As they age, pattern of adult's head and underparts gradually emerges. **Similar species:** Beautiful adult essentially unmistakable, though cf. similarly plumaged (uncannily so) immature Gray-bellied Hawk. Younger Ornates, lacking rufous on foreneck, somewhat resemble Black-and-white Hawk-Eagle; the latter is smaller, lacks pointed crest, has conspicuous black lores and orange cere, and never shows black barring below. Cf. also younger Black Hawk-Eagle and Gray-headed Kite. **Habits:** Similar to Black Hawk-Eagle, though seems not to soar as often or as high, more often just circling fairly low above canopy; seems less likely to soar out over adjacent semiopen fragmented forest than does Black. **Voice:** Flying birds call frequently, with quality similar to Black's though pattern differs, "wheeeeer, whip, whip, whip, whip."

Black-and-chestnut Eagle, *Oroaetus isidori*
Aguila Andina   Plate 14(3)

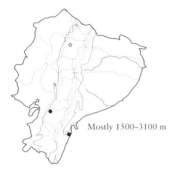

Mostly 1500–3100 m

66–73.5 cm (26–29″). *Rare* in *subtropical and temperate forest* on both slopes. Long erectile pointed crest; legs feathered to toes. Iris yellow; cere and lores gray; feet dull yellow. **Adult** *black above* (including crest) *and on throat; underparts dark chestnut* with sparse black streaking, some black on thighs. Tail fairly long, *pale grayish with broad black subterminal band* and narrow white tip. **In flight** wings broad and rounded, underside with *chestnut underwing-coverts, primaries whitish*, secondaries gray. **Immature** pale grayish brown above, crest tipped black, forehead and superciliary buffyish. *Below basically white* with some brown on sides of chest. Tail boldly banded grayish and black, whiter from below; underwing-coverts whitish. **Similar species:** This impressive montane eagle is unlikely to be confused, mainly because other equally large hawk-eagles do not range to such high elevations. Its chestnut is hard to discern at any distance, but the pale areas in wings and tail are visible in flying birds even from afar. Solitary Eagle is mainly dark gray with a very different flight profile (very broad wings, short tail). **Habits:** Usually seen soaring, generally not ascending too high above its mountain fastnesses; sometimes flies in pairs. Not often seen perched; resting birds mainly remain in the leafy canopy of tall trees and not out in open. Feeds primarily on larger birds and small to midsized mammals. **Voice:** Not very vocal, and unlike the two *Spizaetus* hawk-eagles seems not to vocalize in a flight display.

Perched birds give a rather nasal squeal, "reeeeeeow," sometimes in series or as they launch out from a branch.

Falcons and Caracaras: Falconidae (19)
A large and widespread group of diurnal birds of prey, most species similar to the Accipitridae but differing in their notched upper mandibles and other anatomical characters. As in that family, the **sexes are usually alike** (apart from the males' often smaller size).

Daptrius and *Ibycter* Caracaras
Caracaras with *mainly black plumage* found in lowland forests and borders. *Ibycter* was recently generically separated from *Daptrius*.

Black Caracara, *Daptrius ater*
Caracara Negro   Plate 16(3)

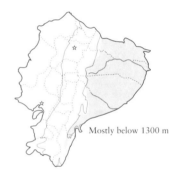

Mostly below 1300 m

40.5–43 cm (16–17″). A *small* caracara found in *semiopen areas such as along rivers and forest borders* in lowlands of east, also following clearings up onto lower slopes of Andes. Iris brown, with *cere and extensive facial skin yellowish orange, yellower on upper throat*; maxilla blackish, mandible pale gray; legs orange-yellow. **Adult** *almost entirely black* with a slight gloss; *base of tail white.* **In flight** all-black wings rather long and narrow. **Juvenile** similar but facial skin yellower, plumage duller black with some buff spotting or barring below. **Similar species:** Red-throated Caracara larger with conspicuous white belly but no white in tail. Black's obvious yellow-orange face unique. **Habits:** A conspicuous bird that often ranges in small groups of up to 3–5 birds, flying along rivers or in other semiopen areas with frequent calling announcing their approach. Almost omnivorous, not only eating carrion but also capturing small mammals, insects, even frogs, fish, and some fruit. **Voice:** Frequently heard call a harsh, far-carrying scream, "kraaaaaaah."

Red-throated Caracara, *Ibycter americanus*
Caracara Ventriblanco   Plate 16(4)

To 800 m

51–56 cm (20–22"). Conspicuous in *canopy and borders of humid forest in lowlands of east*; a few also still occur locally in lowlands of west. Iris reddish; cere and base of bill blue-gray, tip of bill yellow; *lores, orbital skin, and bare skin on throat red*; legs orange-red. **Adult** *glossy black with contrasting white belly*. **Juvenile** similar but facial skin more yellowish and throat black. **Similar species:** Black Caracara smaller with bright bare yellow-orange face, white at base of tail instead of on belly; its voice is unmistakably different. **Habits:** Usually occurs in small, often incredibly noisy groups of up to 5–6 birds. They fly with deep, slow wingbeats, generally through or just a bit above canopy, never soaring. Foraging birds sometimes descend quite low, almost to ground, and at such times they can be notably unsuspicious. This caracara feeds almost entirely on eggs and larvae of bees and wasps, obtained by ripping apart their nests; remarkably, caracaras seem never to be stung, seemingly having some sort of inherent repellent effect. They also eat some fruit. **Voice:** No other birds, not even big macaws, are capable of generating as much noise as a group of this species. Their most frequent call is a raucous "kra-kra-kra-kra-kow" or just "kra-kow." Also given is a somewhat more mellow "kowh" repeated several times,

and flying birds often give a far-carrying "krraah."

Northern Crested-Caracara, *Caracara cheriway*
Caracara Crestado Norteño   Plate 16(8)

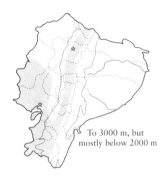

To 3000 m, but mostly below 2000 m

51–58.5 cm (20–23"). Open and agricultural terrain, arid scrub, and woodland borders in *southwest*, also a few in highlands. Formerly called Crested Caracara (*Polyborus plancus*). Iris brown to hazel; *cere, base of bill, and lores orange-red* (duller in juveniles), bill pale blue; rather long legs yellow. **Adult** has *crown and slight bushy crest black* in striking contrast to *white sides of head, neck, throat, and upper chest*, nape and upper back with black barring. Otherwise blackish above with *uppertail-coverts and basal half of tail white with dusky barring*; remainder of tail black. Breast whitish with black barring, belly and thighs black, crissum white. **In flight** long wings black with *prominent patch of white in primaries*. **Immature** already with *blackish crown* but otherwise dark brown overall, with adult's white areas, including wing patch, buffier, upper back and underparts more or less streaked. **Similar species:** Adult unmistakable. Browner younger birds can be confused with young of other caracaras, though this species is larger and generally shows enough head pattern and bill color to be recognizable. **Habits:** Conspicuous, usually perching in open, most often low and often on ground where it strides about with great authority. Flies strongly on steady, deep wingbeats; sometimes ascends to considerable heights, but soars only briefly. An opportunistic feeder, eating mainly carrion when it regularly feeds with vultures; also takes some live prey. **Voice:** Usually quiet, though at times gives low guttural calls, e.g., a "grrk" or a "grr-grr-grr-grraow."

Phalcoboenus Caracaras

Attractive and boldly patterned caracaras found at high elevations in the Andes, mainly in paramo, the Mountain Caracara only in the extreme south.

Carunculated Caracara
Phalcoboenus carunculatus
Caracara Curiquingue   Plate 16(6)

Mostly 3000–4200 m

51–56 cm (20–22″). *Paramo and nearby fields and cliffs* in highlands south locally to El Oro and n. Loja. Iris dark brown; *cere and bare wrinkled facial skin and upper throat reddish to orange-red*, bill bluish gray; legs bright yellow. **Adult** *glossy black above*, feathers of crown recurved; *uppertail-coverts and broad tip to tail white. Underparts black conspicuously streaked with white*, belly and crissum white. **In flight** wings rather long, *underwing-coverts and base of flight feathers white*, flight feathers black very narrowly tipped white. **Immature** very different, with bare face and legs dusky. *Tawny to dark brown* with some whitish mottling on head and underparts; uppertail-coverts whitish with some brown barring. **In flight** shows pale buff patch at base of primaries. **Similar species:** Adult essentially unmistakable, but in extreme south cf. Mountain Caracara (with no streaking below). Cf. certain ages/morphs of Variable Hawk. Younger birds differ from other caracaras in being more uniformly brown but are very similar to Mountain Caracaras of same age. **Habits:** Conspicuous in open areas it favors, this attractive caracara paces about on ground

searching for a wide variety of items; in general occurs singly or in pairs, though larger groups occur in areas where it remains numerous. Wide-ranging, and flight very strong; when windy, often sails gracefully for long periods on set wings. **Voice:** Essentially silent, but reported to give "harsh barking calls" (Fjeldså and Krabbe 1990).

Mountain Caracara
Phalcoboenus megalopterus
Caracara Montañero   Plate 16(7)

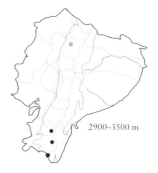

2900–3500 m

51–56 cm (20–22″). *Paramo in far south.* Iris dark brown; *cere and facial skin reddish*, bill bluish gray; legs yellow. Resembles much more widespread Carunculated Caracara. **Adult** differs in having less extensive bare red skin on face with virtually none behind eye or on lower throat, and in *plain black lower throat to lower breast* with no white streaking. **Immature** also similar but uppertail-coverts *plain buffy whitish* (with no barring, hence standing out more). **Habits and Voice:** Similar to Carunculated Caracara.

Yellow-headed Caracara, *Milvago chimachima*
Caracara Bayo   Plate 16(5)

40–45 cm (15¾–17¼″). A *small* caracara with weak bill and talons found *along larger rivers in lowlands of northeast.* Iris pale brown to hazel; cere and orbital area pale yellow, tip of bill pale bluish gray; legs pale blue-gray to greenish. **Adult** *mostly creamy to yellowish buff* with *narrow dark postocular streak*; back and wings contrastingly blackish brown. *Uppertail-coverts buff; rather long and rounded tail yellowish buff with dusky bars and broad dusky tip.* **In flight** wings dark brown with *large buff patch on*

Below 300 m

Mostly below 2000 m

primaries. **Immature** with overall pattern like adult's but head and neck streaked brown, and throat and breast streaked and mottled with brown. **Similar species:** Not likely confused in its limited range, where only other caracaras are the very different Black and Red-throated. Cf. Laughing Falcon. **Habits:** Usually seen flying low over sandbars in larger rivers, often pausing to perch on piles of driftwood; only occasionally seen out on nearby pastures—its typical haunt elsewhere—though in the future it may begin to spread into that habitat. Frequently accompanies cattle, even perching on their backs to pick off ticks. Usual flight consists of several shallow flaps followed by a glide on down-bent wings. Scavenges for carrion; also searches for live food while walking on ground. **Voice:** Infrequently gives a rather weak, nasal scream, "wreeeah."

Micrastur **Forest-Falcons**
A distinctive group of raptors found primarily in lowland forests, though two species (Barred and Collared) range well up into the subtropics as well. Forest-falcons have short rounded wings, long graduated tails (especially Collared and Buckley's), rather long legs, and a fairly distinct facial ruff. They are furtive and are heard much more often than seen, though sometimes they respond to tape playback. Nests, so far as known, are placed inside tree cavities.

Barred Forest-Falcon, *Micrastur ruficollis*
Halcón Montés Barreteado   Plate 15(6)
33–38 cm (13–15″). *Widespread* but inconspicuous inside humid lowland and subtropical forest and secondary woodland of

east and west. Iris brown; *cere, base of bill, lores, and wide orbital ring bright yellow;* legs yellow. **Adult** *slaty gray above,* wings somewhat browner (especially in ♀♀); graduated tail blackish with 3–4 narrow white to pale gray bars and white tip. Throat pale gray; *remaining underparts white finely and evenly barred with black.* **Immature** *dark brown above,* blackest on head, *usually with partially broken whitish to pale buff nuchal collar. Buff below* (creamy whitish to rather deep), *generally with at least some coarse dusky barring;* some birds have underparts entirely barred, whereas others are unmarked. Tail as in adult. **Similar species:** Lined Forest-Falcon (*only in e. lowlands*) adult has staring white iris, orange facial skin and legs; cf. also rare Plumbeous Forest-Falcon (*only in northwest*). Adult Tiny Hawk much smaller (especially ♂♂), lacks extensive yellow facial skin (only on cere), and tail banding gray (not white) and wider; it regularly perches high and in open, which Barred Forest-Falcon rarely or never does. Immature Bicolored Hawk never shows any barring below (the vast majority of Barred Forest-Falcons show at least some), and its tail barring is grayish and wider than in forest-falcon. Cf. also immature of larger Collared Forest-Falcon. **Habits:** Perches quietly inside forest, mainly in low and mid-levels; sometimes confiding, but more often slips away at the first indication of an observer's presence. Sometimes attends swarms of army ants, then often on ground itself, chasing after lizards and large insects flushed by ants. Also eats some birds, though most birds at antswarms don't seem to be terribly afraid of it. Like other forest-falcons, Barred never soars, indeed it never seems to fly above forest canopy. **Voice:** Usual vocalization a slowly repeated sharp, stacatto "our!" or "ahnk!," sometimes likened to bark of a distant small dog; it is given at several-second intervals though sometimes sped up when bird is excited. Like other forest-falcons, it calls primarily around dawn and dusk, sometimes even in full darkness. Also gives a series of 5–7 notes, reminiscent of Lined Forest-Falcon though less nasal (P. Coopmans). Agitated birds (especially) also give a much faster series of notes, also rising and falling in pitch, loudest in middle, e.g., "koh-koh-koh-ko-kó-kó-ke-ke-ke-keh-keh-kuh."

Lined Forest-Falcon, *Micrastur gilvicollis*
Halcón Montés Lineado   Plate 15(7)

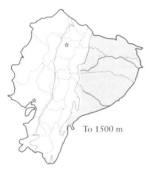

32–37 cm (12¹/₂–14¹/₂″). Scarce inside humid forest (*especially terra firme*) in *lowlands and foothills of east.* Iris white; *cere, base of bill, lores, and wide orbital ring bright orange to reddish orange; legs orange.* **Adult** resembles Barred Forest-Falcon, differing in soft-part coloration (iris dark in Barred, facial skin and legs yellow), shorter tail with *only two white bars* (sometimes only one shows), and reduced barring on lower belly and crissum (often this area looks whitish in Lined). **Immature** resembles Barred Forest-Falcon of similar age but (fide C. Witt) is *uniform slaty gray above* (as in adult) and *upperside of tail has only 1–2 visible whitish bands* (vs. 3–4 in Barred); facial skin yellower than in adults. **Habits:** Similar to Barred Forest-Falcon. Somewhat surprisingly, there seems to be little habitat separation between these two closely similar species in the e. lowlands. Lined seems strictly confined to terra firme, whereas Barred is relatively more wide-ranging (occurring also in várzea and forest borders). **Voice:**

Like Barred Forest-Falcon, heard far more often than seen. Usual vocalization a nasal "cow-káh" or "cow, káw-káw" (first note noticeably lower pitched, unlike Buckley's) repeated every 1–2 seconds, sometimes for prolonged periods; it can be varied to a 4-noted "cow, kao, káw-káw," especially when a bird is excited such as after tape playback. Also gives a series of single calls, similar to Barred's—at about the same rate—but less abrupt and more nasal (P. Coopmans).

Plumbeous Forest-Falcon, *Micrastur plumbeus*
Halcón Montés Plomizo   Plate 15(8)

31–36 cm (12¹/₄–14¹/₄″). *Rare and poorly known* inside very humid forest in *lowlands and foothills of northwest* (mainly Esmeraldas). Iris brown; *cere, base of bill, lores, and wide orbital ring bright orange; legs also orange.* Resembles Barred Forest-Falcon, with which sympatric. **Adult** differs in its *orange* (not yellow) *facial area and legs, single white tail-band* (not 2–3), and tendency toward *only sparse dark barring on underparts.* **Immature** also seems to have sparse dark barring on underparts (which can look essentially plain whitish except on chest); it has two white tail bands. **Habits:** Not well known, but apparently similar to Barred Forest-Falcon. **Voice:** Apparently the most frequent vocalization is a series of single "kew" or "ku" calls, similar to Barred Forest-Falcon but notes lower pitched and more nasal (N. Krabbe recording). Also gives a "kiw, ki-kíw, ki-kíw-kíw" or "kew, kiw, ki-kíw" (K. Berg recording), again similar to Barred but lower pitched; a faster "kiw, ki-ki-ke-kew" (P. Coopmans); and a more leisurely "kew...kew...kah-kooh" (M. Robbins recording).

Color Plates

Dedicated with love to the memory of

William B. Greenfield,
Martha Chara de Kalil,
and Felix Hirschberg

Key

Plate 1 Tinamous

Tinamus Tinamous
Large tinamous found on ground inside humid forest in lowlands and foothills, wary and heard far more often than seen. All 3 species show scaly vermiculated pattern on face and sides of neck, most marked in Gray Tinamou.

1. GRAY TINAMOU, *Tinamus tao*
Very rare and local inside forest in foothills and lower subtropics on e. slope, locally out into adjacent lowlands. Large and dark, mainly lustrous dark gray with black vermiculation; head black with white freckling. p. 29

2. GREAT TINAMOU, *Tinamus major*
2E *T. m. peruvianus*—rufescent crown
2W *T. m. latifrons*—browner crown, somewhat crested
Inside humid forest in lowlands of east and northwest. Large; brown overall plumage. p. 30

3. WHITE-THROATED TINAMOU, *Tinamus guttatus*
Inside terra firme forest in lowlands of east. Small buffy-white spots on upperparts; smaller than Great Tinamou.
p. 30

Nothocercus Tinamous
Fairly large, scarce tinamous found locally on ground inside montane forests. Heard far more often than seen.

4. HIGHLAND TINAMOU, *Nothocercus bonapartei*
Inside subtropical forest on e. slope. Mainly rufescent brown with contrasting blackish crown; throat tawny-buff. p. 31

5. TAWNY-BREASTED TINAMOU, *Nothocercus julius*
Inside temperate forest on e. slope and in northwest. Replaces Highland Tinamou at higher elevations; similar but crown rufescent, throat pure white. p. 31

Crypturellus Tinamous
Small to midsized tinamous found widely on ground in most forested and wooded lowland habitats; most diverse in east. Mainly because of small size, *Crypturellus* are exceptionally difficult to see, often calling close by but remaining invisible. They are best identified by distinctive vocalizations. When actually seen, check especially for comparative size, overall coloration, presence or not of barring above, and breast coloration.

6. CINEREOUS TINAMOU, *Crypturellus cinereus*
Fairly common inside humid forest in lowlands of east, favoring areas near water. Uniform sooty brown. p. 32

7. BERLEPSCH'S TINAMOU, *Crypturellus berlepschi*
Inside humid forest in lowlands of northwest, mainly in n. Esmeraldas. Uniform sooty black. p. 32

8. LITTLE TINAMOU, *Crypturellus soui*
Common and widespread in forest borders, secondary woodland, and even plantations in lowlands and foothills of east and west. Small, richly colored, with blackish crown. p. 32

9. TATAUPA TINAMOU, *Crypturellus tataupa*
Secondary woodland and borders in Zumba area of extreme southeast. Small with gray underparts and purplish red legs and base of bill. p. 35

10. BROWN TINAMOU, *Crypturellus obsoletus*
Rare and local inside forest in foothills along e. slope. Resembles smaller Little Tinamou, but throat gray and shows some dusky flank barring. p. 33

11. UNDULATED TINAMOU, *Crypturellus undulatus*
Common in várzea and riparian forest, forest borders, and adjacent clearings in lowlands of east. Uniform dull brown above, grayish below with white throat. Relatively easy to see (for a tinamou). p. 33

12. BARTLETT'S TINAMOU, *Crypturellus bartletti*
Scarce and apparently local inside terra firme forest in lowlands of east. Barred upperparts, dark brownish gray upper back and breast. p. 34

13. VARIEGATED TINAMOU, *Crypturellus variegatus*
Inside terra firme forest in lowlands of east. A brightly colored tinamou with conspicuously barred upperparts, rich rufous upper back and breast. p. 33

14. PALE-BROWED TINAMOU, *Crypturellus transfasciatus*
Inside deciduous forest and woodland in lowlands (mainly) and lower subtropics of southwest (north to Manabí and Los Ríos). Whitish brow, pale grayish underparts. ♀ depicted; ♂ shows less barring on back and rump. p. 34

Nothoprocta Tinamous
Basically brown tinamous with decurved bills and complex, variegated pattern on upperparts (barring, streaking, and vermiculations). Both are montane species and inhabit more open, grassier terrain than other Ecuadorian tinamous.

15. ANDEAN TINAMOU, *Nothoprocta pentlandii*
Deciduous scrub and fields in highlands of south, mainly in Loja. Gray breast with large buff spots. p. 35

16. CURVE-BILLED TINAMOU, *Nothoprocta curvirostris*
Shrubby paramo and pastures just below treeline. Complex variegated pattern with tawny-buff lower underparts; rufous in wings shows especially in flight. p. 36

Plate 2 Albatrosses, Petrels, and Shearwaters

Phoebastria and *Thalassarche* Albatrosses

Very large, heavy-bodied seabirds with exceptionally long, narrow wings. Glide stiff-winged low over water, flapping very little if at all.

1. WAVED ALBATROSS, *Phoebastria irrorata*

Uncommon off sw. coast, with a few pairs nesting on Isla de la Plata (mainly breeds on Galápagos). Huge size; yellow bill. Golden buff tinge on hindneck, white foreneck contrasting with dark underparts (at close range can be seen to be finely barred).   p. 38

2. BLACK-BROWED ALBATROSS, *Thalassarche melanophris*

Accidental off sw. coast (breeds in subantarctic). Huge size; adults with orange-yellow bill, horn with black tip in immatures. Head, neck, and underparts snowy white; clean-cut black and white underwing pattern. Adults have prominent black eye patch. Juvenile has dark-tipped bill, dusky foreneck collar.   p. 38

3. SOUTHERN FULMAR, *Fulmarus glacialoides*

Accidental off sw. coast (breeds in Antarctic). Gull-like with heavy, mainly pink bill. White and pale gray, with conspicuous white patch in primaries. Glides much like a shearwater low over water, often attracted to boats.   p. 39

4. PINTADO PETREL, *Daption capense*

Very rare off sw. coast (breeds in Antarctic). Unmistakable, with boldly pied black and white pattern on upperside of wings. Glides shearwater-like, following boats for protracted periods.   p. 39

5. DARK-RUMPED PETREL, *Pterodroma phaeopygia*

Uncommon off sw. coast (breeding on Galápagos). White forecrown contrasts with blackish hood; underwing white with black stripe on leading edge and back onto coverts. Flight typically very fast, arching high.   p. 39

Procellaria Petrels

Large, dark petrels with short heavy bills, resembling shearwaters but stockier; they have similar gliding flight.

6. WHITE-CHINNED PETREL, *Procellaria aequinoctialis*

Accidental off sw. coast (breeds in subantarctic). Stout bill greenish ivory, lacking dark tip; larger than Parkinson's.
                                          p. 40

7. PARKINSON'S PETREL, *Procellaria parkinsoni*

Regular off sw. coast, sometimes in fairly large numbers (breeds off New Zealand). Stout bill greenish ivory with dark tip; lacks silvery underwing of smaller and slenderer Sooty Shearwater.   p. 40

Puffinus Shearwaters

Pelagic birds that come to land only to breed and are rarely seen from shore; none nests in mainland Ecuador waters. Coloration and even pattern usually subdued, with species identification often difficult; additional species may occur in Ecuadorian waters. Wings fairly long and narrow; flight typically low over water, a few flaps followed by often long glides, sometimes banking from side to side. Given sufficient wind, shearwaters may glide effortlessly for long periods, not flapping at all.

8. PINK-FOOTED SHEARWATER, *Puffinus creatopus*

Regular off sw. coast (breeds off Chile). Large, heavy-set shearwater with mainly white underparts; bill pinkish with dark tip.   p. 40

9. BULLER'S SHEARWATER, *Puffinus bulleri*

Accidental off sw. coast (breeds off New Zealand). Dark cap contrasting with white underparts, all-black bill, sometimes striking dark M-pattern across upperwing, contrasting gray rump.   p. 41

10. SOOTY SHEARWATER, *Puffinus griseus*

Ecuador's most frequently seen shearwater, sometimes visible even from shore (breeds in subantarctic). Entirely sooty with silvery on underwing; slender, all-black bill.   p. 41

11. AUDUBON'S SHEARWATER, *Puffinus lherminieri*

Casual off coast (breeds on tropical islands, including Galápagos). A small shearwater, dark above and pure white below. Has distinctive "sloppy" flight, a series of shallow flaps followed by short glide.   p. 41

Plate 3 Storm-Petrels; Skuas and Jaegers

Oceanites and *Oceanodroma* Storm-Petrels

Relatively small, vaguely swallow-like seabirds that flutter or swoop over ocean's surface; under low wind conditions they sometimes swim. Some species are attracted to boats. Most species seem scarce, but this may more reflect a lack of pelagic field work than actual rarity. Identification is often difficult, and other unrecorded species are also possible in Ecuadorian waters. The two *Oceanites* have longer legs but are otherwise similar to *Oceanodroma*.

1. WILSON'S STORM-PETREL, *Oceanites oceanicus*
Rare off sw. coast (breeds in Antarctic). Rounded white rump patch extends around to lower flanks; rather long legs protrude beyond squared tail. Fluttery flight, often pattering on surface with dangled legs (sometimes showing yellow in foot webbing). p. 42

2. WHITE-VENTED STORM-PETREL, *Oceanites gracilis*
Rare off sw. coast, mainly quite close to shore (breeding grounds unknown). Appearance and behavior similar to larger Wilson's. Differs in its more extensive white on midbelly (often hard to see), pale suffusion on underwing. p. 42

3. LEAST STORM-PETREL, *Oceanodroma microsoma*
Uncommon off coast during northern winter (breeds off Baja California). The smallest storm-petrel. Essentially all dark, with no white rump; fairly short wedge-shaped or rounded tail. Flight quite fast and direct, with rather deep wingstrokes. p. 43

4. WEDGE-RUMPED STORM-PETREL, *Oceanodroma tethys*
Fairly common off coast (breeds on Galápagos). Extensive white area on rump and uppertail-coverts (can appear "white-tailed"). Typical flight fast and steady. p. 43

5. BAND-RUMPED STORM-PETREL, *Oceanodroma castro*
Casual well off sw. coast (breeds on tropical islands, including Galápagos). White rump patch; short legs do not protrude beyond notched tail. Erratic bounding flight with deep wingstrokes. p. 44

6. ASHY STORM-PETREL, *Oceanodroma homochroa*
Accidental off sw. coast (breeds off California). Ashy brown with no white rump; forked tail; pale suffusion on underwing. p. 45

7. BLACK STORM-PETREL, *Oceanodroma melania*
Apparently regular off coast (breeds off Baja California). A large, brownish black storm-petrel with deeply forked tail. Favors warm water. Flight bounding and erratic, often shifting directions. p. 44

8. MARKHAM'S STORM-PETREL, *Oceanodroma markhami*
Scarce off sw. coast (apparently breeds on islands off Peru). Very similar to Black Storm-Petrel but slightly browner with more prominent pale carpal bar; tail even more deeply forked. Favors cool water. Flight bounding and erratic, often shifting directions. p. 44

9. HORNBY'S STORM-PETREL, *Oceanodroma hornbyi*
Scarce off sw. coast (apparently breeds on islands off Peru). Distinctive, with dark cap and chest band contrasting with white underparts and forehead. p. 45

10. WHITE-FACED STORM-PETREL, *Pelagodroma marina*
Casual far off coast. Distinctive, with white face and underparts with gray patch from eye onto ear-coverts, gray back and rump. p. 43

Catharacta Skuas

Large, bull-necked seabirds with strongly hooked bills, extremely rare in Ecuadorian waters.

11. SOUTH POLAR SKUA, *Catharacta maccormicki*
Accidental visitant to sw. coast (breeds in Antarctic). Variable. Morphs are typically either pale "chamois" color or dark blackish brown; usually shows conspicuous pale nape patch, always lacks Chilean's dark crown. p. 156

12. CHILEAN SKUA, *Catharacta chilensis*
Accidental visitant to sw. coast (breeds off Chile and Argentina). Rather bright cinnamon underparts contrast with dark cap. p. 156

Stercorarius Jaegers

Confusing trio of pelagic birds that resemble falcons and often chase other birds, forcing them to regurgitate food. See text for details on identification, and be aware that certain individuals simply cannot be assigned to species.

13. LONG-TAILED JAEGER, *Stercorarius longicaudus*
Accidental off sw. coast (breeds in Arctic). Nonbreeding adult and juvenile shown. Relatively long and slender wings, almost tern-like in shape. Adults with long central tail feathers easy, but streamers often broken off or molted. In flight at all ages shows only very small white wing-flash, contrast between pale upperwing-coverts and dark flight feathers. Juvenile usually shows solid dark chest. p. 158

14. PARASITIC JAEGER, *Stercorarius parasiticus*
Regular off coast (breeds in Arctic). Shown are light-morph adult in breeding plumage, dark-morph adult in nonbreeding plumage, and light-morph juvenile. Intermediate in size and bulk between larger Pomarine and smaller Long-tailed Jaegers. Adults have fairly long straight central tail feathers (mainly evident in breeding plumage) and quite prominent white wing-flash. Juvenile variable but usually showing buffyish head, especially on nape. p. 157

15. POMARINE JAEGER, *Stercorarius pomarinus*
Regular off coast (breeds in Arctic), seemingly the most numerous jaeger in Ecuadorian waters. Shown are light-morph adults in breeding and nonbreeding plumages and light-morph juvenile. Compared to other jaegers, larger and heavier chested with broad wings, but cf. even larger and stockier skuas. White wing-flash prominent. Breeding adults have quite long, twisted, and rounded central tail feathers; nonbreeders are more barred below. Juveniles have two-toned bill (bill usually all dark in Parasitic), barred underparts and rump. p. 156

Plate 4 Boobies, Pelicans, Cormorants and Shags, Frigatebirds, Etc.

1. RED-BILLED TROPICBIRD, *Phaethon aethereus*
Breeds on cliffs of Isla de la Plata, otherwise a rare and highly pelagic visitant to Ecuadorian seas. Beautiful, mainly white, adults with very long tail streamers and heavy red bill, immatures with yellower bill and coarser black barring on mantle. Flight strong and graceful, usually well above surface except when plunge-diving for prey, most often flying fish.   p. 45

Sula Boobies
Large "streamlined" seabirds with pointed bills, long pointed wings, and wedge-shaped tails that fly strongly and are often highly pelagic. Gregarious, particularly at their nesting colonies. Although they swim, boobies more often rest ashore or at least out of water. Adults of most species are mainly white, often with brown or black on wings; young birds are browner and less patterned. Food obtained by plunge-diving, often from considerable heights and at an angle.

2. BLUE-FOOTED BOOBY, *Sula nebouxii*
Fairly common and widespread along coast, especially where rocky, breeding locally on islands; does not range very far offshore. Bright blue feet and legs in adults (grayer in younger birds), fine brown streaking on head and hindneck (looks solid at a distance), white patches on upper back and rump. Immature more solidly brown on head and neck.   p. 47

3. BROWN BOOBY, *Sula leucogaster*
Very rare off n. coast. Solidly brown with contrasting white breast and belly; bill and feet yellowish. Immature similarly patterned, breast and belly not so pure white, bill and legs dusky.   p. 48

4. NAZCA BOOBY, *Sula granti*
Nests in large numbers on Isla de la Plata, otherwise pelagic. Adult snowy white with black flight feathers and tail; contrasting black mask, orange bill. Immature brownish except for white breast and belly and across hindneck; yellowish bill.   p. 48

5. PERUVIAN BOOBY, *Sula variegata*
Occasional wanderer to sw. coastal waters from Peru. White head, neck, and underparts; mantle brown without obvious white patches on hindneck and rump; bill and legs bluish gray.   p. 47

6. RED-FOOTED BOOBY, *Sula sula*
Breeds in small numbers on Isla de la Plata, otherwise pelagic. Bright red feet and legs; pale blue bill, red facial skin. Two morphs, brown birds decidedly commoner in Ecuador.
    p. 48

Pelecanus Pelicans
Unmistakable large seabirds with short legs, unique long bills whose lower mandible is expanded into a flexible pouch. Gregarious, flying strongly and soaring high as well as gliding low over water, often in lines or V formations. Food obtained mainly by plunge-diving, less often by dipping bill while swimming. Nonbreeding adults of both species lose black on nape.

7. BROWN PELICAN, *Pelecanus occidentalis*
Common and well known along coast. Large; mostly brown, gray, and black, adults with white on head, immatures browner above and more extensively white below.   p. 50

8. PERUVIAN PELICAN, *Pelecanus thagus*
Small numbers with previous species along sw. coast; apparently increasing. Huge size (notably larger even than Brown Pelican), extensive white on upperwing-coverts (even in brown immatures).   p. 51

Phalacrocorax Cormorants and Shags
Dark or mainly dark waterbirds with slender, hooked bills, notable for having feathers that are not fully waterproof; as a result often seen drying themselves with wings outstretched. Swim readily and obtain food by diving.

9. NEOTROPIC CORMORANT, *Phalacrocorax brasilianus*
Widespread near water, both fresh and salt; most numerous in west. Adult all blackish; immature more brownish, with white on underparts. The only cormorant normally found in Ecuador.   p. 49

10. GUANAY SHAG, *Phalacrocorax bougainvillii*
Occasional wanderer to sw. coastal waters from Peru. Mostly black with clean-cut white underparts, bare red skin around eye; longer and thinner neck than Neotropic, very evident in flight.   p. 49

11. ANHINGA, *Anhinga anhinga*
Widespread along rivers and on lakes in lowlands. Long pointed bill, very long and thin neck, large silvery white area on wing-coverts, long fan-shaped tail. ♂ mainly black, ♀ with head, neck and chest contrastingly pale brown. Often soars. Swims low in water, sometimes only head and neck protruding.   p. 50

12. HUMBOLDT PENGUIN, *Spheniscus humboldti*
Casual vagrant to sw. coast from Peru, usually just dead birds washed up on beach. Unmistakable; the only penguin ever recorded in mainland Ecuador. Black and white pattern, bare pink skin on face. Immature browner with grayish cheeks.   p. 37

Fregata Frigatebirds
Very large, unmistakable seabirds most numerous along immediate coast though solitary birds are sometimes seen far out to sea. Soar effortlessly on "crooked" wings, often ascending to great heights before swooping down to obtain food, either snatching a morsel from water's surface or chasing another bird and forcing it to disgorge. Complex plumage variation; the two species are difficult to distinguish, but only Magnificent normally occurs in mainland Ecuadorian waters.

13. MAGNIFICENT FRIGATEBIRD, *Fregata magnificens*
Widespread and conspicuous along coast, soaring birds sometimes wandering a bit inland. Very long and pointed wings, long and deeply forked tail, powerful hooked bill. Adult ♂ all black with inflatable red throat pouch, subadult ♂ retains some white on belly, ♀ with white breast and sides of neck, immature with head and breast white, juvenile with dark spurs on sides of chest.   p. 46

14. GREAT FRIGATEBIRD, *Fregata minor*
Casual vagrant to sw. coast. Resembles much more numerous Magnificent. Adult ♂ virtually identical but with red legs, more obvious brown band on upperwing-coverts. Adult ♀ with pale gray throat. Subadult has white area on belly. Juvenile has buffy head with variable black blotching on sides.   p. 46

Plate 5 Smaller Herons and Ibises; Spoonbill

Butorides Herons

Small, stocky herons, one (Green) very rare, which unlike most other members of family are generally solitary, separating out to feed individually along water's edge, flushing with a distinctive complaining "kyow!" call.

1. GREEN HERON, *Butorides virescens*
Rare boreal migrant to north. Adult with sides of neck and breast rich vinous-chestnut. Immature indistinguishable from immature Striated Heron.   p. 66

2. STRIATED HERON, *Butorides striatus*
Widespread along edge of ponds, lakes, and rivers (also mangroves and marshy areas), mainly in lowlands but some occur locally in central valley. A small, chunky heron with black crown and shaggy crest; adult has gray sides of neck and breast, immature streaked below.   p. 66

3. CAPPED HERON, *Pilherodius pileatus*
Uncommon along rivers and in swampy forest and borders in lowlands of east. Unmistakable, with bright blue bill and facial area, black cap, and pale buff head and underparts.
                                                    p. 67

4. ZIGZAG HERON, *Zebrilus undulatus*
Local and inconspicuous in várzea forest along edge of sluggish streams and ponds in lowlands of east. Small. Adult dark with dense wavy barring; juvenile more rufescent.   p. 61

Ixobrychus Bitterns

Very small herons found locally in marshes and around ponds, one (Stripe-backed) very rare in Ecuador. Both are skulking.

5. LEAST BITTERN, *Ixobrychus exilis*
Very local in freshwater marshes and around ponds in lowlands of northeast (Napo) and southwest (Manabí and El Oro). Black crown and back (browner in ♀ ♀); rufous to pale buff sides of head and neck, and upper back; contrasting buff wing-coverts (especially conspicuous in flight).   p. 60

6. STRIPE-BACKED BITTERN, *Ixobrychus involucris*
Accidental vagrant to ponds in lowlands of northeast. Resembles Least Bittern but larger, paler, and more grayish buff with back conspicuously striped.   p. 61

Eudocimus Ibises

Beautiful ibises with spectacular plumage, one (Scarlet) very rare in Ecuador.

7. WHITE IBIS, *Eudocimus albus*
Locally common (and gregarious) along coast, especially in mangroves but a few also inland to freshwater marshes. Decurved reddish bill. Unmistakable adult pure white, with black wingtips prominent in flight. Juvenile browner, with contrasting white rump conspicuous in flight.   p. 70

8. SCARLET IBIS, *Eudocimus ruber*
Casual visitant to shores of lakes and rivers in lowlands of northeast. An unmistakable bright scarlet version of White Ibis, black wingtips as in that species. Juvenile like juvenile White Ibis, but most birds how a few pink or red feathers, especially on rump.   p. 71

9. BARE-FACED IBIS, *Phimosus infuscatus*
Very rare visitant to rivers (and probably lakes?) in lowlands of northeast. A dark, relatively short-legged ibis with bare red face, reddish bill (duller in juveniles).   p. 70

10. GLOSSY IBIS, *Plegadis falcinellus*
Casual vagrant to marshy areas in lowlands of southwest. A dark, long-legged ibis with blackish bill. Adult mainly bronzy chestnut, juvenile more blackish.   p. 71

11. GREEN IBIS, *Mesembrinibis cayennensis*
Swampy forest and forested margins of ponds and rivers in lowlands of east. A chunky, dark, short-legged ibis with characteristic stiff, jerky flight. Dark bronzy green with iridescent green in ruffled crest.   p. 70

12. BLACK-FACED IBIS, *Theristicus melanopis*
Rare and very local around paramo lakes in highlands of north, often foraging on nearby grasslands. A large ibis, unmistakable with buff head and neck, gray upperparts, salmon pink legs. Juvenile duller with streaked head, neck, and underparts.   p. 69

13. ROSEATE SPOONBILL, *Ajaia ajaja*
Local along coast in southwest (especially in mangroves), a few also along rivers in lowlands of northeast. Unmistakable, with broad spatulate bill. Adult with much bright pink and scarlet, juvenile whiter.   p. 71

Plate 6 Herons and Egrets, Limpkin, and Trumpeter

Egretta Egrets and Herons

Atractive, midsized herons, rather diverse in plumage. Feed by wading in water, often moving about actively. Conspicuous and gregarious; they are especially numerous in marshy and swampy terrain on or near Guayas and El Oro coasts.

1. SNOWY EGRET, *Egretta thula*

Widespread in marshes, mangroves, along rivers, etc.; most numerous near sw. coast. A relatively small, slender, all-white heron with golden yellow feet, slim black bill, yellow lores. Younger birds have yellow up rearpart of dark legs.   p. 64

2. LITTLE BLUE HERON, *Egretta caerulea*

Common in marshes, mangroves, and around ponds near sw. coast; less numerous elsewhere in lowlands (also in east). Bicolored bill; yellowish olive legs. Adult dark and unpatterned, entirely slaty blue and rich vinaceous. Immature white, resembling Snowy Egret except for soft-part differences. Subadult "piebald," white with dark patches coming in.   p. 64

3. TRICOLORED HERON, *Egretta tricolor*

Marshes and mangroves along sw. coast; rare elsewhere. Dark and slender-necked with long bill and contrasting white belly, white rump evident in flight. Immatures more rufescent on foreneck.   p. 65

4. AGAMI HERON, *Agamia agami*

Rare and inconspicuous along forested streams, around oxbow lakes, and in swampy forest in lowlands of east. Extremely long rapier-like bill, long slender neck. Richly colored in chestnut and oily green, with beautiful silvery filigreed pattern on foreneck. Immature browner and duller.   p. 67

5. BOAT-BILLED HERON, *Cochlearius cochlearius*

Scarce and local along forested rivers and around oxbow lakes in lowlands of east. Unmistakable broad shovel-like bill; pale gray back, dark belly. Immature duller and browner, but already with loose floppy crest and unique bill. Mainly nocturnal, roosting by day in trees next to water, often in groups.   p. 69

6. BLACK-CROWNED NIGHT-HERON, *Nycticorax nycticorax*

Local in marshes, mangroves, and around ponds and lakes in lowlands, also a few in n. highlands. Stocky and thick-necked; black crown and back, gray wings, white underparts. Immature (flying) brown with whitish streaking and spotting (spots, especially above, larger than in next species). Rather strictly nocturnal.   p. 68

7. YELLOW-CROWNED NIGHT-HERON, *Nyctanassa violacea*

Fairly common along. sw. coast, especially in mangroves. Stocky, with notably stout, blunt bill. Adult gray with distinctive black-and-white patterned head. Immature (flying) brownish slaty and streaked with whitish streaking and spotting (dorsal spots finer than in previous species). Mainly nocturnal, though feeds by day more than Black-crowned.   p. 68

8. CATTLE EGRET, *Bubulcus ibis*

Common and nearly ubiquitous in open areas of west, smaller numbers and more local in east. Forages in grassy areas and along roadsides, often accompanying domestic animals and at times far from water, but regularly roosting with other herons. A small, "heavy-jowled" egret with short thick yellow bill (brighter in breeding season). Breeding adults have rich buff on crown, foreneck, and back.   p. 65

9. LIMPKIN, *Aramus guarauna*

Local in marshes and rice fields in sw. lowlands, also around a few lakes in ne. lowlands. Very large with superficially ibis-like decurved bill. Brown with profusely white-streaked foreparts. Eats snails.   p. 131

10. GRAY-WINGED TRUMPETER, *Psophia crepitans*

Mainly terrestrial inside terra firme forest in lowlands of east; confined to more remote areas. Large, with unmistakable hunched posture. Mainly velvety black with loosely held pale ashy gray flight feathers covering back. Gregarious. p. 132

Plate 7 Larger Herons, Storks, Flamingo, and Screamer

Ardea Herons and Egrets
Large, long-necked, long-legged herons that stand on shorelines or wade into shallow water after prey. The two herons are relatively solitary, but where the egret is numerous it sometimes gathers in large flocks.

1. GREAT BLUE HERON, *Ardea herodias*
Casual vagrant to ponds, lakeshores, and marshes. Subadult depicted; adults have all-yellow bill, cleaner-cut plumage. Regardless of plumage stage, rufous thighs and rufous on bend of wing diagnostic. Younger Cocoi Herons can be equally gray on neck. p. 63

2. COCOI HERON, *Ardea cocoi*
Widespread in lowlands of east and west; in east mainly along major rivers, in west most numerous coastally. Adult has striking white neck contrasting sharply with entirely black crown and lower underparts. Younger birds dingier and grayer but already show white thighs. p. 63

3. GREAT EGRET, *Ardea alba*
Widespread in marshes, along rivers, etc.; most numerous in sw. lowlands especially near coast. Large and long-necked, pure white plumage, yellow bill, black legs. Cf. other (smaller) egrets on Plate 6. p. 64

Mycteria and *Jabiru* Storks
Very large wading birds found in marshy areas, both species with featherless heads, heavy bills.

4. WOOD STORK, *Mycteria americana*
Generally uncommon in open marshy areas and around lakes in lowlands, most numerous locally along sw. coast. Flying birds can appear almost anywhere, even crossing Andes. Large and ungainly looking, but graceful in flight when it often soars high. Mainly white with black flight feathers; unfeathered head and neck grayish; heavy decurved bill. Juvenile duskier. Gregarious, feeding in shallow water, roosting in trees. p. 72

5. JABIRU, *Jabiru mycteria*
Casual wanderer to lowlands of northeast. Huge. Plumage entirely white (including all of wings); unfeathered black head and neck; massive upswept bill. Adults have red on lower neck; duskier in younger birds. Generally solitary or in pairs. p. 72

Tigrisoma Tiger-Herons
Relatively inconspicuous, solitary herons with heavy bodies, thick necks, and subtly intricate plumage patterns. Young birds with "tiger-like" boldly banded pattern are responsible for group name. Though more reclusive than many other herons, they sometimes feed in the open as well.

6. RUFESCENT TIGER-HERON, *Tigrisoma lineatum*
Uncommon around oxbow lakes and in swampy forest in lowlands of east; now very rare in west. Adult with rich rufous head and neck. Immature coarsely banded buff and black, gradually becoming darker and less patterned with age. p. 62

7. FASCIATED TIGER-HERON, *Tigrisoma fasciatum*
Scarce along rocky streams, and rivers in foothills and subtropics on both slopes, often standing on boulders out in the torrent. Adult looks slaty blackish (but actually is barred and vermiculated with white). Immature's plumages initially duplicate those of Rufescent, but subadults start to look grayer. Bill slightly shorter and stouter. p. 62

8. PINNATED BITTERN, *Botaurus pinnatus*
Rare and local in freshwater marshes and wet grassy areas in lowlands of southwest; usually skulking. Buff and whitish with intricate dark barred and vermiculated pattern, some streaking on underparts. Never shows boldly banded pattern of young tiger-herons. p. 60

9. CHILEAN FLAMINGO, *Phoenicopterus chilensis*
Scarce and local in lagoons and on extensive mudflats along sw. coast. Unmistakable with pink overall coloration, extremely long legs, etc.; the only flamingo in mainland Ecuador. Immatures whiter but still show much pink and red, especially in flight. p. 59

10. HORNED SCREAMER, *Anhima cornuta*
Scarce and local in marshes, and around more remote lakes and rivers in lowlands; in west now only at Manglares-Churute. Nearly unmistakable, a very large and heavy gooselike bird; mostly blackish with white on crown and foreneck. The "horn" is often surprisingly hard to see in the field. p. 51

Plate 8 Grebes and Ducks

1. LEAST GREBE, *Tachybaptus dominicus*
Locally and erratically common on freshwater ponds in low-lands of west; only a few records from east. Small size, thin black bill, conspicuous yellow eye, overall gray plumage. Nonbreeders paler with whitish throat.   p. 36

2. PIED-BILLED GREBE, *Podilymbus podiceps*
Locally common on freshwater ponds in lowlands of west, also on a few lakes in n. highlands; occasional wanderer to salt water. Stout pale bill (with conspicuous dark ring when breeding), overall brownish plumage.   p. 36

3. SILVERY GREBE, *Podiceps occipitalis*
Now very local on a few deep lakes in highlands and paramo, mainly in north. Thin blackish bill, snowy white underparts. Gray plumes on ear-coverts when breeding.   p. 37

Dendrocygna Whistling-Ducks
Large, gangly ducks with long necks and legs that stand with upright posture, swim relatively little.

4. FULVOUS WHISTLING-DUCK, *Dendrocygna bicolor*
Locally common in freshwater marshes, lakes, and rice fields in lowlands of west. Mainly buffy-fulvous, with creamy flank plumes. In flight wings dark, ring on uppertail-coverts white.   p. 52

5. BLACK-BELLIED WHISTLING-DUCK, *Dendrocygna autumnalis*
Locally common in freshwater marshes, lakes, and rice fields in lowlands of west, a few wanderers to east. Conspicuous rosy red bill and legs (gray in juveniles), grayish face, black belly. In flight wings show conspicuous white stripe.   p. 52

Anas Teals and Pintails
"Typical" ducks that frequent freshwater ponds and marshes nearly throughout Ecuador, though numbers of most species are now much diminished because of drainage and excessive disturbance. They fly strongly, and many species have distinctive patterns on upperwings (see text).

6. ANDEAN TEAL, *Anas andium*
Locally fairly common on lakes and ponds in paramo. Small size, dark bill, dusky head.   p. 55

7. WHITE-CHEEKED PINTAIL, *Anas bahamensis*
Locally fairly common on saltwater lagoons and ponds, a few also on adjacent freshwater lakes. Red on bill (less in ♀♀), conspicuous white cheeks and throat, long pointed tail.   p. 55

8. YELLOW-BILLED PINTAIL, *Anas georgica*
Lakes and ponds in paramo, also very locally in central valley. Yellow bill, overall buffy-brown plumage, long pointed tail.   p. 56

9. NORTHERN SHOVELER, *Anas clypeata*
Accidental vagrant to coastal ponds. Large spatulate bill. Breeding ♂ with green head, etc.   p. 57

10. BLUE-WINGED TEAL, *Anas discors*
Locally common boreal migrant to freshwater ponds and marshes in lowlands of west, elsewhere in much smaller numbers. Small size, pale blue patch on wing-coverts prominent in flight. Breeding ♂ with unique white crescent on foreface.   p. 56

11. CINNAMON TEAL, *Anas cyanoptera*
No recent reports; a resident race formerly occurred around lakes in n. highlands, and boreal migrants also recorded. Small size, pale blue patch on wing-coverts (as in Blue-winged Teal) prominent in flight, larger bill than in Blue-winged. ♂ with unmistakable mainly chestnut plumage; ♀ very similar to ♀ Blue-winged Teal (see text).   p. 57

12. LESSER SCAUP, *Aythya affinis*
Accidental vagrant to lakes and ponds in n. highlands; no recent reports. Dives in fairly deep water. ♂ with dark foreparts, white and pale grayish body, ♀ brown with contrasting white patch at base of bill. In flight shows white wingstripe.   p. 58

13. SOUTHERN POCHARD, *Netta erythrophthalma*
Now very rare on freshwater lakes, ponds, and marshes in lowlands of southwest. ♂ all dark with little pattern, ♀ with prominent white facial pattern. In flight shows white wingstripe.   p. 57

14. ANDEAN RUDDY-DUCK, *Oxyura ferruginea*
Local on deeper freshwater lakes in highlands and paramo, often swimming out in open water. Long stiff tail sometimes held cocked out of water. Breeding ♂ with unmistakable bright blue bill, black head, and chestnut body. Nonbreeding ♂♂ duller; they and ♀♀ look very dark and unpatterned.   p. 58

15. MASKED DUCK, *Nomonyx dominicus*
Very local and secretive on shallow overgrown lakes and ponds with much aquatic vegetation in lowlands of west, a few wanderers in east. Long stiff tail usually not raised. Breeding ♂ with bright blue bill, black foreface, and chestnut body with much black spotting. ♀ has two obvious dark facial stripes; nonbreeding ♂ much like ♀ but less cinnamon-tinged.   p. 59

16. TORRENT DUCK, *Merganetta armata*
Widespread (but numerous only locally) along swift-flowing, rocky rivers and streams from foothills up into paramo. Conspicuous red bill and legs, small head and slender neck, streaked upperparts. ♂ has mainly white face and underparts, ♀ rufous below.   p. 54

17. MUSCOVY DUCK, *Cairina moschata*
Local around forest-fringed freshwater ponds and lakes in more remote lowlands of east, also a few persisting in southwest. Very large, plumage mainly dark glossy greenish. ♂ larger than ♀, has large white patch in wing, caruncles on bill.   p. 53

18. ORINOCO GOOSE, *Neochen jubata*
Very local on sandbars along larger rivers in lowlands of east, now mainly along Río Pastaza. Unmistakable: very large, with head and neck buffy whitish, much chestnut in body. Conspicuous, standing and walking about in the open.   p. 53

19. COMB DUCK, *Sarkidiornis melanotos*
Rare and local along rivers and in marshes and ponds in lowlands of southwest, mainly s. Loja; seems prone to wandering. Large (♂ considerably bigger); mainly white head, neck, and underparts. Adult ♂ has large "comb" on upper bill. In flight wings all dark.   p. 54

Plate 9 American Vultures and Osprey

1. ANDEAN CONDOR, *Vultur gryphus*

Now local and scarce in open highlands, especially in remote paramo regions. Soars steadily, often high, on flat out-stretched wings, usually with primaries widely spread; not often seen perched. Generally solitary; several may gather at a carcass. Huge size renders the condor unmistakable. Adults show conspicuous and extensive white on upper wing and a prominent white ruff; ♂♂ have bare skin on head red, black-ish in ♀♀. ♂ has large upstanding comb and dewlap. Younger birds browner, without ruff or white on wing.

p. 73

2. KING VULTURE, *Sarcoramphus papa*

More remote lowlands, especially where forest remains extensive. Soars on flat wings, frequently high above ground, sometimes with other vultures. Not often seen perched, then usually inside forest. Very large. Adult unmistakable, with white body and multicolored bare skin on head and neck; in flight note boldly contrasting black flight feathers. Younger birds more blackish, gradually acquiring white; cf. much smaller but similarly shaped Black Vulture.

p. 74

Cathartes Vultures

Very large vultures that soar on long, narrow wings held characteristically uptilted (especially in Turkey Vulture). Note adults' distinctive bare head colors.

3. GREATER YELLOW-HEADED VULTURE, *Cathartes melambrotus*

Widespread in lowland forest of east. Very large; mainly yellow head, deep black plumage. In flight note contrastingly darker inner primaries, steadier flight on flatter wings than in Turkey Vulture.

p. 75

4. TURKEY VULTURE, *Cathartes aura*

4E *C. a. ruficollis*—yellowish nape band
4W *C. a. jota*—solid reddish head

Numerous and widespread in lowlands of west, much less so in lowlands of east; local in open areas in highlands. Large, with bare skin on head mainly or entirely red (blackish in young birds). Soaring birds tilt from side to side; underside of flight feathers uniform silvery gray. Some boreal migrants probably occur, but their numbers and range remain unclear because of close similarity to resident *jota*.

p. 75

5. BLACK VULTURE, *Coragyps atratus*

Omnipresent and locally abundant in lowlands, though less so in extensively forested areas; often along roads, and gathers in flocks at garbage dumps. Smaller numbers range into highlands, especially around towns. Smaller than other vultures; all black with grayish bare skin on head. Proportionately short tail and white wing patches at base of pri-maries evident in flight. Soars on flat wings, flapping more than *Cathartes*.

p. 74

6. OSPREY, *Pandion haliaetus*

Boreal migrant, with some present throughout year though there are more during northern winter months. Widespread near water (both fresh and salt); most numerous in lowlands. Hunts fish, often captured after hovering. Large, with white underparts and mainly white head, dark mask. In flight note "crooked" wings with blackish carpal patch.

p. 76

Plate 10 Diurnal Raptors I

1. SWALLOW-TAILED KITE, *Elanoides forficatus*
Widespread from lowlands up into subtropics, mainly in forested terrain but tolerates substantial habitat disturbance. Unmistakable, with long, deeply forked tail and snowy white head and underparts. Supremely graceful in flight, and more often seen flying than perched; regular in groups.   p. 78

Ictinia Kites
Predominantly gray kites with square tails; juveniles heavily streaked. Most often seen in flight, sometimes high, regularly in groups; flight buoyant on long, pointed wings.

2. PLUMBEOUS KITE, *Ictinia plumbea*
Widespread in forested lowlands, more numerous in east. Rufous in primaries shows especially in flight; wings very long, in perched birds protruding beyond tail; tail shows narrow white banding from below. Juvenile streaked dusky below, has shorter wings.   p. 81

3. MISSISSIPPI KITE, *Ictinia mississippiensis*
Very rare (perhaps just overlooked) transient in east. Compared to much commoner Plumbeous, wings shorter (not protruding past tail) and tail shorter and showing no bands (in adults). Adult paler gray on head and underparts, with contrastingly pale inner flight feathers evident in flight. Juvenile's streaking below rufescent.   p. 82

4. WHITE-TAILED KITE, *Elanus leucurus*
Rare and local (but apparently increasing) in pastures and open areas in lowlands of north. Nearly unmistakable, with mainly white head, underparts, and tail, conspicuous black shoulders. Juvenile browner and more streaked above, washed buff below. Often hovers.   p. 79

Rostrhamus Kites
Chunky, mainly gray kites with exceptionally slender deeply hooked bills (used for prying open snail shells). Occasionally soar, sometimes high.

5. SNAIL KITE, *Rostrhamus sociabilis*
Around ponds, marshes, and rice fields in lowlands of west (where declining) and east (where local). Conspicuous white basal tail and tail-coverts in all plumages. ♂ plumbeous gray. ♀ with whitish forehead and superciliary, dusky and white-streaked underparts. Juvenile like ♀ but generally browner and buffier. Flies slowly on characteristically bowed wings low over water and fringing vegetation.   p. 79

6. SLENDER-BILLED KITE, *Rostrhamus hamatus*
Local in swampy forest and along streams in lowlands of east. Markedly short tail showing no white; wings broad. Cf. Slate-colored Hawk (Plate 12-6). Often reclusive.   p. 80

7. PEARL KITE, *Gampsonyx swainsonii*
Open and agricultural areas in more arid lowlands of southwest, and (locally) in northeast; often perches on wires. Small, falcon-like kite with pointed wings. Distinctive, with white collar and underparts, buff on face. Cf. American Kestrel (Plate 17-7).   p. 78

Harpagus Kites
Somewhat *Accipiter*-shaped kites with characteristic dark median throat stripe in all plumages; notched bill also often noticeable. Both species often perch tamely at forest edges, Double-toothed regularly following monkey troops.

8. DOUBLE-TOOTHED KITE, *Harpagus bidentatus*
  8W *H. b. fasciatus*—♂ essentially gray-barred below, ♀ more rufescent
  8E *H. b. bidentatus*—both sexes with uniform rufous underparts

Widespread in forest from lowlands up into subtropics. Most young birds prominently streaked below, in a few (age?) underparts essentially white with streaking much sparser. In flight note "puffy" white undertail-coverts, pale underwings contrasting with darker body.   p. 80

9. RUFOUS-THIGHED KITE, *Harpagus diodon*
Casual vagrant to forest in lowlands of east. Adult mostly gray with contrasting rufous thighs. Cf. Bicolored Hawk (Plate 15-4). Juvenile like juvenile Double-toothed but with thighs solid rufous.   p. 81

Plate 11 Diurnal Raptors II

1. HOOK-BILLED KITE, *Chondrohierax uncinatus*

Local in forested lowlands and subtropics. Plumages vary, but the small patch of yellowish skin in front of eye and heavy and deeply hooked bill always impart an odd visage. Most ♂♂ gray above and variably gray-barred below (cf. Gray Hawk, Plate 13-1), but a few are uniformly blackish to gray below. ♀♀ brown above with obvious rusty nuchal collar, below boldly rufous-barred. Younger birds typically white or buffyish below with some scattered light barring. In flight wings typically held forward with their base pinched in at rear; flight feathers usually boldly banded (cf. Roadside Hawk, Plate 13-2, often surprisingly similar).   p. 77

2. GRAY-HEADED KITE, *Leptodon cayanensis*

Humid forest in lowlands of west and east. Looks small-headed. Adult unique with pearly gray head. Younger birds more variable and difficult, but always with yellowish cere and unfeathered tarsus. Light morph with mainly white head and underparts, black crown patch (cf. Black-and-white Hawk-Eagle, Plate 14-6); scarcer dark morph with blackish brown head and streaking on underparts. Adult in flight readily known by contrasting black underwing-coverts, boldly banded flight feathers; younger birds more difficult (see text).   p. 76

3. CINEREOUS HARRIER, *Circus cinereus*

Scarce in paramo and higher grasslands. Obvious white rump in all plumages, seen mainly in low tilting flight with wings held in shallow dihedral. Not often seen perched, but then note effect of pale-outlined facial disks. Attractive ♂ pearly gray above and rufous-barred below. ♀ mainly brown, mottled and streaked paler; rufous barring below much as in ♂. Immature like ♀ but underparts streaked.   p. 82

Buteogallus Hawks

Large, solidly built raptors with notably long legs (shorter in Common Black-Hawk) but fairly short tails. All three Ecuadorian species are found mainly in lowlands and soar frequently on broad wings.

4. SAVANNA HAWK, *Buteogallus meridionalis*

Fairly common in open areas of southwest, perching conspicuously, often on ground. Adult nearly unmistakable, with body mainly tawny to rufescent (with subdued dusky barring) and mainly rufous wings (evident both at rest and in flight). Young birds resemble similarly aged Great Black-Hawks but show rufous on wings even at an early age.   p. 89

5. COMMON BLACK-HAWK, *Buteogallus anthracinus*

Local in mangroves along coast. Small for genus. Adult mostly dull slaty, often somewhat mottled; tail crossed by one white band, wings show buffyish patch at base of secondaries and inner primaries (most obvious in flight). Immature coarsely streaked below and with bold creamy brow, tail with several narrow whitish bands; usually best identified by habitat.   p. 89

6. GREAT BLACK-HAWK, *Buteogallus urubitinga*

Widespread though never numerous in forest and woodland in lowlands of west and east, in southwest ranging higher. Adult slaty black with conspicuous white basal half of tail. Immature coarsely streaked below with creamy brow and blackish malar, tail with several narrow whitish bands (more than in Common). Though often near water, rarely or never in mangroves.   p. 89

7. BLACK-COLLARED HAWK, *Busarellus nigricollis*

Scarce and local around lakes and rivers in lowlands of far northeast. Large, with distinctive whitish head, black collar on chest, generally bright rufous plumage. Generally perches low along water's edge, but also soars high.   p. 91

8. SOLITARY EAGLE, *Harpyhaliaetus solitarius*

Rare and local in montane forest, mainly on e. slope and in subtropics. Very large but with very short tail. Adult mostly plumbeous gray (Great Black-Hawk markedly blacker), tail crossed by one white band. Immature much like immature Great Black-Hawk aside from its much larger size. Usually seen in flight, soaring on very broad wings.   p. 90

Plate 12 Diurnal Raptors III

Leucopternis Hawks

Attractive raptors found primarily in humid lowland forests; most species uncommon and relatively inconspicuous. Three species soar frequently: White, Gray-backed, and Barred. All have gray (usually) or black at least on mantles, and many have brightly colored ceres. Note the positioning of each species' single white tail band.

1. WHITE HAWK, *Leucopternis albicollis*

Lowlands of east, favoring terra firme and hilly terrain near Andes. Large; mostly white with white fringing on black scapulars and wing-coverts; tail with terminal white band; cere gray. p. 87

2. GRAY-BACKED HAWK, *Leucopternis occidentalis*

Very local in humid and sometimes deciduous forest of west, especially in foothills and lower subtropics. Distinctive in range, where the only large *Leucopternis*. Gray-mantled with prominent streaking on crown and nape; tail mainly white with broad black subterminal band. p. 88

3. BLACK-FACED HAWK, *Leucopternis melanops*

Scarce in terra firme in lowlands of east. Fairly small. Striking orange-red cere and small black mask; tail crossed by median white band. p. 87

4. SEMIPLUMBEOUS HAWK, *Leucopternis semiplumbea*

Scarce in humid forest in lowlands of northwest. Fairly small. Striking orange cere; bicolored, with gray upperparts and white underparts. p. 86

5. PLUMBEOUS HAWK, *Leucopternis plumbea*

Rare in humid lowland and foothill forest in northwest. Fairly small. Striking orange cere, bright red eye; plumage uniform gray. p. 86

6. SLATE-COLORED HAWK, *Leucopternis schistacea*

Humid forest in lowlands of east, often near water. Striking orange-red cere, yellow eye; plumage uniform plumbeous gray, tail crossed by one median white band. Cf. Slender-billed Kite (Plate 10-6). p. 86

7. BARRED HAWK, *Leucopternis princeps*

Forest (sometimes even where patchy) in foothills and subtropics on both slopes. Very large. Usually seen soaring, often high, when contrast between black chest and pale lower underparts evident even at long distances; tail crossed by one median white band, conspicuous yellow cere. Barring often not prominent at a distance. Cf. similarly patterned but shorter-tailed Black-chested Buzzard-Eagle (Plate 14-7). p. 88

8. VARIABLE HAWK, *Buteo polyosoma*

Conspicuous and locally numerous in open and semiopen terrain from coastal deserts up into highlands. Formerly considered to represent two species, Red-backed Hawk (*B. polyosoma*) and Puna Hawk (*B. poecilochrous*), now treated as conspecific. Variable, but all adults have mainly white tail with black subterminal band. Typical ♂ all-gray above, white below; typical ♀ similar but with rufous patch on back. Rarer but very striking dark morph (both sexes) has mainly rufous underparts in addition to back; in some birds rufous below is confined to breast. Higher elevation birds more frequently are dark, often entirely slaty gray to blackish (aside from tail); these are the birds formerly known as Puna Hawk. Immatures variable but have tail more uniform and grayish (finely vermiculated), upperparts brown, underparts creamy whitish with some dark streaking. Other *Buteo* spp. are shown on Plate 13. p. 96

Plate 13 Diurnal Raptors IV

Buteo Hawks

Variable, sometimes confusing (especially in younger birds) group of compactly built, usually broad-winged raptors. One or more species is found in most forested and wooded areas, though generally not inside forest. Most soar habitually, often spreading tails broadly as they circle ever higher. Note the number, positioning, and color (gray or white) of tail bands. For Variable Hawk, see Plate 12-8.

1. GRAY HAWK, *Buteo nitidus*

Lowlands, especially in deciduous woodland and borders in west; scarce and local in east. Lovely adult distinctive, essentially pearly gray and generally barred; cere pale, iris dark. Immature with bold creamy buff brow and coarse breast streaking. p. 92

2. ROADSIDE HAWK, *Buteo magnirostris*

Common, widespread, and conspicuous from more humid lowlands up locally into subtropics; often in cutover terrain, frequently seen along roads and rivers (most numerous raptor in such situations). Adult mainly gray with orange cere and yellow iris; lower underparts with dull rufous barring. In flight rufous area in primaries diagnostic (but sometimes hard to discern against light); usually does not spread tail. Calls distinctive. p. 93

3. BROAD-WINGED HAWK, *Buteo platypterus*

Boreal migrant to forest, woodland, and borders, especially in subtropics. Adult brown above with dusky malar area; breast and sides broadly barred rufous. Immatures somewhat variable, but typically with boldly streaked underparts; also show creamy brow and dark malar. In flight note essentially unmarked whitish underwing, adult's single prominent white tail-band. Call distinctive. p. 94

4. SHORT-TAILED HAWK, *Buteo brachyurus*

Widespread, typically shaped *Buteo*, almost invariably seen only in soaring flight (very infrequently perched). Two morphs. Light morph more numerous: white below with contrastingly blackish head with "hooded" effect. Dark morph all blackish except for white forehead (usually hard to see). In flight note only narrowly banded tail (looks plain from a distance); light morph has entirely whitish underwing, in dark morph note contrast between dark coverts and white flight feathers. p. 94

5. WHITE-THROATED HAWK, *Buteo albigula*

Confusing, scarce hawk of highlands, like Short-tailed usually seen in soaring flight. Most resembles immature Broad-winged but has solid brown head (showing no brow or malar), adults with blotchier streaking confined to chest; in flight wings look somewhat narrower. p. 95

6. WHITE-RUMPED HAWK, *Buteo leucorrhous*

Uncommon in montane forest and woodland. A small, attractive *Buteo*, mainly black with staring yellow iris; rufous thighs diagnostic if seen, but white rump usually not visible. Easy in flight when striking white wing coverts contrast with blackish flight feathers. p. 93

7. SWAINSON'S HAWK, *Buteo swainsoni*

Very rare boreal migrant; usually seen only in flight. Variable in plumage, but note relatively long, narrow wings for a *Buteo*; sometimes flies with a slight dihedral, often shows whitish on rump. Typical light-morph adult distinctive, with white throat, contrasting dark brown chest. In flight whitish underwing-coverts contrast with darker flight feathers. Dark morph less numerous, essentially uniform sooty brown, with confusing intermediates also occurring (for all of these, best to identify by shape). For immatures, see text. p. 95

8. ZONE-TAILED HAWK, *Buteo albonotatus*

Widespread in lowlands (especially in west), but never numerous. Usually seen in flight (often quite low), with distinctive Turkey Vulture-like dihedral, relatively narrow wings and tail, and two-toned effect on underwing with paler flight feathers. Perched birds are more difficult: they look uniform slaty except for having several tail bands. Immature similar except for sparse white spotting below, variable in extent.

p. 96

Plate 14 Diurnal Raptors V

1. CRESTED EAGLE, *Morphnus guianensis*

Very rare in humid lowland and montane forest; now local and found almost entirely in remote areas. Very large, almost as big as Harpy but somewhat slighter overall, with proportionately longer tail; both have quite broad, rounded wings. Variable in plumage, but always shows a single-pointed crest (often laid back and not very prominent, however); iris usually amber, but cere and lores always blackish imparting vaguely "masked" look. Light morph has gray foreneck. Rare dark-morph adult has entirely blackish foreparts, profuse bold barring below. Most immatures resemble light-morph adult but are even paler on foreparts, almost whitish in some. Inconspicuous and rarely seen, usually remaining inside forest but occasionally perching at edge or circling low over canopy.   p. 97

2. HARPY EAGLE, *Harpia harpyja*

Very rare and now local in humid lowland forest (only marginally more "numerous" than Crested), now mainly in east. Huge, with massive legs and talons. All birds have bifurcated crest, often raised but sometimes just ruffled (even then distinctly lower in middle). Adult unmistakable, with bold black chest band contrasting with gray head. Juveniles difficult to separate from Cresteds of comparable age, but note their larger size (including heavier bill), crest shape, and lores only dusky (not distinctly black); even at an early age there is usually a shadow of adult's breast band and barred thighs. In flight note Harpy's black on underwing-coverts (uniformly pale in all Cresteds, regardless of age), but this is generally hard to see. Remarkably inconspicuous, usually remaining in cover but occasionally perching at edge; bold, often totally indifferent to one's presence.   p. 97

3. BLACK-AND-CHESTNUT EAGLE, *Oroaetus isidori*

Spectacular, scarce eagle of montane forest (at higher elevations than other forest eagles). Very large. Dark generally, usually appearing blackish with chestnut below not very apparent. Most often seen soaring, when whitish basal tail and primaries are conspicuous. Immature less distinctive, though nothing similar normally occurs with it; it already shows adult's pale "wing panels."   p. 100

Spizaetus Hawk-Eagles

Pair of rather dissimilar, large eagles found primarily in humid lowland forest. Both species soar frequently (especially Black) and vocalize often, but neither is often seen perched. They have barred thighs in all plumages.

4. BLACK HAWK-EAGLE, *Spizaetus tyrannus*

Uncommon but conspicuous, locally ranging up into subtropics on w. slope. Basically black, with white-barred thighs, white speckling in short bushy crest, gray-barred tail. In flight note long, rounded wings often held slightly forward with notably indented rear margin; flight feathers boldly banded.   p. 99

5. ORNATE HAWK-EAGLE, *Spizaetus ornatus*

Rare (especially in west). Spectacular adult unmistakable with long spikelike crest, bright rufous sides of head and neck, boldly barred belly. Juvenile already crested but with white head, neck, and underparts; it shows heavy black barring on belly much as in adult. In flight wings somewhat broader and less rounded than Black's.   p. 99

6. BLACK-AND-WHITE HAWK-EAGLE, *Spizastur melanoleucus*

Rare and local in lowland and foothill forest, mainly in east. A beautiful raptor, somewhat smaller than *Spizaetus*. Clean-cut and nearly unmistakable, with bright orange cere, contrasting black lores, short black crest contrasting with immaculate white head and underparts with no barring (unlike young Ornate). Note feathered tarsi (cf. immature Gray-headed Kite, Plate 11-2). In flight wings somewhat less rounded than *Spizaetus*, whiter below with less dark barring than in Ornate; distinctive leading edge of wing white (most noticeable from above).   p. 98

7. BLACK-CHESTED BUZZARD-EAGLE, *Geranoaetus melanoleucus*

Widespread in open terrain in highlands and paramo. Large, with tail extremely short, though less markedly so in young birds. Distinctive adult mainly gray with more blackish chest contrasting with whitish lower underparts. Immature not so easy: brown above, variably streaked and blotched below, only gradually acquiring dark chest. In flight all ages show very broad, somewhat tapered wings which impart a characteristic silhouette often apparent even in young birds.
                                                    p. 92

Plate 15 Diurnal Raptors VI

Accipiter Hawks

Bold, rapacious, bird-eating hawks, none of them particularly numerous in Ecuador; all tend to be secretive, rarely occurring in the open with the exception of Plain-breasted. In flight show relatively short, rounded wings and fairly long, squared tails with several gray bands (in *Micrastur* bands are white). Most species have a distinctly fierce and capped look, rather different from the more owl-like expression of *Micrastur*, with which certain species are readily confused. There is marked sexual variation in size.

1. TINY HAWK, *Accipiter superciliosus*
Scarce in humid forest in lowlands of east and west, sometimes perching high in canopy. Very small. Adult with narrow even gray barring below. Immatures have two morphs, one similar to adult ♀ but with browner barring below, other (rarer) rufous above sometimes with dark barring, rufous-barred below.   p. 84

2. SEMICOLLARED HAWK, *Accipiter collaris*
Rare in subtropical forest on both slopes. Adult blackish brown above with partial whitish nuchal collar, whitish streaking on cheeks, and extensive coarse black barring below (browner in ♀). Immatures have two morphs, one like adult but with collar and barring on underparts more rufescent, other rufous brown above with conspicuous cinnamon collar and underparts tawny barred with rufous brown.
                                          p. 83

3. PLAIN-BREASTED HAWK, *Accipiter ventralis*
Widespread in montane areas from treeline down occasionally to upper tropics; the most frequently seen *Accipiter* (even soaring regularly), and less tied to forest than others. Very variable, but except in rare black morph always shows rufous thighs. Adults have gray to brownish gray upperparts, browner in young birds; young birds may also be more streaked below. Pale morph strikingly white below; rufous morph variably barred and mottled with rufous below; dark morph entirely sooty, sometimes with rufous thighs and lower underparts. Unlike somewhat larger Bicolored, Plain-breasted is never gray below.   p. 83

4. BICOLORED HAWK, *Accipiter bicolor*
Scarce in variety of forested and wooded habitats from lowlands up into subtropics. Fairly large. Adult basically gray with contrasting rufous thighs (sometimes hard to see); note also dark cap. Juvenile variable, brown above with creamy whitish to ochraceous underparts and partial nuchal collar.
                                          p. 84

5. GRAY-BELLIED HAWK, *Accipiter poliogaster*
Very rare in humid forest in lowlands of east. The largest *Accipiter*. Adult slaty above with blackish head extending down over sides of neck (some birds have whitish-streaked auriculars); below white or (usually) slightly tinged gray. Juvenile strikingly different, brownish above aside from blackish crown and rufous face and sides of neck, blackish malar streak, and coarse blackish barring on lower underparts (pattern remarkably like adult Ornate Hawk-Eagle, Plate 14-5).   p. 85

Micrastur Forest-Falcons

Complicated, difficult genus of shy, reclusive forest raptors; all species have extensive bare skin around eye and on cere, in some brightly colored. Adults of most species reasonably distinctive (except Buckley's), but all go through several plumage stages when younger and can then be hard to separate. Further complications come from certain *Accipiter* hawks, but latter have gray (not white) tail banding and usually show distinctly darker crown (crowns usually uniform with upperparts in *Micrastur*). All species are most often recorded—and most readily identified—by their far-carrying calls, heard especially at dawn and dusk.

6. BARRED FOREST-FALCON, *Micrastur ruficollis*
The most numerous and widespread forest-falcon, occurring in humid forest and woodland from lowlands of west and east up into subtropics (but comparatively scarce in lowlands of east). Adult has bright yellow facial skin, underparts with narrow even gray barring, and 3 white tail bands (in the field often only two show, and in east they are often faint or even lacking). Juveniles variable and confusing, but all show a prominent whitish to buff nuchal collar and variable amount of dark barring on whitish to buff underparts (barring often coarse and extensive, but can be fainter and confined mainly to sides).   p. 103

7. LINED FOREST-FALCON, *Micrastur gilvicollis*
Scarce in terra firme forest in lowlands of east. Resembles Barred Forest-Falcon (voices differ characteristically), but adult with white iris, bright orange facial skin, only two white tail bands (often only one shows), and usually more faintly and sparsely barred below (can look quite whitish). Juveniles of the two very similar (see text).   p. 104

8. PLUMBEOUS FOREST-FALCON, *Micrastur plumbeus*
Rare in lowland and foothill forest of northwest. Resembles commoner Barred Forest-Falcon, differing in reddish orange facial skin and single white tail band. Barring on underparts of young birds apparently faint and sparse; they may show two white tail bands.   p. 104

9. SLATY-BACKED FOREST-FALCON, *Micrastur mirandollei*
Rare in terra firme forest in lowlands of east. Adult uniform gray above, including face (showing no capped look, unlike Gray-bellied Hawk) with bright yellow facial skin; all whitish below. Juvenile creamy whitish below with sparse but distinct dusky shaft streaking; may also show coarse spotting or chevroning on breast.   p. 105

10. COLLARED FOREST-FALCON, *Micrastur semitorquatus*
Widespread but never numerous in forest and woodland in lowlands and subtropics. Large and lanky, with long tail showing 3–5 white tail bands; facial skin dull olive greenish; conspicuous blackish crescent down across auriculars. Adults have 3 morphs, two commoner ones either white or buff below and on nuchal collar; in addition a rare melanistic morph is mainly sooty black and shows no collar. Juveniles buffyish below with variable amounts of coarse blackish barring (most when young); dark crescent and pale collar are often more obscure than in adults.   p. 105

11. BUCKLEY'S FOREST-FALCON, *Micrastur buckleyi*
Smaller, rarer version of Collared Forest-Falcon found in lowlands of east, mainly or entirely in floodplain and várzea forest. Very similar aside from size, but outer tail feathers have only 4 white bands (not 6), remaining tail feathers only 3 (never more, unlike Collared). ♀♀ (only?) show some small white spots on inner secondaries (and in some on scapulars as well); Collared never shows such spotting.
                                          p. 106

Plate 16 Diurnal Raptors VII

1. CRANE HAWK, *Geranospiza caerulescens*
Widespread but scarce in forest and woodland in lowlands of west and east. Lanky shape with long, reddish legs. Basically gray, some birds with whitish barring on lower underparts; cere dark gray and iris red. Cf. various *Leucopternis* spp. (Plate 12). Soars fairly often, in flight showing distinctive white bar across primaries.   p. 85

2. HARRIS'S HAWK, *Parabuteo unicinctus*
Fairly common in semiopen, often arid areas and deciduous woodland in southwest, locally ranging up in intermontane valleys, even in north. Adult distinctive, sooty blackish with contrasting rufous wing-coverts and thighs (but can look all dark), conspicuous white basal tail and coverts. Immatures blotchier and more streaked, especially below, but already show rufous on wings and pale basal tail. In flight shows rufous underwing-coverts.   p. 91

3. BLACK CARACARA, *Daptrius ater*
Numerous and conspicuous along rivers and in clearings in lowlands of east, now spreading up into foothills. Adult black with extensive bright orange face (yellower in juveniles) and conspicuous white band across base of tail (visible only from above). Often in pairs or small groups.   p. 100

4. RED-THROATED CARACARA, *Ibycter americanus*
Widespread in humid forest in lowlands of east. Unmistakable very raucous voice draws attention even from long distances. Bare red throat; conspicuous white belly and crissum. Usually in pairs or small groups.   p. 101

5. YELLOW-HEADED CARACARA, *Milvago chimachima*
Along major rivers in lowlands of northeast, locally spreading into clearings. Adult distinctive, with yellowish buff head and underparts and blackish eyeline. In flight note conspicuous buff patches in wings and buffyish basal tail. Immature similarly patterned on wings and tail, but head and body heavily streaked brownish.   p. 102

Phalcoboenus Caracaras
Attractive caracaras found in paramo, Mountain only in far south. Both species have bare facial skin extending to sides of chin, usually reddish orange but can vary to bright red (especially or only in Mountain?) to yellowish. They also have flashy wing patterns in flight, with contrasting white underwing-coverts and white basal tail and tail-tip. Immatures much duller with gray facial skin, brown to tawny with variable amount of whitish mottling and streaking; in flight both show large pale wing patch at base of primaries.

6. CARUNCULATED CARACARA, *Phalcoboenus carunculatus*
Local in paramo south to n. Loja. Boldly white-streaked foreparts.   p. 102

7. MOUNTAIN CARACARA, *Phalcoboenus megalopterus*
Only in paramo of s. Loja. Like Carunculated but with solid black foreparts.   p. 102

8. NORTHERN CRESTED-CARACARA, *Caracara cheriway*
Common and conspicuous in semiopen and agricultural areas of west, spreading up into arid montane areas. Adult unmistakable with striking reddish facial skin, white foreneck contrasting with black crown and mainly blackish upperparts. In flight note large white patch in primaries and basal tail. Immature browner and more streaked, but some of adult's pattern usually apparent (especially wing and tail pattern).   p. 101

Plate 17 Diurnal Raptors VIII

1. LAUGHING FALCON, *Herpetotheres cachinnans*
1W *H. c. fulvescens*—cinnamon-buff crown and underparts
1E *H. c. cachinnans*—paler crown and underparts
Widespread in forested and wooded lowlands, often taking prominent perches at edge. Virtually unmistakable, with conspicuous large black mask, large and "puffy"-headed silhouette. In low flight shows caracara-like patch on wings but does not soar. Often very vocal, with far-carrying forest-falcon-like calls.   p. 106

Falco Falcons
Well-known raptors with characteristically pointed wings capable of exceptionally fast flight; most species also soar. All show either a dark moustache (broad and prominent in some) or dark sides of head. ♀♀ markedly large than ♂♂. Falcons are conspicuous birds which favor open or semiopen habitats (even forest-based species are almost always at edge), generally perching fully in open.

2. PEREGRINE FALCON, *Falco peregrinus*
Uncommon boreal migrant to semiopen areas in highlands and w. lowlands, favoring areas near water and most numerous near coast; also a tiny population resident very locally in Andes, nesting on cliffs. Large and heavily built. Adult gray above with wide black moustache, variable amount of blackish barring below but throat and upper chest always pure white. Immatures similarly patterned (already with broad moustache) but browner above, more streaked below, often with creamy forehead and superciliary. In often very fast flight note broadly based wings, very powerful and deep wingstrokes, and relatively short tail; often soars.   p. 109

3. APLOMADO FALCON, *Falco femoralis*
Uncommon in open areas in highlands and paramo. A handsome large falcon with bold buff superciliary, dark "vest," and buff on lower underparts. In flight note (compared to Peregrine) comparatively narrow wings and long tail.   p. 108

4. ORANGE-BREASTED FALCON, *Falco deiroleucus*
Rare and local in foothills and subtropics on e. slope, occasionally out into lowlands; no recent confirmed records from northwest. A heavily built falcon, with about same proportions as Peregrine. Compared to much more numerous (and similar) Bat Falcon, Orange-breasted larger and stockier with more massive bill, much larger and more powerful talons, blacker upperparts, more extensive rufous on chest (contrasting with white throat), and coarser and more conspicuous buff or white barring across black "vest." Nests on inaccessible cliffs and (rarely) snags, but can be seen hunting almost anywhere.   p. 108

5. BAT FALCON, *Falco rufigularis*
5E *F. r. rufigularis*—uniform buffy whitish foreneck
5W *F. r. petoensis*—throat whitish, chest buffier or orangey
Widespread and conspicuous at edge of forest and woodland in lowlands of west and east; frequently seen perched high on dead snags. A small, attractive falcon with narrow, almost swift-like wings. Contrasting pale collar and foreneck, black "vest" with only faint white scaling, rufous lower underparts. Cf. much more numerous Orange-breasted Falcon, which overly hopeful birders frequently confuse with Bat Falcon.   p. 108

6. MERLIN, *Falco columbarius*
Scarce boreal migrant, mainly to open areas near coast. A comparatively stocky falcon, with dashing flight and rather short wings and tail. Underparts streaked in all plumages. ♂ gray above with gray tail bands (like an *Accipiter*). ♀ brown above with no barring.   p. 107

7. AMERICAN KESTREL, *Falco sparverius*
7N *F. s. aequatorialis*—♂ more richly colored below
7S *F. s. peruvianus*—♂ paler below, more profusely spotted
Fairly common and conspicuous in open and semiopen areas in highlands, and locally in lowlands of southwest (mainly El Oro and Loja). Regular in agricultural regions, even towns. Distinctive facial pattern in both sexes. ♂ with blue-gray wings, mainly solid rufous tail. ♀ has upperparts entirely rufous barred and spotted with black, underparts streaked, tail barred with black. Often hovers; frequently perches on wires.   p. 107

Plate 18 Cracids

Penelope Guans

Midsized to large, arboreal cracids found in lowland and montane forests. All are basically similar, but for the most part only one species occurs in any area. Small-headed and slender-necked, all species are dark overall with bare red skin on throat (the "dewlap") and white streaking on foreneck. The larger species especially are often hunted for food, and therefore in many areas are much reduced in numbers. They are less vocal than chachalacas, but do have a characteristic wing-whirring display given mainly at dawn, sometimes in the dark.

1. CRESTED GUAN, *Penelope purpurascens*
Now very local in forests of west, mainly in foothills and subtropics. The largest Ecuadorian guan, but cf. similar Baudó. No more "crested" than other guans.   p. 113

2. BAUDÓ GUAN, *Penelope ortoni*
Rare and local in lowland and foothill forests of northwest. Closely resembles Crested (often hard to separate), but smaller and generally more uniform darker brown (showing little or none of Crested's rufescence on lower belly and rump).   p. 112

3. SPIX'S GUAN, *Penelope jacquacu*
Not uncommon in more remote forests in lowlands of east, where the only *Penelope* present.   p. 112

4. ANDEAN GUAN, *Penelope montagnii*
4E   *P. m. brooki*—more conspicuous scaling on foreneck, back
4W   *P. m. atrogularis*
Local in montane forest on both slopes south to Azuay and s. Morona-Santiago (replaced southward by Bearded). A fairly small, compact guan with small dewlap and little facial pattern.   p. 111

5. BEARDED GUAN, *Penelope barbata*
Now scarce and local in montane forest in south, mainly Loja. Replaces Andean Guan in this area (no overlap known); differs in whitish grizzling on face, rufous tail-tipping.   p. 111

Ortalis Chachalacas

Small, relatively plain cracids with restricted bare red skin on throat found in lowlands (mainly) on either slope. Shaped much like *Penelope* guans but slighter and less robust. Often shy and inconspicuous—though, being less hunted, they better tolerate human proximity than guans—and are best known from their raucous gabbled calls given at dawn and dusk.

6. SPECKLED CHACHALACA, *Ortalis guttata*
Forest borders and secondary woodland in lowlands of east. Essentially brown with white-spotted foreneck; rufous in tail evident in flight.   p. 110

7. RUFOUS-HEADED CHACHALACA, *Ortalis erythroptera*
Local in semihumid and deciduous forest borders and woodland in lowlands of west, up into lower subtropics in south. Rufous head, flight feathers, and tips to outer tail feathers.   p. 110

8. COMMON PIPING-GUAN, *Pipile pipile*
Arboreal and often conspicuous in forest and borders in lowlands of east. Nearly unmistakable, black with conspicuous white on face, crown, and wings; bill and dewlap blue.   p. 113

9. WATTLED GUAN, *Aburria aburri*
Scarce and very inconspicuous guan found mainly inside foothill and subtropical forest on e. slope, locally also in Pichincha. All black with bright blue on bill and long dangling dewlap bright orange-yellow.   p. 114

10. SICKLE-WINGED GUAN, *Chamaepetes goudotii*
10W   *S. g. fagani*—small (chachalaca-sized), blacker above
10E   *S. g. tschudii*—considerably larger, browner above
Local in subtropical and lower temperate forest and borders on both slopes, most numerous in northwest. A plain, two-toned (rufous belly) guan with extensive bright blue facial skin.   p. 114

11. NOCTURNAL CURASSOW, *Nothocrax urumutum*
A small, rufescent curassow found in terra firme forest in lowlands of east. Bright reddish bill, colorful bare skin around eye. Strictly nocturnal so very rarely seen without making a big effort to see a singing bird at night. Apparently forages on ground like other curassows, but sings from subcanopy.   p. 115

Crax Curassows

Very large, heavily built cracids found in remote areas, both species perhaps extirpated in Ecuador. Both sexes have fancy recurved crest feathers, ♂♂ with enlarged and colorful bill protuberances. Very low-pitched booming song of ♂♂ given mainly at night.

12. GREAT CURASSOW, *Crax rubra*
Extremely rare and local in lowlands forest of west. Strongly dimorphic; crest feathers very long. ♂ mainly black with cere and prominent knob bright yellow. ♀ mainly rufous, head contrastingly black and white; tail boldly barred.   p. 116

13. WATTLED CURASSOW, *Crax globulosa*
Extremely rare and local in lowland forests of northeast, apparently mainly in riparian areas. Both sexes mainly black, including entire tail (which has no white tip). ♂ with large knob and wattles bright red. ♀ with rufous belly.   p. 116

14. SALVIN'S CURASSOW, *Mitu salvini*
Local in more remote lowland forests of east. Sexes alike; shorter crest feathers than in *Crax*. Mainly black with red bill, white belly; white on tip of tail diagnostic. Feeds mainly on ground, though also perching freely in trees.   p. 115

Plate 19 Wood-Quail and Seedsnipes

Odontophorus Wood-Quail

Plump, short-tailed quail found in pairs and small coveys inside humid and montane forest. Hard to see (and when they are, often not seen well) but regularly heard. Often confused, but usually only one species occurs in any area. Intricate patterns of brown, rufous, buff, and black predominate; all species have a bare ocular area (brightly colored in both species of e. lowlands).

1. MARBLED WOOD-QUAIL, *Odontophorus gujanensis*
Lowlands of east, mainly in terra firme. Conspicuous bright orange-red ocular area; no rufous on underparts.   p. 117

2. RUFOUS-FRONTED WOOD-QUAIL, *Odontophorus erythrops*
Lowlands and foothills of west. Conspicuous white crescent across black foreneck; rufous on forecrown and head.
p. 117

3. DARK-BACKED WOOD-QUAIL, *Odontophorus melanonotus*
Subtropics of northwest. Relatively unpatterned (head concolor); throat and breast plain rufous.   p. 118

4. RUFOUS-BREASTED WOOD-QUAIL, *Odontophorus speciosus*
Local in foothills and lower subtropics on e. slope. Black throat and lower face, white-speckled superciliary. ♂ mainly rufous below, ♀ mainly gray below.   p. 118

5. STARRED WOOD-QUAIL, *Odontophorus stellatus*
Rare or local in lowlands of east, perhaps mainly in southeast. Conspicuous yellowish ocular area, gray throat, neck, and upper back, rufous underparts. "stars" (on underparts) are not obvious. ♂ with orange-rufous on crest, ♀'s crest darker.   p. 118

6. TAWNY-FACED QUAIL, *Rynchortyx cinctus*
Scarce in lowlands of far northwest. Smaller than wood-quail. ♂ has obvious tawny face, gray breast. ♀ has whitish superciliary, prominent coarse barring on underparts.
p. 119

7. RUFOUS-BELLIED SEEDSNIPE, *Attagis gayi*
Local in paramo at high elevations. Well camouflaged, crouching and shuffling on ground, but capable of flying strongly; ranges in pairs and small groups. Fairly large and plump. Ornate scalloped pattern above; lower underparts cinnamon-rufous.   p. 147

8. LEAST SEEDSNIPE, *Thinocorus rumicivorus*
Apparently extirpated in Ecuador. Inhabited open arid terrain on Santa Elena Peninsula. Small with stubby bill. Both sexes camouflaged by intricate dusky and buff pattern above. ♂ with gray foreneck accented by black median stripe.
p. 148

Plate 20 Jacana, Smaller Rails, Sunbittern, and Sungrebe

1. WATTLED JACANA, *Jacana jacana*
1W *J. j. scapularis*—paler mantle
1E *J. j. intermedia*—solid black below
Conspicuous and noisy in marshes and around ponds in lowlands, much more numerous in west. Unmistakable, using extremely long toes to walk on floating vegetation; in flight shows extensive pale yellowish green in wings. Adult rufous (west) or chestnut (east) and black with red lobe and wattles at base of bill. Very different immature has white underparts and prominent brow.   p. 132

2. UNIFORM CRAKE, *Amaurolimnas concolor*
Apparently rare inside swampy forest and woodland in lowlands of east and northwest. Uniform rufous brown with entirely olive bill, reddish legs. Best known from loud voice.   p. 122

3. CHESTNUT-HEADED CRAKE, *Anurolimnas castaneiceps*
Widespread but secretive in dense growth in terra firme forest and secondary woodland, not always near water, in lowlands of east. Foreparts contrastingly rich rufous. Upper mandible mainly black; legs reddish northward, as shown, but dusky south of Río Napo. Best known from loud voice.   p. 121

Laterallus Crakes
Small, sneaky rails with short stout bills whose distinctive voices are (unlike *Neocrex*) heard far more often than birds are seen. All but one species (Russet-crowned) show prominent black flank barring. They favor marshy areas and edges of ponds and lakes in lowlands, but a few occur in more wooded situations, and some range up into lower subtropics.

4. WHITE-THROATED CRAKE, *Laterallus albigularis*
Locally common in damp grassy areas and marshes in lowlands and foothills of west. Small; foreneck rich rufous, extensive bold black and white barring on rearparts.
                                                              p. 120

5. RUFOUS-SIDED CRAKE, *Laterallus melanophaius*
Marshes and damp grassy areas in lowlands and foothills of east. Small; face and sides of breast broadly rich rufous, extensive bold black and white barring on flanks.   p. 120

6. GRAY-BREASTED CRAKE, *Laterallus exilis*
Local in damp grassy areas and marshy lake edges in lowlands of west and east. Very small; gray head and breast, rufous patch on upper back, bold flank barring.   p. 119

7. BLACK-BANDED CRAKE, *Laterallus fasciatus*
Apparently scarce and local in damp second-growth and grassy areas in lowlands and foothills of east. Rich rufous-chestnut foreparts, bold ochraceous and black banding on lower rearparts.   p. 121

8. RUSSET-CROWNED CRAKE, *Laterallus viridis*
Apparently rare and local in damp second-growth in lowlands and foothills of east. Entire underparts cinnamon-rufous; gray on face contrasting with chestnut crown; black bill.   p. 121

9. SORA, *Porzana carolina*
Scarce boreal migrant to marshes in highlands and lowlands of west. Stout bright yellow bill; streaked back. Adult has black foreface, gray head and foreneck. Immature duller, buffy brownish with bold flank barring.   p. 122

Neocrex Crakes
Secretive crakes with basal half of bill bright orange-red, legs salmon pink, and head and underparts entirely gray. They may have been overlooked, in part because their voices are barely known.

10. PAINT-BILLED CRAKE, *Neocrex erythrops*
Apparently rare and local in grassy areas in lowlands of southwest. Lower flanks and crissum barred black and white.
                                                              p. 123

11. COLOMBIAN CRAKE, *Neocrex colombianus*
Apparently rare and local in grassy areas in lowlands of west. Flank barring faint at best, crissum unmarked buff. p. 124

12. SUNBITTERN, *Eurypyga helias*
12E *E. h. helias*—browner above
12W *E. h. major*—grayer above
Scarce and infrequently seen along streams and around ponds and lakes in lowlands and foothills. Unique and unmistakable, with long slender bill but rather short legs, intricately marked and beautiful plumage, bursts of orange-rufous on wings in flight.   p. 130

13. SUNGREBE, *Heliornis fulica*
Local on forest-fringed ponds and lakes and sluggish shaded streams in lowlands. Superficially duck-like, usually encountered swimming low in water with head pumping back and forth. Bold black and white striping on head and neck; weirdly colorful feet conspicuous on birds perched along water's edge. ♂ lacks buff cheeks.   p. 131

Plate 21 Larger Rails, Gallinules, and Coots

Pardirallus Rails
Midsized, dark rails with fairly long, decurved, highly colored bills found locally in marshes and wet fields in lowlands or subtropics.

1. BLACKISH RAIL, *Pardirallus nigricans*
Marshes and wet areas with luxuriant grass along e. base of Andes, up locally into lower subtropics. Dark overall with entirely lime green bill. p. 125

2. PLUMBEOUS RAIL, *Pardirallus sanguinolentus*
Local in wet grassy areas and near streams in highlands of Loja. Dark overall with base of bill bright blue and red. p. 125

3. SPOTTED RAIL, *Pardirallus maculatus*
Local in reedbeds in coastal lowlands of w. Esmeraldas and from se. Guayas into El Oro. Unmistakable, with bold white spotting and streaking; bill yellowish with red spot at base. p. 126

Rallus Rails
Fairly large rails with long slender bills and barred flanks, one species found in highlands, the other very locally in mangroves.

4. ECUADORIAN RAIL, *Rallus aequatorialis*
Local in marshes and wet grassy areas in highlands, where the only long-billed rail present. Gray face, extensive rufous on wings, dull cinnamon-buff underparts. Juvenile much more blackish. p. 124

5. CLAPPER RAIL, *Rallus longirostris*
Very local and apparently rare in mangroves along coast; recorded only from n. Esmeraldas and near Guayaquil. Dull and grayish overall, with boldly banded flanks. p. 124

Aramides Wood-Rails
Large, colorful, vaguely chicken-like rails with black rearparts; stout fairly long bills some shade of greenish yellow, legs coral red; all species have rufous in primaries (mainly visible in flight). They occur in swampy places in lowlands and favor more wooded or forested environments than many other rails. So far as known, all species have loud cackling calls.

6. GRAY-NECKED WOOD-RAIL, *Aramides cajanea*
Swampy forest and woodland and along streams in lowlands of east. Head and neck all gray contrasting with cinnamon-rufous breast and upper belly. p. 127

7. RED-WINGED WOOD-RAIL, *Aramides calopterus*
Poorly known, apparently rare and local along streams in hilly terra firme and foothill forest in east. Maroon-chestnut sides of neck, mainly gray underparts. p. 127

8. BROWN WOOD-RAIL, *Aramides wolfi*
Rare and local along streams and in swampy areas in lowlands and foothills of west. Mainly dark brown with contrasting ashy gray head and neck. p. 127

9. RUFOUS-NECKED WOOD-RAIL, *Aramides axillaris*
Local in mangroves and deciduous forest in lowlands and foothills of west (mainly southwest). Head, neck, and underparts rich rufous; gray patch on upper back. Juvenile much duller and grayer below (cf. larger Brown Wood-Rail). p. 126

Porphyrula Gallinules
Colorful waterbirds with bright yellow legs found in thick vegetation around lakes and in freshwater marshes. Adults dissimilar (though both species have conspicuous white crissums, especially obvious in flight), but buffier younger birds can be confused.

10. PURPLE GALLINULE, *Porphyrula martinica*
Locally fairly common in marshes and lake margins in lowlands of west and northeast, vagrants elsewhere. Beautiful adult unmistakable with rich blue head and underparts, multicolored bill and frontal shield, etc. Immature much plainer and browner, but some blue already showing on wings. p. 128

11. AZURE GALLINULE, *Porphyrula flavirostris*
Local in grassy margins of certain lakes in lowlands of east. Small and delicate-looking, often appearing pale. Unmistakable adults extensively pale blue, but they seem to be outnumbered by browner young birds, which always already show blue on wings. p. 128

12. COMMON GALLINULE, *Gallinula chloropus*
Locally common on ponds and in marshes in lowlands of west, also around certain highland lakes. Vaguely duck-like, often swimming out in open water, pumping head. Mainly slaty adult has bright red bill and frontal shield, white stripes on sides. Immature drabber and paler gray, but early on shows side striping and reddish on bill and shield. p. 129

Fulica Coots
Gray, superficially duck-like rails, with white crissums. Coots are considerably less secretive than most other rails and frequently swim out on open freshwater, their heads nodding back and forth.

13. AMERICAN COOT, *Fulica americana*
Extirpated in Ecuador, formerly having occurred on Yaguarcocha in Imbabura highlands. Similar to Andean Coot, differing in dark ring on bill, small chestnut frontal shield. p. 130

14. ANDEAN COOT, *Fulica ardesiaca*
Mainly on certain lakes in highlands, also near coast on Santa Elena Peninsula. Uniform slaty gray. Bill and large frontal shield vary in coloration, the 3 primary combinations shown. p. 129

Plate 22 Shorebirds I

1. PERUVIAN THICK-KNEE, *Burhinus superciliaris*
Rare, local resident of open, often barren areas in arid areas of southwest. Mainly crepuscular and nocturnal, by day lethargic and usually inconspicuous though sometimes roosting fully in open. A large shorebird, distinctive in range and habitat; note bold head striping, large eye, long legs.
p. 148

2. AMERICAN OYSTERCATCHER, *Haematopus palliatus*
Uncommon local resident on sandy coastlines of southwest. Conspicuous. Large and spectacular, with heavy bright red bill, pinkish legs, black head and foreneck. Note bold white wingstripe in flight. p. 149

Vanellus **Lapwings**
Large, attractive shorebirds with bold patterns and broad white wingstripe and rump. Noisy and conspicuous, often flying at an intruder on broad, rounded, and somewhat bowed wings. Both species have carpal spur on bend of wing.

3. SOUTHERN LAPWING, *Vanellus chilensis*
Scarce and local (but increasing) resident in open grassy areas and river sandbars in lowlands of northeast. Virtually unmistakable, with long wispy crest, white foreface, large black breast shield. p. 150

4. ANDEAN LAPWING, *Vanellus resplendens*
Locally numerous in paramo, favoring areas with short grass especially around lakes (but sometimes ranging far from water). Elegant, with dove gray head and foreneck; legs shorter than in Southern Lapwing, not protruding past tail in flight. p. 151

5. PIED PLOVER, *Hoploxypterus cayanus*
Uncommon on sandbars along larger rivers in lowlands of east and west (now very rare in latter). Conspicuous. Exceptionally attractive, with boldly pied pattern, salmon red legs.
p. 152

Pluvialis **Plovers**
Fairly large, chunky plovers which resemble each other in nonbreeding plumage. Calls differ (see text).

6. GRAY PLOVER, *Pluvialis squatarola*
Common boreal migrant to coast, favoring beaches and mudflats (occasional on fields); rare inland. Breeding adult has black and white-spotted upperparts (looking gray or silvery at any distance), mainly black underparts with bold white bordering stripe. Nonbreeding birds much duller, whitish below with variable amount of dark speckling. In flight note white wingstripe, white basal tail, black axillars. p. 151

7. AMERICAN GOLDEN-PLOVER, *Pluvialis dominica*
Rare boreal migrant throughout, favoring short-grass fields and sandbars, not necessarily near water. Breeding adult has gold-spangled upperparts, all-black underparts (no white lower belly and crissum). Nonbreeders trickier, typically more gold- or buff-spotted below than Gray (but beware juvenile Grays which can be buff-spotted), and showing more prominent pale superciliary. In flight has all-dark upperwing (no wingstripe) and tail, no black axillars. p. 151

8. PACIFIC GOLDEN-PLOVER, *Pluvialis fulva*
Accidental vagrant to sw. coast. Resembles American Golden-Plover but more yellowish buff generally (especially on brow), and with more "gold" spangling above. See text.
p. 152

Limosa **Godwits**
Very large shorebirds with characteristic long and upswept bills, basal half pinkish.

9. HUDSONIAN GODWIT, *Limosa haemastica*
Very rare boreal transient to mudflats and shallow water, inland as well as on coast; few records. Bill can look almost straight, but always bicolored. In all plumages shows white basal tail, white wingstripe, black underwing-coverts. Breeding adults rich chestnut below; nonbreeders and juveniles duller and more uniform, mainly grayish on mantle and foreneck. p. 136

10. MARBLED GODWIT, *Limosa fedoa*
Casual boreal transient to mudflats and shallow water; only a few records, all from *sw. coast.* Essentially uniform tawny-buff. In flight shows no marked pattern; prominent cinnamon underwing-coverts. p. 137

11. WHIMBREL, *Numenius phaeopus*
Numerous boreal migrant along entire coast, occurring on all types of shoreline (sandy, rocky, muddy), even sometimes on short-grass fields; casual inland. Unmistakable, with striking long and decurved bill. Crown boldly striped whitish and dark brown; otherwise brownish. p. 136

12. TAWNY-THROATED DOTTEREL, *Oreopholus ruficollis*
Extirpated in Ecuador, formerly on arid plains of Santa Elena Peninsula. An elegant dry-ground plover, nearly unmistakable: bold creamy brow, rich tawny throat and chest, black belly patch. p. 155

13. WILLET, *Catoptrophorus semipalmatus*
Numerous boreal migrant along entire coast, favoring sandy and muddy shorelines; no inland records. Fairly heavy, straight, grayish bill; legs also grayish. In all plumages note striking black and white wing pattern. Nonbreeding birds nondescript and grayish; breeding-plumage birds browner, vermiculated dusky. Cf. Greater Yellowlegs (Plate 24-5).
p. 134

14. BLACK-NECKED STILT, *Himantopus mexicanus*
Locally common resident in marshes, ponds (both fresh and salt), and rice fields in lowlands of southwest. Unmistakable. Large, gangly, with exceptionally long and shockingly pink legs; black upperparts. In flight upperwing solidly black.
p. 149

15. AMERICAN AVOCET, *Recurvirostra americana*
Casual boreal visitant to saltwater ponds near coast. Unmistakable. Long, slender, upswept bill (stilt's is straight). Boldly pied black and white pattern above; head and foreneck usually grayish (buff in breeding plumage). p. 150

Plate 23 Shorebirds II

Charadrius Plovers

Compact, rather small plovers which usually show a white nuchal collar and dark breast band (incomplete in a few, doubled in one). Voices of many are distinctive.

1. SEMIPALMATED PLOVER, *Charadrius semipalmatus*
Common boreal migrant along coast, rare inland; favors mudflats and pond margins. Breeding adult has orange base to stubby bill, blackish in other plumages; legs orange-yellow.
p. 153

2. SNOWY PLOVER, *Charadrius alexandrinus*
Local around salt lagoons of sw. coast. Small and dainty, with slender black bill, grayish legs. Black chest band restricted to sides.
p. 154

3. COLLARED PLOVER, *Charadrius collaris*
Sandbars along rivers and around coastal lagoons in lowlands of west and east; the only *Charadrius* normally found away from coast. Slender black bill, rufous on hindcrown and sides of head, neat but narrow black chest band.
p. 154

4. PIPING PLOVER, *Charadrius melodus*
Accidental boreal migrant to sw. coast. A pale, sandy plover with stubby blackish bill, yellowish legs. Breeding birds have partial black chest band, orange bill base.
p. 153

5. WILSON'S PLOVER, *Charadrius wilsonia*
Local around coastal lagoons. Stout black bill (markedly heavier than in other *Charadrius*); broad chest band (brown in ♀).
p. 153

6. KILLDEER, *Charadrius vociferus*
Large *Charadrius*, local but increasing in agricultural areas and near water in lowlands of southwest, to some extent elsewhere in west. Distinctive, with obvious double black chest band; unique bright cinnamon-rufous rump shows in flight.
p. 154

Calidris Sandpipers

Diverse group of boreal migrant shorebirds, many with series of plumages and thus often confusing and difficult to distinguish. In flight most have white rump crossed by black central stripe, and also show at least a vague white wingstripe.

7. RED KNOT, *Calidris canutus*
Casual on mudflats of sw. coast. Chunky, in nonbreeding plumage nondescript grayish (but strikingly rufous when breeding), even in flight showing little pattern. Cf. nonbreeding Stilt Sandpiper (Plate 24-8).
p. 138

8. BAIRD'S SANDPIPER, *Calidris bairdii*
Mainly around ponds in paramo; rare elsewhere. Fairly large "peep" with wings extending past tail, black legs. Basically brownish (juveniles with scaly back pattern) with buffyish breast, no streaking on flanks.
p. 140

9. WHITE-RUMPED SANDPIPER, *Calidris fuscicollis*
Rare, principally around ponds in highlands. At rest resembles commoner Baird's, but in nonbreeding plumage grayer generally with grayish breast streaking extending sparsely down flanks. In flight note all-white rump.
p. 140

10. DUNLIN, *Calidris alpina*
Casual on mudflats of sw. coast. Generally with hunched posture. Bill fairly long and decurved at tip. Nonbreeding birds nondescript, but in breeding plumage have black belly patch and bright reddish back. Cf. Stilt Sandpiper (Plate 24-8).
p. 141

11. PECTORAL SANDPIPER, *Calidris melanotos*
Uncommon, but can turn up almost anywhere; favors damp short-grass areas. Fairly large; legs yellowish. Basically brownish, with marked contrast between streaked breast and white belly.
p. 141

12. LEAST SANDPIPER, *Calidris minutilla*
Widespread, like Pectoral favoring moist grassy areas and pond margins. Small and "dumpy," looking short-tailed in flight. Bill short and thin, legs pale greenish to yellowish. Basically brownish, juveniles more rufescent; darker and browner than Semipalmateds and Westerns.
p. 140

13. SEMIPALMATED SANDPIPER, *Calidris pusilla*
Common locally along coast, favoring mudflats; very rare inland. Legs black; bill comparatively short, straight. Looks basically grayish regardless of plumage, even breeding birds showing little brown or rufous. Cf. very similar Western Sandpiper; often they cannot be distinguished.
p. 139

14. WESTERN SANDPIPER, *Calidris mauri*
Common locally along coast, favoring mudflats; often with very similar Semipalmated Sandpiper (and likewise very rare inland); wades more deeply. Bill slightly longer, more drooped at tip (often longer than head, but beware individual variation). Nonbreeders almost impossible to distinguish; see text. Arriving juveniles may show distinctive rufous scapulars; breeding adults more rufescent above (especially on crown) and more extensively streaked below. Voices differ slightly.
p. 139

15. SANDERLING, *Calidris alba*
Sandy coasts. Pale overall, pearly gray above and white below, often with black carpal patch. In flight shows bold white wingstripe (more conspicuous than other *Calidris*). Breeding plumage more rufescent (see text).
p. 138

16. BUFF-BREASTED SANDPIPER, *Tryngites subruficollis*
Scarce boreal migrant to grassland and paramo. Delicate, looking small-headed. Uniformly brown and buffy, with bold scaly pattern above; legs yellow. In flight shows pure white underwing.
p. 143

Phalaropus Phalaropes

Distinctive boreal migrants generally found on open ocean or coastal lagoons. In breeding plumage (rarely seen in Ecuador) ♀♀ brighter than ♂♂. Unique behavior among shorebirds, often alighting on water, swimming about daintily.

17. WILSON'S PHALAROPE, *Phalaropus tricolor*
Locally common on coastal lagoons of southwest, a few elsewhere (especially on highland lakes). Needle-like black bill. Nonbreeders uniformly gray above with only vague eye patch. Breeding ♀ unmistakable with rich chestnut on foreneck; ♂ similar but duller. In flight note lack of wingstripe (unlike other phalaropes).
p. 147

18. RED PHALAROPE, *Phalaropus fulicaria*
Rare along coast and offshore. Resembles more numerous Red-necked Phalarope, differing in stouter bill which may show some yellowish (Red-necked's never does), smoother gray back (Red-necked's typically more patterned). Breeding plumage utterly different (see text).
p. 146

19. RED-NECKED PHALAROPE, *Phalaropus lobatus*
Scarce along coast and offshore. Slender bill. Contrasting black ear patch; usually shows some white striping on back. Breeding plumage very different (see text).
p. 147

Plate 24 Shorebirds III

1. SURFBIRD, *Aphriza virgata*
Local on rocky coasts, often with turnstones. Stocky with thick short bill, yellowish legs. Nonbreeders mainly plain gray. Breeding plumage densely streaked and chevroned. In flight shows white rump and basal tail. p. 137

2. RUDDY TURNSTONE, *Arenaria interpres*
Common along coast, mainly in rocky areas. Short orange legs. Complex "harlequin" pattern always evident though most marked in breeding plumage. Nonbreeders have black chest, may show little rufescence above. p. 137

3. SPOTTED SANDPIPER, *Actitis macularia*
Common and widespread on coast and along rivers and streams, some even in highlands. Frequent teetering; flies with stiff, shallow wingbeats. Nonbreeders plain but with distinctive smudge on sides of breast. Black-spotted below in breeding plumage. p. 135

Tringa Sandpipers and Yellowlegs
Nicely proportioned shorebirds with long legs and fairly long bills. Often wade in shallow water.

4. SOLITARY SANDPIPER, *Tringa solitaria*
Mainly occurs inland, favoring secluded shallow freshwater ponds. Olive legs. Dark olive brown above with narrow white eye-ring. In flight shows mainly white sides to tail. p. 134

5. GREATER YELLOWLEGS, *Tringa melanoleuca*
Widespread—but usually only in small numbers—around freshwater, a few also along coast. Bright yellow legs. Larger than the following species, with proportionately longer, upswept bill. Plumages of the two similar, with breeding-plumage birds darker and more streaked on foreneck. Cf. Willet (Plate 22-13). p. 133

6. LESSER YELLOWLEGS, *Tringa flavipes*
Most common in coastal lagoons, a few elsewhere. Bright yellow legs. Delicate straight bill all black. In flight shows dark wings, white rump. p. 133

7. WANDERING TATTLER, *Heteroscelus incanus*
Local on rocky coastlines. Short yellowish legs. Nonbreeders predominantly dark slaty gray. Fine barring below in breeding plumage. In flight uniformly slaty gray above. p. 135

8. STILT SANDPIPER, *Micropalama himantopus*
Local on coastal lagoons, especially at Ecuasal. Droopy bill; rather long yellowish olive legs. Nonbreeders dull and grayish with fairly prominent white brow. Breeding-plumage birds barred below with rufescent cheeks. Cf. nonbreeding Red Knot (Plate 23-7). p. 142

9. CURLEW SANDPIPER, *Calidris ferruginea*
Accidental on sw. coast at Ecuasal. Fairly long, evenly decurved bill. Nonbreeders closely resemble equally rare Dunlin (Plate 23-10); see text. Breeding plumage unmistakable, with rufous-chestnut underparts. In flight shows all-white rump. p. 142

Plate 25 Shorebirds IV

Gallinago Snipes

Fairly large shorebirds with long straight bills and cryptic, mostly brown plumage, inhabiting heavy cover in damp situations; much less often in the open than other shorebirds and often only seen as they flush at your feet. Feed by probing deeply into damp soil. Several species are the only shorebirds that breed in Ecuador. Three have aerial displays during which characteristic calls are given.

1. ANDEAN SNIPE, Gallinago jamesoni

Widespread in paramo and grassland in highlands; regularly far from open water, though most often feeding where damp and muddy. A large, robust snipe with copious barring on breast and belly. Roding display is frequent: they fly high overhead at dawn and dusk, calling loudly.   p. 145

2. NOBLE SNIPE, Gallinago nobilis

Local in bogs and marshy lakeshores in highlands; infrequent any distance from open water. A large, very long-billed snipe; fairly white belly with dark chevrons on flanks. Rufous near tip of tail usually evident as bird flushes.   p. 145

3. IMPERIAL SNIPE, Gallinago imperialis

Local in humid treeline forest and woodland, mainly on e. slope. Large and rufescent overall, with heavy blackish banding below. Mainly recorded during roding display at dawn and dusk, with loud raucous call.   p. 146

4. SOUTH AMERICAN SNIPE, Gallinago paraguaiae

Rare in damp grassy areas and marshy lakeshores in lowlands of northeast, where the only snipe known to be present. Midsized; rufous in tail much as in Noble Snipe.   p. 144

5. COMMON SNIPE, Gallinago gallinago

Boreal migrant, with only a few records, perhaps most likely in highlands. Cannot be distinguished in field from South American Snipe; smaller than Noble (with which Common might occur). See text.   p. 144

6. PUNA SNIPE, Gallinago andina

One sighting from paramo in extreme south (sw. Zamora-Chinchipe). Small (other Ecuadorian snipes are markedly larger) with yellowish legs.   p. 144

7. SHORT-BILLED DOWITCHER, Limnodromus griseus

Locally common boreal migrant to coastal mudflats and lagoons. Long straight bill; proportionately short olive legs. Nonbreeders mainly grayish, becoming more rufescent (especially below) in breeding plumage. In flight shows white rump extending up back in a point. Unlike snipes, feeds in the open, wading in shallow water.   p. 143

8. UPLAND SANDPIPER, Bartramia longicauda

Scarce transient to grasslands and paramo (usually not near water) in highlands. Distinctive small-headed, long-necked, long-tailed silhouette. Bill short and slender, legs yellowish. Mottled brownish with white belly.   p. 135

Plate 26 Gulls

Larus Gulls

Large to fairly large aquatic birds, related to but more heavily built than terns, most gulls range along the coast (principally in southwest), with only one (Andean) regularly found away from it. Most gulls occur in Ecuador only as nonbreeding visitors—only 3 species breed—and a number of species are only vagrants. Identification of some species poses substantial difficulties, a problem exacerbated by the lengthy series of plumages required before full adult plumage is attained. Some Ecuadorian gulls are more straightforward, however, having only breeding and nonbreeding adult and juvenal plumages. Especially note size and color of bill, color of legs and mantle, and upperwing pattern on birds in flight.

1. GRAY GULL, *Larus modestus*
Fairly common visitor to sw. coast, especially on Santa Elena Peninsula. Adult mainly gray, with head whitish in breeding plumage, brownish when not breeding; narrow white trailing edge to wing. Juvenile browner.   p. 159

2. KELP GULL, *Larus dominicanus*
Scarce along sw. coast, mainly on outer Santa Elena Peninsula; breeds in small numbers at Ecuasal. Very large with heavy bill. Black and white adult distinctive, younger birds browner and more mottled.   p. 159

3. HERRING GULL, *Larus argentatus*
Accidental; one record from along Río Napo. A large gull with fairly heavy bill and pinkish legs. This and the next 3 species go through a series of age-related plumages; see text. Shown for Herring is a subadult.   p. 160

4. CALIFORNIA GULL, *Larus californicus*
Accidental; one record from Santa Elena Peninsula coast. Closely resembles larger Herring Gull but with dark eye; see text. Shown is a subadult.   p. 161

5. RING-BILLED GULL, *Larus delawarensis*
Accidental; one record from Santa Elena Peninsula coast. Resembles larger Herring Gull but with less heavy bill, distinctively "ringed" in adults (pinkish with black tip in younger birds). Shown is a nonbreeding adult.   p. 160

6. LESSER BLACK-BACKED GULL, *Larus fuscus*
Accidental; one record from Santa Elena Peninsula coast. In shape much like Herring Gull; see text. As illustrated, adult of race occurring in Ecuador has slaty gray mantle.   p. 160

7. GRAY-HOODED GULL, *Larus cirrocephalus*
Locally numerous breeder along sw. coast. Attractive adult has pearly gray hood, reddish bill and legs, prominent white wedge in primaries; underwing blackish. Nonbreeders lose most of gray hood. Juvenile browner and more mottled above; bill yellowish, ear patch dusky.   p. 161

8. ANDEAN GULL, *Larus serranus*
Locally numerous around lakes in paramo and temperate zone, where normally the only gull; not known to range down into lowlands. Breeding adult has conspicuous black hood with white eye-crescents; in flight shows extensive white in primaries, blackish underwing. Nonbreeders have hood reduced to spot on ear-coverts.   p. 162

9. LAUGHING GULL, *Larus atricilla*
Boreal migrant along coast, where locally common (usually the most numerous gull), a few elsewhere. Mantle all gray, with white only on trailing edge; more leaden in adults, browner in juveniles. Usually shows dusky smudge behind eye and on hindneck, but breeding-plumage adults have full black hood.   p. 162

10. FRANKLIN'S GULL, *Larus pipixcan*
Rather uncommon boreal migrant, mainly along coast. Resembles more numerous Laughing Gull; somewhat broader winged. Adults differ in having obvious white in primaries, nonbreeders in having a fairly well-defined dark "half-hood" on head. Black subterminal tail band in juveniles does not extend to outer feathers.   p. 163

11. SWALLOW-TAILED GULL, *Creagrus furcatus*
Uncommon offshore visitant from Galápagos; hardly ever seen from shore. Adult large and strikingly patterned, with obviously forked tail. Conspicuous whitish spot at base of bill, red eye-ring; in flight note bold white triangle on flight feathers. Adult had blackish hood, reduced to area around eye and an earspot when not breeding. Juvenile has brown mantle with feathers boldly edged white, black tipping on tail fork.   p. 163

12. SABINE'S GULL, *Xema sabini*
Uncommon boreal migrant, mainly occurring offshore. A small dainty gull with slender yellow-tipped bill and shallowly forked tail. Flight pattern striking (recalling much larger Swallow-tailed Gull) with white flight feathers and black outer primaries. Breeding adults have dark gray hood. Juvenile browner above with black tipping on tail fork.   p. 163

Plate 27 Terns and Black Skimmer

Sterna Terns

Attractive aquatic birds, generally smaller, slimmer, and more graceful than gulls, found mainly along coast. Two species range along rivers in east. Most terns occur in Ecuador only as visitants, with only a few species nesting; many are notably gregarious. Terns have relatively narrow, pointed wings, and all have notched or forked tails, deeply so in some species. Most feed by flying above water, diving in after small fish; a few simply pluck prey from water's surface. They swim little or not at all. Identification can be difficult, especially because of difficulties imposed by plumage sequencing.

1. GULL-BILLED TERN, *Sterna nilotica*
Locally fairly common resident around coastal lagoons in southwest, breeding locally. Heavy black bill. Rather short tail, not very deeply forked. Overall plumage very pale.
p. 164

2. ROYAL TERN, *Sterna maxima*
Widespread and often common nonbreeding visitant along entire coast, occurring throughout year. A large tern with heavy bill, reddish orange in breeding plumage, more yellow-orange at other times.
p. 165

3. CASPIAN TERN, *Sterna caspia*
Accidental vagrant to near Manabí coast. Resembles Royal Tern, but even heavier bill blood red with blackish tip, entire crown black with fine white streaking, primaries blackish.
p. 164

4. ELEGANT TERN, *Sterna elegans*
Boreal migrant to coast, most numerous in w. Guayas. Closely resembles better-known Royal Tern, but smaller and with more slender bill (shape of Sandwich's). Nonbreeders have black of rearcrown extending forward to encompass eye; breeding-plumage birds (especially) may show pink flush on breast.
p. 165

5. SANDWICH TERN, *Sterna sandvicensis*
Boreal migrant to coast, most numerous in w. Guayas. Slender black bill with yellow tip (but tip can be hard to see). Tail longer and more deeply forked than Gull-billed's; Sandwich can also look very pale.
p. 165

6. COMMON TERN, *Sterna hirundo*
Boreal migrant to coast, most numerous in w. Guayas. A mid-sized tern, graceful with deeply forked tail except when molting. Reddish legs at all seasons, brighter when breeding; bill blood red with black tip in breeding plumage, blackish (sometimes with red at base) at other times. Birds in Ecuador usually show a dark carpal bar on closed wing.
p. 166

7. ARCTIC TERN, *Sterna paradisaea*
Scarce transient mainly to offshore waters, a few sometimes reaching coastal lagoons (then often with Commons). Closely resembles more numerous Common Tern; legs slightly shorter. In all plumages shows crisp narrow black margin to underside of wing. Breeding birds have blood red bill, slightly grayer underparts. Nonbreeders difficult but have less distinct carpal bar, whiter tail (no dusky on outermost feather), whiter flight feathers.
p. 166

8. SOUTH AMERICAN TERN, *Sterna hirundinacea*
Casual wanderer to coast of Santa Elena Peninsula. Closely resembles Arctic Tern, but larger with longer legs, longer and heavier bill.
p. 167

9. YELLOW-BILLED TERN, *Sterna superciliaris*
Along rivers in lowlands of east. Small. Slender yellow bill.
p. 167

10. LEAST TERN, *Sterna antillarum*
Casual boreal migrant to coast, so far only in w. Guayas. Small. Slender, narrowly black-tipped yellow bill in breeding adult, otherwise brownish or blackish.
p. 167

11. PERUVIAN TERN, *Sterna lorata*
Scarce austral visitant to sw. coast. Small. Bill basally olive yellowish (apparently at all seasons). Underparts pearly gray.
p. 168

12. BRIDLED TERN, *Sterna anaethetus*
Very local breeder on islands off w. Guayas coast; forages mostly offshore. Distinctive, with brown mantle and whitish nuchal collar.
p. 168

13. INCA TERN, *Larosterna inca*
Rare, erratic visitant to sw. coast (none present most years). An unmistakable large, dark tern with bright red bill, conspicuous curling white moustache.
p. 169

14. BLACK TERN, *Chlidonias niger*
Scarce boreal migrant to coast. A fairly small, gray-backed tern with only slightly notched tail. Nonbreeders have pied head pattern, dusky patch on sides of breast. Breeding-plumage birds have head and underparts black.
p. 169

15. LARGE-BILLED TERN, *Phaetusa simplex*
Generally uncommon along rivers in lowlands of east; less numerous than Yellow-billed. A large tern with heavy lemon yellow bill; flashy black, gray, and white wing pattern in flight.
p. 168

16. BLACK SKIMMER, *Rynchops niger*
Generally uncommon along rivers in lowlands of east, also a few along sw. coast. Unmistakable, with spectacular laterally compressed black and red bill; black upperparts. Feeds by skimming low over water, bill open wide, with lower mandible slicing surface.
p. 170

Plate 28 Pigeons I

Columba Pigeons

Arboreal pigeons found mainly in canopy of humid and montane forests. Despite their large size, many species are often quite inconspicuous, though some at least occasionally take prominent perches. A few species closely resemble each other; particularly the Ruddy/Plumbeous/Dusky trio are often best told by voice.

1. BAND-TAILED PIGEON, *Columba fasciata*
Numerous and often conspicuous in subtropical and temperate forest and woodland. Wide pale tail-band (most obvious in flight), narrow but conspicuous white nuchal collar, yellow bill. p. 171

2. PLUMBEOUS PIGEON, *Columba plumbea*
Lowlands and foothills of east; foothills and subtropics of west. Mainly grayish brown, darker in west; iris whitish. Distinctive voice. p. 173

3. RUDDY PIGEON, *Columba subvinacea*
Lowlands of east and west, and up to lower subtropics on both slopes. Mainly vinaceous brown; iris reddish. Very similar to Plumbeous Pigeon (see text), often best told by distinctive voice. p. 172

4. DUSKY PIGEON, *Columba goodsoni*
Humid forest canopy in lowlands and foothills of northwest. Somewhat contrasting gray head and foreneck. Distinctive voice. p. 173

5. SCALED PIGEON, *Columba speciosa*
Local in lowlands of east and west, in east only near Andes. Nearly unmistakable, with mainly red bill and eye-ring, boldly scaled foreneck and underparts. p. 171

6. PALE-VENTED PIGEON, *Columba cayennensis*
Woodland edge (normally not in forest) in lowlands of east and west, in east mainly near rivers and lakes, in west rather scarce. Pale belly, two-toned tail. p. 172

7. MARAÑÓN PIGEON, *Columba oenops*
Rare in woodland of extreme southeast in Zumba region, where the only *Columba* known to be present. Red at base of bill, gray on wing. p. 172

Geotrygon Quail-Doves

Plump, short-tailed pigeons found solitarily (occasionally in pairs) walking on ground inside humid and montane forests; shy and inconspicuous, not often encountered. Heard far more often than seen. Note especially their facial patterns (with bold facial and malar stripes) and overall coloration (some highly glossed and colorful). Unlike *Leptotila* doves (Plate 29), *Geotrygon* show no white in tail.

8. SAPPHIRE QUAIL-DOVE, *Geotrygon saphirina*
Inside terra firme forest in lowlands and foothills of east. Bold head pattern with white facial stripe, black malar stripe, gray crown; purple back and blue rump. p. 180

9. INDIGO-CROWNED QUAIL-DOVE, *Geotrygon purpurata*
Inside very humid forest in foothills and adjacent lowlands of northwest. Like Sapphire, but with dark blue hindcrown; breast slightly darker gray. p. 180

10. OLIVE-BACKED QUAIL-DOVE, *Geotrygon veraguensis*
Inside very humid forest in lowlands of Esmeraldas. Mainly dark brown, with sharply contrasting white forehead and stripe on lower face. p. 181

11. RUDDY QUAIL-DOVE, *Geotrygon montana*
Widespread inside humid forest and woodland in lowlands of east and west, some up into lower subtropics. Reddish bill; ♂ mainly rufous-chestnut, ♀ duller, browner, with more subdued facial pattern and brown malar stripe. p. 182

12. VIOLACEOUS QUAIL-DOVE, *Geotrygon violacea*
Recorded from inside humid forest in lowlands of northeast (Cuyabeno). Reddish bill and eye-ring (like Ruddy's), but no strong facial pattern (no malar); white forecrown, strong violet gloss on neck and back, pale grayish mauve breast. p. 182

13. WHITE-THROATED QUAIL-DOVE, *Geotrygon frenata*
Widespread inside substropical and temperate forest on both slopes; the only quail-dove ranging so high in Andes. Large, dark, with gray crown, black malar stripe, white throat. Juvenile shows blackish barring. p. 181

Plate 29 Pigeons II

Zenaida Doves

Brownish doves found in semiopen terrain. White shows on corners of fairly long, graduated tails (especially in flight). Often gregarious (unlike *Leptotila* doves), feeding on ground.

1. EARED DOVE, *Zenaida auriculata*

Often numerous in agricultural land and around towns, both in central and interandean valleys and lowlands of southwest. Dark spot on neck, black spots on inner wing.   p. 174

2. WEST PERUVIAN DOVE, *Zenaida meloda*

Local in stands of taller trees in lowlands of southwest. Conspicuous white in wing, bright blue eye-ring. Distinctive voice.   p. 174

Columbina Ground-Doves

Small doves, usually common in open and agricultural terrain, most species in lowlands. Note color of primaries (easiest to see as birds flush), most often rufous. Gregarious, feeding on ground.

3. COMMON GROUND-DOVE, *Columbina passerina*

Somewhat local in arid scrub and agricultural land in highlands. Scaly breast, rufous in wing (shows mainly in flight).   p. 175

4. PLAIN-BREASTED GROUND-DOVE, *Columbina minuta*

Local in open country in lowlands of northeast and southwest. Small; much like larger and longer-tailed Ruddy, especially ♀♀, but with rufous flash in primaries only.   p. 175

5. RUDDY GROUND-DOVE, *Columbina talpacoti*

Increasing in open country in lowlands of east. ♂ mainly rufous with contrasting gray crown. ♀ more uniform, duller, browner.   p. 176

6. ECUADORIAN GROUND-DOVE, *Columbina buckleyi*

Common in open country in lowlands of west. Black primaries and blackish bill in both sexes.   p. 176

7. CROAKING GROUND-DOVE, *Columbina cruziana*

Common in open arid terrain of southwest up into arid interandean valleys. Conspicuous yellow-orange base of bill, black primaries, chestnut-maroon scapular bar. Distinctive voice.   p. 176

Claravis Ground-Doves

Distinctive, forest-based doves, less conspicuous than the smaller *Columbina* doves, and not gregarious. Strongly dimorphic, but both sexes marked by "bars" across wing; ♀♀ mainly brown.

8. BLUE GROUND-DOVE, *Claravis pretiosa*

Forest borders in lowlands of west and (locally) east. ♂ unmistakable, mostly grayish blue. ♀ with bright rufous rump and tail.   p. 177

9. MAROON-CHESTED GROUND-DOVE, *Claravis mondetoura*

Very rare and local in montane forest and woodland. ♂ unmistakable, with rich maroon breast and conspicuous white in tail. ♀ much like ♀ of commoner Blue, but with tawny foreface, white on tail corners, less rufous on rump and tail.   p. 177

10. BLACK-WINGED GROUND-DOVE, *Metriopelia melanoptera*

Local in small flocks in paramo. Extensive black in wings, all-black tail, white bend of wing, bare orange skin in front of and below eye.   p. 178

Leptotila Doves

Mainly terrestrial, forest- or woodland-based doves which do not gather in flocks. Except for White-tipped, retiring and hard to see, rarely emerging from cover. Fairly large, relatively unpatterned, with square tails showing white tipping. Cf. *Geotrygon* quail-doves (Plate 28).

11. PALLID DOVE, *Leptotila pallida*

Humid forest and woodland in lowlands and foothills of west. Rich rufous upperparts with gray hindcrown and nape, pale underparts with white belly.   p. 179

12. WHITE-TIPPED DOVE, *Leptotila verreauxi*

12W *L. v. decolor*
12E *L. v. decipiens*—less white on forecrown
Relatively widespread in deciduous forest and woodland in west and up into highlands; a few also on Río Napo islands. Occurs at higher elevations than other *Leptotila*. More uniform and grayish brown than Pallid.   p. 178

13. OCHRE-BELLIED DOVE, *Leptotila ochraceiventris*

Now rare and local inside forest and woodland of coastal cordillera and far southwest. Richly colored with ochraceous belly.   p. 179

14. GRAY-FRONTED DOVE, *Leptotila rufaxilla*

Lowlands of east, especially in thick lower growth near water. Forecrown pale gray, blue-gray midcrown, buff lower face.   p. 179

Plate 30 Parrots I

Ara Macaws

Splendid very large, long-tailed, and intensely colorful parrots found primarily in more remote forested areas, with most found in lowlands of east. Macaws are also characterized by their bare facial skins, more extensive than the ocular areas shown by some *Aratinga* parakeets, some of which approach the smaller macaws in size. Raucous voices often draw attention to flying birds, which may pass high overhead; perched birds are usually much quieter. Though generally easy to identify, in low, angled afternoon light Blue-and-yellow and Scarlet Macaws can look uncannily similarly colored.

1. BLUE-AND-YELLOW MACAW, *Ara ararauna*

Lowlands of east, favoring várzea and river edges, locally still numerous. Unmistakable, with rich blue upperparts, golden yellow underparts.   p. 183

2. SCARLET MACAW, *Ara macao*

Lowlands of east, favoring terra firme forest. Mainly bright red, with yellow on wing-coverts.   p. 184

3. RED-AND-GREEN MACAW, *Ara chloroptera*

Lowlands of east, where scarce (Scarlet much commoner) in terra firme forest. Deeper red than Scarlet, with green on wing-coverts; lines of tiny feathers on bare white face.

p. 185

4. GREAT GREEN MACAW, *Ara ambigua*

Now rare and very local in lowlands and foothills of west, in both humid and deciduous forest. Nearly unmistakable in range; very large and basically green with red forecrown, yellowish underwing, red in tail.   p. 184

5. MILITARY MACAW, *Ara militaris*

Scarce and local in montane forest in foothills and lower subtropics on e. slope. Very similar to Great Green Macaw; no overlap. Slightly brighter, purer green; slightly smaller.

p. 183

6. CHESTNUT-FRONTED MACAW, *Ara severa*

Lowlands of east and west, mainly at forest edge. Smaller than the "great" macaws (but still fairly large), with conspicuous red underwing, bare white face.   p. 185

7. RED-BELLIED MACAW, *Orthopsittaca manilata*

Lowlands of east, especially around *Mauritia* palms though also often overflying forest. Bare face pale yellow, yellowish underwing, forehead concolor green.   p. 185

8. YELLOW-EARED PARROT, *Ognorhynchus icterotis*

Now exceedingly rare, found extremely locally in montane forest of subtropical zone in northwest. Like a smaller macaw in shape, showing obvious contrasting yellow on forecrown and face.   p. 188

Plate 31 Parrots II

Forpus Parrotlets
Tiny parrots with stubby, square tails found principally in lowlands, most often in secondary habitats. Often in small, monospecific groups; chattering calls. One of the few Neotropical parrot genera showing sexual dimorphism, ♂♂ with blue on rump and wing.

1. PACIFIC PARROTLET, *Forpus coelestis*
Mainly lowlands of west, most numerous and familiar in arid regions but now spreading into more humid ones. Unique in range.   p. 191

2. DUSKY-BILLED PARROTLET, *Forpus sclateri*
Scarce in lowlands of east. Dusky on maxilla; somewhat darker green than Blue-winged.   p. 191

3. BLUE-WINGED PARROTLET, *Forpus xanthopterygius*
Local in lowlands of east, most often in clearings. Entirely pale bill; bright, pale green plumage.   p. 191

4. BARRED PARAKEET, *Bolborhynchus lineola*
Erratic in subtropical and temperate forest on both slopes. Almost invariably seen as tight, high-flying flocks, rarely noted perched; distinctive shrill, high-pitched calls. Short, pointed tail; dusky barring inconspicuous at any distance.   p. 190

Brotogeris Parakeets
Fairly small parrots with short, pointed tails and rather bulbous bills found in lowlands; conspicuous and often at forest edge.

5. COBALT-WINGED PARAKEET, *Brotogeris cyanoptera*
Common in lowlands of east. Obvious deep blue in wing, small orange chin patch (often inconspicuous), bluish on crown.   p. 192

6. TUI PARAKEET, *Brotogeris sanctithomae*
Very rare in várzea forest and borders in lowlands of northeast. Compared to much commoner Cobalt-winged, shows much less blue on wing, no blue on tail, browner bill, purer white eye-ring, more yellow on forecrown (though Cobalt-wingeds show some).   p. 193

7. GRAY-CHEEKED PARAKEET, *Brotogeris pyrrhopterus*
Deciduous forest and clearings in southwest. Distinctive in range; pale gray cheeks, orange under wing.   p. 192

Touit Parrotlets
Fairly small, chunky parrots with square tails; generally scarce, local, and inconspicuous in canopy of humid and montane forests. Often seen only flying high overhead in tight, small flocks.

8. SAPPHIRE-RUMPED PARROTLET, *Touit purpurata*
Local in lowlands of east. Mostly plain bright green; dark brown scapular bar; blue rump (visible mainly in flight).   p. 193

9. SCARLET-SHOULDERED PARROTLET, *Touit huetii*
Local in lowlands and foothills of east. Dark green head with complex facial pattern and bold white eye-ring, red and blue on wing (and much red under wing).   p. 194

10. BLUE-FRONTED PARROTLET, *Touit dilectissima*
Mainly foothills on w. slope. Blue and red markings on face, ♂ with much red on wing.   p. 194

11. SPOT-WINGED PARROTLET, *Touit stictoptera*
Subtropics on e. slope. ♂ with much brownish dusky on wing and inconspicuous spotting; ♀ mostly green with yellowish face, some dusky spotting on wing.   p. 194

Pyrrhura Parakeets
Slender, long-tailed parrots, most with bright red primary coverts which flash conspicuously as they fly through canopy of humid and subtropical forests (rarely much above it). Cf. larger *Aratinga* parakeets (Plate 32).

12. MAROON-TAILED PARAKEET, *Pyrrhura melanura*
12E   *P. m. melanura*—lowlands of east
12SE   *P. m. souancei*—broad breast scaling; foothills
12NW *P. m. pacifica*—grayish ocular area; foothills
Most widespread *Pyrrhura* in Ecuador. Pale breast scaling (varies racially, narrowest in lowlands of east); reddish in tail.   p. 189

13. EL ORO PARAKEET, *Pyrrhura orcesi*
Local in foothill forests of El Oro and Azuay. Plain green plumage (no scaling), red frontal band.   p. 189

14. WHITE-BREASTED PARAKEET, *Pyrrhura albipectus*
Local in foothills and lower subtropics of southeast. Yellowish white to white collar and breast, red ear patch.   p. 190

15. PAINTED PARAKEET, *Pyrrhura picta*
One sighting from se. lowlands (n. Morona-Santiago); status uncertain. Mainly dark head with reddish foreface, no red on primary-coverts, large red belly patch.   p. 190

16. BLACK-HEADED PARROT, *Pionites melanocephala*
Lowlands of east. Chunky; short tailed. Colorful and nearly unmistakable with black crown, bright orange-yellow foreneck, white underparts.   p. 195

Pionopsitta Parrots
Chunky, short-tailed parrots found in lowland and foothill forests. Despite their brightly colored heads, usually inconspicuous except in twisting flight.

17. ROSE-FACED PARROT, *Pionopsitta pulchra*
Foothills and more humid lowlands of west. Face entirely bright rosy pink.   p. 195

18. ORANGE-CHEEKED PARROT, *Pionopsitta barrabandi*
Lowlands of east. Black head with contrasting bright orange lower cheeks; red underwing-coverts.   p. 196

19. SAFFRON-HEADED PARROT, *Pionopsitta pyrilia*
Very rare in lowlands of northwest; status uncertain. Head bright yellow; red underwing-coverts.   p. 196

20. SHORT-TAILED PARROT, *Graydidasculus brachyurus*
Várzea forest in lowlands of northeast. Chunky; short tailed. Mainly plain bright green with blackish bill and ocular area. Raucous voice.   p. 197

Plate 32 Parrots III

1. GOLDEN-PLUMED PARAKEET, *Leptosittaca branickii*
Local in temperate forest on e. slope, mainly in south. *Aratinga*-like, with long reddish tail. Distinctive in range (not with any *Aratinga*), golden plume crosses face.   p. 188

Aratinga Parakeets
Fairly large parrots with long pointed tails and obvious bare eye-rings. Found in a variety of habitats and areas. Often gregarious, usually noisy; flocks are regularly seen flying high overhead. Cf. smaller *Pyrrhura* parakeets (Plate 31).

2. DUSKY-HEADED PARAKEET, *Aratinga weddellii*
Common in lowlands of east, often at forest borders. Grayish head, blackish bill, large whitish eye-ring.   p. 187

3. RED-MASKED PARAKEET, *Aratinga erythrogenys*
Local in west, in a variety of wooded habitats (both humid and arid). Usually extensive bright red on head (but heads of young birds entirely green), red on underwing-coverts.   p. 186

4. WHITE-EYED PARAKEET, *Aratinga leucophthalmus*
Lowlands of east and lower subtropics on e. slope. Mainly bright green, scattering of red feathers on head, underwing-coverts red and yellow.   p. 187

5. SCARLET-FRONTED PARAKEET, *Aratinga wagleri*
Very rare and local in woodland of highlands in Loja. Resembles commoner Red-masked but considerably larger with red restricted to forecrown (young Red-maskeds may also have red only on forecrown), underwing-coverts green (lacking red except on bend of wing).   p. 186

Pionus Parrots
Fairly large, square-tailed parrots found widely in humid and montane forests, all species with red crissums. Highly gregarious and vocal, often flying high with characteristic deep wingstrokes.

6. BLUE-HEADED PARROT, *Pionus menstruus*
Numerous and widespread in lowlands of east and west. Unique, with rich blue hood (but color can be hard to see in poor light).   p. 198

7. RED-BILLED PARROT, *Pionus sordidus*
Subtropics on both slopes. Bright red bill.   p. 198

8. WHITE-CAPPED PARROT, *Pionus seniloides*
Mainly temperate zone on both slopes. White forecrown, throat, and speckling on face.   p. 198

9. BRONZE-WINGED PARROT, *Pionus chalcopterus*
Locally numerous in lowlands and foothills of west. Distinctive; mainly dark blue (no green), contrasting brownish wings, white on throat.   p. 199

Hapalopsittaca Parrots
Midsized, scarce parrots found locally in temperate-zone forests.

10. RED-FACED PARROT, *Hapalopsittaca pyrrhops*
Southeast. Red on foreface, extensive rosy magenta on shoulders (especially in ♂).   p. 197

11. RUSTY-FACED PARROT, *Hapalopsittaca amazonina*
One sighting from Carchi. Dull reddish foreface, extensive rosy red on shoulders, some reddish at base of tail.   p. 196

Amazona Amazons
Large parrots with square, relatively short tails found widely in humid and montane forests. Most species show brightly colored speculum. Highly gregarious, often gathering in large roosting aggregations (sometimes several species together). Fly with characteristic shallow wingstrokes; flocks comprise obvious pairs which often fly side by side.

12. RED-LORED AMAZON, *Amazona autumnalis*
Local in lowlands of west. Red forehead, yellow-green cheeks.   p. 199

13. FESTIVE AMAZON, *Amazona festiva*
Local in várzea forests of lowlands in northeast. Red rump (hard to see on perched birds), reddish loral band, blackish bill, no wing speculum.   p. 200

14. ORANGE-WINGED AMAZON, *Amazona amazonica*
Often common in várzea and riparian forests in lowlands of east. Yellow cheeks, blue on forecrown, orange wing speculum.   p. 201

15. SCALY-NAPED AMAZON, *Amazona mercenaria*
Local in montane forest on both slopes. Basically green with no head pattern.   p. 201

16. YELLOW-CROWNED AMAZON, *Amazona ochrocephala*
Lowlands of east. Yellow forecrown, narrower white eye-ring than often-sympatric Mealy.   p. 200

17. MEALY AMAZON, *Amazona farinosa*
Humid forest in lowlands of east and west. Large with wide white eye-ring, "powdery" suffusion on plumage.   p. 202

18. RED-FAN PARROT, *Deroptyus accipitrinus*
Rare and local in terra firme forest of lowlands of far southeast. Tail long and squared; hawk-like in flight, with shallow wingstrokes and glides. Unmistakable, with red-and-blue-barred ruff and underparts.   p. 202

Plate 33 Cuckoos I

Coccyzus Cuckoos

Slender cuckoos with long graduated tails whose feathers are white tipped (broadly so in several species). Inconspicuous, tending to sneak around inside shrubby cover; some species are more arboreal. They range principally in lowlands, most occurring in Ecuador entirely or mainly as nonbreeding migrants; except for breeding Gray-cappeds, they vocalize little or not at all. Eye-ring color appears to be individually variable, gray or yellow in most species.

1. BLACK-BILLED CUCKOO, *Coccyzus erythropthalmus*
Rare transient to woodland, forest borders, and scrub, mainly in west. Bill all black; underside of tail gray, feathers with narrow white tips.   p. 203

2. YELLOW-BILLED CUCKOO, *Coccyzus americanus*
Rare transient to woodland and scrub; few records. Lower mandible yellow; rufous flash in primaries; underside of tail black (paler in juveniles), feathers with broad white tips.   p. 203

3. PEARLY-BREASTED CUCKOO, *Coccyzus euleri*
Status uncertain, but certainly rare. Like Yellow-billed Cuckoo but somewhat smaller with no rufous in primaries.
                               p. 204

4. DARK-BILLED CUCKOO, *Coccyzus melacoryphus*
Austral migrant to shrubby areas and borders, mainly in lowlands of east; also apparently a local resident in southwest. Underparts mainly rich buff; distinct black mask.   p. 204

5. GRAY-CAPPED CUCKOO, *Coccyzus lansbergi*
Deciduous woodland and borders in lowlands of west; irregular in many areas. Gray head contrasts with rufous upperparts; underparts rich buff.   p. 204

Piaya Cuckoos

Predominantly rufous cuckoos found in humid lowlands, one (Little) in shrubbery mainly near water, two larger and longer-tailed species (Squirrel, Black-bellied) more arboreal. Soft-part coloration distinctive in each.

6. LITTLE CUCKOO, *Piaya minuta*
  6E *P. m. minuta*—darker generally
  6W *P. m. gracilis*—paler generally
Shrubby lower growth in lowlands of east and west. A small, shorter-tailed version of better-known Squirrel Cuckoo. No pure gray on breast; red orbital skin.   p. 206

7. SQUIRREL CUCKOO, *Piaya cayana*
  7W *P. c. nigricrissa*—orbital skin greenish yellow
  7E *P. c. mesura*—orbital skin red, less black below
Spectacular large, long-tailed cuckoo, widespread in forest and woodland canopy and borders in lowlands and lower Andean slopes. Yellowish bill; rufous-chestnut upperparts.   p. 205

8. BLACK-BELLIED CUCKOO, *Piaya melanogaster*
Scarce in canopy of terra firme in lowlands of east. Striking with bright red bill, gray crown. Note that Squirrel Cuckoo also is "black-bellied."   p. 205

Crotophaga Anis

Distinctive group of fairly large, black cuckoos with unique laterally compressed bills; long tails seem to be only loosely attached to their bodies. Found in semiopen terrain in lowlands, Greater principally near water. Range in groups and can be quite noisy.

9. GREATER ANI, *Crotophaga major*
Numerous and conspicuous near water in lowlands of east, a few also in southwest. Very large. Nearly unmistakable, glossy black with long tail; eye conspicuously pale. p. 206

10. SMOOTH-BILLED ANI, *Crotophaga ani*
Common and widespread in semiopen country in lowlands, often around houses. Large laterally compressed bill smooth but with "hump" at base of upper mandible.   p. 206

11. GROOVE-BILLED ANI, *Crotophaga sulcirostris*
More arid lowlands of west, in south also well up into highlands. Like Smooth-billed but somewhat smaller, usually less disheveled-looking; upper mandible shows grooves (but these often hard to see) and smoothly arched culmen (with no "hump"). Voice often helpful (see text).   p. 207

1NB

2

3

4

5

6E

6W

7W

7E

8

9

10

11

Plate 34 Cuckoos II and Hoatzin

1. STRIPED CUCKOO, *Tapera naevia*
Slender, small, brownish cuckoo of shrubby clearings and agricultural areas with tall grass; mainly in lowlands of west. Bold streaking above; dark malar streak; whitish underparts. Juvenile browner above with bold buff spotting, especially on crown; buffier foreneck. Secretive and heard more often than seen; elevates expressive crest while vocalizing. p. 207

Dromococcyx Cuckoos
Rare, inconspicuous cuckoos found inside humid forests in lowlands of east; both species are heard much more often than seen. Both are notably dark above, have tremendously elongated uppertail-coverts (especially Pheasant Cuckoo).

2. PHEASANT CUCKOO, *Dromococcyx phasianellus*
Rare in lower and middle growth inside humid and swampy forest in lowlands of east. Strange shape, with small head, thin neck, very elongated uppertail-coverts (often raised, producing an odd "humped" profile), and wide (often fanned) tail. Dark upperparts with white postocular stripe; chest speckled or streaked dusky. p. 208

3. PAVONINE CUCKOO, *Dromococcyx pavoninus*
Very rare (only one old record) in forest/woodland undergrowth in lowlands of east; elsewhere favors bamboo. Recalls Pheasant Cuckoo (even their songs are much alike; see text) but smaller with less "exaggerated" shape, uppertail coverts not as elongated. Foreneck fulvous with no dusky spotting or streaking, postocular stripe buff. p. 208

Neomorphus Ground-Cuckoos
Among the most spectacular Neotropical birds, ground-cuckoos are (sadly) only rarely encountered, most often when in attendance at army antswarms. Despite being very large, they are surprisingly inconspicuous. They range locally in extensive humid forests in lowlands and foothills and are essentially terrestrial. The 3 species are basically allopatric and easily recognized by plumage pattern; bushy crests often ruffled, long tails frequently held partially cocked.

4. RUFOUS-VENTED GROUND-CUCKOO, *Neomorphus geoffroyi*
Local inside humid forest in lowlands of east. Yellowish bill; brownish head with no black; brownish underparts. p. 209

5. RED-BILLED GROUND-CUCKOO, *Neomorphus pucheranii*
Recent sightings from inside humid forest in far northeast. Bill and orbital area mostly bright red; crown glossy blue-black; foreneck ashy. p. 209

6. BANDED GROUND-CUCKOO, *Neomorphus radiolosus*
Very rare inside humid forest in lower foothills of northwest, mainly in Esmeraldas. Unmistakable: body essentially black, feathers boldly scaled buffy whitish, extensive maroon-brown on wings and lower back. p. 210

7. HOATZIN, *Opisthocomus hoazin*
Bizarre-looking large cracid-like bird found locally in trees and shrubbery around oxbow lakes and streams in lowlands of east. Unmistakable, with shaggy crest, extensive bright blue facial skin, broad buff tail tipping; in flight shows much rufous in flight feathers. Often in groups and typically quite tame, flushing reluctantly, then perching and peering around in evident befuddlement at the source of disturbance, hissing and grunting loudly. p. 210

Plate 35 Smaller Owls

Otus Screech-Owls

A very confusing group of small owls which usually show short ear-tufts; note interspecific variation in eye color, either yellow or dark. Many species have both grayish brown ("normal") and rufous morphs. They inhabit various types of forest and woodland. Many screech-owls are hard to identify on the basis of plumage characters alone, so it is often best to go by range and, especially, their usually distinctive voices (though no species "screeches").

1. FOOTHILL SCREECH-OWL, *Otus roraimae*
Scarce and local inside forest in lower subtropics and foothills on e. slope, also in adjacent lowlands. Yellow eye, relatively uniform face, large white spots on wing. Also has rufous morph. CHOCÓ SCREECH-OWL (*O. centralis*), found in foothill forests on w. slope, is very similar in appearance but has notably different voice (see text).   p. 211

2. TROPICAL SCREECH-OWL, *Otus choliba*
Fairly common in lighter woodland and borders in lowlands of east. Yellow iris, bold facial rims, obvious herringbone pattern below. Also has gray morph.   p. 212

3. WEST PERUVIAN SCREECH-OWL, *Otus roboratus*
Local in deciduous woodland of southwest. Small; does not occur with any other *Otus*. Both morphs shown.   p. 213

4. TAWNY-BELLIED SCREECH-OWL, *Otus watsonii*
Inside humid forest in lowlands of east, often numerous. Dark iris; plumage relatively dark and unpatterned, with paler tawny belly. Apparently has no rufous morph.   p. 214

5. RUFESCENT SCREECH-OWL, *Otus ingens*
5E *O. i. ingens*
5W *O. i. columbianus*
Local inside subtropical forest on e. slope and in northwest. Dark iris. Upperparts relatively unpatterned and dark, fairly strong herringbone pattern below, with white ground color on belly.   p. 213

6. CINNAMON SCREECH-OWL, *Otus petersoni*
Local inside cloud forest on e. slope. Much like rufous morph Rufescent, but smaller and showing no white below.   p. 213

7. WHITE-THROATED SCREECH-OWL, *Otus albogularis*
Temperate forest on both slopes. Yellow eye, dark plumage with conspicuous white throat.   p. 214

Glaucidium Pygmy-Owls

Another extremely confusing group of very small owls, best identified by range—so far as known all species are allopatric—and voice. They are more diurnal and conspicuous than most other owls. Like *Otus*, *Glaucidium* have both rufous and a grayish brown morphs, and differ only subtly in plumage pattern and coloration. All species show "false eyes" on nape and a collared effect across lower throat.

8. ANDEAN PYGMY-OWL, *Glaucidium jardinii*
Temperate forest and woodland up to treeline on both slopes; occurs above ranges of other pygmy-owls. Relatively unmarked wing; dark morph has distinct white crown dotting, more rufescent morph has relatively plain crown (with subdued mottling). A newly described species, CLOUD FOREST PYGMY-OWL (*G. nubicola*), ranges in subtropics on w. slope south to Pichincha; in appearance it is very close to Andean but differs in voice (see text).   p. 215

9. CENTRAL AMERICAN PYGMY-OWL, *Glaucidium griseiceps*
Rare in humid forest of lowlands of n. Esmeraldas. Indistinct pale dots on grayish crown; rufescent overall plumage.   p. 216

10. SUBTROPICAL PYGMY-OWL, *Glaucidium parkeri*
Local in subtropics on e. slope. Bold white spotting on scapulars and wing-coverts; profuse white crown dotting; plain, dark umber brown back.   p. 216

11. FERRUGINOUS PYGMY-OWL, *Glaucidium brasilianum*
Woodland and borders in lowlands of east. Crown usually finely streaked (but can be nearly plain); relatively unmarked upperparts.   p. 217

12. PACIFIC PYGMY-OWL, *Glaucidium peruanum*
12L lowland form—crown usually streaked
12H highland form—spotted crown, bold white scapular spots
Common in woodland and semiopen situations in southwest. Somewhat variable, with rufous and gray-brown morphs present at least in lowlands (highland form usually, if not always, gray-brown). Lowland form resembles Ferruginous of east (formerly considered conspecific), but voice very different.   p. 217

13. BUFF-FRONTED OWL, *Aegolius harrisii*
Very rare and seemingly local in subtropical and temperate forest and woodland. Small. Unmistakable, rich buff on forehead, face, and underparts.   p. 222

14. BURROWING OWL, *Athene cunicularia*
Terrestrial in open arid situations locally along sw. coast and in highlands. Partially diurnal. Unmistakable, boldly white-spotted pattern, long legs, etc. A highland bird is depicted; coastal birds are smaller, paler, and less boldly marked.   p. 218

Plate 36 Larger Owls

1. BARN OWL, *Tyto alba*
Widespread in open and semiopen situations, most numerous in lowlands of west but also locally in highlands; scarce in east. Very pale below with white, heart-shaped face; upperparts golden buff. Light morph illustrated; tawny morph grayer above, buffier below.   p. 211

2. CRESTED OWL, *Lophostrix cristata*
Humid forest in lowlands of east and west. Unmistakable: large, dark, with conspicuous long flaring white tufts above eyes.   p. 218

3. GREAT HORNED OWL, *Bubo virginianus*
Scarce in paramo woodland and adjacent open terrain. Very large and dark. Conspicuous bushy ear-tufts; coarse barring below.   p. 215

Pulsatrix Owls
Large, round-headed owls with conspicuous facial patterns found in lowland and foothill forests and woodlands. Both species are often vocal and are most active at dusk and dawn.

4. SPECTACLED OWL, *Pulsatrix perspicillata*
Lowlands of east and west, also up into lower subtropics in west. Unmistakable; bold white pattern on face, plain buff underparts, yellow iris. Juvenile has contrasting black face mask.   p. 218

5. BAND-BELLIED OWL, *Pulsatrix melanota*
Foothills and lower subtropics on e. slope. Recalls larger Spectacled Owl. Dark-eyed with white foreneck collar, dark breast band, bold belly banding.   p. 219

Strix Owls
Fairly large, round-headed owls with complex mottled or barred plumage patterns. Found inside humid and montane forest; strictly nocturnal.

6. BLACK-AND-WHITE OWL, *Strix nigrolineata*
Local in humid forest in lowlands and foothills of west. Black and white, underparts white narrowly barred with black.   p. 219

7. BLACK-BANDED OWL, *Strix huhula*
Humid forest in lowlands of east. Blacker than previous species, especially below.   p. 220

8. MOTTLED OWL, *Strix virgata*
Local in humid and semihumid forest in lowlands and lower subtropics of west; only a few records from lowlands of east. Brown and mottled.   p. 220

9. RUFOUS-BANDED OWL, *Strix albitarsis*
Widespread but inconspicuous in subtropical and temperate forest on both slopes. Mainly rich rufous (especially ♂♂), beautifully dappled and marked with black and white.   p. 221

Asio Owls
Fairly large owls with ear-tufts (short in one) and streaking on underparts that range in semiopen terrain, two species in highlands and one (Striped) in lowlands. All are scarce.

10. STRIPED OWL, *Asio clamator*
Scrub and semiopen, often settled, terrain in lowlands; ranges mainly in southwest (in east locally on river islands). Long ear-tufts, black-outlined whitish face, boldly streaked underparts.   p. 221

11. SHORT-EARED OWL, *Asio flammeus*
Paramo and adjacent shrubbery and low trees. Sometimes active at dusk, coursing low with floppy but still graceful flight. Roosts by day on ground, usually in tall grass. In twilight may perch in open. Mainly dusky-brown, with coarse blurry streaking below; ear-tufts inconspicuous.   p. 222

12. STYGIAN OWL, *Asio stygius*
Semiopen areas and woodland of highlands. Roosts by day in trees, rarely perches in open. Almost blackish overall, with long narrow ear-tufts.   p. 221

Plate 37 Oilbird, Potoos, "Fancy" Nightjars

1. OILBIRD, *Steatornis caripensis*
Mainly on lower mountain slopes, but prone to wandering. Roosts by day in caves and dark gorges, locally in large colonies; at dusk emerges to feed by plucking large fruits from various trees (especially palms) in canopy and borders, often flying long distances. Large, with long tail, heavy hooked bill. Rufous brown with white spotting. Noisy, both at night and when disturbed in its diurnal roosts.   p. 223

Nyctibius Potoos
Solitary, arboreal, nocturnal birds with exceptionally large, highly reflective eyes that shine back at you like a beacon when spotlighted at night. By day potoos perch motionless, usually with eyes closed, relying on their cryptic coloration and pattern to escape detection. Unlike nightjars, most of which are smaller, potoos perch vertically, sometimes fully in the open at forest edge and in adjacent clearings; two rarer species (Long-tailed, Rufous) tend more to remain inside forest. Cavernous gapes open very wide, even more so than in nightjars. Each species has a distinctive, far-carrying primary vocalization.

2. GREAT POTOO, *Nyctibius grandis*
Forest canopy and borders in lowlands of east, at night most often seen along lake and river shores, regularly in semiopen. Big-headed and large-bodied, considerably more so than other potoos. Usually looks very pale, some birds almost whitish, but this varies and some can be pale brownish; never gives a streaked effect.   p. 223

3. LONG-TAILED POTOO, *Nyctibius aethereus*
Lower and middle growth of terra firme forest in lowlands of east, even at night mainly remaining inside. Large, long-tailed; basically dark-plumaged (like smaller Common Potoo) but with prominent white malar stripe.   p. 224

4. COMMON POTOO, *Nyctibius griseus*
Widespread in forest and woodland borders and clearings in lowlands and lower subtropics; more often in semiopen than other potoos. Somewhat variable in overall coloration, usually mainly grayish brown, sometimes with some white on wing-coverts; always seems to show band of black streaks across breast and black malar streak.   p. 224

5. ANDEAN POTOO, *Nyctibius maculosus*
Rare and local in subtropical forest and borders on e. slope. More uniform and dark than most Commons, ♂ ♂ with considerable white on wing-coverts (but this may be obscure or hidden).   p. 225

6. RUFOUS POTOO, *Nyctibius bracteatus*
Very rare and local in lowlands of east, apparently favoring seasonally flooded and várzea forests; tends or remain inside and fairly low. By far the smallest and most rufescent potoo; large white spots on scapulars and lower underparts.   p. 225

Uropsalis Nightjars
Dark, relatively unpatterned montane nightjars that mainly segregate by elevation, overlapping only locally (e.g., on Cordillera de Huacamayos). Despite ♂ ♂'s spectacular elongated outer tail feathers, the two species are often surprisingly hard to distinguish. Voices distinctively different.

7. SWALLOW-TAILED NIGHTJAR, *Uropsalis segmentata*
Rare and local near cliffs and seepage areas in upper subtropical and temperate zones on both slopes. Both sexes with upperparts uniformly spotted and mottled rufous; no white in wings. ♂ with very long tail streamers (can be 2–3 times as long as body) with white shafts.   p. 234

8. LYRE-TAILED NIGHTJAR, *Uropsalis lyra*
Local near cliffs and along streams in foothills and subtropics on both slopes. Both sexes have fairly distinct rufous nuchal collar but show much less rufous spotting on upperparts than Swallow-tailed; no white in wings. ♂ with extremely long tail streamers (can be 3–4 times length of body) with whitish tips. Regularly rests and feeds along roads and on roadcuts.   p. 235

Other nightjars are on Plate 39.

Plate 38 Nighthawks

Lurocalis Nighthawks

Dark, short-tailed nighthawks, rarely seen except during a brief period at dusk when they emerge from forest canopy to feed.

1. RUFOUS-BELLIED NIGHTHAWK, *Lurocalis rufiventris*

Uncommon in and near subtropical and temperate forest on both slopes. Usually seen in irregular flight low over forest canopy at dusk, not associating with other birds. Looks like a huge bat, with short tail, and dark and unpatterned underwing; rufous on belly and underwing-coverts is usually hard to discern in the lighting conditions when this species is usually seen. Rests by day atop a large tree limb, where very difficult to spot.   p. 227

2. SHORT-TAILED NIGHTHAWK, *Lurocalis semitorquatus*

Uncommon and local (overlooked?) in and near canopy of humid forest in lowlands of west and east. Like previous species, usually seen flying erratically at dusk over forest canopy, nearby clearings, and rivers; then normally looks very dark. Equally short-tailed. Notably smaller than Rufous-bellied, with blackish barring on underparts and underwing-coverts.   p. 226

Chordeiles Nighthawks

Nighthawks with slim pointed wings that show either a white wing-band across primaries or (Sand-colored) are predominantly white. Wing-bands, throat patches, and tail markings buffier in ♀♀ of Common and Lesser. All 3 species are mainly crepuscular and favor semiopen terrain, principally in lowlands.

3. COMMON NIGHTHAWK, *Chordeiles minor*

Boreal migrant and winter resident, mainly in lowlands of east, but transients (especially) can occur almost anywhere, even in central valley. Most often seen in graceful, bounding high flight with deep wingstrokes, usually in late afternoon or around dusk; then best known by prominent white band crossing wing. By day rests on branch at varying heights, sometimes on open ground; then inconspicuous and unlikely to be noticed unless flushed.   p. 228

4. LESSER NIGHTHAWK, *Chordeiles acutipennis*

Semiopen, often arid, areas in lowlands of west, locally penetrating dry intermontane valleys; also a few recent reports from ne. lowlands (status?). Most often feeds in low bounding flight relatively near ground. Closely resembles Common Nighthawk, differing in position of white wing-band (nearer tip of wing), somewhat less pointed wing shape (with outer 2 primaries about same length, not outermost longer), and buff barring on inner primaries. Calls also differ; see text.   p. 227

5. SAND-COLORED NIGHTHAWK, *Chordeiles rupestris*

Local along major rivers in lowlands of east, resting by day on sandbars (often in large flocks), darting gracefully low over water at dusk. Nearly unmistakable, with much white in wings, tail, and on underparts. Resembles Yellow-billed Tern more than any nighthawk.   p. 228

6. NACUNDA NIGHTHAWK, *Podager nacunda*

Very rare presumed austral migrant to lowlands of east. Large, with somewhat rounded wings less swept back than in other nighthawks; white wing-band broad. Tail short. Lower underparts pure white.   p. 229

7. BAND-TAILED NIGHTHAWK, *Nyctiprogne leucopyga*

Local around certain blackwater lakes in lowlands of northeast. A small, dark nighthawk with no white wing-band; also shows little white on throat, but has one white band on rather long tail. Like several other nighthawks, emerges at dusk from adjacent woodland to feed low over water.   p. 229

Plate 39 Nightjars

1. PAURAQUE, *Nyctidromus albicollis*
Numerous and widespread in semiopen areas and secondary woodland in lowlands, often sitting along roads (more often than *Caprimulgus* tend to). Large, long-tailed, with plain rufescent cheeks and conspicuous black spots down scapulars. Has gray and rufous morphs. ♂ with much white on sides of tail, showing especially in flight (see inset at bottom right). p. 229

Nyctiphrynus Poorwills
Fairly small, forest-loving nightjars found on either side of Andes; somewhat more arboreal than *Caprimulgus*. Considered conspecific until recently.

2. CHOCÓ POORWILL, *Nyctiphrynus rosenbergi*
Humid forest in lowlands and foothills of northwest. Dark with conspicuous large white spots on wing-coverts; narrow white fringe on tail-tips. p. 230

3. OCELLATED POORWILL, *Nyctiphrynus ocellatus*
Inside humid forest in lowlands of east. Large black spots on scapulars, white spots on belly (hard to see in field), broad white tail-tips. ♂ generally sooty; ♀ generally tawny. p. 230

Caprimulgus Nightjars
Confusing group of mainly terrestrial, nocturnal birds found in semiopen and edge habitats; difficult to become familiar with and generally hard to identify, though every species has distinctive voice. Eyes reflect brilliant fiery red. All are cryptically patterned in some shade of mottled brown, with only subtle interspecific pattern differences; note especially facial areas, presence or absence of a nuchal collar, and (especially in flight) positioning of white (or buff) on tail and wings if any is present at all. Gapes open wide to admit insect prey; rictal bristles unusually long.

4. BAND-WINGED NIGHTJAR, *Caprimulgus longirostris*
Widespread in semiopen areas, scrub, and woodland borders in Andes, occurring at higher elevations than other *Caprimulgus*. Both sexes coarsely barred, especially on head and neck. ♂ with white throat crescent, prominent white wing-band, large white tail corners; ♀ browner (less grayish) with throat crescent and wing-band buff, no white in tail. Regularly sits on roads; favors vicinity of cliffs. p. 231

5. WHITE-TAILED NIGHTJAR, *Caprimulgus cayennensis*
Local in arid scrub of n. intermontane valleys in Imbabura. A small nightjar with fairly prominent rufous nuchal collar. ♂ with white throat and malar streak, frosted whitish brow, much white in tail (visible mainly in flight). ♀ has buffier throat and malar, lacks white in tail. p. 231

6. ANTHONY'S NIGHTJAR, *Caprimulgus anthonyi*
Local in arid scrub, grassy areas, and low woodland in lowlands of west, where the only small nightjar. ♂ with prominent white throat patch, white wing-band, limited white in tail (only on inner webs). ♀ buffier with buff wing-band, no white in tail. p. 232

7. BLACKISH NIGHTJAR, *Caprimulgus nigrescens*
Local in open gravelly areas adjacent to humid forest in lowlands and foothills of east. Very dark, even ♂♂ showing little white. Occasionally rests and feeds on roads that go through forest. p. 233

8. RUFOUS NIGHTJAR, *Caprimulgus rufus*
Deciduous woodland in Río Marañón drainage around Zumba. Large, dark, with overall rufescent tone; throat dark with whitish crescent below. Wings with rufous barring but no wide band; tail corners broadly whitish and buff in ♂. Rarely in open, usually staying inside woodland. p. 233

9. SPOT-TAILED NIGHTJAR, *Caprimulgus maculicaudus*
Status uncertain; one specimen from lowlands of northeast. Favors damp grassy fields. Blackish crown and face set off by irregular buff brow; fairly prominent rufous nuchal collar; spotting on breast. ♂ with broad white tail-tipping. p. 232

10. LADDER-TAILED NIGHTJAR, *Hydropsalis climacocerca*
Semiopen areas along rivers and lakeshores in lowlands of east, often feeding from low branches out over water. Both sexes have sandy grayish and relatively unpatterned upperparts. Grayish ♂ has fancy "double-notched" tail shape showing much white. ♀ with finely barred and vermiculated patterning, no white in more normally shaped tail. p. 234

Uropsalis nightjars are on Plate 37.

Plate 40 Swifts

1. WHITE-COLLARED SWIFT, *Streptoprocne zonaris*
Widespread and often numerous in highlands (at times even over paramo), also ranging out over adjacent lowlands. Flies in large noisy flocks, regularly accompanying smaller swifts. Large with notably forked tail, usually conspicuous white collar encircling neck (less obvious in some young birds). p. 235

Cypseloides Swifts
This genus comprises one relatively numerous and distinctive species (Chestnut-collared) and 3 rare and relatively obscure—perhaps merely overlooked—midsized species. They differ from *Chaetura* swifts in larger size, longer and more swept-back wings, and shorter tails; gliding more frequent and typical flight faster than in *Chaetura*. Younger individuals (especially) show pale "frosting" on belly feathers.

2. CHESTNUT-COLLARED SWIFT, *Cypseloides rutilus*
Distinctive rufous-chestnut collar (but color can be hard to see except against dark background). Tail usually looks slightly notched. Some ♀♀ (perhaps younger birds?) lack chestnut in collar. p. 236

3. WHITE-CHESTED SWIFT, *Cypseloides lemosi*
Status uncertain, but may be regular with other swifts on e. slope and over adjacent lowlands. Distinctive white patch on chest (can be deceptively hard to see, however), tail slightly forked. p. 237

4. SPOT-FRONTED SWIFT, *Cypseloides cherriei*
Status uncertain, evidently rare in subtropics on both slopes of north. Striking white markings on face (but you must be very close to see them), short square tail. p. 237

5. WHITE-CHINNED SWIFT, *Cypseloides cryptus*
Status uncertain; evidently scarce in foothills on both slopes, at least in north, sometimes flying over adjacent lowlands with other swifts. Heavy bodied with proportionately short, squared tail (even shorter than in Spot-fronted); uniform blackish, marginally the darkest *Cypseloides*. Larger than Chestnut-collared. p. 236

Chaetura Swifts
Small, relatively stubby swifts with fast wingbeats and more "fluttery" flight than *Cypseloides*, not gliding as much. Rump pattern and its degree of contrast with back are important field characters in many species; also check overall size, degree of throat contrast. Identification is notoriously difficult, and beware varying light angles when attempting to discern what is "paler" and "darker." Most swifts can be identified with confidence only under ideal conditions.

6. CHIMNEY SWIFT, *Chaetura pelagica*
Uncommon transient and boreal winter resident to lowlands (perhaps also highlands, at least as a migrant?); status still unclear. A large, rather pale, uniform-looking *Chaetura*. Rump hardly contrasts at all; throat whitish. p. 238

7. CHAPMAN'S SWIFT, *Chaetura chapmani*
Status uncertain; one sighting from lowlands of east (overlooked?). Closely resembles Chimney, hard to distinguish in field. Differs (subtly) in blacker crown and mantle, slightly more contrasting paler ashy rump, but throat more or less concolor with underparts (not paler). p. 238

8. GRAY-RUMPED SWIFT, *Chaetura cinereiventris*
8E *C. c. sclateri*—rump more contrasting
8W *C. c. occidentalis*—rump less contrasting
Fairly common in lowlands and foothills of east, less so and more local in more humid lowlands and foothills of west. Small. Gray rump of e. birds often contrasts well with back, and in strong light can look pale, but is never whitish as in larger Pale-rumped Swift. Gray rump of w. birds shows less well (often hardly any contrast at all), but must only be compared with distinctive Band-rumped; w. birds marginally paler below than e. birds (but lack Band-rumped's contrasting whitish throat). p. 239

9. BAND-RUMPED SWIFT, *Chaetura spinicauda*
Foothills and lower subtropics of northwest. A small *Chaetura* with strongly contrasting whitish band across rump (easy to see), contrasting whitish throat. p. 239

10. SHORT-TAILED SWIFT, *Chaetura brachyura*
Numerous in cleared areas and lowlands of east. A relatively distinctive, dark *Chaetura* with obviously short tail (looks "tail-less"), highly contrasting pale rump and tail-coverts, all-dark underparts. p. 238

11. TUMBES SWIFT, *Chaetura ocypetes*
Local in semiopen areas and forest borders in lowlands of southwest; in most of its range the only *Chaetura* present. Rather long, bowed wings; rump and uppertail contrastingly paler; throat and foreface contrastingly paler. p. 239

12. PALE-RUMPED SWIFT, *Chaetura egregia*
Scarce in lowlands of east, but apparently overlooked. Considerably larger and heavier-bodied than Gray-rumped (with which it often flies, affording easy comparison), gliding more; rump and uppertail much paler, contrastingly whitish. p. 240

13. LESSER SWALLOW-TAILED SWIFT, *Panyptila cayennensis*
Uncommon in lowlands of east and west. Distinctive, with long tail, forked but usually held closed in a point; highly contrasting white bib and nuchal collar. p. 241

14. WHITE-TIPPED SWIFT, *Aeronautes montivagus*
Uncommon and somewhat local in highlands. Tail with shallow fork, but usually held closed giving squared appearance; conspicuous contrasting white bib, white tail-tipping. p. 241

15. NEOTROPICAL PALM-SWIFT, *Tachornis squamata*
Conspicuous over cleared areas and near water, mainly near palms (in which it nests), in lowlands of east. A small narrow-winged swift with long tail generally held in a tapering, needlelike point; underparts mottled. p. 241

Plate 41 Hummingbirds I

Glaucis Hermits
Small hermits with decurved bills, rounded tails showing rufous. Favor humid forest borders in lowlands, especially *Heliconia* thickets.

1. BRONZY HERMIT, *Glaucis aenea*
Lowlands of northwest. Bronzy green above; pale rufous below. p. 242

2. RUFOUS-BREASTED HERMIT, *Glaucis hirsuta*
Lowlands of east. Green above; pale rufous below. p. 242

Threnetes Barbthroats
Small hummingbirds with decurved bills, black throat patches, cinnamon chest-bands, rounded tails with a bold black and white pattern.

3. PALE-TAILED BARBTHROAT, *Threnetes niger*
Lowlands and foothills of east. Tail mainly buffy whitish. p. 243

4. BAND-TAILED BARBTHROAT, *Threnetes ruckeri*
Lowlands and foothills of west. Broad black subterminal tail band. p. 243

Phaethornis Hermits
Diverse genus of midsized to very small hummingbirds with long usually decurved bills and elongated central tail feathers tipped white. Color of underparts varies and is important. Found in forest and woodland undergrowth (mainly in humid regions), many species favoring *Heliconia*. ♂♂ gather to sing noisily at leks.

5. WHITE-WHISKERED HERMIT, *Phaethornis yaruqui*
Lowlands and foothills of west, often common. Dark overall with contrasting white crissum and malar. p. 244

6. GREEN HERMIT, *Phaethornis guy*
Foothills and subtropics on e. slope. Dark with gray underparts, contrasting buff facial stripes. p. 244

7. TAWNY-BELLIED HERMIT, *Phaethornis syrmatophorus*
Subtropics on both slopes. Bright ochraceous rump and underparts, very long central rectrices. p. 245

8. GREAT-BILLED HERMIT, *Phaethornis malaris*
Numerous in lowlands of east, principally in terra firme forest. Orange-red lower mandible; uniform dull buff underparts. p. 245

9. BARON'S HERMIT, *Phaethornis baroni*
Deciduous forest and woodland in lowlands of west, in south ranging up into subtropics. Lower mandible reddish orange; grayish below, whiter on belly. p. 245

10. WHITE-BEARDED HERMIT, *Phaethornis hispidus*
Várzea and riparian forest, secondary woodland in lowlands of east. Grayish underparts and rump, prominent white facial markings and throat stripe. p. 246

11. STRAIGHT-BILLED HERMIT, *Phaethornis bourcieri*
Terra firme forest in lowlands of east. Almost straight bill, dull facial pattern. p. 246

12. REDDISH HERMIT, *Phaethornis ruber*
Mainly várzea, along streams in lowlands of east. Tiny; mainly rich rufous underparts (♂ with black breast band). p. 246

13. GRAY-CHINNED HERMIT, *Phaethornis griseogularis*
13E *P. g. griseogularis*
13SW *P. g. porcullae*—slightly paler below
Foothills and lower subtropics on e. slope and local in Loja. Gray median chin (hard to see in field), uniform rich rufous underparts. p. 247

14. BLACK-THROATED HERMIT, *Phaethornis atrimentalis*
Uncommon and local in humid forest and secondary woodland (mainly near water) in lowlands of east. Small; blackish streaking on throat, buff underparts (less rich than in Reddish). p. 248

15. STRIPE-THROATED HERMIT, *Phaethornis striigularis*
Humid and deciduous forest and woodland in lowlands and foothills of west, where the only small hermit. Dusky throat streaking, buffy grayish underparts, brighter on belly. p. 247

Eutoxeres Sicklebills
Heavy, hermit-like hummingbirds with heavily streaked underparts, unique sharply decurved bills. Found in humid forest undergrowth and borders, and favor *Heliconia*, clinging while feeding.

16. WHITE-TIPPED SICKLEBILL, *Eutoxeres aquila*
Foothills and lower subtropics on both slopes, in west also locally in humid lowlands. Tail feathers black with white tips. p. 248

17. BUFF-TAILED SICKLEBILL, *Eutoxeres condamini*
Lowlands and foothills of east; local overlap with White-tipped. Tail mainly cinnamon-buff. p. 248

18. TOOTH-BILLED HUMMINGBIRD, *Androdon aequatorialis*
Humid forest of foothills and lowlands in northwest. Long straight bill, blackish-streaked underparts; whitish uppertail-coverts obvious in flight. p. 249

19. WEDGE-BILLED HUMMINGBIRD, *Schistes geoffroyi*
19W *S. g. albogularis*—♀ with white throat
19E *S. g. geoffroyi*
Foothill and subtropical forest undergrowth and borders on both slopes. Short bill, partial or complete white pectoral collar. p. 289

Urosticte Whitetips
Uncommon montane, forest-based hummingbirds, ♂♂ with unique white tips to central rectrices (broader in Purple-bibbed).

20. PURPLE-BIBBED WHITETIP, *Urosticte benjamini*
Foothills and lower subtropics on w. slope. ♂ with conspicuous purple chest. ♀ thickly spangled with green below (cf. ♀ of smaller Booted Racket-tail, Plate 42-10). p. 267

21. RUFOUS-VENTED WHITETIP, *Urosticte ruficrissa*
Subtropics on e. slope. ♂ with glittering green throat. ♀ thickly spangled with green below, buff crissum. p. 267

Doryfera Lancebills
Dull-plumaged, round-tailed hummingbirds of montane forest undergrowth. Strikingly long, almost upswept bills.

22. GREEN-FRONTED LANCEBILL, *Doryfera ludovicae*
Subtropics on e. slope and in northwest, especially along streams. Dark overall with coppery nape, green frontlet. p. 250

23. BLUE-FRONTED LANCEBILL, *Doryfera johannae*
Foothills and lower subtropics on e. slope. Dark and dull bluish overall with violet frontlet (blue-green in ♀). p. 249

24. SPECKLED HUMMINGBIRD, *Adelomyia melanogenys*
Common and widespread in foothill and subtropical forest undergrowth and (especially) borders on both slopes. Short straight bill, white-tipped tail, hermit-like face pattern, speckling below. p. 266

25. SAPPHIRE-SPANGLED EMERALD, *Amazilia lactea*
One sighting from lowlands of east. Like far commoner Glittering-throated Emerald (Plate 44-7) but has glittering violet-blue foreneck. p. 264

26. TUMBES HUMMINGBIRD, *Leucippus baeri*
Arid scrub of s. Loja. Dusty green above; plain pale buffy grayish below. p. 262

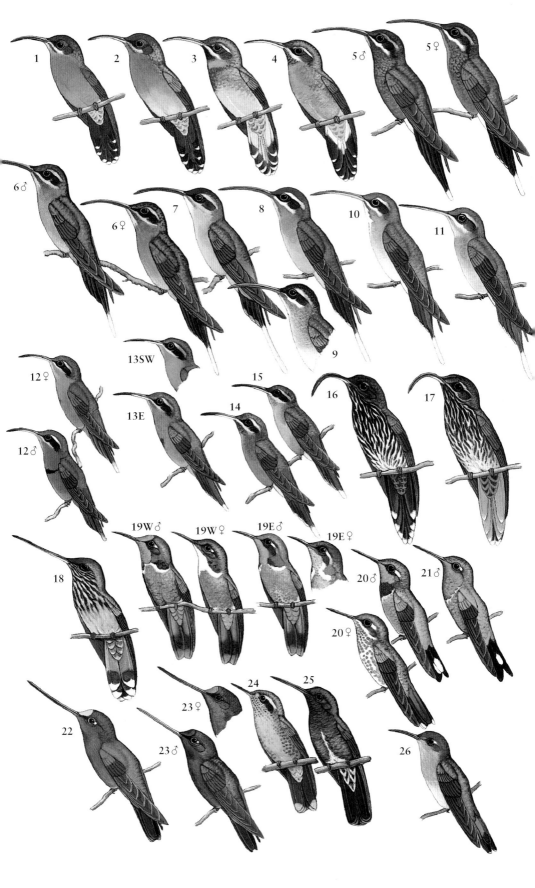

Plate 42 Hummingbirds II

1. FIERY-TAILED AWLBILL, *Avocettula recurvirostris*
Very rare in lowlands of east. Bill upturned at tip (hard to see in field); coppery in tail. ♀ with mango-like dark median stripe on underparts. p. 253

2. VIOLET-HEADED HUMMINGBIRD, *Klais guimeti*
Forest lower growth and borders in foothills and subtropics on e. slope. Short black bill; prominent white eyespot. ♂ with violet-blue head (♀ forecrown only). p. 254

Lophornis Coquettes
Tiny hummingbirds of lowlands and foothills of east, usually found at flowering trees in forest borders and clearings. All Ecuadorian species appear to be rare (or perhaps local? or seasonal?). All have prominent white to pale buff rump bands in both sexes. ♂ ♂ highly ornamented, ♀ ♀ more difficult (see text). Tail is gently wagged in usually slow, bee-like flight.

3. SPANGLED COQUETTE, *Lophornis stictolophus*
Mainly foothills and adjacent lowlands. ♂ with bushy rufous crest, feathers tipped black. ♀ with rufous on forecrown, more or less white throat, no blackish on underparts.
p. 254

4. RUFOUS-CRESTED COQUETTE, *Lophornis delattrei*
Very rare in w. Napo. ♂ like ♂ Spangled but rufous crest narrower and longer, feathers lacking black tips. ♀ has more rufous on throat than ♀ Spangled. p. 255

5. FESTIVE COQUETTE, *Lophornis chalybeus*
Very rare in lowlands. Fairly long square tail. ♂ dark with unique head and neck ornamentation. ♀ lacks thorntails' prominent white flank patch. p. 255

Popelairia Thorntails
Tiny hummingbirds with prominent white rump bands, ♂ ♂ with long, usually pointed tails, wasp-like ♀ ♀ with bold black and white patterns. Tails often held cocked. Canopy and borders of humid forest, often at flowering *Inga* trees.

6. WIRE-CRESTED THORNTAIL, *Popelairia popelairii*
Foothills and lower subtropics on e. slope (Black-bellied lower). ♂ with unique long wispy crest (sometimes short). ♀ has coppery cast above, solid black throat and breast.
p. 255

7. BLACK-BELLIED THORNTAIL, *Popelairia langsdorffi*
Local (erratic?) in lowlands of east. ♂ like ♂ Wire-crested but without crest and lacks coppery cast above. ♀ has dull green spots on throat (hard to see), no coppery cast above.
p. 256

8. GREEN THORNTAIL, *Popelairia conversii*
Lowlands and foothills of west. Both sexes unique in range.
p. 256

9. PURPLE-BACKED THORNBILL, *Ramphomicron microrhynchum*
Infrequent in forest borders and scrub of temperate zone on both slopes. Extremely short bill. ♂ with unique glittering violet back. ♀ densely green-spangled below. p. 285

10. BOOTED RACKET-TAIL, *Ocreatus underwoodii*
10E *O. u. peruanus*—buff leg puffs
10W *O. u. melanantherus*—white leg puffs
Foothill and subtropical forest borders on both slopes. ♂ ♂ with unique tail rackets. W.-slope ♀ ♀ have nearly immaculate white underparts; e.-slope birds more green-spotted below (cf. Purple-bibbed and Rufous-vented Whitetips, Plate 41). p. 283

11. ECUADORIAN PIEDTAIL, *Phlogophilus hemileucurus*
Local in undergrowth and borders of foothill forest on e. slop. Prominent white pectoral collar; bold black and white pattern on tail. p. 268

Calliphlox, Myrtis, Chaetocercus, and *Myrmia* Woodstars
Four closely related genera of tiny, bee-like hummingbirds with characteristic white flank patches (sometimes hidden by wings). Species identification often difficult, especially in ♀ ♀. Usually seen at flowering trees at forest borders, a few in gardens or more arid habitats. Tails often wagged in flight.

12. PURPLE-THROATED WOODSTAR, *Calliphlox mitchellii*
Foothills and lower subtropics on w. slope. ♂ has rufous on lower flanks. ♀ has buffy whitish throat, entire belly rufous.
p. 292

13. AMETHYST WOODSTAR, *Calliphlox amethystina*
Lowlands of east (where the only woodstar), occasionally up to foothills. ♂ has dull green "vest." ♀ with effect of pale pectoral collar. p. 292

14. PURPLE-COLLARED WOODSTAR, *Myrtis fanny*
Mainly scrub in arid intermontane valleys, wandering to humid foothills. ♂ with unique glittering blue throat. ♀ stockier, less bee-like than other woodstars, with less evident flank patch, fairly prominent white tail corners. p. 293

15. WHITE-BELLIED WOODSTAR, *Chaetocercus mulsant*
Widespread in subtropical and temperate zones, often in gardens and scrub. Contrastingly white median belly in both sexes. ♀ has rufous sides and flanks only. p. 294

16. GORGETED WOODSTAR, *Chaetocercus heliodor*
Scarce and local in subtropics on both slopes. ♂ with gorget elongated to sides, darker underparts than other woodstars. ♀ with mainly cinnamon-rufous underparts. p. 294

17. LITTLE WOODSTAR, *Chaetocercus bombus*
Local (erratic?) in woodland and borders in lowlands of west, wandering (?) elsewhere, even to e.-slope foothills. ♂ with unique buff pectoral collar. ♀ with cinnamon-rufous underparts, often a hint of narrow dusky pectoral collar. p. 294

18. ESMERALDAS WOODSTAR, *Chaetocercus berlepschi*
Rare and very local in woodland near coastal cordillera of west ♂ with gorget elongated to sides, white pectoral collar. ♀ has pale buff throat, whitish underparts, white collar.
p. 295

19. SHORT-TAILED WOODSTAR, *Myrmia micrura*
Arid scrub and gardens in lowlands of southwest. Dusty green upperparts, very short tail in both sexes. p. 293

Plate 43   Hummingbirds III

Campylopterus Sabrewings

Fairly large hummingbirds with somewhat decurved bills found on e. slope and in lowlands of east.

1. GRAY-BREASTED SABREWING, *Campylopterus largipennis*
Humid forest and borders in lowlands. Large white tail corners; gray underparts.   p. 250

2. LAZULINE SABREWING, *Campylopterus falcatus*
Very rare in subtropical forest and borders of w. Napo. Rufous tail. ♂ with violet-blue bib, ♀ with whitish malar.
                                                                p. 250

3. NAPO SABREWING, *Campylopterus villaviscensio*
Local in foothills. Dark (including tail; cf. White-tailed Hillstar, Plate 45-3). ♂ with glittering green crown and blue bib. ♀ dark gray below, narrow white tail-tipping.   p. 251

Heliothryx Fairies

Unmistakable hummingbirds with snowy white underparts and tail found in lowland (mainly) and foothill forest and borders.

4. BLACK-EARED FAIRY, *Heliothryx aurita*
East.   p. 290

5. PURPLE-CROWNED FAIRY, *Heliothryx barroti*
West.   p. 290

6. WHITE-NECKED JACOBIN, *Florisuga mellivora*
Lowland (mainly) and foothill forest, woodland, borders in east and west. ♂ unmistakable with blue hood, white nuchal collar, belly, and tail. ♀ thickly spotted dusky-green below except for white belly; tail broadly white-tipped.   p. 251

Colibri Violetears

Mainly montane hummingbirds with violet ear-tufts, dark subterminal tail-bands. ♂♂ give loud, repetitious calls.

7. BROWN VIOLETEAR, *Colibri delphinae*
Scarce and local in foothills and subtropics on e. slope and in northwest. Dull brown with throat patch and pale malar.
                                                                p. 252

8. GREEN VIOLETEAR, *Colibri thalassinus*
Forest borders and clearings in subtropics on both slopes. Lacks violet-blue on chin and belly; smaller than Sparkling.
                                                                p. 252

9. SPARKLING VIOLETEAR, *Colibri coruscans*
Common and widespread in subtropical and temperate zones, often in gardens. Violet-blue belly patch.   p. 252

Topaza Topazes

Large, spectacular hummingbirds found in lowlands of east. ♂♂ have greatly elongated, inwardly curved tail streamers; ♀♀ with glittering orange throats.

10. CRIMSON TOPAZ, *Topaza pella*
Now believed not to occur in Ecuador (early specimens were mislabeled). Mainly rufous tail in both sexes.   p. 271

11. FIERY TOPAZ, *Topaza pyra*
Rare and local, favoring blackwater streams. Mainly dark tail in both sexes.   p. 271

Chalybura Plumeleteers

Fairly large hummingbirds found in west, both species with characteristic white crissums in both sexes.

12. WHITE-VENTED PLUMELETEER, *Chalybura buffonii*
Local in woodland of southwest, mainly in foothills. Blue-black tail.   p. 266

13. BRONZE-TAILED PLUMELETEER, *Chalybura urochrysia*
Humid forest of lowlands and foothills of far northwest. Bronzy tail.   p. 266

Heliodoxa Brilliants

Fairly large hummingbirds with heavy bills, flat crowns; often show malar streak. Forest-based, but most species regularly emerge to feed at edge and in clearings. Cf. Gould's Jewel-front (Plate 44-4).

14. FAWN-BREASTED BRILLIANT, *Heliodoxa rubinoides*
Subtropics on both slopes. Buffy-fawn underparts, bronzy tail.   p. 270

15. VIOLET-FRONTED BRILLIANT, *Helidoxa leadbeateri*
Subtropics on e. slope. ♂ with brilliant violet forecrown. ♀ with blue forecrown, densely spangled throat and breast.
                                                                p. 269

16. GREEN-CROWNED BRILLIANT, *Heliodoxa jacula*
Foothills and subtropics on w. slope. Blue-black tail. ♂ with glittering violet throat patch, ♀ densely green-spangled below. Immatures frequently have rufous on malar and even face. Cf. larger Empress Brilliant.   p. 269

17. BLACK-THROATED BRILLIANT, *Heliodoxa schreibersii*
Local inside forest in lowlands (mainly) and foothills of east, especially along streams. Very dark. ♂ with black throat, violet upper chest. ♀ with obvious buff malar.   p. 270

18. PINK-THROATED BRILLIANT, *Heliodoxa gularis*
Rare and local in foothills on e. slope. Smaller than other brilliants. Pink throat patch; white crissum.   p. 269

19. EMPRESS BRILLIANT, *Heliodoxa imperatrix*
Subtropics of northwest. Large, robust, with long, deeply forked dusky-bronze tail. ♂ with glittering golden green belly.   p. 268

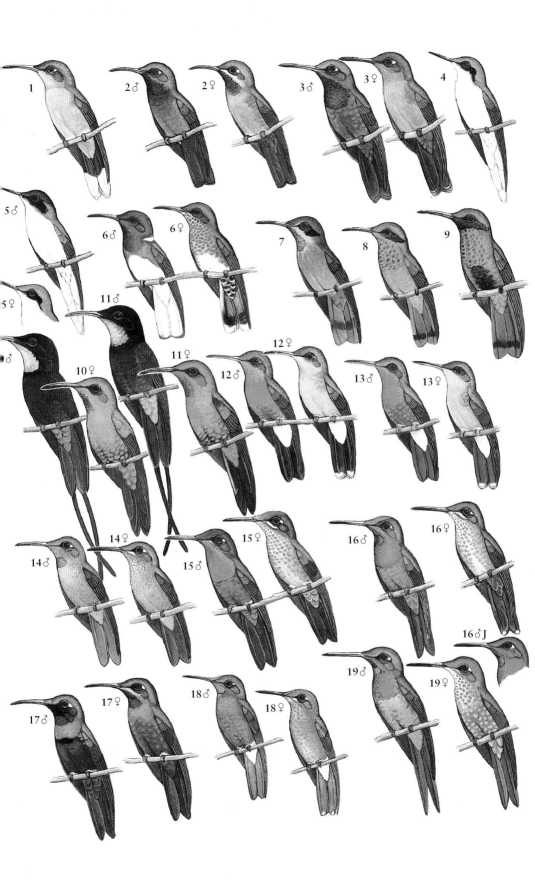

Plate 44 Hummingbirds IV

1. LONG-BILLED STARTHROAT, *Heliomaster longirostris*
Cleared areas and scrub in lowlands. Long, almost straight bill; white rump streak; bold head pattern.   p. 291

2. BLUE-TUFTED STARTHROAT, *Heliomaster furcifer*
Accidental vagrant to lowlands of northeast. Long bill. ♂ unmistakable, with glittering blue underparts and tuft. ♀ has uniform grayish underparts.   p. 291

3. BLACK-THROATED MANGO, *Anthracothorax nigricollis*
Fairly large hummingbird of cleared areas, scrub, and woodland borders in lowlands. Black median stripe down underparts (more obvious in ♀ ♀), mainly brilliant magenta-violet tail.   p. 253

4. GOULD'S JEWELFRONT, *Heliodoxa aurescens*
Inside terra firme forest in lowlands of east. Contrasting rufous chest band in both sexes.   p. 271

5. OLIVE-SPOTTED HUMMINGBIRD, *Leucippus chlorocercus*
Low riparian scrub on river islands in lowlands of east. Dull; whitish underparts with faint dusky speckling.   p. 262

6. MANY-SPOTTED HUMMINGBIRD, *Taphrospilus hypostictus*
Scarce in clearings and forest edge in foothills and lower subtropics on e. slope. Fairly large; dense spotting below; no white malar or tail corners; bronzy green tail.   p. 262

Amazilia Hummingbirds and Emeralds
Typical midsized hummingbirds, all showing at least some reddish on lower mandible. Most species favor forest edge and clearings.

7. GLITTERING-THROATED EMERALD, *Amazilia fimbriata*
Common in semiopen areas in lowlands (mainly) and foothills of east. White median belly stripe.   p. 264

8. BLUE-CHESTED HUMMINGBIRD, *Amazilia amabilis*
Woodland and forest edge in lowlands of west. Relatively dull; both sexes green-spotted below with dull buffy grayish crissum, dull bronzy tail; ♂ with diffuse blue on chest, glittering green crown.   p. 265

9. PURPLE-CHESTED HUMMINGBIRD, *Amazilia rosenbergi*
Humid forest undergrowth and borders of lowlands in northwest. White crissum and blue-black tail in both sexes. ♂ with well-defined purple chest patch.   p. 265

10. RUFOUS-TAILED HUMMINGBIRD, *Amazilia tzacatl*
Common and widespread in gardens, clearings, and woodland in lowlands of west (mainly in humid regions), locally higher. Bright rufous tail. ♀ duller.   p. 263

11. AMAZILIA HUMMINGBIRD, *Amazilia amazilia*
11L *A. a. dumerilii*—bronzy tail; lowlands
11H *A. a. alticola*—mainly rufous tail; highlands
Arid scrub and gardens of southwest. White breast; amount of rufous on belly individually variable in both races.   p. 263

12. ANDEAN EMERALD, *Amazilia franciae*
12W *A. f. viridiceps*—green crown
12SE *A. f. cyanocollis*—blue crown and neck
Foothills, locally also in humid w. lowlands. Mainly pure white underparts, sides contrastingly green.   p. 264

13. BLUE-CHINNED SAPPHIRE, *Chlorestes notatus*
Scarce at forest edge in lowlands of east. Rounded blue-black tail.   p. 256

14. GOLDEN-TAILED SAPPHIRE, *Chrysuronia oenone*
Common in forest edge in foothills on e. slope, locally into lowlands. Golden coppery tail, ♂ with glittering blue head.   p. 261

Hylocharis Sapphires
Amazilia-like hummingbirds with mainly coral red bills, ♂ ♂ with at least some blue on head and throat. Most are rare and little known in Ecuador.

15. BLUE-HEADED SAPPHIRE, *Hylocharis grayi*
Arid scrub, light woodland, and gardens in intermontane valleys of north. Blue-black tail, ♂ with entire head blue.   p. 260

16. HUMBOLDT'S SAPPHIRE, *Hylocharis humboldtii*
Woodland borders near coast in Esmeraldas. Green tail, ♂ with head and throat blue.   p. 261

17. RUFOUS-THROATED SAPPHIRE, *Hylocharis sapphirina*
Rare in forest borders of lowlands of east. Bronzy green tail, orange-rufous chin; blue only on throat.   p. 259

18. WHITE-CHINNED SAPPHIRE, *Hylocharis cyanus*
Lowlands of east (but no recent records). Blue-black tail. ♂ with blue head and bib, tiny white chin spot; ♀ with mainly whitish underparts.   p. 260

Thalurania Woodnymphs
Found in humid lowland forests and borders, all with forked tails and slightly decurved, all-black bills.

19. GREEN-CROWNED WOODNYMPH, *Thalurania fannyi*
Northwest. ♂ with contrasting glittering violet-blue belly, ♀ with bicolored underparts (belly darker).   p. 258

20. EMERALD-BELLIED WOODNYMPH, *Thalurania hypochlora*
Southwest. ♂ entirely glittering green below. ♀ uniform pale grayish below.   p. 259

21. FORK-TAILED WOODNYMPH, *Thalurania furcata*
East. ♂ with dull green crown. ♀ uniform pale grayish below.   p. 258

22. VIOLET-BELLIED HUMMINGBIRD, *Damophila julie*
Lowlands of west in forest borders, plantations. Small, with woodnymph pattern. Bill short, reddish below; rounded tail.   p. 259

Chlorostilbon Emeralds
Small, short-billed hummingbirds with forked tails, ♂ ♂ glittering green, ♀ ♀ with white postocular stripe.

23. BLUE-TAILED EMERALD, *Chlorostilbon mellisugus*
Scarce in forest borders and clearings in lowlands of northeast and subtropics on e. slope in south. ♂ basically brilliant glittering green. ♀ with white postocular, blackish cheeks.   p. 257

24. WESTERN EMERALD, *Chlorostilbon melanorhynchus*
Fairly common in semiopen areas and scrub in highlands south to Quito region, and in lowlands of west (also up onto w. slope). Very similar to Blue-tailed Emerald (see text); ♂'s crown has golden sheen.   p. 257

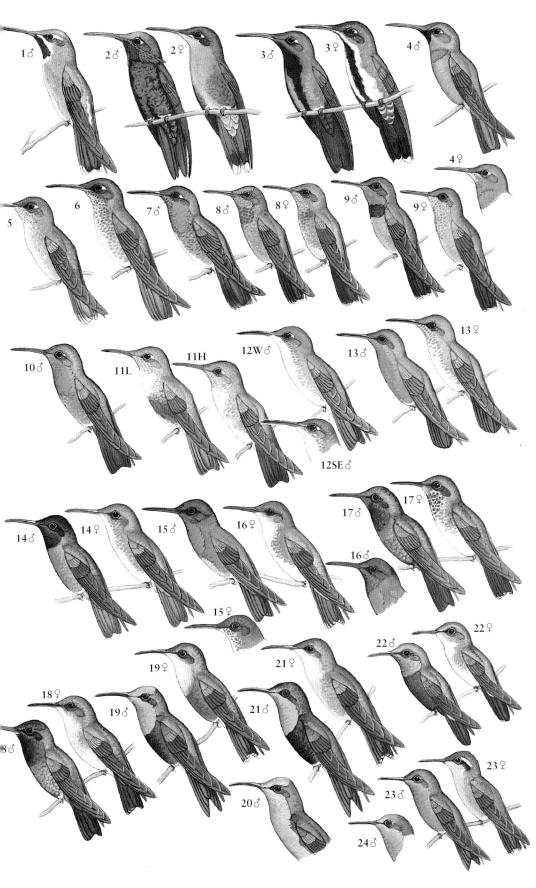

Plate 45 Hummingbirds V

Oreotrochilus Hillstars
Robust, spectacular hummingbirds found in paramo.

1. ECUADORIAN HILLSTAR, *Oreotrochilus chimborazo*
1 *O. c. jamesoni*—♂ with violet-blue hood
1CH *O. c. chimborazo*—♂'s throat green; Volcán Chimborazo only
♂ white below with dark median belly stripe. ♀ dull grayish green above, lightly speckled below.   p. 272

2. ANDEAN HILLSTAR, *Oreotrochilus estella*
Extreme se. Loja. ♂ has dull green crown, glittering green throat, wider belly band. ♀ like ♀ Ecuadorian.   p. 272

3. WHITE-TAILED HILLSTAR, *Urochroa bougueri*
3W *U. b. bougueri*—prominent rufous malar, bronzy upperparts
3E *U. b. leucura*—green upperparts
Subtropical forest on both slopes in north, on w. slope mainly along rocky streams. Dark with conspicuous white in tail. On e. slope, cf. dark-tailed Napo Sabrewing (Plate 43-3).   p. 272

4. GIANT HUMMINGBIRD, *Patagona gigas*
Unmistakably huge hummingbird of arid acrub and gardens in central valley; conspicuous whitish rump.   p. 273

5. SHINING SUNBEAM, *Aglaeactis cupripennis*
Shrubby areas near treeline. Unmistakable: cinnamon and brown. S. birds have shorter bill, mainly rufous tail (with bronzy less extensive). ♀♀ lack iridescence on rump.   p. 273

6. GREAT SAPPHIREWING, *Pterophanes cyanopterus*
Shrubby areas near treeline, mainly in humid regions. Large, hovering with slow wingbeats. ♂ with blue wings. ♀ cinnmon-rufous below.   p. 274

7. SWORD-BILLED HUMMINGBIRD, *Ensifera ensifera*
Temperate forest and scrub. Unmistakably long, upswept bill.   p. 276

Coeligena Incas and Starfrontlets
Fairly large, usually boldly patterned hummingbirds with long straight bills found in montane forest and borders.

8. BRONZY INCA, *Coeligena coeligena*
Subtropics on e. slope. Mainly bronzy brown with paler, streaky foreneck.   p. 275

9. BROWN INCA, *Coeligena wilsoni*
Foothills and subtropics on w. slope. Dark with conspicuous white patch on sides of chest.   p. 275

10. COLLARED INCA, *Coeligena torquata*
Upper subtropical and temperate zones on e. slope and in northwest. Flashy, with conspicuous large white chest shield, much white in tail.   p. 275

11. BUFF-WINGED STARFRONTLET, *Coeligena lutetiae*
Temperate zone on e. slope and in northwest. Conspicuous buff wing patch.   p. 276

12. RAINBOW STARFRONTLET, *Coeligena iris*
12S *C. i. iris*—more rufous on belly and back
12N *C. i. hesperus*—♂ with glittering coppery red crown
Subtropical and temperate scrub and woodland in south. Colorful, glittering crown; rufous belly, rump, and tail.   p. 276

Lesbia Trainbearers
Small but very long-tailed hummingbirds found in montane areas and interandean valleys.

13. BLACK-TAILED TRAINBEARER, *Lesbia victoriae*
Common in scrub and gardens in arid regions, locally up into paramo. Slightly decurved bill; mainly black uppertail.   p. 284

14. GREEN-TAILED TRAINBEARER, *Lesbia nuna*
Local (commoner in south) in montane scrub and forest borders. Short straight bill. Smaller and shorter-tailed than Black-tailed; both sexes brighter green generally (including upper side of tails).   p. 284

Aglaiocercus Sylphs
Montane forest hummingbirds, often numerous, ♂♂ with spectacularly long, colorful tails, ♀♀ with conspicuous rufous below.

15. LONG-TAILED SYLPH, *Aglaiocercus kingi*
15E *A. k. mocoa*—♂ bluer tailed
15NW *A. k. emmae*—♂ green-tailed, lacks throat patch
Subtropical and lower temperate zones on both slopes; in west occurs higher than Violet-tailed. ♂'s speckled throat meets rufous lower underparts.   p. 288

16. VIOLET-TAILED SYLPH, *Aglaiocercus coelestis*
16NW *A. c. coelestis*
16SW *A. c. aethereus*—♂ lacks throat patch
Foothills and lower subtropics of west. ♂ with violet-blue uppertail. ♀ has conspicuous white chest.   p. 289

Boissonneaua Coronets
Montane hummingbirds with short straight bills, strongly patterned tails. Favor forest borders. All expose rufous underwing-coverts while holding wings up after alighting. ♀♀ duller.

17. BUFF-TAILED CORONET, *Boissonneaua flavescens*
Subtropics of northwest, also locally in northeast. Mainly green with prominent buff in tail.   p. 277

18. CHESTNUT-BREASTED CORONET, *Boissonneaua matthewsii*
Subtropics of east and (locally) southwest. Contrasting rufous-chestnut lower underparts and tail.   p. 277

19. VELVET-PURPLE CORONET, *Boissonneaua jardini*
Scarce in foothills and subtropics of northwest. Spectacular: mainly glittering purple and turquoise green, flashing white tail.   p. 278

20. PERUVIAN SHEARTAIL, *Thaumastura cora*
Casual (vagrant?) in scrub of s. Loja. ♂ unmistakable with long tail streamers. ♀ resembles ♀ Purple-collared Woodstar (Plate 42-14) but bill shorter, straighter.   p. 291

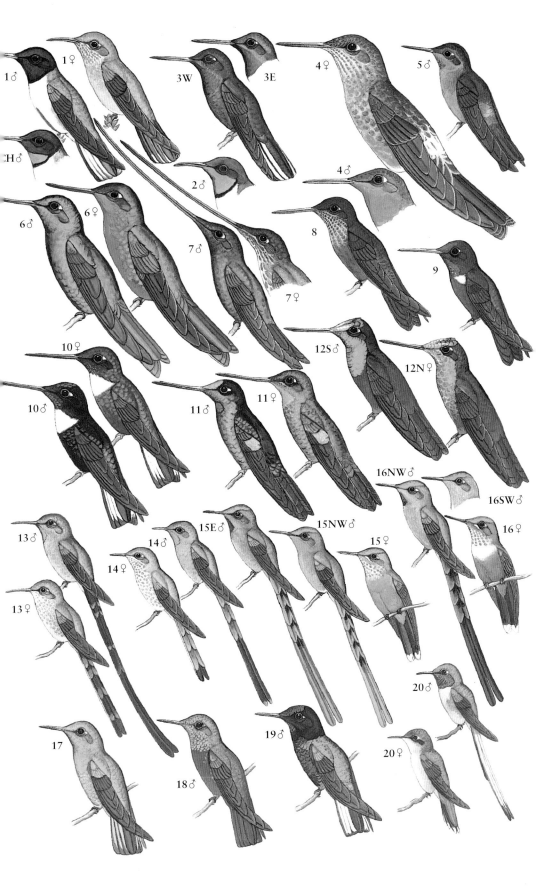

Plate 46 Hummingbirds VI

1. MOUNTAIN VELVETBREAST, *Lafresnaya lafresnayi*
Temperate forest borders and scrub. Decurved bill; much white in tail in both sexes. ♂ with extensive black below.
p. 274

Eriocnemis Pufflegs

Colorful, iridescent hummingbirds with short bills and forked tails found mainly in temperate forest and borders. Conspicuous white leg puffs in all but one species (Black-thighed); glittering crissums in all but one species (Golden-breasted).

2. BLACK-BREASTED PUFFLEG, *Eriocnemis nigrivestis*
Rare and local in forest borders and nearby shrubby areas on nw. slopes of Volcán Pichincha. Short tailed (other sympatric pufflegs are much longer tailed); ♂ with diagnostic black breast shield.
p. 280

3. TURQUOISE-THROATED PUFFLEG, *Eriocnemis godini*
Extremely rare (no recent records; extinct?), apparently in valleys north of Quito; habitat unknown. Closely resembles ♀ Black-breasted; perhaps not distinguishable, though Turquoise-throated occurs (exclusively?) at lower elevations. See text.
p. 281

4. GLOWING PUFFLEG, *Eriocnemis vestitus*
Widespread near treeline on e. slope. Beautiful ♂ with dark glittering green breast shield, purple throat patch, etc.; ♀ has glittering blue disks on buff throat.
p. 280

5. SAPPHIRE-VENTED PUFFLEG, *Eriocnemis luciani*
Local in temperate forest borders and scrub, mainly in north. Long violet-blue tail; brilliant glittering bluish green underparts. Sexes alike.
p. 281

6. GOLDEN-BREASTED PUFFLEG, *Eriocnemis mosquera*
Locally common but inconspicuous inside forest and woodland just below treeline on both slopes, mainly in north. Long bronzy-green tail; breast with obvious golden cast. Sexes alike.
p. 282

7. EMERALD-BELLIED PUFFLEG, *Eriocnemis alinae*
Rare and apparently local at borders of subtropical forest on e. slope. Conspicuous irregular white breast patch. Cf. Greenish Puffleg.
p. 282

8. BLACK-THIGHED PUFFLEG, *Eriocnemis derbyi*
Uncommon and local in temperate forest just below treeline in far north. Glittering green crissum contrasts with short, forked, black tail; ♂ with black leg puffs.
p. 282

Haplophaedia Pufflegs

Dull pufflegs (no glittering feathers in plumage) found in subtropical forests and borders.

9. HOARY PUFFLEG, *Haplophaedia lugens*
Northwest; local. Dull, brownish underparts.
p. 283

10. GREENISH PUFFLEG, *Haplophaedia aureliae*
E. slope, somewhat local. Head bronzy, blue-black tail; solid green underparts.
p. 283

11. MOUNTAIN AVOCETBILL, *Opisthoprora euryptera*
Unique short, upswept bill. Recalls a metaltail; note streaked underparts.
p. 288

Metallura Metaltails

Small, short-billed hummingbirds found in temperate forest borders and shrubby clearings; often common. Note tail and throat colors.

12. VIOLET-THROATED METALTAIL, *Metallura baroni*
Very limited range in Azuay. Violet-purple on throat, dull green tail.
p. 286

13. VIRIDIAN METALTAIL, *Metallura williami*
13NE *M. w. primolinus*—♂ with glittering green gorget
13SE *M. w. atrigularis*—♂ with black gorget
Near treeline mainly on e. slope. Bright green undertail; crissum shows buff. Cf. pufflegs (especially Glowing).
p. 285

14. TYRIAN METALTAIL, *Metallura tyrianthina*
Widespread and usually common. Conspicuous coppery bronze tail. ♀ with conspicuous buff throat and chest.
p. 286

15. NEBLINA METALTAIL, *Metallura odomae*
Large metaltail found locally near treeline in far southeast. Glittering rosy red on throat. ♀♀ similar but duller.
p. 286

Chalcostigma Thornbills

Short-billed hummingbirds with beautiful elongated, pointed gorgets found mainly at high elevations in semiopen areas.

16. RUFOUS-CAPPED THORNBILL, *Chalcostigma ruficeps*
Local in subtropics of far southeast, favoring semiopen areas such as roadsides. Rather small. Prominent rufous crown; dull buffyish underparts; brownish tail lacks white tipping.
p. 287

17. BLUE-MANTLED THORNBILL, *Chalcostigma stanleyi*
At treeline and in paramo, sometimes feeds on ground. Very dark overall; long, forked, blue-black tail.
p. 288

18. RAINBOW-BEARDED THORNBILL, *Chalcostigma herrani*
Temperate forest edge. Rufous crown; conspicuous white tail-tipping.
p. 287

Heliangelus Sunangels

Fairly large hummingbirds with short bills, prominent glittering gorgets (at least in ♂♂), and forked tails found at edge of montane forest and in shrubby clearings. Hold wings up after alighting.

19. AMETHYST-THROATED SUNANGEL, *Heliangelus amethysticollis*
Locally common in subtropics in southeast. Conspicuous white pectoral band; rosy pink gorget. ♀ has rufous on throat.
p. 278

20. GORGETED SUNANGEL, *Heliangelus strophianus*
Subtropics on w. slope. Conspicuous white pectoral band.
p. 279

21. TOURMALINE SUNANGEL, *Heliangelus exortis*
Temperate zone in northeast. Some ♀♀ with distinctive white throat; ♂ lacks pectoral collar.
p. 279

22. FLAME-THROATED SUNANGEL, *Heliangelus micraster*
Local in temperate zone in southeast. ♂ with stunning flame-orange throat.
p. 279

23. PURPLE-THROATED SUNANGEL, *Heliangelus viola*
Widespread and common in south, often in scrub far from forest. Large brilliant violet-purple gorget (duller in some ♀♀).
p. 279

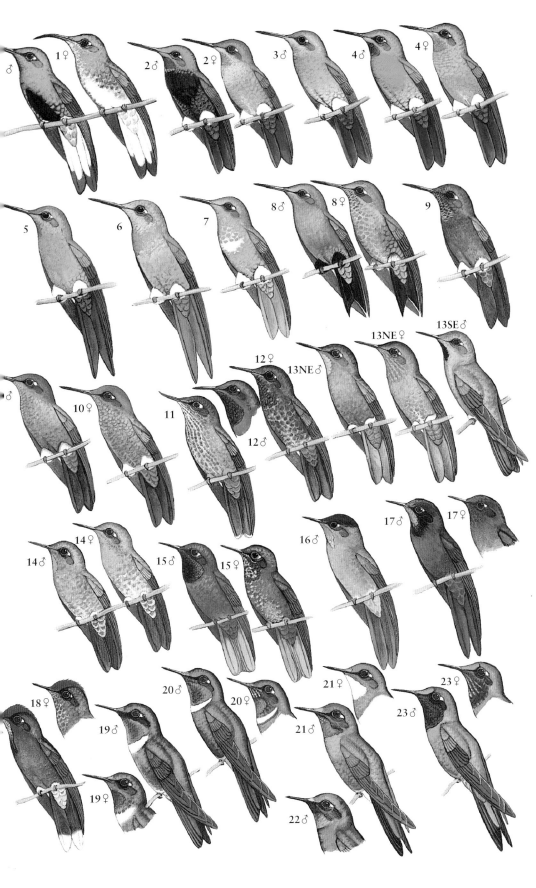

Plate 47 Trogons

Trogon Trogons

Fairly large, colorful humid or montane forest birds which tend to perch stolidly but tamely, often fully in open. Regularly found in pairs, ♂♂ more brightly colored than more sombre ♀♀. Note especially belly colors (red or yellow), undertail patterns, and bill and eye-ring colors. Voices are important—many more trogons will be heard than seen—but various species can be somewhat confusing to separate.

1. SLATY-TAILED TROGON, *Trogon massena*
Lowlands of far northwest, scarce and little known. All or mainly black undertail; salmon color on bill; dark iris.
p. 299

2. BLACK-TAILED TROGON, *Trogon melanurus*
Lowlands of east. A large trogon with red lower underparts; tail all or mainly black.
p. 297

3. ECUADORIAN TROGON, *Trogon mesurus*
Lowlands of west. Whitish iris in both sexes. Resembles Chocó Trogon, ♂ differing in red eye-ring and faint white breast band; for very similar ♀♀, see text.
p. 298

4. CHOCÓ TROGON, *Trogon comptus*
Humid foothills of northwest. Very like Ecuadorian Trogon; both sexes have similar whitish irides. ♂ differs in lack of eye-ring and white breast band, bluer uppertail. ♀♀ of the two not distinguishable in field (see text).
p. 298

5. AMAZONIAN WHITE-TAILED TROGON, *Trogon viridis*
Numerous in lowlands of east. Blue eye-ring, gray bill, yellow belly. ♂ with blue on foreparts, undertail largely white and unbarred. ♀ gray above and on foreparts.
p. 299

6. WESTERN WHITE-TAILED TROGON, *Trogon chionurus*
Lowlands of west. Blue eye-ring, gray bill, yellow belly. ♂ with blue on foreparts, solid white undertail. ♀ gray above and on foreparts; resembles ♀ of preceding species.
p. 300

7. BLACK-THROATED TROGON, *Trogon rufus*
Lowlands of northwest and east, in lower growth of terra firme, more inside forest than most trogons. Yellow on bill, yellow belly. ♂ with yellow eye-ring, green foreparts. ♀ brown above and on foreparts.
p. 301

8. AMAZONIAN VIOLACEOUS TROGON, *Trogon violaceus*
Humid forest in lowlands of east. Yellow belly. Resembles larger Amazonian White-tailed Trogon. ♂ differs in yellow eye-ring, barred undertail. ♀ has broken whitish eye-ring.
p. 302

9. NORTHERN VIOLACEOUS TROGON, *Trogon caligatus*
Humid and deciduous forest in lowlands of west. Yellow belly. Resembles larger Western White-tailed Trogon. ♂ differs in yellow eye-ring, black crown, barred undertail. ♀ has broken whitish eye-ring; resembles ♀ of preceding species.
p. 303

10. COLLARED TROGON, *Trogon collaris*
Lowlands and foothills. Red belly. ♂ has boldly banded undertail, green foreparts. ♀ brown above and on foreparts, undertail mottled and relatively unpatterned, dull facial mask. Occurs at lower elevations than Masked Trogon.
p. 300

11. MASKED TROGON, *Trogon personatus*
11W *T. p. assimilis*
11E *T. p. temperatus*—♂ with faint undertail barring
Subtropical and temperate zones on both slopes, at higher elevations than other trogons. On e. slope *temperatus* is found higher than *T. p. personatus* (not shown, but very similar to *assimilis*). Red belly. Compared to Collared Trogon, ♂ has narrower tail barring, bolder eye-ring; ♀ has blacker more contrasting face, all-yellow bill, barred undertail.
p. 301

12. BLUE-CROWNED TROGON, *Trogon curucui*
Lowlands of east. Red belly. ♂ like ♂ Collared but with blue on foreparts, yellow eye-ring. ♀ much like ♀ Violaceous but with red belly, all-yellow bill.
p. 302

Plate 48 Larger Woodpeckers and Quetzals

1. LINEATED WOODPECKER, *Dryocopus lineatus*
1E *D. l. lineatus*—more heavily barred below
1W *D. l. fuscipennis*—browner above
Widespread in forest borders, woodland, and clearings in lowlands. Narrow white stripe extending from face down neck, black auriculars; white back stripes parallel (not converging).   p. 339

Campephilus Woodpeckers
Large woodpeckers, boldly patterned with conspicuous crests (usually pointed). Sexes much alike, though differing in extent of red, black, and white on head. Identification to species rests primarily on head patterns and pattern and extent of white on back. Vocally all are somewhat alike; each species also gives loud whacking series of 2–4 raps (very different from Lineated Woodpecker's loud drum). Found widely in taller forests, especially in lowlands, though two species (Powerful, Crimson-bellied) are montane.

2. CRIMSON-CRESTED WOODPECKER, *Campephilus melanoleucos*
Humid forest and borders in lowlands of east. White V on back; heavy barring below. ♂ has mainly red head with white at base of bill. ♀ has black on front of entire crest, broad white malar stripe.   p. 343

3. GUAYAQUIL WOODPECKER, *Campephilus gayaquilensis*
Humid and deciduous forest borders in lowlands and foothills of west. White V on back; heavy barring below. ♂ has mainly red head. ♀ also has mainly red head; broad white malar stripe.   p. 344

4. RED-NECKED WOODPECKER, *Campephilus rubricollis*
Scarce inside terra firme in lowlands of east. Underparts unmarked, red and rufous; black back also unmarked.
                                                              p. 344

5. CRIMSON-BELLIED WOODPECKER, *Campephilus haematogaster*
5E *C. h. haematogaster*—black extends to chest, ♀ buff on neck
5W *C. h. splendens*—somewhat more black barring below
Rare inside foothill and subtropical forest. Facial stripes buff, underparts and rump mainly red, bold buff or whitish barring and spotting in wings (visible especially in flight).
                                                              p. 345

6. POWERFUL WOODPECKER, *Campephilus pollens*
Scarce in subtropical and temperate forest. ♂ has back stripes converging into white lower back and rump, underparts with barring black and rich buff. ♀ unmistakable, with no red on head.   p. 344

Pharomachrus Quetzals
Beautiful large trogons, two (Crested, Golden-headed) found in montane forests, one (Pavonine) in e. lowlands. ♂♂ have lovely shimmering green plumage with contrasting bright red lower underparts; ♀♀ less brilliant but still readily identified. Both sexes, especially ♂♂, have elongated wing-coverts (overlaying wings) and tail-coverts (overlaying uppertail). ♂♂ have characteristic loud and far-carrying vocalizations.

7. CRESTED QUETZAL, *Pharomachrus antisianus*
Uncommon in subtropical and lower temperate forests and borders on both slopes. Red iris. ♂ with frontal crest protruding over bill, mainly white undertail. ♀ with white barring on underside of outer tail feathers.   p. 296

8. GOLDEN-HEADED QUETZAL, *Pharomachrus auriceps*
Foothill, subtropical, and lower temperate forests and borders on both slopes. ♂ with golden sheen on head, all-black undertail. ♀ has head bronzy, all-black undertail.
                                                              p. 296

9. PAVONINE QUETZAL, *Pharomachrus pavoninus*
Scarce and local in terra firme forest in lowlands of east, where the only quetzal present. ♂'s bill salmon red, duskier in ♀.   p. 297

Plate 49 Kingfishers, Motmots, and Jays

Megaceryle Kingfishers
Large kingfishers with prominent crests, blue-gray upperparts.

1. RINGED KINGFISHER, *Megaceryle torquata*
Widespread. Large; bushy crest, blue-gray upperparts, mainly rufous underparts.   p. 303

2. BELTED KINGFISHER, *Megaceryle alcyon*
Accidental boreal migrant. Smaller than Ringed, with bands across mainly white underparts (blue-gray in ♂, blue-gray and rufous in ♀). Drawn to smaller scale than other kingfishers.   p. 304

Chloroceryle Kingfishers
Four species with dark oily green upperparts. Two larger species are mainly white below and favor larger and more open bodies of water, where they are conspicuous. Two smaller species are mainly orange-rufous below and range mainly in shady backwater areas where typically hard to see.

3. AMAZON KINGFISHER, *Chloroceryle amazona*
Larger bodies of water in lowlands of east. The largest "green" kingfisher, with heavy bill, no white spotting in wings and tail.   p. 304

4. GREEN KINGFISHER, *Chloroceryle americana*
Widespread near water in lowlands and (in smaller numbers) lower subtropics, even in salt water along coast. Green and white; smaller than Amazon, less crested and with slighter bill; shows conspicuous white spotting in wings and tail. W. birds are large.   p. 304

5. GREEN-AND-RUFOUS KINGFISHER, *Chloroceryle inda*
Inconspicuous along sluggish streams and in várzea forest in lowlands of east and far northwest. Green and rich orange-rufous.   p. 305

6. AMERICAN PYGMY KINGFISHER, *Chloroceryle aenea*
Inconspicuous along sluggish streams and in várzea forest in lowlands of east and west (where scarce and local). Tiny; green and rich orange-rufous plumage, white midbelly.
                                    p. 305

7. BROAD-BILLED MOTMOT, *Electron platyrhynchum*
7W *E. p. platyrhynchum*
7E *E. p. pyrrholaemum*—no rackets, smaller bill
Humid forest in lowlands and foothills of east and west. Broad flat bill with keeled culmen; head and breast mainly rufous with large black chest spot, blue-green belly.   p. 306

8. RUFOUS MOTMOT, *Baryphthengus martii*
Humid forest in lowlands and foothills of east and west. A larger version of Broad-billed Motmot, differing in narrower and more arched bill, small black chest spot, contrasting blue in primaries. As in Broad-billed, e. birds lack rackets.
                                    p. 306

Momotus Motmots
Large motmots with prominent rackets on tail-tips and a blue "diadem" on crown. Surprisingly inconspicuous, ranging in forest and woodland undergrowth.

9. BLUE-CROWNED MOTMOT, *Momotus momota*
9W *M. m. argenticinctus*—nape turquoise blue
9E *M. m. microstephanus*—nape deep violet-blue
Widespread in woodland and forest undergrowth in lowlands of west (also into subtropics in southwest), less numerous in lowlands of east. Extensive blue in crown, mainly green upperparts.   p. 307

10. HIGHLAND MOTMOT, *Momotus aequatorialis*
Lower growth of foothill and subtropical forest on e. slope (where the only motmot). Larger than similar Blue-crowned Motmot of e. lowlands (no overlap), but in color of nape and underparts more resembles w. birds.   p. 307

Cyanolyca Jays
Sleek jays found in montane forests. Primarily blue with black masks; note especially color and degree of contrast on crown.

11. BLACK-COLLARED JAY, *Cyanolyca armillata*
Very rare and local in temperate forest and borders on e. slope south to w. Napo. Mainly ultramarine blue, patterned much like more numerous Turquoise Jay; crown and throat show less contrast.   p. 564

12. TURQUOISE JAY, *Cyanolyca turcosa*
Widespread and often common in upper subtropical and temperate forest and borders. Mainly greenish blue with black pectoral collar; throat and crown contrastingly paler than rest of body.   p. 564

13. BEAUTIFUL JAY, *Cyanolyca pulchra*
Scarce and local in subtropical forests of northwest. Notably dark with strikingly contrasting bluish white crown. p. 565

Cyanocorax Jays
Strikingly patterned jays, larger and heavier bodied than *Cyanolyca*. Range primarily in lowlands, one (Inca) in lower montane regions. All 3 have black face and bib but otherwise differ strikingly in color and pattern.

14. VIOLACEOUS JAY, *Cyanocorax violaceus*
Common, noisy, and conspicuous in lowlands of east. Mostly dull violaceous with contrasting bluish white nape; head and foreneck black.   p. 565

15. INCA JAY, *Cyanocorax yncas*
Widespread in subtropical forest, woodland, and borders on e. slope. Unmistakable; the only Ecuadorian jay with green and yellow in plumage.   p. 566

16. WHITE-TAILED JAY, *Cyanocorax mystacalis*
Deciduous woodland and scrub in southwest, where the only jay present. Unmistakable, with handsome blue and white pattern; striking white in tail, especially conspicuous in flight.   p. 565

Plate 50 Jacamars and New World Barbets

1. WHITE-EARED JACAMAR, *Galbalcyrhynchus leucotis*
Conspicuous around margins of lakes and rivers in lowlands of east, often perching low and in the open. Unmistakable, dumpy and short tailed with oversized pink bill, chestnut plumage with obvious white ear patch.   p. 308

2. BROWN JACAMAR, *Brachygalba lugubris*
Local at borders of certain lakes and rivers in lowlands of east, sometimes in small loose groups. Short squared tail. Small, relatively dull, and brownish.   p. 308

Galbula Jacamars
"Classic' jacamars, with long, sharply pointed bills. Elegant and dazzling, they tend to perch on open branches, often in sedentary pairs, sallying out after passing large insects (often bees, dragonflies, even small butterflies). All but one are humid forest-based birds ranging primarily in lowlands.

3. YELLOW-BILLED JACAMAR, *Galbula albirostris*
Understory of terra firme forest and secondary woodland in lowlands of east. Bill mainly yellow, also eye-ring; no green on chest.   p. 308

4. WHITE-CHINNED JACAMAR, *Galbula tombacea*
Lower growth at forest borders, mainly in várzea, in lowlands of east. Whitish chin, glittering green breast, rufous belly.   p. 309

5. COPPERY-CHESTED JACAMAR, *Galbula pastazae*
Local in shrubby borders and lower growth in foothill and lower subtropical forest on e. slope. Yellow-orange eye-ring (often inconspicuous), bluish crown, deep rufous belly (also throat in ♀).   p. 309

6. RUFOUS-TAILED JACAMAR, *Galbula ruficauda*
Humid forest and woodland borders in lowlands and foothills of west, where the only *Galbula* present.   p. 310

7. PURPLISH JACAMAR, *Galbula chalcothorax*
Terra firme forest in lowlands and foothills of east, at times ranging up into mid-levels and even subcanopy. White lower throat and mottling on lower belly and crissum (replaced by buff in ♀), gray underside of tail, purplish breast.   p. 310

8. PARADISE JACAMAR, *Galbula dea*
Scarce and local in canopy and subcanopy of terra firme forest in lowlands of far east and southeast; often much higher above ground than other jacamars. Unmistakable: large but slender with a long pointed tail; looks dark overall with contrasting white throat.   p. 310

9. GREAT JACAMAR, *Jacamerops aureus*
Mid-levels and subcanopy of terra firme forest in lowlands and foothills of east; also locally in far northwest. Surprisingly inconspicuous, especially given its large size and beautiful shining dorsal coloration, but distinctive vocalizations often draw attention to it. Heavy arched bill diagnostic. ♀ lacks ♂♂ white on lower throat.   p. 311

Capito Barbets
Colorful, heavy-set frugivorous birds with notably heavy bills found in canopy and borders of forest, mainly in lowlands.

10. FIVE-COLORED BARBET, *Capito quinticolor*
Humid forest in lowlands of n. Esmeraldas. ♂ has red crown, white throat, yellow belly. ♀ with dense black spotting below.   p. 320

11. SCARLET-CROWNED BARBET, *Capito aurovirens*
Common and conspicuous in várzea and riparian forest and woodland in lowlands of east. Yellow-orange throat and breast. ♂ with scarlet crown, white in ♀.   p. 319

12. ORANGE-FRONTED BARBET, *Capito squamatus*
Widespread in humid forest and woodland in lowlands of west. Conspicuous orange forecrown. ♂ with entirely whitish and creamy underparts, ♀ with black throat and breast.   p. 320

13. GILDED BARBET, *Capito auratus*
Common in humid forest and woodland in lowlands and foothills of east. Both sexes predominantly black and yellow, ♂ with orange throat, ♀ with large black spots below.   p. 321

Eubucco Barbets
Similar to *Capito* but somewhat smaller, green-backed. Show strong sexual dimorphism, ♂♂ being very colorful, ♀♀ with more subdued colors but patterns more complex. Heavy bills either yellow or pale green.

14. RED-HEADED BARBET, *Eubucco bourcierii*
Foothill and subtropical forest and woodland on both slopes. ♂ unmistakable, with bright red hood. ♀ with complex head pattern showing blue on face.   p. 322

15. LEMON-THROATED BARBET, *Eubucco richardsoni*
Terra firme forest in lowlands of east. ♂ with red head, blue-gray nape, yellow foreneck. ♀ has black mask, gray throat, orange band across breast.   p. 321

16. TOUCAN BARBET, *Semnornis ramphastinus*
Subtropical forest and borders on w. slope south to Cotopaxi. Unmistakable: large, multicolored, with heavy bill. Despite its bright colors, most often located by far-carrying sonorous vocalizations. Orange-yellow on rump conspicuous in flight.   p. 322

Plate 51 Puffbirds

Notharchus Puffbirds

Puffbirds of varying sizes found in humid lowland forests; united by bold black and white patterns.

1. WHITE-NECKED PUFFBIRD, *Notharchus macrorhynchos*

Widespread in humid forest, woodland, and borders in lowlands. Large; forehead and extensive area on foreneck white.
p. 311

2. BLACK-BREASTED PUFFBIRD, *Notharchus pectoralis*

Rare in humid forest and borders in lowlands of far northwest. Recalls larger White-necked but lacks white on forecrown; discrete white patches on throat and ear-coverts.
p. 312

3. PIED PUFFBIRD, *Notharchus tectus*

3E *N. t. picatus*—larger; white crown spotting
3W *N. t. subtectus*—smaller; narrow black breast band
Canopy and borders of humid forest and woodland in lowlands, more numerous in west. A small version of White-necked; superciliary white (but none on hindneck); white scapulars.
p. 312

Bucco Puffbirds

Inconspicuous puffbirds with complex, relatively colorful plumage patterns. Found in lowlands of east.

4. CHESTNUT-CAPPED PUFFBIRD, *Bucco macrodactylus*

Scarce in forest borders and shrubby clearings. Small. Complex head pattern with chestnut crown, cinnamon nuchal collar, neat black chest band.
p. 313

5. SPOTTED PUFFBIRD, *Bucco tamatia*

Very rare inside humid forest in southeast. Large black malar area; conspicuously black-spotted underparts; cinnamon throat.
p. 313

6. COLLARED PUFFBIRD, *Bucco capensis*

Scarce inside terra firme forest. Unmistakable: heavy orange bill, bright orange-rufous upperparts, narrow black breast band.
p. 314

Nystalus Puffbirds

Mainly brownish puffbirds, arboreal in humid forests on either side of Andes. Inconspicuous except for loud and frequently heard vocalizations.

7. BARRED PUFFBIRD, *Nystalus radiatus*

Borders of humid and foothill forest in west. Unmistakable: prominent black barring all over, obvious buff nuchal collar.
p. 314

8. STRIOLATED PUFFBIRD, *Nystalus striolatus*

Borders of humid and foothill forest in east. Pale underparts with black shaft streaking.
p. 314

Malacoptila Puffbirds

Notably inconspicuous puffbirds with at least somewhat streaked patterns found in understory of humid or montane forests. The 3 Ecuadorian species are basically allopatric.

9. BLACK-STREAKED PUFFBIRD, *Malacoptila fulvogularis*

Scarce and local inside foothill and subtropical forest on e. slope. All-black bill; red iris; fulvous "bib"; extensive narrow streaking.
p. 315

10. WHITE-CHESTED PUFFBIRD, *Malacoptila fusca*

Inside terra firme forest in lowlands of east. Extensive orange on bill; dark iris; white pectoral crescent (sometimes doesn't show); extensive narrow buff streaking.
p. 315

11. MOUSTACHED PUFFBIRD, *Malacoptila mystacalis*

Not recorded in Ecuador, but found close to border on w. slope of Andes in Colombia. Like White-whiskered (of lowlands) but lower mandible bluish gray; shows little streaking below.
p. 316

12. WHITE-WHISKERED PUFFBIRD, *Malacoptila panamensis*

Widespread and relatively numerous in humid forest and woodland in lowlands and foothills of west, where the only *Malacoptila*. Typical of genus; belly boldly streaked. Sexually dimorphic: ♂ ♂ more rufescent above and rufous on breast, ♀ ♀ grayer above and only buff on breast.
p. 316

13. LANCEOLATED MONKLET, *Micromonacha lanceolata*

Rare, local, and inconspicuous in lower growth and borders of humid lowland and foothill forest and woodland. Unmistakable: small; prominent white on face; conspicuous black streaking on white underparts.
p. 316

Nonnula Nunlets

Relatively small, inconspicuous puffbirds found in lower growth of humid forest in lowlands of east.

14. RUSTY-BREASTED NUNLET, *Nonnula rubecula*

Very rare and local in humid forest in lowlands of far northeast. Like Brown Nunlet but has much more conspicuous white eye-ring; duller on breast and whiter on belly. p. 317

15. BROWN NUNLET, *Nonnula brunnea*

Scarce in humid forest in lowlands of east. Unpatterned, with rufescent tone below; inconspicuous pink eye-ring. p. 317

16. WHITE-FACED NUNBIRD, *Hapaloptila castanea*

Rare and local in borders of subtropical forest and adjacent clearings in northwest and on e. slope. Unmistakable in range: conspicuous white on face, rich rufous underparts.
p. 317

Monasa Nunbirds

Large, mainly dark gray puffbirds with brightly colored bills found in forests and woodlands of lowlands of east. Conspicuous and noisy, usually in small groups.

17. BLACK-FRONTED NUNBIRD, *Monasa nigrifrons*

Common in várzea and riparian forest and woodland in lowlands of east. All blackish (no white) with bright red bill.
p. 318

18. WHITE-FRONTED NUNBIRD, *Monasa morphoeus*

Mid-levels and subcanopy of terra firme forest in lowlands of east. White foreface, bright red bill. p. 318

19. YELLOW-BILLED NUNBIRD, *Monasa flavirostris*

Borders of humid forest and woodland in lowlands of east; quieter and less numerous than other, larger *Monasa*. Bright yellow bill; white shoulders (sometimes hidden). p. 319

20. SWALLOW-WINGED PUFFBIRD, *Chelidoptera tenebrosa*

Semiopen areas and forest borders, especially along rivers and roads, in lowlands of east. Always conspicuous, perching in open and making long aerial sallies. Silhouette plump, short-tailed. Mainly blackish with rufous lower belly; extensive white on rump obvious in flight. p. 319

Plate 52 Toucans

Aulacorhynchus Toucanets

Fairly small, predominantly green toucans found in montane forests at varying elevations. So far as known all are allopatric.

1. CRIMSON-RUMPED TOUCANET, *Aulacorhynchus haematopygus*

Numerous in foothill and subtropical forest on w. slope. The only "green" toucan with red rump; much reddish on bill.
p. 324

2. CHESTNUT-TIPPED TOUCANET, *Aulacorhynchus derbianus*

Scarce and local in foothill and lower subtropical forest on e. slope (below Emerald's elevations). Bill mostly black (with no yellow).
p. 323

3. EMERALD TOUCANET, *Aulacorhynchus prasinus*

3N *A. p. albivitta*—whitish throat, much yellow on culmen
3S *A. p. cyanolaemus*—bluish throat, yellow reduced to tip
Numerous in subtropical and lower temperate forest on e. slope. Yellow on bill (extent varying geographically); chestnut crissum and underside of tail.
p. 323

Selenidera Toucanets

Sexually dimorphic, fairly small toucans with complex plumage patterns and quite short, heavy bills. Range mainly in subcanopy and mid-levels of humid forest, primarily in lowlands. As toucans go, relatively inconspicuous, rarely perching in open.

4. GOLDEN-COLLARED TOUCANET, *Selenidera reinwardtii*

Terra firme forest in east. Basal half of bill dark red. ♂ with bright golden ear-tufts. ♀ has black replaced by rich tawny brown; ear-tufts olive.
p. 324

5. YELLOW-EARED TOUCANET, *Selenidera spectabilis*

Very rare in humid forest in lower foothills of n. Esmeraldas. Prominent greenish yellow along culmen. ♂ with yellow ear-tufts. ♀ lacks ear-tufts, has dark brown crown.
p. 324

Pteroglossus Araçaris

Midsized toucans with long bills found primarily in lowland forests, most species relatively numerous and conspicuous. Unlike previous two genera, araçaris usually range in small flocks. Key identification characters involve bill pattern and coloration and pattern of banding (or lack thereof) across underparts.

6. PALE-MANDIBLED ARAÇARI, *Pteroglossus erythropygius*

Only araçari in humid and semihumid forest and woodland in most of west. Black breast spot, whitish lower mandible.
p. 325

7. STRIPE-BILLED ARAÇARI, *Pteroglossus sanguineus*

Replaces similar Pale-mandibled northward, in Esmeraldas and adjacent Imbabura. Black lower mandible.   p. 326

8. MANY-BANDED ARAÇARI, *Pteroglossus pluricinctus*

Widespread in forests of east. Two obvious bands across underparts.
p. 326

9. IVORY-BILLED ARAÇARI, *Pteroglossus azara*

Terra firme forest in east. A small araçari. Wide red chest band, bordered below by black; mainly ivory whitish bill.
p. 327

10. CHESTNUT-EARED ARAÇARI, *Pteroglossus castanotis*

Mainly várzea and riparian forest in east. One red belly band.
p. 326

11. LETTERED ARAÇARI, *Pteroglossus inscriptus*

Widespread in forests of east. A small araçari, with unmarked lower underparts, dark scribbling on maxilla.
p. 327

Andigena Mountain-Toucans

Large, spectacular, boldly patterned toucans with colorful bills found in montane forests. All are allopatric. Like *Aulacorhynchus* toucanets, only infrequently perch in open. Far-carrying vocalizations often attract attention.

12. PLATE-BILLED MOUNTAIN-TOUCAN, *Andigena laminirostris*

Subtropical and lower temperate forest in northwest. Multicolored, with blue-gray underparts, yellow plate on maxilla.
p. 327

13. GRAY-BREASTED MOUNTAIN-TOUCAN, *Andigena hypoglauca*

Temperate forest on e. slope, also locally above interandean valleys in south. Underparts entirely gray, yellow on bill. S. birds have reddish pink maxilla, maxilla more orange and iris dark in n. birds.
p. 328

14. BLACK-BILLED MOUNTAIN-TOUCAN, *Andigena nigrirostris*

Local in subtropical forest on e. slope. Whitish foreneck, mainly black bill.
p. 328

Ramphastos Toucans

"Classic" toucans: large, predominantly black with obvious large bib either white or yellow. Bills enormous, longer in ♂ ♂ than ♀ ♀. Conspicuous in humid lowland forests, often perching in open; two white-bibbed species occur in east, two yellow-bibbed species in west, and a last in e. foothills. Species identification can be tricky, and often is best done by characteristic voices.

15. WHITE-THROATED TOUCAN, *Ramphastos tucanus*

Lowlands (mainly) and foothills of east. Large. White bib, long bill. Best distinguished from Channel-billed by yelping voice.
p. 330

16. CHANNEL-BILLED TOUCAN, *Ramphastos vitellinus*

Lowlands (mainly) and foothills of east. Plumage identical to larger White-throated. Bill averages shorter, is keeled. Best distinguished from White-throated by croaking voice.
p. 329

17. CHESTNUT-MANDIBLED TOUCAN, *Ramphastos swainsonii*

Lowlands and foothills of west. Large. Yellow bib, long bill with extensive chestnut at base. Often best distinguished from Chocó by yelping voice.
p. 330

18. CHOCÓ TOUCAN, *Ramphastos brevis*

Lowlands and foothills of west. Plumage identical to larger Chestnut-mandibled. Bill averages shorter, is keeled, and black replaces chestnut. Often best distinguished from Chestnut-mandibled by croaking voice.
p. 329

19. BLACK-MANDIBLED TOUCAN, *Ramphastos ambiguus*

Scarce and local in foothills and lower subtropics on e. slope. Large. Yellow bib, long yellow and black bill. Yelping voice.
p. 330

Plate 53 Woodpeckers I

Piculus Woodpeckers

Midsized woodpeckers found mostly in subcanopy and canopy of humid lowland and foothill forest. Most species have plain olive upperparts, boldly barred or banded underparts; facial patterns of virtually all are distinctive. Most are relatively inconspicuous, heard more often than seen.

1. CRIMSON-MANTLED WOODPECKER, *Piculus rivolii*
Widespread in upper subtropical and temperate forests, adjacent clearings. Nearly unmistakable, with mainly red upperparts.   p. 334

2. GOLDEN-OLIVE WOODPECKER, *Piculus rubiginosus*
2W *P. r. rubripileus*—♂ with black only on upper throat
2E *P. r. buenavistae*—somewhat brighter above
Widespread in forest, woodland, and clearings in west (both humid and arid areas), from lowlands up into subtropics; in east less numerous, only in subtropics. Contrasting whitish face, plain olive above, dusky-olive barring below.   p. 334

3. YELLOW-THROATED WOODPECKER, *Piculus flavigula*
Humid forest in lowlands of east. Solid bright yellow face and throat.   p. 335

4. WHITE-THROATED WOODPECKER, *Piculus leucolaemus*
Humid forest in lowlands and foothills of east. Yellow facial stripe (only); broad malar stripe red (♂) or olive (♀).
                                    p. 335

5. LITA WOODPECKER, *Piculus litae*
Scarce in humid forest in lowlands and foothills of northwest. Extensive yellow in face (shared by no other woodpecker in west).   p. 336

6. GOLDEN-GREEN WOODPECKER, *Piculus chrysochloros*
Humid forest in lowlands of northeast. Entire underparts evenly banded with olive; prominent yellow facial stripe bordered by olive. ♀ has no red on head.   p. 336

Celeus Woodpeckers

Bushy crested woodpeckers with pale yellowish bills. Almost all are mainly some shade of rufous, chestnut, or cinnamon (one exception, Cream-colored, is shockingly yellow). The vast majority are found in canopy and subcanopy of humid forests in lowlands of east, one exception (Cinnamon) being western in distribution. All are relatively inconspicuous, heard more often than seen.

7. CHESTNUT WOODPECKER, *Celeus elegans*
Generally the most numerous *Celeus*. Head and underparts plain dark chestnut.   p. 336

8. SCALE-BREASTED WOODPECKER, *Celeus grammicus*
Smaller than Chestnut (the two species are often together), with profuse black chevrons on underparts and scaling on wing-coverts.   p. 337

9. CINNAMON WOODPECKER, *Celeus loricatus*
Humid forest in lowlands and foothills of west, where the only *Celeus* and thus unique: the only woodpecker there that shows extensive cinnamon-rufous.   p. 337

10. CREAM-COLORED WOODPECKER, *Celeus flavus*
More apt to occur at forest borders and in várzea than other *Celeus*, but also ranges in terra firme. Unmistakable: mainly creamy yellow with contrastingly darker wings and tail. Some birds show extensive rufous in wings.   p. 337

11. RUFOUS-HEADED WOODPECKER, *Celeus spectabilis*
Rare and local in riparian and várzea forest and woodland. Upperparts (including wing-coverts) yellowish buff with bold black banding and spotting; rufous head.   p. 338

12. RINGED WOODPECKER, *Celeus torquatus*
Scarce, mainly in terra firme canopy. Distinctive, with cinnamon head, broad black breast shield, upperparts (including tail) rufous-chestnut barred black, belly barred black and buff.   p. 338

13. ANDEAN FLICKER, *Colaptes rupicola*
Rocky paramo in extreme south on Cordillera Las Lagunillas. An unmistakable large, partially terrestrial woodpecker with gray crown and malar, densely barred upperparts, rich cinnamon-buff to yellowish underparts.   p. 333

Plate 54 Woodpeckers II and Scythebills

Picumnus Piculets

Tiny woodpeckers found widely in forested and wooded habitats, mainly in lowlands; all but one species (Rufous-breasted) primarily arboreal. Their short tails are generally not used for support while tapping; the various species are marked by dotted crowns.

1. RUFOUS-BREASTED PICULET, *Picumnus rufiventris*

Scarce in lower growth of humid forest borders and regenerating clearings in lowlands and foothills of east. Distinctive rufous underparts. p. 331

2. PLAIN-BREASTED PICULET, *Picumnus castelnau*

Riparian and várzea forest and woodland in lowlands of east; no confirmed Ecuadorian records (only old specimens, perhaps from ne. Peru). Distinctive uniform yellowish white underparts. p. 332

3. OLIVACEOUS PICULET, *Picumnus olivaceus*

Woodland and forest borders in more humid lowlands and foothills of west. Rather plain overall, with unmarked olivaceous breast. p. 332

4. LAFRESNAYE'S PICULET, *Picumnus lafresnayi*

Humid forest, woodland, and borders in lowlands and foothills of east. Most of body coarsely barred. p. 332

5. ECUADORIAN PICULET, *Picumnus sclateri*

5S *P. s. sclateri*—El Oro and Loja; more heavily marked below

5N *P. s. parvistriatus*—Manabí and Guayas

Deciduous forest and woodland of southwest. Brownish above, underparts barred and streaked. p. 333

6. SPOT-BREASTED WOODPECKER, *Chrysoptilus punctigula*

Semiopen areas and borders (nonforest) in lowlands and foothills of east. Boldly patterned head, prominent barring above, black spotting below. p. 333

Veniliornis Woodpeckers

Small, inconspicuous woodpeckers found widely in humid and montane forests. With two exceptions (very different Smoky-brown and Scarlet-backed), olive above (often shaded brighter) and barred below.

7. BAR-BELLIED WOODPECKER, *Veniliornis nigriceps*

Scarce in temperate forest and woodland. Dense barring on entire underparts; larger than Yellow-vented. p. 342

8. YELLOW-VENTED WOODPECKER, *Veniliornis dignus*

Scarce in subtropical forest and woodland on e. slope and in northwest. Belly yellow and unmarked. p. 342

9. LITTLE WOODPECKER, *Veniliornis passerinus*

Várzea and riparian forest and woodland in lowlands of east. Whitish facial stripes, no yellow on nape. p. 341

10. RED-STAINED WOODPECKER, *Veniliornis affinis*

Humid forest in lowlands of east. Golden yellow nuchal collar; no pale facial stripes. p. 341

11. CHOCÓ WOODPECKER, *Veniliornis chocoensis*

Humid forest in lowlands and foothills of northwest. Heavy dark barring below; no red rump. p. 341

12. RED-RUMPED WOODPECKER, *Veniliornis kirkii*

Humid and deciduous forest and woodland in lowlands and foothills of west. The only *Veniliornis* with red rump, but this can be hard to see. Throat whitish, barring below less heavy than in Chocó. p. 342

13. SMOKY-BROWN WOODPECKER, *Veniliornis fumigatus*

Numerous and widespread in foothill and subtropical forest and woodland. Uniform dark brown without barring. p. 340

14. SCARLET-BACKED WOODPECKER, *Veniliornis callonotus*

14S *V. c. major*—whitish postocular p. 340

14N *V. c. callonotus*—less extensive barring below (on average)

Fairly common in deciduous woodland and scrub in lowlands and foothills of west, also following clearings into more humid areas. A small woodpecker with unmistakable red upperparts. p. 343

Melanerpes Woodpeckers

Conspicuous, noisy woodpeckers found at forest edge in lowlands on either slope.

15. BLACK-CHEEKED WOODPECKER, *Melanerpes pucherani*

Canopy and borders of humid forest and in adjacent clearings in lowlands and foothills of west. Colorful, with black upperparts, white rump, red on belly. p. 340

16. YELLOW-TUFTED WOODPECKER, *Melanerpes cruentatus*

Common in clearings and forest borders in lowlands and foothills of east; favors dead snags. Colorful, mainly black with bright yellow postocular, extensive bright red on belly, white rump. p. 339

Campylorhamphus Scythebills

Distinctive woodcreepers with unmistakable long, slender, deeply decurved bills. Range inside humid and montane forests, all but one species (Red-billed) rare and inconspicuous.

17. RED-BILLED SCYTHEBILL, *Campylorhamphus trochilirostris*

Humid and semihumid forest and woodland in lowlands and subtropics of west; scarce and local inside terra firme forest in lowlands of east. Long bill reddish brown; back lightly streaked; streaks on breast relatively wide, long, dark-edged. p. 389

18. CURVE-BILLED SCYTHEBILL, *Campylorhamphus procurvoides*

Very rare (overlooked?) inside humid forest in lowlands of northeast. Very similar to Red-billed (bill colors alike), but buff streaking on underparts narrower and without blackish edging; streaking on back absent or very sparse. See text. p. 389

19. BROWN-BILLED SCYTHEBILL, *Campylorhamphus pusillus*

Uncommon and local inside foothill and subtropical forest on both slopes. Bill relatively short (for a scythebill) and dark; narrower streaking on underparts than in Red-billed. p. 389

20. GREATER SCYTHEBILL, *Campylorhamphus pucherani*

Very rare and local (overlooked?) in upper subtropical and temperate forest, mainly on e. slope. A large scythebill with relatively short, heavy bill; uniform plumage, with two bold white facial stripes. p. 388

Plate 55 Woodcreepers

Dendrocincla Woodcreepers

Midsized, rather plain woodcreepers with little streaking found in humid and montane forests. Two species (Plain-brown, White-chinned) frequently follow army antswarms.

1. TYRANNINE WOODCREEPER, *Dendrocincla tyrannina*

Subtropical and temperate zones on both slopes, generally scarce. Large; plain overall appearance. All sympatric woodcreepers show some streaking.   p. 378

2. PLAIN-BROWN WOODCREEPER, *Dendrocincla fuliginosa*

Widespread and often numerous in lowlands and foothills of east and west. Plain overall appearance with dusky malar stripe, pale face.   p. 378

3. WHITE-CHINNED WOODCREEPER, *Dendrocincla merula*

Rare and local in humid forest in lowlands of northeast, even there outnumbered by Plain-brown though occasionally the two attend the same antswarm. Bluish iris, whitish chin contrasting with dark face.   p. 378

Deconychura Woodcreepers

Rare woodcreepers found in lower growth of humid and montane forests on e. slope. Rather unpatterned, with vague speckling on foreparts.

4. LONG-TAILED WOODCREEPER, *Deconychura longicauda*

Rare and local in montane forest in subtropical zone and foothills on e. slope, also locally in lowlands of east. Confusing (see text), but is rather long-tailed.   p. 379

5. SPOT-THROATED WOODCREEPER, *Deconychura stictolaema*

Rare and local in terra firme forest in lowlands of northeast. Rather small and dark, "normal" woodcreeper bill (cf. much more common Wedge-billed).   p. 379

6. WEDGE-BILLED WOODCREEPER, *Glyphorynchus spirurus*

Common in lower growth of humid forest and woodland in lowlands of east and west. Small; short, slightly upturned bill. Typically forages on large trunks.   p. 380

7. OLIVACEOUS WOODCREEPER, *Sittasomus griseicapillus*

7W *S. g. aequatorialis*
7E *S. g. amazonus*—darker and grayer

Distinctive small woodcreeper found in middle and upper levels of deciduous forest and woodland (west) and várzea forest (east), in lowlands and foothills. Unstreaked grayish head and underparts.   p. 380

8. CINNAMON-THROATED WOODCREEPER, *Dendrexetastes rufigula*

Middle and upper levels of forest (usually their borders, often in palms) in lowlands of east. Fairly large and uniform, with pale greenish bill, band of white streaks on breast.   p. 381

9. STRONG-BILLED WOODCREEPER, *Xiphocolaptes promeropirhynchus*

9H *X. p. promeropirhynchus*—montane; dusky malar
9E *X. p. orenocensis*—e. lowlands; reddish bill

Uncommon in montane forest on both slopes and várzea forests in lowlands of east. Large, massive, dark bill. Only slightly smaller Buff-throated (e. lowlands) has straighter bill (less arched) with pale lower mandible.   p. 381

Dendrocolaptes Woodcreepers

Fairly large woodcreepers of humid forests with heavy dark bills, barring at least on underparts. Often follow army antswarms.

10. BLACK-BANDED WOODCREEPER, *Dendrocolaptes picumnus*

Scarce in humid forest of lowlands and foothills of east. Dusky barring on underparts, buff streaking about head.
                    p. 383

11. AMAZONIAN BARRED-WOODCREEPER, *Dendrocolaptes certhia*

Humid forest in lowlands of east. Generally barred appearance; reddish bill.   p. 382

12. NORTHERN BARRED-WOODCREEPER, *Dendrocolaptes sanctithomae*

Humid forest in lowlands of northwest. Generally barred appearance; blackish bill.   p. 383

Xiphorhynchus Woodcreepers

Variable group of large to midsized woodcreepers, many with slightly decurved bills (straight in some), most with prominent buff to whitish streaking (lacking in a few). Most occur in lowland forests, a few ranging up onto Andean slopes.

13. STRAIGHT-BILLED WOODCREEPER, *Xiphorhynchus picus*

Várzea forest and woodland in lowlands of east, often conspicuous and numerous. Distinctive straight whitish bill, whitish streaking on foreparts.   p. 383

14. BUFF-THROATED WOODCREEPER, *Xiphorhynchus guttatus*

Humid forest in lowlands of east; often foraging high, usually numerous. Large, long straight bill.   p. 385

15. OCELLATED WOODCREEPER, *Xiphorhynchus ocellatus*

Lower growth inside terra firme in lowlands of east. Somewhat decurved blackish bill, deep buff guttate spots on breast, essentially unstreaked back.   p. 384

16. SPIX'S WOODCREEPER, *Xiphorhynchus spixii*

Rare in lowlands of east, mainly (?) in várzea. Much like Ocellated, but with prominently streaked back. See text.
                    p. 385

17. STRIPED WOODCREEPER, *Xiphorhynchus obsoletus*

Várzea forests of lowlands of east. Bill somewhat decurved and pale brownish; pale buffish streaking on mantle and underparts. Scarcer than similar Straight-billed.   p. 384

18. BLACK-STRIPED WOODCREEPER, *Xiphorhychus lacrymosus*

Humid forest of lowlands and foothills of far northwest. Unmistakable, with bold black-and-white streaking. p. 386

19. SPOTTED WOODCREEPER, *Xiphorhynchus erythropygius*

Humid and montane forest and woodland in lowlands and (especially) foothills and subtropics of west. Olivaceous tone, spotted underparts, eye-ring.   p. 386

20. OLIVE-BACKED WOODCREEPER, *Xiphorhynchus triangularis*

Montane forest in subtropical zone on e. slope. Much like Spotted (no overlap), but with spotted crown.   p. 386

Lepidocolaptes Woodcreepers

Fairly small woodcreepers with slender decurved bills, prominently streaked underparts.

21. LINEATED WOODCREEPER, *Lepidocolaptes albolineatus*

Subcanopy of terra firme forest in lowlands of east. Unstreaked crown and back.   p. 388

22. STREAK-HEADED WOODCREEPER, *Lepidocolaptes souleyetii*

Deciduous and semihumid woodland in lowlands of west, often numerous. Streaked crown, blurrily streaked underparts.   p. 387

23. MONTANE WOODCREEPER, *Lepidocolaptes lacrymiger*

Subtropical and temperate forest and woodland on both slopes. Crown lightly spotted.   p. 387

24. LONG-BILLED WOODCREEPER, *Nasica longirostris*

Spectacular, large woodcreeper with very long whitish bill. Mainly in várzea forests in lowlands of east.   p. 381

Plate 56 Furnariids I

Synallaxis Spinetails

A fairly diverse and confusing group of small, skulking birds with graduated tails found in a variety of shrubby habitats, a few species in forest or woodland undergrowth or on river islands. One or more is found almost anywhere in Ecuador. Many are most often identified by voice. Look for tail color, presence or absence of rufous on crown and a throat patch, and color of underparts.

1. AZARA'S SPINETAIL, *Synallaxis azarae*
1 *S. a. media*
1SW *S. a. ochracea*—paler, some with superciliary
Common and widespread in shrubby, nonforest habitats in Andes. Rufous tail, throat patch. p. 349

2. DUSKY SPINETAIL, *Synallaxis moesta*
Scarce and local in shrubby forest borders in foothills on e. slope, also locally in lowlands. Dark generally, with short rufous-chestnut tail. p. 349

3. SLATY SPINETAIL, *Synallaxis brachyura*
Common in rank shrubbery and woodland borders in lowlands and foothills of west. For a *Synallaxis*, easy to see. Dark gray underparts, blackish tail. p. 350

4. DARK-BREASTED SPINETAIL, *Synallaxis albigularis*
Common in tall grass and shrubbery in lowlands and foothills of east. Gray underparts with obvious throat patch; dusky tail. p. 350

5. MARAÑÓN SPINETAIL, *Synallaxis maranonica*
Only in Zumba area of extreme southeast, in woodland undergrowth and borders. Dark overall (including belly), no rufous on crown. p. 351

6. PLAIN-CROWNED SPINETAIL, *Synallaxis gujanensis*
Locally numerous in woodland undergrowth on islands in Río Napo and lower Río Aguarico. Pale brownish overall, no crown or throat patch. p. 350

7. WHITE-BELLIED SPINETAIL, *Synallaxis propinqua*
Locally numerous in early-succession scrub on river islands in lowlands of east. Dull brownish gray overall with hoary throat patch. p. 351

8. BLACKISH-HEADED SPINETAIL, *Synallaxis tithys*
Local in deciduous woodland undergrowth in lowlands of southwest. Dark with black face, blackish tail. p. 352

9. RUFOUS SPINETAIL, *Synallaxis unirufa*
Dense undergrowth of subtropical and temperate forest on both slopes of Andes. Uniform bright rufous with long tail, no barring on wings (cf. Rufous Wren, Plate 80-4). p. 352

10. RUDDY SPINETAIL, *Synallaxis rutilans*
Scarce and local near ground in terra firme forest in lowlands of east. Mostly rufous-chestnut with dark tail, black throat patch (latter sometimes hard to see). p. 352

11. CHESTNUT-THROATED SPINETAIL, *Synallaxis cherriei*
Scarce and inexplicably local in undergrowth of younger woodland in foothills and adjacent lowlands of northeast. No throat patch, brownish on crown and mantle, gray on belly. p. 353

12. NECKLACED SPINETAIL, *Synallaxis stictothorax*
Locally common in arid scrub of lowlands of southwest. Distinctive (more arboreal than other *Synallaxis*), with white superciliary and underparts, fine streaking on breast, two-toned tail (in most of range). p. 353

13. WHITE-BROWED SPINETAIL, *Hellmayrea gularis*
Temperate forest undergrowth on both slopes. Wren-like, with short tail; conspicuous white throat and brow. p. 353

Cranioleuca Spinetails

Similar to *Synallaxis* in form and appearance (though most show a superciliary), all with rufous wings and tail. *Cranioleuca* are more forest-based and have more arboreal foraging behavior. Unlike *Synallaxis*, they often accompany mixed flocks.

14. RED-FACED SPINETAIL, *Cranioleuca erythrops*
Montane forest and borders in foothills and subtropical zone on w. slope. Contrasting rufous head unique. Juveniles have ochraceous brow (cf. Line-cheeked). p. 354

15. ASH-BROWED SPINETAIL, *Cranioleuca curtata*
Montane forest and borders in foothills and subtropical zone on e. slope. Rufous crown, grayish superciliary. p. 354

16. LINE-CHEEKED SPINETAIL, *Cranioleuca antisiensis*
Montane woodland and scrub in southwest. Rufous crown, white superciliary. p. 355

17. PARKER'S SPINETAIL, *Cranioleuca vulpecula*
Woodland undergrowth and scrub on river islands in lowlands of east. Entirely rufous upperparts, whitish superciliary. p. 355

18. SPECKLED SPINETAIL, *Cranioleuca gutturata*
Tangled lower growth of humid forest and borders in lowlands of east, often near water. Rufous crown, speckled underparts. p. 355

Plate 57 Furnariids II

1. ANDEAN TIT-SPINETAIL, *Leptasthenura andicola*
Shrubbery near treeline, foraging actively. Generally streaked appearance, prominent white superciliary, long pointed tail, no rufous in wings. p. 348

Asthenes Canasteros
Small, generally streaked, brown furnariids found near ground in paramo and shrubby grassland; often inconspicuous. They have long pointed tails (sometimes held partially cocked), cinnamon-rufous chin patches.

2. MANY-STRIPED CANASTERO, *Asthenes flammulata*
Widespread in more humid paramo. Attractively streaked with rufous and white. p. 357

3. STREAK-BACKED CANASTERO, *Asthenes wyatti*
3N *A. w. aequatorialis*—more grayish underparts
3S *A. w. azuay*—larger; more rufous in wing, buffier underparts
Local in more arid paramo and shrubby areas; scarcer than Many-striped. Underparts unstreaked. p. 357

Schizoeaca Thistletails
Inconspicuous in shrubbery near treeline, the two species replacing each other from north to south. Very long pointed tails (often frayed), unstreaked upperparts.

4. WHITE-CHINNED THISTLETAIL, *Schizoeaca fuliginosa*
South to n. Morona-Santiago. Upperparts chestnut brown, vague pale superciliary, whitish chin patch. p. 356

5. MOUSE-COLORED THISTLETAIL, *Schizoeaca griseomurina*
North to Azuay and s. Morona-Santiago. Upperparts olivaceous brown, conspicuous white eye-ring, no superciliary. p. 356

Margarornis Treerunners
Distinctive, arboreal furnariids found in montane forests, hitching up trunks and branches; often with mixed flocks.

6. PEARLED TREERUNNER, *Margarornis squamiger*
Widespread in temperate zone. Underparts boldly white-spotted. p. 361

7. STAR-CHESTED TREERUNNER, *Margarornis stellatus*
Rare and very local in mossy forest on w. slope. Contrasting white throat, gorget of white "stars." p. 361

8. RUSTY-WINGED BARBTAIL, *Premnornis guttuligera*
Scarce in lower growth of subtropical forest on e. slope and in northwest. Heavily streaked foreparts; recalls certain small foliage-gleaners. p. 362

9. SPOTTED BARBTAIL, *Premnoplex brunnescens*
Undergrowth of subtropical forest, creeping on branches. Small, dark brown (no rufous on wings or tail), buff spotting below. p. 362

10. RUFOUS-FRONTED THORNBIRD, *Phacellodomus rufifrons*
Light woodland and clearings in Zumba area of extreme southeast. Very dull, but with rufous forecrown. p. 358

11. ORANGE-FRONTED PLUSHCROWN, *Metopothrix aurantiacus*
Second-growth in lowlands of east. Unique, warbler-like. Orange legs, bold orange-yellow forecrown. Juvenile lacks orange forecrown. p. 359

Xenerpestes Graytails
Obscure small grayish birds that forage high in forest canopy. Range in foothills, one species on either side of Andes.

12. EQUATORIAL GRAYTAIL, *Xenerpestes singularis*
Rare in foothills on e. slope. Streaked underparts, rufescent forecrown. p. 359

13. DOUBLE-BANDED GRAYTAIL, *Xenerpestes minlosi*
Very local in lower foothills of northwest. Bold white eyebrow and wing-bars. p. 359

14. PLAIN SOFTTAIL, *Thripophaga fusciceps*
Rare and local in tangled second-growth in lowlands of east. Drab; dull brownish with contrasting rufous wings and tail. p. 358

15. SPECTACLED PRICKLETAIL, *Siptornis striaticollis*
Scarce and local in subtropical forest on e. slope. Xenops-like (including behavior), with short but bold white postocular. p. 358

Xenops Xenops
Small, arboreal furnariids which frequently accompany mixed flocks; creep about on dead twigs and small branches, often hanging upside-down. Most species have an upturned lower mandible and show silvery white crescent on ear-coverts.

16. RUFOUS-TAILED XENOPS, *Xenops milleri*
Scarce in terra firme canopy of lowlands of east. Lacks crescent on ear-coverts and upturn on lower mandible; shorter tailed than other *Xenops*. p. 375

17. SLENDER-BILLED XENOPS, *Xenops tenuirostris*
Scarce in forest canopy of lowlands of east, below range of very similar Streaked. Streaking below slightly sparser; more black shown on upperside of tail. p. 374

18. STREAKED XENOPS, *Xenops rutilans*
Relatively widespread in west and subtropics on both slopes (but not in lowlands of east), in both humid and deciduous habitats. Upturned lower mandible, silvery crescent, relatively prominent streaking. p. 374

19. PLAIN XENOPS, *Xenops minutus*
19E *X. m. obsoletus*—more white on throat and chest
19W *X. m. littoralis*
Common in humid forest in lowlands of east and west. Much less streaking than other *Xenops*, with none on mantle. p. 374

Plate 58 Furnariids III

Hyloctistes Woodhaunters

Obscure foliage-gleaners found in lower growth of humid forest, one species on either side of Andes. Formerly considered conspecific, but voices differ dramatically (see text).

1. EASTERN WOODHAUNTER, *Hyloctistes subulatus*
Lower growth inside humid forest in lowlands and lower subtropics in east. Streaking relatively dull and blurry.
p. 365

2. WESTERN WOODHAUNTER, *Hyloctistes virgatus*
Lower growth inside humid forest in lowlands and lower subtropics in west. Like preceding, but mantle streaking relatively obscure. p. 365

3. CHESTNUT-WINGED HOOKBILL, *Ancistrops strigilatus*
Subcanopy of terra firme forest in lowlands of east; often with flocks. Streaking on mantle and underparts, contrasting rufous wings, heavy bill. p. 366

Syndactyla Foliage-gleaners

Found in lower growth of subtropical forest and woodland. Usually inconspicuous, though foraging with mixed flocks.

4. LINEATED FOLIAGE-GLEANER, *Syndactyla subalaris*
4E *S. s. mentalis*—more prominently streaked above and below
4W *S. s. subalaris*—streaking above mainly confined to nape
Widespread in subtropical forests on both slopes. Prominent buff streaking; contrasting pale throat. Cf. *Thripadectes* treehunters (Plate 59). p. 363

5. BUFF-BROWED FOLIAGE-GLEANER, *Syndactyla rufosuperciliata*
Subtropical forest undergrowth in extreme southeast (Cordillera del Cóndor). Like Lineated (sympatric), but crown and mantle unstreaked. p. 363

6. RUFOUS-NECKED FOLIAGE-GLEANER, *Syndactyla ruficollis*
Scarce and local in subtropical forest and woodland in Loja. Orange-rufous superciliary and sides of neck. p. 363

Anabacerthia Foliage-gleaners

Slender foliage-gleaners with well-marked spectacles found in foothill and subtropical forests, one species on either slope of Andes. Arboreal, easier to see than most foliage-gleaners.

7. SCALY-THROATED FOLIAGE-GLEANER, *Anabacerthia variegaticeps*
W. slope. Bright orange-ochraceous brow and eye-ring.
p. 364

8. MONTANE FOLIAGE-GLEANER, *Anabacerthia striaticollis*
E. slope. Dull; streaking confined to chest (and faint there), whitish brow and eye-ring. p. 364

Philydor Foliage-gleaners

Fairly large, simply patterned furnariids found in humid and montane forests, most species arboreal and reasonably conspicuous; often accompany mixed flocks. All have bold superciliary; most show no streaking.

9. RUFOUS-RUMPED FOLIAGE-GLEANER, *Philydor erythrocercus*
Fairly common in lowlands and foothills of east. Plain underparts (no breast flammulation or streaking), faint rufous on uppertail-coverts. p. 367

10. SLATY-WINGED FOLIAGE-GLEANER, *Philydor fuscipennis*
Local in lowlands of west. Unique in range; contrasting dusky wings. p. 366

11. CINNAMON-RUMPED FOLIAGE-GLEANER, *Philydor pyrrhodes*
Forest undergrowth in lowlands of east. Unique in range; contrasting slaty wings. p. 367

12. BUFF-FRONTED FOLIAGE-GLEANER, *Philydor rufus*
Arboreal in foothill and lower subtropical forest on both slopes. Grayish crown, ochraceous eyebrow and throat, dull-colored tail. Cf. Russet Antshrike (Plate 60-19). p. 368

13. RUFOUS-TAILED FOLIAGE-GLEANER, *Philydor ruficaudatus*
Very rare in lowlands of east. Much like Rufous-rumped, best told by faintly flammulated breast; see text. p. 368

14. CHESTNUT-WINGED FOLIAGE-GLEANER, *Philydor erythropterus*
Subcanopy of terra firme forest in lowlands of east. Essentially unstreaked; contrasting rufous wings, pale ochraceous orange throat. p. 366

Automolus and *Anabazenops* Foliage-gleaners

Fairly large, robust foliage-gleaners, usually rather drab and unpatterned. Tend to skulk in forest undergrowth. Most species occur in lowlands. All are heard more often than seen.

15. OLIVE-BACKED FOLIAGE-GLEANER, *Automolus infuscatus*
Numerous in terra firme in lowlands of east. Dull but with contrasting white throat. p. 369

16. CHESTNUT-CROWNED FOLIAGE-GLEANER, *Automolus rufipileatus*
Mainly várzea undergrowth in lowlands of east. Exceptionally hard to see. Nearly uniform rufous; iris orange. p. 370

17. RUDDY FOLIAGE-GLEANER, *Automolus rubiginosus*
17W *A. r. nigricauda*—blackish tail, very dark
17E *A. r. brunnescens*
Near ground in foothills and adjacent lowlands on both slopes. Uniform and dark-looking. Dark eye, cf. Brown-rumped Foliage-gleaner. p. 371

18. BAMBOO FOLIAGE-GLEANER, *Anabazenops dorsalis*
Scarce in foothills and lowlands on e. slope, mainly in bamboo and *Gynerium* cane. White superciliary and throat separated by dark cheeks. p. 368

19. BUFF-THROATED FOLIAGE-GLEANER, *Automolus ochrolaemus*
19E *A. o. turdinus*
19W *A. o. pallidigularis*—white throat (unique in range)
Humid forest undergrowth in lowlands of east and west. In east, pale buffish throat and brow. p. 369

20. BROWN-RUMPED FOLIAGE-GLEANER, *Automolus melanopezus*
Scarce in lowlands of east. Bright orange eye, ochraceous orange throat. p. 370

21. HENNA-HOODED FOLIAGE-GLEANER, *Hylocryptus erythrocephalus*
Local in undergrowth of deciduous forest and woodland in southwest. Unobtrusive. Unmistakable, with orange-rufous ("henna") hood. p. 371

Plate 59 Furnariids IV

1. SLENDER-BILLED MINER, *Geositta tenuirostris*
Local in arid paramo in Cotopaxi and n. Chimborazo. Mainly terrestrial. Slender decurved bill, streaking on foreparts, extensive rufous in wing visible in flight.   p. 346

Cinclodes Cinclodes
Mainly terrestrial furnariids found in paramo, especially near water; they often occur together. Note prominent white superciliary and throat, rufous wing-band (visible mainly in flight).

2. STOUT-BILLED CINCLODES, *Cinclodes excelsior*
Large; stout, somewhat decurved bill; breast scaling.
    p. 347

3. BAR-WINGED CINCLODES, *Cinclodes fuscus*
Somewhat smaller than Stout-billed, with slenderer, shorter, straight bill. Usually more numerous than Stout-billed.
    p. 346

Furnarius Horneros
Chunky, mainly terrestrial furnariids with short tails, predominantly rufous plumage. Found in lowlands, mainly in semiopen areas.

4. PACIFIC HORNERO, *Furnarius cinnamomeus*
Common and conspicuous in southwest. Unmistakable in range (where the only hornero), with bright rufous upperparts, grayish crown, pale eye.   p. 347

5. BAY HORNERO, *Furnarius torridus*
Very rare in lowlands of far northeast, near rivers. Mainly rufous-chestnut, contrasting white throat.   p. 348

6. LESSER HORNERO, *Furnarius minor*
Local on islands in Río Napo in lowlands of northeast, usually walking on ground inside heavy cover. Small, dull, paler (especially below) than Bay.   p. 348

7. POINT-TAILED PALMCREEPER, *Berlepschia rikeri*
Local in palms (usually *Mauritia*) in lowlands of northeast; often high. Unmistakable; bold black and white streaking on head and underparts.   p. 361

Pseudocolaptes Tuftedcheeks
Large furnariids with unique flaring "tufts" on sides of neck. Arboreal in montane forests, probing into bromeliads; often with mixed flocks.

8. STREAKED TUFTEDCHEEK, *Pseudocolaptes boissonneautii*
Widespread in subtropical and temperate zones. Snowy white neck tufts, streaking on back.   p. 360

9. PACIFIC TUFTEDCHEEK, *Pseudocolaptes johnsoni*
Very local in mossy foothill and lower subtropical forest on w. slope. Unstreaked back, dingy throat (buff-tinged tuft contrasts more).   p. 360

Thripadectes Treehunters
Large, robust furnariids of Andean forests, where generally scarce. Inconspicuous, skulking in thick undergrowth, frequently foraging independently of flocks. Buff streaking varies in extent and prominence.

10. FLAMMULATED TREEHUNTER, *Thripadectes flammulatus*
Temperate zone on both slopes (ranging higher than other treehunters). The largest and most boldly streaked treehunter.
    p. 372

11. STRIPED TREEHUNTER, *Thripadectes holostictus*
Mostly subtropical zone, on both slopes. Streaking narrower (especially below) than in Flammulated.   p. 372

12. BLACK-BILLED TREEHUNTER, *Thripadectes melanorhynchus*
Lower subtropical zone on e. slope (the lowest-ranging treehunter there). Underparts mostly plain, throat ochraceous with black scaling, buff back streaking.   p. 373

13. STREAK-CAPPED TREEHUNTER, *Thripadectes virgaticeps*
Subtropical zone on both slopes, but only in north. Underparts mostly plain, back unstreaked, buff streaking on throat.
    p. 372

14. UNIFORM TREEHUNTER, *Thripadectes ignobilis*
Foothills and lower subtropical zone on w. slope (where the lowest-ranging treehunter). Dark and uniform, with streaking faint.   p. 373

Sclerurus Leaftossers
Short-tailed, mainly dark brown furnariids found on or near ground inside humid and montane forests, especially where damp. Cryptic and rarely encountered. Note especially color and pattern of throat and chest.

15. GRAY-THROATED LEAFTOSSER, *Sclerurus albigularis*
Scarce and local in foothills and lower subtropics on e. slope. Distinctive, with gray throat contrasting with rufous chest.
    p. 376

16. TAWNY-THROATED LEAFTOSSER, *Sclerurus mexicanus*
Lowlands to lower subtropics on both slopes. Rufous throat and chest, rather long drooping bill.   p. 375

17. SHORT-BILLED LEAFTOSSER, *Sclerurus rufigularis*
Rare in lowlands of east. Bill relatively short and straight (cf. Tawny-throated).   p. 376

18. SCALY-THROATED LEAFTOSSER, *Sclerurus guatimalensis*
Local in lowlands and lower foothills of west. White on throat.   p. 377

19. BLACK-TAILED LEAFTOSSER, *Sclerurus caudacutus*
Lowlands of east. Large and dark, with white on throat.
    p. 376

20. SHARP-TAILED STREAMCREEPER, *Lochmias nematura*
Local in foothills on e. slope, especially along streams. Underparts boldly white-spotted.   p. 377

Plate 60 Antbirds I

1. FASCIATED ANTSHRIKE, *Cymbilaimus lineatus*
Humid lowland forest and borders of east and west. Heavy bill, red eye. ♂ narrowly barred black and white. ♀ narrowly barred black and buff. p. 390

2. UNDULATED ANTSHRIKE, *Frederickena unduligera*
Terra firme undergrowth in lowlands of east. Scarce and hard to see. Large with heavy bill, red eye. ♂ vermiculated white. ♀ rufescent with wavy black barring. p. 391

3. GREAT ANTSHRIKE, *Taraba major*
Lowlands in shrubby second-growth and borders. Unmistakable, both sexes obviously bicolored; shaggy crest, heavy bill. p. 391

4. COLLARED ANTSHRIKE, *Sakesphorus bernardi*
Woodland undergrowth and scrub in lowlands of southwest (ranging higher in Loja). Shaggy crest. ♂ unmistakable, contrasting black hood, white collar and underparts. ♀ with buff nuchal collar and underparts, speckled face. p. 392

Thamnophilus Antshrikes
A diverse group found mainly in lowland forest and woodland undergrowth. "Barred group" (first 3 species) have shaggy expressive crests. Usually in pairs, most species usually not with flocks. Vocalizations often helpful. See other *Thamnophilus* on Plate 96.

5. BARRED ANTSHRIKE, *Thamnophilis doliatus*
Local on river islands in lowlands of far northeast. ♂ evenly barred black and white. ♀ buff and rufous, barring only on face and nape. p. 393

6. CHAPMAN'S ANTSHRIKE, *Thamnophilus zarumae*
Scrub and deciduous woodland in montane El Oro and Loja. ♂ a pallid version of Barred, buff on belly. ♀ like ♀ Barred but paler below with vague dusky speckling. p. 393

7. LINED ANTSHRIKE, *Thamnophilus tenuepunctatus*
Clearings and thickets at forest edge in lowlands along e. base of Andes, often common. ♂ a blacker version of Barred. ♀ boldly barred black and white below, chestnut above.
p. 392

8. COCHA ANTSHRIKE, *Thamnophilus praecox*
Very local in thickets of blackwater várzea swamps in lowlands of northeast. ♂ all black. ♀ rufous-chestnut with black hood, no bare blue around eye (cf. ♀ White-shouldered Antbird, Plate 63-5). p. 393

9. CASTELNAU'S ANTSHRIKE, *Thamnophilus cryptoleucus*
Woodland undergrowth on river islands in lowlands of east. Large; heavy-billed. ♂ black with white fringing on coverts. ♀ all dull black. p. 394

10. WHITE-SHOULDERED ANTSHRIKE, *Thamnophilus aethiops*
Scarce and local in humid forest in foothills on e. slope and in adjacent lowlands. Heavy bill; red eye. ♂ all lustrous black, inconspicuous white on wing-coverts. ♂ uniform rich rufous. p. 394

11. UNIFORM ANTSHRIKE, *Thamnophilus unicolor*
Foothills and subtropics on both slopes. Grayish eye. ♂ uniform gray. ♀ with contrasting gray face. p. 395

12. PLAIN-WINGED ANTSHRIKE, *Thamnophilus schistaceus*
Widespread in lowlands of east, mainly in terra firme. Reddish eye. ♂ uniform gray with blackish cap (showing less in south). ♀ plain brown above, tawny below; cap rufous.
p. 395

13. MOUSE-COLORED ANTSHRIKE, *Thamnophilus murinus*
Local in terra firme in lowlands of east (south of Río Napo). Resembles Plain-winged, but iris pale grayish, faint fringing on coverts. ♂ also differs in paler overall color, brownish on wings. ♀ lacks tawny below. p. 396

14. WESTERN SLATY-ANTSHRIKE, *Thamnophilus atrinucha*
The only *Thamnophilus* in lowlands of west, commoner northward. p. 396

15. SPOT-WINGED ANTSHRIKE, *Pygiptila stellaris*
Forest subcanopy in lowlands of east, often with flocks. Distinctive shape, with short tail and bull-headed look. p. 398

16. PEARLY ANTSHRIKE, *Megastictus margaritatus*
Scarce and local in terra firme in lowlands of east. Both sexes with distinctive large round white or buff spots on coverts, tips of inner flight feathers, and tail. p. 398

Thamnomanes Antshrikes
Plain antshrikes found in forest understory in lowlands of east; numerous and relatively conspicuous. Mixed flocks often form around them. Very vocal.

17. CINEREOUS ANTSHRIKE, *Thamnomanes caesius*
♂ uniform gray. ♀ brownish with contrasting rufous belly. Often perches upright. p. 401

18. DUSKY-THROATED ANTSHRIKE, *Thamnomanes ardesiacus*
♂ like ♂ Cinereous but usually shows dusky on throat, tail shorter and narrowly white-tipped. ♀ more olivaceous above, paler (less rufous) on belly. Often best told by voice.
p. 401

19. RUSSET ANTSHRIKE, *Thamnistes anabatinus*
Forest subcanopy on both slopes, primarily in foothills; often with flocks. Heavy bill, short tail, foliage-gleaner-like color and pattern. p. 398

20. WHITE-STREAKED ANTVIREO, *Dysithamnus leucostictus*
Subtropical forest lower growth on e. slope. ♂ gray with blackish on upper chest, small white spots and fringes on coverts. ♀ with bold white streaking below. Cf. other antvireos (Plates 61, 96). p. 400

Plate 61 Antbirds II

Dysithamnus Antvireos
Chunkier and heavier-billed than *Myrmotherula*, with which they often associate. Humid forest undergrowth. See other antvireos (Plates 60, 96).

1. PLAIN ANTVIREO, *Dysithamnus mentalis*
1W *D. m. aequatorialis*—♂ with yellowish belly
1E *D. m. napensis*—♂ uniform gray below
Lowlands and foothills in west, foothills and subtropics on e. slope; in west also in deciduous forest. Dark auriculars. ♂♂ grayish. ♀♀ with rufous crown.   p. 399

2. SPOT-CROWNED ANTVIREO, *Dysithamnus puncticeps*
Lowlands and foothills of northwest. Both sexes with pale gray iris, streaked crown.   p. 399

Terenura Antwrens
Boldly patterned, warblerlike antwrens found in canopy of humid or montane forest. Usually with mixed flocks; often vocal. Another species is on Plate 96.

3. CHESTNUT-SHOULDERED ANTWREN, *Terenura humeralis*
Lowlands of east, in terra firme. Rufous rump; yellow wing-bars. Short unmarked tail, olive upperparts. ♂ with chestnut shoulders (hard to see).   p. 414

4. RUFOUS-RUMPED ANTWREN, *Terenura callinota*
Foothills and lower subtropics on both slopes. Rufous rump; yellow wing-bars. ♂ with yellow shoulders (hard to see).   p. 413

5. DOT-WINGED ANTWREN, *Microrhopias quixensis*
5E *M. q. quixensis* — ♀ with black throat
5W *M. q. consobrina*—♀ all chestnut below
Humid forest undergrowth in lowlands of east and west, often in bamboo; commoner in west. Long graduated tail broadly tipped white; both sexes also with conspicuous white spots on coverts.   p. 410

Herpsilochmus Antwrens
Boldly patterned antwrens with long white-tipped tails found in canopy of humid and montane forest. Often vocal. Another species is on Plate 96.

6. RUFOUS-WINGED ANTWREN, *Herpsilochmus rufimarginatus*
E.-slope foothills; also local in lowlands of west. Conspicuous rufous in flight feathers.   p. 412

7. YELLOW-BREASTED ANTWREN, *Herpsilochmus axillaris*
E.-slope foothills and subtropics. Bright pale yellow underparts, olive on upperparts. ♂ with spotted crown.   p. 412

8. DUGAND'S ANTWREN, *Herpsilochmus dugandi*
Terra firme in lowlands of east. ♂ mostly gray and white. ♀ dull buff below.   p. 411

Myrmotherula Antwrens
Small, short-tailed antbirds found in lowland forests unless otherwise indicated, a few at edge or in foothills. Depending on species, range from near ground to viny tangles in subcanopy. Often hard to identify; note especially throat pattern, wing and tail markings, and dorsal coloration. An additional species is on Plate 96.

9. GRAY ANTWREN, *Myrmotherula menetriesii*
East; common, often well above ground. ♂ pale gray with fringed coverts. Two-toned ♀ has unmarked coverts.
          p. 409

10. RÍO SUNO ANTWREN, *Myrmotherula sunensis*
Scarce in terra firme in east. Short tail. ♂ like ♂ Long-winged but darker and more extensive black below, with dotted coverts, untipped tail. ♀ browner-backed, more uniform than similar species.   p. 409

11. LONG-WINGED ANTWREN, *Myrmotherula longipennis*
11 *M. l. zimmeri*—♀ gray above
11N *M. l. longipennis*—♀ brown above, two-toned below
East, mainly in terra firme. ♂ medium gray with contrasting black bib, fringed coverts, white-tipped tail. ♀ gray above with unmarked wing-coverts, uniform buff below.   p. 408

12. SLATY ANTWREN, *Myrmotherula schisticolor*
12W *M. s. schisticolor*
12E *M. s. interior*—♀ gray-backed
Foothills (mainly) and lower subtropics on both slopes (local in lowlands of west). ♂ slaty with black bib and fringed coverts. ♀ dark-eyed with buff wing-bars.   p. 408

13. PLAIN-WINGED ANTWREN, *Myrmotherula behni*
E.-slope foothills, very local. ♂ with unmarked coverts. ♀ brownish above with unmarked coverts.   p. 409

14. WHITE-FLANKED ANTWREN, *Myrmotherula axillaris*
Widespread and common. Diagnostic white flanks usually visible in both sexes.   p. 407

15. RUFOUS-TAILED ANTWREN, *Myrmotherula erythrura*
East, mainly in terra firme. Long rufous tail in both sexes.
          p. 407

16. ORNATE ANTWREN, *Myrmotherula ornata*
E.-slope foothills and adjacent lowlands, especially in bamboo. ♂ combines black throat and chestnut back. ♂ has black-and-white streaked throat, buff underparts.   p. 407

17. YASUNÍ ANTWREN, *Myrmotherula fjeldsaai*
Lowlands of east, south of Río Napo. Both sexes with buff wing-bars, brown back. ♂ has checkered throat, ♀ has throat streaked black.   p. 406

18. STIPPLE-THROATED ANTWREN, *Myrmotherula haematonota*
Lowlands of far northeast. Both sexes with chestnut back. ♂ with stippled throat, white-dotted coverts. ♂ with short brown tail.   p. 405

19. FOOTHILL ANTWREN, *Myrmotherula spodionota*
E.-slope foothills. ♂ with gray back, checkered throat. ♀ with buff-spotted coverts; sympatric ♀ Slaty is gray-backed.   p. 406

20. CHECKER-THROATED ANTWREN, *Myrmotherula fulviventris*
Lowlands and foothills of west, where the only pale-eyed antwren. ♂'s checkered throat unique in range.   p. 405

21. PLAIN-THROATED ANTWREN, *Myrmotherula hauxwelli*
Near ground inside terra firme in east. White (♂) or buff (♀) tertial spots unique.   p. 404

22. PACIFIC ANTWREN, *Myrmotherula pacifica*
Shrubby areas in more humid lowlands and foothills of west. Nearly unmistakable in range; ♂ streaked black and white, ♀ with bright orange-buff head and underparts.   p. 404

23. AMAZONIAN STREAKED-ANTWREN, *Myrmotherula multostriata*
Local in shrubby areas near water in east. Resembles preceding (calls very different), but ♀ paler with fine black streaking below. Cf. Stripe-chested Antwren of foothills.
          p. 403

24. STRIPE-CHESTED ANTWREN, *Myrmotherula longicauda*
Second-growth in e.-slope foothills. Both sexes unique in range (Amazonian Streaked-Antwren only in actual lowlands).   p. 404

25. PYGMY ANTWREN, *Myrmotherula brachyura*
Common in forest subcanopy and borders in lowlands of east. Streaked black and white above, mostly pale yellow below.   p. 402

26. SHORT-BILLED ANTWREN, *Myrmotherula obscura*
Lowlands of east, mainly in terra firme subcanopy. Both sexes like Pygmy but blacker above with wider black malar.
          p. 403

Plate 62 Antbirds III

Drymophila Antbirds
Attractive antbirds with long tails, generally streaked plumage. Favor bamboo thickets.

1. STRIATED ANTBIRD, *Drymophila devillei*
Rare and local in lowlands of northeast. Smaller than Long-tailed, with sparser streaking below confined to sides of chest, tail showing white spots from above. p. 413

2. LONG-TAILED ANTBIRD, *Drymophila caudata*
Subtropics on both slopes (no known overlap with preceding). Distinctive shape and plumage pattern. p. 412

Hypocnemis Antbirds
Two very different-looking, small, short-tailed antbirds found in lowlands of east, separating by habitat. Both species very vocal, with songs much alike. Cf. much longer-tailed *Drymophila*.

3. WARBLING ANTBIRD, *Hypocnemis cantator*
Favors forest edge, common. Contrasting rufous flanks in both sexes. ♂'s foreparts patterned black and white, ♀ similar but duller. p. 418

4. YELLOW-BROWED ANTBIRD, *Hypocnemis hypoxantha*
Favors interior of terra firme, uncommon. Bright yellow on face and underparts unique among the antbirds. p. 419

Cercomacra Antbirds
Confusing group of slender antbirds with long tails. ♂♂ gray or black with white on coverts and tail-tips; ♀♀ brown, often more rufescent below. Most species skulk in thickets, mainly in second-growth or at forest edge; all are very vocal.

5. GRAY ANTBIRD, *Cercomacra cinerascens*
Lowlands of east, foraging in subcanopy vine tangles (unique for genus). Broad white tail-tips in both sexes. p. 415

6. DUSKY ANTBIRD, *Cercomacra tyrannina*
More humid lowlands of west. ♂ uniform medium gray with narrow fringing on wings and tail-tips. ♀ dull rufescent below with unmarked wings. p. 415

7. BLACKISH ANTBIRD, *Cercomacra nigrescens*
E.-slope foothills and lower subtropics, locally also in lowlands. ♂ uniform dark gray. ♀ has orange-rufous of underparts intruding onto forecrown. p. 415

8. BLACK ANTBIRD, *Cercomacra serva*
E.-slope foothills and lowlands. ♂ similar to ♂ Blackish but blacker. ♀ similar to ♀ Blackish but forecrown concolor with back. Voice often best distinction. p. 416

9. JET ANTBIRD, *Cercomacra nigricans*
Lowlands of west, local in deciduous woodland and borders. Large white tail-tips in both sexes. ♂ jet black. ♀ grayer with variable amount of white streaking below. p. 416

10. WHITE-BACKED FIRE-EYE, *Pyriglena leuconota*
10W *P. l. pacifica*—♀ dull uniform brownish
10E *P. l. castanoptera*—♀ with black head and underparts
Lowlands and foothills in west, foothills and subtropics on e. slope. Forest and woodland undergrowth, often with army ants. Red iris in both sexes. ♂ all deep black with white back patch. p. 424

11. BLACK BUSHBIRD, *Neoctantes niger*
Scarce in terra firme undergrowth in lowlands of east. Unique heavy upswept bill. ♂ all black. ♀ with large chestnut breast patch. p. 423

12. GRAY-HEADED ANTBIRD, *Myrmeciza griseiceps*
Rare and local in woodland undergrowth in montane El Oro and w. Loja. Slender bill. Distinctive in its limited range, recalling a *Cercomacra*. ♂ with dark gray hood and black bib, ♀ paler and lacking black below. Other more typical *Myrmeciza* on Plate 63. p. 425

Schistocichla Antbirds
Myrmeciza-like antbirds found in terra firme undergrowth of lowlands of east. Note eye color.

13. SPOT-WINGED ANTBIRD, *Schistocichla leucostigma*
Often along forest streams. Dark iris. ♂ gray with distinct white spots on wing-coverts. ♀ with gray head, orange-rufous underparts. p. 422

14. SLATE-COLORED ANTBIRD, *Schistocichla schistacea*
Local in far northeast. Gray iris. ♂ like Spot-winged but wing-spots smaller. ♀ easier, with streaky orange-rufous head. p. 423

15. BLACK-CHINNED ANTBIRD, *Hypocnemoides melanopogon*
Várzea streamsides in lowlands of far northeast. Gray iris; short black tail with narrow white tip. ♂ with black throat, ♀ mottled gray and whitish below. p. 419

Myrmoborus Antbirds
Fairly small, short-tailed antbirds with distinct "browed" effect found in e.-slope lowlands and foothills. Another species is on Plate 96.

16. BLACK-FACED ANTBIRD, *Myrmoborus myotherinus*
Forest undergrowth, mainly terra firme. ♂ with pearly gray brow and underparts, black face and throat. ♀ with contrasting white throat. p. 418

17. WHITE-BROWED ANTBIRD, *Myrmoborus leucophrys*
Dense second-growth in e.-slope foothills, only locally out into lowlands. ♂ dark gray with snowy white brow. ♀ with conspicuous bright buff brow. p. 417

18. BLACK-AND-WHITE ANTBIRD, *Myrmochanes hemileucus*
Low shrubby growth on river islands in northeast. Black and white plumage and small size unique there. p. 422

19. SILVERED ANTBIRD, *Sclateria naevia*
Near water in lowlands of east, favoring várzea streams and lakesides. Long pink legs. ♂ gray and white, ♀ rufous brown and white. p. 423

Myrmeciza Antbirds
Short-tailed antbirds found in humid forest undergrowth of west, favoring vicinity of streams. Formerly in genus *Sipia*. Other *Myrmeciza* are on Plate 63.

20. ESMERALDAS ANTBIRD, *Myrmeciza nigricauda*
Mainly foothills. Ruby red iris. ♂ uniform slaty, white spots on coverts. ♂ has dull brown mantle, white-scaled throat. p. 428

21. STUB-TAILED ANTBIRD, *Myrmeciza berlepschi*
Esmeraldas lowlands. Dark iris. ♂ all black. ♀ distinctively white-spotted below. p. 429

Plate 63 Antbirds IV

Myrmeciza Antbirds

A heterogeneous group of small to robust antbirds found in undergrowth of humid forest, mainly in lowlands. Many have conspicuous bare blue skin around eyes. Most species sexually dimorphic. All are heard more often than seen; some (especially Sooty, Immaculate) habitually follow army ants. Other *Myrmeciza* are on Plate 62.

1. CHESTNUT-BACKED ANTBIRD, *Myrmeciza exsul*
Common in lowlands and foothills of west. Blue ocular skin and dark iris distinguish both sexes from sometimes sympatric Esmeraldas (Plate 62-20).   p. 428

2. BLACK-THROATED ANTBIRD, *Myrmeciza atrothorax*
Scarce and local in second-growth and borders in lowlands of east. ♂ very dark with tiny white dots on wing-coverts. ♀ has buff wing-dots, rufous breast contrasting with whitish throat and midbelly.   p. 425

3. CHESTNUT-TAILED ANTBIRD, *Myrmeciza hemimelaena*
Rare and very local in lowlands and foothills of east; favors terra firme. Short rufous tail. ♂'s black throat and breast contrast sharply with white belly. ♀ has gray head, rufescent underparts.   p. 425

4. PLUMBEOUS ANTBIRD, *Myrmeciza hyperythra*
Common in várzea forest undergrowth of lowlands of northeast. Both sexes with bare blue skin around eye, fine wing-dotting.   p. 426

5. WHITE-SHOULDERED ANTBIRD, *Myrmeciza melanoceps*
Common and vocal in thick forest borders (both várzea and terra firme) in lowlands of east. Dull blue skin around eye. ♂ lustrous black (white shoulders usually hard to see). ♀ rufous-chestnut with contrasting black hood.   p. 426

6. SOOTY ANTBIRD, *Myrmeciza fortis*
Terra firme undergrowth in lowlands of east. Conspicuous bright bare blue skin around eye. ♂ uniform sooty black (white under wing hard to see). ♀ with mainly dull gray face and underparts.   p. 427

7. IMMACULATE ANTBIRD, *Myrmeciza immaculata*
Humid forest undergrowth in lowlands and foothills of west. Conspicuous bare bright blue skin around eye. ♂ deep black (white under wing hard to see). ♀ mainly umber brown.   p. 427

Pithys Antbirds

Only one *Pithys*, the classy White-plumed, is known from Ecuador. White-masked known only from a single specimen, taken in adjacent Peru, and may be just a hybrid.

8. WHITE-PLUMED ANTBIRD, *Pithys albifrons*
Terra firme undergrowth in lowlands of east. Unmistakable, with spectacular white head plumes. Frequently with army ants.   p. 429

9. WHITE-MASKED ANTBIRD, *Pithys castanea*
Unknown in life (and not known from Ecuador); to be looked for in lowlands of southeast. All-chestnut body (no gray mantle); white face (but no plumes). See text.   p. 429

Gymnopithys Antbirds

Fairly small, plump antbirds of humid forest undergrowth. Among the most persistent followers of army ants.

10. LUNULATED ANTBIRD, *Gymnopithys lunulata*
Scarce in várzea forest undergrowth of lowlands of east. White throat. ♂ uniform gray, ♀ more ornately patterned.   p. 430

11. BICOLORED ANTBIRD, *Gymnopithys leucaspis*
11W *G. l. aequatorialis*—black cheeks
11E *G. l. castanea*—bluish white ocular area, white cheeks
Humid forest undergrowth in lowlands. Sharply bicolored, rufous and white.   p. 429

12. HAIRY-CRESTED ANTBIRD, *Rhegmatorhina melanosticta*
Local in terra firme undergrowth in lowlands of east; often with army ants. Unmistakable large pale blue ocular area, black facial area, expressive grayish crest. ♂'s mantle unmarked.   p. 430

Hylophylax Antbirds

Small, short-tailed, ornately patterned antbirds of humid forest undergrowth.

13. SCALE-BACKED ANTBIRD, *Hylophylax poecilinota*
Lowlands of east, mainly in terra firme. Both sexes with unmistakable scaling on mantle.   p. 421

14. SPOTTED ANTBIRD, *Hylophylax naevioides*
Lowlands of northwest. Both sexes unmistakable in range, with boldly banded wings, spots on breast. Often at antswarms.   p. 419

15. SPOT-BACKED ANTBIRD, *Hylophylax naevia*
Fairly common in lowlands of east, in terra firme and várzea. Gray face and buff back-spotting in both sexes.   p. 420

16. DOT-BACKED ANTBIRD, *Hylophylax punctulata*
Local in várzea forest undergrowth of lowlands of east. Both sexes with whitish facial band, white spotting on back and rump.   p. 420

17. BANDED ANTBIRD, *Dichrozona cincta*
On ground inside terra firme forest in lowlands of east, mainly in hilly terrain. Unmistakable white band across back almost connects to bold wing-bands.   p. 421

Phlegopsis Bare-eyes

Large, flashy antbirds found in forest undergrowth of lowlands of east. Seen most often at antswarms.

18. BLACK-SPOTTED BARE-EYE, *Phlegopsis nigromaculata*
Especially in várzea. Large rose red ocular area, spotted back, rufous tail.   p. 431

19. REDDISH-WINGED BARE-EYE, *Phlegopsis erythroptera*
Strictly in terra firme, local and usually scarce. Large rose red ocular area. ♂ black with scaled back, rufous on wings. ♀ rufous and brown with conspicuous pale buff wing-banding.   p. 431

20. OCELLATED ANTBIRD, *Phaenostictus mcleannani*
Humid forest undergrowth in lowlands of northwest. Unmistakable ornate pattern, large bare blue ocular area. Often at antswarms.   p. 432

21. WING-BANDED ANTBIRD, *Myrmornis torquata*
Seemingly rare (local?) in lowlands of east, on or near ground inside terra firme. Odd dumpy shape with short tail and legs. Scaly effect on sides of head and neck.   p. 432

Plate 64 Smaller Antpittas, Antthrushes

Grallaricula Antpittas

Small, plump antpittas of montane forest undergrowth (they tend not to be terrestrial), rarely occurring at edge. Hard to see without tape playback.

1. CRESCENT-FACED ANTPITTA, *Grallaricula lineifrons*

Apparently locally not uncommon in temperate forest on e. slope. Unmistakable large white facial crescent; bold streaking below. p. 446

2. SLATE-CROWNED ANTPITTA, *Grallaricula nana*

Uncommon in subtropical forest on e. slope, ranging at elevations below Crescent-faced; often in bamboo. Gray crown; unmarked rich rufous underparts. p. 445

3. OCHRE-BREASTED ANTPITTA, *Grallaricula flavirostris*

Uncommon and seemingly local in foothill and lower subtropical forest on both slopes, ranging at lower elevations than other *Grallaricula*. The only *Grallaricula* on w. slope. Variants shown depict differences in bill color and breast pattern; see text. p. 444

4. PERUVIAN ANTPITTA, *Grallaricula peruviana*

Apparently rare and local in subtropical forest on e. slope in south. White throat, black breast chevrons, bold facial markings. ♂ has crown more rufous. p. 445

5. RUFOUS-CROWNED ANTPITTA, *Pittasoma rufopileatum*

Long-legged, chunky antpitta on ground inside very humid forest in lowlands and foothills of northwest, now mainly in Esmeraldas. Rufous crown, long wide black eye-stripe (with white spots in ♀), dense black barring below (sparser in ♀). p. 436

Hylopezus Antpittas

Midsized antpittas with obvious breast streaking, one species on either side of Andes. Not often seen, but distinctive songs are frequently heard.

6. STREAK-CHESTED ANTPITTA, *Hylopezus perspicillatus*

On or near ground in humid forest of lowlands and foothills of northwest. Bold black breast streaking; prominent buff eye-ring; buff spotting on wing-coverts. p. 443

7. WHITE-LORED ANTPITTA, *Hylopezus fulviventris*

Dense second-growth and borders in lowlands of east. Conspicuous white lores, rufous flanks. p. 444

8. THRUSH-LIKE ANTPITTA, *Myrmothera campanisona*

Fairly common in forest undergrowth of lowlands of east, mainly in terra firme, locally up into foothills. Plain and dull, with extensive blurry breast streaking. p. 444

Chamaeza Antthrushes

Fairly large terrestrial antthrushes with boldly patterned underparts found inside humid forest (both lowland and montane) in east. Distinctive songs are much more often heard than the birds, which are shy, are ever seen.

9. STRIATED ANTTHRUSH, *Chamaeza nobilis*

Inside terra firme forest in lowlands of east. Large; boldly scalloped underparts. p. 435

10. SHORT-TAILED ANTTHRUSH, *Chamaeza campanisona*

Inside foothill and lower subtropical forest on e. slope. Densely streaked underparts. p. 435

11. BARRED ANTTHRUSH, *Chamaeza mollissima*

Rare inside subtropical and lower temperate forest on e. slope. Unmistakable dense barring on underparts and facial stripes. p. 436

Formicarius Antthrushes

Simply patterned but attractive antthrushes found on or near ground inside humid lowland and montane forests. Usually walk with tail held jauntily cocked, reminiscent of certain rails. As with *Chamaeza*, distinctive songs are heard more often than birds are seen.

12. BLACK-HEADED ANTTHRUSH, *Formicarius nigricapillus*

Fairly common in lowlands and foothills of west. Very dark overall, with blackish foreparts, contrasting white eye-ring. p. 434

13. RUFOUS-CAPPED ANTTHRUSH, *Formicarius colma*

Inside terra firme in lowlands of east. Bright orange-rufous crown contrasting with blackish foreparts. p. 433

14. BLACK-FACED ANTTHRUSH, *Formicarius analis*

Generally numerous in forests in lowlands of east. Entire head dull brown; rufous crissum; partial pale blue eye-ring. p. 433

15. RUFOUS-BREASTED ANTTHRUSH, *Formicarius rufipectus*

15W *F. r. carrikeri*—rufous crown
15E *F. r. thoracicus*—duller overall
Subtropics on both slopes, locally down into foothills. Breast rufous to chestnut. p. 434

Plate 65 Antpittas

Grallaria Antpittas

Plump, mainly terrestrial antbirds, secretive in humid montane and lowland forests, a few at borders. All have a characteristic "round" shape with long legs, large heads, very short tails. Except for the common Tawny, all are heard far more often than seen; learn their distinctive voices. An additional species is on Plate 96.

1. UNDULATED ANTPITTA, *Grallaria squamigera*
1 *G. s. squamigera*—upperparts more olivaceous
1SE *G. s. canicauda*—upperparts uniform gray
Temperate forest. A large antpitta with boldly scalloped ochraceous underparts; white throat bordered by blackish malar.   p. 437

2. GIANT ANTPITTA, *Grallaria gigantea*
2NW *G. g. hylodroma*—rich rufous underparts
2E *G. g. gigantea*—ochraceous underparts
Rare and local in subtropical forest. The largest Ecuadorian antpitta. Compared to Undulated, has finer scalloping below, buffier throat with no bordering malar.   p. 437

3. SCALED ANTPITTA, *Grallaria guatimalensis*
Mainly foothill and lower subtropical forest and borders, also locally inside terra firme in lowlands of east. Whitish malar and collar on foreneck; coarse dark scaling above.
                                                             p. 438

4. MOUSTACHED ANTPITTA, *Grallaria alleni*
Local in subtropical forest on both slopes in north. Occurs above range of similar Scaled; see text.   p. 438

5. PLAIN-BACKED ANTPITTA, *Grallaria haplonota*
Very local in foothill and lower subtropical forest and borders on both slopes. Plain and brown, with white throat, buffyish malar.   p. 438

6. CHESTNUT-CROWNED ANTPITTA, *Grallaria ruficapilla*
Widespread in subtropical and temperate forest borders and secondary woodland. Entire head bright orange-rufous; underparts boldly streaked.   p. 439

7. WATKINS'S ANTPITTA, *Grallaria watkinsi*
Deciduous woodland and scrub of southwest. Compared to Chestnut-crowned (which, where sympatric, occurs at higher elevations), paler generally with whitish face, pinkish legs. Songs differ markedly.   p. 439

8. CHESTNUT-NAPED ANTPITTA, *Grallaria nuchalis*
8E *G. n. nuchalis*
8NW *G. n. obsoleta*—rufous confined to nape; dark overall
Temperate and upper subtropical forest, especially in bamboo. Plain and dark, with uniform gray underparts, rufous on crown.   p. 440

9. WHITE-BELLIED ANTPITTA, *Grallaria hypoleuca*
Borders of subtropical forest on e. slope. Distinctly bicolored: rufous above, whitish below.   p. 441

10. YELLOW-BREASTED ANTPITTA, *Grallaria flavotincta*
Scarce in subtropical forest of northwest. Yellowish underparts.   p. 441

11. RUFOUS ANTPITTA, *Grallaria rufula*
Small antpitta, widespread in temperate and upper subtropical forest. Uniform rich rufous.   p. 442

12. TAWNY ANTPITTA, *Grallaria quitensis*
Common and widespread in temperate scrub and paramo. For an antpitta, easy to see. Uniform olivaceous brown, paler below.   p. 442

13. OCHRE-STRIPED ANTPITTA, *Grallaria dignissima*
Spectacular, large antpitta found locally (perhaps overlooked) inside terra firme forest in lowlands of east. Rich rufescent throat and chest, bold flank streaking.   p. 443

Plate 66 Gnateaters and Tapaculos

Conopophaga Gnateaters

Small, plump and round, short-tailed birds found inside humid and montane forests; inconspicuous, not very vocal. ♂♂ attractively plumaged, and both sexes sport a distinctive silvery postocular tuft that can be flared laterally when bird is excited (at other times more or less hidden).

1. CHESTNUT-CROWNED GNATEATER, Conopophaga castaneiceps
1N *C. c. castaneiceps*—♀ with back more olivaceous
1S *C. c. chapmani*—♀ with back more rufescent
Undergrowth inside e.-slope foothill and subtropical forest (at higher elevations than other gnateaters). ♂ has chestnut crown, dark underparts. ♀ has rich rufous foreparts (including crown), white median lower underparts.   p. 446

2. ASH-THROATED GNATEATER, *Conopophaga peruviana*
Undergrowth inside terra firme in lowlands of east, south of Río Napo. Small buff dots on wing-coverts, prominent black scaling on back. ♂ has breast and back gray.   p. 446

3. CHESTNUT-BELTED GNATEATER, *Conopophaga aurita*
Undergrowth inside terra firme forest in lowlands of northeast, north of Río Napo. ♂ has black face contrasting with rufous breast. ♀ brown-backed with less obvious black scaling than in Ash-throated; wings plain.   p. 447

Melanopareia Crescentchests
Boldly patterned tapaculos that skulk near ground in scrubby habitats of s. Ecuador. Heard much more often than seen.

4. ELEGANT CRESCENTCHEST, *Melanopareia elegans*
Scrub and woodland undergrowth in lowlands and (southward) subtropics of southwest. Black head, contrasting buff brow and throat, black crescent on chest.   p. 448

5. MARAÑÓN CRESCENTCHEST, *Melanopareia maranonica*
Scrub and woodland undergrowth in Río Marañón valley around Zumba. Resembles better-known Elegant Crescentchest but larger with extensive silvery wing-edging, more richly colored belly.   p. 448

6. OCELLATED TAPACULO, *Acropternis orthonyx*
Inconspicuous (but often vocal) in dense undergrowth of temperate and upper subtropical forest and woodland. Large, spectacular, unmistakable when seen, with bright rufous face and throat, boldly white-spotted body.   p. 453

7. RUSTY-BELTED TAPACULO, *Liosceles thoracicus*
Inconspicuous (but often vocal) on ground inside terra firme forest in lowlands of east, creeping about furtively with predilection for fallen logs. Prominent white bib (conspicuous even in dim light of forest interior).   p. 447

8. ASH-COLORED TAPACULO, *Myornis senilis*
Inconspicuous (except by voice) in undergrowth of temperate forest and woodland. Resembles a *Scytalopus* tapaculo, but tail markedly longer. Juvenile brown and (unlike juvenile *Scytalopus*) virtually unbarred. Often best recognized by voice; see text.   p. 449

Scytalopus Tapaculos
Very difficult genus of small, secretive birds with rather short tails, found at varying elevations in forest and woodland undergrowth through Andes. Basically gray to blackish, most species with flanks and rump rufescent brown with blackish barring. Sexes typically alike. Most *Scytalopus* are very similar in plumage, and many cannot be recognized by appearance. Far more important are distribution and often characteristic voices (especially primary songs); see text. Fortunately they tend to be very vocal. Three new species were described from Ecuador in 1997, and relationships of several others have only recently been clarified.

9. UNICOLORED TAPACULO, *Scytalopus unicolor*
9 *S. u. latrans*—both sexes uniform blackish
9SW *S. u. subcinereus*—♀ paler and grayer, with brown on flanks
Generally widespread and numerous in subtropical and temperate forest and woodland undergrowth, but less so on e. slope. ♂♂ are blackest and most uniform *Scytalopus*. Only in southwest do ♀♀ show rufescent brown on rump and flanks.   p. 449

10. EQUATORIAL RUFOUS-VENTED TAPACULO, *Scytalopus micropterus*
Undergrowth of subtropical and lower temperate forest and woodland on e. slope. Similar in plumage to Spillman's (northward) and Chusquea (southward), overlapping with both; differs in being longer tailed and slightly paler below. Tends to occur at lower elevations. Best identified by voice.   p. 450

11. NARIÑO TAPACULO, *Scytalopus vicinior*
Undergrowth and borders of subtropical forest in northwest. Similar in plumage to Spillman's, and overlaps with it, though tending to occur at lower elevations. Best identified by voice.   p. 451

12. CHOCÓ TAPACULO, *Scytalopus chocoensis*
Undergrowth and borders of foothill and adjacent lowland forest in far northwest (Esmeraldas), where the only tapaculo.   p. 451

13. EL ORO TAPACULO, *Scytalopus robbinsi*
Uncommon and local in undergrowth and borders of foothill forest in southwest (Azuay and El Oro), where the only tapaculo occurring lower than Unicolored.   p. 451

14. SPILLMANN'S TAPACULO, *Scytalopus spillmanni*
Undergrowth and borders of upper subtropical and temperate forest on both slopes, but only in north; favors *Chusquea* bamboo. Similar in plumage to Equatorial Rufous-vented (e. slope) and Nariño (w. slope), overlapping with both though tending to occur at higher elevations. Best identified by voice. Juvenile brown and barred; most other *Scytalopus* have a similar plumage.   p. 452

15. CHUSQUEA TAPACULO, *Scytalopus parkeri*
Undergrowth and borders of upper subtropical and temperate zone on e. slope, replacing Spillmann's southward. Shows strong predilection for *Chusquea* bamboo. Similar in plumage to Equatorial Rufous-vented, overlapping with it though tending to occur at higher elevations. Best identified by voice.   p. 452

16. NORTHERN WHITE-CROWNED TAPACULO, *Scytalopus atratus*
Undergrowth and borders of foothill and lower subtropical forest on e. slope. Unusual among *Scytalopus*, can usually be identified by appearance: relatively blackish with small white patch on midcrown.   p. 450

17. PARAMO TAPACULO, *Scytalopus canus*
Uncommon and somewhat local in undergrowth of temperate and *Polylepis* woodland and treeline scrub on e. slope, on w. slope only in Carchi. Mainly at higher elevations than other *Scytalopus*. Small, ♀♀ browner above than other *Scytalopus*. Best identified by voice.   p. 452

Plate 67 Tyrant Flycatchers I

Pogonotriccus Bristle-Tyrants

Small tyrannids of foothills and subtropics in Andes with relatively long slender bills and complex facial patterns. They often wing-lift and tend to perch vertically and to remain inside forest at lower and middle levels, accompanying mixed flocks.

1. MARBLE-FACED BRISTLE-TYRANT, *Pogonotriccus ophthalmicus*

Subtropics on e. slope and in northwest. Grizzled facial area, prominent dark ear-crescent, wing-bars yellowish.   p. 476

2. VARIEGATED BRISTLE-TYRANT, *Pogonotriccus poecilotis*

Uncommon in subtropics on e. slope. Grizzled facial area as in Marble-faced, but lower mandible yellow, wing-bars ochraceous.   p. 476

3. SPECTACLED BRISTLE-TYRANT, *Pogonotriccus orbitalis*

Uncommon in foothills on e. slope. Plainer facial pattern than Marble-faced, bolder eye-ring; lower mandible pale. p. 477

Phylloscartes Tyrannulets

Slender tyrannulets that perch horizontally as they forage in canopy of foothill and subtropical forest on e. slope. Frequently cock rather long tails and often wing-lift.

4. ECUADORIAN TYRANNULET, *Phylloscartes gualaquizae*

Uncommon in foothills. Confusing (see text); all-dark bill relatively long and slender, dark eye-line, forecrown concolor (no white).   p. 475

5. RUFOUS-BROWED TYRANNULET, *Phylloscartes superciliaris*

Local in southeast (Cutucú and Cóndor). Distinctive, white cheeks outlined darker, grayish white underparts.   p. 476

6. SULPHUR-BELLIED TYRANNULET, *Mecocerculus minor*

Montane forest and woodland, mainly on e. slope. Gray crown, white superciliary, bold buff wing-bars, yellow underparts.   p. 469

Phyllomyias Tyrannulets

Diverse, difficult group of obscure tyrannids, found mainly in Andean forests and scrub, only one (Sooty-headed) out into lowlands. All have short bills, often imparting a "stubby" look.

7. PLUMBEOUS-CROWNED TYRANNULET, *Phyllomyias plumbeiceps*

Scarce in subtropics of east. Confusing (see text); pale area behind dark ear-crescent, fairly strong wing-edging. p. 455

8. ASHY-HEADED TYRANNULET, *Phyllomyias cinereiceps*

Subtropics on e. slope and in northwest. Bluish gray crown, bold ear-crescent, fine olive breast streaking, no edging on wing-coverts.   p. 456

9. WHITE-FRONTED TYRANNULET, *Phyllomyias zeledoni*

Rare and local in foothills. Confusing (see text); short bill with yellow-orange mandible, white frontal area.   p. 454

10. SOOTY-HEADED TYRANNULET, *Phyllomyias griseiceps*

Mainly lower foothills of west and east, commoner in west; favors forest edge, trees in clearings. Plain, wings without bars. Distinctive voice.   p. 454

11. BLACK-CAPPED TYRANNULET, *Phyllomyias nigrocapillus*

Montane forest and borders in temperate zone on e. slope and in northwest. Crown obviously dark, wing-bars bold.
     p. 455

12. TAWNY-RUMPED TYRANNULET, *Phyllomyias uropygialis*

Montane forest borders and scrub in temperate zone on both slopes. The brownest tyrannulet; rump tawny, wing-bars buff.
     p. 456

13. SOUTHERN BEARDLESS-TYRANNULET, *Camptostoma obsoletum*

13W *C. o. sclateri*—dull, wing-bars buffyish

13E *C. o. olivaceum*—brighter yellow below, wing-bars whitish

Common in scrub and woodland in west up to central and interandean valleys; scarce and local in east, mainly in várzea. Bushy crest. Distinctive voice.   p. 459

14. YELLOW-CROWNED TYRANNULET, *Tyrannulus elatus*

Forest and woodland borders, clearings in lowlands of east and west. Stubby bill, gray face and throat. Unmistakable voice; see text.   p. 461

Ornithion Tyrannulets

Inconspicuous small tyrannulets of humid forest canopy and clearings in lowlands, one species on either side of Andes. Distinctive voices.

15. WHITE-LORED TYRANNULET, *Ornithion inerme*

East. Prominent but short white superciliary, white-spotted wing-bars.   p. 458

16. BROWN-CAPPED TYRANNULET, *Ornithion brunneicapillum*

West. Short tail, bold white superciliary, plain wings. Crown varies from brown to dusky.   p. 459

Phaeomyias Tyrannulets

Nondescript tyrannulets with stubby bills found in scrub and woodland. Best known by distinctive voices.

17. TUMBESIAN TYRANNULET, *Phaeomyias tumbezana*

Arid scrub and woodland of southwest, ranging higher in Loja. Pale lower mandible. Grayish above with buffyish wing-bars.   p. 460

18. MOUSE-COLORED TYRANNULET, *Phaeomyias murina*

Local in clearings and woodland borders in lowlands of northeast. Pale lower mandible. Brownish above with clear yellow belly.   p. 460

19. SUBTROPICAL DORADITO, *Pseudocolopteryx acutipennis*

Local in sedgy marshes of central and interandean valleys. Plain bright olive above, uniform bright yellow below.
     p. 472

20. YELLOW TYRANNULET, *Capsiempis flaveola*

Woodland and humid forest lower growth, especially in bamboo, in lowlands and foothills of west and locally in northeast. Yellow superciliary, wing-bars, and underparts.
     p. 477

Zimmerius Tyrannulets

Small tyrannulets found in humid and montane forests and borders, united by distinctive yellow wing-edgings; they lack wing-bars. Each species' voice distinctive.

21. RED-BILLED TYRANNULET, *Zimmerius cinereicapillus*

Rare and local in e.-slope foothills. Yellow iris, bright yellow underparts; lower mandible reddish (hard to see).   p. 458

22. SLENDER-FOOTED TYRANNULET, *Zimmerius gracilipes*

Forest canopy in lowlands of northeast. Pale grayish iris, gray crown, yellow lower underparts.   p. 457

23. GOLDEN-FACED TYRANNULET, *Zimmerius chrysops*

Widespread in humid lowlands up to subtropical zone, especially common in west. Yellow on face, whitish underparts. Often perches atop dead leaves with tail partially cocked. p. 457

24. LOJA TYRANNULET, *Zimmerius flavidifrons*

Numerous in humid forest borders in foothills and subtropics of southwest, also in Río Marañón drainage. Resembles Golden-faced Tyrannulet, but voice differs (see text); less yellow on face.   p. 457

25. RINGED ANTPIPIT, *Corythopis torquata*

Walks on ground inside humid forest in lowlands of east, pumping tail. Distinctively shaped, with bold black breast streaking.   p. 478

Plate 68 Tyrant Flycatchers II

Mionectes Flycatchers

Small, slender, inconspicuous flycatchers found in understory of humid forest and woodland. Wing-lift frequently.

1. OCHRE-BELLIED FLYCATCHER, *Mionectes oleagineus*
Lowlands of east and west. Distinctive ochre belly.   p. 473

2. STREAK-NECKED FLYCATCHER, *Mionectes striaticollis*
Subtropics (some overlap with Olive-striped). White post-ocular spot. Grayish head (less evident in w.-slope birds), unstreaked midbelly.   p. 473

3. OLIVE-STRIPED FLYCATCHER, *Mionectes olivaceus*
Foothills and humid lowlands near Andes, both east and west. White postocular spot. More extensive streaking on belly than Streak-necked.   p. 473

Leptopogon Flycatchers

Slender flycatchers of humid or montane forest undergrowth, two species with characteristic dark auriculars. All wing-lift regularly.

4. SLATY-CAPPED FLYCATCHER, *Leptopogon superciliaris*
Common in foothills and lower subtropics on both slopes. Gray crown. Cf. smaller *Pogonotriccus* bristle-tyrants (Plate 67).   p. 474

5. SEPIA-CAPPED FLYCATCHER, *Leptopogon amaurocephalus*
Lowlands of east, favoring várzea forest. Brownish crown.   p. 474

6. RUFOUS-BREASTED FLYCATCHER, *Leptopogon rufipectus*
Local in subtropics on e. slope. Orange-rufous throat and chest. Cf. Handsome Flycatcher (Plate 71-20).   p. 475

Tolmomyias Flatbills

Midsized olive flycatchers, among the hardest Ecuadorian tyrannids to identify; see text. Voice is often best clue. Bills fairly wide and flat.

7. YELLOW-OLIVE FLATBILL, *Tolmomyias sulphurescens*
Deciduous woodland in lowlands of west, and montane forest in foothills and lower subtropics on both slopes; most often in understory or at edge. Tends to have pale iris.   p. 489

8. ZIMMER'S FLATBILL, *Tolmomyias assimilis*
Canopy and borders of humid forest in lowland of east. Tends to have dark iris; bright plumage; pale wing speculum.   p. 490

9. YELLOW-MARGINED FLATBILL, *Tolmomyias flavotectus*
Canopy and borders of humid forest in lowlands of north-west. Dark eyed; bold edging on wing-coverts but no bars.   p. 490

10. GRAY-CROWNED FLATBILL, *Tolmomyias poliocephalus*
Canopy and borders of humid forest in lowlands of east. Smaller than previous 3 species. Tends to be pale eyed.   p. 491

11. OLIVE-FACED FLATBILL, *Tolmomyias viridiceps*
Second-growth and várzea forest in lowlands of east. No gray on crown.   p. 491

12. ORANGE-EYED FLATBILL, *Tolmomyias traylori*
Scarce and local in várzea forest and woodland in lowlands of east. Orangey iris. Distinctive voice.   p. 490

Myiopagis Elaenias

Undistinguished small tyrannids with semiconcealed coronal stripes. Often best known by voice; see text. Wooded/forested habitats in lowlands.

13. FOREST ELAENIA, *Myiopagis gaimardii*
East, mainly in canopy and borders of second-growth. White coronal stripe, blurry streaked effect on breast.   p. 462

14. GREENISH ELAENIA, *Myiopagis viridicata*
Deciduous woodland and humid forest borders of west. No wing-bars; rather plain face.   p. 463

15. PACIFIC ELAENIA, *Myiopagis subplacens*
Deciduous woodland of southwest. Dark auriculars outlined by paler gray; plain wings.   p. 463

16. YELLOW-CROWNED ELAENIA, *Myiopagis flavivertex*
Local in lower growth of várzea forest in northeast. Yellow coronal stripe.   p. 462

17. GRAY ELAENIA, *Myiopagis caniceps*
Scarce in canopy of humid forest in east and northwest. Bold wing markings. ♂ mainly gray, some (younger birds?) with olive back. ♀ clouded olive on breast.
   p. 461

18. GRAY-AND-WHITE TYRANNULET, *Pseudelaenia leucospodia*
Local in arid scrub of w. Guayas and Isla de la Plata. Distinctive "horns" outline white coronal patch.   p. 460

19. AMAZONIAN SCRUB-FLYCATCHER, *Sublegatus obscurior*
Scarce and local at edge of humid forest in lowlands of east. Small dark bill, grayish throat and breast blending into pale yellow belly; wing-bars vague. See text.   p. 467

Elaenia Elaenias

Notoriously difficult; individual elaenias often cannot be safely identified to species; voice often characteristic, nonvocalizing birds thus especially difficult. In Ecuador 4 species (22, 23, 25, 26) are particularly similar, all having about same amount of white in crest (often hidden; when visible, usually just a slit shows). Besides voice, note relative size, head and crest shape (and extent of white, if present), and presence and intensity of yellow on belly.

20. YELLOW-BELLIED ELAENIA, *Elaenia flavogaster*
Shrubby areas, clearings, and lighter woodland in lowlands and foothills of west (also Zumba area). Usually shows upstanding bushy crest revealing white. No more yellow-bellied than several other elaenias.   p. 464

21. LARGE ELAENIA, *Elaenia spectabilis*
Rare austral migrant to clearings and borders in lowlands of east. Much like Yellow-bellied but shows little or no crest (and no white), usually a 3d wing-bar.   p. 464

22. WHITE-CRESTED ELAENIA, *Elaenia albiceps*
Widespread in shrubby areas and clearings, borders of subtropical and temperate forest and woodland. Particularly dull: brownish olive above, dingy below with no yellow.
   p. 466

23. SMALL-BILLED ELAENIA, *Elaenia parvirostris*
Uncommon austral migrant to forest borders and clearings in lowlands of east. Bright olive above, gray on breast, obvious white eye-ring.   p. 466

24. MOTTLE-BACKED ELAENIA, *Elaenia gigas*
Uncommon and local in clearings, lighter woodland, and river islands along e. base of Andes. An easy elaenia: large with bifurcated crest revealing much white.   p. 464

25. LESSER ELAENIA, *Elaenia chiriquensis*
Scarce in shrubby clearings in foothills and subtropics of northwest. Dull, often confused. "Intermediate" between White-crested and Sierran; often not separable from duller Sierrans (see text).   p. 465

26. SIERRAN ELAENIA, *Elaenia pallatangae*
Subtropical and temperate forest and woodland borders and clearings, favoring more humid regions than White-crested (with which easily confused). Dull, but with pale yellow belly.
   p. 466

27. HIGHLAND ELAENIA, *Elaenia obscura*
Rare and local in montane forest and woodland in Azuay and Loja. A large elaenia, round headed (no white in crest); bill short.   p. 465

Plate 69 Tyrant Flycatchers III

Todirostrum and *Poecilotriccus* Tody-Flycatchers

Diverse group of small tyrannids with broad flat bills and short tails found in variety of habitats but mostly at edge of humid forest and woodland. Most are difficult to see (Common and Spotted are exceptions), but all have distinctive vocalizations. Several species have recently been transferred to *Poecilotriccus* from *Todirostrum*; former inhabit dense undergrowth, latter are more arboreal.

1. RUSTY-FRONTED TODY-FLYCATCHER,
   Poecilotriccus latirostris
   Dense low second-growth in lowlands of east. Buffy facial area, whitish underparts.   p. 484

2. YELLOW-BROWED TODY-FLYCATCHER,
   Todirostrum chrysocrotaphum
   Forest canopy and borders in lowlands of east. Bold yellow postocular stripe, bright yellow underparts with black streaking.   p. 485

3. BLACK-HEADED TODY-FLYCATCHER, *Todirostrum nigriceps*
   Canopy and borders of humid forest in lowlands and foothills of west. Head glossy black contrasting with yellow-olive back.   p. 484

4. GOLDEN-WINGED TODY-FLYCATCHER,
   Poecilotriccus calopterus
   Low second-growth in lowlands and foothills of east. Bright golden on wing-coverts; dark iris.   p. 483

5. COMMON TODY-FLYCATCHER, *Todirostrum cinereum*
   5W *T. c. sclateri*—whitish throat
   5E *T. c. peruanum*—all yellow underparts
   Conspicuous in clearings and second-growth in lowlands of east near Andes, common and widespread in west. Blackish forecrown shades to gray nape and back; whitish iris.
                                                         p. 485

6. SPOTTED TODY-FLYCATCHER, *Todirostrum maculatum*
   Local in woodland on river islands in lowlands of east. Orange iris, gray head, profusely speckled throat and breast.   p. 485

7. BLACK-AND-WHITE TODY-FLYCATCHER,
   Poecilotriccus capitalis
   Very local in dense thickets in foothills and lowlands of east. Bold yellow tertial edging. ♂ black and white, ♀ with rufous crown.   p. 483

8. RUFOUS-CROWNED TODY-FLYCATCHER,
   Poecilotriccus ruficeps
   8N *P. r. ruficeps*
   8S *P. r. peruvianus*—black malar stripe
   Dense low second-growth and borders in subtropics on both slopes. Rufous crown, whitish bib; amount of black variable.
                                                         p. 483

Hemitriccus Tody-Tyrants

Small tyrannids which resemble *Todirostrum* but have more "normal" bills and tend to perch more vertically. Found in humid or montane forest, most scarce and hard to see, though they vocalize frequently.

9. BLACK-THROATED TODY-TYRANT, *Hemitriccus granadensis*
   9N *H. g. granadensis*—white lores and ocular area
   9SE *H. g. pyrrhops*—buff lores and ocular area
   Local in montane shrubbery of temperate zone, mainly on e. slope. Distinctive black throat.   p. 481

10. WHITE-EYED TODY-TYRANT, *Hemitriccus zosterops*
    Lower and middle growth inside terra firme in lowlands of east. Drab and olive, with plain olive crown.   p. 481

11. BUFF-THROATED TODY-TYRANT, *Hemitriccus rufigularis*
    Rare and local in e.-slope foothill forest. Sides of head and neck, throat, and breast pale dull buff, whitish belly.
                                                         p. 482

12. CINNAMON-BREASTED TODY-TYRANT,
    Hemitriccus cinnamomeipectus
    Rare and local in subtropical forest undergrowth of far southeast (Cordillera del Cóndor). Bright cinnamon throat and breast, yellow belly, bold tertial edging.   p. 482

Lophotriccus Pygmy-Tyrants

Small tyrannids with broad transverse crests, feathers prominently edged, found in woodland and forest undergrowth. Loud voices.

13. SCALE-CRESTED PYGMY-TYRANT, *Lophotriccus pileatus*
    Widespread and often common in foothills and lower subtropics on both slopes, also humid lowlands of west; especially in bamboo. Rufous edging on crest feathers.   p. 480

14. DOUBLE-BANDED PYGMY-TYRANT, *Lophotriccus vitiosus*
    Lowlands of east. Gray edging on crest feathers.   p. 480

15. TAWNY-CROWNED PYGMY-TYRANT,
    Euscarthmus meloryphus
    Thick undergrowth of arid and deciduous scrub of west. Tiny; bright buff foreface. Distinctive voice.   p. 472

Myiornis Pygmy-Tyrants

Minute, short-tailed tyrannids found in borders of humid lowland forest, one on either side of Andes.

16. SHORT-TAILED PYGMY-TYRANT, *Myiornis ecaudatus*
    East. Gray head.   p. 479

17. BLACK-CAPPED PYGMY-TYRANT, *Myiornis atricapillus*
    Northwest. Black on head.   p. 479

Pseudotriccus Pygmy-Tyrants

Inconspicuous small tyrannids found in undergrowth of montane forest, generally not with mixed flocks. Somewhat manakin-like; frequent bill-snapping.

18. BRONZE-OLIVE PYGMY-TYRANT, *Pseudotriccus pelzelni*
    18E *P. p. pelzelni*
    18W *P. p. annectens*—browner upperparts, buffier underparts
    Foothills and subtropics on both slopes. Uniform bronzy olive, brownest on wings.   p. 478

19. RUFOUS-HEADED PYGMY-TYRANT, *Pseudotriccus ruficeps*
    Temperate zone on both slopes. Unmistakable: contrasting rufous head and throat, chestnut wings and tail.   p. 478

Anairetes Tit-Tyrants

Conspicuously crested tyrannids found in shrubby areas of Andes.

20. TUFTED TIT-TYRANT, *Anairetes parulus*
    Widespread in temperate zone. Small; obviously streaked foreneck.   p. 471

21. BLACK-CRESTED TIT-TYRANT, *Anairetes nigrocristatus*
    Very local in extreme s. Loja (Utuana). Unmistakable, mainly black and white; larger, longer crest than Tufted.   p. 471

22. AGILE TIT-TYRANT, *Uromyias agilis*
    Local, mainly in bamboo stands of temperate-zone forest on both slopes. Streaked overall appearance, long flat crest; often looks "disheveled."   p. 471

23 LESSER WAGTAIL-TYRANT, *Stigmatura napensis*
   Riparian scrub on river islands in lowlands of northeast. Long graduated tail, feathers broadly tipped white; large white patch on wing-coverts.   p. 470

Serpophaga Tyrannulets

Two quite different small tyrannids, associated with water.

24. RIVER TYRANNULET, *Serpophaga hypoleuca*
    Inconspicuous in riparian scrub on river islands in lowlands of east. Slender. Uniform dull brownish above, whitish below.
                                                         p. 469

25. TORRENT TYRANNULET, *Serpophaga cinerea*
    Conspicuous along rushing streams in Andes. Mainly pale gray with black head.   p. 470

Plate 70 Tyrant Flycatchers IV

1. NORTHERN TUFTED-FLYCATCHER, *Mitrephanes phaeocercus*
Borders of humid forest in lower foothills of northwest. Pewee-like behavior. Distinctive, with crest, rufescent throat and chest. p. 500

2. RUDDY-TAILED FLYCATCHER, *Terenotriccus erythrurus*
Inside humid forest in lowlands of east and west. Often with understory flocks. Rufous tail and underparts. Cf. much rarer Cinnamon Neopipo (Plate 78-17). p. 495

Myiobius Flycatchers
Unmistakable group with obvious yellow rump, often fanned tail, active and acrobatic behavior with understory flocks inside lowland and foothill forest. Species-level separation often difficult; see text.

3. TAWNY-BREASTED FLYCATCHER, *Myiobius villosus*
Lower story of foothill and subtropical forest on both slopes. Tawny brown across breast and down flanks. p. 497

4. SULPHUR-RUMPED FLYCATCHER, *Myiobius sulphureipygius*
Humid forest undergrowth in lowlands of west. Bright tawny across breast. Note lack of tawny on flanks (cf. Tawny-breasted), brighter chest than Black-tailed. p. 497

5. WHISKERED FLYCATCHER, *Myiobius barbatus*
Humid forest undergrowth in lowlands of east. Grayish olive breast, duller than in Black-tailed. p. 496

6. BLACK-TAILED FLYCATCHER, *Myiobius atricaudus*
Woodland undergrowth in lowlands of east and west. Chest always dull brownish. Sulphur-rumped and Whiskered are more true forest birds. p. 496

7. ORNATE FLYCATCHER, *Myiotriccus ornatus*
7W *M. o. stellatus*
7E   *M. o. phoenicurus*—all-rufous tail
Conspicuous at borders and openings of montane forest and woodland on both slopes. Unmistakable, with prominent yellow rump, obvious white lores. p. 495

8. CINNAMON FLYCATCHER, *Pyrrhomyias cinnamomea*
Conspicuous and often common at edge of montane forest in subtropical and temperate zones on both slopes. Distinctive rufous underparts. p. 500

9. WHITE-HEADED MARSH-TYRANT, *Arundinicola leucocephala*
Casual along Río Napo. White-headed ♂ unmistakable. ♀ brownish above with whitish face. p. 517

Platyrinchus Spadebills
Inconspicuous small flycatchers with very wide bills found in lower growth inside humid and montane forest. Usually solitary (not with flocks).

10. WHITE-CRESTED SPADEBILL, *Platyrinchus platyrhynchos*
Rare in terra firme in lowlands of east. Bright ochraceous underparts, gray head. p. 493

11. WHITE-THROATED SPADEBILL, *Platyrinchus mystaceus*
Widespread in foothill and subtropical forest on both slopes, locally also in lowlands of west. Complex facial pattern, contrasting white throat. p. 492

12. GOLDEN-CROWNED SPADEBILL, *Platyrinchus coronatus*
Scarce in terra firme in lowlands of east and northwest. Complex facial pattern, orange-rufous crown patch. p. 492

13. YELLOW-THROATED SPADEBILL, *Platyrinchus flavigularis*
Rare in subtropical forest on e. slope. Rufous head, yellow underparts. p. 493

14. CINNAMON-CRESTED SPADEBILL, *Platyrinchus saturatus*
Very rare and local in terra firme in lowlands of far northeast. Plain and dull, with white throat, cinnamon in crown. p. 492

Rhynchocyclus Flatbills
Sombre, mainly olive, midsized flycatchers with lethargic behavior found in humid and montane forest undergrowth. Exceptionally wide flat bills with lower mandible pale. *Tolmomyias* flatbills are smaller; cf. Plate 68.

15. OLIVACEOUS FLATBILL, *Rhynchocyclus olivaceus*
Scarce in lowlands of east. No other *Rhynchocyclus* in range; has broad olive wing-edging but no bars, bold whitish eyering. p. 489

16. PACIFIC FLATBILL, *Rhynchocyclus pacificus*
Lowlands and foothills of west. Dull grayish eye-ring, olive breast with some flammulation, rufescent wing-edging. p. 488

17. FULVOUS-BREASTED FLATBILL, *Rhynchocyclus fulvipectus*
Foothills and lower subtropics on both slopes. Dull grayish eye-ring, dull tawny-fulvous breast, rufescent wing-edging. Occurs above ranges of other *Rhynchocyclus*. p. 488

Ramphotrigon Flatbills
Superficially like *Rhynchocyclus*, and likewise found in humid forest undergrowth (but only in e. lowlands), but with more prominent wing-bars, different facial patterns. Distinctive vocalizations often heard.

18. DUSKY-TAILED FLATBILL, *Ramphotrigon fuscicauda*
Very rare, local, and inconspicuous in terra firme, known only from w. Napo lowlands. Partial white eye-ring, rufous wing-bars, dusky tail, olive-flammulated breast. p. 487

19. RUFOUS-TAILED FLATBILL, *Ramphotrigon ruficauda*
Local in terra firme of east. Unmistakable, with mainly rufous wings and tail. p. 486

20. LARGE-HEADED FLATBILL, *Ramphotrigon megacephala*
Uncommon and local in bamboo stands along e. base of Andes from lower subtropics into adjacent lowlands. Yellowish supraloral and eye-ring, ochraceous wing-bars, yellowish underparts. p. 487

Mecocerculus Tyrannulets
Small to fairly small tyrannulets that glean in Andean forests and shrubbery; characterized by especially bold wing-bars, simple facial patterns. Posture usually horizontal, though atypical White-throated perches quite upright.

21. WHITE-THROATED TYRANNULET, *Mecocerculus leucophrys*
Temperate forest borders, shrubby clearings, and *Polylepis* on both slopes; not as tied to forest as other *Mecocerculus*. Puffy white throat; brown upperparts. p. 467

22. WHITE-TAILED TYRANNULET, *Mecocerculus poecilocercus*
Subtropical forest and borders on both slopes. Pale rump, white in outer tail feathers (conspicuous in flight); wing-bars yellowish. p. 468

23. WHITE-BANDED TYRANNULET, *Mecocerculus stictopterus*
Temperate forest borders and woodland on both slopes. Bold white superciliary and broad wing-bars. p. 468

24. RUFOUS-WINGED TYRANNULET, *Mecocerculus calopterus*
Local in montane forest and woodland and adjacent clearings in foothills and subtropics, mainly on w. slope but also on e. slope in south. Distinctive rufous wing-patch. p. 469

Plate 71 Tyrant Flycatchers V

1. RUFOUS-TAILED TYRANT, *Knipolegus poecilurus*
Local in forest borders in subtropics on e. slope. Drab and pewee-like, with rufescent underparts, red eye.   p. 515

Contopus **Pewees and Flycatchers**
Drab, midsized flycatchers usually seen perched in open at forest edge or in clearings. Identification difficult; voice often most helpful.

2. OLIVE-SIDED FLYCATCHER, *Contopus cooperi*
Boreal migrant, usually perching high in trees. Large but short-tailed, vested look, white tuft behind wings.   p. 503

3. EASTERN WOOD-PEWEE, *Contopus virens*
Boreal migrant, primarily to lowlands of east. Drab, showing no eye-ring (cf. *Empidonax*) but with fairly bold wing-bars. Best distinguished from other pewees by voice.   p. 501

4. WESTERN WOOD-PEWEE, *Contopus sordidulus*
Boreal migrant, primarily to foothills, especially on e. slope. Amost identical to Eastern, but slightly darker with all-dark bill; best to go by voice.   p. 501

5. TUMBES PEWEE, *Contopus punensis*
Lowlands of west. Very similar to wood-pewees, but usually shows whitish lores, more capped look; best to go by voice.
p. 502

6. BLACKISH PEWEE, *Contopus nigrescens*
Very local in canopy of e.-slope lower foothill forest. Very small, all blackish.   p. 502

7. SMOKE-COLORED PEWEE, *Contopus fumigatus*
Common and widespread in subtropical and temperate zones on both slopes. Fairly large; pointed crest, overall dark gray plumage.   p. 503

Empidonax **Flycatchers**
Fairly small flycatchers, all boreal migrants, favoring semi-open areas and woodland lower growth. Identification difficult except by voice; see text. Somewhat smaller and more olivaceous than pewees, showing more distinct wing-bars and eye-rings.

8. ACADIAN FLYCATCHER, *Empidonax virescens*
Lowlands of west, favoring woodland. Relatively bold eye-ring, olivaceous tone, yellowish belly.   p. 503

9. ALDER FLYCATCHER, *Empidonax alnorum*
WILLOW FLYCATCHER, *Empidonax traillii*
Lowlands of east, favoring shrubby areas. These 2 species indistinguishable except by voice. Somewhat duller and browner (less olive) than Acadian. Juveniles of both species have buffier wing-bars.   p. 504

Lathrotriccus **Flycatchers**
Inconspicuous flycatchers found in woodland and forest undergrowth; distinctive voice. Similar to *Empidonax*, showing at least a partial eye-ring.

10. EULER'S FLYCATCHER, *Lathrotriccus euleri*
Scarce in humid forest in lowlands and foothills of east. Rather brown above, ochraceous wing-bars, pale yellowish belly.   p. 505

11. GRAY-BREASTED FLYCATCHER, *Lathrotriccus griseipectus*
Dense woodland undergrowth in lowlands and foothills of west. Gray above and on chest.   p. 505

12. FUSCOUS FLYCATCHER, *Cnemotriccus fuscatus*
Inconspicuous in woodland on river islands in lowlands of east. Dull grayish brown with faint wing-bars, whitish superciliary.   p. 506

13. BROWNISH TWISTWING, *Cnipodectes subbrunneus*
Forest and woodland undergrowth in lowlands of east and west. Often lifts wings. Brown with rufous tail, pale edging on wings.   p. 486

Onychorhynchus **Royal-Flycathers**
Mid-sized flycatchers, inconspicuous in lowland forests. Though it reveals color (red in ♂, orange in ♀) only when spread, spectacular crest always shows hammerhead effect.

14. AMAZONIAN ROYAL-FLYCATCHER, *Onychorhynchus coronatus*
Scarce in lowlands of east. Spectacular crest; breast with dusky scaling; wings plain, tail rufous.   p. 494

15. PACIFIC ROYAL-FLYCATCHER, *Onychorhynchus occidentalis*
Scarce and local in lowlands of west. Similar to preceding (same spectacular crest), but markedly larger and paler, with cinnamon tail.   p. 494

Myiophobus **Flycatchers**
Fairly small flycatchers with bold wing-bars, usually showing a crown patch (but often hard to see). Diverse in behavior and habitat.

16. FLAVESCENT FLYCATCHER, *Myiophobus flavicans*
Undergrowth of subtropical forest on both slopes. Broken eye-ring, cinnamon wing-bars (often only one shows), crown patch usually yellow.   p. 497

17. ORANGE-CRESTED FLYCATCHER, *Myiophobus phoenicomitra*
Local in undergrowth of foothill forest. Weak eye-ring, orange-rufous crown patch.   p. 498

18. OLIVE-CHESTED FLYCATCHER, *Myiophobus cryptoxanthus*
Shrubby clearings in e.-slope foothills and adjacent lowlands. Dull, breast clouded with olive brown.   p. 499

19. BRAN-COLORED FLYCATCHER, *Myiophobus fasciatus*
19W *M. f. crypterythrus*—grayish brown upperparts
19E *M. f. fasciatus*—rufescent upperparts
Shrubby clearings, mainly in lowlands and foothills of west (rare in east, where cf. Olive-chested). Streaking on breast.
p. 498

20. HANDSOME FLYCATCHER, *Myiophobus pulcher*
Borders of subtropical forest on both slopes, mainly in north; with mixed flocks. Orange-ochraceous breast, gray head.   p. 499

21. ORANGE-BANDED FLYCATCHER, *Myiophobus lintoni*
Local in borders and subcanopy of temperate forest and woodland in southeast. Wing-bars of large cinnamon spots, orange on lower mandible.   p. 500

22. RORAIMAN FLYCATCHER, *Myiophobus roraimae*
Very local in undergrowth of subtropical forest in southeast (Cordilleras de Cutucú and del Cóndor). Larger than other *Myiophobus*, brown-backed with more extensive rufous in wing.   p. 498

Plate 72 Tyrant Flycatchers VI

Agriornis Shrike-Tyrants
Large, somewhat thrush-like tyrannids with strongly hooked bills, much white in tail. Range in open country at high elevations in Andes.

1. BLACK-BILLED SHRIKE-TYRANT, *Agriornis montana*
Widespread. Bill comparatively thin, throat only faintly streaked, pale eye.   p. 512

2. WHITE-TAILED SHRIKE-TYRANT, *Agriornis andicola*
Very rare and local. Larger than Black-billed; bill heavier with pale on lower mandible, throat much more boldly streaked. Tail patterns of the two similar.   p. 512

3. SHORT-TAILED FIELD-TYRANT, *Muscigralla brevicauda*
Mainly terrestrial in semiopen, even barren terrain in southwest. Small with very short tail, long legs, brightly colored rump (but often concealed).   p. 514

4. LONG-TAILED TYRANT, *Colonia colonus*
Conspicuous in clearings and borders of humid and foothill forest. Nearly unmistakable, with very long central tail feathers (shorter in ♀♀), conspicuous whitish crown. E. birds lack whitish on back.   p. 516

Muscisaxicola Ground-Tyrants
Slim, mostly terrestrial flycatchers found primarily in open areas of Andes, characterized by thin bills, black tails, outer feathers with white outer webs (often flicked open and shut), long legs. Head patterns important for identification.

5. WHITE-BROWED GROUND-TYRANT, *Muscisaxicola albilora*
Austral migrant to temperate zone (usually not in actual paramo). Rufescent nape, long and narrow white superciliary.   p. 513

6. PARAMO GROUND-TYRANT, *Muscisaxicola alpina*
High elevations in paramo. Prominent short white supraloral.   p. 513

7. LITTLE GROUND-TYRANT, *Muscisaxicola fluviatilis*
Very rare wanderer to open areas in east. Much like Spot-billed, but eye-stripe vague or absent, belly white.   p. 514

8. SPOT-BILLED GROUND-TYRANT, *Muscisaxicola maculirostris*
Barren areas in temperate zone and paramo. Brownish overall, with uniform buffyish underparts. Spot on bill hard to see.   p. 513

9. DARK-FACED GROUND-TYRANT, *Muscisaxicola macloviana*
Accidental austral migrant, one record in far south. Blackish foreface.   p. 514

10. VERMILION FLYCATCHER, *Pyrocephalus rubinus*
Conspicuous in scrub and agricultural areas in arid highlands and southwest. ♂ unmistakable; ♀ with pink belly, streaked breast. Also a rare austral migrant to e. lowlands; ♀ there usually lacks red on belly, is more streaked below.   p. 506

Myiotheretes Bush-Tyrants
Large flycatchers with hooked bills, streaking on throat, cinnamon-rufous in wings (especially obvious in flight). Found in open areas and forest borders in temperate zone of Andes.

11. STREAK-THROATED BUSH-TYRANT, *Myiotheretes striaticollis*
Widespread. Mainly cinnamon-rufous underparts.   p. 510

12. SMOKY BUSH-TYRANT, *Myiotheretes fumigatus*
Forest-based. Sooty brown with faint paler superciliary.
                                                     p. 511

13. RED-RUMPED BUSH-TYRANT, *Cnemarchus erythropygius*
Scarce in paramo. Mainly gray with frosted white foreface, rufous belly, rump, and in tail.   p. 510

14. CLIFF FLYCATCHER, *Hirundinea ferruginea*
Local near cliffs and roadcuts in foothills and subtropics on e. slope. Rufous in wing (conspicuous in flight), grizzled face, rufous underparts.   p. 511

Ochthoeca Chat-Tyrants
Group of boldly patterned midsized tyrannids found in Andes, some in semiopen shrubby areas or forest borders, others less conspicuous and in understory of montane forest. They tend to perch erectly and have conspicuous superciliaries; most have prominent rufous wing-bars.

15. BROWN-BACKED CHAT-TYRANT, *Ochthoeca fumicolor*
Common in open areas in temperate zone and especially shrubby paramo. Mainly rufescent underparts, creamy brow.
                                                     p. 507

16. WHITE-BROWED CHAT-TYRANT, *Ochthoeca leucophrys*
Very scarce and local in montane scrub and woodland borders of Azuay and n. Loja. White brow, pale gray underparts.   p. 507

17. RUFOUS-BREASTED CHAT-TYRANT, *Ochthoeca rufipectoralis*
Edge of temperate forest. Broad rufous chest band, single rufous wing-bar, white brow.   p. 508

18. SLATY-BACKED CHAT-TYRANT, *Ochthoeca cinnamomeiventris*
Near streams in montane forest and woodland. Dark with chestnut belly, white supraloral.   p. 508

19. CROWNED CHAT-TYRANT, *Ochthoeca frontalis*
Inside montane forest near and just below treeline. Golden frontal area, plain wings (with no bars), smoky gray underparts.   p. 508

20. JELSKI'S CHAT-TYRANT, *Ochthoeca jelskii*
Woodland undergrowth and borders in Loja; not on actual e. slope. Prominent rufous wing-bars, golden frontal area.
                                                     p. 509

21. YELLOW-BELLIED CHAT-TYRANT, *Ochthoeca diadema*
Inside temperate forest. Brow entirely yellow, yellow on underparts.   p. 509

22. BLACK PHOEBE, *Sayornis nigricans*
Conspicuous and widespread along streams and rivers in Andes. Mainly black; white belly, wing and tail edging. Wags tail.   p. 506

Fluvicola Water-Tyrants
Conspicuous, white and black tyrannids found near water in open areas.

23. MASKED WATER-TYRANT, *Fluvicola nengeta*
Lowlands of west. Unmistakable, with black eye-stripe.
                                                     p. 516

24. PIED WATER-TYRANT, *Fluvicola pica*
Accidental vagrant to east. Unmistakable, with mainly white head.   p. 517

25. DRAB WATER-TYRANT, *Ochthornis littoralis*
Conspicuous along banks of rivers and larger streams in lowlands of east. Nondescript, uniform sandy brown with white supraloral.   p. 509

Plate 73 Tyrant Flycatchers VII

Also included here are two Cotinga genera, *Laniocera* and *Lipaugus*.

Attila Attilas

Tyrant flycatchers with prominently hooked bills, bull-headed appearance, and pale, usually yellow, rumps. Attilas perch erectly inside forest in lowlands and lower subtropics. Sluggish and inconspicuous, heard much more often than seen.

1. BRIGHT-RUMPED ATTILA, *Attila spadiceus*
Widespread in lowlands of east and west, also in subtropics. Variable, but the only attila with breast streaking and shows stronger wing-bars than the others. Olive morph is by far the most frequent; rufous and gray morphs occur in east.
p. 517

2. CITRON-BELLIED ATTILA, *Attila citriniventris*
Local in terra firme in east. Gray head, yellowish belly, plain wings.
p. 518

3. OCHRACEOUS ATTILA, *Attila torridus*
Local in humid forest and woodland in west. Mainly bright yellow-ochraceous, contrasting black on wings.
p. 519

4. CINNAMON ATTILA, *Attila cinnamomeus*
Várzea in lowlands of east. Mainly cinnamon-rufous, contrasting black on wings. Cf. Várzea Schiffornis (Plate 78-20).
p. 519

5. WHITE-EYED ATTILA, *Attila bolivianus*
Very rare (wanderer?) in várzea in lowlands of northeast. Staring white eye unique among the attilas.
p. 518

Laniocera Mourners

Inconspicuous cotingas found in lower growth inside humid forest in lowlands, one species on either side of Andes. Rounder headed and with more prominent wing-markings than superficially similar and commoner *Rhytipterna* mourners, with which they are illustrated because of superficial similarity.

6. CINEREOUS MOURNER, *Laniocera hypopyrra*
Terra firme in east. Cinnamon-rufous spotting on wings.
p. 546

7. SPECKLED MOURNER, *Laniocera rufescens*
Northwest. Large cinnamon-rufous spots on black wing-coverts.
p. 547

Rhytipterna Mourners

Plain-colored tyrannids found in mid-levels and subcanopy inside forest on either side of Andes. Often with flocks. Shape recalls *Myiarchus*, but in coloration they are much like the only subtly different (and often sympatric) pihas.

8. GRAYISH MOURNER, *Rhytipterna simplex*
Lowlands of east. Plain gray, belly with olivaceous tinge.
p. 520

9. RUFOUS MOURNER, *Rhytipterna holerythra*
Lowlands and foothills of northwest. Rich rufous, crown and wing-coverts slightly darker (not uniform with back).
p. 520

Lathria and *Lipaugus* Pihas

Plainly colored and inconspicuous cotingas found inside humid and montane forest. Superficially resemble smaller *Rhytipterna* mourners (and even certain *Turdus* thrushes), and are placed here because of this. Some species draw attention through loud vocalizations.

10. DUSKY PIHA, *Lipaugus fuscocinereus*
Local in temperate forest on e. slope. Very large; all-gray plumage.
p. 548

11. SCREAMING PIHA, *Lipaugus vociferans*
Common (at least very vocal, not too often seen) in lowlands of east, mainly in terra firme. Uniform gray.
p. 548

12. RUFOUS PIHA, *Lipaugus unirufus*
Lowlands of northwest (now mainly Esmeraldas). Uniform rufous with slightly paler throat.
p. 549

13. GRAY-TAILED PIHA, *Lathria subalaris*
Very local in foothills on e. slope. Tail and belly pale gray.
p. 547

14. OLIVACEOUS PIHA, *Lathria cryptolophus*
Local in subtropics on e. slope and in northwest. Mainly olive, yellower belly and yellow eye-ring.
p. 547

Myiarchus Flycatchers

Very similar, midsized flycatchers, fairly conspicuous in a variety of wooded habitats; most are difficult to identify except by voice and, to some extent, range. All species vary with age and molt stage, showing more rufous wing and tail edging when young, more pale edging in fresh plumage. Pay special attention to color tonality of upperparts, especially the crown.

15. SHORT-CRESTED FLYCATCHER, *Myiarchus ferox*
Lowlands (especially) and foothills in east. Dark overall, with all-black bill.
p. 522

16. SWAINSON'S FLYCATCHER, *Myiarchus swainsoni*
16A *M. s. swainsoni*
16B *M. s. ferocior*—especially pale, dusky ear-coverts
Two austral migrant subspecies to lowlands of east. Pale overall, pinkish usually showing at least at base of lower mandible.
p. 522

17. PALE-EDGED FLYCATCHER, *Myiarchus cephalotes*
Subtropical forest borders and clearings on e. slope. Crown and back uniform brownish olive, pale outer web on outer tail feathers.
p. 522

18. SOOTY-CROWNED FLYCATCHER, *Myiarchus phaeocephalus*
Lowlands and lower subtropics in west, also around Zumba. Dark overall, with indistinctly bicolored crown (forecrown paler, grayer).
p. 523

19. DUSKY-CAPPED FLYCATCHER, *Myiarchus tuberculifer*
19W *M. t. nigriceps*—relatively small, black crown
19E *M. t. tuberculifer*—relatively small, sepia brown crown
19H *M. t. atriceps*—relatively large, black crown
Widespread in variety of habitats. Races vary (see above); voice is often best character, but dark crown contrasts more than in other *Myiarchus*.
p. 521

20. GREAT CRESTED FLYCATCHER, *Myiarchus crinitus*
Very rare boreal migrant to lowlands of east. Broad rufous edging on primaries and tail.
p. 523

Plate 74 Tyrant Flycatchers VIII

1. **WESTERN SIRYSTES**, *Sirystes albogriseus*
Local in canopy of humid forest in lowlands of northwest. Distinctive, *Myiarchus*-like in shape but very different gray, white, and black.   p. 521

2. **EASTERN SIRYSTES**, *Sirystes sibilator*
Canopy of humid forest in lowlands of east. Like preceding but lacking white tail-tip and wing-edging; calls very different.   p. 520

Tyrannus Kingbirds and Flycatchers
Conspicuous, often common and noisy tyrannids found primarily in open and semiopen terrain. Several species are migratory and in Ecuador rather rare. Note especially pattern and coloration of head and foreparts.

3. **FORK-TAILED FLYCATCHER**, *Tyrannus savana*
Austral migrant, primarily to lowlands of east. Long tail streamers (but shorter in worn plumage), pure gray mantle.   p. 534

4. **EASTERN KINGBIRD**, *Tyrannus tyrannus*
Boreal migrant, primarily to lowlands of east. Uniform slaty above, broad white tail-tip (inconspicuous in worn plumage).   p. 533

5. **TROPICAL KINGBIRD**, *Tyrannus melancholicus*
Omnipresent and conspicuous in semiopen areas, especially lowlands. Gray head, olive back, grayish olive chest.
                                  p. 532

6. **WHITE-THROATED KINGBIRD**, *Tyrannus albogularis*
Very rare austral migrant to lowlands of east. Like Tropical, but head pale gray with contrasting black mask, bright olive back, white throat.   p. 532

7. **GRAY KINGBIRD**, *Tyrannus dominicensis*
Vagrant, one record from El Oro coast. Heavy bill, gray upperparts with dusky mask, whitish underparts.   p. 533

8. **SNOWY-THROATED KINGBIRD**, *Tyrannus niveigularis*
Lowlands of west. A small, pale kingbird; black mask, gray back, white throat, pale gray chest.   p. 532

9. **SULPHURY FLYCATCHER**, *Tyrannopsis sulphurea*
Local in lowlands of east, mainly around *Mauritia* palms. Dull; brownish wings and tail, olive mottling on sides of chest, tail not notched.   p. 531

10. **DUSKY-CHESTED FLYCATCHER**, *Myiozetetes luteiventris*
Scarce in canopy and borders of humid forest in lowlands of east. Drab and quite small, rather brown above with unpatterned head, mottling on chest.   p. 526

11. **PIRATIC FLYCATCHER**, *Legatus leucophaius*
Widespread in lowlands of east and west; distinctive call. Stubby bill, dark tail, streaked underparts.   p. 530

12. **VARIEGATED FLYCATCHER**, *Empidonomus varius*
Austral migrant to lowlands of east. Like smaller Piratic, but bill longer, obvious rufous in tail, white edging on wings.
                                  p. 530

13. **CROWNED SLATY FLYCATCHER**, *Griseotyrannus aurantioatrocristatus*
Austral migrant to lowlands of east. Smoky gray, contrasting black crown.   p. 531

Conopias Flycatchers
Less familiar than *Myiozetetes*, with somewhat longer bills and less conspicuous behavior, being much more forest-based. Vocalizations distinctive and often heard.

14. **YELLOW-THROATED FLYCATCHER**, *Conopias parva*
Very local in lowlands of northeast. Underparts all yellow (including throat).   p. 528

15. **WHITE-RINGED FLYCATCHER**, *Conopias albovittata*
Lowlands of Esmeraldas. Wings plain (cf. *Myiozetetes*).
                                  p. 527

16. **THREE-STRIPED FLYCATCHER**, *Conopias trivirgata*
Very local in lowlands of far east. All-yellow underparts (including throat), rather pale olive back, crown and cheeks duskier.   p. 528

17. **LEMON-BROWED FLYCATCHER**, *Conopias cinchoneti*
Foothills and subtropics on e. slope and in extreme northwest. Superciliary all bright yellow.   p. 527

Myiodynastes Flycatchers
Rather large flycatchers with heavy bills found mainly in wooded areas. Most have dark malar stripe, all show at least some rufous in tail.

18. **SULPHUR-BELLIED FLYCATCHER**, *Myiodynastes luteiventris*
Boreal migrant to lowlands of east. Dusky "chinstrap"; no rufous primary edging; belly pale clear yellow, relatively unstreaked.   p. 529

19. **STREAKED FLYCATCHER**, *Myiodynastes maculatus*
19   *M. m. chapmani / maculatus*
19E *M. m. solitarius*—austral migrant; blackish tail, bold streaking
Lowlands of east and west. Generally streaked, much rufous in tail, rufescent primary edging.   p. 528

20. **BAIRD'S FLYCATCHER**, *Myiodynastes bairdii*
Deciduous woodland to arid scrub in lowlands of southwest. Distinctive, with broad black mask, much rufous in wings.   p. 529

21. **GOLDEN-CROWNED FLYCATCHER**, *Myiodynastes chrysocephalus*
Foothills and subtropics on both slopes. Buffyish throat and cheeks, dark malar, breast flammulation.   p. 529

22. **BOAT-BILLED FLYCATCHER**, *Megarynchus pitangua*
Woodland in lowlands and foothills of east and west. Large; broad heavy bill. Distinctive voice.   p. 524

23. **GREAT KISKADEE**, *Pitangus sulphuratus*
Conspicuous and noisy, mainly near water in lowlands of east. Large; fairly heavy bill, rufous wing-edging. Voice easy to learn.   p. 523

24. **LESSER KISKADEE**, *Philohydor lictor*
Near water in lowlands of east. Long slender bill. Distinctive voice.   p. 524

Myiozetetes Flycatchers
Conspicuous and noisy, midsized flycatchers with stubby bills found in semiopen areas in lowlands.

25. **RUSTY-MARGINED FLYCATCHER**, *Myiozetetes cayanensis*
Humid lowlands and foothills in west. Rufous primary edging, black ear-coverts. Distinctive voice.   p. 525

26. **SOCIAL FLYCATCHER**, *Myiozetetes similis*
Lowlands and foothills of west and east. Pale wing-bars and edging on inner flight feathers, dusky ear-coverts.   p. 525

27. **GRAY-CAPPED FLYCATCHER**, *Myiozetetes granadensis*
Lowlands of east and northwest. Head mostly gray (often bushy crested) with only short white superciliary. Distinctive voice (kiskadee-like).   p. 526

Plate 75 Tyrant Flycatchers IX

Pachyramphus Becards

Diverse group of large-headed, arboreal birds, one or another species found almost throughout Ecuador (though none occurs at high elevations). Most show strong sexual dimorphism. ♂♂'s often-given and melodic songs draw attention.

1. YELLOW-CHEEKED BECARD, *Pachyramphus xanthogenys*
Clearings and forest borders in foothills on e. slope. ♂ with bright yellow cheeks and throat. ♀ has throat and sides of head and neck gray, rufous on wing-coverts.   p. 534

2. BARRED BECARD, *Pachyramphus versicolor*
Montane forest on both slopes. Small; faint dusky barring on underparts and sides of neck. ♀ has much rufous in wings.
p. 535

3. SLATY BECARD, *Pachyramphus spodiurus*
Scarce in lowlands of west. Small. ♂ with pale gray lores, whitish edging on wing-coverts and flight feathers. ♀ like commoner Cinnamon but with no pale supraloral; has black patch on primary-coverts.   p. 535

4. CINEREOUS BECARD, *Pachyramphus rufus*
Only a few old, uncertain records from southeast. ♂ pale gray overall with no white on scapulars or white tail-tipping. ♀ rufous and buff with prominent whitish lores.   p. 536

5. CHESTNUT-CROWNED BECARD, *Pachyramphus castaneus*
Local at forest edge in lowlands and foothills of east. Sexes alike. Rufescent with distinctive gray nape band.   p. 536

6. CINNAMON BECARD, *Pachyramphus cinnamomeus*
Numerous in clearings and edge of humid forest in lowlands and foothills of west. Sexes alike. Rufescent with dark lores surmounted by pale supraloral area.   p. 536

7. WHITE-WINGED BECARD, *Pachyramphus polychopterus*
7NW   *P. p. dorsalis*—♂ gray below
7E   *P. p. tenebrosus*—♂ black below
Second-growth in lowlands of east; in northwest only in foothills and lower subtropics. Mainly black ♂ of east distinctive. W.-slope ♂ with gray underparts, black on back, white scapular stripe. ♀♀ throughout have face plain with concolor crown.   p. 537

8. BLACK-AND-WHITE BECARD, *Pachyramphus albogriseus*
Forest and woodland in foothills and subtropics (where the only becard of its type) on both slopes, also locally in lowlands of west. ♂ has plain gray back, prominent pale gray lores. ♀ has chestnut crown outlined by black.   p. 537

9. BLACK-CAPPED BECARD, *Pachyramphus marginatus*
Humid forest canopy in lowlands of east. ♂ like ♂ Black-and-white, but with black on back, white on scapulars. ♀ with rufescent crown.   p. 538

Platypsaris Becards

Larger, heavier-billed becards found in a variety of wooded or forested situations; crown feathers often raised in an expressive bushy crest.

10. ONE-COLORED BECARD, *Platypsaris homochrous*
Widespread in wooded habitats of west, ranging well up into foothills. Relatively large, often bushy crested. ♂ essentially slaty (blacker above) with plain wings. ♀ rufescent with dusky around eyes, no pale supraloral.   p. 538

11. CRESTED BECARD, *Platypsaris validus*
Very rare in canopy and borders of lower temperate forest on e. slope in s. Zamora-Chinchipe. The largest becard, ♂ black and olivaceous gray, ♀ with contrasting slaty crown.
p. 539

12. PINK-THROATED BECARD, *Platypsaris minor*
Humid forest canopy and borders in lowlands of east. ♂ slaty with diffused rosy pink patch on lower throat and chest (often hard to see). ♀ has contrasting slaty crown and back.
p. 539

Tityra Tityras

Easily recognized, chunky, predominantly white or pale pearly gray tyrannids with short tails that range in humid lowlands. Often conspicuous, perching in open at forest edge and in clearings. ♂♂ have black on head, wings, and tail; ♀♀ are less pure white.

13. BLACK-TAILED TITYRA, *Tityra cayana*
Widespread in east. Ocular area and most of bill red. ♂ has all-black head and tail; ♀ prominently streaked.   p. 540

14. MASKED TITYRA, *Tityra semifasciata*
Widespread in more humid lowlands and foothills of west, also along e. base of Andes. Ocular area and most of bill red. ♂ has black on head restricted to mask and forecrown, white on tail; ♀ has brownish head, grayish back.   p. 540

15. BLACK-CROWNED TITYRA, *Tityra inquisitor*
Lowlands in east and more humid parts of west. Bill black with no red. ♂ has black only on crown; ♀ has rufous-chestnut cheeks.   p. 540

Plate 76 Cotingas I

1. PURPLE-THROATED COTINGA, *Porphyrolaema porphyrolaema*
Scarce in canopy of humid forest in lowlands of east. ♂ black above with back feathers fringed white; mostly white below with deep purple throat. ♀ rather uniformly barred with conspicuous plain rufous throat. p. 549

2. RED-CRESTED COTINGA, *Ampelion rubrocristatus*
Widespread and conspicuous in temperate forest borders and woodland up to treeline on both slopes. Sexes alike. Mostly gray with whitish bill, whitish streaking on rump and crissum. White in tail seen mainly in flight; reddish crest often hidden. Immature browner, splotchier, with coarse streaking below. p. 541

3. POMPADOUR COTINGA, *Xipholena punicea*
Very rare and local in canopy of terra firme in lowlands of southeast. ♂ unique, shining crimson-purple with mainly white wings. ♀ ashy gray with pale yellow iris, prominent white wing-edging. p. 551

4. BLACK-TIPPED COTINGA, *Carpodectes hopkei*
Canopy and borders of humid forest in lowlands of northwest. Unmistakable ♂ ethereal white. ♀ much grayer; extensive white wing-edging. p. 551

Cotinga Cotingas
Distinctive arboreal birds found in canopy of humid lowland forests. Perch prominently on high branches. Though mainly solitary, a few will sometimes congregate at fruiting trees. Beautiful ♂♂ mainly some shade of brilliant blue; ♀♀ more obscure, brownish with scaly pattern. They can be recognized from a great distance by distinctive round-headed, dove-like silhouette.

5. BLUE COTINGA, *Cotinga natererii*
Scarce and local in canopy and borders of humid forest in northwest. ♂ unmistakable in range, bright shining blue with dark purple throat and belly patch. ♀ distinctive in range (where the only *Cotinga*), with spotted and scaled underparts. p. 550

6. PLUM-THROATED COTINGA, *Cotinga maynana*
Canopy and borders of humid forest in east (often sympatric with Spangled). ♂ uniform bright shining turquoise blue with relatively small plum-colored throat patch, little black in wings. ♀ generally pale grayish brown, breast somewhat mottled, belly quite ochraceous. p. 550

7. SPANGLED COTINGA, *Cotinga cayana*
Canopy and borders of humid forest in east (often sympatric with Plum-throated). ♂ pale shining turquoise blue with considerable black mottling showing through; wings mostly black; large throat area magenta-purple. ♀ generally dark grayish brown, feathers narrowly scaled paler. p. 550

8. ANDEAN LANIISOMA, *Laniisoma buckleyi*
Very rare and inconspicuous in lower growth inside humid forest along e. base of Andes. Narrow eye-ring pale yellow. Olive above, bright yellow below with considerable black scaling. ♂ with black crown; younger birds have large rufous spots on tips of wing-coverts. p. 546

Pipreola Fruiteaters
Attractive, plump cotingas of Andes, where found in lower and middle growth of montane forest. Lethargic and inconspicuous. Green predominates, with at least ♂♂ being strongly patterned and colored. ♂♂ have high-pitched songs.

9. GREEN-AND-BLACK FRUITEATER, *Pipreola rieferii*
Widespread in subtropical and temperate forest and borders on both slopes; the most frequently seen fruiteater. ♂ has green-suffused black hood with obvious yellow border; white tertial tipping. ♀ has dark iris, green hood, green-mottled underparts. p. 543

10. BLACK-CHESTED FRUITEATER, *Pipreola lubomirskii*
Scarce in subtropical forest on e. slope. Yellowish white iris; greenish gray legs. ♂ with black hood, not bordered with yellow; midbelly solid yellow; no tertial tipping. ♀ with solid green bib. p. 544

11. ORANGE-BREASTED FRUITEATER, *Pipreola jucunda*
Foothill and subtropical forest and borders in northwest. Yellowish white iris; greenish gray legs. ♂ with fiery orange breast. ♀ has entire underparts streaked with yellow. p. 544

12. SCARLET-BREASTED FRUITEATER, *Pipreola frontalis*
Local in foothill and subtropical forest on e. slope. ♂ has mainly yellow underparts (including breast) with red on lower throat and chest. ♀ shows scaly pattern below. p. 544

13. FIERY-THROATED FRUITEATER, *Pipreola chlorolepidota*
Foothill forest along e. base of Andes. The smallest fruiteater; obvious pale tertial tipping. ♂ has well-defined scarlet patch on throat and chest bordered below by green breast. ♀ has wavy barred pattern below, yellower belly than ♀ Scarlet-breasted. p. 545

14. BARRED FRUITEATER, *Pipreola arcuata*
Temperate forest and woodland on both slopes. The largest fruiteater; both sexes with unique heavy barring below, extensive black in wings and tail. p. 543

15. SCALED FRUITEATER, *Ampelioides tschudii*
Uncommon in subcanopy and mid-levels in foothill and subtropical forest on both slopes. Plump, short-tailed. Both sexes with unique complex scaled and scalloped pattern. p. 545

16. WHITE-BROWED PURPLETUFT, *Iodopleura isabellae*
Canopy of humid forest and borders in lowlands of east, often on open branches. Unique: small; short tail, distinctive white facial markings (visible from great distance), white rump band. ♀ lacks purple flank patch. p. 545

17. CHESTNUT-BELLIED COTINGA, *Doliornis remseni*
Rare and very local at treeline on e. slope. Mostly sooty with belly rufous-chestnut; both sexes with reddish chestnut crest, only ♂ with black crown. p. 542

18. CHESTNUT-CRESTED COTINGA, *Ampelion rufaxilla*
Rare and local in canopy and borders of subtropical forest on e. slope. Unmistakable; sexes alike. Sides of head, throat, and chest cinnamon-rufous, bold streaking on belly, long bright chestnut crest often flared. p. 542

Plate 77 Cotingas II

1. PURPLE-THROATED FRUITCROW, *Querula purpurata*
Widespread in humid forest in lowlands of east and west. Black, ♂ with shiny purple throat (feathers often flared). Usually in small noisy groups.   p. 552

2. RED-RUFFED FRUITCROW, *Pyroderus scutatus*
Very rare in mid-levels and subcanopy of montane forest in foothills and lower subtropics of northwest. Very large. Obvious shiny flame red bib; rufous belly.   p. 552

3. BLACK-NECKED RED-COTINGA, *Phoenicircus nigricollis*
Scarce and local inside less-disturbed terra firme forest in lowlands of east. Spectacular ♂ unmistakable: bright scarlet crown, underparts, rump, and tail. ♀ duller and brown above, still with enough red to be easily recognized. ♂ ♂ form small leks.   p. 554

Cephalopterus Umbrellabirds
Spectacular, very large, black cotingas, ♂ ♂ with unique umbrella-shaped crests and extendible wattle on chest. Generally inconspicuous; move by hopping through subcanopy of humid forests, especially in foothills but also locally in lowlands of east.

4. LONG-WATTLED UMBRELLABIRD, *Cephalopterus penduliger*
Scarce and local in humid forest in foothills (mostly) and adjacent lowlands of west. Unmistakable. Dark iris. ♂'s conspicuous umbrella-shaped crest all black; very long, extensible wattle on chest. ♀ slatier with crest less prominent.
                                                        p. 553

5. AMAZONIAN UMBRELLABIRD, *Cephalopterus ornatus*
Local in riparian and várzea forest along rivers (especially islands) and lake margins in lowlands of east, and in montane forest in foothills and lower subtropics on east slope. Unmistakable. ♂ ♂ glossy. White iris. ♂'s conspicuous umbrella-shaped crest shows white shafts; long extensible wattle on chest. ♀ slatier with crest less prominent.   p. 553

6. ANDEAN COCK-OF-THE-ROCK, *Rupicola peruviana*
  6W *R. p. sanguinolenta*—♂ intense blood red, ♀ carmine
  6E *R. p. aequatorialis*—♂ reddish orange, ♀ orangey brown
Lower growth of foothill and subtropical forest on both slopes, favoring ravines and steep slopes above rivers. Unmistakable. Chunky, with conspicuous laterally compressed frontal crest (larger in ♂ ♂). ♂ has wide, "shingle-like" gray tertials. At times surprisingly inconspicuous, but loud raucous calls sometimes attract attention.   p. 554

7. BARE-NECKED FRUITCROW, *Gymnoderus foetidus*
Conspicuous in canopy of humid forest (especially near water) in lowlands of east. Large, mainly black, with small head imparting distinctive silhouette. ♂ with conspicuous turquoise blue crinkles on neck, silvery gray wings (flashing at great distances in often high, looping flight). ♀ smaller with less blue on neck, wings nearly concolor. Immature scaled whitish below.   p. 552

Plate 78 Manakins

Pipra, Dixiphia, and Lepidothrix Manakins

Small frugivorous birds found primarily in humid lowland forest, some species occurring up into subtropics; all were formerly placed in genus *Pipra*. ♂♂ usually unmistakable, but several of the much plainer ♀♀ can be difficult to distinguish. ♂♂ of all species engage in some type of display, in some quite elaborate with loud calls, in others simpler.

1. GOLDEN-HEADED MANAKIN, *Pipra erythrocephala*
Mainly terra firme in lowlands of east. ♂ with golden yellow head. ♀ dull olive; bill pale, flesh colored.   p. 555

2. RED-CAPPED MANAKIN, *Pipra mentalis*
Humid forest and woodland in lowlands of northwest. ♂ with scarlet head. ♀ dull olive, legs dark.   p. 556

3. WHITE-CROWNED MANAKIN, *Dixiphia pipra*
Foothill and subtropical forest on e. slope, also locally out into lowlands of east (in terra firme). Iris dark red. ♂ with white crown and nape. ♀ with gray on crown; underparts vary (can be grayish or olive yellowish).   p. 557

4. BLUE-RUMPED MANAKIN, *Lepidothrix isidorei*
Local in foothill and subtropical forest on e. slope. ♂ with white crown and nape, pale blue rump. ♀ with yellowish forecrown, bright green rump.   p. 557

5. BLUE-CROWNED MANAKIN, *Lepidothrix coronata*
5E *L. c. coronata*—♂ with crown paler azure blue
5W *L. c. miniscula*—♂ with crown deeper ultramarine blue
Humid forest in lowlands of east (mainly terra firme) and northwest. ♂ with blue crown. ♀ brighter, more grass green above than ♀ Golden-headed and Red-capped.   p. 557

6. WIRE-TAILED MANAKIN, *Pipra filicauda*
Humid forest undergrowth, often near streams or where swampy, in lowlands of east. Wirelike tail filaments (longer in ♂). ♂ unique, with bright yellow underparts, bright red crown and nape. ♀ is only ♀ *Pipra* with whitish iris.   p. 556

7. BLUE-BACKED MANAKIN, *Chiroxiphia pareola*
Terra firme lower growth in lowlands of east. Larger than *Pipra*. ♂ with sky blue back, red crown patch. ♀ with pale orange-reddish legs.   p. 558

8. GOLDEN-WINGED MANAKIN, *Masius chrysopterus*
8W *M. c. coronulatus*—♂ with scarlet on nape
8E *M. c. pax*—♂ with brown on nape
Foothill and subtropical forest and woodland on both slopes. ♂ with golden yellow crown curling over bill; pale yellow edging on flight feathers (conspicuous in flight). ♀ has contrasting yellowish throat patch; yellowish midbelly.   p. 558

9. WHITE-BEARDED MANAKIN, *Manacus manacus*
Lower growth of secondary woodland and forest borders in lowlands of east and west. ♂ with conspicuous white "beard" and nuchal collar. ♀ has orange legs. Leks conspicuous, with very loud snapping.   p. 559

Machaeropterus Manakins

Small manakins found in humid and montane forests, reminiscent of *Pipra* though ♂♂ of both species have inner flight feathers modified for display purposes. Inconspicuous, most often found by tracking down ♂♂'s interminably given vocalizations.

10. STRIPED MANAKIN, *Machaeropterus regulus*
Inconspicuous in terra firme forest of lowlands of east. ♂ with bright red crown, underparts streaked reddish chestnut. ♀ has faint streaking below (unique among ♀♀ manakins); pale tertial edging.   p. 559

11. CLUB-WINGED MANAKIN, *Machaeropterus deliciosus*
Local in lower growth of foothill and lower subtropical forest on w. slope. ♂ unique, rufous-chestnut with white edging on peculiar twisted inner flight feathers. ♀ has cinnamon-rufous on face, white edging on inner flight feathers.   p. 560

Chloropipo Manakins

Fairly large, long-tailed manakins found in undergrowth of montane or humid forest. Inconspicuous and, unusual for a manakin, not vocal.

12. JET MANAKIN, *Chloropipo unicolor*
Local inside subtropical forest on e. slope. ♂ all black. ♀ uniform dark sooty-olive.   p. 560

13. GREEN MANAKIN, *Chloropipo holochlora*
13W *C. h. litae*—above duller olive green
13E *C. h. holochlora*—above brighter moss green
Inside humid and foothill forest. Confusing; see text. Larger than ♀♀ *Pipra*; note dark legs, yellowish midbelly. Sexes alike.   p. 560

14. YELLOW-HEADED MANAKIN, *Chloropipo flavicapilla*
Very rare in subtropical forest on e. slope in north. Orange to red iris. ♂ unmistakable, with bright golden yellow crown and nape. ♀ duller but crown and nape still yellowish.
          p. 561

15. ORANGE-CRESTED MANAKIN, *Heterocercus aurantiivertex*
Scarce and inconspicuous in lower growth of várzea forest and woodland in lowlands of east. A large, relatively dull manakin, both sexes with whitish throat; ♂'s orange crest inconspicuous.   p. 561

16. DWARF TYRANT-MANAKIN, *Tyranneutes stolzmanni*
Mainly mid-levels and subcanopy of humid forest in lowlands of east. Very small (smaller even than ♀♀ *Pipra*) and drab; iris pale. Sexes alike. Usually recorded from ♂'s distinctive and oft-heard voice.   p. 562

17. CINNAMON NEOPIPO, *Neopipo cinnamomea*
Rare (overlooked?) in terra firme forest in lowlands of east. Uncannily similar to much more common Ruddy-tailed Flycatcher (Plate 70-2); look for Neopipo's blue-gray legs (not pinkish), lack of rictal bristles, and yellow coronal patch (often hard to see). Sexes alike. Now considered a tyrannid.   p. 495

18. WING-BARRED PIPRITES, *Piprites chloris*
Mid-levels and subcanopy of humid lowland and foothill forest in east. Yellow spectacles, gray nape and sides of neck, bold wing markings. Sexes alike. Distinctive voice.   p. 562

19. BROAD-BILLED SAPAYOA, *Sapayoa aenigma*
Rare in lower growth inside humid lowland forest in far northwest. Confusing; rather long tailed, broad billed. Uniform olive (not yellower on belly), wings unmarked.
          p. 563

Schiffornis

Inconspicuous and retiring "manakins" found in undergrowth of lowland and subtropical forest; larger and longer-tailed than typical manakins, with distinctive wide-eyed look. Sexes alike. Heard more often than seen.

20. VÁRZEA SCHIFFORNIS, *Schiffornis major*
Scarce and local in lower growth of várzea forest in lowlands of east. Bright cinnamon-rufous; gray on face variable in extent. Cf. Cinnamon Attila (Plate 73-4).   p. 563

21. THRUSH-LIKE SCHIFFORNIS, *Schiffornis turdinus*
21 *S. t. rosenbergi / aeneus*—dark overall
21E *S. t. amazonus*—paler generally; more grayish below
Lower growth inside humid and montane forest in lowlands and subtropics of west, and subtropics on e. slope; local in lowlands of east (*amazonus*). Uniform and dark; wings more rufescent. Best told by voice.   p. 562

Plate 79 Swallows

Progne Martins

Largest swallows, found in open habitats primarily in lowlands. Most have steely blue upperparts, somewhat duller in ♀♀. Aside from one brown-backed species, identification can be tricky, but only one blue-backed species (Gray-breasted) is at all numerous in Ecuador. See text.

1. BROWN-CHESTED MARTIN, *Progne tapera*

1   *P. t. tapera*
1E *P. t. fusca*—austral migrant; spots on median breast
Lowlands of east and southwest. The only brown-backed martin; smudgy brownish breast band. Usually flies low, often gliding on bowed wings.   p. 581

2. GRAY-BREASTED MARTIN, *Progne chalybea*

Widespread in lowlands; by far the most common *Progne*. Grayish brown throat and breast, whitish belly. Often flies high overhead.   p. 581

3. PURPLE MARTIN, *Progne subis*

Very rare boreal visitant, so far recorded only from highlands. Shape (including tail fork) like Gray-breasted. ♂ entirely steely blue. ♀ like Gray-breasted but usually with whitish collar and forecrown.   p. 582

4. SOUTHERN MARTIN, *Progne elegans*

Very rare austral visitant to lowlands of east. The largest martin, with deeply forked tail. ♂ entirely steely blue. ♀ sometimes has pale forecrown but never a collar; underparts (including belly) basically dark.   p. 582

Notiochelidon Swallows

Typical swallows, the first two familiar birds of semiopen highlands, the third (Pale-footed) rare and forest-based.

5. BROWN-BELLIED SWALLOW, *Notiochelidon murina*

Slender dark swallow of semiopen areas in highlands and paramo. Rather deeply forked tail; uniform smoky underparts.   p. 584

6. BLUE-AND-WHITE SWALLOW, *Notiochelidon cyanoleuca*

6   *N. c. cyanoleuca*
6E *N. c. patagonica*—austral migrant; less black on crissum
Numerous in highlands, often around houses. Blue above, snowy white below, with obvious black crissum.   p. 584

7. PALE-FOOTED SWALLOW, *Notiochelidon flavipes*

Scarce over temperate forest on e. slope. Pinkish buff throat and chest, dark flanks.   p. 584

Tachycineta Swallows

Small swallows with glossy blue or green upperparts, white underparts. Both Ecuadorian resident species have white rumps; see Tree Swallow on Plate 96.

8. WHITE-WINGED SWALLOW, *Tachycineta albiventer*

Around lakes and rivers in lowlands of east. Conspicuous white on wing.   p. 583

9. TUMBES SWALLOW, *Tachycineta stolzmanni*

Very local in arid scrub of extreme sw. Loja. Dull glossy bluish green above; whitish rump and underparts, both with faint streaks.   p. 583

10. WHITE-BANDED SWALLOW, *Atticora fasciata*

Common along forest-bordered streams and rivers in lowlands of east. Unmistakable and beautiful, steely blue with conspicuous white breast band; tail deeply forked.   p. 585

11. WHITE-THIGHED SWALLOW, *Neochelidon tibialis*

11E *N. t. griseiventris*—somewhat paler, especially on rump
11W *N. t. minima*—particularly small
Local and uncommon (especially in east) at edge of humid forest in foothills and adjacent lowlands. Small, dark.
                    p. 585

12. SOUTHERN ROUGH-WINGED SWALLOW, *Stelgidopteryx ruficollis*

12E *S. r. ruficollis*—uniform brown above
12W *S. r. uropygialis*—conspicuous whitish rump
Widespread in lowlands, especially near water; more common in west. A brownish swallow with cinnamon-buff throat.   p. 585

13. SAND MARTIN, *Riparia riparia*

Boreal migrant, especially to lowlands. A small, brown-backed swallow with distinct dusky-brown breast band.
                    p. 586

Petrochelidon Swallows

Swallows (only one resident) with basically steel blue upperparts, contrasting throat patterns and colors. Tails essentially square.

14. CHESTNUT-COLLARED SWALLOW, *Petrochelidon rufocollaris*

Local in open areas and around towns in southwest. Rufous rump prominent in flight; rufous nuchal collar and breast band, contrasting white cheeks and throat.   p. 586

15. CLIFF SWALLOW, *Petrochelidon pyrrhonota*

Boreal migrant, especially to lowlands. Cinnamon-rufous rump prominent in flight; throat dark, conspicuous pale forehead.   p. 586

16. BARN SWALLOW, *Hirundo rustica*

Common boreal migrant, especially to lowlands. Long tail streamers (less obvious in molting birds) with white spots on inner webs; mainly buff underparts. Molting young birds can look faded and "ratty."   p. 586

Plate 80 Wrens

Campylorhynchus **Wrens**
Boldly patterned wrens found in lowlands, favoring forest edge and wooded habitats; arboreal, most often ranging in family groups. The largest wrens. Best known from their loud, frequently heard vocalizations.

1. THRUSH-LIKE WREN, *Campylorhynchus turdinus*
Common in east. Conspicuously dark-spotted underparts.
p. 588

2. FASCIATED WREN, *Campylorhynchus fasciatus*
Common in arid regions of southwest, smaller numbers in subtropics and more humid areas. Conspicuously banded and spotted overall appearance.
p. 589

3. BAND-BACKED WREN, *Campylorhynchus zonatus*
Northwest. Patterned much like Fasciated, but browner (not so grayish) overall with ochraceous on belly.
p. 588

Cinnycerthia **Wrens**
Stocky, unpatterned wrens found in montane forest undergrowth, replacing each other altitudinally. Often in small groups, both species with excellent musical songs.

4. RUFOUS WREN, *Cinnycerthia unirufa*
Temperate zone on both slopes, favoring *Chusquea* bamboo. Uniform rufous brown, with contrasting black lores but barely visible wing and tail barring. Cf. Rufous Spinetail (Plate 56-9).
p. 589

5. SEPIA-BROWN WREN, *Cinnycerthia olivascens*
Subtropical zone on both slopes. Uniform brown with wings and tail distinctly barred black. Some birds show variable amount of white on face (5A).
p. 590

Thryothorus **Wrens**
Midsized wrens found in variety of wooded and forested habitats at differing elevations; favor dense tangled growth, skulk in pairs. Predominantly brown or rufescent, boldly patterned on head, many with streaked cheeks. Songs loud, vigorous, and complex, often given as duet.

6. BAY WREN, *Thryothorus nigricapillus*
6   *T. n. nigricapillus*
6NW *T. n. connectens*—more extensively barred below
Humid lowlands of west, often common. Black crown, complex facial pattern, bold black and white barring below.
p. 590

7. PLAIN-TAILED WREN, *Thryothorus euophrys*
7W *T. e. euophrys*—boldly spotted breast
7E *T. e. longipes*—breast only faintly speckled
Chusquea bamboo thickets in temperate forest. Mainly bright rufous upperparts, wings and tail unbarred.
p. 591

8. WHISKERED WREN, *Thryothorus mystacalis*
Local in foothills and more humid lowlands of west. Bold black "whisker," rufous-chestnut mantle, wings almost unbarred.
p. 591

9. CORAYA WREN, *Thryothorus coraya*
Tangles at forest edge in lowlands of east, often common. Dark face with wide black malar stripe.
p. 592

10. SPECKLE-BREASTED WREN, *Thryothorus sclateri*
Deciduous woodland and scrub in southwest and Zumba area, often common. Dense black barring and speckling on face and underparts, especially so in Zumba birds.
p. 593

11. BUFF-BREASTED WREN, *Thryothorus leucotis*
Local in thickets at edge of várzea forest in lowlands of east. Whitish on face and throat, buff underparts, no wing barring.
p. 592

12. SUPERCILIATED WREN, *Thryothorus superciliaris*
Arid scrub and thickets in lowlands of southwest. White face, bold superciliary, and underparts; bright rufous upperparts.
p. 592

13. STRIPE-THROATED WREN, *Thryothorus leucopogon*
Scarce and local in tangles of humid forest and woodland in lowlands of northwest. Small and dull, with face and throat boldly streaked.
p. 593

Troglodytes **Wrens**
Small, more or less unpatterned wrens that often hold tails cocked. Distinctive musical songs.

14. HOUSE WREN, *Troglodytes aedon*
Widespread, usually common and familiar around houses and in semiopen and agricultural terrain; scarcer in east. Small and plain, with weak eyebrow, indistinct wing and tail barring. Some birds on El Oro coast are more or less sooty (14A).
p. 594

15. MOUNTAIN WREN, *Troglodytes solstitialis*
Montane forest, woodland, and borders on both slopes. Short-tailed. Rufescent with conspicuous buff superciliary.
p. 594

16. GRASS WREN, *Cistothorus platensis*
Small, usually secretive wren of paramo and temperate zone grasslands. Basically buffy with back prominently streaked.
p. 590

Henicorhina **Wrens**
Small wrens with stubby tails, boldly streaked cheeks. Found in humid or montane forest undergrowth.

17. WHITE-BREASTED WOOD-WREN, *Henicorhina leucosticta*
17E   *H. l. hauxwelli*—black crown, breast pure white
17NW *H. l. inornata*—brown crown, breast dingier white
Humid forest undergrowth in lowlands. Breast white to whitish.
p. 594

18. GRAY-BREASTED WOOD-WREN, *Henicorhina leucophrys*
Montane forest and woodland undergrowth on both slopes. Breast gray (but nw. White-breasteds only slightly paler).
p. 595

19. BAR-WINGED WOOD-WREN, *Henicorhina leucoptera*
Only on remote Cordillera del Cóndor in far southeast; occurs with Gray-breasted. White wing-bars; breast grayish white.
p. 595

Cyphorhinus **Wrens**
Fairly chunky wrens found on or near ground inside humid or montane forest. Beautiful songs are heard more often than birds are seen.

20. CHESTNUT-BREASTED WREN, *Cyphorhinus thoracicus*
Scarce and local inside subtropical forest on e. slope. Larger than other *Cyphorhinus*, with heavy arched bill; crown all dark, unbarred wings and tail.
p. 595

21. MUSICIAN WREN, *Cyphorhinus arada*
Inside terra firme forest in lowlands of east. Bare blue ocular skin; orange-rufous forecrown, brow, and breast.
p. 596

22. SONG WREN, *Cyphorhinus phaeocephalus*
Inside humid forest and woodland in lowlands of west. Conspicuous bare blue ocular skin.
p. 596

Microcerculus **Wrens**
Inconspicuous, short-tailed, nearly terrestrial wrens found inside humid forest. Walk and hop on long legs, often bobbing. Songs distinctive.

23. SOUTHERN NIGHTINGALE-WREN, *Microcerculus marginatus*
23   *M. m. marginatus / occidentalis*—underparts white
23SW *M. m. taeniatus*—dense wavy scaling below
Lowlands of east and west, more widespread and numerous in east. White bib; dark brown upperparts.
p. 597

24. WING-BANDED WREN, *Microcerculus bambla*
Local in foothills and adjacent lowlands in east. Bold white wing-band; breast gray.
p. 597

25. GRAY-MANTLED WREN, *Odontorchilus branickii*
Canopy of foothill and subtropical forest, mainly on e. slope but also in lower foothills of northwest. A distinctive arboreal wren with gray upperparts, boldly banded tail.
p. 589

Plate 81 Mimids, Donacobius, Gnatcatchers and Gnatwrens, Vireos and Greenlets, Pipits, and Dippers

Mimus Mockingbirds
Conspicuous, somewhat thrush-like slender birds with long tails found in open country.

1. LONG-TAILED MOCKINGBIRD, *Mimus longicaudatus*
Common in arid scrub and gardens of southwest. Distinctive, with long tail broadly tipped white, complex facial pattern. p. 580

2. TROPICAL MOCKINGBIRD, *Mimus gilvus*
Recently found in Imbabura highlands. Pale gray and whitish with obvious white tail corners. p. 580

3. BLACK-CAPPED DONACOBIUS, *Donacobius atricapillus*
Marshy areas and wet pastures in lowlands of east. Distinctive, with pale eye, buff underparts, long tail broadly tipped white. Commanding loud voice. p. 587

Polioptila Gnatcatchers
Distinctive small, slender birds whose long narrow tails are flipped around animatedly.

4. TROPICAL GNATCATCHER, *Polioptila plumbea*
4W *P. p. bilineata*—white face
4E *P. p. parvirostris*—fully black/gray crown
Widespread in west, scarce in forest canopy in east. Gray and white, ♂♂ with black on crown; much white in tail. p. 599

5. SLATE-THROATED GNATCATCHER, *Polioptila schistaceigula*
Scarce in humid forest canopy of northwest. Mostly slaty with white belly. p. 599

6. LONG-BILLED GNATWREN, *Ramphocaenus melanurus*
6E *R. m. duidae*—browner back
6W *R. m. rufiventris*—grayer back, larger white tail-tips
Forest and woodland tangles in lowlands of east and west. Long slender bill; frequently flips around fairly long tail. p. 598

Microbates Gnatwrens
Small, short-tailed gnatwrens found in humid forest understory, regularly with mixed flocks.

7. TAWNY-FACED GNATWREN, *Microbates cinereiventris*
Lowlands of east and west. Bright tawny face; streaks on chest. p. 598

8. COLLARED GNATWREN, *Microbates collaris*
Very local in lowlands of northeast. White face patterned with black; black pectoral collar. p. 598

Cyclarhis Peppershrikes
Stocky, bull-headed vireos with heavy hooked bills; varying amounts of chestnut on head. Arboreal in woodland and forest; oft-heard loud songs.

9. RUFOUS-BROWED PEPPERSHRIKE, *Cyclarhis gujanensis*
9W *C. g. virenticeps*—bright yellow breast, rufous brow
9SE *C. g. contrerasi*—mainly rufous crown, gray and olive below
The only peppershrike in lowlands of west, locally ranging higher in south; also in montane forest and borders in subtropics of southeast. p. 566

10. BLACK-BILLED PEPPERSHRIKE, *Cyclarhis nigrirostris*
Foothill and subtropical forest and borders of north. Short narrow rufous brow, gray and olive underparts. p. 567

11. SLATY-CAPPED SHRIKE-VIREO, *Vireolanius leucotis*
11W *V. l. mikettae*
11E *V. l. leucotis*—white cheek stripe
Humid forest canopy and borders in foothills (especially) and lowlands of east and west. Heard more often than seen. Heavy hooked bill, gray head, bold yellow brow. p. 567

Vireo Vireos
Dull, fairly chunky small birds with superciliaries and rather heavy bills. Arboreal in woodland and forest borders, foraging lethargically.

12. RED-EYED VIREO, *Vireo olivaceus*
12E *V. o. olivaceus*
12W *V. o. griseobarbatus*—yellow sides, flanks, and crissum
Mainly lowlands. Bold white superciliary outlined in black. p. 568

13. YELLOW-GREEN VIREO, *Vireo flavoviridis*
Boreal migrant, mainly to lowlands of east. Washed-out facial pattern; pale yellow sides, flanks, and crissum. p. 568

14. BROWN-CAPPED VIREO, *Vireo leucophrys*
Common in foothill and subtropical forest and woodland on both slopes. Brown crown, whitish facial area and throat. p. 568

Hylophilus Greenlets
Confusing dull, small vireos found in humid forest or borders, most in canopy, a few lower. Forage more actively than *Vireo*, and regularly accompany mixed flocks; greenlets have more pointed bills. Note especially color of bill, eye, and underparts. Voice also often important.

15. RUFOUS-NAPED GREENLET, *Hylophilus semibrunneus*
Local in foothills of northeast. Rufous crown and nape, whitish face and throat. p. 569

16. DUSKY-CAPPED GREENLET, *Hylophilus hypoxanthus*
Lowlands of east. Brown crown and back, yellowish lower underparts. p. 569

17. LEMON-CHESTED GREENLET, *Hylophilus thoracicus*
Scarce and local in lowlands of east. Pinkish bill, pale iris, yellow chest band. p. 570

18. OLIVACEOUS GREENLET, *Hylophilus olivaceus*
Shrubby clearings and borders in foothills and subtropics on e. slope. Uniform yellowish olive underparts; pinkish bill, pale iris. p. 570

19. LESSER GREENLET, *Hylophilus decurtatus*
Lowlands and foothills of west. Plump, puffy-headed, short-tailed. Mainly whitish underparts, whitish eye-ring. p. 570

20. TAWNY-CROWNED GREENLET, *Hylophilus ochraceiceps*
20E *H. o. ferrugineifrons*—more grayish below
20NW *H. o. bulunensis*—more olivaceous below
Humid forest undergrowth in lowlands of east and northwest. Obvious pale eye, tawny forecrown. p. 571

21. PARAMO PIPIT, *Anthus bogotensis*
Grasslands in temperate zone and paramo. Slim shape with slender bill, notched tail with white outer feathers; streaked above but mainly dull buff below. p. 600

22. WHITE-CAPPED DIPPER, *Cinclus leucocephalus*
Unmistakable plump, short-tailed, blackish and white bird of rocky Andean streams and rivers. p. 580

Plate 82 Thrushes

1. ANDEAN SOLITAIRE, *Myadestes ralloides*
Subtropical forest and woodland on both slopes, locally down into foothills. Leaden gray underparts; distinctive silvery gray flashes in wings and tail in flight.   p. 571

2. RUFOUS-BROWN SOLITAIRE, *Cichlopsis leucogenys*
Very local in foothill forest of northwest. Rich rufous brown with throat and supraloral reddish chestnut, orangey crissum.   p. 572

3. BLACK SOLITAIRE, *Entomodestes coracinus*
Scarce in foothill and subtropical forest of northwest. Unmistakable. Jet black with large white cheek patch; white in wings and tail conspicuous in flight.   p. 572

Catharus Nightingale-Thrushes and Thrushes
Shy and inconspicuous thrushes found mainly on or near ground inside forest. First two species resident in montane areas and notable for bright orange bill, eye-ring, and legs and beautiful songs; second two species relatively dull-plumaged boreal migrants.

4. SPOTTED NIGHTINGALE-THRUSH, *Catharus dryas*
On or near ground inside foothill and subtropical forest and woodland on both slopes. Unmistakable. Apricot yellow underparts with bold spotting.   p. 573

5. SLATY-BACKED NIGHTINGALE-THRUSH, *Catharus fuscater*
On or near ground inside subtropical forest and woodland on both slopes, at higher elevations than preceding species. Staring white iris; mainly gray (darker above, paler below).   p. 572

6. GRAY-CHEEKED THRUSH, *Catharus minimus*
Scarce boreal migrant, mainly inside forest in lowlands of east. Dull, with speckled breast; grayish lores and cheeks.   p. 573

7. SWAINSON'S THRUSH, *Catharus ustulatus*
Boreal migrant, much commoner and more widespread than Gray-cheeked, especially numerous along e. base of Andes. Dull, with speckled breast; buffyish lores and cheeks (spectacled look usually obvious).   p. 574

8. PALE-EYED THRUSH, *Platycichla leucops*
Scarce and local in montane forest and borders on both slopes. ♂ lustrous black with conspicuous white iris. ♀ more difficult, mostly dark brown with lower underparts paler and more mottled; iris pale grayish or brownish.   p. 574

Turdus Thrushes
Widespread thrushes found in variety of forested, wooded, or semiopen habitats. Some are familiar and common, others decidedly shyer and more obscure, more or less confined to forest interior. Coloration and plumage pattern vary considerably, and for many species identification can be difficult; pay particular attention to soft-part colors and quality of songs. Sexes alike unless indicated.

9. CHIGUANCO THRUSH, *Turdus chiguanco*
Semiopen, usually arid terrain in central valley from Cotopaxi south. Pale overall; ashy brown with orange-yellow bill and legs.   p. 574

10. GREAT THRUSH, *Turdus fuscater*
Common and conspicuous in more humid highlands and central valley up to edge of paramo. Large. Uniform sooty. ♀ lacks eye-ring.   p. 575

11. GLOSSY-BLACK THRUSH, *Turdus serranus*
Montane forest on both slopes (more forest-based than Great). ♂ glossy black; bold eye-ring. ♀ essentially uniform dull brown, not paler on belly; yellowish eye-ring.   p. 575

12. ANDEAN SLATY-THRUSH, *Turdus nigriceps*
Local rainy-season breeder in montane woodland of Loja. ♂ easy, mostly gray, darker above becoming black on crown, sharp throat streaking; bright yellow soft parts. Browner ♀ trickier: eye-ring yellow but bill dark, throat streaking prominent, no white chest patch.   p. 579

13. PLUMBEOUS-BACKED THRUSH, *Turdus reevei*
Woodland and forest in southwest. Nearly unmistakable with bluish white iris, blue-gray upperparts, creamy buff on lower underparts.   p. 576

14. CHESTNUT-BELLIED THRUSH, *Turdus fulviventris*
Local in subtropical forest and borders on e. slope. Unmistakable: bright rufous belly diagnostic.   p. 575

15. MARAÑON THRUSH, *Turdus maranonicus*
Numerous in woodland and clearings in Río Marañón drainage of s. Zamora-Chinchipe. Dark brown above with heavy brown scaling below.   p. 576

16. BLACK-BILLED THRUSH, *Turdus ignobilis*
Semiopen habitats in lowlands of east. Dull; olivaceous brown with white on foreneck.   p. 577

17. LAWRENCE'S THRUSH, *Turdus lawrencii*
Forest canopy in lowlands of east. Dark brown overall, ♂ with yellow bill and eye-ring (♀'s bill dark, eye-ring narrower). ♂ has remarkable mimicking song.   p. 577

18. HAUXWELL'S THRUSH, *Turdus hauxwelli*
Scarce inside humid forest in lowlands of east, mainly near water. Warm brown with pale lower belly and crissum (variable in extent); no eye-ring.   p. 578

19. DAGUA THRUSH, *Turdus daguae*
Local inside humid forest in lower foothills of west. Narrow eye-ring yellow, conspicuous white chest crescent, brownish underparts.   p. 579

20. WHITE-NECKED THRUSH, *Turdus albicollis*
Inside terra firme forest in lowlands and foothills of east. Conspicuous white chest crescent, underparts mainly gray.   p. 578

21. PALE-VENTED THRUSH, *Turdus obsoletus*
Very local inside forest in foothills and subtropics of northwest. Uniform dark brown with contrasting white at least on crissum and lower belly.   p. 577

22. ECUADORIAN THRUSH, *Turdus maculirostris*
Woodland and forest borders of west, where the most widespread thrush. Uniform dull olivaceous brown with olive bill, yellow-orange eye-ring.   p. 578

Plate 83 New World Warblers

1. BLACK-AND-WHITE WARBLER, *Mniotilta varia*
Boreal migrant mainly to Andean slopes of north. Creeps on trunks and branches. Obvious black-and-white striping above. p. 605

2. PROTHONOTARY WARBLER, *Protonotaria citrea*
Very rare boreal migrant to lowlands of north, usually near water. Golden head and underparts (♀ duller), blue-gray wings. p. 605

3. TENNESSEE WARBLER, *Vermivora peregrina*
Rare boreal migrant to Andean slopes of north. Plain, olive above with thin yellowish superciliary, some yellow below but crissum white. p. 601

4. TROPICAL PARULA, *Parula pitiayumi*
Widespread and often common in humid and arid lowlands and subtropics of west, only subtropics in east. Small; blue-gray upperparts with black face, orange on breast (♀ duller). p. 601

Dendroica **Warblers**
Diverse group of arboreal boreal migrants found in variety of wooded habitats; only one species (Mangrove) is resident.

5. MANGROVE WARBLER, *Dendroica petechia*
Resident locally in mangroves. Predominantly yellow and olive, ♂ with rufous crown. Younger birds often grayer and whiter. p. 602

6. YELLOW WARBLER, *Dendroica aestiva*
Uncommon boreal migrant to lowlands. Both sexes (especially ♂♂) predominantly yellow with yellow tail spots. ♀♀ less bright generally, lack streaking below. p. 602

7. CERULEAN WARBLER, *Dendroica cerulea*
Boreal migrant to canopy and borders of foothill and lower subtropical forest on e. slope (few records in west). Adult ♂ azure blue above with black chest band. ♀ bluish green above with bold yellowish superciliary. p. 602

8. BAY-BREASTED WARBLER, *Dendroica castanea*
Casual boreal migrant to north. Breeding ♂ unmistakable; in other plumages note unstreaked whitish underparts, often showing bay on flanks. p. 603

9. BLACKBURNIAN WARBLER, *Dendroica fusca*
Common boreal migrant to montane forest and woodland. Adult ♂ has unmistakable bright orange on foreparts (yellower in other plumages, but pattern the same). p. 603

10. BLACKPOLL WARBLER, *Dendroica striata*
Boreal migrant to clearings and borders in lowlands of east. Legs usually pale. Breeding ♂ with black crown, white cheeks. ♀ and nonbreeding ♂ dull, with vague streaking below; see text. p. 603

11. CHESTNUT-SIDED WARBLER, *Dendroica pensylvanica*
Casual boreal migrant. Breeding ♂ unmistakable; in other plumages mainly bright lime green above, pale gray below. p. 604

12. MOURNING WARBLER, *Oporornis philadelphia*
Scarce boreal migrant to borders and thickets in north. Gray hood, duller in ♀ (♂ with black on chest). p. 607

13. GOLDEN-WINGED WARBLER, *Vermivora chrysoptera*
Casual boreal migrant to montane forest and woodland in north. Dusky cheeks and throat (black in ♂), extensive yellow on wings. p. 600

14. CANADA WARBLER, *Wilsonia canadensis*
Boreal migrant to undergrowth and borders in foothills and subtropics, mostly e. slope. Bold yellow spectacles; prominent necklace (duller in immatures). p. 608

15. AMERICAN REDSTART, *Setophaga ruticilla*
Scarce boreal migrant to woodland and borders. Adult ♂ mainly black with orange patches. ♀ has yellow patches. p. 605

16. NORTHERN WATERTHRUSH, *Seiurus noveboracensis*
Scarce boreal migrant, mainly terrestrial near water. Often teeters rearparts. Streaked underparts, creamy superciliary. p. 606

17. OVENBIRD, *Seiurus aurocapillus*
Casual boreal migrant to forest undergrowth. Streaked underparts, orange crown stripe. p. 606

Myioborus **Whitestarts**
Spritely warblers that flash conspicuous white in tail. Common in montane forests and borders.

18. SLATE-THROATED WHITESTART, *Myioborus miniatus*
Foothills and subtropics. Plain slaty head and throat. p. 608

19. SPECTACLED WHITESTART, *Myioborus melanocephalus*
19N variant shown by some birds near Colombian border. Temperate zone. Bold yellow spectacles. p. 608

Geothlypis **Yellowthroats**
Mainly olive and yellow warblers found in shrubbery and rank grass (not forest) in lowlands and foothills of west.

20. OLIVE-CROWNED YELLOWTHROAT, *Geothlypis semiflava*
♂ with large black mask. ♀ shows little facial pattern. p. 606

21. BLACK-LORED YELLOWTHROAT, *Geothlypis auricularis*
♂ has small black mask, shows gray on crown. ♀ shows some gray on crown; narrow ocular area and short superciliary yellow. p. 607

Basileuterus **Warblers**
Predominantly olive warblers found in forest and woodland undergrowth and shrubby areas, most species in Andes. Note head pattern details; songs often distinctive.

22. BLACK-CRESTED WARBLER, *Basileuterus nigrocristatus*
Common in shrubby areas and borders in temperate zone on both slopes. Narrow black crown stripe. p. 609

23. CITRINE WARBLER, *Basileuterus luteoviridis*
Temperate zone on e. slope. Short yellow superciliary, concolor olive crown. p. 609

24. THREE-STRIPED WARBLER, *Basileuterus tristriatus*
24W *B. t. daedalus*—dull buffy yellowish underparts
24E *B. t. tristriatus*—brighter yellow underparts
Widespread in subtropics on both slopes. Bold facial pattern with black cheeks. p. 610

25. CHOCÓ WARBLER, *Basileuterus chlorophrys*
Foothills and lower subtropics of northwest. Olive overall, with orange-rufous, black, and olive crown stripes. p. 610

26. THREE-BANDED WARBLER, *Basileuterus trifasciatus*
Foothills and subtropics of El Oro and Loja. Olive-gray crown stripe and superciliary, grayish throat and chest. p. 610

27. RUSSET-CROWNED WARBLER, *Basileuterus coronatus*
27W *B. c. elatus*—lower underparts bright yellow
27E *B. c. orientalis*—lower underparts gray and whitish
Subtropics and temperate zone. Mainly gray head with obvious orange-rufous crown. p. 611

28. GRAY-AND-GOLD WARBLER, *Basileuterus fraseri*
28S *B. f. fraseri*—yellow coronal streak
28N *B. f. ochraceicrista*—orange coronal streak
Mainly deciduous forest and woodland in lowlands and subtropics of southwest. Bluish gray upperparts, white supraloral streak. p. 611

29. BUFF-RUMPED WARBLER, *Basileuterus fulvicauda*
Near streams in lowlands of east and west. Conspicuous buff rump and basal tail, tail often fanned. p. 611

Plate 84 Bananaquit and Tanagers I

1. BANANAQUIT, *Coereba flaveola*
Clearings, woodland, and borders in lowlands and foothills of west (especially) and east (where scarce away from Andes). Often at flowering trees. Sexes alike. Short decurved bill, white wing speculum and bold superciliary.   p. 612

Conirostrum Conebills
Small, warbler-like tanagers with sharply pointed bills found primarily in Andes. Most species favor canopy of forest and woodland, often ranging with mixed flocks, but two (Cinereous, Bicolored) occur in scrubbier habitats.

2. BICOLORED CONEBILL, *Conirostrum bicolor*
One sighting from a Río Napo island. Nondescript but with orange-red eye; underparts dingy grayish buff. Sexes alike, immatures yellower below.   p. 618

3. CHESTNUT-VENTED CONEBILL, *Conirostrum speciosum*
Scarce and very local in woodland along e. base of Andes. ♂ blue-gray with chestnut crissum. ♀ has bluish gray crown and nape, bright olive mantle, pale lores (cf. ♀ Blue Dacnis, Plate 85-1).   p. 617

4. CINEREOUS CONEBILL, *Conirostrum cinereum*
Widespread in scrub and gardens in temperate zone and paramo. Buffyish superciliary and underparts, white wing speculum.   p. 618

5. BLUE-BACKED CONEBILL, *Conirostrum sitticolor*
Temperate forest and woodland. Distinctive: rich rufous lower underparts, black hood, blue mantle.   p. 618

6. CAPPED CONEBILL, *Conirostrum albifrons*
Upper subtropical and temperate forest. Frequent tail-wagging. ♂ black with blue crown (often hard to see). ♀ has bluish crown, gray head and foreneck, bright olive upperparts.   p. 619

7. GIANT CONEBILL, *Oreomanes fraseri*
Local in *Polylepis* woodland, hitching along trunks and on branches. Long, sharply pointed bill. Sexes alike. Bold white malar streak, entirely chestnut underparts.   p. 619

8. TIT-LIKE DACNIS, *Xenodacnis parina*
Very local in shrubby areas and *Polylepis* woodland in paramo of south. Stubby bill (not hooked at tip). ♂ all deep blue. ♀ with blue forehead and ocular area, uniform cinnamon-buff underparts.   p. 619

Diglossa and *Diglossopis* Flowerpiercers
Distinctive small tanagers with upper mandibles sharply hooked, lower mandibles upturned; range in montane forest and clearings in Andes, from foothills up into shrubby paramo. Most are simply patterned in various shades of blue or black, some with rufous or white accenting. They are nectarivorous, piercing corolla of flowers, but two species in particular (Indigo, Golden-eyed) also eat more insects.

9. BLUISH FLOWERPIERCER, *Diglossopis caerulescens*
Local in subtropical and temperate zones, more numerous on e. slope. Uniform grayish blue with little facial pattern; bill straighter, less hooked than in other flowerpiercers.   p. 620

10. MASKED FLOWERPIERCER, *Diglossopis cyanea*
Widespread and often numerous in temperate zone. Bright blue with black mask, red eye.   p. 620

11. GLOSSY FLOWERPIERCER, *Diglossa lafresnayii*
Montane woodland at and just below treeline. Black with grayish blue shoulders; larger than Black Flowerpiercer.   p. 621

12. BLACK FLOWERPIERCER, *Diglossa humeralis*
Widespread and often numerous in shrubby areas and gardens from temperate zone up into paramo. All black; relatively small.   p. 622

13. RUSTY FLOWERPIERCER, *Diglossa sittoides*
Local in cleared areas and gardens in subtropical and temperate zones. ♂ bicolored: bluish gray above, cinnamon-buff below. ♀ dull, olivaceous with blurry breast streaking.   p. 622

14. WHITE-SIDED FLOWERPIERCER, *Diglossa albilatera*
Montane forest borders in subtropical and temperate zones. Distinctive white "tuft" usually protrudes from under wing. ♂ slaty; ♀ two-toned brown.   p. 622

15. INDIGO FLOWERPIERCER, *Diglossopis indigotica*
Rare and local in foothills and lower subtropics of northwest. Bright blue overall; red eye.   p. 621

16. GOLDEN-EYED FLOWERPIERCER, *Diglossopis glauca*
Foothills and subtropical zone on e. slope. Bold golden eye; dark blue overall.   p. 621

Cyanerpes Honeycreepers
Small tanagers with decurved bills, short tails, brightly colored legs (♂♂). Range in lowlands, especially in humid forest, and gregarious, congregating in flowering trees, often accompanying mixed flocks.

17. PURPLE HONEYCREEPER, *Cyanerpes caeruleus*
Lowlands (primarily) and foothills of east and west. ♂ has bright yellow legs, black throat patch. ♀ has buff facial area, blue malar streak.   p. 613

18. RED-LEGGED HONEYCREEPER, *Cyanerpes cyaneus*
Local in lowlands of northwest, a few records in east. Long decurved bill. ♂ has bright red legs, pale blue crown. ♀ has reddish legs, plain face except for whitish brow.   p. 613

19. SHORT-BILLED HONEYCREEPER, *Cyanerpes nitidus*
Scarce and local in forest canopy of lowlands in northeast. Short decurved bill; legs dull reddish. ♂ has large black bib on throat. Note ♀'s dark lores.   p. 613

20. GOLDEN-COLLARED HONEYCREEPER, *Iridophanes pulcherrima*
Forest canopy and borders in lower subtropics on e. slope, a few records also from northwest. Golden nuchal collar. Unmistakable ♂ has black head, opalescent rump and underparts. Duller ♀ echoes ♂'s pattern.   p. 614

21. GREEN HONEYCREEPER, *Chlorophanes spiza*
Forest canopy and borders, clearings in lowlands and foothills of east and west. Bill with much yellow (especially in ♂♂). ♂ lustrous green with contrasting black head. ♀ uniform pale bright green.   p. 614

Dacnis Dacnises
Two rare dacnises of lowland forests. See also Plate 85.

22. SCARLET-BREASTED DACNIS, *Dacnis berlepschi*
Northwest. Iris golden yellow; scarlet breast (brighter and more extensive in ♂♂). ♂ unmistakable; ♀ notably brown.   p. 617

23. WHITE-BELLIED DACNIS, *Dacnis albiventris*
East. Iris golden yellow. ♂ bright cobalt blue with white belly. ♀ greenish (see text).   p. 617

Plate 85 Tanagers II

Dacnis Dacnises

Small warbler-like tanagers with strongly dimorphic plumage. ♀♀ often dull-plumaged; note eye colors. Forest canopy and borders in lowlands and foothills. See also Plate 84.

1. BLUE DACNIS, *Dacnis cayana*
  1E *D. c. glaucogularis*—♂ turquoise
  1W *D. c. coerebicolor*—♂ ultramarine
Humid lowlands. Legs pink, iris red. ♂ with black bib and lores. ♀ green with pale blue head.   p. 615

2. YELLOW-TUFTED DACNIS, *Dacnis egregia*
Lowlands of west. Iris yellow to orange-yellow. ♂ bright turquoise green and black, yellow pectoral tuft and belly. ♀ dull olivaceous with yellow pectoral tuft and belly.   p. 615

3. BLACK-FACED DACNIS, *Dacnis lineata*
Lowlands of east. Iris yellow to orange-yellow. ♂ turquoise and black with white belly. ♀ dull olivaceous with whitish belly, no pectoral tuft.   p. 615

4. YELLOW-BELLIED DACNIS, *Dacnis flaviventer*
Lowlands of east. Iris red. ♂ yellow below with black mask and bib. ♀ dull olivaceous with mottled breast.   p. 616

5. SCARLET-THIGHED DACNIS, *Dacnis venusta*
Lowlands of northwest, scarce. Iris red. ♂ black below with contrasting turquoise blue head. ♀ has turquoise-tinged upperparts, buffy grayish underparts.   p. 616

Chlorophonia Chlorophonias

Plump, short-tailed, with predominantly bright green plumage; ♀♀ duller. Mainly Andean, all species scarce or local. Montane forest canopy and borders, favoring mistletoe.

6. CHESTNUT-BREASTED CHLOROPHONIA, *Chlorophonia pyrrhophrys*
Subtropical and temperate zones on e. slope and in northwest. Strongly patterned, with blue crown. ♂ has black brow, broad chestnut stripe down belly. ♀ with chestnut brow (cf. ♀ Golden-rumped Euphonia).   p. 626

7. BLUE-NAPED CHLOROPHONIA, *Chlorophonia cyanea*
Subtropics and foothills on e. slope. ♂ has blue back and rump. ♀ with blue restricted to nape.   p. 626

8. YELLOW-COLLARED CHLOROPHONIA, *Chlorophonia flavirostris*
Foothills of northwest. Salmon orange bill and legs; iris white, eye-ring yellow. ♂ gaudy, with yellow collar. ♀ more uniform, underparts yellowish green.   p. 626

Euphonia Euphonias

Small, plump, short-tailed tanagers, most species strongly dimorphic in plumage. Most ♂♂ basically bicolored (blue-black above, yellow to orange below), ♀♀ predominantly olive; especially note head and lower belly/undertail patterns. They occur in canopy and borders of forest and woodland, some species into clearings and gardens, many favoring mistletoe; mainly in lowlands, a few montane.

9. GOLDEN-RUMPED EUPHONIA, *Euphonia cyanocephala*
  9NW *E. c. pelzelni*—♂ with black frontlet
  9SW *E. c. insignis*—♂ with orange frontlet
Highlands, mainly on w. slope, wandering to foothills. Blue crown and nape. ♂ with yellow rump. ♀ (both races) has tawny frontlet.   p. 627

10. ORANGE-BELLIED EUPHONIA, *Euphonia xanthogaster*
Widespread and common. ♂ with yellow forecrown extending to behind eye, white undertail spots. ♀ has tawny-yellow forecrown, buffyish lower underparts.   p. 628

11. WHITE-VENTED EUPHONIA, *Euphonia minuta*
Lowlands of east and northwest. White crissum and undertail. ♂ has small yellow frontlet. ♀ with grayish white throat.   p. 628

12. FULVOUS-VENTED EUPHONIA, *Euphonia fulvicrissa*
Lowlands and foothills of northwest. Tawny crissum and lower midbelly. ♂ has yellow forecrown, no white undertail. ♀ with rufous frontlet, olive breast.   p. 629

13. ORANGE-CROWNED EUPHONIA, *Euphonia saturata*
Lowlands of west. ♂ has entire crown and underparts deep orange, no white undertail. ♀ nearly uniform olive (paler below), lores not pale.   p. 629

14. THICK-BILLED EUPHONIA, *Euphonia laniirostris*
Lowlands of east and west; common, especially in west. Bill heavy. ♂ has entirely yellow underparts (including throat). ♀ olive above, yellower below, with pale grayish lores. Immature ♂ like ♀ but with black mask.   p. 627

15. RUFOUS-BELLIED EUPHONIA, *Euphonia rufiventris*
Lowlands of east. ♂ with all-dark head (no yellow on forecrown), orange-rufous underparts. ♀ has tawny crissum, gray median underparts.   p. 630

16. WHITE-LORED EUPHONIA, *Euphonia chrysopasta*
Lowlands of east. Prominent white lores in both sexes.
          p. 631

17. BRONZE-GREEN EUPHONIA, *Euphonia mesochrysa*
Foothills and subtropics on e. slope. ♂ olive with bronzy sheen above; forecrown yellow. ♀ lacks yellow on forecrown.   p. 630

18. PURPLE-THROATED EUPHONIA, *Euphonia chlorotica*
Woodland and clearings in Río Marañón drainage around Zumba. Resembles Orange-bellied Euphonia but smaller. ♂ differs in its smaller yellow forecrown patch, brighter yellow underparts. ♀ differs in lacking ochraceous on forecrown and belly.   p. 629

Plate 86 Tanagers III

1. SWALLOW TANAGER, *Tersina viridis*
Erratic (usually in groups) at forest borders in lowlands and (especially) foothills. ♂ mostly bright blue with black mask. ♀ mostly bright green with prominent flank barring.
p. 648

Tangara Tanagers
Fairly small tanagers usually with bold patterns and bright colors found in virtually all wooded or forested habitats; sexes alike or nearly so in most species. Species presented here (more are on Plate 87) are found in lowlands, some also ranging up into foothills. Many typically associate in mixed flocks. None is especially vocal.

2. OPAL-RUMPED TANAGER, *Tangara velia*
Uncommon in east. Predominantly dark blue with rufous lower underparts; opalescent straw rump.
p. 639

3. OPAL-CROWNED TANAGER, *Tangara callophrys*
Fairly common in east. Mainly dark blue (no rufous below) with conspicuous opalescent brow; opalescent straw rump.
p. 640

4. PARADISE TANAGER, *Tangara chilensis*
Fairly common in east, often in groups and most numerous in foothills. Unmistakably gaudy and colorful with apple green head, red rump, and bright blue underparts.   p. 640

5. GREEN-AND-GOLD TANAGER, *Tangara schrankii*
Common in east. Bright green and yellow with conspicuous black mask.
p. 640

6. EMERALD TANAGER, *Tangara florida*
Uncommon and local in foothills of northwest. Bright lime green with conspicuous black ear patch, yellow on head.
p. 633

7. BLUE-WHISKERED TANAGER, *Tangara johannae*
Scarce in lowlands of northwest. Black face with blue malar.
p. 641

8. YELLOW-BELLIED TANAGER, *Tangara xanthogastra*
Uncommon in east. Bright green speckled with black; yellow midbelly.
p. 641

9. SPOTTED TANAGER, *Tangara punctata*
Fairly common in e.-slope foothills and subtropics. Boldly black-spotted; bluish cast to head; whitish midbelly.
p. 641

10. BLUE-NECKED TANAGER, *Tangara cyanicollis*
10E *T. c. caeruleocephala*—straw rump, coppery wing-coverts
10W *T. c. cyanopygia*—blue rump, greener wing-coverts
Common in foothills and lower subtropics, also local in lowlands of west; a nonforest *Tangara*, often in cutover terrain. Strongly contrasting wing-coverts; bright blue hood.
p. 638

11. MASKED TANAGER, *Tangara nigrocincta*
Uncommon in east. Dusty blue hood, black breast, white belly.
p. 638

12. GOLDEN-HOODED TANAGER, *Tangara larvata*
Lowlands of west. Golden buff hood, black breast.   p. 638

13. TURQUOISE TANAGER, *Tangara mexicana*
Fairly common in east. Mainly cobalt blue with contrasting yellow belly.
p. 639

14. GRAY-AND-GOLD TANAGER, *Tangara palmeri*
Foothills of northwest. Gray with band of black and opalescent speckles across breast.
p. 632

15. BAY-HEADED TANAGER, *Tangara gyrola*
Common in foothills and lowlands (less so in east). Rufous-chestnut head, turquoise blue underparts. Young birds much duller. W. birds *lack* yellow on nape.   p. 642

16. RUFOUS-WINGED TANAGER, *Tangara lavinia*
Foothills of northwest (especially Esmeraldas). Stunning ♂ with golden yellow mantle bright rufous wings. ♀ much duller but shows dull rufous on wings (never seen in Bay-headed).
p. 642

Hemithraupis Tanagers
Warbler-like tanagers found in lowland forests and woodlands.

17. YELLOW-BACKED TANAGER, *Hemithraupis flavicollis*
Terra firme forest in east. ♂ with yellow throat and rump, mostly black upperparts. ♀ with uniform yellowish underparts.
p. 623

18. GUIRA TANAGER, *Hemithraupis guira*
Lowlands, more common in west. ♂ with black face and throat, orange-rufous breast. ♀ dull; yellow around eye and on foreneck, pale grayish lower flanks.
p. 623

19. SCARLET-AND-WHITE-TANAGER, *Erythrothlypis salmoni*
Local in foothill forest of northwest. ♂ unmistakable, bright scarlet with flanks broadly white. ♀ much duller, brownish with broadly white flanks as in ♂.
p. 624

Plate 87 Tanagers IV

1. **FAWN-BREASTED TANAGER,** *Pipraeidea melanonota*
Widespread but never really common in semiopen areas and forest borders on Andean slopes and in central valley. Buff underparts, blue crown (duller in ♀♀), red iris.   p. 625

Chlorochrysa Tanagers
Mainly brilliant green tanagers of montane forests on lower Andean slopes. Smaller and less chunky than *Tangara*, often found with them in mixed flocks.

2. **ORANGE-EARED TANAGER,** *Chlorochrysa calliparaea*
Fairly common on e. slope. Orange rump patch, red ear patch (orange in ♀). ♂ with black throat.   p. 631

3. **GLISTENING-GREEN TANAGER,** *Chlorochrysa phoenicotis*
Uncommon and local on w. slope, where mainly bright green plumage is unique.   p. 631

Tangara Tanagers
These brightly colored and boldly patterned tanagers are a feature of Andean forests; up to 6–8 species may range together in the same flock. Most are easy to identify, though young birds are duller; sexual dimorphism occurs in only a few. *Tangara* found in lowlands are depicted on Plate 86; in foothills some of those species may occur with species shown on this plate.

4. **RUFOUS-THROATED TANAGER,** *Tangara rufigula*
Foothills on w. slope, where locally common. Rufous throat, black head, scaly pattern.   p. 632

5. **GOLDEN TANAGER,** *Tangara arthus*
5W   *T. a. goodsoni*—golden yellow underparts
5E   *T. a. aequatorialis*—rufous tinge below
Foothills and subtropics on both slopes, often common. Golden with conspicuous black ear patch.   p. 633

6. **SILVER-THROATED TANAGER,** *Tangara icterocephala*
Locally common in foothills on w. slope. Mainly bright lemon yellow with opalescent throat.   p. 633

7. **SAFFRON-CROWNED TANAGER,** *Tangara xanthocephala*
Subtropics on both slopes, much commoner in east. Contrasting bright yellow head.   p. 634

8. **GOLDEN-EARED TANAGER,** *Tangara chrysotis*
Uncommon in lower subtropics on e. slope. Deep golden face, black crown, rufous midbelly.   p. 634

9. **FLAME-FACED TANAGER,** *Tangara parzudakii*
9W   *T. p. lunigera*—mainly orange head, greener underparts
9E   *T. p. parzudakii*—larger with redder face
Subtropics on both slopes. Brightly colored head, black back.   p. 634

10. **BLUE-BROWED TANAGER,** *Tangara cyanotis*
Lower subtropics on e. slope, uncommon and local. Turquoise blue brow (cf. ♂ Black-faced Dacnis, Plate 85-3).

11. **METALLIC-GREEN TANAGER,** *Tangara labradorides*
Subtropics in northwest (where more common) and southeast. Opalescent buff brow.   p. 635

12. **GOLDEN-NAPED TANAGER,** *Tangara ruficervix*
Subtropics on both slopes. Mainly bright turquoise blue with golden nape patch.   p. 635

13. **SCRUB TANAGER,** *Tangara vitriolina*
Dry woodland and gardens in intermontane valleys of north. Dull opalescent greenish with rufous crown, black mask. ♀ duller.   p. 637

14. **BERYL-SPANGLED TANAGER,** *Tangara nigroviridis*
Subtropical and temperate zones on both slopes, often common. Unique generally spangled appearance.   p. 636

15. **BLUE-AND-BLACK TANAGER,** *Tangara vassorii*
Temperate zone on both slopes (the highest-ranging *Tangara*). Mainly bright blue (cf. Masked Flowerpiercer, Plate 84-10).   p. 636

16. **BLACK-CAPPED TANAGER,** *Tangara heinei*
Subtropics on both slopes in north, favoring clearings. Scaly effect on breast. ♂ with black crown. ♀ with scaled and dusky crown, bright green mantle.   p. 636

17. **SILVER-BACKED TANAGER,** *Tangara viridicollis*
Montane forest and scrub in south (mainly Loja and s. El Oro). Orange-buff throat. ♂ striking with shiny silvery back, mainly black underparts. ♀ mostly bright green with brown crown. Cf. rare and local Straw-backed Tanager (Plate 96-19).   p. 637

18. **RUFOUS-CRESTED TANAGER,** *Creurgops verticalis*
Subtropics on e. slope and in extreme northwest. Chunky shape. Gray upperparts, rufous underparts. ♂'s crown patch inconspicuous, ♀ has none.   p. 648

Plate 88 Tanagers V

Iridosornis Tanagers
Beautiful, predominantly blue tanagers of montane forest lower growth, all species with rufous crissums. Often inconspicuous. Sexes alike.

1. YELLOW-THROATED TANAGER, *Iridosornis analis*
Local in subtropics on e. slope. Bright yellow throat, dull buffyish underparts. p. 643

2. PURPLISH-MANTLED TANAGER, *Iridosornis porphyrocephala*
Rare in subtropics of northwest. Bright yellow throat contrasts with blue underparts. p. 642

3. GOLDEN-CROWNED TANAGER, *Iridosornis rufivertex*
Temperate zone on e. slope and in northwest. Vivid blue with bright golden crown patch, black head and neck. p. 643

Anisognathus Mountain-Tanagers
Fairly large, colorful tanagers, arboreal and conspicuous in montane forests; all have at least some blue in wing. Usually conspicuous, regularly occurring with flocks. Sexes alike.

4. SCARLET-BELLIED MOUNTAIN-TANAGER, *Anisognathus igniventris*
Widespread and often common in temperate forest borders, shrubby areas; often up to treeline. Unmistakable, with vivid red belly and cheek patch, blue shoulders and rump.
p. 643

5. LACRIMOSE MOUNTAIN-TANAGER, *Anisognathus lacrymosus*
Fairly common in temperate-zone forests on e. slope. Mustard yellow underparts; two yellow spots on face.
p. 644

6. BLUE-WINGED MOUNTAIN-TANAGER, *Anisognathus somptuosus*
6 *A. s. cyanopterus / alamoris / somptuosus*—black back
6NE *A. s. baezae*—green back
Common in subtropics on both slopes. Bright yellow underparts and crown patch; large bright blue wing-patches.
p. 644

7. BLACK-CHINNED MOUNTAIN-TANAGER, *Anisognathus notabilis*
Local in foothills and subtropics on w. slope. Rich orange-yellow underparts, bright moss green back. p. 644

Buthraupis Mountain-Tanagers
Large, hefty tanagers found in temperate-zone forests up to treeline; appearance and behavior vary among species. Sexes alike.

8. HOODED MOUNTAIN-TANAGER, *Buthraupis montana*
Often common and conspicuous in temperate forest on e. slope and in northwest. Bright blue back, ruby red eye, surprisingly conspicuous dark thighs. p. 645

9. MASKED MOUNTAIN-TANAGER, *Buthraupis wetmorei*
Scarce and local near treeline on e. slope. Bold yellow brow, large yellow rump. p. 645

10. BLACK-CHESTED MOUNTAIN-TANAGER, *Buthraupis eximia*
Uncommon in upper temperate forest on e. slope and in northwest. Blue crown, rich green upperparts. p. 646

Bangsia Tanagers
Large-headed, chunky tanagers of northwest found in lower and middle growth of humid foothill forests. Yellow chest patch in both species.

11. GOLDEN-CHESTED TANAGER, *Bangsia rothschildi*
Local in lower foothills of Esmeraldas. Mainly blue-black. p. 646

12. MOSS-BACKED TANAGER, *Bangsia edwardsi*
Locally common in foothills south to nw. Pichincha. Blue face. p. 646

13. BUFF-BREASTED MOUNTAIN-TANAGER, *Dubusia taeniata*
Inconspicuous (but vocal) in lower growth of temperate forest on both slopes. Conspicuous spangled blue brow. p. 647

14. VERMILION TANAGER, *Calochaetes coccineus*
Locally fairly common in forest canopy in subtropics on e. slope. Mostly brilliant scarlet; black bib. p. 652

Piranga Tanagers
Boldly patterned tanagers found in montane forest. Other *Piranga* are on Plate 89.

15. RED-HOODED TANAGER, *Piranga rubriceps*
Scarce and local in temperate zone on e. slope, also a few recent records from northwest. Contrasting red hood. Sexes much alike, ♀ with less red on underparts. p. 654

16. WHITE-WINGED TANAGER, *Piranga leucoptera*
Foothills and lower subtropics on both slopes. Bold white wing-bars. ♂ rosy red; ♀ yellow and olive. p. 653

17. WHITE-CAPPED TANAGER, *Sericossypha albocristata*
Spectacular large tanager of subtropical forest canopy on e. slope, scarce and local. Moves in noisy, conspicuous groups. Unmistakable, with snowy white crown, red bib (brighter in ♂♂). p. 666

18. GRASS-GREEN TANAGER, *Chlorornis riefferii*
Fairly common in temperate forest on both slopes. Showy, mainly bright green with rufous face, red bill and legs. Sexes alike. p. 648

Plate 89 Tanagers VI

Thraupis Tanagers

Usually common and conspicuous tanagers found in semi-open areas and forest borders. Sexes usually alike.

1. BLUE-GRAY TANAGER, *Thraupis episcopus*
1W *T. e. quaesita*—plain blue wings
1E *T. e. coelestis*—white on wing-coverts
Familiar bright pale blue tanager, widespread in lowlands, spreading up into montane valleys in cleared areas.   p. 649

2. PALM TANAGER, *Thraupis palmarum*
Common in lowlands, often but not always in palms. Grayish olive with contrasting black outer half of wings.   p. 649

3. BLUE-CAPPED TANAGER, *Thraupis cyanocephala*
Forest edge and clearings in subtropics and temperate zone. Bright blue crown; bright olive mantle.   p. 650

4. BLUE-AND-YELLOW TANAGER, *Thraupis bonariensis*
Gardens and light woodland in arid sectors of central and interandean valleys. Colorful ♂ unmistakable. ♀ dull, washed with blue on head, buffyish below.   p. 650

Ramphocelus Tanagers

Colorful, conspicuous, common tanagers of shrubby clearings and forest edge situations in lowlands. ♂♂ (at least) have prominent silvery on bill.

5. MASKED CRIMSON TANAGER, *Ramphocelus nigrogularis*
East; in groups, especially near water. Unmistakable, boldly patterned in brilliant red and black.   p. 651

6. SILVER-BEAKED TANAGER, *Ramphocelus carbo*
Very common in east; usually in groups. ♂ often looks blackish but is actually mostly rich velvety maroon. ♀ mostly brick red with heavy dark bill.   p. 650

7. LEMON-RUMPED TANAGER, *Ramphocelus icteronotus*
Very common in west. ♂ unmistakable with conspicuous bright yellow rump and lower back. ♀ shares yellow rump, is yellow below.   p. 651

8. BLACK-AND-WHITE TANAGER, *Conothraupis speculigera*
Seasonal and local in shrubby clearings and arid woodland, mainly in Loja. ♂ unmistakable, black and white (cf. *Sporophila* seedeaters, Plate 92). ♀ olive with streaking on breast (cf. Streaked Saltator, Plate 91-6).   p. 665

Chlorothraupis Tanagers

Chunky, heavy-billed, predominantly olive tanagers found in lower growth of humid forest, especially in foothills. Sexes alike. See also Olive Tanager (Plate 96-21).

9. OCHRE-BREASTED TANAGER, *Chlorothruapis stolzmanni*
Foothills and subtropics on w. slope. Drab, with ochre wash below.   p. 655

10. LEMON-SPECTACLED TANAGER, *Chlorothraupis olivacea*
Lowlands and lower foothills of Esmeraldas. Prominent yellow "spectacles."   p. 654

11. GRAY-HEADED TANAGER, *Eucometis penicillata*
Local in várzea forest undergrowth in lowlands of east. Gray head, expressive bushy crest.   p. 656

12. SCARLET-BROWED TANAGER, *Heterospingus xanthopygius*
Humid forest canopy in lowlands and foothills of northwest. Yellow rump, white pectoral tuft. ♂ blacker with scarlet brow.   p. 659

13. FULVOUS SHRIKE-TANAGER, *Lanio fulvus*
Humid forest canopy in lowlands and foothills of east. ♂ bright ochraceous yellow with black hood. ♀ duller and browner with ochre-buff rearparts (cf. smaller but similar ♀ Flame-crested Tanager, Plate 90-4).   p. 658

Piranga Tanagers

Strongly dimorphic tanagers (♂♂ mainly or entirely some shade of red, ♀♀ olive and yellow) found in canopy and borders of forest and woodland. Other *Piranga* are on Plate 88.

14. SCARLET TANAGER, *Piranga olivacea*
Boreal migrant, mainly to lowlands of east. Bill dark. Breeding-plumage ♂ unmistakable, scarlet with black wings. ♀ and nonbreeding ♂♂ with contrasting dark wings.   p. 653

15. SUMMER TANAGER, *Piranga rubra*
Boreal migrant, widespread. Bill not always as pale as shown. ♂ rosy red. ♀ with concolor olive wings, orangey tinge to underparts.   p. 653

16. HIGHLAND HEPATIC-TANAGER, *Pirange lutea*
Wooded habitats, mainly in west, also foothills of southeast. Dark lores and bill. ♂ uniform carmine red. ♀ can be confused with ♀ Summer, but bill always dark; see text.   p. 652

17. RED-CROWNED ANT-TANAGER, *Habia rubica*
Forest undergrowth in lowlands of east. ♂ reddish with red crest. ♀ can be difficult, dull brownish with orange in crest.   p. 655

18. DUSKY-FACED TANAGER, *Mitrospingus cassinii*
Humid forest borders in west, especially lower foothills; usually near streams, in noisy groups. Staring white eye, contrasting grayish face and throat. Sexes alike.   p. 656

19. MAGPIE TANAGER, *Cissopis leveriana*
Conspicuous in small groups at forest edge and clearings in lowlands and foothills of east. Unmistakable: large with long graduated tail, black and white plumage. Sexes alike.   p. 665

Plate 90 Tanagers VII

Tachyphonus Tanagers

Mainly lowland tanagers, most species found in humid forest at varying levels, often with flocks. ♂♂ predominantly black, usually with at least some white on wing; ♀♀ browner or more olive.

1. WHITE-SHOULDERED TANAGER, *Tachyphonus luctuosus*

Lowlands and foothills of east and west, much commoner in west. ♂ with prominent white shoulders. ♀ olive and yellow with contrasting gray hood. p. 658

2. TAWNY-CRESTED TANAGER, *Tachyphonus delattrii*

Lowlands and (especially) foothills of northwest. Favors understory, regularly in monospecific groups. ♂ with conspicuous orange crest. ♀ uniform dull tobacco brown. p. 658

3. FULVOUS-CRESTED TANAGER, *Tachyphonus surinamus*

Lowlands of east, favoring forest understory. ♂ with rufous and white on flanks. ♀ olive-backed with contrasting gray head, buffyish underparts. p. 657

4. FLAME-CRESTED TANAGER, *Tachyphonus cristatus*

Lowlands of east, favoring forest canopy. ♂ with small yellowish throat patch; orange in crest often not as prominent as shown. ♀ dull brownish (cf. ♀ Fulvous Shrike-Tanager, Plate 89-13). p. 657

5. WHITE-LINED TANAGER, *Tachyphonus rufus*

Local in clearings of lowlands and foothills of east and west. ♂ with white under wing (conspicuous in flight). ♀ uniform rufous brown. p. 656

Thlypopsis Tanagers

Small, warbler-like tanagers of secondary habitats, Ecuadorian species showing prominent orange. Sexes nearly alike. An additional, recently found species is on Plate 96.

6. RUFOUS-CHESTED TANAGER, *Thlypopsis ornata*

Highlands. Orange-rufous head and underparts, contrasting white midbelly. p. 624

7. ORANGE-HEADED TANAGER, *Thlypopsis sordida*

Lowlands of east, especially in riparian areas. Contrasting yellow-orange hood. p. 624

8. BLACK-FACED TANAGER, *Schistochlamys melanopis*

Shrubby clearings in Río Marañón drainage of s. Zamora-Chinchipe. Unmistakable, gray with black face and foreneck. Juvenile olive (see text). p. 666

Chlorospingus Bush-Tanagers

Midsized, predominantly gray and olive tanagers of montane forest and borders in Andes; many species are numerous and conspicuous, often accompanying mixed flocks. Sexes alike.

9. COMMON BUSH-TANAGER, *Chlorospingus ophthalmicus*

Subtropical zone on e. slope, and in El Oro. Dingy, with grayish head, pale iris. p. 659

10. YELLOW-THROATED BUSH-TANAGER, *Chlorospingus flavigularis*

10W *C. f. marginatus*—dingy breast
10E *C. f. flavigularis*—gray breast
Often common in foothills and subtropics on both slopes, favoring understory, especially near streams. Yellow on throat; iris hazel. p. 661

11. YELLOW-WHISKERED BUSH-TANAGER, *Chlorospingus parvirostris*

Local in subtropics on e. slope, mainly in understory and edge. Flaring orange-yellow "whiskers"; iris grayish white. p. 661

12. ASHY-THROATED BUSH-TANAGER, *Chlorospingus canigularis*

12W *C. c. paulus*
12E *C. c. signatus*—white postocular
Foothills and subtropics on both slopes (local in west); arboreal. Gray head; dark iris; bright yellow-green chest band. p. 660

13. DUSKY BUSH-TANAGER, *Chlorospingus semifuscus*

Common in subtropics in northwest. Dark and patternless, but with pale iris. p. 660

14. YELLOW-GREEN BUSH-TANAGER, *Chlorospingus flavovirens*

Very rare and local in mossy forest in foothills of northwest. Uniform olive, somewhat yellower below. p. 660

15. GRAY-HOODED BUSH-TANAGER, *Cnemoscopus rubrirostris*

Montane forest in temperate zone on e. slope, locally in northwest. Pink bill, contrasting gray hood; wags tail. p. 661

16. BLACK-BACKED BUSH-TANAGER, *Urothraupis stolzmanni*

Woodland near treeline on e. slope, often in small groups. Unmistakable, with black upperparts, snowy white throat. p. 662

Hemispingus Hemispinguses

Small, mainly olive or gray tanagers of montane forest, some species recalling *Basileuterus* warblers (see Plate 83). Usually seen with mixed flocks, most species in understory. Sexes alike.

17. BLACK-CAPPED HEMISPINGUS, *Hemispingus atropileus*

Forest understory (favors bamboo) in temperate zone on e. slope and in northwest. Black head with conspicuous white superciliary; ochraceous foreneck. p. 662

18. SUPERCILIARIED HEMISPINGUS, *Hemispingus superciliaris*

Local in forest (especially at edge) in temperate zone on both slopes. Bold white superciliary; bright yellow underparts. p. 663

19. OLEAGINOUS HEMISPINGUS, *Hemispingus frontalis*

Scarce in forest understory in subtropics on e. slope. Uniform olive, yellower below; weak yellowish superciliary. p. 663

20. BLACK-EARED HEMISPINGUS, *Hemispingus melanotis*

Uncommon and local in forest understory in subtropics on e. slope, favoring bamboo understory. Gray head with black face, cinnamon-buff breast. p. 663

21. WESTERN HEMISPINGUS, *Hemispingus ochraceus*

Rare and local in forest understory in subtropics on w. slope. Very dull, with dusky face. p. 664

22. PIURA HEMISPINGUS, *Hemispingus piurae*

Very local in montane woodland undergrowth of s. Loja. Striking, with black head, long white brow, rich rufous breast. p. 664

23. BLACK-HEADED HEMISPINGUS, *Hemispingus verticalis*

Forest (favoring edge) in temperate zone, especially near treeline, on e. slope. Gray with black head, pale iris, brownish crown stripe. p. 664

Plate 91 Saltators, Grosbeaks, Siskins, etc.

Saltator Saltators and Grosbeaks

Large arboreal "finches" found widely in forested and wooded areas, a few species in more open terrain. Bills heavy and "swollen"; most have prominent superciliary. Clear, melodic songs are frequently given. Sexes usually alike.

1. BUFF-THROATED SALTATOR, Saltator maximus

Common and widespread in clearings and forest canopy in lowlands of east and west. Buff throat, black malar; olive upperparts.   p. 667

2. BLACK-WINGED SALTATOR, Saltator atripennis

Foothills, lower subtropics, and adjacent humid lowlands on w. slope. Black head with bold white markings; contrasting black wings.   p. 667

3. GRAYISH SALTATOR, Saltator coerulescens

Locally common in riparian areas and clearings in lowlands and foothills of east. White throat, black malar; gray upperparts.   p. 668

4. BLACK-COWLED SALTATOR, Saltator nigriceps

Montane scrub and forest borders mainly in Loja. Bright red bill; gray with contrasting black hood.   p. 668

5. MASKED SALTATOR, Saltator cinctus

Rare in subtropical forest on e. slope. Black face, throat, and pectoral band; bluish gray upperparts; reddish on bill, orange eye.   p. 669

6. STREAKED SALTATOR, Saltator striatipectus

6N S. s. striatipectus—grayish upperparts, breast streaks

6W S. s. flavidicollis—unstreaked yellowish below, long brow

6S S. s. peruvianus—olive upperparts, breast streaks; Zumba

Common in light woodland, scrub, and semiopen areas in arid intermontane valleys of north and more arid lowlands of west. W. juveniles have sparse blurry streaking below, shorter white brow.   p. 668

7. SLATE-COLORED GROSBEAK, Saltator grossus

Humid forest in lowlands of west and east. Heavy red bill, mostly slaty gray plumage. Juveniles lack white throat.
                                                    p. 669

8. YELLOW-SHOULDERED GROSBEAK, Parkerthraustes humeralis

Inconspicuous in canopy of terra firme forest in lowlands of east. Gray and olive with black mask, scaly malar and throat, yellow crissum. Sexes alike.   p. 672

9. RED-CAPPED CARDINAL, Paroaria gularis

Common in shrubbery around lakes in lowlands of east. Sexes alike. Colorful adult unmistakable with red head, black and white body. Juveniles brown above with buff face and bib.   p. 669

Pheucticus Grosbeaks

Large, heavy-set "finches" with massive bills, bold plumage patterns. Black and yellow predominate in the two resident species, found in the highlands. Arboreal, with rich melodic songs.

10. SOUTHERN YELLOW-GROSBEAK, Pheucticus chrysogaster

Common and widespread in scrub, gardens, and agricultural areas in more arid highlands and w. lowlands. ♂ has entire head, neck, and underparts golden yellow. ♀ duller; head and neck streaked blackish.   p. 670

11. BLACK-BACKED GROSBEAK, Pheucticus aureoventris

Uncommon and local in scrub, gardens, and agricultural areas in more arid intermontane valleys south to Chimborazo. ♂ has all-black head and back. ♀ like ♀ Southern Yellow, but head and neck more solidly dark (little or no streaked effect). See text.   p. 670

12. ROSE-BREASTED GROSBEAK, Pheucticus ludovicianus

Scarce boreal migrant to forest borders and clearings. ♂ unmistakable, black and white with large rosy patch on chest. ♀ and juveniles browner above, buffy below with fine streaking; bold superciliary.   p. 671

13. BLUE-BLACK GROSBEAK, Cyanocompsa cyanoides

13E C. c. rothchildii—azure facial markings and shoulders (♂)

13W C. c. cyanoides—♂ more uniform

Inconspicuous in lower growth of humid forest and woodland in lowlands and foothills of east and west. Heavy bill. ♂ dusky blue. ♀ uniform rich chocolate brown. Cf. Oryzoborus seed-finches (Plate 92).   p. 671

Carduelis Siskins and Goldfinches

Small, gregarious finches with conical, pointed bills found mainly in highlands (Saffron Siskin in sw. lowlands). ♂ ♂ contrastingly patterned in black and yellow; ♀ ♀ duller, more olive. Many are often best identified by range (especially 17, 18, 19); ♀ ♀ of some species are easier to separate than respective ♂ ♂. Siskins have prominent yellow wing patches, usually at least some white on tertials.

14. LESSER GOLDFINCH, Carduelis psaltria

Very local (sporadic?) in clearings and shrubby areas, mainly in subtropics on both slopes. Both sexes have white in wing, but no yellow. Bill pale. ♂ black above, all yellow below.
                                                    p. 709

15. YELLOW-BELLIED SISKIN, Carduelis xanthogastra

Scarce and local in montane forest and clearings in foothills and subtropics on w. slope. ♂ black with contrasting yellow breast and belly. ♀ dark olive above; olive chest contrasts with yellow breast.   p. 709

16. ANDEAN SISKIN, Carduelis spinescens

Scarce and local in paramo, montane woodland, and agricultural areas in highlands of north. Black on head restricted to crown; underparts tinged olive. Sexes nearly alike (juveniles lack black crown).   p. 708

17. HOODED SISKIN, Carduelis magellanica

Common and widespread in semiopen areas, clearings, and gardens in highlands and on w. slope. ♂ with black hood, olive-yellow underparts, mainly olive upperparts (rump yellow in south). ♀ has grayish underparts, no black on crown.   p. 707

18. OLIVACEOUS SISKIN, Carduelis olivacea

Subtropical forest and clearings on e. slope. ♂ very like ♂ Hooded. ♀ olive below (not grayish of Hooded).   p. 708

19. SAFFRON SISKIN, Carduelis siemiradzkii

Local in deciduous forest and borders in lowlands of southwest. ♂ like ♂ Hooded but brighter generally with back more golden olive. ♀ yellower generally; olive-yellow below.   p. 708

Sicalis Finches and Yellow-Finches

Midsized finches of open terrain, gregarious when not breeding. Two species are predominantly yellow.

20. SAFFRON FINCH, Sicalis flaveola

Locally common and conspicuous around towns and in agricultural areas in Loja and El Oro, spreading into Guayas. Adult mainly bright yellow with orange forecrown. Immature brownish, streaky, with pale yellow pectoral band.
                                                    p. 684

21. GRASSLAND YELLOW-FINCH, Sicalis luteola

Local in fields and pastures, often near water, in highlands. Brownish streaked upperparts, mainly yellow underparts.
                                                    p. 684

22. SULPHUR-THROATED FINCH, Sicalis taczanowskii

Rare and erratic in barren open ground, mainly on Santa Elena Peninsula. Massive bill. Very drab pale grayish brown; yellow on throat hard to see.   p. 685

Plate 92 Emberizine Finches I

1. BLUE-BLACK GRASSQUIT, *Volatinia jacarina*
Common in agricultural regions and clearings in lowlands of west; scarcer and more local in east. Pointed bill. ♂ glossy blue-black. ♀ has dusky-streaked underparts.   p. 673

Sporophila Seedeaters
Often common and conspicuous small finches of open, shrubby terrain, especially where grassy. Thick, stubby bills. Usually sexually dimorphic, ♂♂ generally strongly patterned. ♀♀ much duller and hard to identify; are usually not referred to here (see main text). Nonbreeders often range in mixed flocks.

2. SLATE-COLORED SEEDEATER, *Sporophila schistacea*
Rare and sporadic at forest borders in lowlands and foothills of northwest and lowlands of east. ♂ has rich yellow bill; mostly gray with white wing speculum and one bar. p. 676

3. VARIABLE SEEDEATER, *Sporophila corvina*
Common in more humid lowlands and foothills of west. ♂ black and white with black pectoral band. ♀ predominantly yellowish buff.   p. 676

4. CAQUETÁ SEEDEATER, *Sporophila murallae*
Relatively scarce in lowlands of east. ♂ black and white with incomplete black pectoral band, narrow white wing-bars.   p. 676

5. BLACK-AND-WHITE SEEDEATER, *Sporophila luctuosa*
Locally common breeder in highlands of far north and south, in nonbreeding season into e. lowlands. ♂ black with white belly, white wing speculum.   p. 678

6. YELLOW-BELLIED SEEDEATER, *Sporophila nigricollis*
More humid parts of west, locally up into highlands. ♂ has black hood, olive upperparts, dull pale yellow belly. p. 678

7. LESSON'S SEEDEATER, *Sporophila bouvronides*
Visitant (Nov.–Apr.) to lowlands of east, favoring grassy areas near rivers. ♂'s conspicuous white malar contrasts with black midthroat. ♀'s bill yellowish below.   p. 677

8. LINED SEEDEATER, *Sporophila lineola*
Very rare austral migrant to lowlands of east. ♂ like Lesson's but has narrow white crown stripe.   p. 677

9. PARROT-BILLED SEEDEATER, *Sporophila peruviana*
Grassy areas and scrub in more arid parts of southwest. Oversized bill. ♂ with variable black bib, white neck patch.   p. 679

10. CHESTNUT-THROATED SEEDEATER, *Sporophila telasco*
Common in lowlands of west. ♂ mostly white below with small chestnut throat patch. ♀ shows streaking above.   p. 679

11. DRAB SEEDEATER, *Sporophila simplex*
Local in highlands of south. Sexes much alike. Dull brownish; 2 pale wing-bars.   p. 679

12. RUDDY-BREASTED SEEDEATER, *Sporophila minuta*
Scarce and local in northwest. ♂ has rump and underparts rufous.   p. 680

13. CHESTNUT-BELLIED SEEDEATER, *Sporophila castaneiventris*
Common in lowlands and foothills of east. ♂ slaty with median underparts chestnut. ♀ small, relatively brown.   p. 680

Tiaris Grassquits
A pair of seedeater-like finches, differing in their more pointed bills and buzzier songs.

14. DULL-COLORED GRASSQUIT, *Tiaris obscura*
Locally common in shrubby clearings in more humid lowlands and foothills of west. Bill distinctly bicolored, paler below. Dull; sexes much alike.   p. 674

15. YELLOW-FACED GRASSQUIT, *Tiaris olivacea*
Local in grassy pastures in foothills and subtropics of northwest. ♂ with unique black and yellow face pattern. ♀'s face pattern echoes ♂'s.   p. 674

16. BLUE SEEDEATER, *Amaurospiza concolor*
Rare and local in undergrowth and borders of montane forest and borders on w. slope. "Typical" seedeater bill. ♂ uniform dusky-blue. ♀ uniform tawny-brown, no streaking below.   p. 680

17. SLATY FINCH, *Haplospiza rustica*
Scarce and erratic in understory of montane forest and woodland (especially in bamboo) on both slopes. Slender, pointed bill. ♂ uniform gray. ♀ dull olive brown with blurry breast streaking.   p. 685

Oryzoborus Seed-Finches
Small to fairly small finches with huge, squared-off bills, markedly larger than bills of *Sporophila* seedeaters. ♂♂ basically black, ♀♀ rich brown.

18. LESSER SEED-FINCH, *Oryzoborus angolensis*
18E *O. a. torridus*—♂ with chestnut breast and belly
18W *O. a. funereus*—♂ all black
Widespread in shrubby clearings and borders in lowlands. ♀ uniform brown, more rufous below.   p. 674

19. BLACK-BILLED SEED-FINCH, *Oryzoborus atrirostris*
Rare and local in marshy lake margins and clearings in lowlands of east. Huge bill, black in ♂. ♀ see text.   p. 675

20. LARGE-BILLED SEED-FINCH, *Oryzoborus crassirostris*
Rare and very local in lowlands of west and east. Bill not quite so massive as Black-billed's, white in ♂. ♀ see text.   p. 675

Catamenia Seedeaters
Small finches found in grassy and shrubby areas in highlands. Streaky with colored bills, buff to chestnut crissums.

21. PLAIN-COLORED SEEDEATER, *Catamenia inornata*
Grassy areas in highlands and paramo. ♂ with brownish pink bill; pale grayish with back streaking. ♀'s bill duller; underparts uniform with fine breast streaking.   p. 681

22. PARAMO SEEDEATER, *Catamenia homochroa*
Local in shrubby montane forest borders on both slopes. Bill pinkish, duller in ♀. ♂ dark slaty gray with blackish foreface. ♀ dark, uniform, with little or no streaking below.   p. 681

23. BAND-TAILED SEEDEATER, *Catamenia analis*
Agricultural areas, gardens, and scrub in central and interandean valleys, mainly where arid. White band across tail, visible mainly in flight. ♂ with butter yellow bill, chestnut crissum.   p. 682

Phrygilus Sierra-Finches
Small to midsized finches of shrubby and open areas, mainly in higlands. Larger than *Catamenia*, bills less stubby.

24. PLUMBEOUS SIERRA-FINCH, *Phrygilus unicolor*
Common in paramo and near treeline. ♂ uniform leaden gray. ♀ coarsely streaked.   p. 682

25. ASH-BREASTED SIERRA-FINCH, *Phrygilus plebejus*
Common (especially southward) in scrub, agricultural, and settled areas in arid highlands; also locally near coast in El Oro. Gray with vague back streaking, whitish on face. Juveniles generally streaky.   p. 683

26. BAND-TAILED SIERRA-FINCH, *Phrygilus alaudinus*
Open arid areas in highlands and locally near coast in southwest. Contrasting white belly, white band across midtail. ♂ has bright yellow bill and legs, legs dull yellowish in streaked ♀.   p. 683

27. CRIMSON-BREASTED FINCH, *Rhodospingus cruentus*
Seasonally common in shrubby areas and woodland borders in lowlands of west. ♂ unmistakable, black and crimson. ♀ nondescript, seedeater-like but with slender pointed bill; strong buff wash below.   p. 673

Plate 93 Emberizine Finches II and House Sparrow

Atlapetes and *Buarremon* Brush-Finches

Midsized finches found in lower growth of montane forest and (especially) borders and secondary woodland in Andes. Note color of underparts (whether basically yellow or white) and facial patterns. Identification to species is usually not a problem, though racial variation can cause confusion. Often not particularly shy, though usually remaining in cover; White-rimmed and the two *Buarremon* species are more secretive and forage more on ground.

1. PALE-NAPED BRUSH-FINCH, *Atlapetes pallidinucha*
Shrubbery near treeline on e. slope. Narrow stripe on hindcrown and nape white, forecrown ochre-yellow, mostly yellow underparts.   p. 686

2. RUFOUS-NAPED BRUSH-FINCH, *Atlapetes latinuchus*
2N   *A. l. spodionotus*—plain wing, no malar
2SW *A. l. comptus*—black malar, yellow lores
2SE *A. l. latinuchus*—white wing speculum
Widespread and often common in montane forest borders and second-growth, but northward not on e. slope of Andes. All-rufous crown, mostly yellow underparts.   p. 686

3. TRICOLORED BRUSH-FINCH, *Atlapetes tricolor*
Lower growth of montane forest and borders in foothills and lower subtropics on w. slope. Crown uniform brownish gold, mostly yellow underparts.   p. 687

4. WHITE-WINGED BRUSH-FINCH, *Atlapetes leucopterus*
4N *A. l. leucopterus*—solid black mask
4S *A. l. dresseri*—more black on forecrown, variable amount of facial white (extremes shown)
Shrubbery and lighter woodland, mainly in more arid regions on slopes of interandean valleys. White wing speculum, mostly white underparts.   p. 687

5. SLATY BRUSH-FINCH, *Atlapetes schistaceus*
Shrubby forest borders in temperate zone on e. slope (but not in far south). Dark and gray overall with chestnut crown, white wing speculum.   p. 687

6. BAY-CROWNED BRUSH-FINCH, *Atlapetes seebohmi*
Secondary woodland and scrub in subtropics of Loja. Chestnut crown, no wing speculum.   p. 688

7. WHITE-HEADED BRUSH-FINCH, *Atlapetes albiceps*
Undergrowth of deciduous woodland and scrub in s. Loja; at higher elevations than other *Atlapetes*. Unique white face contrasts with black hindcrown.   p. 688

8. PALE-HEADED BRUSH-FINCH, *Atlapetes pallidiceps*
Extremely rare and local in arid scrubby woodland of montane s. Azuay. Drab with head pattern faded, brownish back.   p. 688

9. WHITE-RIMMED BRUSH-FINCH, *Atlapetes leucopis*
Rare and seemingly local on or near ground inside temperate forest on e. slope and in far northwest. Dark; conspicuous white ocular region, olive underparts.   p. 689

10. CHESTNUT-CAPPED BRUSH-FINCH, *Buarremon brunneinucha*
10   *B. b. frontalis*—black chest band
10SW *B. b. inornata*—no chest band
Undergrowth of montane forest and woodland in foothills and subtropics on both slopes. Black chest band in most of range, puffy white throat, chestnut crown.   p. 689

11. STRIPE-HEADED BRUSH-FINCH, *Buarremon torquatus*
Undergrowth and borders of temperate forest and woodland, ranging lower in southwest. Gray and black striped head, puffy white throat.   p. 689

12. OLIVE FINCH, *Lysurus castaneiceps*
Secretive in foothill and subtropical forest undergrowth, often near streams, on e. slope and in northwest. Plain and dark, with gray face and throat, olive body.   p. 690

13. TANAGER FINCH, *Oreothraupis arremonops*
Rare and very local at edge of subtropical forest in northwest (Pichincha). Unique, rufescent with black head, broad white superciliary.   p. 690

Arremon Sparrows

Attractively patterned sparrows found on or near ground in lowland forest and woodland. Resemble brush-finches but smaller.

14. ORANGE-BILLED SPARROW, *Arremon aurantiirostris*
Undergrowth of humid forest and woodland in lowlands of east and west. Unmistakable bright orange bill, bold head pattern. Juvenile duller with dark bill.   p. 690

15. BLACK-CAPPED SPARROW, *Arremon abeillei*
15W *A. a. abeillei*—gray back
15S *A. a. nigriceps*—olive back; Zumba region
Undergrowth of deciduous woodland and scrub in lowlands of west and far south. Black head with bold white superciliary; in most of range back gray.   p. 691

16. BLACK-STRIPED SPARROW, *Arremonops conirostris*
Shrubby clearings and woodland borders in lowlands of west. Pale gray head with narrow black striping, grayish underparts.   p. 691

17. RUFOUS-COLLARED SPARROW, *Zonotrichia capensis*
Common and familiar in shrubby areas, gardens, etc., in highlands, locally down into foothills. Distinctive, with rufous collar, puffy-crested look. Streaky juveniles are often seen.   p. 693

Ammodramus Sparrows

Small, plain, "streaky" sparrows with pointed tails found in open grassy terrain.

18. GRASSHOPPER SPARROW, *Ammodramus savannarum*
Perhaps extirpated; at most very local in fields in central valley. Small, buffyish, with spiky tail, crown striping.   p. 692

19. YELLOW-BROWED SPARROW, *Ammodramus aurifrons*
Common and widespread in grassy areas in lowlands of east, smaller numbers up into subtropics. Drab, but with yellow on face. Distinctive song.   p. 692

20. TUMBES SPARROW, *Aimophila stolzmanni*
Arid scrub and shrubby areas in Loja. Gray head with rufous striping, black malar, chestnut shoulders.   p. 692

21. COLLARED WARBLING-FINCH, *Poospiza hispaniolensis*
Local in arid scrub and woodland borders in lowlands of southwest. Bold facial pattern, pale wing-edging. ♂ mainly gray above, incomplete black pectoral band. ♀ browner overall, throat contrasting white. Many birds on Isla de la Plata (where common) have at least some orange on bill (21A).   p. 693

22. HOUSE SPARROW, *Passer domesticus*
Spreading in urban areas, where tame and aggressive. Chunky. ♂ unmistakable with large black bib, etc. ♀ much duller with buffyish eye-stripe.   p. 710

Plate 94 Icterids I

All species on this plate exhibit marked sexual dimorphism in size. All caciques depicted are ♂♂, which are larger than respective ♀♀. All oropendolas depicted are ♀♀, which are smaller than respective ♂♂. Thus the 2 groups here appear more similar in size than they actually are.

Cacicus Caciques

Mainly black icterids, some entirely so, others with bright red or yellow on rump or bright yellow on wings; smaller than oropendolas and show less yellow on tail. Bills long, pointed, usually pale; irides also pale (typically blue, at least in adults). Most species are arboreal and conspicuous, found in both lowland and montane situations; loud vocalizations attract attention. Majority nest in colonies, sometimes with oropendolas but more often on their own.

1. YELLOW-RUMPED CACIQUE, *Cacicus cela*
1E *C. c. cela*—ivory bill
1W *C. c. flavicrissus*—duskier bill, less yellow on tail
Lowlands. Common in east, especially at edge and near water; local in west, in both humid and deciduous situations. Yellow rump extends to basal tail. p. 694

2. NORTHERN MOUNTAIN-CACIQUE, *Cacicus leucoramphus*
Montane forest and borders on e. slope. Yellow rump and wing-coverts. p. 695

3. RED-RUMPED CACIQUE, *Cacicus haemorrhous*
Rare and local in terra firme forest in lowlands of east. Lower back and rump red. p. 695

4. SCARLET-RUMPED CACIQUE, *Cacicus microrhynchus*
Humid forest and borders in lowlands of west. Red rump. p. 696

5. SUBTROPICAL CACIQUE, *Cacicus uropygialis*
Foothill and subtropical forest and borders on e. slope. Red restricted to rump. Tail longer than in Red-rumped. p. 696

6. ECUADORIAN CACIQUE, *Cacicus sclateri*
Rare and local in lowlands of east, mainly in várzea and riparian situations. All black with blue iris. p. 696

7. SOLITARY CACIQUE, *Cacicus solitarius*
Dense lower growth, mostly near water, in lowlands of east. Usually singly or in pairs. All black with dark iris. p. 697

8. YELLOW-BILLED CACIQUE, *Amblycercus holosericeus*
Disjunct, in woodland undergrowth in lowlands of west and temperate-forest undergrowth (especially bamboo) on e. slope. All black with straw yellow iris. p. 697

9. BAND-TAILED OROPENDOLA, *Ocyalus latirostris*
Very rare in várzea forest in lowlands of east. Black band at tip of tail, two-toned bill, velvety black and maroon-chestnut plumage. p. 698

10. CASQUED OROPENDOLA, *Clypicterus oseryi*
Local in lowlands of east, mainly in terra firme. Swollen bill casque; mainly chestnut with yellowish olive foreparts. p. 698

11. CHESTNUT-HEADED OROPENDOLA, *Zarhynchus wagleri*
Local in humid forest and woodland in lowlands of west, where the only oropendola. Prominent swollen frontal shield above proportionately large bill; rich chestnut and black plumage. p. 698

Psarocolius Oropendolas

Impressive large birds characterized by their mainly yellow tails; otherwise coloration varies from black through chestnut to greenish. Bills long, sharply pointed, often brightly colored; as in caciques, irides of adults are often blue. Colonial breeders, with conspicuous pouch nests suspended from isolated trees, usually at forest edge. ♂♂ give loud slashing calls combined with spectacular lunging display.

12. CRESTED OROPENDOLA, *Psarocolius decumanus*
Common and widespread in lowlands of east. Mainly black; bill ivory. p. 699

13. RUSSET-BACKED OROPENDOLA, *Psarocolius angustifrons*
13W *P. a. atrocastaneus*—orange-yellow bill, rufescent plumage
13SE *P. a. alfredi*—like 13W, but duller and more olivaceous
13E *P. a. angustifrons*—black bill, dull plumage
In west only in subtropics, where the only oropendola present. 13E common and conspicuous in lowlands of east, spreading up into adjacent subtropics; in both areas the only oropendola with black bill. 13SE in subtropics (only) from Morona-Santiago southward. p. 699

14. GREEN OROPENDOLA, *Psarocolius viridis*
Local in terra firme forest in lowlands of east. Bill greenish yellow with orange-red tip; plumage mostly greenish yellow. p. 700

15. OLIVE OROPENDOLA, *Psarocolius yuracares*
Uncommon in lowlands of east, mainly in terra firme. The largest oropendola, with unique bare pink cheek patch; bill black with orange-red tip. Plumage chestnut (including wings) and bright yellow-olive. p. 700

Plate 95 Icterids II

Sturnella Blackbirds and Meadowlarks

Gregarious, conspicuous blackbirds of open grassy situations, one on either side of Andes. Wheezy songs, often given in flight, draw attention.

1. RED-BREASTED BLACKBIRD, *Sturnella militaris*

Local in grassy fields in lowlands of east. Slender pointed bill. ♂ unmistakable, with mostly bright red underparts (fresh-plumaged birds more brownish, especially above). ♀ blackish above with prominent buff head striping; mainly buff below, usually tinged red.   p. 706

2. PERUVIAN MEADOWLARK, *Sturnella bellicosa*

Common in pastures and scrub in more arid lowlands of west, spreading into more humid regions and into highlands. Showy ♂ unmistakable with bright red throat and breast, bold whitish superciliary. ♀ much like ♂ but not as black; more "scaly" on belly; usually with strong red tinge on breast.   p. 706

3. BOBOLINK, *Dolichonyx oryzivorus*

Scarce transient to grassy areas in lowlands (especially in east). Sparrow-like, with "spiky" tail. ♀ (nonbreeding ♂ similar) buffy with bold brown head striping. Breeding ♂ (seen infrequently on northward passage) unmistakable: black underparts, obvious buff nape, white rump and scapulars.   p. 707

4. ORIOLE BLACKBIRD, *Gymnomystax mexicanus*

River islands and sandbars in lowlands of east; conspicuous but not common. A large icterid, unmistakable: bright golden yellow head and underparts, black mantle.   p. 706

Icterus Orioles and Troupials

Slender, long-tailed blackbirds with strikingly patterned yellow or orange and black plumages. Favor semiopen areas and borders and have good songs.

5. YELLOW-TAILED ORIOLE, *Icterus mesomelas*

Secondary woodland and clearings in more humid lowlands of west. Yellow lateral tail feathers (often hidden on perched birds); extensive yellow on wing-coverts, reaching narrow whitish edging on secondaries.   p. 705

6. WHITE-EDGED ORIOLE, *Icterus graceannae*

Arid scrub and woodland in drier lowlands of southwest. Tail mainly black with white on outer web of outermost tail feather; obvious white patch on inner secondaries. Often confused with Yellow-tailed, which outnumbers it except in truly arid regions.   p. 705

7. ORANGE-BACKED TROUPIAL, *Icterus croconotus*

Shrubby areas especially near water in lowlands of east. Unmistakable: brilliant orange with black throat, wings, and tail.   p. 704

8. BALTIMORE ORIOLE, *Icterus galbula*

Casual boreal migrant to borders and clearings in lowlands. ♂ has black hood and back, mainly orange underparts. ♀ much duller but with yellowish orange underparts, brightest on breast.   p. 704

9. MORICHE ORIOLE, *Icterus chrysocephalus*

Uncommon in canopy and borders of humid forest in lowlands of east. Mainly black with conspicuous yellow crown and nape.   p. 703

10. PALE-EYED BLACKBIRD, *Agelaius xanthophthalmus*

Very local (perhaps regular only at Limoncocha) in marshy vegetation around oxbow lakes in lowlands of east. All black with yellow iris.   p. 703

11. SCRUB BLACKBIRD, *Dives warszewiczi*

Generally common (especially southward), noisy, and conspicuous in agricultural and settled regions and woodland borders in lowlands of west, southward also in highlands. All glossy black. Very vocal.   p. 702

12. SHINY COWBIRD, *Molothrus bonariensis*

12W   *M. b. aequatorialis*— ♀ dark brown (e. ♀♀ similar)
12SW *M. b. occidentalis*— ♀ much paler and more mottled
Semiopen areas, mainly in lowlands; more common in west. ♂ glossy purplish black. Often in flocks. Parasitizes a variety of smaller birds.   p. 701

13. VELVET-FRONTED GRACKLE, *Lampropsar tanagrinus*

Local and scarce in várzea forest and along lake margins in lowlands of northeast. Slender pointed bill. All black, more blackbird- than grackle-like. Usually in small flocks. p. 703

14. GREAT-TAILED GRACKLE, *Quiscalus mexicanus*

Locally common along coast, especially in mangroves. Bright straw yellow iris (brown in younger birds). ♂ unmistakable, with long creased tail, glossy blue-black plumage. ♀ smaller, basically brown above with buff superciliary and underparts.   p. 702

15. GIANT COWBIRD, *Molothrus oryzivorus*

Forest borders and semiopen areas in lowlands of east and west (in east frequent along rivers), smaller numbers up onto lower Andean slopes. Parasitizes oropendolas and caciques, ♀♀ often hanging around active colonies. Iris usually orange or orange-red in ♂, yellower in ♀. ♂ looks small headed, and ruff usually apparent. ♀ smaller, duller, more sooty.   p. 701

Plate 96 Miscellaneous Additional Species

Included here are species only recently discovered in Ecuador or which for various reasons were omitted from the previous 95 plates. A few, we have to admit, were forgotten!

1. YELLOW-BREASTED CRAKE, *Porzana flaviventer*
Tiny rail, brown and buff with bold flank barring, known only from Bahía de Caráquez marshes in Manabí. Legs yellow. Sexes alike.　　　　　　　　　　p. 123

2. AMAZONIAN ANTSHRIKE, *Thamnophilus amazonicus*
Lower growth of blackwater várzea woodland in lowlands of far northeast. ♂ gray with prominent white wing markings. ♀ with orange-rufous head, neck, and underparts.
　　　　　　　　　　p. 397

3. MARAÑÓN SLATY-ANTSHRIKE, *Thamnophilus leucogaster*
Deciduous woodland in Río Marañón drainage near Zumba. Both sexes resemble Western Slaty-Antshrike (Plate 60-14) but have whiter bellies; calls differ, and they do not occur together.　　　　　　　　　　p. 397

4. BICOLORED ANTVIREO, *Dysithamnus occidentalis*
Rare and local in lower growth of subtropical forest on e. slope and in far northwest. ♂ uniform sooty (including underparts); ♀ has gray underparts with no streaking. Cf. more common White-streaked Antvireo (Plate 60-20).
　　　　　　　　　　p. 400

5. GRISCOM'S ANTWREN, *Myrmotherula ignota*
Humid forest subcanopy and borders in lowlands and foothills of northwest. Resembles Pygmy and Short-billed Antwrens (Plate 61), neither of which occurs west of Andes; see text.　　　　　　　　　　p. 402

6. ASH-WINGED ANTWREN, *Terenura spodioptila*
Terra firme forest canopy in lowlands of northeast (north of Río Aguarico). Like Chestnut-shouldered Antwren (Plate 61-3), but both sexes whiter below, ♂ lacking chestnut shoulders.　　　　　　　　　　p. 414

7. ANCIENT ANTWREN, *Herpsilochmus gentryi*
Terra firme canopy in lowlands of far southeast. Both sexes with yellow underparts; cf. Dugand's Antwren (Plate 61-8), with whitish underparts.　　　　　　　　　　p. 411

8. ASH-BREASTED ANTBIRD, *Myrmoborus lugubris*
Riparian woodland undergrowth on a Río Napo island in lowlands of far northeast. Both sexes with no brow, plain or almost plain wings. ♂ two-toned gray, ♀ with underparts pale gray. See other *Myrmoborus* antbirds on Plate 62.
　　　　　　　　　　p. 417

9. JOCOTOCO ANTPITTA, *Grallaria ridgelyi*
Unmistakable large antpitta recently described from lower temperate forest of s. Zamora-Chinchipe. Black crown, bold white stripe on lower cheeks. Sexes alike.　　　　p. 440

10. TREE SWALLOW, *Tachycineta bicolor*
Casual vagrant to lowlands of w. Esmeraldas. Glossy greenish blue above, pure white below; no white rump or black crissum.　　　　　　　　　　p. 583

11. JOHANNES'S TODY-TYRANT, *Hemitriccus iohannis*
Riparian woodland in lowlands of far southeast. An obscure, dull flycatcher with brownish olive face, blurry foreneck streaking. Sexes alike. Cf. Spotted Tody-Flycatcher (Plate 69-6).　　　　　　　　　　p. 481

12. AMAZONIAN BLACK-TYRANT, *Knipolegus poecilocercus*
Undergrowth of blackwater várzea woodland in lowlands of far northeast. ♂ all glossy black with blue bill. ♀ dull and brown, blurry olive brown streaking below, some rufous in tail, vague buff wing-bars.　　　　　　　p. 515

13. RIVERSIDE TYRANT, *Knipolegus orenocensis*
Local in scrub on Río Napo islands in lowlands of northeast. ♂ uniform dull black. ♀ dull and olive grayish, blurry olive grayish streaking below, plain wings, no rufous in tail.
　　　　　　　　　　p. 515

14. SHARPBILL, *Oxyruncus cristatus*
Canopy of foothill forest on slopes of remote Cordillera del Cóndor in far southeast. Sharply pointed bill; conspicuous black scaling and spotting below. Sexes alike.　　　p. 541

15. BLACK-THROATED GREEN WARBLER, *Dendroica virens*
Accidental vagrant to subtropical forest borders in northwest. Extensive yellow on sides of head, black throat (mottled in juveniles), plain olive back.　　　p. 604

16. CONNECTICUT WARBLER, *Oporornis agilis*
Accidental vagrant to lowlands of w. Esmeraldas. Conspicuous, complete white to buffy whitish eye-ring in all plumages; see text. Cf. similar Mourning Warbler (Plate 83-12).
　　　　　　　　　　p. 607

17. GREEN-TAILED GOLDENTHROAT, *Polytmus theresiae*
Very rare in lowlands of far southeast; no recent records. Decurved bill with red at base; both sexes bright green below.
　　　　　　　　　　p. 261

18. BUFF-BELLIED TANAGER, *Thlypopsis inornata*
Secondary woodland and borders in Río Marañón drainage near Zumba. ♂ buff and gray, deeper rufous on crown; ♀ duller but still buff below.　　　　　　　p. 625

19. STRAW-BACKED TANAGER, *Tangara argyrofenges*
Canopy and borders of subtropical forest in remote far southeast. Both sexes resemble Silver-backed Tanager (Plate 87-17) but have throat green (not coppery). Unmistakable ♂ has bright opalescent "straw" mantle, black wings. Duller ♀ has some yellow on back and sides.　　　　p. 637

20. ORANGE-THROATED TANAGER, *Wetmorethraupis sterrhopteron*
Canopy and borders of foothill forest on slopes of remote Cordillera del Cóndor in far southeast. Unmistakable, with unique orange throat and chest. Sexes alike.　　　p. 647

21. OLIVE TANAGER, *Chlorothraupis frenata*
Very local in lower growth of foothill forest on e. slope (mainly Sucumbíos). A heavy-set, mainly dark olive tanager with stout black bill. ♀ shows more yellow on foreface.
　　　　　　　　　　p. 654

22. PLUSHCAP, *Catamblyrhynchus diadema*
Undergrowth of subtropical and temperate forest on both slopes, especially in bamboo. Thick stubby bill; bright golden yellow forecrown; rich chestnut underparts. Sexes alike.
　　　　　　　　　　p. 666

23. BLUE GROSBEAK, *Guiraca caerulea*
Accidental vagrant to clearings in lowlands of northeast. Heavy bill. ♂ deep blue with 2 prominent rufous wing-bars. ♀ rufescent brown, same wing-bars as ♂.　　p. 671

24. RED PILEATED-FINCH, *Coryphospingus cucullatus*
Shrubby second-growth in Río Marañón drainage near Zumba. Both sexes essentially reddish, with narrow white eye-ring; ♂ brighter with scarlet coronal stripe often apparent.　　　　　　　　　　p. 685

25. CINEREOUS FINCH, *Piezorhina cinerea*
Casual wanderer to open arid terrain in lowlands of s. Loja. Very heavy bill bright yellow; pale gray plumage. Sexes alike.
　　　　　　　　　　p. 683

26. DICKCISSEL, *Spiza americana*
Accidental vagrant to grassy clearings in lowlands of northeast. Sparrow-like, with irregular yellow area on breast, rufous in shoulders. Breeding ♂ brighter with V-shaped black bib on chest.　　　　　　　　　　p. 672

Slaty-backed Forest-Falcon
Micrastur mirandollei
Halcón Montés Dorsigris   Plate 15(9)

To 400 m

Collared Forest-Falcon
Micrastur semitorquatus
Halcón Montés Collarejo   Plate 15(10)

To 2000 m

40.5–45 cm (16–17¾"). *Rare* inside humid forest (primarily terra firme) in *lowlands of east*. Iris hazel to brown; *cere, lores, and orbital ring bright yellow;* legs orange-yellow. **Adult** *dark slaty gray above and on sides of neck*; somewhat graduated tail blackish with three narrow whitish bars. *Below grayish white to creamy buff*, some individuals with very fine dark shaft streaks. **Immature** like adult but underparts whitish *with coarse brownish scalloping*. **Similar species:** Potentially confusing, in part because it is such a relatively unfamiliar bird. Adult resembles adult of shorter-legged and equally rare Gray-bellied Hawk though latter has a more "capped" look, less extensive yellow on facial area, and is grayer below. Immature Barred Forest-Falcons can have sparse coarse barring below somewhat like markings of immature Slaty-backeds; however, the larger Slaty-backed is never as brown above. Cf. also immature Bicolored Hawk. **Habits:** A deep forest bird, rarely encountered in Ecuador, with overall behavior similar to that of other forest-falcons, though Slaty-backed apparently feeds more on birds than do the previous three species. **Voice:** Far-carrying call a series of nasal notes, at first soft, then gradually rising and becoming louder, "aaah, ooow, ooow, ooow, ooow, ooow, ooów, ooów, ooów" (about one note/second), vaguely reminiscent of Laughing Falcon. Also gives a rising series of shorter and more rapidly delivered notes, e.g., "koh-koh-koh-koh-oh-oh-oh-oh oow ooów ooów," the last 3 notes notes longer and lower pitched (P. Coopmans).

51–58.5 cm (20–23"). A *large, lanky* forest-falcon with *exceptionally long and graduated tail*, scarce but widespread inside humid lowland and subtropical forest, woodland, and borders in both east and west. Iris brown; cere, base of bill, lores, and orbital ring olive; legs yellow. **Adult** blackish above, black of crown *continuing down across cheeks as a crescent*; tail blackish with 3–4 narrow whitish bands and white tip. *White to buff (a few even tawny) below*, this color *extending up onto sides of neck and forming nuchal collar*. Rare **dark morph** *uniform sooty black to blackish brown*, some birds with breast and belly spotting and barring. **Immature** like adult above though somewhat browner above, some birds with buff spotting or barring; nuchal collar may be less distinct but is almost always present. Below varies from whitish to deep buff, *coarsely barred or chevroned with dark brown*. **Similar species:** Facial crescent and nuchal collar are conspicuous in all plumages and—regardless of an individual's overall coloration—should identify this species, together with its large size and "elongated" shape. In e. lowlands, however, cf. smaller (and rarer) Buckley's Forest-Falcon. **Habits:** Bold and rapacious, at times almost fearless but typically furtive to the point of being invisible, remaining in dense leafy or viny cover. Feeds primarily on birds. **Voice:** Vocalizes mainly around dawn and dusk; even calling birds usually remain hidden, only rarely perching in open. Most frequent call a series of hollow and resonant "oow" notes repeated steadily every 2–3 seconds, sometimes continuing for long periods. Also gives a rising series of 8–11 "ko" notes that ends with 2 lower-pitched "oow" notes (P. Coopmans), and occasionally gives a faster series with more laughing quality.

Buckley's Forest-Falcon, *Micrastur buckleyi*
Halcón Montés de Buckley   Plate 15(11)

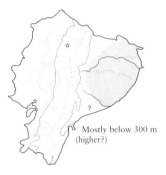

Mostly below 300 m (higher?)

41–46 cm (16–18"). *Rare* and little known inside humid forest and borders in *lowlands of east*. A *small* and proportionately shorter-tailed and shorter-legged version of Collared Forest-Falcon, thus overall proportions look rather more "normal"; often best identified by *voice*. Closely resembles that species, aside from size; outer rectrix has only four white bars (vs. six in Collared, but this is difficult to see with certainty in field—bird must be preening). ♀♀ also differ in having *white spots on scapulars and inner secondaries* (lacking in all Collareds). Birds with buff underparts are infrequent but have been seen (P. Coopmans). **Habits:** Not well known, but apparently similar to other forest-falcons, and equally furtive. Buckley's appears to favor várzea and riparian habitats. **Voice:** Far-carrying call a distinctive phrase, "kawa-káw" or sometimes "kawa-káw . . . kow," repeated at slow intervals (often 5 or more seconds). Also gives a series of 15–16 nasal "anh" calls, increasing in pitch and volume in middle and then trailing off, recalling Slaty-backed but notes shorter and with faster delivery, and a series of about 25 "ko" notes ending with two more drawn-out and nasal notes (P. Coopmans).

Laughing Falcon, *Herpetotheres cachinnans*
Halcón Reidor   Plate 17(1)

46–51 cm (18–20"). A *distinctive* "puffy-headed" raptor, conspicuous in canopy and

Mostly below 800 m

borders of humid and deciduous forest in lowlands of east and west, also ranging out into trees in adjacent clearings. Iris brown; cere yellow, orbital skin grayish horn; legs dull yellow. *Head and underparts cinnamon-buff to pale buff* (paler in **eastern birds**) with *highly contrasting broad black mask extending from lores to around nape*, some blackish streaking on crown. Upperparts dark brown. Rather long tail blackish with 3–4 buff bands, underside buff with 4–5 blackish bands. **In flight** blackish wings show a prominent buff patch at base of primaries. **Similar species:** Much slighter Yellow-headed Caracara has similar overall buff coloration but has no broad mask, only a thin eye-stripe. **Habits:** Usually seen singly, perched upright on a prominent perch where it may remain motionless for long periods; there it quietly surveys its surroundings, watching for its primary prey, snakes. Flies with fast, stiff, shallow wingbeats (almost recalling an *Amazona* parrot), and never soars. **Voice:** Well known from its distinctive, loud, "laughing" vocalizations, given mainly around dawn and dusk but also at other times (even at night). Most frequent is a "guá-co, guá-co, guá-co . . ." or simply "guá, guá, guá . . . ," either sometimes repeated for as long as several minutes. At times calls are less measured, and bird may even break into what can only be described as maniacal laughter. On occasion members of a pair will vocalize together, calling in syncopation.

Falco Falcons
The "true" falcons vary markedly in size, some being small (e.g., American Kestrel), others (Peregrine and Orange-breasted) notably large and powerful. Females are much larger than males but are usually

similar in plumage. *Wings are long and pointed*, tails fairly long, and legs quite short. They occur mainly in semiopen habitats in Ecuador.

American Kestrel, *Falco sparverius*
Cernícalo Americano   Plate 17(7)

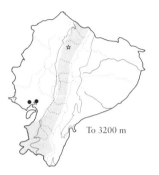

To 3200 m

25.5–29 cm (10–11″). An attractive *small* falcon that is fairly common and conspicuous in open and semiopen agricultural terrain and around towns in more arid *highlands*, in the southwest (mainly El Oro and Loja) also ranging in lowlands. Iris brown; cere, orbital ring, and legs yellow to orange-yellow. ♂ *mainly rufous above*, with *blue-gray crown* and *white face* crossed by *black moustache and stripe on ear-coverts*; *wing-coverts contrastingly blue-gray*; *fairly long tail rufous with black subterminal band and narrow white tip. Below cinnamon-buff*, deepest on breast, whitest on throat; belly with scattered black spots. **Northern birds** are more richly colored below with less black spotting. **In flight** wings pointed, rather long and narrow, underside whitish, flight feathers with dusky barring. ♀ differs in having *entire upperparts, including wing-coverts, rufous narrowly barred blackish*; below whitish, breast and flanks with rufous-brown streaking; tail rufous with numerous black bars. **Similar species:** Merlin more compactly built with shorter tail; it is never rufous above. Similarly shaped and sized Pearl Kite also often perches on wires, but its upperparts and shorter tail are solid gray (with no barring). Flying Pearl Kites are very pale below; that species rarely flies high overhead and *never hovers*. **Habits:** A familiar raptor, often living in close proximity to people and in agricultural areas, sometimes even in towns. Often seen perched

along roads, frequently on wires and fences. Hovers frequently on rapidly beating wings, then plunges to ground in pursuit of insects, less often small mammals or lizards. **Voice:** Breeding birds give a shrill "kiilly-killy-killy . . ." or "kree-kree-kree. . . ."

Merlin, *Falco columbarius*
Esmerejón   Plate 17(6)

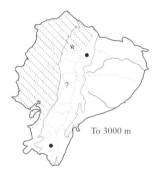

To 3000 m

26.5–31.5 cm (10½–12½″). A *scarce boreal migrant* to semiopen terrain in lowlands of west and highlands, most numerous along coast and near water; recorded mostly late Oct.–early Mar. Small but stocky and *compact*. Iris dark brown; cere, orbital ring, and legs yellow. **Adult ♂** *mostly dark slaty blue-gray above*, superciliary (especially) and face whitish, streaked dusky, and with short narrow blackish moustache; tail black with three pale gray bars and white tip, underside blackish with three narrow white bars. *Below whitish with dusky streaking, often coarse.* **In flight** wings pointed, underside appearing dark with white spots and bars. **Adult ♀** and **immature** similar but *upperparts dark brown to grayish brown*, streaking below usually heavier. **Similar species:** American Kestrel more lightly built with longer wings and tail; ♀ kestrel *barred* above. Peregrine Falcon similarly plumaged but much larger with broader wings, proportionately shorter tail and much wider moustache (Merlin's is often quite inconspicuous). **Habits:** A dashing falcon that flies rapidly with fast powerful wingstrokes. Hunts primarily birds, dashing close to ground, relying on surprise and speed for a successful outcome. Usually perches close to ground.

Aplomado Falcon, *Falco femoralis*
Halcón Aplomado   Plate 17(3)

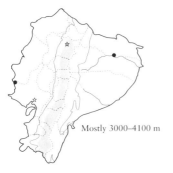

Mostly 3000–4100 m

Mostly below 1000 m

37–43 cm (14½–17″). A beautiful, strongly marked falcon, *scarce and local in paramo and more open arid areas of highlands.* Rather slender with proportionately long wings and tail. Iris dark brown; cere, orbital ring, and legs yellow. **Adult** bluish gray above with *prominent buff superciliary* encircling gray crown, blackish postocular stripe, and black moustache; tail blackish with 5–6 narrow grayish bars and narrow white tip. Throat white, *chest and sides of neck buff; sides and narrow band across breast blackish narrowly barred white; lower underparts rufous.* **In flight** wings pointed, underside appears dark with white bars and spots, *narrow white trailing edge* often apparent. **Immature** similar but browner above, chest more streaked, lower underparts paler. **Similar species:** Most apt to be confused with the larger and more heavily built Peregrine Falcon, though that lacks extensive rufous in plumage, has broader wings and shorter tail. Neither Bat nor Orange-breasted Falcon shows Aplomado's obvious buff brow, and neither occurs in high open terrain. **Habits:** Usually seen singly, perching in the open, often on a rock or promontory, sometimes even on ground. Hunts a wide variety of prey, capturing birds in fast level flight, also hawking many insects. Soars regularly. **Voice:** Occasionally gives a loud repeated scream (mostly when nesting?), but usually silent.

Bat Falcon, *Falco rufigularis*
Halcón Cazamurciélagos   Plate 17(5)

24–28 cm (9½–11″). *Widespread* at borders of humid and deciduous forest and wood-land, also in trees isolated in nearby cleared areas, in *lowlands and foothills of east and west;* tends to avoid arid regions. Iris dark brown; cere, orbital ring, and legs yellow. *Head and entire upperparts black to dark slaty gray,* blackest on head. *Throat, sides of neck, and chest whitish to buff or even orange-rufous;* in **east**, this area tends to be uniform buffy whitish, whereas in **west** birds tend to have throat whitish with sides of neck and chest buff to bright buffy orange. *Broad "vest" across breast and down flanks black with narrow white to pale cinnamon barring;* lower belly and crissum deep rufous. **In flight** wings pointed and rather narrow, underwing blackish with white flecking and barring. **Similar species:** For distinctions from similar but larger (and much rarer) Orange-breasted Falcon, see under that species. Otherwise the handsome and highly colored Bat Falcon is unlikely to be confused, though high-flying individuals can be mistaken for White-collared Swift (with which they occasionally mingle). **Habits:** Most often seen in pairs that may perch for protracted periods on a favored high dead snag, where they are some-times quite unwary. Flight very fast and dashing. Prey—mainly birds, large insects, and bats—is captured almost entirely on the wing; often seen flying at dusk in pursuit of bats. **Voice:** Both sexes, but especially ♂ ♂, give a loud shrill "kee-kee-kee-kee . . ." or "kiy-kiy-kiy-kiy. . . ."

Orange-breasted Falcon, *Falco deiroleucus*
Halcón Pechinaranja   Plate 17(4)

35.5–41.4 cm (14–16″). *Rare* at borders of humid lowland and subtropical forest, *mainly in foothills and lower subtropics*

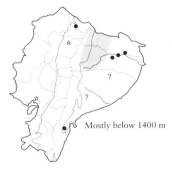

Mostly below 1400 m

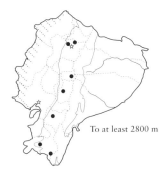

To at least 2800 m

but also occasionally ranging higher or out into adjacent lowlands; *only in east.* A spectacular *large* and *heavy-bodied* version of much more numerous Bat Falcon, the *very similar Orange-breasted must always be identified with care.* Iris dark brown; cere, orbital area, and legs greenish yellow to olive; *bill heavier and talons much larger and more powerful than in Bat Falcon.* Plumage as in Bat Falcon, with the following more notable differences: blacker upperparts, feathers edged bluish gray; *throat pure white in contrast to orange-rufous chest and sides of neck*, sometimes with a few black streaks on chest; and black "vest" across breast with *coarser and more prominent buff or whitish barring.* Similar species: Cf. also Peregrine Falcon, which is larger but has similar build; color pattern rather different. Habits: Always infrequently encountered. Pairs apparently hold very large territories to which—if undisturbed—they remain faithful for many years. Perches on cliffs and dead snags, usually nesting on former. Feeds mainly on a variety of small to midsized birds, pursuing them in swift and powerful flight; unlike Peregrine, however, the Orange-breasted usually does not stoop down on prey. Voice: Infrequently heard call a loud, penetrating "kyah-kyah-kyah-kyah . . . ," often continued 5–10 seconds, lower pitched and less shrill than Bat Falcon's. Most vocal around nest sites.

Peregrine Falcon, *Falco peregrinus*
Halcón Peregrino   Plate 17(2)

38–48 cm (15–19"). A *large* and *heavily built* falcon with long and broad-based wings. Boreal migrants range widely in open country, principally near water and along coast; also nests very locally in highlands (only one breeding pair is known, but there may be more). Iris dark brown; cere, orbital ring, and legs yellow (in juveniles paler, sometimes even grayish). **Boreal migrant adult** *dark bluish gray above*, paler on rump and blacker on head; *wide black moustache* contrasts with *white ear-coverts and sides of neck*; tail blackish with 4–6 gray bars and white tip, underside with whitish bars. Below white, sometimes tinged pinkish buff, *breast and belly barred with black.* **Resident adult** similar but darker above and blacker on sides of head including ear-coverts; underparts more tinged with buff. **In flight** shows *long and broad-based pointed wings*, underside with extensive blackish barring. **Immature** similar but *dark to grayish brown above* with head paler and more extensively buff, forehead and superciliary often whitish. Below whitish to creamy buff with *dark streaking and spotting.* Similar species: So much larger than other falcons (aside from Orange-breasted, which see) that confusion is unlikely; ♀♀ and juvenile Merlins are similarly plumaged. Cf. also Aplomado Falcon. Habits: A magnificent large falcon that perches on prominent vantage points, launching out periodically to hunt; most numerous along coast, often where there are concentrations of shorebirds. Feeds primarily on larger birds, capturing them in flight, often after a spectacular stoop; also overtakes prey in level, direct pursuits. Also eats bats as these emerge from roosts at dusk. Pairs of the tiny resident population nest on highland cliffs. Voice: Usually quiet away from nesting sites, where it gives various cackles and screams.

Galliformes
Curassows, Guans, and Chachalacas:
Cracidae (14)

Superficially pheasant-like birds with small heads and slender necks found exclusively in the Neotropics. Although cracids are handsome and have an elegant carriage, their plumages tend to be sombre, with only their featherless parts (bill, cere, dewlap, and legs) brightly colored. They are primarily forest birds, and most species are arboreal; curassows, however, are partly terrestrial. Cracids feed mainly on fruit, curassows especially on fruits that have fallen to the ground. Highly esteemed gamebirds, many species have declined markedly, primarily because of hunting. A low reproductive rate—clutches are small—results in their being less able to withstand even modest hunting pressure than their ecological counterparts (such as pheasants and grouse) elsewhere. Cracids have a long looped trachea that enables them to produce deep, resonant calls; some species also give mechanical wing rattles during a flight display. They build simple open cup nests, usually hidden in low vegetation; their eggs have a rough, often pitted, surface.

Ortalis Chachalacas

Small and plain cracids with only a small bare red patch on the throat, one species on either side of the Andes. Chachalacas inhabit the borders of humid lowland forest and woodland and are best known from their raucous far-carrying calls given as a gabbling chorus mainly soon after dawn. **Sexes are alike.**

Speckled Chachalaca, *Ortalis guttata*
Chachalaca Jaspeada   Plate 18(6)

Mostly below 1100 m

49.5–52 cm (19½–20½″). Fairly common in forest borders, secondary woodland, and riparian areas in *lowlands of east*; generally not found in terra firme, and most numerous near water. Bill dusky blue; bare throat patch reddish; legs coral pink. Brown above, somewhat darker on head and neck. Tail bronzy brown, *outer feathers rufous-chestnut. Foreneck and throat dark brown conspicuously spotted with white*; underparts pale grayish brown, crissum rufescent. **Similar species:** Not likely confused as it is so much smaller than other cracids found in e. lowlands. **Habits:** An arboreal bird that occurs in groups of up to 4–6 (rarely more), usually remaining inside thick leafy cover (especially in forest borders), though regularly perching in the open in early morning. Rarely drops to ground and does not ascend high in trees. Where not much persecuted can become quite tame, and often persists in inhabited areas (though there quite shy). **Voice:** Very vocal. This species' loud raucous chorus is frequently heard (especially soon after dawn) and is often given by several birds at once with a rhythmic effect; individual birds give various phrases, among them the classic "cha-cha-la-cak" but with numerous variants. An ascending, squealing call is given in alarm; also gives various peeping notes.

Rufous-headed Chachalaca
Ortalis erythroptera
Chachalaca Cabecirrufa   Plate 18(7)

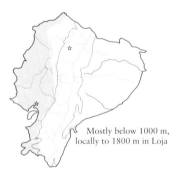

Mostly below 1000 m, locally to 1800 m in Loja

56–61 cm (22–24″). Now local in semihumid and deciduous forest borders and secondary woodland in *lowlands and lower subtropics of west*. Bill gray, slatier toward base and tip paler; bare throat patch dull red; legs slaty gray. *Head and neck rufous*; otherwise mostly olive brown above. *Flight feathers mostly rufous*; tail bronzy, *outer feathers rufous-chestnut*. Breast grayish brown; lower underparts whitish, buffier on lower flanks and crissum. **Similar species:** The only chachalaca in its range, and as such this striking species should be easily recognized. Cf. various *Penelope* guans, especially the relatively small Baudó Guan, and the comparatively small western race of Sickle-winged Guan. **Habits:** Usually found in small groups of up to 4–6 birds, ranging in trees at various heights above ground though usually not too high. In many areas now very shy and elusive (and even quiet?), but as a result can persist in some heavily settled and even almost entirely deforested areas; most numerous in more remote and better-forested districts. In the few sites where not excessively persecuted, can become relatively tame. **Voice:** This species' loud cacaphonous calling is given at varying times during day (not necessarily around dawn) and occasionally even at night; often the calling from members of one group elicits a response from another, and we have heard as many as four groups countersinging at one site. Common phrases include a low "cha-cha-kaw" and a shriller "kra-kra-ka." In alarm, groups also have more querulous, guan-like honking and yelping calls.

Penelope Guans

Midsized to quite large cracids of lowland or montane forests, the smaller species about the same size as chachalacas, the larger ones almost as big as curassows. *Penelope* guans have a sometimes large *bare red dewlap* on the throat and *relatively plain dark plumage with some white streaking*. **Sexes are alike.** These guans give a characteristic wing-whirr display during the breeding season, when they glide between two trees and produce a mechanical sound through modification of their outer primaries. Most or all guans in other genera also do this.

Bearded Guan, *Penelope barbata*
Pava Barbada   Plate 18(5)

56–61 cm (22–24″). Now scarce and local in *subtropical and temperate forest and woodland in south (El Oro southward)*. Bare skin around eye bluish gray; bare dewlap and legs coral red. Above bronzy brown, head and

Mostly 1900–2700 m

neck more blackish with *distinct silvery whitish streaking above and behind eye and on sides of head*; tail bronzy *with rufous tip* (sometimes vague, but usually quite apparent, especially in flight). Upper throat blackish; breast dusky brown with *distinct silvery whitish streaking*; lower underparts brown, darkening on crissum. **Similar species:** Easily confused with Andean Guan, though in general these two small montane guans replace each other geographically, Bearded occurring southward. Throat patterns of the two are similar; note Andean's uniform dark tail (with no paler tip, though beware certain Beardeds on which this can be obscure), dark crown (with no silvery streaking on brow, usually prominent in Bearded), and more chevroned pattern on breast (Bearded is clearly streaked). **Habits:** Usually encountered singly or in pairs, foraging at varying levels in trees, sometimes even briefly dropping to ground. Where not much persecuted, can be quite tame. **Voice:** Various whistling and honking calls are given, often in a fast series and higher pitched than in most other *Penelope*, especially when birds are disturbed. Wing-whirr display given mainly around dawn.

Andean Guan, *Penelope montagnii*
Pava Andina   Plate 18(4)

53.5–58.5 cm (21–23″). Locally fairly common (though scarce in more settled areas) in *temperate forest and woodland on both slopes south to Azuay and sw. Morona-Santiago*. Bare skin around eye bluish gray; small bare dewlap and legs coral pink. Above bronzy brown, more rufescent on rump and uppertail-coverts; *tail uniform bronzy blackish. Sides of head and neck with silvery*

Mostly 2500–3600 m

whitish chevrons. Upper throat blackish; breast dusky brown with narrow but distinct silvery whitish chevrons; lower underparts brown, more rufescent on crissum. **Similar species:** Cf. Bearded Guan, which replaces Andean in s. Ecuador. Other montane Ecuadorian guans (Wattled, Sickle-winged) are more uniform, showing no whitish patterning. **Habits:** Usually found singly or in pairs, less often in small (likely family) groups, foraging at all levels though most often at edge and generally not too high above ground. Can be astonishingly tame where not persecuted. **Voice:** Disturbed birds give a variety of soft "dok" or "kit" notes, sometimes repeated for long periods; when flushed may fly off with loud honking on squealing calls. Wing-whirr display given before and at dawn, usually when still too dark to see clearly; it is usually two-parted.

Baudó Guan, *Penelope ortoni*
Pava del Chocó   Plate 18(2)

56–61 cm (22–24"). A *rare and (now) local guan of humid and foothill forest in west*. Iris red, bare skin around eye slaty; large bare dewlap red; legs coral red. Above dark

? To 1000 m

bronzy brown, darkest on head and neck. Below brown, darkest on foreneck, with *prominent white streaking on breast and belly*. **Similar species:** Often confused with Crested Guan (locally sympatric) though that is much larger; the two species have much the same overall coloration and pattern, but Crested's rump and lower belly are more rufescent (sometimes markedly so, but this often hard to see in field). In the field Baudó Guan tends to behave differently, approached birds crouching in midstory and uttering low calls, not fleeing quickly with loud honking calls like Crested Guan (fide O. Jahn). **Habits:** Not well known, but in overall behavior differs little from congeners, though thought to be very tame, this perhaps accounting for its disappearance under even very light hunting pressure (O. Jahn). Not known to be numerous anywhere. **Voice:** What is probably an alarm call is a soft and rather prolonged rising whistle lasting about 3 seconds (O. Jahn recording).

Spix's Guan, *Penelope jacquacu*
Pava de Spix   Plate 18(3)

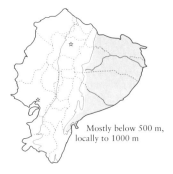

Mostly below 500 m, locally to 1000 m

76–84 cm (30–33"). A *large* guan found in *humid forest (both várzea and terra firme) in lowlands of east*. Iris reddish, bare skin around eye bluish slate; *large bare dewlap orange-red*; legs coral red. Above dark brown, darker on head and neck, with sparse white streaking on back; rump more rufescent and tail decidedly bronzy. Breast dark brown *prominently streaked white*; *belly and crissum rufous brown*. **Similar species:** *The only Penelope guan in the e. lowlands.* Much larger than Common Piping-Guan, with which it regularly occurs; piping-guan has obvious white on face and wings, blue (not red) dewlap, etc. **Habits:** Usually occurs singly or in pairs, most often fairly close to ground. For much of day often lingers in heavy viny cover inside forest; early and late more apt to perch in open. **Voice:** Commonest call a loud deep honking (a repeated "honh"), sometimes with a more querulous tone ("kwee-onh"), often given just prior to bird's launching off its perch with clumsy heavy wingbeats. Also has a weird and amazingly loud squealing yelp, "oworrrrr-onnh-ááánh!" or "ohhhh-wánhhh-rúhh." Wing-whirr display given mainly at night, especially just before dusk.

Crested Guan, *Penelope purpurascens*
Pava Crestada   Plate 18(1)

To 1500 m

84–91.5 cm (33–36"). A *large* guan, now *rare and local in foothill and lower subtropical forest in west*. Iris red, bare skin around eye bluish slate; large bare dewlap red; legs coral red. Somewhat more crested than other *Penelope* guans. Above dark olive brown with slight gloss, darker on head and neck; *rump chestnut* and tail decidedly bronzy. Breast dark brown with prominent white streaking; *belly and crissum chestnut*. **Similar species:** Considerably larger than the Baudó Guan, with which Crested is sometimes found; the two species are similar in overall coloration and pattern, though chestnut on Crested's rump and lower underparts is distinctive if this can be made out (this area is simply dull dark brown in Baudó). **Habits:** Usually found singly or in pairs, less often in small family groups; ranges at all heights in trees, sometimes very high but not often dropping to ground. Now usually very shy, this a result of heavy hunting pressure where this declining bird yet survives. **Voice:** Sometimes

quite noisy, giving a variety of far-carrying yelping or honking calls, sometimes startlingly loud, e.g., a low guttural "kwee-ohh," a very piercing "whulééur," and a "konh-konh-konh-konh . . ." often repeated for 30 or more seconds before it flushes with heavy ponderous wingbeats. The wing-whirr display seems infrequent and is given especially at night.

Common Piping-Guan, *Pipile pipile*
Pava Silbosa Común   Plate 18(8)

Mostly below 400 m

68.5–73.5 cm (27–29"). An attractive arboreal guan found in *terra firme and várzea forest (including borders) in lowlands of east*. In settled areas scarce or even extirpated, but fairly common in more remote districts. Ecuador birds belong to a population that has sometimes been separated as a distinct species, Blue-throated Piping-Guan (*P. cumanensis*). Bill pale bluish with black tip; iris reddish brown, bare skin around eye white; bare throat on chin pale blue, becoming *dusky purplish or bluish on large dewlap*; legs coral red. **Sexes alike.** *Mainly black with contrasting shaggy white crest and nape* and *large white patch on wing-coverts (conspicuous even on perched birds)*. Emarginated outer primaries hard to see. **Similar species:** Not likely confused. Spix's Guan larger and shows no white on crown or wings; smaller Speckled Chachalaca likewise shows no white; Nocturnal Curassow is mainly rufescent. **Habits:** Regularly seen in small groups, often perching in open especially in early morning. Quite tame where not overly persecuted. Very graceful and agile, running and hopping about from branch to branch with great agility, bursting into flight with a few strong wingbeats, then gliding in a gradual descent. **Voice:** The "piping" for which this species is named is heard quite often: it consists of a series of 6–8 clear piercing whistled notes that gradually rise in pitch (with quality and cadence of Scale-backed Antbird, though much louder). Piping-guans also wing-whirr frequently and seem to engage in this display more often during daylight hours than *Penelope* guans; the sound is distinctly two-parted, and often is preceded by sharp wing-claps as bird launches from its perch. Various soft peeping notes are also given.

Wattled Guan, *Aburria aburri*
Pava Carunculada   Plate 18(9)

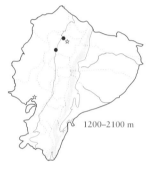

1200–2100 m

73.5–81.5 cm (29–32"). A scarce and secretive *large* guan of *subtropical forest, mainly on e. slope* but also now known from *Mindo area. Bill powder blue with black tip; long thin dangling dewlap bright yellow; legs yellow.* **Sexes alike.** *Entirely black* with strong bluish green gloss. Emarginated outer primaries hard to see. **Similar species:** Liable to be confused only with Sickle-winged Guan, with which Wattled is locally sympatric; w.-slope Sickle-wingeds are, however, so much smaller (chachalaca-sized) that confusion unlikely. On e. slope the two species are more similar in size (though Wattled is still substantially bigger), Sickle-winged differing in its mainly rufous underparts. Both species can look comparably dark, especially in dim light. **Habits:** Not often encountered in Ecuador. Usually found in pairs, difficult to see as they slip gracefully and quietly through foliage of heavily vegetated trees; unlike Sickle-wingeds, Wattleds hardly ever perch in the open along roads. Easiest to see at dawn when vocalizing. **Voice:** Breeding birds regularly give a loud but brief vocal-

ization, hard to transcribe but with a reedy quality, "bree-ee-ee-ee-ah"; this sometimes is delivered at intervals (sometimes long) steadily through night, especially when calm and clear. It slightly resembles Swallow-tailed Nightjar's song.

Sickle-winged Guan, *Chamaepetes goudotii*
Pava Ala de Hoz   Plate 18(10)

900–2600 m

Western birds 51–54.5 cm (20–21½"); eastern birds 61–63.5 cm (24–25"). Relatively widespread, numerous, and conspicuous in *subtropical and lower temperate forest and forest borders on both slopes.* Bill black; iris red with *extensive bare loral and orbital area cobalt blue;* legs coral red. **Sexes alike.** **West-slope birds** above mostly slaty blackish with slight green gloss, head and neck grayer. *Throat and chest brownish gray; lower underparts rufous-chestnut.* Highly modified "sickle-shaped" outer primaries hard to see in field. **East-slope birds** *considerably larger and proportionately longer-tailed; underparts mostly rufous-chestnut* (extending up over chest) with only throat brownish gray. **Similar species:** Extensive bare blue area on face of this montane guan is unique in Ecuador. *Penelope* guans all have red dewlaps and show at least some white streaking. Wattled Guan larger, all black (no rufous below), and has skinny pendulous dewlap. **Habits:** Typically found singly or in pairs, often perching low at forest edge. Though elsewhere described as wary, in Ecuador can be quite tame (especially smaller w.-slope birds). Basically arboreal, though elsewhere reported to drop to ground. **Voice:** Quiet on the whole, apparently with no loud vocal calls. Brief wing-whirring displays are frequent during breeding season, but are given mainly during predawn darkness so are hard to observe.

Nocturnal Curassow, *Nothocrax urumutum*
Pavón Nocturno   Plate 18(11)

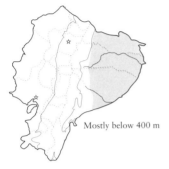

Mostly below 400 m

66–71 cm (26–28″). A *small, rufescent* curassow *found in terra firme forest in lowlands of east*; by voice evidently not rare, but mainly nocturnal and extremely difficult to see without a great deal of effort (or luck!). *Bill reddish orange; bare skin in front of eye blue, above it greenish yellow, and below it slaty*; legs dull orangey brown. **Sexes alike.** *Head and neck rufous-chestnut* with *expressive crest of long and somewhat recurved black feathers*; above otherwise brown with dense blackish vermiculations, tail narrowly tipped buff. Breast and belly rufous-buff. **Similar species:** So much smaller than the true curassows that confusion with them is unlikely. No guan is so rufescent; Speckled Chachalaca (found in different habitat) is smaller, spotted on breast, lacks crest, etc. **Habits:** Known almost entirely from its far-carrying, booming song, delivered at night from forest canopy. Birds reportedly roost by day in holes in ground (if they routinely remained above ground, surely they would be encountered more often than is the case), or perhaps inside a hollow log. They apparently emerge to feed at twilight when—very rarely (and with great good fortune)—they can be encountered, perhaps feeding on fallen fruit. **Voice:** ♂'s song, delivered only in full dark, a deep series of booming hooting notes, far-carrying and all-too ventriloquial, "oo-oo-oó, oo-oo-oóh?"; after a pause of several seconds, phrase is often followed by a sharply accented and somewhat higher-pitched "unh!" Sings at a rate of about one

call/minute, the calling bird usually perched high in a forest tree, occasionally lower.

Salvin's Curassow, *Mitu salvini*
Pavón de Salvin   Plate 18(14)

Mostly below 400 m

84–89 cm (33–35″). *Generally rare* (more numerous in remote regions) *in terra firme and várzea forest in lowlands of east*. Has sometimes been placed in genus *Crax. Bill orange-red with upper mandible compressed*; legs coral red. **Sexes alike.** Mainly black, glossed with blue on crest, back, upperside of tail, and breast; *lower belly and tail-tip contrastingly white*. Expressive crest feathers most often held flat, but sometimes ruffled upward. **Similar species:** Other than the very different Nocturnal, *Salvin's is the only curassow left in e. lowland forests*. On the optimistic assumption that the Wattled Curassow still occurs in Ecuador, both sexes can easily be separated from Salvin's by absence of white on tail-tip. **Habits:** Usually occurs in pairs that feed mainly on ground but often are found resting or roosting low in trees, rarely very high up and often in dense shrubby viny growth near water. Most active in early morning when pairs sometimes walk into the open, though never far from cover, or nervously descend to a secluded riverbank to drink. **Voice:** ♂'s song a deep low booming that seems to be given primarily at night, "oo-oooonh, wooónh-unh . . . oooúp-óó-óóóú!" Both sexes give various short high-pitched squealing calls when nervous or alarmed.

Crax Curassows
Large and heavily built cracids, both Ecuadorian *Crax* are now sadly rare as a result of overhunting and destruction of their humid

forest habitats. They are easily known by their great size and *curly crest feathers*; males have *ornamented bills* and are *mainly black*. Salvin's Curassow (in genus *Mitu*) is similar, differing mainly in its bill structure and less recurved crest feathers. *Crax's* deep booming songs are given mainly at night.

Great Curassow, *Crax rubra*
Pavón Grande   Plate 18(12)

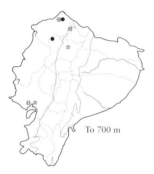

To 700 m

89–94 cm (35–37″). Now *extremely rare and local—if indeed still extant—in humid and deciduous forest in lowlands of west*. Both sexes have long recurved crown feathers that form *expressive bushy crest*, these feathers black in ♂, with white barring in ♀. ♂ has *cere and prominent knob bright yellow* and dusky-flesh legs; ♀'s bill yellowish with dusky cere. ♂ *black* with *white belly*. ♀ *mostly bright rich rufous*, buffier on belly; *head and neck black barred with white*; *tail handsomely barred rufous, buff, and black*. **Similar species:** The only curassow in w. Ecuador; as such should not be confused. Much heavier than Crested Guan (the largest *Penelope*) and very differently marked. **Habits:** Essentially unknown in Ecuador. Elsewhere occurs mainly in pairs, less often in small groups, especially where feeding on fallen fruit. **Voice:** ♂'s song (in Middle America) a deep low-frequency booming consisting of several notes on varying pitches, but so low-pitched you almost feel rather than hear it. Alarmed or nervous birds give various descending squealing calls.

Wattled Curassow, *Crax globulosa*
Pavón Carunculado   Plate 18(13)

84–89 cm (33–35″). Now *extremely rare and local—if indeed still extant—in várzea and*

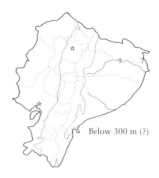

Below 300 m (?)

riparian forest and on river islands in low-lands of northeast. Both sexes have fairly long recurved crown feathers forming expressive bushy crest. ♂ has *base of bill, large knob on cere, and two large knoblike wattles on either side of lower mandible bright red*; ♀ lacks knob and wattles. ♂ black with *white belly*. ♀ black with *rufous belly*. **Similar species:** Both sexes of Salvin's Curassow have obvious white tail-tips and are white-bellied; ♂ Wattled's bill adornments unmistakable. **Habits:** Very poorly known, with numbers throughout its range much reduced by its easy accessibility to hunters. In Ecuador there are no confirmed recent reports, but we still hope it may be found in some remote backwater region. **Voice:** Not certainly known. Whistled "song" ascribed to this species by del Hoyo (1994, p. 325) is likely an alarm call; species probably has a booming true song similar to that of other *Crax*.

New World Quails: Odontophoridae (6)
An exclusively American family, recently separated from the more wide-ranging Partridges, Grouse, Turkeys, and Old World Quail (Phasianidae). Ecuadorian members are shy terrestrial birds found inside humid lowland and montane forests. They eat mainly vegetable matter and nest on the ground.

Odontophorus Wood-Quails
Plump and *short-tailed* quail that range inside humid and montane forest where they are infrequently seen but *regularly heard*; members of pairs often duet. All are basically brown with rufous, black, or gray patterning; most have *bare ocular areas*, brightly colored in several species.

Marbled Wood-Quail
Odontophorus gujanensis
Corcovado Carirrojo   Plate 19(1)

To 900 m

25.5–28 cm (10–11″). A *relatively unpat-terned* wood-quail, locally fairly common on ground inside humid forest (mainly terra firme) in *lowlands of east*. Like other wood-quail, *heard much more often than seen*. **Sexes alike.** *Conspicuous bare skin around eye red to orange-red.* Short bushy crest dark brown; *otherwise mostly brown*, more grayish on upper back and foreneck, breast and belly with faint black and buff barring and spotting, wing-coverts mottled blackish. **Similar species:** *The only wood-quail com-monly found in e. lowlands*; cf. much rarer Starred Wood-Quail. Tinamous are very dif-ferently shaped with long slender necks, slender bills, and small heads. **Habits:** Ranges on forest floor in pairs or small coveys, favor-ing ravines and areas with dense tangled undergrowth. Cryptic plumage makes finding this species difficult; it is typically encoun-tered only by chance. Most often startled birds flush explosively, one by one, and are almost impossible to relocate; occasionally one will scurry a short distance and then freeze, affording best chance for a protracted view. Rarely a flushed bird will fly to a low horizontal branch where if not pressed it may remain for a protracted period. **Voice:** Best known from its far-carrying and hollow, rollicking song, a rapidly repeated and ringing duet, e.g., "corcorovádo, corcorovádo ..." or "cocoro-kó, cocoro-kó ...," with first part given by ♂, second by ♀. Sometimes varied to a slower "kow-wáw, koo-wáw, koo-wáw ..." or a hollow "koo-

kororo, koo-kororo ...," the latter similar to Starred Wood-Quail. Songs are given most frequently at dusk, less often at dawn and other times (at some seasons even at intervals through night). Alarmed birds give a variety of peeping notes, fast cackles, and even a swelling and rising "too-too-too-too-too-too-too" (J. Moore recording).

Rufous-fronted Wood-Quail
Odontophorus erythrops
Corcovado Frenticolorado   Plate 19(2)

Mostly below 1200 m, but to 1600 m in Loja

23–25.5 cm (9–10″). Locally fairly common on ground inside humid and montane forest and secondary woodland in *lowlands and lower subtropics of west*. Inconspicuous bare skin around eye dark purplish in ♂, dusky in ♀. *Forehead and face mostly rufous*; above (including short bushy crest) grayish brown with faint dusky vermiculations, buff feather edging, and *some large black spots on wing-coverts*. *Throat black bordered below by conspicuous white crescent; underparts rufous-chestnut* becoming brown on lower belly. ♀ similar but darker and duller below. **Similar species:** Dark-backed Wood-Quail replaces this species at higher elevations in nw. Ecuador; it differs in having an unmarked dark brown head and back and entirely rufous throat and breast (paler and brighter than in Rufous-fronted) with no black throat and white crescent. **Habits:** Similar to other wood-quail (see Marbled), though Rufous-fronted seems more capable of persisting in degraded and fragmented habitat. **Voice:** Frequently heard song a rapidly repeated gabbling phrase, loud and resonant, e.g., "koo-klaw, koo-klaw, koo-klaw. ..."

Dark-backed Wood-Quail
Odontophorus melanonotus
Corcovado Dorsioscuro   Plate 19(3)

1200–2700 m

23–25.5 cm (9–10″). A *simply patterned* wood-quail found on ground inside *subtropical forest on w. slope south to w. Cotopaxi.* Inconspicuous bare skin around eye dusky. **Sexes alike.** *Above uniform very dark brown* with faint blackish vermiculations. *Throat and breast uniform bright rufous*; belly brown with faint black vermiculations. **Similar species:** Rufous-fronted Wood-Quail ranges at lower elevations (some overlap?); it differs in having more patterning on head (rufous forehead and face, black throat, and white crescent) and is paler brown above, darker rufous below. **Habits:** Similar to Marbled Wood-Quail. **Voice:** Frequently heard song a rapidly repeated "keeeoro-keeroro-keeroro . . . ," at times given as a fast duet, at times as a slower series by one individual; quality is harsh and throaty (P. Coopmans). Also gives soft whistles.

Rufous-breasted Wood-Quail
Odontophorus speciosus
Corcovado Pechirrufo   Plate 19(4)

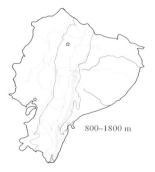

800–1800 m

24–26.5 cm (9½–10½″). Scarce and local on ground inside *foothill and subtropical forest on e. slope.* Inconspicuous bare skin around eye dusky. ♂ above (including short bushy crest) brown with faint dusky vermiculations, buff feather edging, and some large black spots on wing-coverts; *white-speckled superciliary.* *Lower face and throat black*; *underparts uniform rufous.* ♀ like ♂ above. *Throat black* bordered below by *rufous chest band*; *remaining underparts gray.* **Similar species:** So far as known, Rufous-breasted occurs at *higher elevations* than either of the other wood-quail found in e. Ecuador, both of which (Marbled, Starred) have *colored* bare skin around eye, lack solid black on throat, etc. **Habits:** Similar to Marbled Wood-Quail. **Voice:** Song a rapidly repeated "keeoróko-keeoróko-keeoróko . . . ," with quality similar to Dark-backed's though pitch usually a little higher. Also gives soft whistles.

Starred Wood-Quail, *Odontophorus stellatus*
Corcovado Estrellado   Plate 19(5)

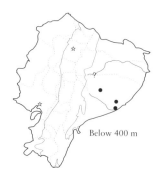

Below 400 m

24–26.5 cm (9½–10½″). *Rare and local* on ground inside humid forest in *lowlands of east* (mainly/entirely in southeast?); probably favors terra firme, but elsewhere also found in swampy transitional or várzea forest. *Bare skin around eye yellow.* *Rather long bushy crest rufous-chestnut* (browner in ♀; **sexes otherwise alike**). *Lower face, throat, neck, and upper back gray*; otherwise brown above with faint dusky vermiculations, scapulars with some large black spots and pale shaft streaks, wing-coverts with buffy whitish spotting. *Underparts mostly rufous* with *diamond-shaped spots on sides of breast (the "stars").* **Similar species:** Much commoner Marbled Wood-Quail is brown (not rufous) below with dark crest and *reddish* bare skin about eye. **Habits:** Hardly known at all in Ecuador; elsewhere behavior appears similar to Marbled Wood-Quail. **Voice:** Song (in Peru) a repeated "koo-kororo, koo-kororo, koo-kororo . . . ," last note with an almost trilled quality. This is often delivered more slowly than the typically fast vocalizations of other wood-quail (though some calls are very similar to Marbled).

Tawny-faced Quail, *Rhychortyx cinctus*
Codorniz Carirrufa   Plate 19(6)

18–19 cm (7–7½"). Scarce and local on ground inside *humid forest in lowlands of far northwest*. ♂ has *face bright tawny* with brown crown and postocular stripe. Above dark brown with dusky and buff vermiculations and black spots on wing-coverts; upper back grayer. Throat whitish; *breast gray*, belly cinnamon-buff, whiter medially, with dusky barring on lower flanks and crissum. ♀ rufescent brown above with *whitish superciliary*, buffier on lower back, rump, and tail; wings barred dusky and buff, scapulars with large black spots and whitish shaft streaks. Throat whitish and chest brown; *breast and belly white coarsely barred blackish*. **Similar species:** *Smaller* than *Odontophorus* wood-quail, both sexes also differing markedly in plumage pattern. **Habits:** An inconspicuous and shy quail that usually ranges in pairs, scurrying on forest floor and foraging in leaf litter. **Voice:** Infrequently heard (or at least not often recognized) song has hollow and rather tinamou-like quality, e.g., "kwoh, kwoh, kwo-hah," but individual notes are given almost randomly, apparently by both sexes; may commence with an evenly pitched series of pure tinamou-like whistled notes. Sometimes heard at night, when birds

occasionally call from roosting perches a meter or so off ground.

Gruiformes
Rails, Gallinules, and Coots:
Rallidae (25)
A nearly cosmopolitan group of marsh- and swamp-inhabiting birds, most of them skulking and secretive to varying degrees and best known from their *vocalizations*. Their *long legs and toes* are adapted for wading and walking in water and on floating vegetation, and their *thin, laterally compressed bodies* are perfect for slipping through grass and dense vegetation. Their short tails are usually held cocked. Small, short-billed rails are called "crakes." Gallinules and coots are more duck-like; some of these swim regularly, the coots (with lobed toes) even diving. **Sexes are alike.** Nests are platforms or cups made of grasses and reeds, well hidden in marshy vegetation; crake nests are often domed, whereas those of wood-rails are placed low in a shrub or tree.

Laterallus Crakes
Small and inconspicuous rails, heard far more often than seen, found mainly in marshy areas in the lowlands. Plumage patterns vary, though all but one species show *black barring on their flanks*; bills are *short but fairly stout*. These crakes walk and run with their head and neck held forward and their tail cocked up.

Gray-breasted Crake, *Laterallus exilis*
Polluela Pechigris   Plate 20(6)

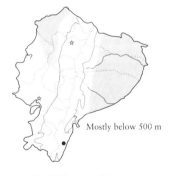

13–14 cm (5–5½"). Local in wet areas with tall grass and shrubby vegetation (including moist pastures) and marshy vegetation around lakes in lowlands of east and northwest; in east can also be numerous on river islands. Bill mostly black above, yellow-green below; iris bright red; legs dull grayish brown. *Head, neck, and breast gray* contrasting with *chestnut nape and upper back* and white throat. Otherwise olive brown above, often with some white barring on wing-coverts; lower underparts white with black barring on flanks and crissum. **Similar species:** Smaller than other Ecuadorian crakes except the very rare Yellow-breasted; none combines the chestnut nape and gray head and foreneck. Gray-breasted often occurs with Rufous-sided and White-throated Crakes. **Habits:** Furtive and generally nearly invisible as it scurries about mouse-like inside dense grassy cover, mainly on ground but sometimes creeping up grass stems. Occurs away from open water and marshes more often than Rufous-sided and White-throated Crakes. Emerges only rarely from concealment, then never straying far from cover. **Voice:** Typical call a short descending churring, often introduced by one or more scratchy notes; typically harsher than comparable churring calls of Rufous-sided and White-throated Crakes. In alarm gives high-pitched tinkling calls, "ti, tee-tee-tee-tee." Most likely seen in response to tape playback.

White-throated Crake, *Laterallus albigularis*
Polluela Goliblanca   Plate 20(4)

Mostly below 1000 m, locally higher near Mindo

15.5–16 cm (6–6¼"). Locally common in damp grassy areas and freshwater marshes in *lowlands and foothills of west*. Bill pale greenish, dusky on culmen; legs dull yellowish brown. Warm brown above, more rufescent on upper back. Throat white with *face, sides of neck, and breast rich rufous*; *belly and crissum boldly banded black and white*.

Similar species: Rufous-sided Crake occurs only east of Andes. No other crake found west of Andes has both rufous breast and prominent belly banding. **Habits:** Though often numerous, this small rail is secretive and far more often heard than seen. Almost impossible to flush, preferring to slip away into tall grass. In early morning sometimes seen walking about more or less in open, but always remains close to cover, to which it quickly retreats if startled. **Voice:** Common call an explosive, abrupt descending churring that often continues for several seconds. Sometimes its mate will answer from nearby, or they may even call almost simultaneously. Another call, perhaps given in alarm, is a higher-pitched "treeeeeng." A bird may call almost underfoot without being seen—not even the grass moves as it slips around—but sometimes responds strongly to tape playback.

Rufous-sided Crake, *Laterallus melanophaius*
Polluela Flanquirrufa   Plate 20(5)

Mostly below 700 m, but locally to 1350 m

15.5–16 cm (6–6¼"). Marshy margins of lakes and in damp pastures with luxuriant grass and shrubs in *lowlands and foothills* of *east*. Bill mostly blackish above, pale green below; legs brownish. Uniform olive brown above. *Face, sides of neck, and sides of breast rufous* contrasting with *white median underparts*; *flanks white boldly banded with black*; crissum rufous. **Similar species:** White-throated Crake occurs only west of Andes; it is more rufescent above, much more extensively rufous across breast, and has black-and-white barred crissum. Black-banded Crake is larger, *shows no white at all below*, and its head and neck are entirely rich rufous. **Habits:** Similar to White-throated Crake, though less often in tall grass away from margins of ponds or marshes. In early morning sometimes emerges to feed on mats of floating vegetation surrounding oxbow lakes, but more often remains hidden in cover, its presence revealed only by its frequent calling. **Voice:** Churring call similar to White-throated Crake's but often not quite as harsh; usually longer than comparable call of Gray-breasted Crake (which regularly occurs with Rufous-sided). Also gives high-pitched tinkling calls similar to Gray-breasted's and the short "treeeeeng" call given by White-throated.

Black-banded Crake, *Laterallus fasciatus*
Polluela Negrilineada   Plate 20(7)

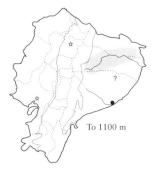

To 1100 m

17–18 cm (6¼–7″). Scarce in *dense thickets and grassy areas near streams or places where soil is saturated* (also sometimes on river islands, where it favors more mature habitat than Gray-breasted) in *lowlands and foothills of east*. Bill black; iris orange-red with narrow pink eye-ring; legs dusky reddish. *Head, neck, and entire breast rich rufous-chestnut* contrasting with uniform brownish olive upperparts. *Lower underparts boldly banded ochraceous and black.* **Similar species:** Smaller Rufous-sided Crake has white down median underparts and black-and-white barring on flanks. Russet-crowned Crake (which occurs in similar, nonmarsh, habitat) is somewhat smaller, has gray sides of head and olive brown hindneck, and is uniform cinnamon-rufous below (with no banding). Chestnut-headed Crake (another nonmarsh rail) is somewhat larger and also has no banding below. **Habits:** Even more secretive than previous three crakes, and hardly ever seen without benefit of tape playback; mainly favors thick and tangled habitat. **Voice:** Call

a long descending churring, similar to Rufous-sided Crake's but often substantially longer (it can continue up to 8–10 seconds) and more musical; presumed ♀ may follow with similar but shorter call.

Russet-crowned Crake, *Laterallus viridis*
Polluela Coronirrojiza   Plate 20(8)

650–1200 m

15.5–16 cm (6–6¼″). *Rare to locally uncommon* in dense undergrowth of secondary woodland and regenerating clearings (not necessarily near water) in lowlands and foothills of east; perhaps most numerous in *Zumba region. Bill blackish*; iris red with narrow red eye-ring; legs pale reddish. *Crown rufous* contrasting with *gray sides of head*; otherwise olive brown above. *Below uniform cinnamon-rufous*, somewhat paler on throat. **Similar species:** Larger Uniform Crake, another "dry (or at most 'moist') ground" crake that also is rare, has yellowish green bill, no rufous on cap, and no gray on face. Chestnut-headed Crake has richly colored head and foreneck contrasting with brown belly, bicolored bill. **Habits:** Creeps around inside dense thickets where extremely hard to see, though occasionally perching partially in the open in early morning. Seems less terrestrial than most rails. **Voice:** Call a descending churring lasting about 5–10 seconds, becoming more sputtering and hesitant toward end; more staccato than Rufous-sided Crake's call.

Chestnut-headed Crake
Anurolimnas castaneiceps
Polla Cabecicastaña   Plate 20(3)

20.5–21.5 cm (8–8½″). Fairly common (but recorded almost entirely by voice) *on ground*

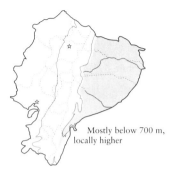

Mostly below 700 m,
locally higher

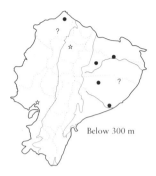

Below 300 m

inside secondary woodland and humid forest in lowlands of east, sometimes near forest streams but *not around open ponds or marshes*. Short thick bill *mainly black above and lime green below*; iris golden orange; legs red (northward) or dusky (southward), the dividing line between the two forms apparently just south of Río Napo. *Forecrown, head, throat, and breast rich rufous* contrasting with olive brown upperparts and brown belly. **Similar species:** So much larger than any *Laterallus* crake that confusion is unlikely; the duller Russet-crowned is the most similar. Cf. also much scarcer Uniform Crake. **Habits:** Ranges in pairs, walking on ground, often with head and neck held erect like a wood-rail, not crouching forward like the true crakes. Favors damp situations with heavy shady cover, picking at leaf litter and suspended dead vegetation. Furtive and hard to see, freezing motionless or slipping away at one's (almost inevitably noisy) approach. **Voice:** Often-heard melodic call, somewhat wood-quail-like, a loud and far-carrying antiphonal duet that may go on for several minutes, one bird's repeated "tee-toh" alternating with mate's "tee-turro" (can be paraphrased as "fi-ga-ro"); sometimes syncopation breaks down, both calls being given at once. Often not responsive to tape playback; when it does approach, usually remains hidden by dense vegetation, uttering low growls.

Uniform Crake, *Amaurolimnas concolor*
Rascón Unicolor   Plate 20(2)

20.5–21.5 cm (8–8½"). *Rare*—inexplicably so (overlooked?)—and local *inside swampy forest and secondary woodland and near streams* in lowlands of northwest and east. *Bill mainly olive*; iris red; legs dusky-pink.

More or less uniform rufous brown, somewhat brighter and paler below with whitish throat. **Northwestern birds** slightly smaller and less rufescent below. **Similar species:** Chestnut-headed Crake has similar, somewhat wood-rail-like shape with upright carriage and cocked tail, and the two could conceivably be found to occur together though to date they have not been; Chestnut-headed differs in its bicolored bill, much more richly colored foreparts, darker and more olive upperparts, and contrasting dark brown belly. **Habits:** Hardly known in Ecuador. Elsewhere found singly or in pairs, almost never leaving dense cover and very hard to see. Walks erectly, often flicking or pumping cocked tail; when alarmed, crouches and usually scurries off rapidly. **Voice:** Distinctive loud song a series of upslurred whistled notes that first rise and become louder, then fall off and fade away, basically a repetition of a "tooeee" note (up to 5–6 times, almost like whistling for a dog). Seems almost always to sing in calm at dusk. Alarm call a sharp harsh "tsjek" (O. Jahn recording).

Sora, *Porzana carolina*
Sora   Plate 20(9)

20–23 cm (7¾–9"). *A scarce and local boreal winter visitant* (Dec.–Mar.) to freshwater marshes, damp grassy situations, and around lakes in lowlands of west and in central and interandean valleys. *Plump*, with *short stout bright yellow bill*; iris orange; legs olive-yellow. **Adult** has *black foreface and throat patch* contrasting with *pale gray of remaining face and foreneck*. Otherwise brown above streaked and spotted with black and white; *mainly gray below*, whiter on median belly and buff on crissum, with sides and

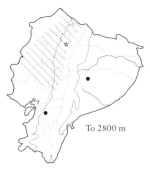

To 2800 m

flanks boldly banded blackish and white. ♀ with less distinct face pattern. **Immature** lacks black face and throat; its face is buffy brown, throat whitish, breast buff, and flank barring browner. **Similar species:** Adult unlikely to be confused. Younger birds are duller, but few other Ecuadorian rallids combine short bill, buffy brown overall coloration, and boldly barred flanks. **Habits:** Furtive and usually keeping to cover, but emerges more often to feed in semiopen, especially in early morning, than do many other rails; also swims regularly. Walks with short tail held cocked. Flushes more readily than many other rails, flying off weakly with legs dangling. **Voice:** Even on its nonbreeding grounds, more often heard than seen. Most frequent call a sharp "keek," often given when startled by a noise; sometimes gives a descending whinny (heard more often when breeding).

[Yellow-breasted Crake, *Porzana flaviventer*
Polluela Pechiamarilla]   Plate 96(1)

13.5–14 cm (5¼–5½″). *Rare and local* in grassy marshes near *head of Bahía de Caráquez in Manabí. Tiny.* Fairly heavy blackish bill; *legs straw yellow. Crown and*

stripe through eye blackish, separated by *whitish superciliary*; otherwise brown above, spotted and streaked with white, tertials and scapulars broadly edged buff. *Sides of neck and breast rich buff*; throat and belly whitish; *sides, flanks, and crissum boldly barred with black.* **Similar species:** Not likely confused on account of its very small size and unique (among Ecuador rallids) coloration; cf. the larger Sora. On flushed birds, dangling yellow legs and buff foreneck prominent. **Habits:** Like so many other grassland-inhabiting crakes, Yellow-breasted is generally furtive, remaining in heavy cover except in early morning when it may emerge to perch atop a grass stem or feed more in open. **Voice:** Has a variety of calls, most of them short, including a squeal, "kree-ee"; a higher-pitched "kii kii"; a gruffer, mechanical-sounding "shrr-shrr"; and a more musical, trilled "chree-yr" (G. B. Reynard and R. Sutton recordings, from West Indies).

Neocrex Crakes
Quite small, *notably gray* crakes with *brightly colored bills* found in grassy areas (not necessarily where marshy) in the lowlands and foothills of the west.

Paint-billed Crake, *Neocrex erythrops*
Polluela Piquipinta   Plate 20(10)

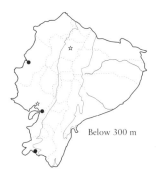

Below 300 m

18–18.5 cm (7–7¼″). *Rare and local* (overlooked?) in rank tall grass in damp or wet areas, rice fields, and marshes in *lowlands of southwest. Bill basally bright orange-red*, maxilla otherwise dusky and mandible bright olive; iris red; legs salmon pink. *Head and most of underparts gray* with median throat white; hindcrown and upperparts uniform olive brown. *Lower flanks and crissum barred black and white*; underwing-coverts whitish mottled dusky. **Similar species:** Bright color at base of bill in conjunction with extensively gray underparts should preclude confusion with all but similar Colombian Crake (which see). **Habits:** Secretive, usually creeping around on or near ground in heavy grass; soon after dawn one occasionally emerges to feed in semiopen, either on muddy margins or floating vegetation. **Voice:** Not well known. A long, seemingly *Laterallus*-like descending churring has been described (Fjeldså and Krabbe 1990), but all we have ever heard are various piping notes and some deep guttural "arrk" notes.

Colombian Crake, *Neocrex colombianus*
Polluela Colombiana   Plate 20(11)

Mostly below 500 m

18–18.5 cm (7–7¹/₄"). *Rare and local* in damp areas with tall grass and muddy margins of ponds and ditches in *lowlands of west*. Bill basally red, otherwise yellowish green; iris red; legs salmon pink. Resembles Paint-billed Crake. Differs in having *lower flanks and crissum unbarred cinnamon-buff* and *unbarred gray underwing-coverts*. **Habits:** Similar to Paint-billed Crake. **Voice:** Presumed song a slow, slightly descending series of inflected whistled notes, "tuee tuee tuee tuee . . ." delivered at a rate of about 1 note/second for 10–12 seconds (O. Jahn recording), similar to song of Uniform Crake though notes somewhat shorter. Alarm call a series of loud grunts (O. Jahn).

Rallus Rails
A wide-ranging genus, though only two *Rallus* occur in Ecuador. They differ from

Pardirallus rails in their differently colored bills and barred flanks.

Clapper Rail, *Rallus longirostris*
Rascón Manglero   Plate 21(5)

33–37 cm (13–14¹/₂"). *Very rare and local in mangroves* along Pacific coast (a few records from Esmeraldas and Guayas). A *large, dull-plumaged* rail with *fairly long slightly decurved bill* showing yellow or orange at base; legs dusky brownish. Above olive grayish with whitish supraloral and dusky streaking on back. *Throat white*; sides of head and foreneck grayish becoming buffy whitish on lower underparts; *flanks boldly banded dusky-brown and white*. ♀ smaller than ♂. **Similar species:** Only possible confusion is with similarly sized Rufous-necked or Brown Wood-Rail, which also occur in mangroves; these are much more richly colored (not looking "faded"), and neither has any barring on flanks. Cf. also Ecuadorian Rail (smaller and not known from mangroves). **Habits:** Very poorly known in Ecuador, where single birds have rarely been seen feeding on mudflats exposed at low tide, quickly retreating back into mangroves when disturbed. **Voice:** Though a noisy bird elsewhere (at least when breeding), Clapper Rail has never knowingly been heard to vocalize in Ecuador. Elsewhere gives a rapid series of loud "kak" or "kek" notes, also various grunting calls.

Ecuadorian Rail, *Rallus aequatorialis*
Rascón Ecuatoriano   Plate 21(4)
20–21 cm (7³/₄–8¹/₄"). *Local in marshes and wet grassy areas in highlands*. Formerly

Mostly 2200–3800

400–1650 m

usually considered conspecific with Virginia Rail (*R. limicola*) of North America. *Fairly long slightly decurved bill* with *extensive bright orange at least at base*; legs dull orange. Above brown, mantle with coarse blackish streaking and *wing-coverts extensively rufous*; *face and sides of neck bluish gray* with blackish lores. Throat white; underparts dull cinnamon-buff, lower flanks blackish barred with white. **Similar species:** The only long-billed rail in most of highlands. Cf. short-billed Sora (a scarce boreal migrant) and (in Loja) Plumbeous Rail. No other crakes occur in the highlands. **Habits:** Generally secretive, creeping about in the cover of reedbeds or other marshy vegetation, only occasionally scurrying across an open area. In early morning one sometimes emerges to feed more in the open, but rarely ventures far from cover. Often flicks tail. **Voice:** Not often heard in Ecuador (inexplicably). Call a descending series of squeals and grunts, considerably higher-pitched than those of Virginia Rail (L. Navarrete recording).

Pardirallus Rails

Midsized rails with fairly long, slender, and somewhat decurved *brightly colored* bills found locally in marshes and swamps, mainly in the lowlands. The genus has sometimes been merged into *Rallus*.

Blackish Rail, *Pardirallus nigricans*
Rascón Negruzco   Plate 21(1)

27.5–29.5 cm (10¾–11½″). A *dark, long-billed* rail found locally around marshy ponds and in wet pastures with luxuriant grass *along e. base of Andes* (but not ranging

out into lowlands). *Entire bill lime green*; iris red; *legs coral red. Head and underparts mostly slaty gray*, blacker on crissum and with *median throat whitish*; mantle olive brown. **Similar species:** In its limited range the only long-billed rail. Cf. Plumbeous Rail (in Ecuador found only in far south). **Habits:** Though favoring dense lush cover, this dark rail is less reclusive than most, sometimes poking along in semiopen though never getting far from cover; sometimes seen rapidly scurrying across an opening (even a road). Often flicks tail. **Voice:** Distinctive call a loud duet consisting of a shrill and sharply rising "drüü-ee-ee-eet?" (presumably given by ♂) together with various softer and more guttural clucking calls and growls (presumably given by ♀).

Plumbeous Rail, *Pardirallus sanguinolentus*
Rascón Plomizo   Plate 21(2)

1500–1900 m

28–30 cm (11–11¾″). Local in wet grassy areas, along streams, and in adjacent sugarcane fields in *highlands of Loja. Rather long bill lime green with base of maxilla turquoise and base of mandible bright red*; iris red; legs coral red. Resembles Blackish Rail, differing mainly in having *blue and red at base of bill*, no white on median throat, and more extensive blackish on lower belly. The two species do not occur together in Ecuador. **Similar species:** The only long-billed rail known from the Loja highlands; Ecuadorian Rail (very rare or local in Loja) has bold barring on flanks, etc. **Habits:** Similar to Blackish Rail, likewise usually occurring in pairs with generally furtive behavior. **Voice:** Distinctive call somewhat like that of Blackish, also a duet, with ♂ giving a repeated squealing or shrieking "zhee-reet!" and ♀ accompanying with repeated low-pitched "hoo" hooting or grunting notes.

Spotted Rail, *Pardirallus maculatus*
Rascón Moteado   Plate 21(3)

25.5–27 cm (10–10½"). An unmistakable, *boldly patterned* rail found locally in *freshwater marshes* (especially cattails) in lowlands of west, so far only from *s. Guayas to El Oro and in w. Esmeraldas. Rather long bill greenish yellow with red spot at base of mandible*; iris red; legs coral pink. *Above blackish boldly spotted and streaked with white*, wings and back browner. *Throat and foreneck spotted and streaked black and white*, throat whiter; *breast and belly coarsely barred black and white*, crissum whitish. **Immature** has duller softparts and blackish is replaced by brown, with underparts dark brownish to olive with variable amount of barring (can be nearly solidly dark). **Similar species:** Striking black-and-white adults are impossible to confuse; younger birds could be mistaken for another *Pardirallus*, though Spotted not known to overlap with any. **Habits:** Usually remains in

thick marshy cover, but occasionally (especially at dawn and dusk) emerges to feed on mud or floating vegetation. **Voice:** Gives a variety of loud grunting or squealing calls, e.g., "skeey, skeeuh-skeeuh."

Aramides Wood-Rails
Large rails with *stout and fairly long bills*, black rearparts, and *coral red legs* found in swampy habitats in the lowlands, though usually not out in open marshes. They typically walk with their *head and long neck held up* (not forward like most rails) and often flick their short cocked tails. Despite their large size and bold color patterns, wood-rails are inconspicuous and infrequently seen. They are best known from their *rollicking calls*.

Rufous-necked Wood-Rail, *Aramides axillaris*
Rascón Montés Cuellirrufo   Plate 21(9)

Mainly at sea level, locally to 1400 m

29.5–31 cm (11½–12¼"). *Local in mangroves along coast of Guayas and El Oro* (once in Esmeraldas); also inland very locally south into w. Loja, there in deciduous forest and woodland. Stout bill greenish yellow with orange at base; legs coral red. *Head, neck, and almost entire underparts rich rufous*; throat white. *Upper back bluish gray*; back and wing-coverts olive brown; rump, tail, and lower belly black. Flight feathers rufous, underwing-coverts barred black and white (both evident mainly in flight). **Juvenile** much duller generally and grayish below. **Similar species:** Only other wood-rail in the west is the dissimilar Brown, with grayish head and throat contrasting with plain chestnut brown body plumage; juvenile of smaller Rufous-necked does not show head-body contrast. Clapper Rail is paler and more washed-out, shows flank barring, etc. **Habits:** Usually seen singly as it emerges warily to feed on mud exposed at low tide, quickly retreating back amongst mangrove roots when disturbed. Birds seen in woodland have been walking on ground, sometimes far from water. **Voice:** Call a loud and incisive series of "kyow" notes repeated steadily for 5–10 seconds or sometimes even longer, occasionally varied to a more irregular "kip-kyow-kip . . . ."

Brown Wood-Rail, *Aramides wolfi*
Rascón Montés Moreno   Plate 21(8)

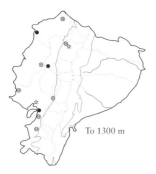

32–35 cm (12½–13¾"). Now *very rare and local* along streams and in swampy areas inside humid forest and secondary woodland, and in mangroves, in *lowlands and foothills of west*. Stout bill greenish yellow; legs coral red. *Head ashy gray* with red eye-ring and contrasting with chestnut brown upperparts. Throat white; *underparts chestnut brown*. Rump, tail, and lower belly black. Flight feathers rufous, underwing-coverts barred chestnut brown and black (both evident mainly in flight). **Similar species:** Rufous-necked Wood-Rail (the only other wood-rail occurring west of Andes) is smaller, paler, more brightly colored (especially below), and has no gray on head. **Habits:** Poorly known. Has been seen emerging to feed on mudflats exposed by receding tides, but apparently more often ranges along streams and in swampy places, where it is reclusive and hard to see; seems to come into open less often than Gray-necked Wood-Rail. **Voice:** Far-carrying call a loud, repeated cackling with cadence and quality much like Gray-necked Wood-Rail; for some reason Brown does not seem to vocalize often, even in the few areas where it is known still to occur.

Gray-necked Wood-Rail, *Aramides cajanea*
Rascón Montés Cuelligris   Plate 21(6)

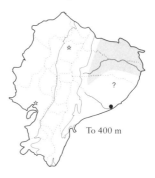

33–38 cm (13–15"). A *beautifully patterned and colorful* wood-rail, widespread along streams, around ponds, and in swampy and marshy areas in *lowlands of east*. Stout greenish yellow bill; legs coral red. *Head and neck gray*, somewhat browner on crown and whiter on throat, contrasting with *cinnamon-rufous breast and upper belly*. Above otherwise mostly brownish olive. Rump, tail, and lower belly black. Flight feathers rufous, underwing-coverts boldly barred cinnamon-rufous and black (both evident mostly in flight). **Similar species:** Much rarer Red-necked Wood-Rail has maroon-chestnut sides of neck, dark gray underparts, etc. **Habits:** Usually wary and remaining in wooded or shrubby cover, but sometimes comes out to feed on muddy margins, especially in early morning; occasionally wades belly-deep in water. Walks on ground with erect carriage, probing into mud or leaf litter, sometimes flicking leaves aside with bill. **Voice:** Best known from its loud cackling calls, often given as an antiphonal duet or even a chorus; heard most often at dawn or dusk, sometimes even at night. Phraseology varies, but a repeated "kok" or "ko-kee" is often followed by a "kow-kow-kow-kow-kow"; this can be varied to a "kok-a-lok" or "ko-wey-hee." During vigorous singing bouts, birds sometimes sound truly maniacal.

Red-winged Wood-Rail, *Aramides calopterus*
Rascón Montés Alirrojizo   Plate 21(7)

32–35 cm (12½–13¾"). *Very rare and apparently local along streams inside hilly terra firme forest in lowlands and foothills of east.*

To 900 m

Stout bill greenish yellow; legs coral red. Above mostly brownish olive with *sides of neck and wing-coverts contrastingly rich maroon-chestnut.* Throat whitish; *underparts uniform bluish gray.* Rump, tail, and crissum black. Flight feathers brown; underwing-coverts boldly barred black and white. **Similar species:** This handsome, *dark* wood-rail should be readily recognized if you are lucky enough to see one. Much commoner Gray-necked Wood-Rail has entirely gray neck and is extensively bright cinnamon-rufous below. **Habits:** Poorly known; seems to be genuinely rare and not just overlooked. Single birds or (less often) pairs have been encountered as they forage near forested streams. **Voice:** Not known.

Porphyrula Gallinules
Two dissimilar waterbirds favoring thick marshy vegetation around freshwater lakes and ponds in the lowlands. Adults have substantial *blue* in their plumage.

Purple Gallinule, *Porphyrula martinica*
Gallareta Púrpura   Plate 21(10)
28–32 cm (11–12½"). *Locally common in freshwater marshes and pond and lake*

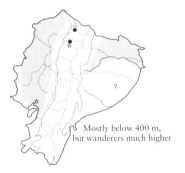

Mostly below 400 m, but wanderers much higher

margins *in lowlands* of east and west, more numerous in west. Has been placed in genus *Porphyrio*. Beautiful adult has *pale blue frontal shield, mostly red bill with terminal third greenish yellow,* and *very long legs and long toes yellow*; in immatures bill and legs duller yellowish. **Adult** unmistakable with *head, neck, and entire underparts deep violet-blue*; median lower belly blacker and *crissum snowy white* (latter often puffed out and conspicuous, especially on flushed birds). *Above bronzy bluish green.* ♂ somewhat larger than ♀. **Immature** *much duller: essentially brown above* with *bluish tinge on wings; whitish below*, tinged buff especially across breast, with *puffy white crissum* as in adult. **Similar species:** Immature Common Gallinule much grayer generally (especially below). In the east, cf. also immature of smaller Azure Gallinule. **Habits:** Usually seen walking about on floating vegetation, using long toes to good advantage; tail usually held cocked, exposing fluffy white crissum. Rarely swims (unlike Common Gallinule), but does regularly clamber about inside and atop shrubby vegetation. Flight seems relatively weak, but this is belied by the species' tendency to vagrancy; numbers found at many Ecuadorian sites seem to vary seasonally. **Voice:** Has various clucking and cackling calls, usually given in a fast series, e.g., "kuhkuhkuhkuh-kurrah-kuh."

Azure Gallinule, *Porphyrula flavirostris*
Gallareta Azulada   Plate 21(11)

Below 300 m

23–25 cm (9–10"). A *small* gallinule with *"faded-looking" plumage, uncommon and local on floating vegetation mats and emergent grass around oxbow lakes in lowlands of east.* Bill and frontal shield yellowish *green*; legs yellow to orange-yellow (brighter when breeding?). **Adult** mottled olive brownish above, back with some dusky streaking; *wings strongly tinged cerulean blue* and tail dusky. *Face and sides of neck and chest azure blue*, breast tinged azure blue; underparts otherwise white. **Immature** similar but much browner above and buffier on face and sides of neck; *wings already tinged blue*. **Similar species:** So much smaller and more delicate than other gallinules that confusion unlikely; much larger immature Purple is similarly colored except for lacking mottling on back. Cf. also immature Sora. **Habits:** Shyer and more skulking than Purple Gallinule, only infrequently walking in the open; tends to remain hidden in grassy vegetation that fringes oxbow lakes. When pressed, flushes a short distance, crashing back into vegetation a short distance away, as it lands sometimes holding up wings as if for balance. **Voice:** In our experience generally silent, but reported to give a trilled call (Hilty and Brown 1986).

Common Gallinule, *Gallinula chloropus*
Gallareta Común   Plate 21(12)

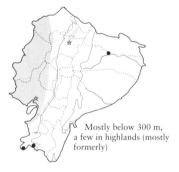

Mostly below 300 m, a few in highlands (mostly formerly)

33–35.5 cm (13–14″). *Locally numerous on and around freshwater ponds and marshes in lowlands of west*, a few also in highland lakes of north. Sometimes called Common Moorhen. *Frontal shield and most of stout bill red, bill with yellow tip*; legs yellowish olive. **Adult** *mostly slaty gray* (browner on back and wings, blacker on head and neck) with *conspicuous white stripes down sides and flanks* and *prominent snowy white sides of crissum*. **Immature** drabber and (especially below) paler, but *already showing white on flanks and crissum*; bill dusky. **Similar**

species: Andean Coot lacks red on bill (but one of its morphs does have a dark red frontal shield) and has no white on sides and flanks; latter is best character when dealing with young birds with dull bill colors and patterns. **Habits:** Often swims (unlike Purple Gallinule), head nodding back and forth; walks freely on marshy vegetation or damp ground, jerking tail with each step. Gathers in large flocks (hundreds) in favorable locales. Flight weak, usually low over water. **Voice:** Gives a variety of cackled calls, often a long-continued "kruunh . . . kruunh . . . ," a harsh "kreeenh," and a more complex "krehdehdehdeh, kreh, kreh, kreh, kreh."

Fulica Coots
Stocky, *somewhat duck-like, mainly gray* waterbirds usually seen swimming on the open water of ponds and lakes, *mostly in the highlands*.

Andean Coot, *Fulica ardesiaca*
Focha Andina   Plate 21(14)

2200–3900 m, and near sea level

39–43 cm (15¼–17″). *Locally fairly common on highland lakes*, also on Santa Elena Peninsula. Sometimes called Slate-colored Coot. *Color of bill and frontal shield varies*, with *three main morphs*: *bill and frontal shield entirely white*; *bill white with contrasting yellow frontal shield*; or *bill yellow with dark reddish frontal shield*, bill often paler toward tip. The two white-billed morphs are more frequent. Legs of first two morphs are slaty, those of the last olive. *Mostly slaty gray*, blacker on head and neck; *crissum usually blackish*, sometimes a little white on its sides. **Similar species:** Cf. American Coot (extirpated). Otherwise not likely confused, but cf. Common Gallinule, with which Andean Coot is sometimes found. **Habits:** Usually seen swimming on open water of a reed-fringed lake; gathers in sizable flocks on larger lakes that support substantial populations, but also occurs in small numbers on smaller and more remote lakes and ponds. Often shy, retreating to cover when approached, sometimes hurriedly pattering along surface. Pairs comprising differing morphs are regularly seen at most or all localities. **Voice:** Gives a repeated cluck-ing, "kituk," and a growling descending "keerro-keerro-keerro."

American Coot, *Fulica americana*
Focha Americana   Plate 21(13)

About 2200 m

35.5–38 cm (14–15"). *Apparently extirpated in Ecuador.* Formerly resident on Yaguar-cocha in Imbabura highlands. *Bill white with broken chestnut ring near tip*, some yellow near base, and *small* dark red frontal shield; legs dull yellowish dusky. *Mostly slaty gray*, blacker on head and neck; *sides of crissum snowy white.* **In flight** shows narrow white tips to secondaries. **Immature** paler generally, often whitish on face and foreneck. **Similar species:** Only Andean Coots now occur where formerly both coot species were resi-dent. In the unlikely event that Americans in being smaller and should ever wander in or recolonize, they would differ from Andeans in being smaller and in having *dark ring on invariably white bill* and *small dark frontal shield*; recall that Andeans are polymorphic. **Habits:** Similar to Andean Coot.

Sunbittern: Eurypygidae (1)
A unique, vaguely heron-like bird with beau-tiful and intricate patterning and colors found in small numbers near forested water-courses. Its nest is a bulky cup placed on a branch near or even overhanging the water. **Sexes are alike.**

Sunbittern, *Eurypyga helias*
Garceta Sol   Plate 20(12)

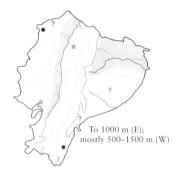

To 1000 m (E); mostly 500–1500 m (W)

43–48 cm (17–18"). Scarce *along forested streams and rivers* (both sluggish and swift, sometimes rocky) in lowlands and foothills of east and west; in east also around *oxbow lakes. Bill long and straight, mandible yellow to orange* (sometimes even reddish); iris red; *short orange legs.* Unmistakable, with complex plumage pattern; *small head* and *slender neck. Head black* with *white super-ciliary and another long white stripe below cheeks;* throat white, neck and breast rufous barred and vermiculated black. Upperparts dusky brown above *with buff banding* (**east**) or grayer above *with wider blackish banding* (**west**); lower underparts buff with some black barring, median belly whiter. Wing-coverts with large white spots, but wings come into their own in flight or when flashed open, *revealing large "sunburst" of buff and orange-rufous in primaries;* tail vermiculated gray and white and crossed by two wide black and chestnut bands. **Habits:** A solitary bird, usually found walking deliberately along water's edge, often with odd mincing gait, extending head and neck back and forth; sometimes wades into shallow water. Catches insect or vertebrate prey with light-ning-fast jabs of long neck. When threatened leans forward and swivels body from side to side, spreading and flaring open wings and raising and fanning tail, exposing all its subtle but gorgeous colors. Flight charac-teristically jerky, then glides down to perch on set wings. **Voice:** Often gives a long, high-pitched, penetrating whistled note with quality of a tinamou (most recalling Cinereous); alarmed birds give a hissing and a loud "kak-kak-kak-kak" call.

Finfoots: Heliornithidae (1)

A slender aquatic bird found locally on quiet waters in lowlands; other species are found in Africa and s. Asia. The Sungrebe is unique in that males are capable of carrying their young in a pouch under each wing. The nest is cup shaped and placed low over the water.

Sungrebe, *Heliornis fulica*
Ave Sol Americano   Plate 20(13)

Below 400 m

28–31 cm (11–12¼″). An inconspicuous aquatic bird with small head and slender neck found locally on *sluggish forest-fringed rivers and streams and marshy lakes and ponds in lowlands of east and west*. Legs striped black and yellow, *lobed feet boldly banded black and yellow* (prominent when out of water); short straight bill yellowish below and blackish above (but red above in breeding ♀, which also has red eye-ring). *Crown and hindneck black* with *white superciliary and another white stripe down neck*; ♀ has cinnamon-buff cheeks. Otherwise olive brown above and white to whitish below. Rather long and wide tail black narrowly tipped white. **Similar species:** Superficially grebe- or duck-like, though differently shaped; no grebe or duck has black-and-white striped head and neck. Cf. immature Wattled Jacana. **Habits:** Usually seen swimming singly, often low in water, sometimes only neck protruding; pumps head and neck back and forth. Remains close to cover, favoring areas where shoreline vegetation overhangs water; when pressed, swimming

birds may clamber into thick low vegetation, sometimes disappearing without a trace. Flight weak and usually not long-sustained, flushed birds at first pattering along surface. **Voice:** Usually quiet, but occasionally gives (often unrecognized) loud and nasal cackling calls, e.g., "kah, ka-ka!" or "kra, kah-kah" or deeper "kro-kro, ko-kwa!," vaguely recalling a wood-rail.

Limpkin: Aramidae (1)

A unique, superficially ibis-like bird found locally in marshy areas. The nest is a stick platform placed in dense vegetation over the water. **Sexes are alike.**

Limpkin, *Aramus guarauna*
Carrao   Plate 6(9)

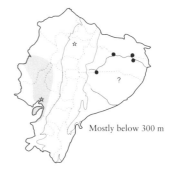

Mostly below 300 m

66–71 cm (26–28″). A *large, long-necked* "wading bird" found locally in and around *freshwater marshes and nearby rice fields* in lowlands of southwest and around marshy lakes in *lowlands of northeast*. Nearly unmistakable. *Long somewhat drooping bill* yellowish at base (especially on mandible); *long legs* dusky to blackish. *Dark brown* with *white streaking on head and neck*. **Similar species:** Ibises have more slender and decurved bills, bare facial skin, and unlike Limpkin never run on ground. Immature White Ibis, also vaguely streaked on neck, has white belly, etc. Cf. also immature Black-crowned Night-Heron (much chunkier with short neck, heavier straight bill, etc.). **Habits:** Usually conspicuous, walking in open in well-vegetated marshy or damp areas, also perching freely in shrubs and low trees. Nervous birds often wing-flick, but where not persecuted Limpkins can be fairly tame. Flight strong though stiff and usually not long-sustained, with neck outstretched and legs often dangled; there is a characteristic upward jerk of wings on the upstroke. Feeds almost entirely on apple snails (*Pomacea*). **Voice:** Often noisy (regularly vocalizing at night), with variety of loud wailing calls, typically "carr-rr-rao" or "carr-reé-ow."

Trumpeters: Psophiidae (1)

Terrestrial birds found in upland forests of Amazonia where they eat mainly fallen fruit but also larger insects, small snakes, and other vertebrates. Trumpeters are often kept in captivity by local people. **Sexes are alike.**

Gray-winged Trumpeter, *Psophia crepitans*
Trompetero Aligris   Plate 6(10)

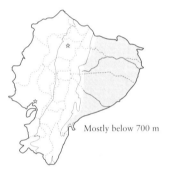

Mostly below 700 m

46–52 cm (18–20½"). A vaguely chicken-like bird with slender neck and *distinctively hunched posture* found *in groups on and near ground inside terra firme forest in lowlands of east, mainly in more remote areas.* Unmistakable. Bill greenish; rather long legs greenish and whitish. *Mostly black* with iridescent purple feathers on lower foreneck; feathers of head and neck short, dense, and velvety. *Wings held loosely and fanned outward*, covering rump and usually sides, with feathers lax; *inner flight feathers contrastingly pale ashy gray*, with brownish band over midback. **Habits:** Groups of 6–8 birds roam forest floor, when threatened running off rapidly or flopping laboriously up to low branches. Wings are flicked and shuffled almost constantly. Where not persecuted— sadly, a rare circumstance in Ecuador—they can be quite tame. Trumpeters roost in trees on low horizontal branches, but can also be quite active (at least vocally) at night. **Voice:** Most frequent call a repeated low-

frequency, throaty moaning or humming, e.g., "hhrrrrruuuummmmm, hrrruuumm, hrrrmm, hrrrm-hrrm-hrm," slowing toward end. In alarm they give a variety of loud harsh grunts and cackles.

Charadriiformes
Jacanas: Jacanidae (1)

Spectacularly long toes characterize this attractive marshbird, which is much more conspicuous than most. Jacanas are polyandrous, a single female laying eggs in nests constructed by several males, which then incubate and care for the young. Females are slightly larger than males. The family is pantropical. **Sexes are alike.**

Wattled Jacana, *Jacana jacana*
Jacana Carunculada   Plate 20(1)

Mostly below 300 m

23–24 cm (9–9½"). *Conspicuous and noisy in marshes and around ponds* in lowlands of east and west; especially common and widespread—even in rice fields and along canals— in west. Unique, with *exceedingly long toes and nails*—readily apparent in the field— *enabling it to walk on floating vegetation.* Bill yellow with *lobed red frontal shield and lappets*. **Adult** has *head, neck, and most of underparts black*, with some chestnut on belly; *upperparts otherwise rufous* with black on scapulars. **Eastern birds** are markedly darker (chestnut) above, lack black on scapulars and rufous on belly. **In flight** shows *very obvious entirely pale greenish yellow flight feathers* (outer 2 feathers almost whitish in **western birds**). Both sexes have a carpal spur on wing, often visible when *wings are held aloft for a few seconds* after alighting. **Immature** very different, lacking red on bill though with *same unmistakable greenish yellow* *flight feathers*: brown above with blackish crown and hindneck and *conspicuous white superciliary*; *underparts white*. Subadults mottled with black are frequently seen. **Similar species:** Even immatures should not be confused; no rail has such long toes, any yellow on wing, or eye-stripe. Cf. Sungrebe. **Habits:** Individuals or small groups parade around on marsh vegetation or grass, also sometimes on mud. Flight usually low on stiff—often bowed—wings, neck out-stretched, long legs and toes dangling loosely; upon landing, often stretches wings upward. **Voice:** Gives a variety of loud cackling and chattering calls. Can be very noisy, flushed birds especially so as they retreat a short distance, but—unlike so many marsh birds—usually remaining in view.

Sandpipers, Snipes, and Phalaropes: Scolopacidae (34)

A widespread group of shorebirds (in Britain collectively called "waders"), the vast majority of this family are highly migratory, *only the various snipes being resident in Ecuador*. This family's abundance and diversity are much greater along the coast than inland. Bill length varies strikingly between species and is an indication of feeding methods. There often is substantial individual variation in bill length, with bills of females longer in many species. Sexual dimorphism in size occurs in some species and is quite striking in a few; males are larger in some species, females in others. Many species show seasonal variation (often striking) in plumage, but only of body feathering: flight patterns remain the same. Voice for many species is often a major clue to identity (though this often requires much experience); many species call especially (or only) in flight.

Identification can be tricky and may require substantial experience and good views. Oftentimes it is less helpful to look at plumage details—often confusingly similar—than it is to note a bird's comparative size, overall form, bill length and shape, color and length of legs, and vocalizations. Unless otherwise indicated, **sexes are alike.**

Tringa Yellowlegs and Sandpipers

Elegant shorebirds with long legs that often wade in shallow water, sometimes even swimming. Bills are thin and quite long.

Greater Yellowlegs, *Tringa melanoleuca*
Patiamarillo Mayor   Plate 24(5)

To at least 3500 m

30.5–33 cm (12–13″). A widespread boreal migrant (most numerous Aug.–Oct.), a few ranging up to highland and paramo lakes; favors freshwater. Long straight bill, *often perceptibly upswept*, blackish with blue-gray base; *legs orange-yellow to yellow*. **Nonbreeding plumage** brownish gray above spotted and flecked with white; head, neck, and chest streaked grayish and white, becoming white on lower underparts. **Breeding plumage** similar but darker above and more coarsely blackish streaked on foreneck and barred on flanks. **In flight** shows *dark wings, white rump*, and pale grayish tail. **Similar species:** Lesser Yellowlegs smaller with proportionately shorter, finer, and blacker bill; calls differ. Cf. also Willet (somewhat alike at rest aside from leg color, but very different in flight). **Habits:** Often in small groups, frequently associating with other shorebirds (including Lessers). Often feeds by sweeping bill sideways in shallow water; also picks insects from surfaces. **Voice:** Call a frequently heard, loud and ringing "tew-tew-tew."

Lesser Yellowlegs, *Tringa flavipes*
Patiamarillo Menor   Plate 24(6)

25.5–28 cm (10–11″). A widespread boreal migrant, with largest numbers around coastal lagoons, only scattered birds elsewhere; few present May–Jul. Fairly long straight bill black; *legs orange-yellow to yellow*. *Plumages essentially identical to Greater Yellowlegs*. **Similar species:** Differs from Greater in its somewhat smaller size and more delicate shape, proportionately shorter and finer *black* bill that lacks any upturn, and different calls. Smaller and more compact Solitary

To at least 3500 m

Sandpiper is darker above, has shorter olive legs. Stilt Sandpiper has bill slightly drooped and in nonbreeding plumage has whitish superciliary; it feeds more like a dowitcher, probing in deeper water (not prancing around shallow water like a yellowlegs). **Habits:** Much like Greater Yellowlegs (with which Lessers often associate), but tends to feed by picking insects from surface (rarely or never sweeping water's surface). **Voice:** Call much less strident than that of Greater Yellowlegs, and only rarely trebled, often just a single "tip" or "kyew."

Solitary Sandpiper, *Tringa solitaria*
Andarríos Solitario   Plate 24(4)

To at least 3000 m

20.5–21.5 cm (8–8½″). A widespread boreal migrant, true to its name often occurring *alone* around shallow freshwater pools or ponds; regular in *wooded, less open situations* where other shorebirds do not occur. Fairly long slender bill black with grayish base; *legs olive*. **Nonbreeding plumage** *mainly dark olive brown above and on foreneck* with *prominent white eye-ring*; lower underparts white. **Breeding plumage** more white-spotted above and white-streaked on

head and neck. **In flight** shows *dark wings* and center of rump and tail, with *sides of tail white barred with dark brown*. **Similar species:** Spotted Sandpiper teeters more (and nods less), has a less upright posture and paler legs, and flies with stiff shallow wing-beats (not with Solitary's deep, quick wing-strokes). **Habits:** Most often solitary, feeding at edge of shallow water; occasionally in loose groups of up to 6–8 birds. Frequently nods head, especially when nervous. When flushed often briefly towers upward. **Voice:** Most frequent call a sharp clear "pt-weet," given especially in flight.

Willet, *Catoptrophorus semipalmatus*
Vadeador Aliblanco   Plate 22(13)

35.5–38 cm (14–15″). A fairly common boreal migrant to mudflats and beaches *along coast*, most numerous Nov.–Feb. *Bill quite heavy and long*, bluish gray basally; *legs bluish gray*. **Nonbreeding plumage** *very plain*: pale *brownish gray above and on foreneck*, with white supraloral and eye-ring; whitish below. **Breeding plumage** (not often seen in Ecuador) similar but sparsely marked with brown above and with some brown streaking and chevrons below. *A drab, essentially unmarked shorebird at rest*, but **in flight** *displays striking wing pattern* with *very bold white wing-stripe contrasting with black primaries*, white rump. **Similar species:** Greater Yellowlegs has yellow legs, more slender bill, very different wing pattern in flight. Cf. also nonbreeding Hudsonian Godwit. **Habits:** Usually in small flocks, regularly associating with other large shorebirds. Feeds both by probing into mud and by picking from sandy or rocky substrates. At high tide sometimes roosts in mangroves, often with Whimbrels.

Voice: Can be very noisy, giving a variety of loud shrill calls, most frequent a "kip-kip-kip" or "kyee-yee-yee."

Wandering Tattler, *Heteroscelus incanus*
Playero Vagabundo   Plate 24(7)

26.5–28 cm (10½–11″). A scarce and local boreal migrant to *rocky coasts*, small numbers occurring throughout year. Straight blackish bill; *rather short legs dull yellow.* **Nonbreeding plumage** *uniform plain slaty gray* with small white supraloral stripe and white lower underparts. **Breeding plumage** (rarely seen in Ecuador) similar but *underparts with even, narrow blackish barring.* **In flight** shows *uniform slaty gray wings, rump, and tail.* **Similar species:** Not likely confused, with characteristic habitat. Spotted Sandpiper smaller and paler with more brownish upperparts, etc. Cf. Surfbird. **Habits:** Most often solitary, sometimes associating with groups of turnstones or Surfbirds, and usually inconspicuous. Feeding birds probe into crevices and often teeter as they move along. **Voice:** Quiet, only infrequently giving its loud "ti-lee-lee" call.

Spotted Sandpiper, *Actitis macularia*
Andarríos Coleador   Plate 24(3)

18–19 cm (7–7½″). A *widespread, often common* boreal migrant that can occur along shorelines almost anywhere (even along streams in Andes), but is most numerous along coast; very few records May–Jul. *Easily recognized by its near-constant teetering.* Bill flesh or yellowish tipped blackish, duskier in nonbreeding plumage; legs dull yellowish. **Nonbreeding plumage** olive brown above

To about 3500 m

with short white superciliary and some wing-covert barring; white below with distinctive *gray smudge on sides of chest* and *white shoulder mark.* **Breeding-plumage** birds (seen prior to northward migration in Apr.) have *black spotting* (larger and denser in ♀♀) *below.* **In flight** shows narrow white wingstripe; *flies with distinctive shallow and jerky wingbeats below horizontal, interspersed with glides on bowed wings.* **Similar species:** Cf. Solitary Sandpiper. **Habits:** Usually feeds alone, apparently maintaining winter feeding territories though birds often roost together, sometimes in trees such as mangroves. Typical posture more horizontal than in other shorebirds, with body tilted forward and head held low. Spotteds seem equally at home on rocky, sandy, or muddy shores. **Voice:** Most frequent call a loud shrill "peet-weet!," often given in flight.

Upland Sandpiper, *Bartramia longicauda*
Pradero Colilargo   Plate 25(8)

To 4000 m

28–30.5 cm (11–12″). A scarce and erratic transient (mainly Aug.–Oct.) en route to its wintering grounds on Argentinian pampas. Favors open grassy areas, including paramo, *showing no affinity for water.* Profile characteristic, with *small head, long slim neck,* and *long tail* (at rest *extending beyond wingtips*). *Rather short and slender bill yellowish*; legs yellow; *large dark eye imparts distinctive "wide-eyed" expression.* Brown above mottled blackish and with buff feather edging; buffy whitish below with brown streaking, chevrons, and barring. **In flight** blackish primaries contrast with mottled brown upperparts; usually flies with stiff strokes, wings bowed downward. **Similar species:** Cf. smaller Buff-breasted Sandpiper. All plovers are chunkier and thicker-billed. Otherwise readily known by combination of distinctive shape and overall brown appearance. **Habits:** "Uppies" stride, graceful and alert, through grass, with head and neck often nodding back and forth. Upon alighting, they often hold up wings briefly, jacana-like. **Voice:** Call a characteristic mellow "huu-huuit," most often given in flight, sometimes as bird flies high overhead.

Whimbrel, *Numenius phaeopus*
Zarapito Trinador   Plate 22(11)

38–43 cm (15–17″). *Widespread and often common along entire coast*, where flexible in its habitat choice (rocky, sandy, and muddy shores being acceptable); accidental elsewhere. A *large* shorebird with *unmistakable long (8–10 cm; 3–4″) and decurved bill.* ♀♀ average larger and longer-billed than ♂♂. Brown above, feathers edged buffyish; *crown and eye-stripe dark brown, separated by conspicuous buff superciliary*. Below buffy whitish streaked and barred dusky brown, especially on breast and flanks. **In flight** essentially uniform brownish above. **Similar species:** Cf. much rarer Marbled and Hud-sonian Godwits (both with upturned bills, etc.). **Habits:** Scatters out to feed more or less solitarily on beaches and mudflats (less often on fields), but at high tide gathers into groups to roost (in some areas perching in mangroves). Unlike so many shorebirds, only rarely wades into water. **Voice:** Has a variety of vigorous calls, including a series of musical whistled notes ("whi-whi-whi-whi-whi") on one pitch, given especially in flight.

Limosa Godwits
Large shorebirds characterized by their *long, upswept, basally pink bills.*

Hudsonian Godwit, *Limosa haemastica*
Aguja Hudsoniana   Plate 22(9)

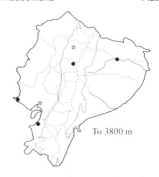

To 3800 m

38–40.5 cm (15–16″). A *rare* boreal migrant, recorded mostly as a transient on lagoons and mudflats on sw. coast, a few elsewhere. *Bill long (8–10 cm; 3–4″) and slightly upturned, pinkish with terminal half blackish.* ♀♀ larger and somewhat longer-billed than ♂♂. **Nonbreeding plumage** brownish gray above with whitish superciliary; *foreneck grayish*, throat and lower underparts whitish. **Juvenile** similar but browner. **Breeding-plumage** birds have face whitish with fine gray streaking, dark brown upperparts with buff and whitish spotting, and *underparts chestnut* (♂♂) or *buff scaled with chestnut* (♀♀). **Flight pattern** striking with *white uppertail-coverts contrasting with black tail*, *bold white wingstripe*, and *black underwing-coverts*. **Similar species:** Cf. even rarer Marbled Godwit. Nonbreeding Willets can look vaguely similar, especially at rest. **Habits:** Often associates loosely with other large shorebirds, but tends to scatter out to feed, often wading into deep water (up to belly) and probing deeply (up to face).

Marbled Godwit, *Limosa fedoa*
Aguja Canela   Plate 22(10)

43–48 cm (17–19″). A *casual* vagrant to lagoons and mudflats on sw. coast. *Bill long (10–12.5 cm; 4–5″) and slightly upturned, pinkish with terminal half blackish.* ♀♀ larger and somewhat longer-billed than ♂♂. At any distance appears essentially *plain brown above and buff below*, but upperparts somewhat mottled and scaled buff and blackish, and underparts can show some dusky barring. In flight *cinnamon inner flight feathers contrast with blackish outer primaries; entire underwing plain cinnamon.* **Similar species:** Regardless of plumage, Hudsonian Godwit always shows flashy black-and-white wing and tail pattern in flight. **Habits:** Behavior much as in Hudsonian Godwit.

Ruddy Turnstone, *Arenaria interpres*
Vuelvepiedras Rojizo   Plate 24(2)

21.5–23 cm (8½–9″). A widespread and locally numerous boreal migrant to *coast, favoring rocky areas* though sometimes on sand and mud. *Short legs bright orange;* short black bill slightly turned up at tip (the better to turn over pebbles and seaweed as it feeds). **Nonbreeding plumage** brown above with varying amounts of rufous (less in immatures); *throat patch white, outlined by smudgy blackish brown chest band;* lower underparts white. **Breeding-plumage** birds more clean-cut and much brighter (especially ♂♂): *head white with complex black-pied pattern; upperparts rufous-chestnut with black scapulars and V on mantle; "double-lobed" black band on chest.* In flight shows white midback and *striking white rump and basal tail that contrast strongly with black outer tail;* white wingstripe and another stripe along wing's base. **Similar species:** Nearly unmistakable, even in duller plumage. Cf. Surfbird. **Habits:** Most often in small groups, regularly associating with other shorebirds, e.g., Surfbirds and Sanderlings. Feeding birds scurry along industriously, poking bills into crevices, never remaining long in one place. **Voice:** Most frequent call a distinctive abrupt "kutikuk", often given in alarm or in flight; feeding birds give a soft chattering.

Surfbird, *Aphriza virgata*
Rompientero   Plate 24(1)

24–25.5 cm (9½–10″). A scarce boreal migrant to *rocky areas along coast* (Aug.–Apr.). *Stocky* with *rather thick* short bill showing a bit of yellow-orange on mandible's base; *legs olive yellowish.* **Nonbreeding plumage** *very plain,* with *dull slaty gray upperparts, throat, and chest;* lower underparts white. **Breeding plumage** (not often seen in Ecuador): *head, neck, and breast white with dense black streaking,* becoming chevrons on flanks; mantle more blackish with variable amount of rufous on scapulars.

In flight shows *bold white rump and basal tail that contrast strongly with black outer tail* and white wingstripe. **Similar species:** Regardless of plumage, Ruddy Turnstones always differ in their bright orange legs; nonbreeders are browner than the always *gray* Surfbird. Cf. also nonbreeding Red Knot. **Habits:** Much like Ruddy Turnstone (with which Surfbird often associates) though much less active as a feeder.

Calidris Sandpipers

Small to midsized sandpipers, the smaller species collectively called "peeps" in America and "stints" in Britain. All are strongly migratory. Their black bills are straight to somewhat decurved, typically not very long. Identification of some species is easy, of others very difficult.

Red Knot, *Calidris canutus*
Playero Rojo   Plate 23(7)

25.5–27 cm (10–10½″). A *very rare* boreal migrant to lagoons and mudflats on sw. coast (Aug. and Jan.). *Chunky* with relatively short black bill and *olive legs*. **Nonbreeding plumage** *very plain*, with *uniform gray upperparts* (juveniles with feathers edged pale, giving scaly effect) and vague whitish superciliary; white below, grayer on foreneck with dusky scaling on flanks. **Breeding plumage** very different, with *face and underparts rich cinnamon-rufous* (crissum and lowermost belly white); upperparts blackish with feathers conspicuously edged and checked buff and whitish. **In flight** shows *only faint white wingstripe*, and at any distance *rump looks gray and noncontrasting* (but actually is white narrowly barred dusky). **Similar species:** Cf. breeding-plumage

Short-billed Dowitcher (also with rusty red underparts but much *longer-billed*). Nonbreeding Stilt Sandpiper similar but with longer more drooping bill, longer legs, and (in flight) much more contrasting white rump. **Habits:** In Ecuador noted singly or in at most small groups, often associating with other smaller shorebirds. Feeds by picking and probing in mud and shallow water.

Sanderling, *Calidris alba*
Playero Arenero   Plate 23(15)

19–20 cm (7½–8″). An often common boreal migrant to *sandy beaches on coast*, smaller numbers on nearby lagoons and rocky areas; few present May–Jul. Accidental elsewhere. Legs and fairly short bill black. *The palest small shorebird* when in **nonbreeding plumage**: *pale pearly gray above* with *blackish lesser wing-coverts sometimes showing at bend of wing* (but often hidden); *immaculate white below* marred only by small dusky smudge on sides of chest. **Juvenile** has mantle more blackish with feathers edged and spangled buff and whitish; this plumage, however, is being lost by time they arrive in Ecuador. **Breeding plumage** striking (but rarely seen in Ecuador as it is attained so late, in Apr.–May): *face, throat, and breast rich rufous* with fine dusky streaking; upperparts also much more rufescent. ♂♂ brighter than ♀♀. **In flight** shows *bold white wingstripe*. **Similar species:** Cf. nonbreeding Red-necked and Red Phalaropes (both with an equally bold wingstripe). No other "peep" has such an obvious wingstripe, and none is as pale or ever shows black at bend of wing. **Habits:** Feeding Sanderlings scamper about actively and on open beaches are well known for "chasing" receding waves. They roost in often tight flocks, sometimes with other small shorebirds. **Voice:** Call a frequently heard sharp "kwip."

Semipalmated Sandpiper, *Calidris pusilla*
Playero Semipalmeado   Plate 23(13)

14.5–15 cm (5¼–6″). A locally common boreal migrant on mudflats and around lagoons *along coast*; few present May–Jul. Legs and *fairly short bill* black; bill *essentially straight* (showing little or no droop, unlike Western Sandpiper), slightly longer in ♀♀ (thus some overlap with Westerns). **Nonbreeding plumage** (by far the most frequently seen plumage in Ecuador) brownish gray above with vague whitish superciliary; white below with *grayish streaking on sides of chest.* **Juvenile** similar but mantle feathers darker, browner, and pale-edged, resulting in somewhat scaly effect, but *with little or (usually) no rufescence*; this plumage is lost rather quickly. **Breeding plumage** (seen to some extent on departing birds in Mar.–Apr. and on arriving birds in Aug.) darker and browner above with feathers edged buff (most so on crown and scapulars); face and breast narrowly streaked dark brown. The few Semis that remain in Ecuador through northern summer months retain nonbreeding plumage. **In flight** shows weak white wingstripe and dark center to white rump. **Similar species:** Semipalmated and Western Sandpipers are difficult to distinguish in Ecuador as most seen are in their nearly identical nonbreeding plumages. Semipalmated has streaking only on sides of chest (not all the way across); bill length and calls help, but many birds must be left as "semiwesterns." Cf. also Least Sandpiper. **Habits:** Swarms of "semiwesterns" are frequent wherever suitable mudflat habitat is found. Semipalmateds

tend to feed by probing into mud (Westerns wade into water more, but this by no means invariable). **Voice:** Most frequent calls a sharp "kyip" and a short, harsh, somewhat guttural "churk."

Western Sandpiper, *Calidris mauri*
Playero Occidental   Plate 23(14)

15–16 cm (6–6¼″). A small, plain "peep," a locally common boreal migrant to mudflats and around lagoons *along coast*; very few present May–Jul. Very similar to Semipalmated Sandpiper when in nonbreeding plumage, as vast majority of Ecuadorian birds always are; see full discussion under that species. *Bills of Western average longer* (especially in longer-billed ♀♀) and *typically show distinct droop at tip*, but longer-billed ♀♀ Semipalmateds and shorter-billed ♂♂ Westerns overlap in bill length (and even shape), so this is not an infallible character. **Juvenile** Westerns show *at least some rusty on upperparts, especially on scapulars*, but this already has been mainly or entirely lost by the time most juveniles arrive in Ecuador (they then resemble dull nonbreeding adults). **Breeding plumage** Westerns are snappy, showing *considerable rufescence on upperparts (especially crown, ear-coverts, and scapulars)*, but this plumage is only starting to be assumed by departing Westerns in Mar.–Apr. **Habits:** Behavior much like Semipalmated Sandpiper, though often wading into deeper water. **Voice:** Most frequent flight call a rather shrill "cheet" or "jyeep," quite different from anything Semipalmated gives, but other Western calls are more similar, and in any case it can be very hard to pick out a single individual's voice from another's when there is a mass of birds in front of you, as is often the case.

Least Sandpiper, *Calidris minutilla*
Playero Menudo   Plate 23(12)

14.5–15 cm (5¾–6″). Well named: *the smallest shorebird*. A common and relatively widespread boreal migrant to pools and lagoons and marshy or damp situations; few/none present May–Jul. Most numerous near coast but—unlike Western and Semipalmated—*does occur on both fresh and salt water*. Short, slightly drooped bill black; *legs dull yellowish to olive* (brighter on breeding adults). **Nonbreeding plumage** brownish gray above with indistinct whitish superciliary; white below with dusky streaking across chest. **Juveniles** have feathers of upperparts edged rufous, buff, and whitish (sometimes forming a V on midback), but by the time they reach Ecuador this edging is so abraded that most resemble adults. **Breeding-plumage** adults also more rufescent above, with quite bold rufous or buff feather edging; they are extensively streaked dusky-brown on foreneck. **In flight** shows faint white wingstripe and dark center to white rump. Usually not recognized by plumage characters so much as by small size, leg color, and characteristic *hunched posture* and *short-necked silhouette*. **Similar species:** Leasts are never as gray as nonbreeding "semiwesterns." Also cf. larger (but similarly plumaged) Pectoral Sandpiper. **Habits:** Usually feeds in groups, often together with other shorebirds but generally keeping to more vegetated places than do Semipalmateds and Westerns. Foraging birds may allow very close approach, crouching almost at one's feet, then bursting up and often towering or circling close at hand; they then look surprisingly short-tailed. **Voice:**

Flying birds give a distinctive shrill, reedy "kree-eep."

White-rumped Sandpiper, *Calidris fuscicollis*
Playero Lomiblanco   Plate 23(9)

18 cm (7″). A *very rare* southbound transient (Aug.–Oct.) to marshy margins of lakes in highlands and paramo, and along rivers in lowlands of east; at least so far not found along coast. *Long wings extend beyond tail at rest* (as in Baird's Sandpiper, but unlike other peeps). Pale base to black bill. **Nonbreeding plumage** *gray to brownish gray above* with whitish superciliary widest behind eye; white below with *distinct band of dusky streaking across chest, extending as sparse streaks down flanks*. **Juvenile** similar but with at least some rufous on crown and scapulars, sometimes tinged buff on breast. **Breeding plumage** (unlikely to be seen in Ecuador) much like juvenile's but more extensively streaked below and with no buff tinge. In flight shows faint white wingstripe and *completely white rump* (no black down center). **Similar species:** More numerous Baird's Sandpiper is similarly shaped and sized, but its upperparts are browner (regardless of plumage), belly white (*never showing flank streaking*), and in flight it shows dark-centered rump. **Habits:** Much like Western and Semipalmated Sandpipers, feeding on mud and in shallow water (less often in moist grassy areas than Baird's). **Voice:** Most frequent flight call a distinctive, almost squeaky "jeeyt," sometimes doubled.

Baird's Sandpiper, *Calidris bairdii*
Playero de Baird   Plate 23(8)

18 cm (7″). A transient (mostly Jul.–Nov. and Mar.) *mainly to highlands and paramo,*

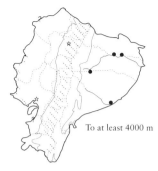

To at least 4000 m

To at least 3500 m

favoring shallow margins of ponds and lakes and damp grassy areas (but can turn up even in relatively dry areas). A very few overwinter, and small numbers are occasionally found in lowlands, principally on sw. coast and along rivers in east. *Long wings extend beyond tail at rest* (as in White-rumped, but unlike other peeps). Bill and legs black. **Nonbreeding plumage** drab brown to grayish brown above with indistinct whitish superciliary; white below with buffyish wash and grayish brown streaking across chest. **Juvenile** more distinctive, brighter and buffier above with *back and scapular feathers edged buffy whitish imparting distinct scaly appearance*, and usually with *buffier face and sides of neck*. **Breeding plumage** similar to juvenal but upperparts more mottled with blackish and less buff on face and underparts. **In flight** shows faint white wingstripe and dark center to white rump. **Similar species:** Rare White-rumped Sandpiper has similar size and comportment; see that species. Pectoral Sandpiper has yellow (not black) legs, more streaked upperparts, and shows strong *contrast* between streaked breast and white belly; its posture more upright. Other "peeps" are markedly smaller. Buff-breasted Sandpiper more uniformly buff below, has yellow legs, etc. **Habits:** Often in small groups, foraging on muddy or short-grass areas (infrequently wading into water); feeds by picking up insects from substrate. **Voice:** Common flight call a gravelly low "krrrit," lower pitched than Pectoral's.

Pectoral Sandpiper, *Calidris melanotos*
Playero Pectoral   Plate 23(11)
20.5–23 cm (8–9″), ♂♂ markedly larger than ♀♀. A widespread but usually not very numerous boreal migrant to *moist grassy*

areas, marshes, and (less often) mudflats and sandbars along rivers; avoids salt water. Bill basally pale; *legs yellowish*. **Adult** dark brown above with prominent buff to whitish streaking and feather edging. *Face, throat, and breast pale buff prominently streaked dusky-brown, ending abruptly against white belly*. **Juvenile** similar but feathers of upperparts more sharply edged, whitish superciliary more prominent, and foreneck ground color buffier. **In flight** shows virtually no wingstripe, dark center to white rump. **Similar species:** Relatively *long-necked* compared to other *Calidris*, typically with more upright posture. Sharp contrast on Pectoral's underparts, though not always easy to see, is unique. Cf. Baird's Sandpiper (differently shaped and with black legs, etc.) and Upland Sandpiper. **Habits:** Usually in small groups which may spread out as they feed, then coalesce into a flock when flushed. Foraging birds can be surprisingly inconspicuous, especially in dense low vegetation. **Voice:** Flushed birds usually give a throaty "krrik" or "krurk," sometimes doubled.

[Dunlin, *Calidris alpina*
Playero Ventrinegro]   Plate 23(10)
19–20 cm (7½–8″). A *casual* vagrant to lagoons and mudflats along sw. coast (Dec.–Apr.). A *dumpy, "dun-colored"* shorebird with distinctive *hunched posture. Bill fairly long and slightly decurved, especially toward tip*; bill of ♂♂ slightly longer than ♀♀. **Nonbreeding plumage** *drab and uniform brownish gray upperparts and foreneck*; lower underparts whitish. **Breeding plumage** (unlikely to be seen in Ecuador) much brighter and more striking with *rufous on back and crown*, whitish face and underparts with sparse blackish streaking, and con-

spicuous black belly patch. **In flight** shows narrow white wingstripe and dark center to white rump. **Similar species:** Nonbreeding Curlew Sandpiper (which see) is even rarer. Nonbreeding Stilt Sandpiper has longer olive or yellowish legs, straighter bill, whiter face and foreneck, and (in flight) an all-white rump but no wingstripe. Nonbreeding Red Knot larger and paler with straight bill, olive legs. **Habits:** Forages on mudflats and in shallow water.

Curlew Sandpiper, *Calidris ferruginea*
Playero Zarapito   Plate 24(9)

20.5–21 cm (8–8¼″). An *acidental* vagrant to sw. coast (Aug.). Resembles Dunlin in shape but not quite so "dumpy," with longer neck. *Bill fairly long and decurved, more slender than Dunlin's and curved through much of its length* (not so much only at tip); legs longer than Dunlin's. **Nonbreeding plumage** much like Dunlin's but paler and purer gray above, and with more pronounced whitish superciliary. **Breeding plumage** very different, with *rich rufous-chestnut face and underparts*, often partially scaled whitish; ♂♂ brighter than ♀♀. **In flight** shows white

wingstripe and *all-white rump* (contra Dunlin's dark-centered rump). **Similar species:** Cf. nonbreeding Dunlin and breeding Red Knot. **Habits:** As in Dunlin, though tending to wade into deeper water.

Stilt Sandpiper, *Micropalama himantopus*
Playero Tarsilargo   Plate 24(8)

To 3500 m

20.5–22 cm (8–8½″). A very local boreal migrant to *coastal lagoons in w. Guayas* (especially Ecuasal), only a few records from elsewhere. Often placed in genus *Calidris*. *Bill fairly long, nearly straight but with perceptible droop at tip; long legs pale olive to yellowish*. **Nonbreeding plumage** plain gray above with whitish superciliary; white below with variable amount of fine gray streaking on foreneck. **Juvenile** similar but feathers of upperparts with buff edging. **Breeding plumage** (seen on departing birds in Apr. and on arriving birds in Aug.) handsome and very different, with *rufous ear-coverts* and sides of crown, and *dense dark barring on underparts and streaking on throat*; back dark brown, feathers conspicuously edged buff and rufous. **In flight** shows *plain wings, contrasting white rump*. **Similar species:** Nonbreeding Short-billed Dowitcher similarly plumaged (and the two feed much alike), but the dowitcher is notably *longer*-billed (bill *straight* with no doop) and *shorter*-legged; in flight white extends up back as a point (very unlike Stilt). Lesser Yellowlegs behaves differently and is daintier bird with slender bill, etc. Cf. also chunkier Red Knot and dumpier Dunlin. **Habits:** Gathers in flocks at favored locales, often associating with other midsized shorebirds such as dowitchers and yellowlegs. Feeds by wading out into water up to belly, there submerging head and probing mud with repeated fast up-and-down thrusts. **Voice:** Not very vocal on its wintering grounds.

Buff-breasted Sandpiper
Tryngites subruficollis
Praderito Canelo   Plate 23(16)

19–20 cm (7½–8″). A *scarce* transient (mainly on southward passage, Jul.–Oct.) on *short-grass* fields and meadows, paramo, and sandbars along major rivers; recorded principally from highlands and in lowlands of east. Short black bill; *legs yellow*. **Adult** has crown and upperparts blackish brown, *feathers margined with buff and imparting scaly appearance*; *face and entire underparts buff*, fading to whitish on lower belly; whitish eye-ring accentuates dark eye in "blank" face. **Juvenile** similar but feather-edging above whiter, *imparting an even more marked scaly effect*. **In flight** dark flight feathers contrast somewhat with brown coverts, but *underwings contrastingly white*. **Similar species:** An attractive and often absurdedly tame shorebird, not likely confused, but cf. Upland and Baird's Sandpipers. **Habits:** Like Upland, Buff-breasted most often is found far from any water. Usually occurs in small groups of its own species and is quiet. When flushed may fly a considerable distance but often eventually returns to near where it started.

Short-billed Dowitcher, *Limnodromus griseus*
Agujeta Piquicorta   Plate 25(7)

25.5–28 cm (10–11″). A locally common boreal migrant to coastal lagoons and mud-flats *along coast*, most numerous in Guayas and El Oro, accidental elsewhere. Occurs throughout year, but few present May–Jul. *Very long (5–6.5 cm; 2–2½″) straight bill;* relatively short olive legs. **Nonbreeding plumage** gray to brownish gray above with white superciliary; throat and breast also gray, latter sometimes also speckled darker, and belly white with some dark barring on flanks. **Juvenile** much brighter with feathers of upperparts (including scapulars and tertials) broadly edged rusty or buff, and foreneck and breast tinged buff. **Breeding-plumage** birds known by *rusty red underparts* with variable amount of black breast spotting (little or none in *hendersoni*, more in other races), whitish on lower belly (except *hendersoni*), and dark flank barring. **In flight** shows narrow white trailing edge to inner flight feathers and *distinctive white rump that extends up lower back in a V*. **Similar species:** Ignoring plumage and racial complexities, dowitchers can be easily recognized by unique snipe-like bills and characteristic feeding behavior. Cf. nonbreeding Stilt Sandpiper and Red Knot. **Habits:** In favored locales occurs in flocks, sometimes sizable. Scatters out to feed in water often deep enough to submerge belly, there repeatedly jabbing bill with fast perpendicular motion, sewing-machine-like. **Voice:** Call, given mainly in flight, a distinctive mellow "chu-tu-tu" or "tu-tu-tu."

Gallinago Snipes
Fairly large shorebirds with *long straight bills* and *cryptic, mostly brown plumage* that inhabit heavy cover in damp situations and are much less often in the open than other shorebirds. They feed by probing deeply into damp soil. *Snipes are the only sandpipers that breed in Ecuador*, and unlike most other shorebirds they exhibit no seasonal variation in plumage. Several remain poorly known. At least three species have *aerial displays*

(termed "roding") during which characteristic calls are given.

[Common Snipe, *Gallinago gallinago*
Becasina Común]   Plate 25(5)

25.5–26.5 cm (10–10½″). A *casual* vagrant to marshes, wet fields and pastures, and pond margins, most likely in highlands. Bill *very long (6.5–7 cm; 2½–2¾″) and straight* but on average slightly shorter than South American Snipe's. *Virtually identical to South American Snipe*, and not known to be distinguishable in field. Apart from slightly shorter bill, Common also has longer wings (as befits a long-distance migrant), somewhat coarser and more extensive flank barring, and slightly less white on sides of tail. Common also could occur with Noble Snipe, which is similar but much larger with proportionately even longer bill, no white trailing edge on wing, and less white on sides of tail. **Habits:** Much like South American Snipe, but flushed birds often fly in zigzag manner (this not reported for South American). **Voice:** Flushed birds often utter a raspy "scraik."

South American Snipe, *Gallinago paraguaiae*
Becasina Sudamericana   Plate 25(4)

25.5–26.5 cm (10–10½″). A *rare and local* visitant (perhaps resident?) to wet fields and pastures and margins of ponds and lakes in *lowlands of northeast. Very long (6.5–7.5 cm; 2½–3″) bill*; short olive legs. *Cryptically colored. Dark brown above with buff and white streaking* (forming pair of V's on back), *head with obvious blackish and buff striping.* Foreneck buffy whitish streaked and mottled with dusky; lower underparts white with

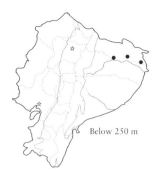

Below 250 m

dark barring on flanks and crissum. **In flight** has dark wing with *narrow white trailing edge on inner flight feathers*, barred rump, and *short mostly orange-rufous tail* with blackish subterminal band and white sides and narrow white tip. **Similar species:** South American is *only snipe known to occur in e. lowlands*, but Common Snipe (which see) could occur there, and they would be impossible to distinguish in field. **Habits:** Poorly known in Ecuador, where overlooked until recently. A close sitter like other snipes, favoring heavy dense cover, only rarely emerging to feed a short distance out in open. **Voice:** Typically flushes abruptly almost at your feet, giving a raspy call and flying a long distance. Displaying birds fly high overhead emitting a loud winnowing call; as this vocalization has not been heard in Ecuador, it seems possible that birds here are only visitants from Colombia.

[Puna Snipe, *Gallinago andina*
Becasina de Puna]   Plate 25(6)

23–25 cm (9–9¾″). One sighting from *paramo in Cordillera Las Lagunillas in*

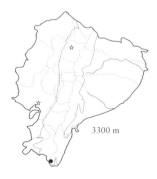

3300 m

extreme s. Ecuador. Bill long (5–6 cm; 2–2¼″) and straight but *proportionately somewhat shorter than in other Ecuadorian snipes. Legs yellow.* Plumage very similar to South American Snipe. **Similar species:** Small size and yellow leg color should distinguish this species from other Ecuadorian snipes; the other snipe (Andean) with which it is known to occur is considerably larger, darker, etc. **Habits:** In Peru favors bogs and wet areas along streams, also marshes. Circling display flight is interspersed with shallow dives. **Voice:** Gives a repeated "dyak-dyak-dyak . . ." or "dyuc-dyuc-dyuc" from ground and a hoarse, wheezy "shushushu . . ." during display flight (Fjeldså and Krabbe 1990).

Noble Snipe, *Gallinago nobilis*
Becasina Noble   Plate 25(2)

2900–4100 m

30–32 cm (11¾–12½″). A fairly large, scarce snipe found in *marshes, bogs, and wet areas around ponds and lakes* in highlands and paramo. *Bill very long (8–10 cm; 3¼–4″), two-toned with olive basal half and dusky terminal half. Dark brown above with buff streaking* (forming an obvious pair of V's on back), *head with blackish and buff striping.* Foreneck buffy whitish heavily streaked and mottled with dusky; lower underparts white with dark barring on flanks and crissum. **In flight** dark *wings relatively broad* and *show no white trailing edge*; often shows considerable rufous on rump and uppertail. **Similar species:** Andean Snipe often occurs in same general areas as Noble, though Andean is less tied to vicinity of water. The two are often confused, being about same size (Noble slimmer but has longer bill); Andean is darker and more rufescent brown generally

with less obvious pale striping on upperparts and extensive dark barring across belly (*median belly not white and unmarked*). Cf. also smaller South American and Common Snipes (neither known to occur with Noble), both of which have white trailing edge to wing. **Habits:** Infrequently encountered; usually one has to walk a marsh or bog in order to kick one up. Rarely in the open and almost never on dry ground. **Voice:** Display behavior remains unknown; the "assembly" mentioned at Cotopaxi (Fjeldså and Krabbe 1990, p. 178) is in error (fide N. Krabbe).

Andean Snipe, *Gallinago jamesoni*
Becasina Andina   Plate 25(1)

3100–4400 m

28.5–30 cm (11¼–11¾″). A *large, heavy-bodied* snipe of paramo, pastures, and adjacent patches of shrubbery and woodland (including *Polylepis*) in highlands. *Bill long (7.5–8.5 cm; 3–3¼″) and heavy with slight droop, blackish with grayish base.* Blackish brown above, feathers with rufous and buffy brown edging but *lacking* the prominent longitudinal striping of most snipes; crown dusky-brown, *face buff speckled with blackish except on plain brow.* Throat buffy whitish; breast buff prominently streaked dusky-brown, becoming whitish on belly *coarsely and more or less uniformly banded dusky-brown.* **In flight** wings lack much pattern and there is no trailing white edge. **Similar species:** Noble Snipe almost as big (though not so heavy-bodied) but differs in its more typical, variegated snipe pattern with striping above, rufous and white on tail, white trailing edge on wing, and unmarked white median belly. **Habits:** By day most often found singly as it crouches on ground in lush paramo; then generally seems inactive and may be mainly a crepuscular feeder. Flushed birds usually remain low and rarely fly far. **Voice:** Displaying males rode high in predawn or postdusk darkness (generally at most a silhouette is visible) and periodically call loudly "wíkko-wíkko-wíkko-wíkko . . ." for up to 30 or more seconds, then dive toward ground accompanied by a jet-like but muffled whining sound.

Imperial Snipe, *Gallinago imperialis*
Becasina Imperial   Plate 25(3)

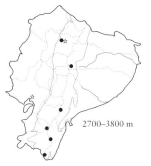

2700–3800 m

29–30.5 cm (11½–12″). A spectacular, *rare* snipe found locally *in temperate woodland and forest at and just below treeline.* Sometimes called Banded Snipe. *Bill long (9 cm; 3½″) and heavy with slight droop,* dark grayish. *Above rich rufous-chestnut barred black,* crown blackish with rufous median stripe. *Throat and chest streaked and banded rufous-chestnut and blackish, belly boldly banded whitish and black.* **Similar species:** Not likely confused: similarly shaped Andean Snipe is nowhere near so rufescent, etc. **Habits:** Until recently unknown in life (and unrecorded in Ecuador), Imperial Snipe turns out not to be as rare and elusive as was believed, though actually seeing one on the ground remains very difficult. Though species is mainly crepuscular or nocturnal, feeding birds have been seen during damp late afternoons on trails inside woodland (e.g., at Cajanuma). **Voice:** Displays are given in gathering gloom of dusk and just before dawn, and continue into night during breeding season. Males rode high into sky, periodically emitting an extraordinary, raucous (almost chachalaca-like), far-carrying "wok, wok-i-tuk, wok-i-tuk, wokka-ti-kow-kow-kuw-ku-ku-ku" with many variations. A

muffled, apparently mechanical sound is heard as the bird descends back toward ground; it usually pulls up and resumes territorial flight and calling.

Phalaropus Phalaropes
Phalaropes are *the most aquatic of the shorebirds, swimming regularly*—Red and Red-necked often alight on the ocean—and sometimes spinning around like little dervishes, daintily picking up insects or zooplankton. All are highly migratory. Breeding plumages are, for shorebirds, unusually colorful, with females brighter than males.

Red Phalarope, *Phalaropus fulicaria*
Falaropo Rojo   Plate 23(18)

20–21.5 cm (8–8½″). A *rare* boreal migrant to offshore waters and locally along immediate Pacific coast. *Bill stout and broad for a phalarope,* often with *some yellow showing at base* (mainly yellow in breeding plumage). **Nonbreeding plumage:** *crown patch and postocular patch black,* head otherwise and entire underparts white; *hindneck and upperparts pale gray, usually unmarked.* **Breeding plumage** (rarely seen in Ecuador) very different, ♀ with *white face,* black foreface and crown, *rich rufous-chestnut underparts,* and blackish upperparts with rufous feather edging. ♂ similar but duller, whitish face contrasting less, underparts paler and more mottled. **In flight** shows *bold white wingstripe.* **Similar species:** A good view is required to distinguish Red and Red-necked Phalaropes in nonbreeding plumage; some birds, especially when seen at sea, can only be identified as "phalarope sp." Red-necked differs in its smaller size, finer bill, and somewhat more variegated (less smooth) back pattern. Nonbreeding Wilson's Phalarope also has a fine bill but has no wingstripe; it shows less well-defined face pattern and has entirely white rump. **Habits:** The least numerous phalarope in Ecuador, most often found offshore. Behavior as in Red-necked.

Red-necked Phalarope, *Phalaropus lobatus*
Falaropo Picofino   Plate 23(19)

18–19 cm (7–7½″). An uncommon boreal migrant to *offshore waters and along immediate coast*. Formerly placed in genus *Lobipes*, and called Northern Phalarope. *Bill fine, black.* **Nonbreeding plumage:** *postocular patch black*; hindneck and upperparts gray, usually with white feather edgings on back; head and entire underparts white. **Breeding plumage** (rarely seen in Ecuador) very different, ♀ with *head, neck, and breast gray* and *rufous-chestnut sides of neck and upper chest* outlining *white throat*; feather edging on upperparts buff. ♂ similar but markedly duller. **In flight** shows *white wingstripe*, slightly *less* bold than in Red. **Similar species:** Cf. Red Phalarope. Nonbreeding Wilson's Phalarope has a similar needle-like bill but is larger, lacks conspicuous black postocular patch, and in flight shows white rump but no wingstripe. **Habits:** Occurs most often in small groups, flying low over water or spinning lightly on surface.

Wilson's Phalarope, *Phalaropus tricolor*
Falaropo Tricolor   Plate 23(17)

21.5–24 cm (8½–9½″). A locally common boreal migrant to *coastal lagoons* (most numerous in w. Guayas), a few also on lakes in highlands. Sometimes placed in genus *Steganopus*. *Very slender, needle-like black*

To 3500 m

bill; legs olive to yellow in nonbreeding plumage, black in breeding. **Nonbreeding plumage** *unmarked pale gray above*; face and underparts pure white with *dusky auricular patch*. **Breeding plumage** (regularly seen in Ecuador) very different, ♀ *beautifully patterned and colorful*: *crown pale blue-gray* becoming white on hindneck, *black mask continuing down sides of neck and becoming chestnut on lower neck and across chest, back blue-gray with broad chestnut stripes,* and browner wings. ♂ similar but duller. **In flight** shows *unpatterned wings* with no wingstripe, *white rump*, and grayish tail. **Similar species:** Wilson's has the weakest facial pattern of the phalaropes (its auricular patch sometimes barely shows). It is larger but finer-billed than others, and in flight also differs by lacking an obvious wingstripe. Cf. also Lesser Yellowlegs. **Habits:** Gathers in large aggregations on favored lagoons, flocks sometimes spinning on water en masse, picking insects off surface. Unlike the other two phalaropes, Wilson's rarely or never alights on the sea. Sometimes forages on mud, where it dashes around, often with rearparts held characteristically high.

Seedsnipes: Thinocoridae (2)
Seedsnipes reach their northern limit in Ecuador, where a pair of species is found; the family is exclusively South American. Compact and short-legged, they inhabit open barren terrain, subsisting by browsing vegetation.

Rufous-bellied Seedsnipe, *Attagis gayi*
Agachona Ventrirrufa   Plate 19(7)

29–30.5 cm (11½–12″). A compact, plump, vaguely tinamou-like bird of *barren slopes at very high elevations* on the highest volcanos

4000–4600 m

(mainly Cayambe south to Chimborazo). Fairly heavy bill; *short yellowish legs*. **Sexes alike.** Above blackish, *each feather intricately patterned with buff and whitish resulting in a beautiful ornate effect. Below rufous*, breast feathers with much the same intricate crescentic pattern as on upperparts; *belly plain rich rufous*. **In flight** shows no strong pattern above; underwing-coverts rufous like belly. **Similar species:** Not likely confused on the windswept open slopes it favors, where few birds of any other kind are found. Tinamous have rounded (not pointed) wings, no rufous on belly, etc. **Habits:** Inconspicuous and easily overlooked; when discovered often crouches and freezes (and then very hard to spot), but sometimes shuffles away; if pressed, flies off strongly. Usually in pairs, less often small groups. **Voice:** Generally quiet, but alarmed birds give a repeated throaty "gulla-gulla-gulla. . . ."

Least Seedsnipe, *Thinocorus rumicivorus*
Agachona Chica   Plate 19(8)

16–17 cm (6¼–6¾"). *Very rare*—if not extirpated—on open sandy or gravel plains with sparse vegetation on *Santa Elena Penin-*

sula. Last reported in 1974. Bill yellowish brown; short legs (usually hidden) yellowish. *Very small.* ♂ mostly pale brown above, feathers intricately scalloped and fringed buff and blackish resulting in an intricate pattern. *Face and sides of neck and chest blue-gray bordered below by black stripe that extends up as a median stripe outlining white throat patch*; lower underparts white. ♀ similar but head and foreneck buffyish streaked dusky (lacking ♂'s complex pattern). **In flight** shows indistinct white wingstripe, blackish flight feathers. **Similar species:** Should this species ever be found again in Ecuador, not likely to be confused. Cf. nonbreeding American Golden-Plover. **Habits:** In Peru occurs in pairs or small groups that crouch low to the ground and are hard to see until flushed, or unless they happen to be near a road (sometimes they feed on grit and spilled grain along roadsides). **Voice:** Flushed birds erupt with a low "juk" call, sometimes doubled; territorial ♂♂ give, sometimes from a low perch but also in flight, a long series of throaty "kuk" notes.

Thick-knees: Burhinidae (1)

Large, cryptically patterned shorebirds with long legs, thick-knees are entirely terrestrial and mainly nocturnal. Their large eyes reflect strongly at night. **Sexes are alike.**

Peruvian Thick-knee, *Burhinus superciliaris*
Alcaraván Peruano   Plate 22(1)

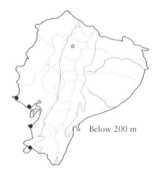

Below 200 m

39.5–42 cm (15½–16½"). A *large* distinctive but *cryptically colored* shorebird, *rare and local* in open grassy scrub and barren areas (often large plowed fields) in arid zones of *w. Guayas, sw. El Oro, and s. Loja. Iris large and bright yellow*; *long legs yellowish*. Above pale grayish brown with *bold white superciliary surmounted by black stripe*; *wing-coverts gray*. Below brownish gray with belly white. **In flight** shows *large white patch at base of primaries*. **Similar species:** Not likely confused in its limited range. **Habits:** Mainly crepuscular and nocturnal, by day resting in sheltered spots, sometimes under a bush but often fully in open. There it stands or crouches, motionless, hoping to escape detection, warily walking away upon discovery. At night foraging birds are sometimes encountered standing on little-traveled dirt roads. When breeding, solitary or in pairs; at other times a dozen or more may gather on a favored field. **Voice:** Can be noisy at night, with loud chattering calls given especially in flight.

Oystercatchers: Haematopodidae (1)

Stocky shorebirds with *heavy bright red bills* found on temperate and tropical coasts, oystercatchers are relatively scarce and local in Ecuador. **Sexes are alike.**

American Oystercatcher, *Haematopus palliatus*
Ostrero Americano   Plate 22(2)

40.5–44.5 cm (16–17½″). An unmistakable *large* and *boldly pied* shorebird found locally *on sandy beaches along coast of southwest*. *Long, laterally compressed bill bright coral red*; *fairly short legs dull pink*; iris pale yellow with narrow red eye-ring. *Head, neck, and chest black* contrasting with dark brown upperparts and *pure white underparts*. **In flight** shows *conspicuous white stripe on inner flight feathers*, *white rump*, and black tail. **Habits:** Very conspicuous, most often found in pairs, but small groups gather when

not breeding; generally wary. Feeds primarily by prying open shells of various molluscs, especially at low tide. **Voice:** Often noisy (sometimes calling even at night), giving a loud piercing "wheep!" or "kleep!," sometimes repeated many times or run together, e.g., "kee-ee-ee-ee-ee-ee-ee."

Stilts and Avocets: Recurvirostridae (2)

Elegant shorebirds found locally throughout much of the world. They nest in open areas near shallow water, typically in small colonies. **Sexes are alike** or nearly so.

Black-necked Stilt, *Himantopus mexicanus*
Cigüeñuela Cuellinegra   Plate 22(14)

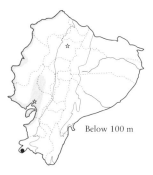

Below 100 m

36–39 cm (14–15½″). An unmistakable *slim* and *very long-legged* shorebird found on coastal lagoons (both salt and fresh) and rice fields in coastal lowlands of w. Ecuador; locally common, but numbers at many sites fluctuate. Has been considered conspecific with Black-winged (or Common) Stilt (*H. himantopus*) of Old World. *Needle-like black bill*; *legs extremely long, almost garish reddish pink*. Essentially *black above* and *immaculate white below* with white forehead and patch above eye. ♀ somewhat browner on mantle. **In flight** wings all black with white rump extending up lower back as a wedge; *long legs trail far behind tail* and *often dangle loosely*. **Habits:** Gregarious and conspicuous, stilts are usually found in loose groups that feed mostly while wading in deep water, probing into mud. **Voice:** Noisy, excitable, and alert, stilts quickly become aware of your approach and will often circle around giving short strident barking calls, repeated endlessly especially if young birds are about.

American Avocet, *Recurvirostra americana*
Avoceta Americana   Plate 22(15)

43–46 cm (17–18″). An *accidental* vagrant
to lagoons along coast. Unmistakable, with
*boldly pied pattern. Long, slender, distinctly
upturned bill* (slightly longer and straighter
in ♂♂); *very long blue-gray legs*. **Nonbreeding plumage:** head and neck pale gray,
becoming white on underparts; midback and
rump white, sides of back black, scapulars
white, wings mainly black. **Breeding plumage**
similar but with *head and neck orange-
cinnamon*. **In flight** wings mainly black with
white on tertials and at base of wing-coverts.
Similar species: Black-necked Stilt mainly
black above (no pied pattern) with straight
bill and pink legs. **Habits:** Much like Black-
necked Stilt, with which vagrant birds in
Ecuador have associated. Feeds by sweeping bill sideways through shallows. **Voice:**
Most frequent call a loud oystercatcher-like
"kleeyp" or "kleet."

Plovers and Lapwings: Charadriidae (13)
A generally distributed group of shorebirds, many plovers are strongly migratory
though almost half of the Ecuadorian
species (including the lapwings) are residents.
Like the typical sandpipers—with which
they regularly consort—plovers and lapwings favor open terrain in the vicinity
of water. Most differ from sandpipers in
their shorter and heavier bills and overall
chunkier proportions. **Sexes are alike** or
nearly so.

Vanellus Lapwings
Strikingly patterned shorebirds that are
resident in Ecuador, where they occupy very

different habitats. Conspicuous, with bold
demeanor and loud strident calls.

Southern Lapwing, *Vanellus chilensis*
Avefría Sureña   Plate 22(3)

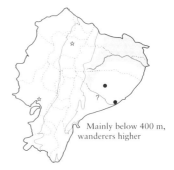

Mainly below 400 m,
wanderers higher

33–35 cm (13–14″). An unmistakable *boldly
patterned* large plover now increasing *in lowlands of east, favoring open areas along rivers
and damp clearings with short grass*. *Fairly
long wispy crest* unique among Ecuadorian
shorebirds. *Bill reddish pink tipped black*; iris
and eye-ring reddish pink; legs pink. *Head
and neck brownish gray* becoming whitish
on foreface and black on forehead and
midthroat; *breast glossy black*, belly white.
Above brownish gray with bronze and green
scapulars and mainly wing-coverts. **In flight:**
*flight floppy and loose, wings broad and
rounded* with a large carpal spur at bend of
wing; from above shows *bold white band on
wing-coverts* (from below *white coverts contrast with black flight feathers*), white rump,
mainly black tail. **Similar species:** Andean
Lapwing has (appropriately enough) an
Andean range, no crest or black on breast,
etc. **Habits:** Conspicuous and beautiful, elsewhere Southern Lapwings are numerous and
often taken for granted, though this is not the
case—at least not yet—in Ecuador. Usually in
pairs or small groups that attract attention
by their bold demeanor and frequent, noisy
vocalizations (audible from a long way off).
Nesting birds are aggressive in defense of
their often small patch of "turf," flying at
the intruder, protesting loudly, sometimes
landing with wings held outstretched for
several seconds or more. **Voice:** Calls include
a strident "keh-keh-keh-keh-keh . . . ," given
at the slightest provocation and quickly
becoming tiresome.

Andean Lapwing, *Vanellus resplendens*
Avefría Andina   Plate 22(4)

Mostly 3500–4400 m

33–34 cm (13–13½″). Locally common and conspicuous in *short-grass situations around lakes, ponds, and bogs in paramo*, ranging occasionally into drier situations or wandering to somewhat lower elevations. Bill pinkish with black tip; iris and eye-ring pinkish red; rather short legs pink (unlike Southern Lapwing, not protruding beyond tail in flight). No crest, but nape feathers often ruffled giving squared-off shape to back of head. *Head, neck, and breast pale brownish gray*, paler on crown and somewhat darker on breast, with dusky lores; *back contrasting bronzy green*, with lesser wing-coverts purplish, greater-coverts white. Belly white. **In flight** shows broad rounded wings but carpal spur quite small; pattern similar to Southern Lapwing's. **Habits:** Similar to Southern Lapwing. Svelte Andean is likewise conspicuous, often in small loose groups that parade around with an erect carriage. **Voice:** Like the Southern, Andean Lapwing is noisy, quickly flying up to mob an approaching observer, especially when nesting, voicing loud "kree!-kree!-kree! . . ." and other calls.

Pluvialis Plovers
Fairly large plovers found on shorelines and in open country. All three Ecuadorian species are strongly migratory. Bill and legs are black. Birds in full breeding plumage with mainly black underparts—among the most attractive of all the shorebirds—are in Ecuador seen relatively rarely.

Gray Plover, *Pluvialis squatarola*
Chorlo Gris   Plate 22(6)
28–30.5 cm (11–12″). A widespread boreal migrant *along coast*, favoring lagoons, mud-

flats, and beaches; accidental elswhere. In North and South America often called Black-bellied Plover. Bill rather short and stout. **Nonbreeding plumage** *pale grayish to brownish gray above* with whitish mottling; superciliary whitish, ear-coverts dusky. Below white with variable amount of dusky mottling and streaking on breast. **Juvenile** more streaked brownish below. **Breeding plumage** (seen on arriving birds in Aug. and departing birds in Apr.) stunning: mottled silvery white and black above (*looking silvery at a distance*); forecrown white extending back as broad stripe around sides of head to sides of breast; *face and underparts black* with only crissum white. **In flight** shows white wingstripe, *white rump and pale tail* (latter with some dusky barring), and white underwing with *contrasting black axillars*. **Similar species:** Cf. scarcer American Golden-Plover. **Habits:** Scatters out to feed but usually roosts in compact flocks. Posture often hunched though usually more erect while feeding, birds standing motionless then running ahead a short distance before pausing or picking at food item. **Voice:** Characteristic call, given especially in flight, a lovely but melancholy slurred whistle, "whee-oo-ee."

American Golden-Plover, *Pluvialis dominica*
Chorlo Dorado Americano   Plate 22(7)
24–26.5 cm (9½–10½″). A *scarce* transient to open grassy or sandy areas; can occur in small numbers just about anywhere in Ecuador. Shape and comportment similar to Gray Plover but somewhat smaller with slimmer bill. **Nonbreeding plumage** grayish brown above mottled with whitish or golden and with *fairly prominent whitish superciliary and dusky crown*. Whitish below, breast

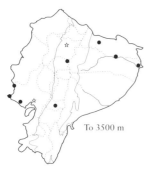

To 3500 m

and flanks mottled grayish. **Juvenile** more heavily mottled with golden above, grayer below. **Breeding plumage** blackish brown above *heavily spangled with golden yellow*; forehead white extending back as stripe around face and broadly down to sides of breast; *face and underparts otherwise entirely black*. **In flight** shows *dark wings and rump* and *smoky gray underwing*. **Similar species:** Nonbreeding Gray Plover slightly larger and not so dark above with less obvious super-ciliary and crown; in flight Gray is easily separated by its white rump and wingstripe, contrasting black axillars. **Habits:** Much like Gray Plover, though Golden is more likely to occur on grassy areas and is by far the more likely of the two away from coast. **Voice:** Common flight call a distinctive "kweedlee."

[Pacific Golden-Plover, *Pluvialis fulva*
Chorlo Dorado del Pacífico]   Plate 22(8)

23–24 cm (9–9½"). An *accidental* vagrant to sw. coast. Very similar to slightly larger American Golden-Plover. **Nonbreeding adult** and **juvenile** *more yellowish buff* (not so brownish gray) with more golden spangling

above and mottling on breast; often have prominent buff brow and dark auricular patch. **Breeding adult** differs in showing *more white on sides and flanks* (this area black in Americans), but beware molting birds. **Habits and Voice:** Much like American Golden-Plover.

Pied Plover, *Hoploxypterus cayanus*
Chorlo Pinto   Plate 22(5)

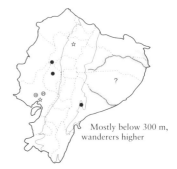

Mostly below 300 m, wanderers higher

22–23 cm (8¾–9"). An elegant, *beautifully patterned* plover characteristic of *sandbars along rivers in lowlands of east*; a few persist in west as well. Bill dusky; *narrow but often conspicuous eye-ring coral red*; *rather long legs also coral red. Face black, extending down hindneck to upper back and then forward as broad pectoral band*; a *conspicuous white diadem* encircles grayish mid-crown. Otherwise grayish brown above with *black scapulars bordered by white stripe down sides of back*. Mostly white below. **In flight** shows *bold 3-part pattern* with grayish brown forewing, white inner flight feathers and coverts, and black outer flight feathers and coverts; a carpal spur shows at bend of wing. **Similar species:** Nearly unmistakable, but cf. larger Southern Lapwing (with different front, crest, etc.). **Habits:** Usually occurs in well-dispersed pairs, nowhere very numerous in Ecuador. Feeds much like a *Charadrius* plover, running forward in short bursts, pausing to pick at prey; wading is infrequent. **Voice:** Most often quiet, though 2-noted "whee-whoot" or single more queru-lous "wheeyp?" calls are characteristic.

Charadrius **Plovers**
Small to midsized, chunky plovers, the Ecuadorian *Charadrius* all have a *dark*

(*usually black*) *breast band*, incomplete in some species and doubled in one. Most are coastal birds, only two (Collared Plover and Killdeer) being regularly found inland.

Semipalmated Plover
Charadrius semipalmatus
Chorlo Semipalmeado   Plate 23(1)

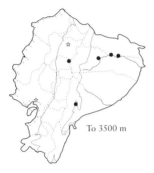

To 3500 m

17–18.5 cm (6¾–7¼"). An often *common* boreal migrant on mudflats and around coastal lagoons; rare inland. *Bill stubby*, black with *orange at base* (*orange* with black tip in breeding plumage); *legs orange to yellow-orange*. **Nonbreeding plumage** brown above with white forehead, vague whitish postocular stripe, and *obvious white nuchal collar*. White below with brown chest band (sometimes broken in middle). **Breeding plumage** similar but face pattern sharper and emphasized by black frontal band and auricular area, and chest band also black. **In flight** shows white wingstripe and white sides to rump. **Similar species:** Wilson's Plover larger with stouter and longer all-black bill, flesh-colored legs. Collared Plover smaller and daintier with more delicate bill; it lacks Semipalmated's nuchal collar and usually shows some rufous on hindcrown. Juvenile of smaller Snowy Plover is perhaps the most similar (back colors are almost the same), but Snowy's breast band *restricted to sides* (at most narrowly broken in middle in Semipalmated). **Habits:** Most often in small groups (larger flocks when migrating), bunching up tightly when at rest but scattering out to feed. Regularly associates with other shorebirds. **Voice:** Most frequent call a distinctive "ch-veet," given especially often in flight; also has various other notes of com-parable quality often run together into a chattering.

Wilson's Plover, *Charadrius wilsonia*
Chorlo de Wilson   Plate 23(5)

18–19.5 cm (7–7¾"). Local *along coast*, favoring lagoons, estuaries, and artificial shrimp ponds. *Bill stout, long, and heavy*; *legs flesh-colored* (brighter when breeding). Much heavier-billed than other single-banded *Charadrius*. **Breeding** ♂ brown above with white forehead and supraloral stripe, black frontal band, often some cinnamon mottling on hindneck, and white nuchal collar. White below, breast crossed by broad black band. **Breeding** ♀ similar but face less crisply patterned with no black frontal band; breast band brown, sometimes mottled cinnamon, and narrower. **Nonbreeding plumage** similar but lacking any cinnamon. In flight shows narrow white wingstripe, white sides to rump. **Similar species:** Collared Plover considerably smaller and more delicate, with no white nuchal collar. **Habits:** Usually occurs in pairs, at most small groups, but otherwise behavior resembles Semipalmated (with which Wilson's regularly consorts). **Voice:** Most frequent call an emphatic whistled "f-whit!" or "kwik."

Piping Plover, *Charadrius melodus*
Chorlo Silbador   Plate 23(4)
17–18.5 cm (6¾–7¼"). An *accidental* vagrant to *Santa Elena Peninsula*. Else-where favors sandy beaches and lagoons. *Bill stubby*, black; *legs orange*. **Nonbreeding plumage** *pale silvery grayish above* with fore-head, superciliary, and nuchal collar white; below white with grayish patches on sides of chest. **Breeding plumage** similar but with

basal half of bill orange, frontal band and patch on sides of chest black. **In flight** shows white wingstripe and white rump and tail, tail with black subterminal band not extending to sides. **Similar species:** Snowy Plover (almost equally pale above) is smaller with more delicate bill, grayish legs. **Habits:** Much like Snowy Plover. **Voice:** Call a charming liquid "pee-po."

Snowy Plover, *Charadrius alexandrinus*
Chorlo Níveo   Plate 23(2)

15.5–16 cm (6–6¼"). *Locally common around margins of salt-evaporation ponds along coast of w. Guayas.* In Old World called Kentish Plover, or American birds are considered a separate species (*C. nivosus*). *Fairly slender bill black; legs gray.* **Adult** *pale sandy brown above* with white forehead, lores (usually), superciliary, and nuchal collar; black frontal band and auricular region. White below with *small black patch on sides of chest.* **Juvenile** similar but lacking black (replaced by sandy brown). **In flight** shows white wingstripe and sides to rump. **Similar species:** Similarly sized Collared Plover has paler legs, is darker above with

cinnamon on hindneck and no white collar, has *complete* breast band. **Habits:** An attractive, dainty plover with limited Ecuadorian range, though perhaps increasing and spreading. Usually in pairs that scamper along rapidly and often are charmingly tame. **Voice:** Most frequent call a dry gravelly "chrrt."

Collared Plover, *Charadrius collaris*
Chorlo Collarejo   Plate 23(3)

To 500 m

15.5–16 cm (6–6¼"). *An attractive, dainty plover, resident along rivers in lowlands of east and west,* also locally around lagoons and estuaries along coast. *Fairly slender bill black; legs pale, yellowish to pinkish.* Adult sandy brown above with *large white area on forecrown* contrasting with *black loral stripe and broad black frontal band; hindcrown, nape, and sides of neck at least tinged cinnamon (often quite rufescent).* Below white with narrow black chest band. **In flight** shows faint white wingstripe and white sides to rump and tail. **Similar species:** Dapper Collared is the only *Charadrius* showing *no white nuchal band* and is the only *Charadrius* likely to be seen away from coast. Semipalmated Plover further differs in its stubby bill, orangey legs, lack of rufescence, etc. Snowy Plover is more grayish above and has incomplete chest band, grayish legs. **Habits:** When nesting usually in pairs on sand or gravel bars. When not breeding may gather into groups that sometimes range away from rivers onto wet grassy areas and airstrips. **Voice:** Most frequent call a simple sharp "chip" or "krip."

Killdeer, *Charadrius vociferus*
Chorlo Tildío   Plate 23(6)

24–25.5 cm (9½–10"). An unmistakable *Charadrius, larger than its congeners and*

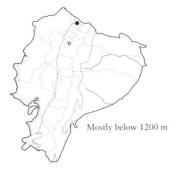

Mostly below 1200 m

with *doubled breast band*. Favors wet pastures, rice fields, and vicinity of ponds and lakes in *lowlands of southwest* (also locally in Carchi); has spread considerably since late 1980s and may continue to do so. Boreal migrants used to occur but have not been found recently. *Tail long and graduated.* Bill black; narrow eye-ring red; legs grayish to yellowish flesh. Brown above with white forehead, postocular stripe, and nuchal collar; black frontal band. Below white, *breast crossed by two conspicuous black bands*. **In flight** shows white wingstripe and *bright cinnamon-rufous rump and basal tail* extending up back as wedge, tail also with *black subterminal band* and white tipping. **Similar species:** Other *Charadrius* plovers smaller, have *single* breast bands, no rusty on rump, etc. **Habits:** Usually in pairs, less often small groups, and normally bold and conspicuous. **Voice:** Presence often made known by oft-given (especially in flight) and far-carrying calls, most frequent being an insistent onomatopoeic "kil-deéah," sometimes repeated several times.

Tawny-throated Dotterel, *Oreopholus ruficollis*
Chorlo Cabezón Cuellicanelo   Plate 22(12)
25.5–28 cm (10–11″). *Apparently extirpated from Ecuador.* Known only from two 19th-century specimens taken on *Santa Elena Peninsula.* Bill fairly long and slender; legs dull pinkish. *A beautiful, elegant plover* of open terrain; erect carriage, relatively long neck. Unmistakable. Brownish gray above, *scapulars and wing-coverts boldly streaked blackish and tawny*; *face mostly white* surmounted by *dusky crown. Lower throat and upper chest orange-tawny*, breast gray, *black patch on median belly*. **In flight** shows white

wingstripe on primaries, but rump and tail uniform brownish; *underwing mostly white*. **Similar species:** Cf. nonbreeding American Golden-Plover, which in general behavior this species recalls. **Habits:** Elsewhere favors open steppes and plains, either barren (also often on plowed fields) or with at most short grass and scattered shrubs. When not breeding frequently in small groups, running rapidly on ground and often quite wary. **Voice:** Most common flight call a tremulous, plaintive "tr-tr-traalü" with quality reminiscent of Gray Plover; usually quiet when on ground.

Skuas and Jaegers: Stercorariidae (5)
Piratic or predatory seabirds that breed in polar regions, migrating toward the equator when not nesting. They differ from gulls in their strongly hooked bills and horny cere; a flash of white in the primaries is conspicuous in flight. They are vocal only on their breeding grounds, and voices are not described here. **Sexes are alike.**

Catharacta Skuas
Stocky, heavy chested seabirds with broad wings (more so than the jaegers, though Pomarine Jaeger is somewhat "intermediate") with a large patch of white at the base of the primaries. Flight is powerful, steady, and—despite typically slow wingbeats—deceptively fast. They are nearly omnivorous. Skuas occur only as vagrants in Ecuadorian waters. The taxonomy of the genus is debated, and it may be better subsumed into *Stercorarius*; formerly both species were often considered austral races of the holarctic Great Skua (*C. skua*).

[Chilean Skua, *Catharacta chilensis*
Salteador Chileno] Plate 3(12)

53–58.5 cm (21–23″). An *accidental* visitant
to w. Guayas coast. Adult's bill blue-gray,
juvenile's duller. **Adult** brown above with
dark brown or blackish crown that *contrasts
with usually rather bright cinnamon underparts* (a few birds duller and more faded);
upperparts somewhat spotted and streaked
cinnamon. **In flight** shows *prominent white
wing flash at base of primaries*. **Juvenile**
similar but tending to be even brighter cinnamon below. **Similar species:** Distinctly
capped appearance in conjunction with
brightly colored underparts usually distinguishes this skua. Cf. South Polar Skua.
Habits: In Humboldt Current waters tends to
feed in inshore waters, sometimes even entering harbors.

[South Polar Skua, *Catharacta maccormicki*
Salteador del Polo Sur] Plate 3(11)

53–58 cm (21–23″). An *accidental* visitant to
w. Guayas coast. Adult's bill black, juvenile's
blue-gray with black tip. **Pale-morph adult**
two-toned with *pale chamois to whitish head*

and underparts (palest on nape, forming an
often obvious "hackled" patch) *contrasting
with uniform blackish brown upperparts*.
Dark-morph adult *essentially uniform blackish brown*, nape paler. **In flight** shows *prominent white wing flash at base of primaries*.
Juveniles resemble respective adults though
tending to be more grayish; they already
show *contrasting pale area on nape*. **Similar
species:** This skua always lacks the contrasting dark crown of Chilean; despite confusing variation in overall plumage coloration,
South Polars can almost always be known by
their pale nape patches, often conspicuous
even at a distance. **Habits:** Nonbreeders tend
to be more pelagic than Chilean Skua.

Stercorarius Jaegers

Hawk- or falcon-like seabirds that chase
other birds, forcing them to regurgitate food;
jaegers also pick up food items from the
ocean's surface. In Ecuador jaegers are generally found so *far offshore* as to be only
rarely seen from land. All three species breed
in the high Arctic, migrating south; pre-
breeding birds may remain in the tropics
year-round. Breeding-plumage adults with
characteristic elongated central tail feathers
(longer in males) are relatively easy to recognize, but otherwise jaeger plumages are so
complex as to be bewildering, such that pos-
itive identification is often impossible.

Pomarine Jaeger, *Stercorarius pomarinus*
Págalo Pomarino Plate 3(15)

43.5–51 cm (17–20″). The *largest* jaeger, *distinctly larger than Laughing Gull*; scarce
(under-recorded?). *Thick necked* and *heavy*

chested, with *relatively broad wings. Heavy, strongly hooked bill, pale at base. Fairly long twisted central tail feathers rounded at tip* (*spoon-shaped*) project beyond rest of tail in breeding-plumage adults but are shorter or broken off at other times. **Light-morph breeding adult** blackish brown above with blackish crown and creamy nuchal collar; yellowish white below with dark barring across chest (*typically forming prominent dark band*) and down sides to lower belly and crissum. **Dark-morph breeding adult** (*scarce*) uniform dark brown with blackish crown, *sometimes mottled paler below*, often with yellowish face. **Nonbreeding adult** similar but with some pale barring above (*especially on rump*) and more extensively dark-barred below. **Immature** much like nonbreeding adult but often with more pale barring or mottling above and on underwing-coverts, and with shorter central tail feathers. **Juvenile** *uniform dark brown* with under-parts evenly and coarsely barred blackish. **In flight** shows *prominent white flash at base of primaries* (visible from above and below; from below, younger birds show *second pale patch at base of primary coverts*). **Similar species:** Cf. Chilean and South Polar Skuas; Pomarine never as distinctly "capped" as the former, nor does it show "hackled" effect on nape seen in vast majority of South Polars. The three jaegers are notoriously difficult to identify, and this is especially the case in the tropics where breeding-plumage adults are so infrequently seen. Pomarine is the *largest* species, and confusion is most likely with the midsized Parasitic. Pomarine looks *relatively larger-headed and barrel-chested*, with *broader wings, especially at base. Somewhat more white at base of primaries* is visible in flight, but the amount actually seen depends on how much flight feathers are spread; a *second pale patch on underwing* of younger Pomarines is diagnostic if seen. Pomarine's bill is *notably heavier and more distinctly two-toned*. Juveniles and immatures tend to be darker and more uniform, rarely or never showing pale nape, and they have *bold and even dark barring below and on uppertail-coverts*. **Habits:** Pelagic, and in Ecuadorian waters typically solitary, flying steadily often well above water, quickly accelerating when harassing other seabirds.

Parasitic Jaeger, *Stercorarius parasiticus*
Págalo Parásito   Plate 3(14)

40.5–45 cm (16–18″). Apparently the *most numerous* jaeger in Ecuadorian waters, but even so infrequently recorded; *midsized, about same size as Laughing Gull*. Proportionately less heavy-bodied than Pomarine, with falcon-like narrower wings. *Bill strongly hooked* but *less heavy than Pomarine's, uniformly dark* (paler base in younger birds). *Fairly long, straight, pointed central tail feathers* project beyond rest of tail in breeding-plumage adults, shorter in other plumages. **Light-morph breeding adult** grayish brown above with blackish crown and creamy nuchal collar; yellowish white below with grayish brown wash on sides of chest (usually not a complete chest band) and dark crissum (but no barring on sides). **Dark-morph breeding adult** *uniform dark smoky brown* (showing *little or no mottling*) with blackish crown. **Immature** variable, paler birds *warm* brown with rusty feather edging producing scaly effect on back and wings and with indistinct brown and buff barring on uppertail-coverts; *head and (especially) nape pale buffy brown, head and foreneck with indistinct streaky effect* (not barred); underparts with irregular, wavy dark barring. Darker birds more uniform (little or no barring) but still have *pale buff nape*. **In flight** shows fairly prominent white flash in primaries (visible from above and below). **Similar species:** Confusing. See comparisons under (larger) Pomarine and (smaller) Long-tailed Jaegers. **Habits:** Similar to Pomarine Jaeger, though more often pursues somewhat smaller seabirds, especially terns.

[Long-tailed Jaeger, *Stercorarius longicaudus*
Págalo Colilargo]   Plate 3(13)

37.5–40.5 cm (14–16″). The *smallest* and *most slender* jaeger, and by far the *rarest* in Ecuadorian waters; may be more numerous *far offshore*, passing by unrecorded. *Graceful and almost tern-like*, slimmer-bodied than Parasitic with wings proportionally longer and narrower. Bill hooked, black in adults but with grayish blue basal half in younger birds. *Very long, straight, and pointed central tail feathers extend far beyond rest of tail* in breeding-plumage adults, but shorter in other plumages. **Breeding-plumage adult** *smooth brownish gray above* with *neat, contrasting black crown* and white nuchal collar; *white below* (with no chest band and no barring on sides), *gradually darkening to dark gray on lower belly and black on crissum.* **Nonbreeding adult** less clean-cut, with less contrasting crown, some dark mottling on mantle, some white flecking on rump, and some dark barring below (may coalesce into a chest band); **immature** similar but with pale barring on underwing-coverts. **Juvenile** variable, but typically *cold grayish brown* with *whitish nape* and *fine whitish barring on mantle* and *strongly black-and-white-barred uppertail-coverts, flanks, and crissum*; head usually pale but *chest usually solidly dark*. In **flight** shows *only small flash of white in primaries* (on outer 1–2 shafts), with *entire underwing dark in adults and immatures* (in juveniles white shows as patch on underside of primaries); in all plumages there is a *striking contrast between pale upperwing-coverts and blackish flight feathers*. **Similar species:** Long-tailed is smallest of the three jaegers, and comparison is made here to midsized Parasitic (Pomarine being so much larger and

bulkier that confusion is unlikely). Birds with elongated central tail feathers are easy but are only infrequently seen in tropics. Long-tailed's slimmer, more delicate proportions usually evident, as are its narrower wings. In flight from above, wings show distinct pale-dark contrast never seen in Parasitic (in which wings are more uniformly dark); Parasitic's white primary flash is considerably greater. Juveniles of the two are the most similar, and central tail feathers are similar (though more pointed in Parasitic); Parasitics are typically "warmer" brown (not "cold" grayish brown), with buffier (not so white) nape and mantle barring, and streakier foreneck. **Habits:** Much like other jaegers though typical flight more agile and buoyant; at least when breeding, hovers much more often. Tends to harass smaller seabirds, especially terns.

Gulls and Terns: Laridae (28)

Familiar and cosmopolitan, most gulls occur along the coast though a few are found exclusively along rivers and one is found in the high Andes. Gulls are generally larger than terns and have somewhat heavier and hooked bills, longer legs, broader and more rounded wings, and squared tails. Terns are slimmer and tend to be smaller and have slender straight bills, narrower and more pointed wings, and usually forked tails. Gulls regularly swim, whereas terns do so only rarely. Gulls tend to be generalist feeders, often scavenging for refuse; most terns plunge-dive into the water in pursuit of small fish, but others pluck fish from the surface or even capture aerial insects. **Sexes are alike.**

Larus Gulls

A diverse genus with two basic groups: *usually large white-headed species*, and *usually smaller species that develop a dark hood when breeding.* Larger gulls are omnivorous, feeding on virtually anything organic, but smaller gulls are more specialized, feeding on fish or other aquatic organisms, some species even on aerial insects. Few gulls breed in Ecuador, a majority being boreal migrants (some very rare). Many gulls, especially the larger species, require 3–4 years to attain full adult plumage, and they can present major identificiation difficulties (not entirely addressed here). Pay special attention to *mantle color*, *bill size and coloration*, *leg color*, and *upperwing pattern*. Gull voices are generally not important for identification, and they are usually not mentioned here.

Gray Gull, *Larus modestus*
Gaviota Gris Plate 26(1)

44.5–46 cm (17½–18″). A locally numerous visitor to sandy coastlines, lagoons, and inshore coastal waters in w. Guayas and s. Manabí, *largest numbers on Santa Elena Peninsula*. Bill and legs black. **Breeding adult** *uniform plain gray* with *contrasting whitish hood*. **Nonbreeding adult** lacks the hood but is more uniform and slightly browner. **In flight** shows mainly blackish flight feathers with *contrasting white trailing edge to secondaries*; *tail gray* with black subterminal band and white tip. **Juvenile** more brownish gray with pale buffish feather edging (especially marked on wing-coverts and tail-tip). **Similar species:** Juvenile Laughing Gull at rest can also look quite uniformly gray, but in flight rump and basal tail obviously white. **Habits:** Groups loaf on sandy beaches, foraging mainly by chasing waves back and forth almost like gigantic Sanderlings, feeding mainly on small crabs. Also scavenges with other gulls in harbors and around boats.

[Band-tailed Gull, *Larus belcheri*
Gaviota Colifajeada] Not illustrated
51–56 cm (20–22″). A *casual* visitor to El Oro coast; one 1999 sighting from near Machala. Also called Belcher's Gull. *Bill very heavy*, in adult *yellow with broad red tip* and some black on upper mandible, in immature yellowish with blackish terminal half and small red tip; legs yellow. **Breeding adult** has

mainly white body and *contrasting blackish mantle*. **In flight** shows *broad white trailing edge to wing* and white tail with *broad black subterminal band*. **Nonbreeding adult** similar but bill colors duller, *hood contrastingly blackish*. **Immature** mostly grayish brown, feathers of upperparts edged paler; *head and neck uniform dark brown*. **In flight** shows dusky flight feathers and blackish tail, whitish rump. **Similar species:** Breeding adult could be confused only with larger Kelp Gull, which has proportionately *less* heavy bill, shows narrower white rear margin to wing, and has all-white tail. Band-tailed Gulls in other plumages look distinctly dark-hooded. **Habits:** Most likely to be seen in harbors and around fishing villages. In Peru often tame.

Kelp Gull, *Larus dominicanus*
Gaviota Dominicana Plate 26(2)

61–66 cm (24–26″). *The only large gull likely to be encountered in Ecuador*; a scarce (but increasing?) resident on coast and lagoons of w. Guayas, *principally on Santa Elena Peninsula*. Adult has *heavy yellow bill* with red spot on lower mandible, *yellowish legs*, and pale iris; first-year bird's bill blackish, iris brown, and legs dull pinkish to grayish. **Adult** has mainly white body and *contrasting blackish mantle.* In flight shows narrow white trailing edge to wing, small white spots near tips of primaries, and *entirely white tail.* Younger birds go through a complex series of plumage stages, requiring four years to attain full adult plumage. **First-year birds** *dark brown* speckled and mottled with buffy whitish on head, neck, and underparts, pale feather edging on mantle. In flight shows dusky-brown flight feathers and tail, tail with broad blackish tip. **Similar species:** So much larger than other gulls normally occurring on the Ecuadorian coast that confusion is unlikely. Adult's black back unique, but cf. accidental Lesser Black-backed Gull. **Habits:** A powerful, aggressive gull that dominates other coastal birds. Usually found singly or in small groups. **Voice:** Various loud, complaining calls are given, e.g., a repeated nasal "keeyow" and a "ka-ka-ka-ka."

Lesser Black-backed Gull, *Larus fuscus*
Gaviota Dorsinegra Menor   Plate 26(6)

56–61 cm (22–24″). An *accidental* vagrant to w. Guayas coast. Resembles Kelp Gull, but smaller with proportionately thinner bill; *legs yellow.* **Adult** (of the likely race, *graellsii*) differs in having *mantle slaty gray* (not black), against which black primaries contrast. **First-year birds** dark brown above with pale feather edging, whitish below, *flight feathers blackish*, and wide blackish subterminal band on tail; bill blackish and legs duskier. Younger stages are probably not

safely distinguished from Kelp Gull. **Habits:** Much as in Kelp Gull.

[Herring Gull, *Larus argentatus*
Gaviota Argéntea]   Plate 26(3)

56–61 cm (22–24″). An *accidental* vagrant to Río Napo near Coca. A *large* gull, *pale-mantled* when adult. Fairly heavy bill yellow with red spot near tip (dusky in first-year birds, gradually becoming paler, in second- and third-year birds yellowish tipped black); iris pale yellow; *legs flesh-colored.* **Breeding adult** has mainly white body and *pale gray mantle.* In flight shows black outer primaries with white spots near their tips, white tail. **Nonbreeding adult** similar but with dusky streaking on head and hindneck. **First-year birds** mainly brown with paler feather edging, flight feathers entirely blackish and tail with wide blackish terminal band; legs dusky. **Similar species:** Cf. Lesser Black-backed Gull (adults easy to distinguish, younger birds rather less so though juvenile Lesser Black-backeds show more extensive black on inner flight feathers). Cf. also Ring-billed and California Gulls; all these gulls are extremely rare in Ecuador. **Habits:** Much as in Kelp Gull.

Ring-billed Gull, *Larus delawarensis*
Gaviota Piquianillada   Plate 26(5)

46–51 cm (18–20″). An *accidental* vagrant to w. Guayas coast. Adult has *bill yellow with conspicuous black band around tip* (flesh with black tip in first-year birds); iris pale yellow; legs greenish yellow. **Breeding adult** has mainly white body and *pale gray mantle.* In flight shows black outer primaries with

white spots near their tips, white tail. **Nonbreeding adult** similar but with dusky streaking on head and hindneck. **First-year birds** variably speckled with blackish and have *grayer* mantle than comparable stages of larger gulls, *narrower* black subterminal tail band, and blackish wingtips *without* white spots; bill pinkish with dusky tip; legs dull pinkish. **Similar species:** Cf. larger California and Herring Gulls (both equally rare or even rarer in Ecuador than Ring-billed). **Habits:** Much as in Kelp Gull, though less aggressive; never occurs far offshore; in its usual range regularly occurs inland.

[California Gull, *Larus californicus*
Gaviota de California]   Plate 26(4)

51–53.5 cm (20–21″). An *accidental* vagrant to w. Guayas coast. Adult has *rather long* yellow bill with *black and red spots near tip of lower mandible* (flesh colored with black tip in first-year birds); *eye dark brown*; *legs yellowish*. Plumages resemble those of Herring Gull; California differs mainly in its smaller size and soft-part colors; adult's

mantle somewhat less pale gray. **Similar species:** Cf. also somewhat smaller Ring-billed Gull. **Habits:** Much as in Kelp Gull.

Gray-hooded Gull, *Larus cirrocephalus*
Gaviota Cabecigris   Plate 26(7)

41–43 cm (16–17″). An attractive gull, locally fairly common on *coast and lagoons in w. Guayas* (mainly on *Santa Elena Peninsula*), smaller numbers elsewhere in southwest; breeds locally. **Adult** has *fairly long deep red bill tipped blackish* (duller in nonbreeders, yellowish tipped dusky in first-year birds), *straw-colored iris with narrow red eye-ring*, and *salmon-red legs*. Hood pearly gray *narrowly outlined with blackish* (hood paler and not outlined in nonbreeders), whiter on forehead; mantle pale gray; underparts, rump, and tail white. **In flight** relatively broadwinged, showing *large white wedge on leading edge of outer wing* and mainly black primaries; *underside of outer wing extensively blackish*. **Juvenile** has brownish hood, narrow black tail-tip, and duskier wings with obscured pattern and browner coverts; **first-year birds** similar to juveniles but hood reduced to *dusky patch on ear-coverts* and less black on tail. **Similar species:** A distinctively lanky and long-necked gull. Adults with their gray heads are easy, but younger stages can be confused with other gulls. Cf. especially smaller Franklin's (which can also look "hooded" but never shows as much white on wing) and immature of larger Swallow-tailed Gull (more pelagic than Gray-hooded). **Habits:** Seen in largest numbers at its nesting colonies on islets in Ecuasal lagoons, foraging there and in nearby harbors. Feeds on a variety of food including (in addition to fish and marine invertebrates) flying insects, eggs, and garbage; around the Santa Elena Peninsula even kleptoparasitizes Brown Pelicans. **Voice:** Breeding birds have a loud, harsh, growling call (e.g., "craw, craw"), incessantly given near nesting colonies.

Andean Gull, *Larus serranus*
Gaviota Andina   Plate 26(8)

Mostly 3000–4200 m

46–48 cm (18–19"). A striking, *uniquely high-elevation* gull found around lakes and ponds in *paramo and temperate zone.* Bill and legs dusky-red; iris dark. **Breeding adult** has *glossy black hood* with conspicuous white eye-crescents; otherwise white with mantle pearly gray. **In flight** shows distinctive and complex pattern with *white outer wing crossed by black band across primaries*, primaries also black-tipped; underside of primaries black with white patch showing in outer primaries. **Nonbreeding adult** similar but with *hood reduced to black patch on ear-coverts*, also a narrow black eye-ring. **Juvenile** resembles preceding but with brownish mottling on wing-coverts and a subterminal black tailband. **Similar species:** *The only gull normally found in highlands.* Cf. younger plumages of Gray-hooded Gull, a species known only from coast. **Habits:** Usually seen in small groups, mainly around water but also flies high over paramo ridges and slopes. Feeds on a variety of prey items including insects and worms taken on fields and grasslands; also catches aerial insects and eats some garbage where available. Nests in small scattered colonies, sometimes even as solitary pairs in surprisingly small and isolated ponds. **Voice:** Agitated birds give a tern-like "keeyr" call, often repeated.

Laughing Gull, *Larus atricilla*
Gaviota Reidora   Plate 26(9)

38–43 cm (15–17"). *By far the most widespread gull along coast; a common boreal winter resident* occupying a range of aquatic habitats, but rarely venturing far to sea and only occasionally occurring a short distance inland (e.g., over rice fields); a few records from along rivers in lowlands of northeast and even in highlands. Occurs year-round; numbers greatest Oct.–Apr. Bill and legs black (former redder when breeding), bill looks "drooped." **Nonbreeding adult** has head and underparts white with brownish gray wash or mottling around eyes and on nape; *mantle leaden gray*; rump and tail white. **In flight** gray of mantle *blends into black wingtips*, and trailing edge of wing is white; wings relatively long and slender. **Breeding adult** (seen prior to northward migration) similar but with black hood and narrow white eye-crescents. **First-year birds** more brownish gray generally, *including variable but often extensive smudge or mottling across breast*; *rump and tail white* with *wide black subterminal band.* **Second-year birds** more like nonbreeding adult but with some gray on breast and dusky on tail. **Similar species:** Learning to recognize this gull is helpful as it can then be used as basis of comparison with other scarcer species. Cf. especially Franklin's and non-adult Gray-hooded Gulls. **Habits:** Often occurs in quite large flocks, loafing on shores and around lagoons, swimming more often than most gulls. **Voice:** The "laughing" call heard so often around breeding grounds is sometimes given in Ecuador just prior to onset of migration.

Franklin's Gull, *Larus pipixcan*
Gaviota de Franklin   Plate 26(10)

35.5–38 cm (14–15″). A transient and boreal winter resident (Oct.–May) along entire coast, with numbers greatest in Guayas. A few occur inland over rice fields. Bill and legs blackish (former red when breeding). **Non-breeding adult** has head and underparts white with *well-defined blackish half-hood from hindcrown to sides of head* and *white eye-crescents*; mantle gray; rump and tail white. **In flight** shows *distinct white bar separating gray of mantle from black of wingtips*; *tips of primaries also white*. **Breeding adult** (seen occasionally on northward passage) similar but with full black hood and conspicuous white eye-crescents. **First- and second-year birds** resemble respective stages of Laughing Gull but have *half-hood similar to nonbreeding adult's*, are whiter below (with less gray), and *lack black subterminal band on outermost tail feathers*. **Similar species:** All plumages recall those of much commoner Laughing Gull. Adults are told in flight by differing wing patterns (Laughing shows no white at all in wingtips) and by Laughing's smudgy, less clean-cut effect on head. Cf. also subadult Gray-hooded Gull. **Habits:** Similar to Laughing Gull, though Franklin's is more often pelagic and regularly migrates in flocks well offshore. Flight more buoyant and graceful than Laughing Gull's.

Sabine's Gull, *Xema sabini*
Gaviota de Sabine   Plate 26(12)

33–35.5 cm (13–14″). A striking *small* gull with *shallowly forked tail*; scarce transient and boreal winter visitant (Sep.–Mar.) to *offshore waters*. Bill black *with yellow tip* (tip

obscure or lacking in younger birds); iris dark, but narrow eye-ring red; legs black. **Nonbreeding adult** has dusky half-hood from hindcrown to sides of head; otherwise head and underparts white; mantle gray; rump and tail white. **In flight** shows *striking 3-part pattern*: gray wing-coverts, *contrasting white secondaries and inner primaries*, and *black outer primaries*. **Breeding adult** has *slaty gray hood* with black border. **Immature** much browner above, *feathers scaled whitish in younger birds*; *wing pattern the same* (though coverts brown); *narrow black tipping on tail-fork*. **Similar species:** This elegant little gull with bouyant flight is unlikely to be confused; Swallow-tailed Gull has much the same flight pattern but is much larger, etc. **Habits:** Usually seen singly, sometimes in association with terns (especially Commons and Arctics). For a gull, wingbeats are atypically deep, more tern-like.

Swallow-tailed Gull, *Creagrus furcatus*
Gaviota Tijereta   Plate 26(11)

53.5–58.5 cm (21–23″). A scarce *pelagic* visitant from Galápagos Islands to *offshore waters of southwest*. A *large* gull with *quite*

deeply forked tail, nearly unmistakable in any plumage. Bill black with *pale greenish tip* and *whitish spot at base*; *red eye-ring* surrounds an unusually large dark eye; *legs pink*. Elegant **breeding adult** has *blackish hood* becoming dark gray on neck; *mantle and breast paler gray*, with line on scapulars white; rump, tail, and belly white. Birds in this plumage have not been seen in mainland waters. **Nonbreeding adult** loses black hood but *retains large blackish patch around eyes and on ear-coverts*. **In flight** shows contrasting pattern with gray wing-coverts, *mainly white flight feathers*, and *black outer primaries*. **Immature** very different but also striking, with brown mantle feathers *boldly edged white* and *broad black tipping on tail-fork*; head pattern as in nonbreeding adult, but bill all black. **Similar species:** Not likely confused, but flight pattern is similar to that of much smaller Sabine's Gull. **Habits:** Seen singly or in at most small groups, most often resting inactively on surface water. Feeds mainly at night (on squid). **Voice:** Seems essentially silent away from breeding grounds.

Sterna Terns

Most terns are now classified in this large and quite variable genus. Few of them nest in Ecuador, and of the four species that do, only two (Gull-billed and Bridled) are coastal; the others (Yellow-billed and Large-billed) breed along eastern rivers. Almost all other terns are boreal migrants; two (Peruvian and Inca) disperse from farther south. As with gulls, identification can be difficult. Pay particular attention to *overall size, bill shape and color*, and *details of wing and tail patterns* (the last best seen in flight).

Gull-billed Tern, *Sterna nilotica*
Gaviotín Piquigrueso   Plate 27(1)

33–38 cm (13–15″). *Locally fairly common on coastal lagoons of southwest, favoring salt-evaporation and shrimp-production ponds*; breeds locally. Formerly placed in genus *Gelochelidon*. A *very pale* tern with *tail only shallowly forked; looks short-tailed in flight. Heavy, gull-like bill black*; rather long legs also black. **Breeding adult** has black crown and nape; otherwise white with *very pale gray mantle and upperwing*. **Nonbreeding adult** similar; no black on crown, but has

dusky patch through eyes onto ear-coverts; primaries somewhat duskier-tipped. **Juvenile** resembles nonbreeding adult though head tinged brownish and feathers of back and wing-coverts tipped brown (resulting in scaly effect). **Similar species:** Sandwich Tern can also look very white but has notably slender bill and longer, more deeply forked tail; it has black on rearcrown (not as patch through eyes). **Habits:** Forages principally by hawking for insects over shallow bodies of water and adjacent open terrain, dropping down to seize prey from water's surface or land, sometimes even capturing insects while walking around (especially near its nesting colonies). Unlike most other terns rarely or never plunge-dives, and hardly ever seen over open ocean. **Voice:** Frequently heard call (especially near nesting colonies) a distinctive sharp, raspy "kay-wék, kay-wék."

[Caspian Tern, *Sterna caspia*
Gaviotín Piquirrojo]   Plate 27(3)

51–56 cm (20–22″). An *accidental* vagrant to near Manabí coast. Formerly placed in genus *Hydroprogne*. A *very large* tern with *heavy blood-red bill* usually tipped blackish; legs black. Tail only shallowly forked. **Breeding**

adult has black crown and nape; otherwise white with pale gray mantle and upperwing. **Nonbreeding adult** similar but *entire crown narrowly streaked with white*. **In flight** looks broad-winged; *primaries edged blackish, this most prominent from below*. **Similar species:** Much more numerous Royal Tern has more orange and somewhat slimmer bill, broadly white forehead in nonbreeding plumage, more deeply forked tail, and whiter underwing (with no blackish). **Habits:** Ecuador bird was seen over a shallow freshwater lake; though often frequenting coastal lagoons, Caspians rarely or never feed over ocean. **Voice:** Most common call, given especially in flight, a distinctive and startlingly loud harsh "krrr-árk!"

Royal Tern, *Sterna maxima*
Gaviotín Real   Plate 27(2)

46–51 cm (18–20″). Generally a *numerous and widespread* transient and visitant along entire coast; occurs year-round but does not breed. *Fairly heavy bill reddish orange to yellow-orange*; legs black. Tail moderately forked. **Breeding adult** has black crown and nape, but quickly molts into **nonbreeding plumage** that is normally seen in Ecuador: mostly white with *rearcrown and nape black* that *contrasts with white forecrown*, feathers forming a *slight bushy crest* (from behind can show some white streaking); mantle and upperwing pale gray. **In flight** shows blackish-edged primaries, visible mainly from above. **Similar species:** Elegant Tern (which see) is smaller and slenderer. Cf. also much rarer Caspian Tern. **Habits:** A strong-flying tern that forages by plunge-diving for fish, often from considerable heights; Royals often feed well out to sea. Roosting birds often gather in flocks that rest together on sandy shorelines, sometimes with other terns; also frequently perchs on rocks, pilings, etc. **Voice:** Most common call a distinctive shrill "chirrik," often given in flight.

Elegant Tern, *Sterna elegans*
Gaviotín Elegante   Plate 27(4)

40.5–43 cm (16–17″). A transient (especially) and boreal winter visitant along entire coast, often with usually larger numbers of more widespread and larger Royal Tern, *which Elegant closely resembles* (size difference usually apparent only when direct comparison is possible). Main points of distinction are as follows. Elegant's *yellow-orange to reddish orange* bill (reddest at onset of breeding season) is *longer, more slender, and very slightly decurved*; crest *slightly longer*; fully solid black crown retained longer (and perhaps more often seen in Ecuador than fully black-crowned Royals); in nonbreeders *black of rearcrown extends forward to encompass eye* (in Royals dark eye typically stands out in a white face); a *rosy-pink flush on breast* is sometimes evident, especially on breeding-plumage birds. **Habits:** Similar to Royal Tern, though Elegants rarely forage as far offshore; flock size can occasionally be larger. Most frequent on Santa Elena Peninsula.

Sandwich Tern, *Sterna sandvicensis*
Gaviotín de Sandwich   Plate 27(5)

40.5–43 cm (16–17″). A transient and boreal winter visitant along coast, often with usually larger numbers of more widespread and somewhat larger Royal Tern. *Long slender black bill with yellow tip* (but tip color hard to discern at a distance, and yellow can even

be lacking); legs black. Tail quite deeply forked. **Nonbreeding adult** mostly white with rearcrown and nape contrastingly black, feathers forming slight bushy crest; mantle pale gray. **Breeding adult** similar but with all-black crown. **In flight** shows blackish-edged primaries, visible mainly from above. **Similar species:** Royal and Elegant Terns have bill some shade of orange; Elegant is virtually identical to Sandwich in form, but Royal is larger and heavier-billed. Gull-billed Tern's bill is much shorter and heavier, and its tail shorter and less deeply forked; non-breeders differ in patterning of black on head (an *ear-patch* in Gull-billed). Non-breeding Common Tern somewhat smaller and slighter with a dark carpal bar, reddish legs, and usually at least some reddish at base of bill. **Habits:** Similar to Royal Tern; as with Elegant Tern, flock size in Sandwich can occasionally be larger than it ever seems to be with Royal.

Common Tern, *Sterna hirundo*
Gaviotín Común   Plate 27(6)

33–38 cm (13–15″). A locally common transient and boreal winter visitant to sandy

coastlines and lagoons *along coast*, numbers greatest around Santa Elena Peninsula; accidental in lowlands of northeast. *Bill blackish with some red (yellowish* in first-year birds) *near base (coral red with black tip* in breeding adults); *legs reddish* (brighter in breeding adults). Tail deeply forked. **Nonbreeding adult** mostly white with *black hindcrown and nape*; mantle pale gray with *dark bar along leading edge of inner wing* (the carpal bar). **Breeding adult** similar but with solid black crown, no carpal bar, and gray tinge below. **In flight** shows *blackish tipping to primaries* and *dusky outer web on outer pair of tail feathers*. **Similar species:** Cf. very similar Arctic Tern (much less numerous in Ecuador). Somewhat larger Sandwich Tern is whiter generally with longer yellow-tipped bill and black legs. **Habits:** A graceful tern, with light and buoyant flight and deep wingbeats. Feeding birds often hover before plunging into water. Usually feeds in coastal waters, rarely foraging beyond sight of land. **Voice:** Generally silent in Ecuador but may give a sharp excited-sounding "kip" call, sometimes in series.

Arctic Tern, *Sterna paradisaea*
Gaviotín del Artico   Plate 27(7)

33–38 cm (13–15″). A transient (mainly) and boreal winter visitant (mostly Aug.–Nov. and Apr.–May) to *offshore waters* and sandy coastlines and lagoons along coast, primarily on Santa Elena Peninsula; accidental in lowlands of northeast. In all plumages closely resembles more numerous Common Tern; major points of distinction are as follows. *Bill somewhat shorter, entirely bright red* in breeding-plumage adults (blackish at other times); *legs somewhat shorter* (this often evident on birds resting side by side); breeding-plumage birds grayer below with narrow white band between gray and black crown; carpal bar in nonbreeding birds less distinct. In flight *primaries white* (this evident both from above and below) with *only narrow black trailing edge to flight feathers* (quite different from broader blackish wedge seen on underside of Common's primaries); *tail entirely white* (*lacking* Common's dusky outer web to outermost rectrix). **Habits:** Similar to Common Tern.

[South American Tern, *Sterna hirundinacea*
Gaviotín Sudamericano]   Plate 27(8)

40.5–43 cm (16–17″). A *casual* visitant to Santa Elena Peninsula coast. Resembles smaller Arctic Tern in all plumages, but *bill longer and somewhat heavier* and legs longer. Individuals identified in Ecuador have been in breeding plumage, with *entirely blood red bills*. These have occurred at a time (Jul.–Aug.) when any Arctic Terns present would likely not be in breeding plumage. **Habits:** As in Arctic and Common Terns. **Voice:** Common call, especially when breeding, a harsh drawn-out "kyarrr," also a "kip" sometimes repeated.

Yellow-billed Tern, *Sterna superciliaris*
Gaviotín Amazónico   Plate 27(9)

23–25.5 cm (9–10″). Fairly common and widespread *along larger rivers in lowlands of east*, also feeding over nearby oxbow lakes. *Bill entirely yellow*; legs greenish yellow to lime green. Tail quite deeply forked. **Breeding adult** has black crown and nape with *white forehead extending back as narrow stripe over eye*; otherwise pale gray above, white below. **Nonbreeding adult**

To 400 m

similar but with crown mottled gray and black (remaining blacker on nape). **In flight** upperwing mainly pale gray with outer two primaries black and middle primaries dusky. **Similar species:** So much smaller than other terns found on e. rivers that confusion unlikely; Least and Peruvian Terns (which see) are similar but in Ecuador are strictly coastal. **Habits:** Usually seen in pairs or small groups, often resting on sandbars or winging purposefully over water. Forages mostly by hovering with very fast wingbeats, plunging straight down after small fish. Nests in small colonies, mainly during latter months of year. **Voice:** Occasionally gives various sharp penetrating calls, e.g., a repeated "kik" or "keek," also a "kirrik," especially in flight.

[Least Tern, *Sterna antillarum*
Gaviotín Menor]   Plate 27(10)

21.5–23 cm (8½–9″). A *casual* boreal winter visitant to coast. Closely resembles somewhat larger Yellow-billed Tern, *which does not occur in w. Ecuador*. Differs from Yellow-billed in having *bill slightly shorter and*

slimmer; breeding adult's bill yellow *narrowly tipped black*, in nonbreeders *brown to blackish* (which Yellow-billed's never is). Legs yellow, duller in nonbreeding plumage. In plumage the two species are similar (including wing pattern); nonbreeding Leasts, however, generally show *well-marked carpal bar* that is never present in Yellow-billeds. **Similar species:** Peruvian Tern slightly larger and distinctly grayer below. **Habits:** Similar to Yellow-billed Tern. In Ecuador, Least would be expected to forage mainly over inshore waters or lagoons.

Peruvian Tern, *Sterna lorata*
Gaviotín Peruano   Plate 27(11)

23–24 cm (9–9½″). A *scarce* austral winter visitant to *sw. coast*; *most years not reported at all.* *Bill yellow with terminal third black*, but mainly blackish in nonbreeders; legs brownish yellow. **Breeding adult** has black crown and nape with white forehead extending back as narrow stripe over eye; otherwise gray above, *pale gray below.* **Nonbreeding adult** similar but crown mottled gray and black. **In flight** upperwing mainly gray with *at least outer four primaries blackish.* **Similar species:** Least Tern slightly smaller and somewhat paler, especially below (white where Peruvian looks distinctly gray); bill of breeding Peruvian more broadly tipped black. **Habits:** Found singly or in small groups, favoring sandy beaches and flats. Forages by hovering over shallow water in bays, estuaries, and lagoons (usually not open ocean), plunging in after fish. **Voice:** Most frequent call, given especially in flight, a mellow "churi," often repeated in series.

Bridled Tern, *Sterna anaethetus*
Gaviotín Embridado   Plate 27(12)

35.5–38 cm (14–15″). A *pelagic* tern, known in Ecuador only as a breeder on *a single islet off nw. Guayas.* Bill and legs black. *Tail deeply forked.* **Adult** has *white forehead extending back as narrow stripe to just behind eye;* crown and nape black; *collar whitish, blending into dark brownish gray upperparts.* Tail pale gray with outer feathers white. Underparts white. **Juvenile** similar but crown streaked whitish and black, and mantle with pale feather edging. **Similar species:** No other tern occurring in Ecuador combines dark upperparts with deeply forked tail. **Habits:** A long-winged tern that normally approaches land only to nest; sometimes rests on flotsam in drift lines, but most often seen in steady flight with deep wingstrokes. Feeds principally by swooping low over water and snatching prey near surface; sometimes plunges in a short distance. **Voice:** Mainly around breeding colonies gives a nasal "kyaar."

Large-Billed Tern, *Phaetusa simplex*
Gaviotín Picudo   Plate 27(15)

Mostly below 250 m

38–40.5 cm (15–16″). A *large* tern with *bold wing pattern* and *quite short tail* found *along rivers in lowlands of east.* Very heavy bill yellow; dull yellowish green legs. Tail only slightly forked. **Breeding adult** has crown and ear-coverts black; *back, rump, and tail gray* (darker than in many other terns); frontlet and entire underparts white. **Nonbreeding adult** similar but with some white on forecrown. **In flight** shows very contrasty pattern with *large area of white on greater-coverts and secondaries* and *black primaries.* **Similar species:** Large size, stout yellow bill, and flashing wing-pattern combined with riverine habitat should preclude confusion. **Habits:** Often found in small groups, regularly resting on sandbars but also sometimes perching on low branches. Nests in colonies, often with Yellow-billed Terns and Black Skimmers, on more remote sandbars. **Voice:** Most often silent, but can be quite vocal around nesting colonies, there giving loud squealing calls reminiscent of a Laughing Gull though shriller.

Black Tern, *Chlidonias niger*
Gaviotín Negro   Plate 27(14)

23–25.5 cm (9–10″). A scarce transient and boreal winter visitant (mostly Aug.–Apr.) to *inshore waters along coast and on adjacent lagoons* (mainly saltwater); a few records from along rivers in lowlands of northeast. A *small* tern with *tail short and only notched.* Bill and legs black. **Nonbreeding plumage** *mostly gray above* but head white with *black patch on crown extending down behind eye onto ear-coverts,* crown pale-streaked. White below with *dusky smudge on sides of chest* (just in front of

wing). **Breeding plumage** (rarely seen in Ecuador) quite different, *much darker generally: entire head, neck, and underparts velvety black* (head deeper black in ♂) blending into smooth gray mantle, rump, and tail; lower belly and crissum white. Splotchy molting birds are frequent. **In flight** shows uniform gray underwing. **Similar species:** Small size together with pied head pattern and mainly gray upperparts distinctive. **Habits:** Usually seen singly or in small groups, though elsewhere wintering birds can congregate in larger flocks. Flight graceful and buoyant, often erratic like a nighthawk's but at other times steadier and more purposeful. Plunge-dives only rarely, instead pausing to hover while daintily picking up morsels from water's surface.

Inca Tern, *Larosterna inca*
Gaviotín Inca   Plate 27(13)

40.5–43 cm (16–17″). A *very rare* and erratic austral visitant to coast of w. Guayas, favoring harbors and rocky headlands; *not present at all in most years. Beautiful and unmistakable.* Tail somewhat forked. *Rather heavy bill dark red* with yellow wattle at gape; legs also dark red. **Adult** *slaty gray,* crown blacker, with *conspicuous white plumes springing from base of bill and curling down over sides of neck.* Wings and tail blackish, wings with *obvious white trailing edge on inner flight feathers.* **Immature** browner with much less prominent and grayer tufts. **Habits:** Flight tends to be fluttering with rather shallow wingbeats. Feeds mainly by swooping low over water, diving relatively little. In Peru it roosts and nests on cliffs, locally even on buildings, and can be very tame.

Skimmers: Rynchopidae (1)

A distinctive tern relative with a *unique narrow bill and feeding behavior*. **Sexes are alike.**

Black Skimmer, *Rynchops niger*
Rayador Negro   Plate 27(16)

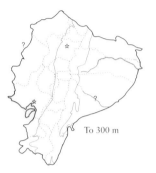

To 300 m

40.5–46.5 cm (16–18½″), ♂♂ larger than ♀♀. Striking and unmistakable, *found in small numbers along larger rivers in lowlands of east*; some may also persist along sw. coast and rivers, but recent records few. *Bill stout but very compressed laterally, with lower mandible considerably longer than upper*; *basal half bright red and outer half black*. Legs also red. **Breeding adult** *black above* with *forehead and underparts white*. Wings long, narrow, and pointed, black above sometimes (in fresh plumage) with narrow white trailing edge to inner flight feathers (often lacking or obscure); underwing smoky gray. Rather short tail somewhat forked, dusky. **Nonbreeding adult** similar but somewhat browner above with whitish collar. **Juvenile** browner and more scaled above, usually with dusky on crown and through eye; bill and legs duller. **Habits:** In east usually seen in small groups, often loafing on sandbars with Large-billed and Yellow-billed Terns; at least locally in more remote areas, larger numbers may gather to nest colonially. Flight languid with slow graceful wingbeats. Feeding unique: skimmers fly back and forth over a stretch of water, bill open wide with lower mandible "plowing" water's surface and snapping shut upon contacting a small fish or crustacean. Nocturnal feeding is frequent. **Voice:** Has a distinctive sharp, nasal, barking call, e.g., "aow," given mainly in flight and around colonies.

Columbiformes

Pigeons and Doves: Columbidae (28)

A cosmopolitan group of attractive but usually subtly colored birds of varying sizes; the term "pigeon" refers to larger species, "dove" to smaller ones, but the names can be used more or less interchangeably. They are proportionately large-bodied birds with small heads and slender bills with a fleshy cere; legs are short. The plumage is dense and soft, and some species have patches of iridescent color. In Ecuador pigeons and doves range widely in both lowland and montane forests and in semiopen terrain, with some species being arboreal but others (e.g., the ground-doves, *Leptotila*, and the quail-doves) more or less terrestrial. **Sexes are usually alike,** though not in the ground-doves or some quail-doves. Their simple cooing songs are often important for species identification. Pigeons and doves feed on fruit and seeds, and they can—uniquely among birds—drink by directly sucking up water. Nests are flimsy twig structures, often not well hidden; nestlings are at first fed regurgitated "pigeon's milk" produced by the lining of their parents' crops.

Columba Pigeons

Fairly large to large *arboreal* pigeons found primarily in the canopy of humid and montane forests. *Columba* are some shade of vinaceous to grayish or chestnut brown with little pattern except in two distinctive species (Band-tailed and Scaled). Most are inconspicuous, heard more often than seen.

Rock Pigeon, *Columba livia*
Paloma Doméstica   Not illustrated

33–35.5 cm (13–14"). A feral non-native resident in towns and cities, with largest numbers in highlands. Often called Rock Dove. Plumage notably variable. Ancestral form *basically gray*, darker above, with green sheen on neck and *two black bars on wing-coverts*; *rump usually contrastingly pale (often white)*; tail gray with blackish subterminal band. Variants range from mostly or entirely white to mainly blackish, beige, or even fawn; patterns are often blotchy. **Similar species:** Can cause confusion with various native *Columba* pigeons. In flight shape reminiscent of a falcon, especially Peregrine. **Habits:** Gregarious around houses or other buildings, where often tame and sometimes maintained in semicaptivity; originally nested on cliffs, but this has not been reported in Ecuador. Feeds on ground in built-up areas and on adjacent lawns or fields. Flight powerful and direct. **Voice:** Frequently gives a soft cooing.

normally found in highlands. Plumbeous and Ruddy Pigeons do occur up into subtropical forests but are smaller, more uniform, and much less conspicuous, rarely gregarious and rarely flying high above canopy as Band-tailed so often does. **Habits:** An arboreal pigeon most often seen in fast-flying flocks that may sweep by overhead or suddenly burst from cover with a great wing clapping. Seems to move about seasonally in response to food availability. Though sometimes perching in the open, at rest usually not very conspicuous, remaining in cover of leafy branches; almost always stays high. **Voice:** Not very vocal, less so than other *Columba*. Song a weak series of deep low-pitched cooing notes, e.g., "cuh-hooo, cuh-hoo, cuh-hoo . . . ," repeated up to 6–10 times; pitch is similar to that of White-throated Quail-Dove's song. In flight sometimes gives a growly "wrrreenh."

Band-tailed Pigeon, *Columba fasciata*
Paloma Collareja   Plate 28(1)

Mostly 1500–3000 m, locally (seasonally?) lower (W)

Scaled Pigeon, *Columba speciosa*
Paloma Escamosa   Plate 28(5)

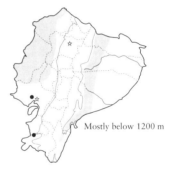

Mostly below 1200 m

35.5–37 cm (14–14½"). A *large montane* pigeon, *generally numerous and widespread in canopy and borders of subtropical and (especially) temperate forest and woodland*, regularly occurring even where forest has been reduced to small degraded patches. *Bill bright orange-yellow*; iris pale purplish, narrow eye-ring red; legs yellow. Crown and most of underparts vinaceous, grayer on throat. *Conspicuous white crescent on hindneck*; upperparts brownish gray, glossed bronzy green on hindneck and upper back. Basal half of tail bluish gray, *terminal half pale ashy gray, the two halves separated by a blackish band*. **Similar species:** This handsome large pigeon is the only *Columba*

33–35.5 cm (13–14"). A *uniquely boldly scaled pigeon*, scarce and local in canopy and borders of humid forest and secondary woodland in lowlands and foothills of west and along e. base of Andes. *Bill red with yellow tip*; iris reddish with *red eye-ring*; legs purplish. *Head and upperparts rich purplish chestnut*; tail blackish. *Neck boldly scaled white and blackish, upper back boldly scaled rufous and blackish*. Breast and belly vinaceous *with heavy dusky scalloping*, fainter on whiter lower belly and crissum. **Similar species:** Scalloped pattern can be hard to discern in poor light, when the mainly red bill stands out more. Most apt to be confused with Pale-vented Pigeon, which likewise

often perches in the open and flies by overhead. **Habits:** Infrequently seen in Ecuador.
Usually noted singly or in pairs, often resting
on an exposed limb in canopy; seems most
numerous (perhaps just more easily seen?) in
partially deforested country. **Voice:** Usual
song a low-pitched, lazy, and rhythmic
"whooo, wh-wh-whooo, wh-wh-whooo."

Pale-vented Pigeon, *Columba cayennensis*
Paloma Ventripálida   Plate 28(6)

Below 500 m

28–30.5 cm (11–12″). *Widespread* in *borders*
of humid forest and woodland, and in clearings in lowlands of east and west; *most
numerous along river edges, on islands, and
around certain lakes in the east.* Iris reddish
brown with narrow red eye-ring; legs
reddish. Head bluish gray with more vinaceous forecrown and green iridescence on
nape. Above rich vinaceous *becoming gray
on rump and uppertail-coverts*; *tail contrastingly pale grayish brown.* Throat whitish;
breast vinaceous, *becoming pale gray on
belly and crissum.* **Similar species:** Smaller
Columba pigeons more uniformly dark than
this richly colored species, and lack paler
belly; in flight Pale-vented's gray rump and
pale tail are usually obvious. Cf. range-
restricted Marañón Pigeon. **Habits:** An
arboreal but essentially *nonforest* pigeon.
Often perches in the open and, unlike smaller
Columba, regularly flies high. In display
flight climbs up with strong deep wingstrokes, then glides back down in an exaggerated dihedral. **Voice:** Frequently heard
song a rather fast "woooh; wok, wuh-
woooh; wuk, wuh-woooh" with phraseology
similar to Scaled Pigeon's but somewhat
faster and higher-pitched.

[Marañón Pigeon, *Columba oenops*
Paloma del Marañón]   Plate 28(7)

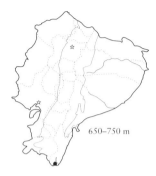

650–750 m

30.5–33 cm (12–13″). Apparently rare in
canopy and borders of deciduous and semihumid forest and woodland in *Río Marañón
drainage around Zumba.* Formerly called
Peruvian Pigeon. *Bill bluish gray with some
red at base*; iris dark red; legs coral pink. Rich
vinaceous above with *outer wing-coverts,
rump, and uppertail-coverts gray*; tail blackish. Throat and breast vinaceous; *belly gray,
becoming darker gray on crissum.* **Similar
species:** The only *Columba* known to occur
around Zumba (though Ruddy Pigeon is
found north toward Valladolid). Marañón
most resembles Pale-vented Pigeon, but latter
has black bill, paler belly, paler terminal band
on tail. **Habits:** Hardly known in Ecuador
(only a few sightings). Behavior similar to
Pale-vented Pigeon's, likewise occurring
singly or in small groups, often perching in
semiopen and flying just above canopy.
Voice: Song (in Peru) a slow "wa-oooo, wa-
wa-oooo."

Ruddy Pigeon, *Columba subvinacea*
Paloma Rojiza   Plate 28(3)

Mostly below 1700 m

28–30.5 cm (11–12″). Fairly common in canopy and borders of humid forest in *lowlands of east and west, also ranging up into lower subtropics in montane forest on both slopes.* Bill black; *iris reddish*; legs reddish. *Mostly vinaceous.* **Eastern birds** slightly darker generally and have darker more contrasting bronzy wings; **western birds** paler and more uniform, with more brownish wings. **Similar species:** Very closely resembles Plumbeous Pigeon, with which sympatric in e. lowlands as well as in foothills and subtropics on both slopes. Often best distinguished by voice (see below). Plumbeous somewhat heavier billed, and its iris is pale (not reddish); these differences can be made out on close perched birds. In the east, Plumbeous slightly paler and grayer below (not so dark a vinaceous), and bronzy wings therefore contrast more. In the west, Plumbeous slightly darker below, and wings darker and bronzier (not so rufescent). Recall that Plumbeous does not occur in lowlands of west; there, however, one does have to deal with similar Dusky Pigeon (which see). **Habits:** Usually found singly or in pairs, remaining in canopy and not often perching in open; several may gather at fruiting trees. Typically flies through canopy, rarely at any height above it. **Voice:** Often heard song a 4-noted mellow rhythmic "wut, wu-whuú-wu," somewhat faster and higher-pitched than Plumbeous Pigeon's song, more syncopated; Ruddy's song does not vary geographically. A useful onomatopoeic transcription is "hit-the-foul-pole." Also gives a throaty growl, "rrrow," similar to other small *Columba*.

Plumbeous Pigeon, *Columba plumbea*
Paloma Plomiza   Plate 28(2)

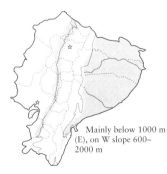

Mainly below 1000 m (E), on W slope 600–2000 m

29.5–32 cm (11½–12½″). Fairly common in canopy and borders of humid forest in *lowlands and foothills of east*, but *in west found only in foothills and subtropical zone* (not in lowlands). Bill black; *iris pale grayish in west, pale yellow in east* (not reddish, as in Ruddy Pigeon); legs pinkish red. *Mostly vinaceous,* wings and tail darker and bronzier. **Eastern birds** paler and grayer on head, neck, and underparts (except that in far southeast they are duller below and darker above); **western birds** darker generally, such that wings contrast less with underparts. **Similar species:** Easily confused with Ruddy Pigeon; for full discussion, see that species. **Habits:** Similar to Ruddy Pigeon, routinely occurring with it, especially in e. lowlands; there seems to be little consistent habitat differentiation. **Voice:** Often heard song east of Andes a 3-noted rhythmic "whuk-whuk-whuoó;" west of Andes similarly patterned but a little faster and more clipped, "wop, wop, wh-ohh." Also has a throaty growl similar to Ruddy's.

Dusky Pigeon, *Columba goodsoni*
Paloma Oscura   Plate 28(4)

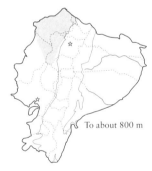

To about 800 m

27–28 cm (10½–11″). *Canopy and borders of humid forest in lowlands and foothills of northwest.* To about 800 m. Bill black; iris red, eye-ring reddish; legs pinkish red. Dark vinaceous above, distinctly *grayer on head* and browner on wings. Throat whitish; *underparts vinaceous gray.* **Similar species:** Closely resembles sympatric race of Ruddy Pigeon; most easily distinguished by song (see below). Ruddy more uniform overall, being vinaceous (not so gray) on head (especially) and underparts; Dusky's bill very small. Cf. also Plumbeous Pigeon (perhaps locally overlapping with Dusky in foothill zone). **Habits:**

Similar to Ruddy Pigeon, and often with it. **Voice:** Frequently heard song a fast rhythmic "whoóa? pup-pup," with emphasis on first syllable. This differs strikingly from Ruddy Pigeon's 4-noted song; compared to Plumbeous, note that *Dusky's last 2 notes are short and quick* (in Plumbeous, first 2 notes are short, last drawled). Dusky has throaty growl similar to Ruddy's.

Zenaida Doves

Rather plain brownish doves, larger than ground-doves, found in semiopen terrain and groves of trees; tails are somewhat graduated with *conspicuous white on corners*. They feed mainly on the ground and (unlike *Leptotila*) can be gregarious.

Eared Dove, *Zenaida auriculata*
Tórtola Orejuda   Plate 29(1)

To 3200 m above Quito

25.5–26 cm (10–10¼"). A plain, midsized dove *common in semiopen and agricultural areas as well as towns and cities in more arid highlands*, smaller numbers also in *drier lowlands of west*. Bill black; legs coral pink. Above dull brown with bluish gray crown, *two dark spots on ear-coverts* (the "ears"), and purple iridescence on neck. Wings with *several large black spots on tertials; graduated tail broadly tipped and edged white* (conspicuous in flight). Below pale vinaceous, lower belly pale buff. **Similar species:** Ground-doves much smaller. Larger and heavier White-tipped Dove lacks head and wing spots and has more ample tail that shows only a narrow terminal band of white. In flight note that Eared shows more white in tail (but only on corners); White-tipped usually seen singly (not in flocks, as Eared so often is). Black-winged Ground-Dove occurs

in paramo, above elevations where Eared typically ranges. **Habits:** Conspicuous in some areas, especially in settled parts of highlands where locally becomes quite tame; regularly perches on buildings and wires. Potters about on ground, head nodding back and forth, often in small groups; larger flocks congregate to feed on agricultural fields. Flight strong and fast, flocks often winging past overhead. **Voice:** Not especially vocal, merely giving a subdued cooing "whoo-oo" that does not often attract attention.

West Peruvian Dove, *Zenaida meloda*
Tórtola Melódica   Plate 29(2)

Mostly below 200 m, but to 700 m in Loja

28.5–29 cm (11¼–11½"). *Woodland and groves in more arid lowlands of southwest.* Formerly considered conspecific with White-winged Dove (*Z. asiatica*) of sw. United States to Panama, which has very different song. Bill black; iris reddish with *prominent blue eye-ring*; legs coral red. Above dull brown with dark spot on ear-coverts and magenta iridescence on neck. *Large white patch on wing-coverts* (conspicuous in flight but prominent on perched birds as well) and blackish flight feathers; somewhat rounded tail with *black subterminal band and obvious white tips.* Below uniform soft buffy grayish, grayest on crissum. **Similar species:** No other Ecuadorian dove has such prominent white in wing (Eared Dove has none). **Habits:** Feeds mainly on open ground but perches and roosts freely in trees (regularly in palms). Often in small groups. **Voice:** Song a distinctive and often-heard, mournful, rhythmic "coo, coo-ooo-poop, coo-ooo-poop, coo-ooo" (with some variation in phrasing), repeated at intervals through day.

Columbina Ground-Doves

Small, short-tailed doves of open country, often feeding in flocks on the ground. Most species show *extensive rufous in the primaries*, conspicuous in flight. Males are somewhat more colorful and boldly marked.

Common Ground-Dove, *Columbina passerina*
Tortolita Común   Plate 29(3)

Mostly 1300–3000 m

16–16.5 cm (6¼–6½"). A *small, scaly-breasted* ground-dove found in *open and semiopen terrain in arid highlands south to Azuay*. Bill basally *pale dull reddish* (even duller in ♀); legs pale pink. ♂ above pale olive brown, gray on nape; *forehead, face, and entire underparts pale vinaceous, feathers of breast and sides of neck dark-centered imparting scaly or scalloped effect.* Wings with a few large black spots on coverts, *primaries contrastingly rufous* (conspicuous in flight, but mainly hidden at rest); tail mainly blackish (central feathers grayish brown), outer feathers narrowly tipped white. ♀ differs in its pale drab grayish buff underparts (though *scaly breast pattern much the same*); spots on wing-coverts shiny rufous. **Similar species:** Likely confused only with equally small Plain-breasted Ground-Dove, which is not known to occur in highlands; neither sex of Plain-breasted has scaly pattern on breast or neck. Croaking Ground-Dove also has pale bill base, but it has no breast scaling and in flight shows no rufous in wings. **Habits:** Feeds mainly on open ground, usually in pairs or small groups, allowing a close approach, then flushing up suddenly with a flash of rufous in wings. Often found along roadsides. **Voice:** Song, usually delivered from a low perch, a monotonously repeated "whoo-oop, whoo-oop, whoo-oop. . . ."

Plain-breasted Ground-Dove
Columbina minuta
Tortolita Menuda   Plate 29(4)

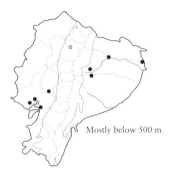

Mostly below 500 m

15.5–16 cm (6–6¼"). A *small* and *uniform* ground-dove, *scarce and local* (but apparently increasing) in open grassy areas of *lowlands in east and west*. Bill brownish, paler at base; legs pale pink. ♂ pale olive brown above, gray on nape and crown as well as uppertail-coverts; *below pale grayish vinaceous*, whiter on throat. Wings with a few large shiny violet spots on coverts and rufous primaries (conspicuous in flight) and underwing; tail mainly blackish (central feathers brown), outer feathers *narrowly tipped white*. ♀ like ♂ above but lacking gray; below pale drab grayish buff, whiter on throat and median belly. **Similar species:** ♀ Ruddy Ground-Dove (locally sympatric in e. lowlands) similar to ♀ Plain-breasted but somewhat larger and longer-tailed; Ruddy is more rufescent on rump, uppertail, and crissum, and its less extensive tail tipping is buff. In flight ♀ Ruddy shows less rufous in wings than Plain-breasted always does. In west, cf. larger Ecuadorian Ground-Dove (in flight easily told by black underwing-coverts and *lack* of rufous in primaries). **Habits:** Found singly or in pairs, less often in small groups. Like Common, Plain-breasted frequently feeds along roads, flushing up when approached. **Voice:** Song a steadily repeated hollow-sounding "whoop, whoop, whoop . . . ," pace somewhat faster than Common's (faster than one note/second).

Ruddy Ground-Dove, *Columbina talpacoti*
Tortolita Colorada   Plate 29(5)

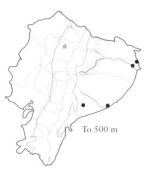

To 500 m

To 2000 m in Loja

16.5–18 cm (6½–7″). *Local in cleared areas and around towns in lowlands of east*; increasing. Bill blackish; tarsus pale pink. ♂ *mostly ruddy vinaceous* with paler face and throat and *contrasting bluish gray crown*. Wing-coverts with scattering of black spots and bars, primaries extensively rufous, axillars black; tail mainly black (central feathers rufous), outer webs of outer feathers rufous. ♀ *much paler and duller*: pale olive brown above and pale grayish buff below; primaries with less rufous than ♂; outer tail feathers narrowly tipped buff. **Similar species:** ♂ Ruddy distinctive, but ♀ can be confused with smaller and shorter-tailed Plain-breasted Ground-Dove (which see). These two are only *Columbina* in e. lowlands. Cf. also ♀ Blue Ground-Dove. **Habits:** Usually in pairs or small groups that potter about on ground in open areas; tame, but when pressed flush with a whirr and usually land in a nearby shrub or tree. First found in Ecuador only in mid-1970s, but now increasing in many areas. **Voice:** Song a steadily repeated "k-whoo, k-whoo, k-whoo. . . ."

Ecuadorian Ground-Dove, *Columbina buckleyi*
Tortolita Ecuatoriana   Plate 29(6)
16.5–18 cm (6½–7″). Fairly common and widespread in clearings and agricultural areas in *more humid lowlands of west*, in the south ranging up into subtropics. Also called Buckley's Ground-Dove; has been considered conspecific with Ruddy Ground-Dove. *Bill blackish*; legs pinkish. ♂ *soft pale gray above*, wings somewhat browner with scattering of large black spots on coverts. *Primaries and underwing-coverts black*; tail

mainly blackish (central feathers brownish gray), outer feathers tipped white. Below pale vinaceous, paler on face and forehead. ♀ like ♂ above but browner; pale dingy buff below, paler on face and whiter on throat and median belly. **Similar species:** Croaking Ground-Dove favors arid regions, but it and Ecuadorian do occur together in some areas. Both sexes of Croaking Ground-Dove differ in their orange base to bill, iridescent purple scapular bar, and pale underwing. Plain-breasted Ground-Dove is smaller and shorter-tailed, has rufous underwing and primaries. **Habits:** Similar to Ruddy Ground-Dove. Often occurs in quite large groups, sometimes together with Croaking Ground-Dove. **Voice:** Song a slow-paced "whoo-oo . . . whoo-oo . . . whoo-oo . . ."; similar to Ruddy Ground-Dove's song.

Croaking Ground-Dove, *Columbina cruziana*
Tortolita Croante   Plate 29(7)

Mostly below 2200 m

16.5–18 cm (6½–7″). *Common in arid scrub and agricultural and settled areas in more arid lowlands of west*, in south also ranging up into highland valleys. *Basal half of bill orange to yellow-orange* (not so bright in ♀); iris whitish; legs pink. ♂ pale grayish brown above except for *soft blue-gray head and neck*; *scapulars with iridescent chestnut-maroon bar* and wing-coverts with scattering of large black spots, flight feathers blackish, underwing-coverts grayish. Below mostly pale vinaceous. ♀ like ♂ above but decidedly browner; pale dingy buff below, whiter on belly. **Similar species:** Ecuadorian Ground-Dove lacks this species' conspicuous orange on bill and obvious scapular bar. **Habits:** Often in groups, numerous and widespread in arid regions; regularly frequents town plazas and other urban areas and can be quite tame. **Voice:** Song unmistakable and very different from other *Columbina*, a weird and mechanical-sounding "wreeoh" or "creeoh," repeated slowly but steadily at a rate of one note every 2 seconds.

Claravis Ground-Doves

Somewhat larger and longer-tailed than *Columbina* ground-doves, *Claravis* are more forest-based and arboreal, and generally are less numerous and less gregarious. There is strong sexual dimorphism, the distinctive males being notably colorful.

Blue Ground-Dove, *Claravis pretiosa*
Tortolita Azul   Plate 29(8)

Mostly below 1000 m

20.5–21.5 cm (8–8½"). Undergrowth and borders of humid secondary woodland and forest and adjacent clearings in lowlands of east and west, more numerous in west. Bill dusky; legs pink. Unmistakable ♂ *mainly bluish gray*, paler on face and underparts. Wing-coverts with black bars and large spots, flight feathers blackish; tail mainly black, central feathers blue-gray. ♀ brown above, *rump and central tail feathers contrastingly rufous* (conspicuous in flight). *Wing-coverts*

with large shiny chestnut bars and large spots*; outer tail feathers blackish. Breast pale grayish brown, belly pale bluish gray. **Similar species:** ♀ somewhat recalls ♀ ♀ of smaller Ruddy or Ecuadorian Ground-Doves, though those lack chestnut wing-spotting and russet rump and uppertail. Cf. also much rarer Maroon-chested Ground-Dove. **Habits:** Less conspicuous than *Columbina* ground-doves, much more often found inside forest and woodland. Usually in pairs and, though regularly walking and feeding on ground, rarely ranges far from cover. Often seen only in flight as a pair rapidly shoots past, regularly flying higher above ground than *Columbina*. **Voice:** Far-carrying song a distinctive slow-paced series of abrupt "boop" or "whoop" notes, hard to track to source. Usually calls from a hidden perch, often during midday.

Maroon-chested Ground-Dove
Claravis mondetoura
Tortolita Pechimarrón   Plate 29(9)

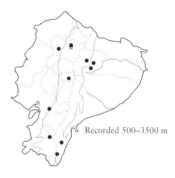

Recorded 500–3500 m

21.5–23 cm (8½–9"). *Very rare, local, and erratic* in undergrowth of *montane forest on both slopes*; few records. Iris mainly red; legs reddish pink. Unmistakable ♂ *dark bluish gray above* with white foreface. *Wings crossed by three bold violet bars*; tail gray, *outer feathers mostly white* (flashing conspicuously in flight). *Breast deep purplish maroon*; belly dark bluish gray, becoming whitish on midbelly and crissum. ♀ brown above with *contrasting pale tawny forehead and face*, rump and tail more rufescent, *outer feathers mostly buffy-white*; *wings crossed by three bold violet bars*. Throat whitish, breast grayish brown becoming buffy brown on flanks and whitish on median belly. **Similar** species: ♀ Blue Ground-Dove has no white in tail, lacks buff on foreface, and has more numerous but smaller chestnut patches in wing (not wide bands); it occurs at lower elevations. Extensive white on Maroon-chested's tail is easily seen, even on fast-flying birds. **Habits:** This enigmatic dove remains poorly known in Ecuador. Elsewhere its presence in an area is sometimes associated with brief periods of bamboo seeding, when it can be temporarily numerous. Even more than Blue Ground-Dove, Maroon-chested tends to remain inside dense cover. **Voice:** Song a far-carrying and long-continued "whoo-oóp; whoo-oóp; whoo-oóp; . . . ," sometimes (P. Coopmans) varied to "whoo-roó-oop, whoo-roó-oop. . . ."

Black-winged Ground-Dove
Metriopelia melanoptera
Tortolita Alinegra   Plate 29(10)

3300–4300 m

22.5–23.5 cm (8¾–9¼"). *Paramo and adjacent fields from Pichincha south locally to Azuay.* Bill black; iris grayish, with *prominent patch of bare orange-yellow skin in front of and below eye*; legs black. ♂ grayish brown above with *conspicuous white patch on bend of wing, flight feathers and underwing black; tail all black.* Below pinkish buff. ♀ similar but drabber and browner below. **Similar species:** Occurs at higher elevations than other Ecuadorian ground-doves. Most likely confused with similarly sized Eared Dove (which ranges well up into temperate zone), which differs in having white in tail but none on wing, etc. **Habits:** Feeds on open, nearly barren ground, often in small groups, huddling behind clumps of grass or rocks. Usually inconspicuous until it flushes with a loud wing-whirr; flight strong and swift. Often most easily spotted when perched atop a boulder, which it frequently does. **Voice:**

Very quiet. Breeding ♂♂ reported to give a rolling "trre-ooi" (Fjeldså and Krabbe 1990).

Leptotila Doves
Plump, square-tailed, mainly terrestrial mid-sized doves found mainly inside forest and woodland, primarily in the lowlands. One species (White-tipped) ranges higher and is more often in the semiopen. All have *outer tail feathers tipped white*, conspicuous as they flush or fly past; underwing-coverts are rufous. Bills are black, irides yellow, and legs pink to reddish pink.

White-tipped Dove, *Leptotila verreauxi*
Paloma Apical   Plate 29(12)

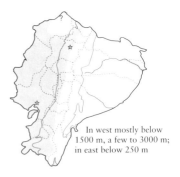

In west mostly below 1500 m, a few to 3000 m; in east below 250 m

26.5–28 cm (10½–11"). Fairly common on or near ground in deciduous and semihumid forest and woodland and clearings in *lowlands of west, also ranging up on w. slope and locally in interandean valleys*; also around *Zumba* in Río Marañón drainage, and in woodland on a few Río Napo islands. Orbital ring purplish red. Grayish brown above, whitish on forehead; tail blackish, *several outer feathers broadly white-tipped* (in flight, looks like a terminal band). Throat white; *underparts pale vinaceous*, becoming whitish on lower belly. **Río Napo birds** similar but with *orbital ring blue* and forecrown less contrasting. **Similar species:** Pallid Dove occurs with White-tipped in west; it shows blue-gray on crown and is more rufescent above (less grayish) and more extensively white on belly. Gray-fronted Dove (the common *Leptotila* in east) likewise has blue-gray forecrown and is distinctively buff-tinged on face and sides of neck; it has red eye-ring. Cf. also Eared Dove. **Habits:** Usually found singly as it walks about on ground, often inside woodland or forest but also coming out into open more often than other *Leptotila*, especially early in day when on little-traveled roads or tracks. Usually wary; a flushed bird sometimes lands on a low perch where it may nod head, raise rearparts, and pace back and forth nervously. Flight fast and strong, and generally low; white in tail often flashes conspicuously, but no more so than in congeners (its extent *not* a useful field character). **Voice:** Song a soft, hollow "who-whooó" with distinctive 2-noted effect (other *Leptotila* give single notes).

Pallid Dove, *Leptotila pallida*
Paloma Pálida   Plate 29(11)

26–27.5 cm (10¼–10¾″). On or near ground inside humid and semihumid forest and secondary woodland in *lowlands of west.* Orbital ring purplish red. Resembles White-tipped Dove but forehead whiter and *mid-crown and nape bluish gray*, *mantle and uppertail much more rufous* (contrasting sharply with pale vinaceous breast), and *belly more extensively white.* **Similar species:** White-tipped Dove often occurs with Pallid but ranges more often out into semiopen terrain; Pallid is more notably bicolored. Cf. also rare Ochre-bellied Dove (in a few places all three species range together). **Habits:** Similar to White-tipped Dove, though Pallid seems less likely to leave cover of forest or woodland. **Voice:** Song a simple mournful single-noted cooing, "whoooh."

Gray-fronted Dove, *Leptotila rufaxilla*
Paloma Frentigris   Plate 29(14)
26–27.5 cm (10¼–10¾″). On or near ground inside humid forest and secondary woodland,

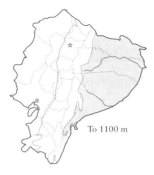

especially in rank growth near water (also frequent on islands), in *lowlands and foothills of east.* Orbital ring purplish red. Above mostly olive brown with *forecrown pale grayish becoming bluish gray on mid-crown*; tail blackish, outer feathers broadly white-tipped. *Face and sides of neck buff*; throat white, underparts pale vinaceous, whiter on lower belly. **Similar species:** The only *Leptotila* east of Andes except for White-tippeds in Zumba region (where Gray-fronted does not occur) and on Río Napo islands (where sympatric with Gray-fronted). White-tipped is plainer, lacking gray on crown and buff on face. **Habits:** Similar to White-tipped Dove. Gray-fronted favors such dense habitats it is much harder to see. **Voice:** Heard much more often than seen. Song a mournful single-noted cooing, "whooh," similar to Pallid's but somewhat higher pitched and sometimes slightly more downslurred.

Ochre-bellied Dove, *Leptotila ochraceiventris*
Paloma Ventriocrácea   Plate 29(13)
26–27.5 cm (10¼–10¾″). A handsome *Leptotila*, *now rare and local*, found on or near

ground *inside humid and semideciduous forest and mature secondary woodland in lowlands and foothills of southwest.* Orbital ring purplish red. Forehead whitish *shading to rusty purplish on crown and dull purplish on hindneck and upper back.* Above otherwise dark olive brown with subdued bronzy sheen; tail dark brown to dusky, outer feathers broadly white-tipped. Face buffyish, throat buffy white; breast pale vinaceous, *becoming ochraceous on belly and crissum.* **Similar species:** Richly colored, not likely confused with other *Leptotila.* Pallid much more rufous above and whiter on belly, White-tipped lacks purplish tones to foreparts and has whiter belly. **Habits:** Similar to White-tipped Dove, which nearly always outnumbers it. Seems shyer, only rarely walking in open. May engage in seasonal movements. **Voice:** Song a distinctive throaty "rrroowww" delivered slowly at about 10-second intervals, quite different from songs of White-tipped and Pallid Doves.

Geotrygon Quail-Doves

Plump, short-tailed pigeons ranging inside humid and montane forest where they walk on the ground. All are shy and inconspicuous, not encountered often and mainly heard. *Geotrygon* are relatively boldly marked and colorful, and the sexes differ in some species. Note their bold facial patterns (with *prominent facial and malar stripes*) and often glossy plumage (especially above). Unlike *Leptotila,* quail-doves often flush with little wing-whirr. Their low flight is strong and fast, and they sometimes rocket down roads or across clearings.

Sapphire Quail-Dove, *Geotrygon saphirina*
Paloma Perdiz Zafiro   Plate 28(8)

23–24 cm (9–9¹/₂"). A beautiful short-tailed quail-dove found on or near ground *inside terra firme forest in lowlands and foothills of east.* Bill, narrow eye-ring, and loral line purplish red; legs purplish pink. *Forehead whitish, midcrown gray, nape iridescent dark green; upper back bronzy, midback and scapulars iridescent purple, lower back and rump dark rich blue.* Wings bronzy chestnut with small white spot near tip of inner secondaries; tail dusky. *Broad stripe on*

Mostly below 1100 m

lower face white bordered below by black malar stripe; throat white, breast pale gray, belly white with buff-tinged lower flanks and crissum. **Similar species:** Colors may be hard to discern in dim light of forest interior, but bold facial pattern always obvious; no other *Geotrygon* in e. lowlands is so strongly marked. Indigo-crowned Quail-Dove occurs only west of Andes. **Habits:** Usually encountered solitarily, walking on forest floor; shy, when discovered often freezing, then either flushing or abruptly scurrying off. Has predilection for vicinity of water and fond of damp shady ravines with rank vegetation. **Voice:** Relatively high-pitched (for a dove) song a distinctive quavering "k-whohh . . . k-whohh . . . k-whohh . . ." with pause of about 3 seconds between calls.

Indigo-crowned Quail-Dove
Geotrygon purpurata
Paloma Perdiz Corona Indigo   Plate 28(9)

23–24 cm (9–9¹/₂"). A *stunning* quail-dove found on or near ground inside *humid and (mostly) foothill forest in northwest;* now

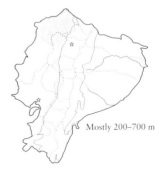

Mostly 200–700 m

scarce and local. Formerly considered con-specific with Sapphire Quail-Dove. *Bill black*; narrow eye-ring and loral line purplish red; legs purplish pink. *Forecrown and broad stripe on lower face white, in striking con-trast to deep blue crown and nape and black malar stripe*; otherwise similar to Sapphire Quail-Dove though lacking white spot on inner secondaries. **Similar species:** Sapphire Quail-Dove found only east of Andes. Olive-backed Quail-Dove also has contrasting white forecrown and facial stripe but other-wise is nowhere near as colorful as Indigo-crowned; Olive-backed mainly occurs at lower elevations. **Habits:** Similar to Sapphire Quail-Dove, though Indigo-crowned more often ranges on slopes away from water. **Voice:** Seems to vocalize infrequently (or only briefly?). Song (in Colombia) described as a soft, hollow "whot, whoo-oó-oit," weak and repeated at short intervals (Hilty and Brown 1986).

Olive-backed Quail-Dove
Geotrygon veraguensis
Paloma Perdiz Dorsioliva   Plate 28(10)

Below 300 m

23–24 cm (9–9½"). A *very dark* quail-dove found *on or near ground inside humid forest in lowlands of far northwest*. Bill black; iris yellow to pinkish, narrow eye-ring and loral line purplish red; legs purplish pink. ♂ *mostly dark olive brown above*, nape and upper back glossed purplish, with *contrast-ing white forehead and broad facial stripe*. Throat white, underparts dull purplish brown becoming whiter on median belly and buff on flanks and crissum. ♀ darker with buff-tinged forehead. **Similar species:** Con-trasting forehead and facial stripe stand out even in deep forest shade. Cf. Indigo-

crowned Quail-Dove (with similar head pattern, but much more colorful and boldly marked). **Habits:** Usually seen walking alone on forest floor, head nodding back and forth; favors areas near streams. Often unsuspi-cious, either freezing or quickly walking a short distance away, sometimes flushing to a low perch. **Voice:** Seems notably unvocal; in nearly 3 years of intensive field work in its range, O. Jahn (pers. comm.) has never knowingly heard it sing. Alarm call a series of abrupt, soft and low-pitched, frog-like "kwoúw" notes (O. Jahn recording). In Costa Rica reported to give a low, resonant, ventriloquial, twanging "thum" or "kuunk" like a faraway frog (Stiles and Skutch 1989).

White-throated Quail-Dove, *Geotrygon frenata*
Paloma Perdiz Goliblanca   Plate 28(13)

Mostly 1300–2600 m

29.5–32 cm (11½–12½"). A *large* quail-dove found on or near ground *inside subtropical and temperate forest and woodland* (less often out to borders) *on both slopes*. Bill black; iris yellow; legs pale pink. *Crown gray* (darker to rear), forecrown and lower face buff bordered below by *conspicuous black malar stripe*; above dark ruddy brown with purple gloss on upper back. *Throat white* contrasting with grayish foreneck that has effect of fine radial lines; lower underparts brownish gray. A few examples from e. slope are darker and browner below. Birds in Loja have forecrown whiter. **Juvenile** with rufes-cent and dusky barring on back, wing-coverts, and (especially) underparts; already shows obvious white throat. **Similar species:** Other quail-doves smaller and none occurs so widely in Andean forests, though there is some overlap with smaller and much more rufescent Ruddy Quail-Dove in lower subtropics. **Habits:** Widespread but inconspicuous, occasionally foraging along edge of little-traveled roads and trails in early morning. Usually forages solitarily on forest floor, flushing to a low branch when disturbed, there nodding nervously and raising rearparts. **Voice:** Heard much more often than seen. Song a low-pitched, hollow, and mournful "hooop," rather short and almost clipped, given at intervals of 2–4 seconds.

Ruddy Quail-Dove, *Geotrygon montana*
Paloma Perdiz Rojiza   Plate 28(11)

Mostly below 1300 m

21.5–24 cm (8½–9½"). Widespread on or near ground inside humid forest and secondary woodland in lowlands of east and west, smaller numbers up locally into lower subtropics. *Bill, orbital ring, and legs purplish red*; iris yellow. ♂ *above rufous-chestnut glossed with purple*; *face pinkish cinnamon with prominent malar stripe*. Breast pale vinaceous, lower underparts dull buff. ♀ much duller: face dull cinnamon with *brown malar stripe*; otherwise dark olive brown above. Breast brownish to grayish, becoming dull buff on belly. **Juvenile** like ♀ but feathers of upperparts with extensive cinnamon edging. **Similar species:** Extensive purplish on face of this quail-dove is equalled only in the very rare Violaceous (which see). Ruddy ♂♂ are easily recognized; even ♀♀ should show enough facial pattern to be recognized. **Habits:** Usually found singly inside forest; like other quail-doves, shy and not often seen. **Voice:** Song a soft, descending "oooo" (lower pitched than Gray-fronted Dove's song) given at intervals of 2–3 seconds from a usually hidden perch close to ground.

Violaceous Quail-Dove, *Geotrygon violacea*
Paloma Perdiz Violácea   Plate 28(12)

250 m

21.5–24 cm (8½–9½"). *Very rare and local* on or near ground inside humid forest in *lowlands of northeast* (Cuyabeno). *Bill, orbital ring, and legs purplish red*; iris yellow. ♂ has *forecrown white* becoming gray on hindcrown and *rich reddish chestnut strongly glossed violet on nape and upper back*; above otherwise rich chestnut brown. Throat white; breast grayish mauve, belly white. ♀ duller and more olive brown above with much less purple gloss; breast grayer. **Similar species:** *The only Ecuador quail-dove showing no malar stripe.* Therefore somewhat reminiscent of a *Leptotila* dove (even to its pale forecrown) though *Leptotila* do not have purplish red bill and have white tail-tipping. **Habits:** Similar to Ruddy and other quail-doves. **Voice:** Song a short hollow "co-ooo" usually given at intervals of 2–3 seconds from a branch 3–6 m above ground (thus often higher up than other quail-doves); somewhat higher pitched than Ruddy or other quail-doves.

Psittaciformes
Parrots and Macaws: Psittacidae (46)
A pantropical group of familiar and often colorful birds, with diversity greatest in the Neotropics and Australasia. Green predominates in a majority of Ecuadorian parrots, though some—notably certain of the large macaws—are vividly hued in other colors. Parrots have short, thick, and hooked bills, flexible tongues, and dextrous feet; the feet are often used to lift food up to the bill. Species vary in size from the meter-long *Ara* macaws to the sparrow-sized *Forpus* parrotlets; the **sexes are alike** except in *Forpus*

parrotlets. Young birds often have dark irides (vs. pale in adults). Parrots occur widely in Ecuador, but the majority occur in humid forests, especially in the lowlands. They are notably gregarious, but only rarely do several species actually flock together; at times, however, several will congregate in a fruiting tree. Parrots are notably vocal, the larger species having very loud calls, the smaller species with higher pitched and more chattering or "twittery" calls. These vocalizations are often helpful for identification, especially of birds flying overhead (where often all one sees is a silhouette) though in many cases— or without much experience—only to generic level. Parrots feed on a wide variety of fruit and seeds; in the east some species descend at times to eat mineral-impregnated soil at clay licks along rivers (locally called "salados"). They nest in tree cavities, certain smaller species sometimes in holes dug into arboreal termitaries; a small clutch of white eggs is laid, and young often have a long period of dependence after fledging. Many parrots are esteemed as pets, for they are social birds that readily bond with their human "owner," and some can learn to imitate various human sounds.

Ara Macaws

Large parrots—*by far the largest in Ecuador*—macaws personify wild lowland forests, and the sight of flying birds in good light is breathtaking. Populations have declined greatly because of deforestation and, to a lesser degree, direct persecution. Macaws are characterized by their *bare facial skin* (in some species crossed by lines of tiny feathers) and *very long graduated tails*. Some are mainly rich green, but others are vividly clad in red, blue, and yellow. Their *raucous vocalizations* always command attention.

Blue-and-yellow Macaw, *Ara ararauna*
Guacamayo Azuliamarillo   Plate 30(1)

81.5–86.5 cm (32–34"). Locally fairly common in *várzea forest and swampy places within terra firme forest* in lowlands of east (still in west?); now found primarily in more remote regions, though can overfly almost anywhere. Unmistakable. *Very long pointed tail.* Bill black; bare facial skin white with lines of small black feathers. *Bright rich blue*

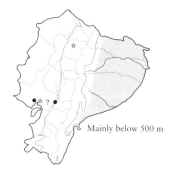

Mainly below 500 m

above, somewhat darker on flight feathers. Small throat patch black; *underparts entirely rich golden yellow*. From below wings and tail yellow. **Similar species:** Though seemingly hard to confuse, flying birds against the sky in low angled light can look deceptively red. **Habits:** Most often seen in pairs or small (presumed family) groups; also regularly gathers into large flocks (up to 30–50 birds, rarely even more) in more remote areas. Often commutes long distances between roosting and feeding sites, then flying high overhead; flight strong and steady but deceptively fast, with long tail streaming behind; the sight of flying "Blue-and-gold" Macaws in good light can be beautiful indeed. Perched birds are often surprisingly hard to spot, especially when feeding, and are then often quiet; such birds are sometimes best located by listening for the sound of bits of falling fruit or debris. **Voice:** Large macaws are well known for their raucous, far-carrying calls, given especially in flight and heralding their approach long before they can be seen. Blue-and-yellow's voice is somewhat less harsh than that of other large macaws, but it still can produce a prodigous amount of noise. Most characteristic is a loud throaty "rraaah!" given especially in flight (when perched mainly in alarm or just before taking flight); also gives a variety of other calls, including a distinctive "kurreeorek."

Military Macaw, *Ara militaris*
Guacamayo Militar   Plate 30(5)

66–71 cm (26–28"). *Rare and now local in foothill and subtropical forest on e. slope. Very long pointed tail.* Bill black; bare facial skin white with lines of small black feathers. *Mostly bright green* with *red forehead*; lower

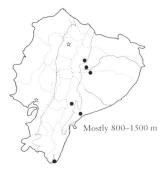

Mostly 800–1500 m

back, rump, and crissum pale blue. Flight feathers blue; tail mostly blue, feathers with red bases. From below wings and tail olive yellow. **Similar species:** Given decent light not likely confused. Similar Great Green Macaw occurs only west of Andes. Only other large macaw regularly occurring at elevations where Military is found is the very different Red-and-green. Much smaller Chestnut-fronted Macaw is similarly colored aside from its red under wings and tail. **Habits:** Not well known in Ecuador, where at least now it seems to be found only very locally. Usually seen in small groups flying high overhead, often during what are presumed to be long-distance flights between roosting and feeding sites. **Voice:** Raucous calls similar to those of other large macaws, most frequently a loud "rraaah!"

Great Green Macaw, *Ara ambigua*
Guacamayo Verde Mayor   Plate 30(4)

76–84 cm (30–33″). *Rare and very local* in more remote areas of humid and deciduous forest in lowlands and foothills of *west*, now confined to *Esmeraldas* and *around Chongón Hills in Guayas. Very long pointed tail*. Bill black with grayish tip; bare facial skin

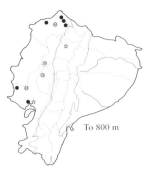

To 800 m

usually dull pink (sometimes whitish, also sometimes flushing to deeper pink) with lines of small black feathers. *Mostly pale yellowish green* with *red forehead*; lower back, rump, and crissum pale blue. Flight feathers mostly blue; tail feathers basally orange-red, terminally blue. From below wings and tail olive yellow. **Similar species:** Not likely confused in its *western* range, *where the only large macaw present*. Military Macaw occurs only on e. slope; it is smaller with proportionately smaller bill and is deeper (not so yellowish) green generally. **Habits:** Usually seen in pairs, less often in small groups of up to 6–10 birds, most often as they fly overhead, calling very noisily. Behavior similar to other large macaws, but seems notably unwary, a habit that may have contributed to its steep decline in Ecuador. **Voice:** Similar to other large *Ara*, but perhaps even more powerful than most, about on a par with Red-and-green.

Scarlet Macaw, *Ara macao*
Guacamayo Escarlata   Plate 30(2)

Below 400 m

84–91.5 cm (33–36″). Locally fairly common in *terra firme forest in lowlands of east*; now found mainly in more remote areas, and certainly most numerous in such regions. *Very long pointed tail*. Bill bicolored, maxilla mostly whitish, mandible black; bare facial skin white, with no lines of feathers. *Mostly bright scarlet*; lower back, rump, and crissum pale blue. *Wing-coverts with large area of bright yellow* but feathers tipped green, flight feathers blue; tail mostly red, feathers tipped blue. From below wings and tail red. **Similar species:** Likely confused only with much rarer (in Ecuador) Red-and-green Macaw, which see. **Habits:** Similar to Blue-and-yellow

Macaw, with which Scarlet occasionally flocks, especially in small groups that are resting in the leafy canopy of trees during midday. At least in Ecuador flocks of Scarlets rarely or never are as large, typically no more than 10–15 birds being together; most often, as with other macaws, seen in pairs or presumed family groups. **Voice:** Very raucous calls similar to those of other large macaws; there is so much individual and situational variation that distinguishing them can be tricky, though Scarlet's tend to be more drawn out and less deep than Red-and-green's, and perhaps not as varied as Blue-and-yellow's.

Red-and-green Macaw, *Ara chloroptera*
Guacamayo Rojo y Verde   Plate 30(3)

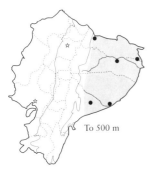

To 500 m

89–96.5 cm (35–38″). *Rare and now local in humid forest in lowlands of east*, where by far the least numerous of the great macaws. *Very long pointed tail.* Bill bicolored, maxilla mostly whitish, mandible black; bare facial skin white with lines of small red feathers. *Mostly deep red*; lower back, rump, and crissum pale blue. *Wing-coverts mostly green*, flight feathers blue; tail carmine, feathers tipped blue. From below wings and tail red. **Similar species:** More numerous Scarlet Macaw not quite so large, is a somewhat paler more scarlet red (though difference is subtle, and varying light conditions can affect it) with obvious area of yellow on wing-coverts (easy to see on flying birds from above, but hard from below), and white facial skin is plain (with no "lines"). **Habits:** Similar to Blue-and-yellow and Scarlet Macaws, though in Ecuador the Red-and-green seems to occur—on the rare occasions when it is found at all—almost entirely

in pairs. Sometimes consorts with Scarlets, rarely with Blue-and-yellows. **Voice:** Similar to Scarlet Macaw's.

Chestnut-fronted Macaw, *Ara severa*
Guacamayo Frenticastaño   Plate 30(6)

Mostly below 1400 m

43–46 cm (17–18″). Widespread in humid forest borders and adjacent clearings in *lowlands of east and west*, now much more numerous in east. Long pointed tail. Bill blackish; bare facial skin creamy white with lines of small blackish feathers. *Mostly green* with small area on forehead reddish chestnut, crown bluish green; bend of wing red and flight feathers bluish. *Underside of wings and tail dull reddish.* **Similar species:** Red-bellied Macaw has bare yellowish facial skin and shows a mealy suffusion to underparts as well as some red on belly. The two are easily told apart in flight, both by distinctly different calls and Red-bellied's yellowish (not reddish) underwing; Red-bellied's wings are slimmer and more pointed, resulting in a decidedly different silhouette. Cf. also larger *Aratinga* parakeets and larger green macaws. **Habits:** Usually in pairs or small groups, favoring openings and borders and thus usually conspicuous; often perches on snags. Tends to remain active through midday hours, more so than many other parrots. Occasionally descends to eat mineral-impregnated soil at salados. **Voice:** Especially vocal in flight, then constantly giving "kraaa" calls that, although loud, do not approach the deep raucous tones of larger macaws.

Red-bellied Macaw, *Orthopsittaca manilata*
Guacamayo Ventrirrojo   Plate 30(7)

46–48 cm (18–19″). *Canopy and borders of várzea forest and swampy areas in terra firme*

To 400 m

Mostly below 1300 m, smaller numbers higher

in lowlands of east; strongly favors *Mauritia* (moriche) palms. Formerly in the genus *Ara*. Bill black; *extensive area of facial skin yellowish* (can be quite bright). Mostly green, bluer on crown and with mealy suffusion on throat and breast; *small patch on midbelly red*. Flight feathers bluish. *Underside of wings and tail pale greenish yellow*. **Similar species:** Chestnut-fronted Macaw differs in having whitish facial skin, brighter and deeper green plumage, and conspicuous red under wings and tail. Voices also differ strikingly, and though the two seem similar, with even minimal experience they should not be confused. **Habits:** Usually in groups, sometimes gathering in flocks of 25 to even 50 birds. Most often seen as they fly high overhead to and from roosting and feeding areas, these typically in (or at least in association with) *Mauritia* palms. Often roosts inside dead, curled-up palm fronds. In flight looks slender with slim pointed wings and narrow tail; wingbeats shallow. **Voice:** Distinctive call much higher pitched than that of other macaws, a repeated "kree-ee-ee" or "kree-ee-ak," often uttered more or less simultaneously by members of flock in a chorus; this carries far, and often heralds the approach of a flying group.

Aratinga **Parakeets**
Fairly small to midsized, mostly green parrots with long graduated tails, *Aratinga* parakeets—sometimes called "conures"—differ from macaws in lacking bare facial skin; in its stead, they have *bare whitish orbital rings* (sometimes called periophthalmic rings), conspicuous in some species. Their bills are proportionately heavy. They mainly range in lowland forests and woodland and are notably gregarious and vocal.

33–35.5 cm (13–14"). *Still locally fairly common (though declining)* in canopy and borders of deciduous forest and woodland, agricultural areas, and arid scrub in *west*, ranging from lowlands up into highlands of Loja; locally also in more humid forest. Long pointed tail. Bill whitish to dusky ivory; wide orbital ring yellowish white. Mostly bright green with *contrasting bright red crown and face* (extending behind eye); *bend of wing and underwing-coverts red*, in some birds thighs also red. Juvenile has little or no red (starts out green), though apparently even youngest birds have some red on underwing-coverts. Underside of wings (aside from coverts) and tail yellowish olive. **Similar species:** Aside from the rare Scarlet-fronted Parakeet (which see), beautiful Red-masked is nearly unmistakable in its w. range, *where it is the only large parakeet*. **Habits:** An arboreal parakeet that tends to be gregarious in flocks of up to 50 or even more birds, and may be nomadic or erratic in its appearances. Roosting flights in bygone years could be huge, numbering in the thousands. Flocks sometimes fly very high. Feeds on a variety of fruits and flowers, foraging with much agility; rarely descends to the ground. **Voice:** Noisy, giving a variety of raspy screeching calls both in flight and while perched, e.g., "scree-screeáh" or "scrah-scrah-scra-scra."

Scarlet-fronted Parakeet, *Aratinga wagleri*
Perico Frentiescarlata   Plate 32(5)
38–40 cm (15–16"). *Rare and local* in montane forest and woodland borders and adjacent agricultural areas in *highlands of Loja*. Bill dull brownish ivory; wide orbital

1000–2500 m

33–35 cm (13–14″). *Mainly in riparian and várzea forest in lowlands of east* (overflying terra firme), also ranging (seasonally?) up into foothills and lower subtropics on e. slope. Long pointed tail. Bill brownish ivory; wide orbital ring yellowish white (the "white eye"; as in other *Aratinga*, White-eyed's iris is some shade of hazel). Mostly bright green with *scattering of red feathers* (often quite extensive; more in older birds?) *on sides of neck and foreneck.* Edge of forewing red; *lesser underwing-coverts red, greater-coverts bright yellow* (flashing conspicuously in flight); underside of flight feathers and tail yellowish olive. **Similar species:** Considerably larger than the other *Aratinga* with which regularly sympatric, Dusky-headed (which also has black bill, grayish head, etc.). **Habits:** Most often seen in flocks as they fly overhead (sometimes high) between mainly riverine roosting areas and feeding sites; usually not in extensive forest, instead favoring borders, secondary growth, and even clearings. Occasionally descends to eat mineral-impregnated soil at salados. **Voice:** Loud raspy shrieking calls similar to Red-masked.

ring yellowish white. Long pointed tail. Mostly bright green with *contrasting bright red forecrown*; *bend of wing and edge of forewing red*, in some birds thighs also red. Underside of wings and tail yellowish olive. **Similar species:** Easily confused with much more numerous Red-masked Parakeet, a somewhat smaller *Aratinga*. Adult Red-masked differs in having much more red on head (extending down over cheeks). Juvenile Red-masked shows no red, however, and subadults with less red could be confused, though they would be unlikely to have clear-cut red forecrown patch and at the same time none elsewhere. Red-masked has extensive red on underwing-coverts, conspicuous in flight from below; *Scarlet-fronted shows no red on wing from below* (red only on bend of wing). **Habits:** Hardly known in Ecuador, where in recent years seen only a few times, generally in small flocks, most often just in flight. Behavior seems similar to Red-masked's, though in Peru the Scarlet-fronted nests semicolonially in crevices on cliffs. **Voice:** Very like Red-masked Parakeet.

White-eyed Parakeet
Aratinga leucophthalmus
Perico Ojiblanco   Plate 32(4)

Dusky-headed Parakeet, *Aratinga weddellii*
Perico Cabecioscuro   Plate 32(2)

Mostly below 500 m

25.5–27 cm (10–10½″). Fairly common at borders of humid forest and in adjacent clearings in *lowlands of east*. Long pointed tail. *Bill black* (not pale as in all other Ecuadorian *Aratinga*); *very wide orbital ring whitish* (in conjunction with whitish irides, imparts a *"goggle-eyed" look*). *Head and sides of neck grayish dusky*, contrasting with otherwise bright green plumage; flight feathers and tips of tail feathers blue. Underside of flight feath-

Mostly below 1100 m

ers and tail blackish. **Similar species:** Considerably smaller than White-eyed Parakeet, which also differs in having green head and underside of wings with red and yellow. In a brief view this small *Aratinga* can even be confused with Maroon-tailed Parakeet. **Habits:** Usually in small groups, rarely more than 8–12 together, usually fewer (except when at salados). Often quite tame, perching in the open and quite low, showing a predilection for various palms. Usually does not fly too high above canopy. Regularly descends to eat mineral-impregnated soil at salados. **Voice:** Similar to White-eyed Parakeet's but distinctly screechier and higher pitched, less raspy, e.g., "jee-jeek," often given by many members of a flock, more or less simultaneously.

Golden-plumed Parakeet
Leptosittaca branickii
Perico Cachetidorado   Plate 32(1)

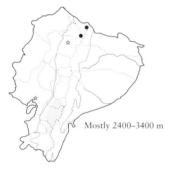

Mostly 2400–3400 m

35.5–38 cm (14–15"). A *large* and *very long-tailed* montane parakeet, *scarce and local (nomadic?) in temperate forest on e. slope, mainly in south*. Bill grayish; iris orange-red, orbital ring creamy whitish. Mostly bright green with *orange-yellow lores* and *small golden yellow tuft behind eye; belly paler and more yellowish with scattering of reddish orange feathers*. Underside of flight feathers yellowish, underside of tail strongly reddish. **Similar species:** Nearly unmistakable in its high-elevation forests, where there is no other large, long-tailed parakeet. No overlap with even larger (and much rarer) Yellow-eared Parrot. **Habits:** This slim and elegant parakeet usually ranges in groups of 5–15 individuals, though in some areas great wheeling flocks of up to 35–40 birds occur, at least sea-

sonally. Golden-plumeds tend to be more conspicuous than many other parrots when perched, often landing in outer crowns and on exposed limbs, moving about actively and often noisily continuing to call. **Voice:** Frequently uttered call (given both in flight and when landed) a repeated shrill "kreeah! kreeah!"

Yellow-eared Parrot, *Ognorhynchus icterotis*
Loro Orejiamarillo   Plate 30(8)

1800–3200 m

43–46 cm (17–18"). *Extremely rare and local* in canopy and borders of *subtropical forest in northwest*, with *recent records only from Carchi and nw. Cotopaxi*. Critically endangered. Heavy bodied and macaw-like, with *massive black bill*; orbital ring dark gray. Bright green above with *conspicuous bright yellow forecrown extending back across cheeks onto ear-coverts*. Throat green; underparts greenish yellow. Underside of tail reddish. **Similar species:** Large size with long tail and conspicuous yellow on head diagnostic for this perilously rare montane parrot. Golden-plumed Parakeet more slender and longer tailed, shows much less yellow; in Ecuador it occurs only on e. slope. **Habits:** Not well known. Quite gregarious, perhaps even nesting semicolonially (apparently mainly using holes in *Ceroxylon* wax palms). A flock observed recently by N. Krabbe and F. Sornoza was faithful to a certain palm left standing in a clearing, roosting there and often clinging to its fronds and trunk. **Voice:** Noisy, with most frequent call (given both in flight and when perched) a raucous but somewhat nasal "raanh" (F. Sornoza recording) often given more or less simultaneously by members of flock, producing a loud and far-carrying cacophony.

Pyrrhura Parakeets

Fairly small parakeets—smaller and more slender than *Aratinga*—*Pyrrhura* are confined to humid lowland and subtropical forests. As with *Aratinga* there is a bare ocular area, but plumage patterns are more complex and *tails are reddish* (not green). *Pyrrhura* range in small flocks and are readily seen in flight but hard to spot when perched.

Maroon-tailed Parakeet, *Pyrrhura melanura*
Perico Colimarrón   Plate 31(12)

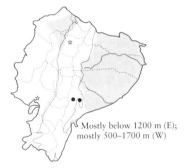

Mostly below 1200 m (E);
mostly 500–1700 m (W)

23–24 cm (9–9½″). Fairly common in canopy and borders of humid forest (both terra firme and várzea) in *lowlands and foothills of east,* ranging up locally into lower subtropics; also in *foothills and lower subtropics of northwest.* Long pointed tail. Bill dusky; orbital ring whitish, but gray in birds of *northwest.* Mostly bright green; crown grayish brown; breast grayish brown, *feathers edged buffyish to white producing distinct scaly effect.* Some blue in primaries, greater primary-coverts bright red (conspicuous in flight); tail dark maroon, feathers basally green. Considerable geographic variation in extent of breast scaling: narrowest in birds of **northwest** and **e. lowlands,** somewhat wider in birds from near base of Andes south to nw. Pastaza, and much wider and whiter in birds from **nw. Morona-Santiago** (in which breast can look almost solidly white). **Similar species:** The only *Pyrrhura* parakeet in most of its range, as such readily recognized. In se. lowlands, cf. very rare Painted Parakeet. Along e. base of Andes in s. Ecuador, cf. White-breasted Parakeet; this can resemble white extremes of Maroon-tailed though White-breasted has orange-yellow auricular patch and yellower wash on breast (where it

never looks "scaly"). **Habits:** Usually in small groups of up to 10–12 birds (often fewer) that fly swiftly through forest canopy (never high above it) in tight compact groups, seeming to "disappear" in leafy foliage as they alight, only rarely perching on exposed limbs. Perched birds are inconspicuous, clambering around noiselessly on limbs and leafy branches. Generally quiet except when flying; upon one's approach they voice soft alarm notes, then suddenly burst from cover. If flushed from a fruiting tree, sometimes after swooping around they may return. **Voice:** Common call, given especially in flight, a rather shrill "keey" or "kree," either often repeated in series or given by several flock members more or less simultaneously.

El Oro Parakeet, *Pyrrhura orcesi*
Perico de Orcés   Plate 31(13)

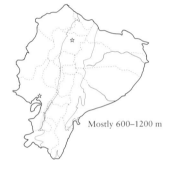

Mostly 600–1200 m

23–24 cm (9–9½″). Very local in *foothill and lower subtropical forest on w. slope in south* (El Oro and Azuay). A recently discovered species. Bill dusky; orbital ring pale pinkish. Long pointed tail. Mostly bright green with *forehead bright red; shows no pale scaling on breast.* Some blue in primaries, greater primary-coverts bright red (conspicuous in flight); tail dark maroon, feathers basally green. **Similar species:** No other *Pyrrhura* occurs in or near its limited range, so unlikely to be confused. Maroon-tailed Parakeet differs in having pale breast scaling, no red on forehead, and brown crown. Red-masked Parakeet much larger and shows much more red on face. **Habits:** Similar to Maroon-tailed Parakeet, though group size can be larger, flocks of up to 40–60 birds having been seen on rare occasions. **Voice:** Similar to Maroon-tailed Parakeet.

White-breasted Parakeet, *Pyrrhura albipectus*
Perico Pechiblanco   Plate 31(14)

Mostly 900–1700 m

24–25.5 cm (9½–10″). *Canopy and borders of foothill and subtropical forest on e. slope in south* (Morona-Santiago and Zamora-Chinchipe). Sometimes called White-necked Parakeet. Bill blackish; orbital ring whitish. Long pointed tail. Bright green above with dusky-brown crown; *auricular patch orange-yellow, nuchal collar white* (somewhat variable in extent). *Throat and breast white variably washed with peachy yellow*; lower underparts green. Primaries with considerable blue, greater primary-coverts bright red; tail dusky-maroon, outer feathers edged green. **Similar species:** This colorful *Pyrrhura* is unlikely to be confused in its limited range, but at least at its northern end it overlaps with Maroon-tailed Parakeet which is broadly white-scaled on breast (and thus can superficially look like White-breasted). **Habits and Voice:** Similar to Maroon-tailed Parakeet.

[Painted Parakeet, *Pyrrhura picta*
Perico Pintado]   Plate 31(15)

Below 300 m

23–25.5 cm (9–10″). Known only from one sighting in *Morona-Santiago lowlands*. Following description is of geographically most likely race. Long pointed tail. Bill blackish; orbital ring whitish. Bright green above with dusky-brown crown and some blue on forehead; *cheeks reddish maroon* and *auricular patch whitish*. Throat and breast dusky-brown, *feathers broadly edged buffy whitish giving scaly or chevroned pattern*; lower underparts green with *carmine patch on median belly*. Flight feathers mainly blue (*no red on wing*); tail reddish. **Similar species:** Only possible confusion is with more simply patterned Maroon-tailed Parakeet, which lacks red and whitish on head, has no belly patch, and shows red flash on primary-coverts (conspicuous in flight). **Habits and Voice:** Similar to Maroon-tailed Parakeet.

Barred Parakeet, *Bolborhynchus lineola*
Perico Barreteado   Plate 31(4)

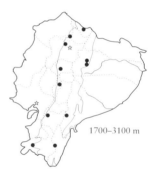

1700–3100 m

17–18 cm (6¾–7″). A *small* parakeet of *subtropical and temperate forest and woodland on both slopes, almost always seen flying high overhead in compact flocks. Short pointed tail*. Bill pale horn; narrow orbital ring grayish. Green, *brighter and paler below* with *upperparts, sides, and flanks narrowly barred black; wing-coverts also mostly black*. **Similar species:** The barring is surprisingly hard to see in field, so usually identified through its *Brotogeris*-like size and shape in conjunction with Andean distribution. **Habits:** Almost invariably found in flocks, sometimes of 50 or more birds, in fast direct flight high overhead (often so high as to be invisible in clouds); they always seem to be on their way to someplace else. Almost never seen perched, landing birds seeming to "vanish" in dense green foliage; they then are generally silent. Sometimes their presence in an area has been correlated with bamboo seeding. **Voice:** Vocal in flight, with distinctive shrill squealing or chattering calls, not really very loud but carrying well (and often hard to locate as they wing by), e.g., "chir-ree-chii."

Forpus Parrotlets

Tiny sparrow-sized parrots, the smallest in Ecuador, that range in semiopen areas and forest borders, mainly in the lowlands. *Tails are very short and wedge-shaped. Forpus* are predominantly bright green and—unusual among the Neotropical parrots—they exhibit sexual dimorphism, males having blue on the wings and rump.

Blue-winged Parrotlet, *Forpus xanthopterygius*
Periquito Aliazul   Plate 31(3)

Mostly below 500 m

12–12.5 cm (4¾–5″). A *nonforest* parrotlet of clearings and woodland and forest borders in *lowlands of east. Very small.* Bill whitish. ♂ green, brighter and paler on head and underparts; *greater wing-coverts, secondaries, and rump rich blue.* ♀ similar but lacking blue. **Similar species:** Dusky-billed Parrotlet has mainly black maxilla (though rest of bill is just as pale as Blue-winged's) and is darker (not so yellowish) green generally; blue on ♂'s wing and rump is darker, more violet-blue. Their calls differ, and Dusky-billed is more forest-based. **Habits:** Usually in small groups that show a predilection for perching in semiopen (often in *Cecropia* trees; also regularly feed on *Cecropia* catkins), but because of small size and green coloration still hard to see. **Voice:** Gives a near-constant high-pitched screechy chattering, "tzit" or "tzeet."

Pacific Parrotlet, *Forpus coelestis*
Periquito del Pacífico   Plate 31(1)

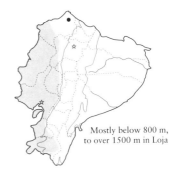

Mostly below 800 m, to over 1500 m in Loja

12.5–13.5 cm (5–5¼″). *Common and widespread* in borders of deciduous forest and woodland, arid scrub, and agricultural and settled areas in *lowlands of west*, in Loja ranging higher. *Very small.* Bill whitish. ♂ green, brighter and paler on head and underparts, somewhat grayer and "dustier" on mantle; *indistinct streak behind eye pale blue; greater wing-coverts, secondaries, and rump deep blue.* ♀ similar but lacking the blue. **Similar species:** The only *Forpus* west of Andes, and so much smaller than any other parrot there as to be easily recognized. Cf. Gray-cheeked Parakeet. **Habits:** Numerous and familiar, adapting well to habitat change and often common in densely settled regions, even in towns and cities: all this parrotlet requires is a few trees. Usually in flocks, sometimes quite large (50 or more birds); often perches in the open, even on wires. Regularly feeds on grass seeds on or near ground. Flight somewhat bounding. Nests in small holes in a variety of situations, often in semiopen. **Voice:** A high-pitched chattering (e.g., "tchit" or "tzit," often rapidly run together in a series) is given almost continuously.

Dusky-billed Parrotlet, *Forpus sclateri*
Periquito Piquioscuro   Plate 31(2)

12.5–13.5 cm (5–5¼″). Scarce in canopy and borders of humid forest (primarily terra firme) in *lowlands of east. Very small. Most of maxilla blackish;* remainder of bill whitish. ♂ green, brightest on forehead and face (almost emerald green), paler below and duller above; *wing-coverts, secondaries, and rump deep violet-blue.* ♀ similar but lacking violet-blue, and paler and more yellowish on

Mostly below 500 m

forehead and face. **Similar species:** Easily confused with Blue-winged Parrotlet. On perched birds look especially for Dusky-billed's *bicolored* bill (*all pale* in Blue-winged); Dusky-billed is noticeably darker (less yellowish) green below. In flight listen for its oft-repeated and distinctly different calls. **Habits:** Usually in pairs or at most small groups (rarely more than 6–8 together) that tend to remain high in canopy and are often hard to see well; can come lower at edge or in adjacent clearings, but in general more of a forest-based bird than Blue-winged. The two do not seem to flock together. **Voice:** Distinctive call a very high-pitched, almost mouse-like "dziit" given both in flight and while perched.

Brotogeris Parakeets

Fairly small parrots with bulbous bills and *rather short, wedge-shaped tails. Brotogeris* occur in forest and woodland borders and canopy in the lowlands, and they are highly gregarious.

Gray-cheeked Parakeet
Brotogeris pyrrhopterus
Perico Cachetigris   Plate 31(7)

Mostly below 1000 m

19–20.5 cm (7½–8″). Uncommon in canopy and borders of deciduous and semihumid forest and woodland, smaller numbers persisting in more settled areas, in *lowlands and foothills of southwest*. Bill and orbital ring whitish. Mostly green, paler and yellower below; *crown pale blue* with *face and sides of neck pale ashy gray*. Primary-coverts deep blue; *underwing-coverts orange*. **Similar species:** Not likely confused in its range, *where there are few other small parrots*. Pacific Parrotlet even smaller and differently shaped, with shorter and less pointed tail. **Habits:** Usually in small groups of up to about 12 birds, generally remaining well up in trees though sometimes lower at edge and in clearings. Flight bounding, sometimes briefly tucking wings in close to body; often flies high overhead, the orange under wings flashing. **Voice:** Noisy, giving a variety of rather shrill, chattering calls. Though usually quiet at midday, this parakeet (along with congeners) calls more when perched than do many others.

Cobalt-winged Parakeet
Brotogeris cyanoptera
Perico Alicobáltico   Plate 31(5)

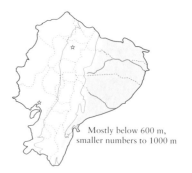

Mostly below 600 m, smaller numbers to 1000 m

19–20.5 cm (7½–8″). *Common and widespread* in canopy of humid forest, secondary woodland, and adjacent clearings in *lowlands of east, where generally the most numerous and conspicuous parrot*. Bill pale yellowish; orbital ring creamy whitish or pinkish white. Mostly green with some yellowish on forecrown and bluish on crown; *orange chin patch* (often inconspicuous). *Considerable blue shows in flight feathers* (obvious in flight but readily visible even on perched birds), also shows some blue on central tail feathers. **Similar species:** Strive to become familiar with this common parakeet so as better to be able to pick out scarcer species. Especially cf. rare Tui Parakeet, and various scarce *Touit* parrotlets (which have *square*, not pointed, tails). **Habits:** Gregarious, sometimes gathering in large flocks of many dozens of birds. Usually remains well above ground, sometimes coming lower at edge and in trees out in clearings. Often perches in the open, but even so usually hard to spot after it has landed. Feeds in flowering as well as fruiting trees. Sometimes descends to eat mineral-impregnated soil at salados, usually inside forest. **Voice:** Noisy, flocks especially keeping up a shrill chattering.

[Tui Parakeet, *Brotogeris sanctithomae*
Perico Tui]   Plate 31(6)

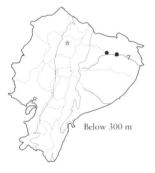

Below 300 m

18–19 cm (7–7½″). *Very rare* (status uncertain) in canopy and borders of *várzea and riparian forest and woodland in lowlands of northeast*, perhaps most likely on river islands. *Bill brownish*; orbital ring white, *iris pale*. Resembles much more numerous Cobalt-winged Parakeet and must be distinguished with care. Major differences to watch for in the Tui are: *markedly darker and browner bill*, *more extensive and brighter yellow on forecrown*, sometimes also with a short streak of yellow back from eye, with more contrasting white eye-ring; *absence of orange chin spot* (though this can be hard to see in Cobalt-winged); *absence of blue in wing* (this usually can be seen on perched Cobalt-wingeds); *absence of blue in tail* (this usually harder to see). **Habits and Voice:** Similar to Cobalt-winged Parakeet.

Touit Parrotlets

Small and chunky parrots with *short and square tails*. Quite brightly colored, and showing sexual dimorphism, *Touit* range in humid lowland and subtropical forests where they always are hard to see well, and often are seen only in flight overhead. They tend to be rare and are apparently nomadic. Their nests are usually dug into arboreal termitaries.

Sapphire-rumped Parrotlet, *Touit purpurata*
Periquito Lomizafiro   Plate 31(8)

Below 300 m

16.5–18 cm (6½–7″). *Rare and seemingly local* in canopy and borders of humid forest in *lowlands of east*. Bill pale yellowish; orbital ring grayish. ♂ mostly green, paler and brighter on uppertail-coverts and underparts; *rump blue* (but this usually hard to see in field). *Scapulars and tertials contrastingly brown*, bend of wing blue, greater primary-coverts and primaries mainly black; *tail mostly magenta*, feathers narrowly edged and tipped black. ♀ differs in having narrow green terminal band on outer tail feathers, which also lack black margins. **Similar species:** Scarlet-shouldered Parrotlet has bold orbital ring, conspicuous blue on upperwing and red on underwing. Cf. also differently shaped Cobalt-winged Parakeet (with pointed tail). **Habits:** Usually in pairs or small groups, usually noted only in flight as they zoom by low over canopy. Like other *Touit*, very hard to spot when perched, rarely resting in open and tending to "freeze" once they are aware of observer's presence; after giving a few alarm notes, they may suddenly burst from cover, usually never to be seen again. **Voice:** Flight call a distinctive nasal "nyaah," often repeated several times in succession. Usually quiet when perched, though perched birds occasionally give the same call.

Scarlet-shouldered Parrotlet, *Touit huetii*
Periquito Hombrirrojo   Plate 31(9)

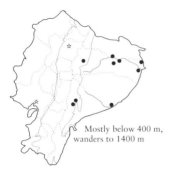

Mostly below 400 m, wanders to 1400 m

Mostly 500–1400 m

15–16.5 cm (6–6½″). *Scarce and local* (overlooked?) in canopy and borders of terra firme forest in *lowlands and foothills of east*. Bill yellowish; *bold orbital ring white*. ♂ mostly green, brightest on scapulars, rump, and uppertail, paler on underparts; crown browner with *forehead black* and *foreface blue*. *Wing-coverts mainly dark blue*, primaries mainly black; *bend of wing and under-wing-coverts bright red* (conspicuous in flight). *Outer tail feathers magenta* tipped black. ♀ differs in yellowish green outer tail feathers. **Similar species:** Confusion most likely with plainer Sapphire-rumped Parrotlet, which lacks black and blue on face, has no blue and red on wing, and lacks obvious orbital ring. Red underwing-coverts resemble Orange-cheeked Parrot's, and therefore these two species can be confused in flight; Orange-cheeked larger with very different head pattern, etc. **Habits:** Similar to Sapphire-rumped Parrotlet. Apparently erratic, not encountered regularly anywhere; at least in late 1980s and early 1990s occurred semiregularly at a salado inside forest south of Río Napo near La Selva. Can occur in large flocks of 50+ birds. **Voice:** Flight call a semimusical "tree-ee-ee" often given as a group flies by high overhead. Usually quiet when perched.

Blue-fronted Parrotlet, *Touit dilectissima*
Periquito Frentiazul   Plate 31(10)
14.5–15 cm (5¾–6″). Scarce and local in canopy and borders of *foothill and lower*

subtropical forest on w. slope, occasionally into adjacent humid lowlands. Formerly sometimes considered conspecific with Red-fronted Parrotlet (*T. costaricensis*) of Costa Rica and w. Panama, then being called Red-winged Parrotlet. Bill yellowish; orbital ring gray. ♂ mostly green, brightest on scapulars, rump, and uppertail, paler on underparts becoming pale yellow on throat; *crown pale blue* with *a little red in front of and behind eye*. *Wing-coverts mostly bright red* with *bright yellow bend of wing and underwing-coverts* (latter conspicuous in flight); greater primary-coverts and primaries mainly black. Outer tail feathers orange-yellow tipped black. ♀ with duller face pattern and *wing-coverts mainly black* (showing little or no red). **Similar species:** Nothing really similar on *w.* slope. **Habits:** Usually in pairs or small groups that tend to perch very quietly high in trees; seen more often at forest edge than other *Touit*. Rarely noticed except in flight, which is fast and twisting, the contrasty yellow and red on wing flashing prominently. **Voice:** Flight call a soft high-pitched "tu-eee," often repeated in series.

Spot-winged Parrotlet, *Touit stictoptera*
Periquito Alipunteado   Plate 31(11)
16–17 cm (6¼–6¾″). Scarce and local in canopy and borders of *subtropical forest on e. slope*. Bill pale olive grayish; narrow orbital ring whitish. ♂ mostly green, somewhat paler below; *wing-coverts contrastingly dusky-brown, feathers pale-tipped giving obscurely spotted appearance*, small patch on outer greater-coverts orange. ♀ similar but foreface yellower and *wing-coverts green with blackish spotting*. **Similar species:** The only *Touit* on e. slope of Andes; Scarlet-

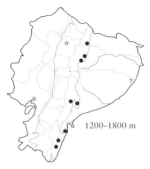

1200–1800 m

shouldered ranges up onto lower slopes (possible occasional overlap?) but has flashy red underwing-coverts, etc. Barred Parakeet has pointed tail (not short and squared-off) resulting in a very different flight profile. **Habits:** Usually in small groups (rarely more than 4–6 birds together) that fly through or just above canopy, usually not high above it. Behavior much like other *Touit*, and equally difficult to see perched. **Voice:** Flight call a harsh repeated "ddreet-ddreet-ddreet-ddreet."

Black-headed Parrot, *Pionites melanocephala*
Loro Coroninegro   Plate 31(16)

Below 400 m

21–22.5 cm (8¼–8¾"). An attractive and colorful, midsized parrot, *fairly common and conspicuous in canopy and borders of humid forest in lowlands of east.* Bill black; iris red, orbital ring gray. *Crown black with throat and chest bright orange-yellow extending back around neck as a buffy orange nuchal collar;* otherwise bright green above. *Breast and belly white* (sometimes stained brownish); *lower flanks and thighs contrastingly yellow or orange-yellow.* **Similar species:** Nearly unmistakable; cf. similarly sized (but

very different) Orange-cheeked Parrot. **Habits:** Usually in groups of 3–8 birds that tend to fly through or just above canopy, rarely very high above it. Often perch on high protruding limbs for protracted periods. Rarely associates with other parrots, even when feeding; seems especially attracted to small fruits of various palms. Can be quite tame. **Voice:** Distinctive flight call a wheezy or squealing screech, e.g., "screeéyr, screeyr-screeyr-screeyr-screeyr." At rest gives a variety of calls, some more musical, others rather un-birdlike; perched Black-headeds are more vocal than most other parrots.

Pionopsitta Parrots
Midsized, stocky, and colorful parrots with rather short, squared tails found in the canopy of humid lowland and foothill forests.

Rose-faced Parrot, *Pionopsitta pulchra*
Loro Cachetirrosa   Plate 31(17)

To 1200 m

21.5–23 cm (8½–9"). A chunky, short-tailed parrot, *uncommon in canopy and borders of humid lowland and foothill forest in west.* Bill pale creamy whitish; iris pale gray, orbital ring whitish. *Face rosy pink extending back over ear-coverts and sides of neck and paling on sides of throat,* crown contrastingly brownish; otherwise bright green above. Greater wing-coverts with some blue, flight feathers mainly black; underwing-coverts blue, axillars red. Chest dull brownish yellow, becoming bright pale green on underparts. Outer tail feathers with some red toward base, tipped blue. **Juvenile** has head more yellowish. **Similar species:** Pale rosy face unique among parrots and makes this attractive species nearly unmistakable. **Habits:** Usually in small groups, sometimes perching in open (e.g., on dead snags) but more often staying hidden in leafy canopy of tall trees. Can persist in fragmented forest. Flight fast and direct, frequently quite high, often twisting from side to side, sometimes lifting wings a bit above horizontal. **Voice:** In flight gives a harsh, far-carrying "shreek! shreek!"

[Saffron-headed Parrot, *Pionopsitta pyrilia*
Loro Cabeciazafrán]   Plate 31(19)

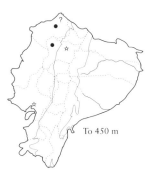

21.5–23 cm (8½–9″). *Very rare* (status uncertain) in canopy and borders of humid forest in *lower foothills of northwest* (Esmeraldas and nw. Pichincha). Bill whitish; iris pale gray, orbital ring whitish. *Head and neck bright yellow, more orange on ear-coverts*; otherwise bright green above. *Large area on bend of wing bright orange-yellow*; greater wing-coverts with some blue, flight feathers mainly black; *underwing-coverts bright red*. Chest yellowish olive; underparts bright pale green. Tail green, yellower toward base and with blue tip. **Similar species:** No other Ecuadorian parrot has an all-yellow head, but beware juvenile Rose-faced Parrots, whose heads are yellowish brown. **Habits:** Hardly known in Ecuador. Habits similar to Rose-faced Parrot. **Voice:** In Panama, flight call a high-pitched, typically doubled "chek-chek" or "cheeyk-cheeyk" (Ridgely and Gwynne 1989).

Orange-cheeked Parrot
Pionopsitta barrabandi
Loro Cachetinaranja   Plate 31(18)

24–25.5 cm (9½–10″). A striking, chunky parrot found in canopy and borders of humid forest in *lowlands of east*. Bill dusky, somewhat paler below; orbital ring whitish. *Head*

Mostly below 400 m

and neck black with *conspicuous large malar patch orange*; otherwise mostly bright green with yellowish olive breast. Shoulders yellow-orange; flight feathers mainly black; *bend of wing and underwing-coverts bright red*; tail tipped blue. **Similar species:** Nearly unmistakable. Black-headed Parrot also has black on head but differs strikingly otherwise. Scarlet-shouldered Parrotlet has similar scarlet on underwing, but is hardly half the size, lacks black head, etc. **Habits:** Usually seen in small flocks (up to 10–20 birds) that like so many other parrots are noted mainly in flight; rarely perches on open branches, preferring to stay in leafy cover. Flight fast and direct, often seeming to toss from side to side as if to show off red underwing. Occasionally descends to eat mineral-impregnated soil at salados, both along rivers and inside forest. **Voice:** Typical flight call a far-carrying and distinctive "chuwít," usually not given in series.

Hapalopsittaca **Parrots**
Similar to *Pionopsitta* but found exclusively in montane forests, both *Hapalopsittaca* in Ecuador are rare birds. There is red on the face and wings of both species.

[Rusty-faced Parrot
Hapalopsittaca amazonina
Loro Carirrojizo]   Plate 32(11)

21.5–23 cm (8½–9″). *Very rare* (status uncertain) in canopy and borders of temperate forest on e. slope in far north (Cerro Mongus). Bill pale grayish; orbital ring gray. Mostly green, paler below and with more brownish olive breast; *foreface rusty red, ear-coverts bright olive with yellow shaft streaks*. *Shoulders extensively dull red*, flight feathers extensively violet-blue, with some red on

underwing-coverts; tail dull reddish broadly tipped blue. **Similar species:** Does not overlap with similar Red-faced Parrot of s. Ecuador, which differs in having redder face, no red in tail, etc. *Pionus* parrots are larger, with the dissimilar White-capped being the species most likely to occur with Rusty-faced. **Habits:** Not well known. Behavior in Colombia appears to differ little from Red-faced Parrot's. **Voice:** Flight call a repeated "chek-chek-chek-chek."

Red-faced Parrot, *Hapalopsittaca pyrrhops*
Loro Carirrojo   Plate 32(10)

21.5–23 cm (8½–9″). *Scarce and local in canopy and borders of temperate forest and woodland in south from Cañar and Morona-Santiago southward* (mainly on interandean slopes). Formerly considered conspecific with Rusty-faced Parrot. Bill pale grayish; orbital ring gray. Mostly green, somewhat bluer on crown and more olive on breast; *forecrown, front of cheeks, and chin red*, ear-coverts brownish olive with yellow streaking. *Shoulders extensively rosy magenta* (more so in ♂♂?), flight feathers mostly violet-blue, with

some red on underwing-coverts; tail green, feathers broadly tipped blue. **Similar species:** Cf. Rusty-faced Parrot (no overlap). Otherwise this fairly small, chunky parrot is unlikely to be confused. **Habits:** Usually in pairs or small groups of up to 4–6 individuals, rarely more. Flight fast and direct, often well above forest canopy. Perched birds are generally hard to see, tending to remain hidden in foliage, but occasionally they land on open or dead branches. **Voice:** Flight calls rather soft and weak, e.g., "kerree-kerree-kerree" (J. Flanagan recording).

Short-tailed Parrot, *Graydidasculus brachyurus*
Loro Colicorto   Plate 31(20)

21.5–23 cm (8½–9″). A *chunky, short-tailed parrot, uncommon in várzea and riparian forest and woodland in lowlands of northeast.* Heavy bill dusky; iris yellow-orange, orbital ring pale gray *extending in front of eye as thin dark line* (imparting a "fierce" expression). *Entirely plain green*, slightly paler on uppertail-coverts and underparts. **Similar species:** Bull-headed and short-tailed shape unique among parrots, the former when perched and the latter especially noticeable in flight; Short-tailed's distinctive loud raucous calls are also helpful. *Amazona* larger and more patterned, fly with shallow wingbeats. Blue-headed Parrot can, especially in poor light, also look plain and unpatterned. **Habits:** Usually in noisy conspicuous groups, in Ecuador most often small (rarely more than 10–15 together). Regularly perches in the open, often on exposed branches or stumps. Flight fast and direct, with fairly deep wingbeats. **Voice:** Unpleasant, loud, and harsh squealing calls easy to recognize and include a "shreeyk" and a sharp, fast "jeek!-jeek!-jeek!-jeek!"

Pionus Parrots

Midsized parrots (somewhat larger than the previous several genera) with short square tails, *Pionus* range in the canopy and borders of humid and montane forests; they tend to be noisy and conspicuous. Tails are short and square, and all species show *red on the crissum. In flight they show characteristic deep wingstrokes.*

Blue-headed Parrot, *Pionus menstruus*
Loro Cabeciazul   Plate 32(6)

Mostly below 1100 m

27–29 cm (10½–11¼"). *Fairly common, conspicuous, and widespread* in canopy and borders of humid forest and woodland in lowlands of east and west. *Unique blue head.* Bill blackish with some red at base; orbital ring pale gray. *Head, neck, and breast blue* (averaging deeper in **eastern birds**, also in ♂♂) with black patch on ear-coverts and red patch on foreneck (latter often more extensive in **western birds**). Otherwise bright green with *conspicuous* (especially in flight) *red crissum and base of tail.* **Similar species:** The most familiar *Pionus*. Cf. other *Pionus*, in Ecuador all of which are more montane. Bronze-winged can be sympatric with Blue-headed in more humid w. lowlands. **Habits:** Noisy and generally familiar, regularly perching on dead snags and in semiopen, often flying about in fair-sized groups. Seems to tolerate disturbed and fragmented forest better than most parrots. Readily told in flight by deep wingstrokes, wings almost touching below body, strikingly different from shallow wingbeats of *Amazona* (other *Pionus* similar). In Amazonia regularly descends to

eat mineral-impregnated soil at salados along rivers, along Río Napo sometimes in large numbers. **Voice:** Common flight call a distinctive, relatively high-pitched "keewink, keewink."

Red-billed Parrot, *Pionus sordidus*
Loro Piquirrojo   Plate 32(7)

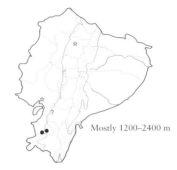

Mostly 1200–2400 m

27–29 cm (10½–11¼"). Canopy and borders of *subtropical forest* and trees in adjacent clearings on both slopes. *Bill red*; inconspicuous orbital ring gray. Mostly green, more bluish on head (especially crown) with *feathers scaled darker blue*; midthroat and band across chest blue (variable in extent and deepness); *conspicuous red crissum and base of tail.* **Similar species:** Resembles Blue-headed Parrot of lowlands, differing especially in its red bill (usually obvious in field); Red-billed looks "scalier," with unmarked blue confined to chest. Looks more solidly green than other *Pionus*. **Habits:** Similar to Blue-headed Parrot, though Red-billed less familiar because of its restricted elevational range. Group size typically smaller, though local and seasonal concentrations can occur. **Voice:** Calls similar to Blue-headed Parrot's, most frequent being a "keewank, keewank."

White-capped Parrot, *Pionus seniloides*
Loro Gorriblanco   Plate 32(8)

28–30 cm (11–11¾"). Uncommon in canopy and borders of *subtropical and temperate forest on both slopes.* Formerly sometimes considered conspecific with Plum-crowned Parrot (*P. tumultuosus*), found farther south in Andes, and then called Speckle-faced Parrot. *Bill yellowish horn*; orbital ring whitish. *Forecrown white*, some birds with

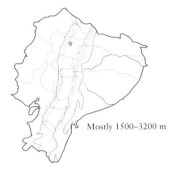

Mostly 1500–3200 m

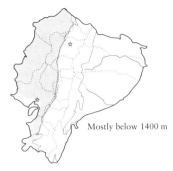

Mostly below 1400 m

scattered pink feathers; *head, neck, and throat dusky violet with white mottling and speckling*; above otherwise green. Below mostly plain dusky violet, lower flanks green, *conspicuous red crissum and base of tail*. Similar species: Mottled and often even messy-looking; this species' unique white on crown and pale bill stand out at long distances and usually preclude confusion. Cf. other parrots of high-elevation forests, e.g., smaller Red-faced Parrot and the large Scaly-naped Amazon. **Habits:** Usually in small groups that are hard to see perched, generally remaining in cover. Even flying birds seem most active when cloud cover hangs low, often preventing good views; flight profile and style much like other *Pionus*, though wingstrokes are sometimes shallower. Seem highly nomadic and may undertake seasonal movements up- and downslope; does not seem to be resident anywhere. **Voice:** Calls quite different from those of Blue-headed and Red-billed Parrots; they more resemble those of a large *Aratinga* parakeet, e.g., "kreeyah-kreeyah-kreeyahkreeyah," given both when perched and flying.

Bronze-winged Parrot, *Pionus chalcopterus*
Loro Alibronceado   Plate 32(9)

27–28 cm (10½–11″). A handsome, *largely blue* parrot of canopy and borders of humid and semihumid forest and woodland and adjacent clearings with large trees in *lowlands and foothills of west*, ranging locally up into lower subtropics. *Bill pale greenish yellow; orbital ring buffy whitish to pale purplish. Mostly rich dark blue*, back more bronzy green and with *contrasting bronzy brown shoulders and wing-coverts. Throat patch contrastingly white*, some pink at its lower edge; crissum red. In flight primaries

bright rich blue from above, paler turquoise blue from below; underwing-coverts rich blue. **Similar species:** A dark and mainly blue parrot, rather differently colored from other *Pionus* (though like others it can look black in poor light), *showing essentially no green*; bronzy wings, white throat, and pale bill and ocular ring stand out. **Habits:** Similar to Blue-headed Parrot, locally (seasonally?) occurring with it at some localities. Bronze-winged likewise tolerates disturbed conditions relatively well. **Voice:** Similar to Blue-headed; typical flight call a repeated "kree-ink."

Amazona Amazons
Rather large, green parrots with *distinctive facial patterns* and usually a *colored speculum on the secondaries*, visible mainly in flight. They range primarily in the canopy of forests, but especially in the early morning they regularly overfly more open areas, en route to feeding sites. Amazons often fly high overhead, and they can then readily be recognized to genus by their squared tails and characteristic *stiff and shallow* (almost "fluttery") *wingbeats*. However, unless giving their *distinctive calls*, they often are hard to identify to species. Pairs are usually apparent within the flock as they remain side by side, sometimes accompanied by what are presumed to be still semi-dependent offspring. Amazons are sometimes called simply "parrots."

Red-lored Amazon, *Amazona autumnalis*
Amazona Frentirroja   Plate 32(12)

33–34.5 cm (13–13½″). *Decidedly local* in canopy and borders of deciduous and humid forest, locally also in adjacent mangroves, in *lowlands of west*. Bill bicolored, yellowish horn above and dusky below and on tip of

Mostly below 700 m

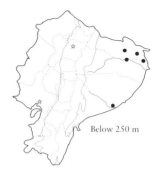

Below 250 m

maxilla; orbital ring yellowish white. Mainly green with *red forehead and lores extending back as narrow line to just back of eye*; feathers of crown, nape, and sides of neck broadly edged lavender, face contrastingly bright pale green. Red speculum on secondaries prominent in flight (but usually hidden at rest); terminal half of tail yellowish green and contrastingly paler, tail with some red at base. **Similar species:** Cf. Mealy Amazon (only other *Amazona* in w. lowlands). Mealy is larger with even wider pale orbital ring (standing out more) and lacks red on forehead and lavender feather edging on top of crown (though it has some lavender on hindcrown)—but both red and lavender can be hard to see in field, especially on flying birds, so be careful. **Habits:** Usually seen in pairs or small groups, mainly as they fly to and from roosting sites *early* in morning and *late* in afternoon. Early and late they perch in open, often on high exposed dead branches, but for the rest of the day they are inconspicuous, remaining in leafy canopy and only rarely revealing their presence by the occasional dropping of fruit pieces or other debris as they feed. **Voice:** Typical loud flight call a distinctively bi- or multisyllabic "cheekorák, cheekorák . . ." or "cheekák, cheekák, cheekák," with harsh quality; perched birds give a variety of other calls, some more musical and complex.

Festive Amazon, *Amazona festiva*
Amazona Festiva   Plate 32(13)

33–33.5 cm (13–14″). Local in canopy and borders of *várzea and riparian forest and woodland in lowlands of northeast*, mainly in lower Río Aguarico drainage and along lower Río Napo. Bill blackish; inconspicuous orbital ring gray. Mainly green with *narrow reddish frontal band extending back as stripe*

to above eye, blue tinge behind eye, and *red on rump extending up onto lower back* (fairly obvious in flight, but almost always hidden at rest). Wings show no red speculum. **Similar species:** Cf. other amazons with which Festive can occur; all of them show a colored wing speculum conspicuous in flight. Orange-winged often occurs with Festive but has very different face pattern with yellow cheeks and no red. **Habits:** Of all the amazons, Festive shows strongest affinity for water and rarely is seen any distance away from the edge of rivers, streams, or oxbow lakes. Behavior generally similar to other amazons, though in some areas it seems unusually tame and conspicuous, perching in open and allowing close approach. **Voice:** Distinctive call a repeated "roww-roww-roww-roww . . ." with nasal quality, given both in flight and while perched; recalls Yellow-crowned Amazon though without that species' two-parted effect.

Yellow-crowned Amazon
Amazona ochrocephala
Amazona Coroniamarilla   Plate 32(16)

34.5–37 cm (13½–14½″). Generally uncommon in canopy and borders of humid forest in *lowlands of east*. Bill horn with dusky to

To 400 m

blackish tip; orbital ring white. Mainly green, with *yellow patch on midcrown*. Red speculum on secondaries prominent in flight (but usually hidden at rest), *as is extensive red area on shoulders* (though latter variable in extent); terminal half of tail yellowish green and contrastingly pale. **Similar species:** Mealy Amazon larger and has wider orbital ring. There seems to be some variation in plumage of both species (especially in extent of yellow in crown and red on shoulders), so best to go by size, orbital ring, and unmistakably different vocalizations (see below). Orange-winged Amazon has grayer orbital ring and extensive yellow on cheeks and crown, and blue can usually be seen on face; its wing speculum is, as name implies, orange (not red). Two species of amazons found in Middle America were formerly considered conspecific with *A. ochrocephala*; the enlarged species was then called Yellow-headed Amazon. **Habits:** Generally not numerous, tending to be found in extensive terra firme. Small numbers occasionally descend to eat mineral-impregnated soil at salados along Río Napo. **Voice:** Most frequent flight call a distinctive throaty, not very raucous (almost semimusical) "ra-raow" or simply "raow," often repeated multiple times (has been paraphrased as "bow-wow"); cf. somewhat similar call of Festive Amazon. Also gives a variety of other calls, especially when perched; all amazons are prized as "good-talking" pets (actually all they do is imitate what they hear as young birds), but Yellow-crowned generally has best reputation.

Orange-winged Amazon, *Amazona amazonica*
Amazona Alinaranja   Plate 32(14)

31–33 cm (12¼–13″). *Numerous* in canopy and borders of várzea and riparian forest and

Below 500 m

woodland in *lowlands of east*. Bill horn with dusky tip; orbital ring pale grayish. Mainly green, with *yellow patch on forecrown and another on cheeks separated by blue on lores and narrowly above bill. Bright orange speculum on secondaries* prominent in flight (but usually hidden at rest); tail more yellowish green with reddish subterminal band. **Similar species:** There is some individual variation in extent of blue and yellow on face, but normally yellow on cheeks is extensive, visible at long distances even on flying birds. Wing speculum of most other amazons is red (not orange), in Festive lacking. **Habits:** Generally the most frequently seen amazon in the east. Favors river-edge situations, overflying terra firme but only rarely landing there, then mainly at edge. Has regular and conspicuous flights to and from its island roost sites, where it sometimes assembles in the hundreds. Does not, however, seem to come to clay licks along rivers, at least not regularly. **Voice:** Most common flight call a rather shrill "kee-wik, kee-wik, kee-wik . . ." or "kwik-kwik, kwik-kwik . . . ," often repeated rapidly. Perched birds give, like other amazons, a wider variety of calls.

Scaly-naped Amazon, *Amazona mercenaria*
Amazona Nuquiescamosa   Plate 32(15)

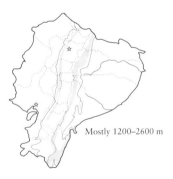

Mostly 1200–2600 m

31–33 cm (12¼–13″). Local and uncommon in *subtropical and temperate forest on both slopes*. Bill dusky with pale area at base of maxilla; orbital ring whitish. Mainly green, *feathers of crown, chest, and especially nape and sides of neck edged black giving scaly effect.* In most of Ecuadorian range shows *little or no colored wing speculum* (in certain birds some maroon shows), but in far south birds showing a prominent large red speculum have been seen; tail with fairly wide reddish subterminal band and dark blue toward base. **Similar species:** *The only montane amazon in Ecuador.* Looks relatively uniform, scaling on foreparts being hard to see except at close range. Other amazons that might overlap with Scaly-naped along e. base of Andes all show *conspicuous* wing speculum. Cf. White-capped Parrot. **Habits:** Only infrequently seen perched, then often wary, and generally not often landing on open branches. Usually noted as it wings high overhead en route to and from feeding and roosting sites. **Voice:** Far-carrying flight calls reminiscent of Mealy Amazon, but often interspersed with other more musical notes.

Mealy Amazon, *Amazona farinosa*
Amazona Harinosa   Plate 32(17)

Mostly below 700 m

38–41 cm (15–16″). Canopy and borders of humid forest in *lowlands of east and west*, now more local in west. Bill mostly dark horn with base of maxilla paler yellowish; *wide and conspicuous orbital ring white*. Mainly green, feathers of hindcrown and nape edged lavender, some birds with a powdery "bloom" on mantle. Red speculum on secondaries prominent in flight (but usually hidden at rest), also some red on bend of wing; terminal half of tail yellowish green and contrastingly pale. **Similar species:** The largest amazon in Ecuador, with a wider and therefore more prominent orbital ring than the others. Otherwise Mealy is somewhat devoid of field marks; beware occasional individuals showing yellow on crown (though never as much as Yellow-crowned Amazon). **Habits:** Similar to Red-lored Amazon, though Mealy seems rarely to gather in such large aggregations, typically

no more than 4–8 birds being together; the exception is at salados, where Mealies regularly congregate to feed on mineral-impregnated soil, especially along Río Napo. Mealies also usually do not join in large roosts of various *Amazona* on river islands in e. lowlands. **Voice:** Has a wide variety of calls, most of them extremely loud and raucous, e.g., a repeated "chok-chok" and a "chap-chap-chap-chaow"; when perched repertoire is even more extensive.

Red-fan Parrot, *Deroptyus accipitrinus*
Loro de Abanico   Plate 32(18)

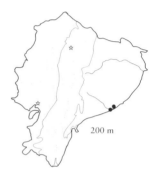

200 m

34–35 cm (13¼–14″). A *spectacular and uniquely colored*, *long-tailed* parrot found locally in *terra firme forest in lowlands of se. Pastaza.* Iris yellow; bill black. *Forecrown white* contrasting with otherwise brown head, feathers with prominent white shaft streaks. *Feathers of hindneck and most of underparts dark red broadly tipped pale blue*; otherwise green above and on flanks. Primaries and underside of tail black. **Similar species:** Unlikely to be confused, often actually looking rather hawk-like. Basic coloration very dark, but *the white forecrown stands out in almost all light conditions.* **Habits:** Usually in noisy pairs or small groups that remain high in forest trees but often remain for long periods on dead snags. Perched birds sometimes raise their long hindneck feathers in a fan-shaped ruff (almost halo-like) and may posture at each other for protracted periods. Flight very distinctive (totally unlike any other parrot's), consisting of several shallow flaps interspersed with long glides on bowed wings; even wing shape is reminiscent of an *Accipiter*. Red-fans sometimes associate with *Amazona* spp. **Voice:** Has a variety of high-pitched calls including a shrill "keeya-keeya-keeya-keeya" and a more piping "peeu-peeu-peeu-peeu."

Cuculiformes
Cuckoos and Anis: Cuculidae (17)
A diverse family, split into separate families by some taxonomists. Most cuckoos are furtive and rarely seen birds of lowland forest and woodland, though the anis provide a striking exception. Many are vocal, some being heard much more often than seen. Nesting behavior is highly varied: some species form pairs, others nest communally, and still others are brood parasites on other bird species. **Sexes are alike.**

Coccyzus **Cuckoos**
Slender and sleek arboreal birds with long graduated tails that are inconspicuous in forest, woodland, and borders. The status of all five Ecuadorian species remains poorly understood.

Black-billed Cuckoo
Coccyzus erythropthalmus
Cuclillo Piquinegro   Plate 33(1)

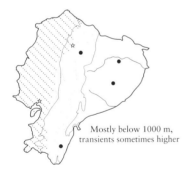

Mostly below 1000 m,
transients sometimes higher

28–29 cm (11–11½"). A *rare transient* (mainly Mar.–Apr., also Nov.) in a variety of habitats from semiopen arid scrub to canopy and borders of humid forest, primarily in lowlands; more numerous on northward passage, at least in southwest. *Slightly decurved bill black*; narrow eye-ring usually yellow (becoming red on breeding grounds, rarely or never seen in Ecuador). Brownish olive above with slightly darker mask; white below, usually with faint buff tinge on throat and chest. *Underside of tail gray, feathers*

with narrow white tips. **Juvenile** similar but often more strongly tinged buff below and can show some rufous in primaries. **Similar species:** Yellow-billed Cuckoo has lower mandible mainly or entirely yellow, shows rufous flash in primaries, and has underside of tail black (not gray) with broader white tips. Cf. also very rare Pearly-breasted Cuckoo. Other *Coccyzus* are much more strongly buff or rufous below. **Habits:** Generally furtive, found singly as it sneaks about in dense leafy cover at varying heights. Migrants are occasionally in more open, scrubby terrain where they can be easier to see. **Voice:** Seems to be silent away from breeding grounds.

Yellow-billed Cuckoo, *Coccyzus americanus*
Cuclillo Piquiamarillo   Plate 33(2)

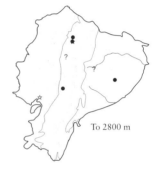

To 2800 m

29–30.5 cm (11½–12"). A *rare transient* (mainly) and boreal winter resident (with scatter of records Sep.–May) to deciduous woodland, scrub, and clearings. *Slightly decurved bill black with lower mandible mostly yellow or orange-yellow*; narrow eye-ring yellow (gray in a few—young?—individuals). Grayish brown above with slightly darker mask; white below, tinged pale gray. *Primaries with rufous edging (prominent as a flash in flight, but usually visible on perched birds as well); underside of tail black, feathers with large white tips.* **Juvenile** similar but often with less yellow on bill; underside of tail grayer (consequently white tail-tips contrast less). **Similar species:** Black-billed Cuckoo always has *all-dark* bill and gray underside to tail (never black); it never shows as much rufous in wing as Yellow-billed. Very rare Pearly-breasted Cuckoo is even more similar to Yellow-billed (it also has yellow lower mandible), differing in smaller size and lack of rufous in wing. **Habits and Voice:** Much like Black-billed Cuckoo.

Pearly-breasted Cuckoo, *Coccyzus euleri*
Cuclillo Pechiperlado   Plate 33(3)

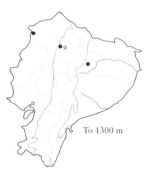

To 1300 m

25.5–27 cm (10–10½″). *Status uncertain*; two specimens from northwest (Mindo and Muisne) and a sighting from Jatun Sacha. Closely resembles better-known Yellow-billed Cuckoo, differing in smaller size and *lack of rufous edging in primaries*; despite the implication of its English name, color of underparts is not any grayer. Pearly-breasted's narrow eye-ring is at least sometimes yellow, contra some sources, so this too not a distinguishing point. **Habits:** Much like Black-billed and Yellow-billed Cuckoos. One of the Ecuador specimens is a juvenile and may have been a transient; it was obtained in "disturbed humid forest." **Voice:** Song in Brazil a simple series of low hollow guttural notes, usually slowly delivered, "kuow, kuow, kuow . . . " (J. Vielliard recording).

Dark-billed Cuckoo, *Coccyzus melacoryphus*
Cuclillo Piquioscuro   Plate 33(4)

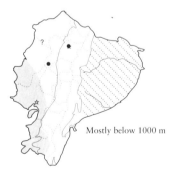

Mostly below 1000 m

27–28 cm (10½–11″). An *uncommon austral migrant* (Apr.–Oct.) to shrubby clearings and forest and woodland borders in *lowlands of east*, a few records from central valley; *apparently resident locally in deciduous scrub and woodland in lowlands and foothills of southwest* (mainly El Oro and Loja). Slightly decurved bill entirely black; narrow eye-ring usually yellow (but sometimes gray, and therefore inconspicuous against dark face). Olive brown above, more grayish on crown with *black mask through eyes and on cheeks* and narrow gray band from below mask down sides of neck; *pale buff below*, deepest on breast and flanks. Flight feathers show no rufous; underside of tail black, feathers with large white tips visible mainly from below. **Similar species:** Usually the presence of extensive buff on underparts of this cuckoo is enough to clinch identification. In west, cf. more richly colored Gray-capped Cuckoo. **Habits:** Usually seen singly, creeping about in dense foliage, generally not very high above ground. **Voice:** Most often silent, austral migrants always so. Infrequently heard and subdued song a descending series of guttural notes, e.g., "ko-ko-ko-ko-kolp-kolp."

Gray-capped Cuckoo, *Coccyzus lansbergi*
Cuclillo Cabecigris   Plate 33(5)

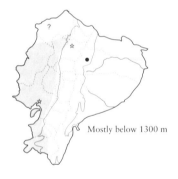

Mostly below 1300 m

27–28 cm (10½–11″). *Scarce and inconspicuous in dense lower growth of woodland, scrub, and adjacent gardens in lowlands and foothills of west* (Manabí and Los Ríos south, in some years farther north). Slightly decurved bill black; narrow eye-ring can be yellow or gray (even in breeding birds). *Head dark gray* contrasting with *rufescent brown upperparts*, wings (especially flight feathers) more rufous; *below rich buff*, deepest on breast. Tail black, feathers with large white tips visible mainly from below. **Similar species:** This handsome cuckoo is more richly colored than any other *Coccyzus* and as such should be easily recognized. Only possible confusion is with Dark-billed Cuckoo (olive brown above, only pale buff below, etc.). **Habits:** Like other *Coccyzus*, usually inconspicuous, creeping about in thick vegetation, sometimes winging swiftly across roads or other open areas. **Voice:** Song, apparently given only while breeding, a fast series of low-pitched hollow notes, "co-co-co-co-co-co." Also gives a low guttural growl when disturbed (e.g., after tape playback).

Piaya Cuckoos

Handsome, *predominantly rufous* cuckoos with *very long and graduated tails* (less extreme in Little) that are found mainly in the lowlands.

Squirrel Cuckoo, *Piaya cayana*
Cuco Ardilla   Plate 33(7)

To 2000–2500 m

40.5–46 cm (16–18″). A *large*, slender cuckoo with *very long, graduated tail*, widespread in canopy and borders of more humid forest and woodland in lowlands of east and west, smaller numbers up into subtropics. *Bill greenish yellow*; iris red, with *orbital skin red* (**east of Andes**) *or greenish yellow* (**west of Andes**). *Uniform rich rufous-chestnut above*, fading to paler vinaceous buff on throat and chest; *lower underparts contrastingly gray*, becoming black on lower belly and crissum (black more extensive in birds **west of Andes**). Underside of tail black, feathers with large white tips visible from below. **Similar species:** Less arboreal Little Cuckoo similarly colored but hardly half the size (and proportionately shorter-tailed); it lacks con-

trast in coloration below. In terra firme forests of east, cf. scarcer Black-bellied Cuckoo. **Habits:** Usually in pairs, creeping about in foliage and hopping along larger branches, tail often held loosely; sometimes moves swiftly with almost squirrel-like agility. Generally not hard to see, at times boldly foraging at close range. Rarely flies far—preferring to move about by running and hopping—but occasionally launches itself across a more open area, usually gently gliding downward on flat wings with occasional weak bursts of flapping. **Voice:** Fairly vocal, with a variety of calls. What is apparently its song a fast series of "kweep" or "kweeyp" notes, often repeated for a protracted period, usually from a hidden perch. More often heard are several characteristic calls, notably an abrupt and loud "cheek! kwahh" and a nasal "weeyadidu."

Black-bellied Cuckoo, *Piaya melanogaster*
Cuco Ventrinegro   Plate 33(8)

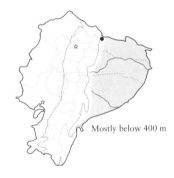

Mostly below 400 m

38–40.5 cm (15–16″). *Scarce and perhaps local in terra firme forest canopy in lowlands of east. Bill bright deep red*; iris dark red with *orbital skin blue and spot in front of eye yellow. Crown gray* contrasting with otherwise rufous upperparts; throat and breast cinnamon-rufous becoming *black on belly and crissum.* Underside of tail black, feathers with large white tips visible from below. **Similar species:** Squirrel Cuckoo is much more frequently encountered, in some places even occurring in terra firme canopy. *Both species show black on belly.* Black-bellied is best known by brightly colored facial soft parts, gray crown, and lack of gray below. **Habits:** Much like more familiar Squirrel Cuckoo, though Black-bellied comes less often into open and usually remains higher above ground. **Voice:** Not very vocal. Distinctive song a steadily repeated "jerreé-jew, jerreé-jew, jerreé-jew . . . ," sometimes continued for a minute or more but hard to track to its source as the singing bird typically remains motionless in dense cover. Also gives other growling notes.

Little Cuckoo, *Piaya minuta*
Cuco Menudo   Plate 33(6)

Mostly below 600 m, locally higher

25.5–28 cm (10–11″). *A small relative of Squirrel Cuckoo, with proportionately shorter tail*, found in shrubby growth and woodland and forest borders (*most often near water*) in *lowlands of east and west*. Bill greenish yellow; iris reddish brown to red with red eye-ring. *Uniform rufous-chestnut above*; throat and breast tawny (paler than upperparts), with belly grayish and crissum blackish. **Western birds** paler than **eastern birds**. Underside of tail black with white tips visible from below. **Similar species:** Squirrel Cuckoo is so much larger that confusion unlikely; Little is, in addition, much less arboreal. **Habits:** Unlike Squirrel Cuckoo, not a bird of forest. Furtive, usually seen singly as it sneaks about in dense vegetation, usually not far above ground. **Voice:** Though usually quiet, has several distinctive vocalizations including a nasal drawn-out "wyahhh, deh-deh-deh" and a much sharper "chik! wreeanh."

Crotophaga Anis
Conspicuous *all-black* cuckoos with *laterally compressed bills* and long tails. Anis range in open terrain (Greater only near

water), and they nest communally, groups sharing in incubation and nestling care.

Greater Ani, *Crotophaga major*
Garrapatero Mayor   Plate 33(9)

Mostly below 400 m, locally higher in river valleys

46–48 cm (18–19″). *A very large, long-tailed ani found in shrubbery along rivers and lakeshores in lowlands of east*, also locally in swampy terrain of southwest. *Iris strikingly pale straw yellow* (dark brown in juveniles); black bill laterally compressed with arched ridge on base of maxilla *imparting a characteristic "broken-nose" profile. Entirely glossy blue-black*, feathers of mantle edged bronzy green and tail glossed purple. **Similar species:** Smooth-billed and Groove-billed Anis are much smaller, have dark eyes, and are nowhere near as glossy. Cf. also ♂ Great-tailed Grackle (in Ecuador found only along immediate coasts, where Greater Ani does not range). **Habits:** Usually found in groups that forage at varying levels in shrubbery and woodland near water, usually not very high; group size typically small (5–15 birds) but occasionally large numbers flock together (RSR once counted a group of 130!). Usually occurs independently of other birds. **Voice:** Quite vocal, with strange low-pitched growling calls, sometimes very abrupt and loud or given as a long-continued weird bubbling chorus by many birds at once. Most characteristic is a fast "koro-koro-koro" often given in flight.

Smooth-billed Ani, *Crotophaga ani*
Garrapatero Piquiliso   Plate 33(10)

33–35.5 cm (13–14″). *Numerous in semiopen agricultural and settled areas in lowlands*

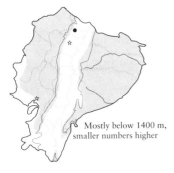

Mostly below 1400 m, smaller numbers higher

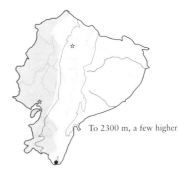

To 2300 m, a few higher

of east and west, in west confined to more humid regions. *Black bill laterally compressed and smooth, with arched hump on basal half of culmen.* Entirely dull black. Tail long and rounded, often appearing loosely attached to body. **Similar species:** Groove-billed Ani occurs only west of Andes; it and slightly larger Smooth-billed can be hard to distinguish, with Groove-billed's grooves on maxilla often hard to discern (and Smooth-billed can give illusion of grooving). Groove-billed's culmen is evenly arched (no hump as in Smooth-billed), and it usually looks sleeker and less disheveled than Smooth-billed. Cf. also much larger Greater Ani. **Habits:** Ranges in small straggling groups of up to 6–10 birds, perching on bushes, fences, and wires, rarely at any great height above ground. Often quite tame. Associates with cattle, feeding on insects they flush and sometimes even perching on them to pick off ticks. Flight labored and weak, consisting of a few quick flaps and an unsteady glide. **Voice:** Most frequent call a distinctive upslurred "oooo-eeek?" (or "aaaaa-ní") often given in alarm or during flight, unlike anything given by Groove-billed. Also has a variety of other whining and clucking vocalizations, some fairly similar to calls of Groove-billed.

Groove-billed Ani, *Crotophaga sulcirostris*
Garrapatero Piquiestriado　　　　Plate 33(11)

28–30 cm (11–12″). Numerous in scrub and agricultural regions, and around towns and settled areas in *more arid lowlands of west*, ranging up into highlands of south, also in Río Marañón drainage around Zamora. *Black bill laterally compressed with culmen forming unbroken arch and maxilla showing*

several grooves. Entirely black. Tail long and rounded, often appearing loosely attached to body. **Similar species:** Resembles Smooth-billed Ani, sometimes occurring with it though Smooth-billed favors more humid regions; rarely or never, however, do the two flock together. Often they are best distinguished by voice; further, slightly larger Smooth-billed is duller black and bill profile shows "hump" on culmen (not smoothly arched as in Groove-billed). **Habits:** Similar to Smooth-billed Ani. **Voice:** Has a variety of clucking calls, some (e.g., a repeated "kwik" or "hwik") markedly sharper than any given by Smooth-billed; also a more querulous soft "koo-ilk?" vaguely like Smooth-billed's most frequent call.

Striped Cuckoo, *Tapera naevia*
Cuclillo Crespín　　　　　　　　　Plate 34(1)

28–30 cm (11–12″). A *brownish* cuckoo of *shrubby clearings and pastures with scattered low trees in lowlands of west*, mainly in more humid regions; also spreading into *southeast*. Bill yellowish; iris hazel. *Short expressive*

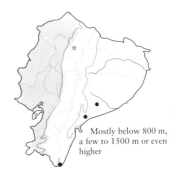

Mostly below 800 m, a few to 1500 m or even higher

crest *rufescent with blackish streaking*; tail fairly long and graduated, uppertail-coverts elongated. *Mostly pale grayish brown above with blackish streaking*; superciliary buffy whitish and face dusky brown. *Dull whitish below* tinged buffy grayish on throat and chest and with narrow black malar streak. **Juvenile** similar but more rufescent above with *conspicuous large buff spots on crown and mantle*; throat and chest buff with faint scaly markings. **Similar species:** Not likely confused in its *semiopen habitat, where the only brown cuckoo.* Cf. much scarcer Pheasant and Pavonine Cuckoos, both found in more forested habitats. **Habits:** Generally secretive, creeping unobtrusively in thick vegetation near ground except when vocalizing. A brood parasite, favoring species that build domed nests. **Voice:** Heard far more often than seen. Most frequent song a pure melancholy 2-noted whistle, "püü-peee," which is quite ventriloquial and far-carrying. Also gives a 5- or 6-noted song of similar quality, the last several notes short and fast. Usually sings from atop a bush or fence post, often ruffling crest and flaring alula.

Dromococcyx Cuckoos
Scarce, forest-inhabiting cuckoos found in the eastern lowlands. Both species are *heard more often than seen*, and both are *brood parasites.*

Pheasant Cuckoo, *Dromococcyx phasianellus*
Cuco Faisán   Plate 34(2)

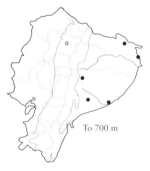

37–41 cm (14½–16"). *Scarce and local* (but overlooked) in várzea and swampy forest and woodland in *lowlands of east. Small-headed* with short expressive crest; *tail long, wide, and graduated (fan-shaped) with uppertail-*

coverts greatly elongated (nearly as long as tail itself). Dark brown above, feathers of wing-coverts and inner flight feathers with white tips; crown dark chestnut bordered below by narrow whitish postocular stripe. Whitish below with *dusky spotting and streaking on throat and chest.* **Similar species:** Profile of this odd cuckoo unique, with small head, thin neck, and often widely spread tail feathers. Striped Cuckoo favors more open terrain, is considerably smaller and paler above with no streaking on foreneck. Cf. also much rarer Pavonine Cuckoo. **Habits:** Very secretive, skulking in dense lower and middle growth, often where viny growth is prevalent. Flight labored, rarely long-sustained; even then the tail is usually spread, and uppertail-coverts are often raised resulting in an odd-looking "humped" shape. A brood parasite, its hosts being mainly species that construct open, cup-shaped nests. **Voice:** Heard much more often than seen. Typical song resembles Striped Cuckoo's short song but with a third trilled note added, e.g., "püü-peee, pr'r'r'r"; sometimes a rising fourth or fifth note is added.

Pavonine Cuckoo, *Dromococcyx pavoninus*
Cuco Pavonino   Plate 34(3)

28–30 cm (11–12"). *One old specimen from w. Napo at Río Suno*; no recent records (surprisingly). Elsewhere inhabits thickets (sometimes of bamboo) inside humid forest and woodland. Resembles Pheasant Cuckoo (with similar strange shape though uppertail-coverts not so elongated) but *considerably smaller* with proportionately shorter tail; *narrow postocular stripe buff* and *plain fulvous throat and breast without any spotting or streaking.* **Similar species:** Cf. similarly sized Striped Cuckoo (upperparts much paler and browner with dusky streaking, and more uniformly whitish below). **Habits:** Unknown in Ecuador. Elsewhere found singly, but almost solely when singing; otherwise elusive and skulking, even more so than Pheasant Cuckoo. **Voice:** Heard much more often than seen, and very ventriloquial. Song resembles that of Pheasant Cuckoo, and sometimes the two almost seem to switch songs. Typical Pavonine song is a whistled "püü-pee, püü-pi-pi" without Pheasant's usual trill at end.

Neomorphus Ground-Cuckoos

Unmistakable and spectacular, *very large* and *mainly terrestrial* cuckoos found at low densities inside humid lowland forest. Their *very long tails* and *expressive bushy crests* are notable, as are their quite striking plumage patterns. Sadly, no ground-cuckoo is often seen in Ecuador, but observers fortunate enough to find an antswarm in or adjacent to extensive forest can always hope.

Rufous-vented Ground-Cuckoo
Neomorphus geoffroyi
Cuco Hormiguero Ventrirrufo   Plate 34(4)

46–51 cm (18–20″). *Rare* on or near ground inside terra firme forest in *lowlands of east.* *Heavy bill greenish yellow*; orbital skin dull bluish. *Very long tail* and expressive bushy crest. Above mostly bronzy green with brown forecrown, head, and neck, and long crest feathers tipped glossy blue-black; rump and upperside of tail bronzy purple. *Pale buffy brown below* becoming rufous on lower belly and crissum; foreneck obscurely scaled dusky and with *narrow black pectoral band.* **Similar species:** *The only ground-cuckoo in most of east*, and essentially unmistakable,

but in far northeast cf. Red-billed Ground-Cuckoo. **Habits:** Surely ranking among the most spectacular Neotropical birds, all ground-cuckoos are elusive (especially considering their large size) and infrequently seen. When encountered they are most apt to be found singly, less often in pairs or small family groups, most frequently while in attendance at a swarm of army ants. They are largely terrestrial, though flushed birds may fly up to low branches. Ground-cuckoos also follow herds of White-lipped Peccaries, and Red-billed (and presumably other ground-cuckoos) is even known to follow along underneath troops of monkeys. Their demeanor varies: though wary and shy at times, running off at the slightest disturbance, at other times they may parade about quite boldly. Excited birds often ruffle crests. The long and full tail is usually held partially cocked, but running birds drop it and extend neck; at times tail seems to be used almost as a rudder. **Voice:** A ground-cuckoo's presence may be revealed by its loud bill snapping, often several snaps in quick succession, apparently given in both alarm and annoyance. Also occasionally gives a low-pitched, dove-like moaning, "oooooo-oóp."

[Red-billed Ground-Cuckoo
Neomorphus pucheranii
Cuco Hormiguero Piquirrojo]   Plate 34(5)

46–51 cm (18–20″). *Rare and local* inside terra firme forest in lowlands of *far northeast. Heavy bill bright red tipped yellowish, orbital skin also bright red* becoming blue behind eye. *Very long tail* and expressive bushy crest. *Crown (including entire crest) glossy blue-black*; above otherwise bronzy green, with rump and upperside of tail bronzy purple. *Face, neck, and chest pale*

ashy, bordered below by *black pectoral band*; lower underparts mostly brown, darkening to dusky on crissum. **Similar species:** Cf. Rufous-vented Ground-Cuckoo (with very different soft-part colors, brown crown and foreneck, etc.). **Habits and Voice:** Poorly known, but probably differ little from Rufous-vented.

Banded Ground-Cuckoo
Neomorphus radiolosus
Cuco Hormiguero Franjeado   Plate 34(6)

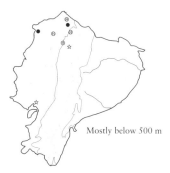

Mostly below 500 m

46–51 cm (18–20″). *Very rare* on or near ground inside humid forest in *lowlands and foothills of northwest* (mainly Esmeraldas). *Heavy bill blackish with paler tip bluish gray. Very long tail* and expressive bushy crest. Unmistakable and spectacular. *Crown (including crest) and hindneck glossy black*; forecrown, upper back, and entire underparts black, *feathers conspicuously edged buffy whitish giving bold scaly appearance. Lower back, rump, and most of wings maroon-chestnut*; upperside of tail bronzy green. **Habits and Voice:** Poorly known, but seem much like Rufous-vented.

Hoatzin: Opisthocomidae (1)
Unique and ungainly, and the sole member of its family, the Hoatzin is found locally near water in the eastern lowlands. Its affinities have long been debated, but present evidence indicates that it is allied to the Cuckoos (Cuculidae). **Sexes are alike.**

Hoatzin, *Opisthocomus hoazin*
Hoazín   Plate 34(7)

61–68.5 cm (24–27″). A *bizarre-looking*, superficially cracid-like bird, *locally numer-*

To 600 m

ous in shrubbery and trees around lakes and along some rivers in lowlands of east. Stout bill dusky olive or blackish; iris red, with *extensive bare skin on face bright blue* (sometimes more faded). Unmistakable. *Loose shaggy crest of long stiff feathers mainly rufous.* Mostly dark olive brown above streaked whitish on neck and back; tail dusky-brown *broadly tipped pale buff.* Bend of wing and conspicuous covert tipping white; *flight feathers mainly rufous. Below mostly buff*, becoming rufous on flanks and lower belly. **Habits:** Notably gregarious, the weird-looking Hoatzin is found in sluggish sedentary groups—sometimes quite large (up to 50 or more birds)—that typically rest in the open during early morning but retreat into shade during midday. They are tame in many areas, allowing a close approach as they peer about looking dazed, clumsily clambering and shuffling in vegetation, often holding their wings partially outstretched as if for balance. Flight weak and never long sustained, typically consisting of a few flaps followed by sail while bird quickly looses height. Threatened nestlings drop out of nest, plopping into water and seeming to disappear, but clambering back out using vestigial claws on each wing. Hoatzins feed mainly on leaves of a variety of plants, also to a limited extent on flowers and fruit. **Voice:** Gives a near-constant wheezy and nasal "whaaah" or "rruh" with distinctive breathless quality.

Strigiformes
Barn Owls: Tytonidae (1)
Allied to the Typical Owls, Barn Owls differ in their heart-shaped facial disks sur-

rounding small eyes and their *long legs*. Sexes are alike.

Barn Owl, *Tyto alba*
Lechuza Campanaria   Plate 36(1)

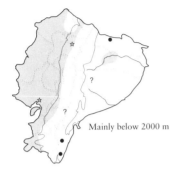

Mainly below 2000 m

35.5–40.5 cm (14–16"). *Widespread in semiopen and agricultural areas*, mainly in lowlands of west and arid interior valleys; scarce and local in east. Iris dark brown. *Distinctive heart-shaped facial disks white to buffy whitish, outlined with dark rim.* **Light morph** mixed grayish and golden buff above, sparsely flecked white; *white below* with sparse scattering of dark spots. **Tawny morph** darker and grayer above; *rich buff below* with same sparse scattering of dark spots. Flight feathers barred darker; *underwing whitish*, imparting characteristic pale ghostly appearance at night. **Similar species:** Not likely confused when perched because of unusual narrow profile (with large head and slender body) and overall pale appearance. In flight might be confused with either Short-eared or Striped Owl. **Habits:** Primarily nocturnal but sometimes active in late afternoon or early morning, especially in dark weather. Hunts mainly through slow and bouyant flapping low over ground, quartering back and forth, often with legs dangled; feeds mainly on small mammals but also on birds and large insects. Usually most numerous around human habitations, feeding in agricultural areas and roosting by day in dark recesses of a tower or other structure, sometimes a natural tree cavity. **Voice:** Has no hooting call. Flying birds give a loud rasping shriek, "sh-h-h-h-h-h." A bird disturbed at its day roost crouches, spreads wings, and sways from side to side, all the while hissing and snapping bill.

Typical Owls: Strigidae (27)

Well-known *nocturnal* predatory birds, owls are rarely seen by the average person, and unless they specifically seek them out, even birders and ornithologists infrequently encounter them. Owls occur widely in Ecuador; diversity is greatest in lowland forests, though a few species occur up to treeline and even into paramo. Owls are characterized by their forward-facing eyes, strongly hooked bills, and powerful talons (the last weaker in smaller, insect-eating species). They are cryptically patterned, mainly in shades of brown, though some species are very handsomely patterned; some have erectile tufts at the sides of their crown. They have superb hearing and locate prey mainly by sound; their rounded wings and the somewhat serrated outer web of the outer primary aid in their nearly silent flight. Owl vocalizations are distinctive and often heard, and in many instances provide the best means of species recognition. Owls feed on small mammals, birds, and larger insects; prey is swallowed whole, with undigestible parts being later cast up as pellets. Nests are placed in a variety of situations, most often in a tree cavity. **Sexes are alike.**

Otus Screech-Owls

A *very confusing* group of small to midsized owls *with ear-tufts* (often small) that range in woodland and forest, most in montane areas; their species-level taxonomy remains, in many instances, controversial. They are intricately patterned and have *facial disks outlined darker to varying degrees*, but there is confusingly little interspecific plumage variation; most species have dark grayish and rufous morphs. Screech-owls are inconspicuous and strictly nocturnal, heard more often than seen, by day perching motionless at regularly used roosting sites. Their *distinctive voices* in conjunction with *range* are by far the best means of identification.

Foothill Screech-Owl, *Otus roraimae*
Autillo Tropandino   Plate 35(1)

20.5–21 cm (8–8¼"). Rare and inconspicuous inside *lower subtropical and foothill forest on e. slope*, also locally in adjacent lowlands. Here regarded as a species distinct from Vermiculated Screech-Owl (*O. vermiculatus*); has also been called Middle American

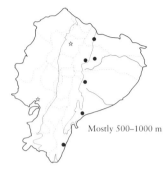

Mostly 500–1000 m

Screech-Owl. A fairly small, *uniform-looking* screech-owl with rather short ear-tufts; *iris yellow*. Grayish to buffy brown above with dusky vermiculations and barring; facial area buffy brown, *indistinctly* outlined with blackish; wing-coverts and scapulars with bold white spots. Below whitish to buff *with narrow wavy dusky brown barring* but *little* vertical streaking. **Rufous morph** more rufescent generally. **Similar species:** Rufescent Screech-Owl considerably larger, brown-eyed, and much more prominently streaked and barred below. Cf. also Tropical Screech-Owl. **Habits:** Strictly nocturnal, tending to remain in heavy cover and thus difficult to spot. Also seems notably shy. **Voice:** Song a fast, quavering, slightly descending trill that starts softly and gradually becomes louder, typically continuing 5–7 seconds and bearing an uncanny resemblance to songs of certain toads, notably *Bufo marinus*. Difficult to lure in with tape playback.

Chocó Screech-Owl, *Otus centralis*
Autillo del Chocó   Plate 35(1)

20.5–21 cm (8–8¼″). Local and inconspicuous *inside foothill forest and secondary woodland on w. slope* south to El Oro. Here

regarded as a species distinct from *O. guatemalae* (Middle American Screech-Owl), with a range from Panama to w. Ecuador. *Virtually identical in appearance to Foothill Screech-Owl* (found east of Andes). One must go by range, and voice, to identify this species. **Habits:** Much as in Foothill Screech-Owl, and equally hard to see. **Voice:** Distinctive song a brief and fast purring trill that descends in pitch and ends abruptly, "kr-r-r-r-r-o," rather soft and usually not carrying very far, very different from other screech-owls.

Tropical Screech-Owl, *Otus choliba*
Autillo Tropical   Plate 35(2)

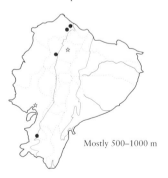

To 650 m

23–24 cm (9–9½″). Clearings as well as borders of várzea and riparian woodland in *lowlands of east; essentially a nonforest owl*, increasing with forest clearance. Fairly conspicuous ear-tufts; *iris yellow*. Grayish to cinnamon brown above, lightly streaked with blackish and mottled with buff; brow and facial area whitish, latter *conspicuously outlined with black rim*; fairly large white spots on scapulars and wing-coverts. Below whitish to pale buffy with *bold herringbone pattern of black streaks and narrow cross-hatching*. **Rufous morph** rare. **Similar species:** Foothill Screech-Owl has much less obvious facial rim and much less streaking below; it is more of a forest bird. Cf. also Tawny-bellied Screech-Owl (dark-eyed and strictly confined to forests). **Habits:** Strictly nocturnal, roosting by day in foliage, often pressed against tree trunks in an effort to escape detection; often in pairs. Feeding birds perch on open branches and regularly range into clearings; generally much easier to see than other screech-owls. **Voice:** ♂'s frequently heard song a short trill that typically ends with distinctive abrupt "ook!" or "ook!-

ook!" Sometimes its presumed mate responds with soft series of hoots, "tu-tu-tú-tú-tú-tu-tu." Responds readily to tape playback.

West Peruvian Screech-Owl, *Otus roboratus*
Autillo Roborado   Plate 35(3)

Mostly below 1200 m

19–20.5 cm (7½–8"). A *very small* screech-owl found in *deciduous woodland and forest as well as scrub—sometimes surprisingly sparse—in lowlands and foothills of southwest.* Has been called Peruvian Screech-Owl. Ear-tufts short; iris yellow. Both morphs look *relatively uniform.* **Gray morph** *gray above* with black and buffy whitish mottling and vermiculations; facial area grayish with *blackish rim indistinct*; white spots on scapulars and wing-coverts. Below whitish with *dense herringbone pattern of blackish streaks and cross-hatching.* Relatively rare **rufous morph** *mainly rufescent*, with patterning much as in gray morph. **Similar species:** Not likely confused in its range and habitat, but cf. Chocó Screech-Owl (confined to humid, mainly foothill, habitats). **Habits:** Much as in Tropical Screech-Owl, usually inhabiting similar semiopen and lightly wooded habitat. **Voice:** ♂'s song a fast, low-pitched but rising churring trill that lasts 2–4 seconds, increasing in volume before fading toward abrupt end. Responds readily to tape playback.

Rufescent Screech-Owl, *Otus ingens*
Autillo Rojizo   Plate 35(5)

25–28 cm (10–11"). Uncommon (overlooked?) inside *subtropical forest* on both slopes. W.-slope birds have been considered a separate species, Colombian Screech-Owl (*O. colombianus*). *Fairly large. Iris brown.* Dusky brown above with blackish and buff vermiculations; wing-coverts and (especially)

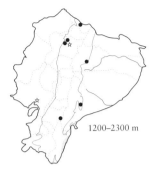

1200–2300 m

scapulars with large white spots; facial area grayish, not strongly outlined. Throat buff with faint dusky barring; *underparts buffy white* with *often prominent dusky shaft streaks and cross-hatching.* **West-slope birds** tend to be more rufescent and show less pattern below. **Similar species:** Cinnamon Screech-Owl, which can occur with this species, is markedly smaller and underparts show less patterning and little or no white. **Habits:** Not well known, with much of range and habitat difficult of access. Strictly nocturnal, generally remaining in heavy cover. **Voice:** Distinctive song a burst of evenly pitched and rapidly delivered notes divided into two sections, second half markedly faster than first, e.g., "bu-bu-bu-bu, bububububu." A second song type consists of a monotonous and prolonged version of the second part of previous song. Call a short wailing "weeaauw" (N. Krabbe recording). Sometimes responds to tape playback.

Cinnamon Screech-Owl, *Otus petersoni*
Autillo Canelo   Plate 35(6)

23–24 cm (9–9½"). Scarce and local inside *subtropical forest on e. slope* (mainly on out-

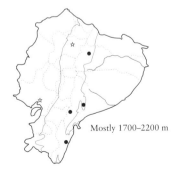

Mostly 1700–2200 m

lying ridges?). A recently described species. *Fairly small. Iris brown.* Rufous brown above with dusky barring; facial area brown, not strongly outlined but sometimes showing whitish brow. Below pale buff with brown shaft streaks and some cross-hatching. **Rufous morph** more cinnamon-rufous generally. **Similar species:** Rufescent Screech-Owl larger with bolder pattern below. Cf. also Foothill Screech-Owl. All three of these *Otus* are best distinguished by voice. **Habits:** Similar to Rufescent Screech-Owl; even less well known, and seems less numerous. **Voice:** Song a simple series of rapidly uttered notes on nearly the same pitch (sometimes the first few notes are lower), lasting about 5 seconds; lower pitched than in Rufescent Screech-Owl. Also gives a long, evenly pitched song similar to alternate song of Rufescent, but lower pitched. Call a wailing "woóouw" (N. Krabbe recording), lower pitched than corresponding call of Rufescent. Sometimes responds to tape playback.

Tawny-bellied Screech-Owl, *Otus watsonii*
Autillo Ventrileonado   Plate 35(4)

Mostly below 500 m

22.5–23.5 cm (8¾–9¼″). *Widespread in lower growth of humid forest in lowlands of east.* A *small, dark* screech-owl with quite long ear-tufts. *Iris brown to orange-brown. Mainly dusky above with a little buffy freckling; facial area tawny, only indistinctly outlined darker. Below ochraceous tawny* with some narrow dusky barring on breast and blackish streaking on belly. **Similar species:** Tropical Screech-Owl nowhere near as dark above, and its pale facial area is strongly outlined; ground color of its underparts is much whiter. *Tawny-bellied is only screech-owl found widely in humid lowland forests of*

east and is much more of a forest bird than Tropical. **Habits:** Strictly nocturnal. Even at night tends to remain in heavy cover where usually hard to see. **Voice:** ♂'s distinctive song a long series of rapidly repeated, low-pitched "who" or "tu" notes that typically begin very softly, gradually swell in volume, and then just as gradually fade away; sequence lasts 10–20 seconds. Also has a shorter and slower, but accelerating and somewhat rising, series of more emphatic hoots. Sometimes sings well before full dark (though where the bird is, inside forest, it is already dark). Sometimes can be coaxed into view with tape playback, but often remains hidden.

White-throated Screech-Owl, *Otus albogularis*
Autillo Goliblanco   Plate 35(7)

Mostly 2500–3400 m

25.5–26.5 cm (10–10½″). *Mainly temperate forest and woodland on both slopes,* regularly up to just below treeline. *Ear-tufts quite short.* Iris yellow. *Dusky to dusky-brown above* with sparse white and buff speckling; facial area dusky, only vaguely outlined darker. *Throat white;* breast dusky with some white spotting, belly tawny-buff with sparse dusky streaking and cross-hatching. **Similar species:** Dark and rather large, this montane screech-owl *occurs at higher elevations than any of its congeners,* and its white throat contrasts more. **Habits:** Strictly nocturnal, and rarely recorded except by tracking down its distinctive voice. Behavior much like other forest-based *Otus.* **Voice:** ♂'s song a fast mellow gabbling with very distinctive cadence, e.g., "whop, whop, whop, whodop, whodop, whodop, whoo!," sometimes continuing 10–20 seconds or more. Also has a fairly short (up to

1½ seconds) descending series of hoots, sometimes given as a duet with one series higher pitched than other. Sometimes responds to tape playback.

Great Horned Owl, *Bubo virginianus*
Búho Coronado Americano   Plate 36(3)

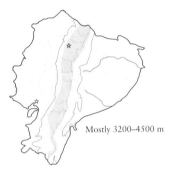

Mostly 3200–4500 m

48–56 cm (19–22"). Patches of *high-elevation woodland* (including *Polylepis* groves) up into paramo, at night sometimes more in open. *The largest Ecuadorian owl, with quite long bushy ear-tufts.* Iris yellow. *Sooty brown above* with buff and whitish mottling; facial area grayish brown bordered with blackish. *Throat white, often puffed and flared out; underparts coarsely barred dusky brown and whitish.* **Similar species:** Even darker Stygian Owl is notably smaller with narrower ear-tufts set closer together. **Habits:** Infrequently encountered in Ecuador, where apparently genuinely scarce. At night hunting birds sometimes take prominent perches, but on the whole inconspicuous and more often heard than seen. **Voice:** ♂'s song a series of deep low hoots with distinctive cadence, typically "hoo, hoó-hoó, hoo," often followed by even lower-pitched (but otherwise similar) song of ♀.

Glaucidium Pygmy-Owls
Very small, rather long-tailed owls lacking ear-tufts that are notable for being relatively *diurnal*; some species are also active at night, especially in the evening. They present a major identification challenge: most are best known by range—they are for the most part allopatric—and voice. Each has a short white superciliary and *distinctive black "false eye-spots"* on either side of the hindneck (often looking like backward-looking eyes). Pygmy-owls are aggressive predators—they have been described as feathered weasels—and pursue a variety of prey including birds their equal in size. Perched birds often are mobbed by flocks of small birds, the agitated owl glaring at them, switching its tail sideways. Imitating the voices of several *Glaucidium* can be an effective means of attracting a wide range of smaller birds.

Andean Pygmy-Owl, *Glaucidium jardinii*
Mochuelo Andino   Plate 35(8)

Mostly 2000–3500 m

14.5–15 cm (5¾–6"). *Scarce in temperate forest and woodland*, especially near borders and occurring up to treeline, on both slopes. Iris yellow; bill and legs yellowish olive. **Dark morph** mainly dark umber brown with *distinct white crown dotting*, some mottling on back, and *relatively unmarked wing-coverts* (only a little white spotting). White below with brown band across chest, splotch on sides of breast (sometimes lightly barred), and broad belly streaking. Tail black with white bars. **Rufous morph** similarly patterned but crown with at most a subdued spotted pattern; tail bars rufous. **Similar species:** *Occurs at higher elevations than other Ecuadorian pygmy-owls.* Subtropical Pygmy-Owl "replaces" it at lower elevations on e. slope, differing in its bold wing and scapular spotting. Cloud-forest Pygmy-Owl "replaces" it at lower elevations in northwest; it is virtually identical in appearance and must be distinguished by voice and range. Highland form of Pacific Pygmy-Owl also can overlap with Andean, but like Subtropical it differs in its boldly marked wing. **Habits:** Usually found singly, sometimes perching high on prominent branch in the open; nowhere does it seem numerous.

Apparently it takes many birds, and small passerines mob it interminably. **Voice:** Most common song a distinctive series of up to 4–5 "wheeu-du-du" phrases followed by series of tooting notes, thus "wheeyr-du-du, wheeyr-du-du, tu-tu-tu-tu-tu-tu."

Cloud-forest Pygmy-Owl, *Glaucidium nubicola*
Mochuelo Nuboselvático   Plate 35(8)

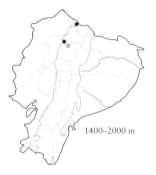

1400–2000 m

14.5–15 cm (5³⁄₄–6″). Uncommon in canopy and borders of *subtropical forest and adjacent clearings on w. slope south to Pichincha in Mindo area*. A recently described species. *Virtually identical in appearance to Andean Pygmy-Owl* (found at *higher elevations*). Go by elevation and voice to identify this species. **Habits:** Much as in Andean Pygmy-Owl. **Voice:** Distinctive song a long-continued series of *paired* phrases, usually with soft introductory note, e.g., "pu, pu-pu, pu-pu, pu-pu. . . ."

Central American Pygmy-Owl
Glaucidium griseiceps
Mochuelo Cabecigris   Plate 35(9)

Mostly 200–400 m

14 cm (5½″). Apparently uncommon (overlooked?) in canopy and borders of humid forest in *lowlands of northwest* (n. Esmeraldas). Formerly considered part of a wide-ranging species then called Least Pygmy-Owl (*G. minutissimum*). Iris yellow; bill and legs yellowish olive. *Mainly rufescent brown above, grayer on head with rather indistinct and sparse whitish crown spotting.* White below with rufous brown band across chest, splotch on sides of chest, and streaking on belly. Tail black with white bars. **Similar species:** *The only pygmy-owl in nw. lowlands.* **Habits:** Usually remains high in canopy and borders of lowland forest where hard to see unless it ventures into a tree in an adjacent clearing. **Voice:** Most common song a usually slightly descending series of 3–5 "too" notes with fairly slow tempo. When an individual is agitated (as after tape playback) sometimes more notes are given, up to 12 or so.

Subtropical Pygmy-Owl, *Glaucidium parkeri*
Mochuelo Subtropical   Plate 35(10)

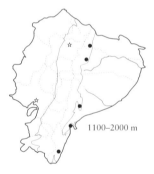

1100–2000 m

14.5 cm (5³⁄₄″). Rare and seemingly local—likely overlooked—in canopy and borders of *subtropical forest on e. slope*. A recently described species. Iris yellow; bill and legs yellowish olive. Grayish brown to dark umber brown above, *crown profusely dotted white*; *scapulars and wing-coverts with rather large bold white spots*, prominent white barring on flight feathers. White below with splotch on sides of chest and belly streaking brown. Tail black with white bars. Rufous morph not known (but may exist?). **Similar species:** Andean Pygmy-Owl occurs at higher elevations (with some overlap?), has much less boldly marked wings. Ferruginous Pygmy-Owl only occurs at much lower elevations. **Habits:** Similar to Central American Pygmy-Owl and thus—unlike Andean—mainly in forest canopy and difficult to see. **Voice:** Most common song a series of 2–4 notes with characteristic hesitation before last note, e.g., "tu-tu, tu" (F. Sornoza recording); it sounds antpitta-like.

Ferruginous Pygmy-Owl
Glaucidium brasilianum
Mochuelo Ferruginoso   Plate 35(11)

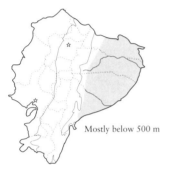

Mostly below 500 m

16–16.5 cm (6¼–6½″). Fairly common in várzea and riparian forest and woodland (also a few moving into terra firme borders) in *lowlands of east*. Iris yellow; bill and legs yellowish olive. Rather variable in color, with similarly patterned brown and rufescent morphs about equally numerous (there are also intermediates). Above grayish brown to rufous brown, *crown typically with fine pale streaking* (but sometimes nearly obsolete); scapulars and wing-coverts with white spots. White below with band across chest, splotch on sides of breast, and streaking on belly grayish to rufous brown. Tail brown with whitish to buff bars. **Similar species:** *The only pygmy-owl in e. lowlands.* **Habits:** Often perches in semiopen and, compared to previous three pygmy-owl species, much more frequently encountered. Flight in open is fast and direct, a burst of quick flaps alternating with a glide; hunting birds may dash after prey into thick cover. **Voice:** Most common song a long series of "pu" notes given steadily and quite rapidly (about 2 notes/second) for up to a minute or more, sometimes starting with a few sharper "wik"

notes; it is easily imitated. Also gives various whinnying or "chirruping" calls.

Pacific Pygmy-Owl, *Glaucidium peruanum*
Mochuelo del Pacífico   Plate 35(12)

Mostly below 1500 m, a few to 2400 m in S Loja

16–16.5 cm (6¼–6½″). *Common and widespread in lowlands and subtropics of southwest*, where it occupies a range of habitats including deciduous woodland and forest, agricultural and settled terrain with scattered trees (even towns and city parks), and desert scrub; in El Oro and Loja also ranges well up into montane forest and scrub. Formerly considered conspecific with Ferruginous Pygmy-Owl. Has been called Peruvian Pygmy-Owl. Two rather different-looking forms occur, considered conspecific because their songs are so similar. **Lowland birds** resemble Ferruginous Pygmy-Owl (found east of Andes, so no overlap) but differ in slightly broader crown streaking and typically paler and more cinnamon dorsal coloration (though a gray-brown morph does occur). **Subtropical birds** usually more grayish brown (a rufous morph may occur, but if so it is rare); crown more spotted with streaking restricted to forehead, and white spots on scapulars and wings larger and more profuse. **Similar species:** *The only pygmy-owl in most of w. lowlands*; Central American occurs well to north of this species' range. Pacifics found in sw. highlands can resemble Andean Pygmy-Owl, though that species is smaller, shows much less scapular and wing spotting, and has no forehead streaking. **Habits:** Similar to Ferruginous Pygmy-Owl, but even more numerous and conspicuous, regularly even seen perching on roadside wires. **Voice:** Most common song a series of rapidly delivered "pü" notes, given at a rate much faster than that of Ferruginous (too fast for most people to effectively whistle it), continued for 10 to upward of 30–45 seconds. Excited birds can break into a "kw-kw-kw-kw-kw-kw-kw-kwík-kwík-kwík."

Burrowing Owl, *Athene cunicularia*
Búho Terrestre   Plate 35(14)

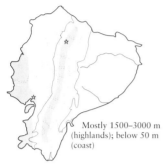

Mostly 1500–3000 m (highlands); below 50 m (coast)

21.5–24 cm (8³/₄–9¹/₂″). A *terrestrial* and *partially diurnal* owl with *rather long legs* found locally in *open arid country in the highlands and in the southwest*. Formerly often placed in genus *Speotyto*. Iris yellow. **Highland birds** brown above with *whitish streaking on crown* and *extensive white spotting on back and wings*; facial area brownish surrounded by white. Buffy whitish below, buffiest on throat, with irregular brown spotting and barring on belly; breast brown with white spots. Tail dark brown barred with white. **Coastal birds** smaller and paler with less extensive brown markings below. **Similar species:** The only truly terrestrial owl in Ecuador and as such nearly unmistakable. **Habits:** Mainly diurnal, though also active in evening. More or less colonial at some sites, with up to 5–10 pairs occupying burrows dug into soft, often sandy soil. Frequently perches on ground, often immediately adjacent to their burrows, bobbing when nervous or disturbed. Also perches on fence posts, but never very high above ground. **Voice:** Generally not very vocal. Occasionally gives a shrieking "kreeey, kik! kik! kik! kik! kik!" and other cackling calls.

Crested Owl, *Lophostrix cristata*
Búho Penachudo   Plate 36(2)

40–42 cm (15³/₄–16¹/₂″). Widespread but uncommon in humid forest and secondary

To 800 m

woodland in lowlands of east and west. *Quite large* with *spectacular, very long white ear-tufts extending back from brow*. Iris usually yellow. Brown above with fine dusky vermiculations and white spotting on scapulars and wing-coverts; facial area rufous bordered with blackish. Below paler brown, more ochraceous on belly, with obscure wavy dusky vermiculations. A scarce **dark morph** is darker brown above and tawny brown below with vermiculations less evident. **Western birds** somewhat paler. **Similar species:** Unique long ear-tufts render this owl nearly unmistakable, but cf. smaller Striped Owl. **Habits:** Strictly nocturnal. Occasionally found by day at its roost in thick undergrowth, often in ravines or along streams. Ear-tufts are raised straight up in alarm (as usually is the case when bird is spotted by day) but at night are usually laid back. More arboreal at night, often perching in subcanopy, generally remaining inside forest; apparently hunts mainly large insects. **Voice:** Characteristic call a low, throaty, and far-carrying rolling growl, "groor-r-r-r," that at close range can be heard to start with soft stutter. Typically comes to tape playback only with reluctantance, if at all.

Pulsatrix Owls

Large owls with round heads and *distinctive facial patterns* found in lowland and foothill forests and borders. Both species are abroad more often in the dim light of dawn and dusk than most other owls.

Spectacled Owl, *Pulsatrix perspicillata*
Búho de Anteojos   Plate 36(4)

43–48 cm (17–19″). Widespread in humid and deciduous forest and woodland (even where patchy) in lowlands of east and west.

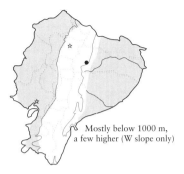

Mostly below 1000 m,
a few higher (W slope only)

A *large and powerful* owl with *no* ear-tufts.
Iris yellow. Dark brown above with *white
brow extending to lores and area around bill*
(forming incomplete "spectacles"); flight
feathers and tail faintly barred paler. Upper
throat and *broad chest band dark brown*
with intervening *buffy white collar across
foreneck*; underparts buff. **Juvenile** whitish
overall with *contrasting blackish facial disks*,
brownish wings. **Similar species:** Not likely
confused, but on e. slope cf. smaller Band-
bellied Owl. **Habits:** Nocturnal, but more
often encountered at its day roost than most
other large owls, in part because it seems to
flush more readily. Hunting birds perch on
large branches more or less in open and
sometimes come out into adjacent clearings.
Voice: Distinctive call a fast series of muffled
hooting notes that start loudly and speed up
but then quickly fade away, e.g., "bup-bup-
buh-buh-buhbuhbuh" (sounding like distant
machine gun). Sometimes duets, and decoys
in quite readily to tape playback. Juvenile
gives a very different short "woauw" call.

Band-bellied Owl, *Pulsatrix melanota*
Búho Ventribandeado   Plate 36(5)

900–1500 m

35.5–38 cm (14–15″). Scarce and local
(perhaps overlooked) in montane forest,
woodland, and borders in *foothills and lower
subtropical zone on e. slope*. Iris brown.
Above dark brown with *white brow extending to lores and area around bill*; wing-
coverts lightly spotted white, flight feathers
banded pale brownish, tail with several
narrow white bands. Throat blackish with
broad collar across foreneck white; *band
across breast dark brown* with some whitish
scaling; *underparts white boldly banded
rufous brown*. **Similar species:** Smaller than
Spectacled Owl, differing notably in its
prominent banding below and brown eye.
Rufous-banded Owl is about same size but is
more prominently marked with rufous above
and irregularly patterned below (without the
evenly banded effect). **Habits:** Similar to
Spectacled Owl, which Band-bellied seems to
replace at higher elevations. **Voice:** Much as
in Spectacled Owl, but (fide P. Coopmans)
Band-bellied's call is slightly faster and higher
pitched, and accelerates noticeably.

Strix Owls

Fairly large, round-headed owls with no
ear-tufts that range in both lowlands and
montane forests. Three of Ecuador's four
species (not Mottled) are beautifully and distinctively patterned. They mainly eat large
insects. All were formerly placed in the genus
Ciccaba.

Black-and-white Owl, *Strix nigrolineata*
Búho Blanquinegro   Plate 36(6)

38–39.5 cm (15–15½″). Humid forest, secondary woodland, and borders in lowlands
and foothills of *west*. Iris brown (but reflect-

Mostly below 900 m,
locally to 1300 m

ing bright red at night); bill bright orange-yellow. *Above sooty black* with nuchal collar of white barring; large facial disk black bordered by white freckling. *Below white narrowly and evenly barred with black.* Tail black with several white bars. **Similar species:** Black-banded Owl occurs only east of Andes. Otherwise only possible confusion is with smaller Mottled Owl, which is essentially brownish (not sharply black and white), etc.; some of their calls are quite similar. **Habits:** Active strictly by night, roosting by day in dense cover and then rarely discovered. Usually perches well above ground, often on quite open limbs where not too hard to see. **Voice:** ♂'s most common call a fast "buh-buh-buh-buh-buh-buh, bwów" with strongly accented last note (sometimes a final "buh" is added), often echoed by ♀'s softer and lower-pitched "buh-buh-bó." Also gives a loud resonant "whoóouw," a screaming, cat-like "keeyow," and a mellow series of 3–7 notes, "whoohów whoohów whoohów. . . ."

Black-banded Owl, *Strix huhula*
Búho Negribandeado   Plate 36(7)

To 900 m

38–39.5 cm (15–15½"). Humid forest (especially terra firme) in lowlands and foothills of *east.* Iris brown (but reflecting bright red at night); bill bright orange-yellow. *Above sooty black* with very narrow white barring (so narrow as to be essentially invisible in field); facial area black surrounded by extensive white freckling. *Below black narrowly and evenly barred with white.* Tail black with several white bars. **Similar species:** Black-and-white Owl occurs only west of Andes. Otherwise only possible confusion is with much browner Mottled Owl, which is very

rare in e. Ecuador. **Habits and Voice:** Very similar to Black-and-white Owl.

Mottled Owl, *Strix virgata*
Búho Moteado   Plate 36(8)

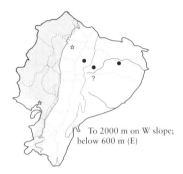

To 2000 m on W slope; below 600 m (E)

30.5–34.5 cm (12–13½"). *Humid forest and woodland in lowlands of west, and in subtropical forest on w. slope of Andes*; rare in forest in lowlands of east (where status not well understood). Iris brown (nonreflective); bill pale grayish. **Western birds** *dark brown above obscurely mottled with grayish buff and dusky,* facial disk brownish *outlined with buffy whitish;* flight feathers dusky barred with grayish. Throat and breast buff *mottled and streaked dusky-brown,* belly buffy whitish *sparsely streaked dusky-brown.* **Eastern birds** apparently differ in their more rufescent upperparts with large whitish scapular spots, and more prominent whitish brow with darker crown. **Similar species:** Rufous-banded Owl may overlap with rather nondescript Mottled on w. slope, though for the most part it occurs at higher elevations; it is somewhat larger, much more rufescent overall, lacks streaking below. **Habits:** Strictly nocturnal, by day roosting in dense thickets, often close to ground, and not apt seen. By night seems more apt to occur in pairs than the previous two species; perches at varying heights but usually not too high. **Voice:** Gives a variety of vocalizations, most frequent a measured series of short emphatic hoots, "whóh whóh whóh whóh whóh!," slower than songs of Black-and-white and Black-banded Owls, and evenly pitched except for the first note often being at slightly lower pitch. Also has descending winnowing or screeching, cat-like "wheeyow?" sometimes followed by "whowhowho."

Rufous-banded Owl, *Strix albitarsis*
Búho Rufibandeado   Plate 36(9)

Mostly 1900–3100 m

To 700 m

35.5–38 cm (14–15″). Lower and middle growth of *subtropical and temperate forest* on both slopes. Iris dark brown (nonreflective); bill greenish gray. Above blackish brown *thickly dappled and barred with rufous*, with *brow, loral area, and throat white*; flight feathers and tail blackish coarsely barred rufous-buff. Breast barred and spotted rufous, blackish, and white; *belly with complex pattern dominated by large blocklike silvery white spots.* ♂ more extensively rufous above and below; ♀ blacker above and with more white below. **Immature** much more uniform and buffier. **Similar species:** A beautiful owl with a complex plumage pattern; notably smaller Mottled Owl is comparatively much plainer. Band-bellied Owl lacks barring above, has white forneck collar, and is more evenly banded on underparts. **Habits:** Similar to Mottled Owl, and likewise strictly nocturnal; when discovered at its day roost in a dense thicket, Rufous-banded usually looks "sleepy" and seems reluctant to flush. **Voice:** Distinctive song a far-carrying "buh-buh-buh-buh-buh-buú!" with strongly accented last note. Call a throaty "rrroo" (P. Coopmans).

Asio Owls
Fairly large, *nonforest* owls with cryptic patterning in brown, buff, and blackish. All three species have *ear-tufts*, much less prominent in Short-eared.

Striped Owl, *Asio clamator*
Búho Listado   Plate 36(10)
35.5–38 cm (14–15″). A fairly large sized owl with *very long buff-edged blackish ear-tufts,*

rare and local in *semiopen areas and agricultural terrain in lowlands of southwest*; also reported from *islands in Río Napo*. Sometimes placed in genus *Rhinoptynx* or *Pseudoscops*. Iris amber brown. *Cinnamon-buff above* coarsely streaked and vermiculated with blackish, *facial area whitish bordered by narrow but conspicuous black rim*; flight feathers and tail grayish buff barred and vermiculated dusky-brown. Throat whitish; *underparts pale buff with conspicuous coarse blackish streaking.* **Similar species:** Somewhat larger Stygian Owl of highlands much darker and more sooty generally, lacks streaking. Short-eared Owl, also of highlands, much darker overall with short (barely visible) ear-tufts, yellow iris, etc. **Habits:** Roosts by day on the ground, often in areas with tall grass. Commences hunting at or just before dusk, sometimes quartering low over open areas but also watching for prey from a fence post or even while balancing on a power line. **Voice:** Not very vocal. Gives a low muffled hoot, "whooh," at long intervals, also other squealing notes.

Stygian Owl, *Asio stygius*
Búho Estigio   Plate 36(12)

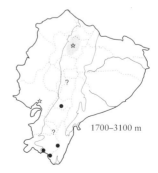

1700–3100 m

41–43 cm (16–17″). A fairly large but slim, *very dark* owl with *quite long blackish ear-tufts* found locally in *semiopen areas in highlands*. Iris orange-yellow. *Blackish brown above* with a few scattered large buff spots, facial area blackish outlined with whitish speckling and with *conspicuous whitish area on forehead* (between "ears"); tail dusky-brown barred buff. Below buffy whitish with *blackish blotching across chest* (where almost solid), *underparts with obvious coarse blackish herringbone pattern*. Similar species: Short-eared Owl favors grassy areas at higher elevations (the two may occur together locally, but unlike Stygian, Short-eared rarely or never roosts in trees). Short-eared is almost equally dark but has blurry *streaked* pattern below, ear-tufts so short as to be invisible under most circumstances, etc. Habits: Roosts singly in a leafy tree, often close to trunk where very hard to spot. Occasionally active before dusk, and where not persecuted not averse to vicinity of human habitation, sometimes feeding around—and even perching on—buildings. Voice: Most characteristic call a very low-pitched "hooo" repeated slowly at intervals of 5–10 seconds; also gives various squeals and screams.

Short-eared Owl, *Asio flammeus*
Búho Orejicorto   Plate 36(11)

Mostly 3000–4000 m

38–40 cm (15–15¾″). Uncommon and local in *paramo and semiopen grassy areas in highlands*. Iris yellow. Above dusky-brown with a few large buff spots and streaks; wings and tail blackish barred with buff. Ear-tufts very short and inconspicuous (usually not visible in field); eyebrow white, facial area buff becoming black around eyes. Below buff

with coarse blurry dusky streaking. Similar species: Striped Owl occurs in lowlands, is much paler generally with long ear-tufts, etc. Even darker Stygian Owl, also found in highlands, differs in *lack* of streaking below, more prominent ear-tufts. Habits: Seen most often at and just before dusk, when it courses over semiopen grassy terrain with characteristic loose and floppy flight, occasionally plunging to ground after prey (most often small rodents). Sometimes perches in open, often on a fence post but rarely much above ground. By day roosts in tall grass. Voice: Usually silent, but elsewhere known to give various barks and squeals when breeding, especially around nest.

Buff-fronted Owl, *Aegolius harrisii*
Buhito Frentianteado   Plate 35(13)

2600–3100 m

19–20 cm (7½–8″). A striking and unmistakable little owl, *very rare* and seemingly local in upper subtropical and *temperate forest and woodland as well as borders* (mainly to feed?) on both slopes. Iris greenish yellow to pale brown. Above umber brown with white spots on scapulars and wings. *Forecrown, facial area, and entire underparts contrastingly rich ochraceous buff, facial area outlined prominently with black*; chin as well as irregular line across chest also black. Habits: Very poorly known, at least in Ecuador. One bird was seen at its day roost in forest undergrowth in a ravine, there being mobbed by small birds (R. Williams et al.). Voice: Song, at least in Brazil, a fast, quavering, rather high-pitched trill (J. Vielliard recording); birds in Bolivia sound similar (fide P. Coopmans).

Caprimulgiformes
Oilbird: Steatornithidae (1)

A distinctive, nocturnal bird found locally in South America. A monotypic family, it is the only nocturnal fruit-eating bird. **Sexes are alike.**

Oilbird, *Steatornis caripensis*

Guácharo   Plate 37(1)

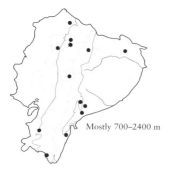

Mostly 700–2400 m

43–47 cm (17–18½"). *Scarce and local in canopy and borders of foothill and montane forest and woodland on both slopes*, occasionally out into lowlands (mainly not far from Andes). *Found mainly at its roosts in caves and deeply shaded ravines*, but most of these are remote. *Heavy hooked bill* pale purplish horn; rictal bristles prominent (though their function seems uncertain in a fruit-eating bird); *eyes reflect bright red* (but are dark brown); pinkish legs set unusually far forward. *Rufous brown above* with a few *large black-encircled white spots on wings*. Paler and less rufescent brown below *with large diamond-shaped white spots*. Wings long and quite pointed; long graduated tail brown narrowly barred black and rufous. **Similar species:** Nearly unmistakable; usually found in cave settings where few or no other birds occur. At night silhouette can look falcon-like. Cf. much smaller Rufous Potoo (also spotted). **Habits:** Roosts by day in caves, at some of which numbers can be very large; also uses very narrow shady ravines into which little or no light penetrates. Rests on ledges, hunching forward on breast and shuffling about at one's approach, sometimes flushing and circling around inside the cave but never actually leaving during daylight hours. Birds stream out at dusk, often flying long distances to feed on large fruits of various forest trees (especially palms and Lauraceae), plucking them while hovering. Foraging birds occasionally rest in trees, perching lengthwise along a limb; very rarely such "stranded" birds are found by day. Nestlings become very fat (weighing half again as much as adults), and in some areas were formerly collected for their oil; we are not aware, however, that this has ever been a regular practice in Ecuador. Infrequently seen away from colonies, though flying birds are sometimes heard or their silhouettes seen as they pass overhead. **Voice:** Often noisy, especially at colonies, also at night when feeding. Even roosting birds vocalize, when disturbed uttering a variety of loud growls, shrieks, and screams; a cacaphony is generated when large numbers exit at dusk. Flying birds also emit loud clicking noises that enable them to navigate and echolocate fruit in pitch darkness.

Potoos: Nyctibiidae (5)

A strictly Neotropical family of solitary nocturnal birds with characteristic and often memorable voices, potoos superficially resemble nightjars, differing most notably in *perching vertically* on often prominent lookouts, from which they sally out after large insects. They lack rictal bristles. *Their eyes reflect light brilliantly*, even from great distances. By day potoos roost in trees, fully in the open but remaining motionless and relying on their cryptic, mottled brownish or grayish coloration to escape detection, which they usually do; if discovered they often stretch their head upward, bittern-like. Bills are relatively small but open wide into a huge gape. Nests are merely small depressions on horizontal limbs; a solitary egg is laid. **Sexes are alike.**

Great Potoo, *Nyctibius grandis*

Nictibio Grande   Plate 37(2)

48–53.5 cm (19–21"). Canopy and borders of humid forest in *lowlands of east. Very large* with *big-headed* silhouette rather different from that of other potoos. Iris brown but *reflecting brilliant orange-red* (visible from great distances). *Looks very pale.* Grayish white to pale brownish above and buffy whitish below variably barred and vermicu-

To 400 m

lated with blackish, usually with at least some blackish mottling on breast. Tail whitish barred with dusky. **Similar species:** So much larger and paler than other potoos that identification is usually straightforward, though certain darker individuals can somewhat resemble Common Potoo (which invariably gives a more streaked effect and typically shows a dark gape mark). Long-tailed Potoo is darker generally with prominent white and dark malar streaks; it rarely perches as high or so much in the open as Great. **Habits:** At night perches high above ground on open branches, sallying out after large insects; occasionally comes lower, especially in clearings adjacent to forest. By day usually roosts in forest canopy, often on a branch or stub with "matching" whitish coloration where, like other potoos, very hard to spot; if the bird is not unduly disturbed, it often uses same site day after day. **Voice:** Far-carrying and unmistakable call an explosive, guttural bawling "bwawrrrr" or "bwawr-rrru," sometimes altered to an abrupt "bawr-bü." Gives a short "gwork" in flight.

Long-tailed Potoo, *Nyctibius aethereus*
Nictibio Colilargo   Plate 37(3)

To 700 m

48–53.5 cm (19–21"). Scarce in *lower and middle growth inside terra firme forest in lowlands of east. Large and very long-tailed.* Iris yellow, reflecting brilliant orange-red. *Rufous brown above* streaked and marbled blackish and with usually prominent buffy whitish brow; shoulders blackish, *bordered below by whitish band. Conspicuous malar stripe white* bordered below by black submalar stripe; underparts mottled and streaked buffy brown and blackish. *Very wide and long tail* boldly banded brown and buff. **Similar species:** Tail is so much larger than that of other potoos that species can usually be identified on that basis alone, but confusion with Common Potoo is possible, despite that species' much smaller size. The two generally segregate by habitat, Common being more of a generalist and rarely or never actually inside forest lower growth; a potoo out in a clearing or in the open at edge is unlikely to be a Long-tailed. Plumage characters are often of minimal value in separating the two, Common being so variable, but the more uniform and less "streaky" Long-tailed never seems to show the patch of black breast streaks usually so obvious on Common, and Common never shows Long-tailed's white malar. **Habits:** Reclusive and not often seen, rarely emerging into open even at night while feeding. Roosts by day inside forest, usually in thick cover no more than 4–6 m above ground and very hard to spot. Active at night, but even then tends not to forage very high above ground. Recorded mostly by voice. **Voice:** Far-carrying and distinctive call a throaty and rather musical "raow-ou," usually given at long intervals; mainly vocalizes during hours just after dusk and before dawn. Also gives a more muffled "huh-huh-huh-huh-huh-huh."

Common Potoo, *Nyctibius griseus*
Nictibio Común   Plate 37(4)

35.5–40.5 cm (14–16"). *Relatively widespread and numerous* in borders of humid forest and woodland and adjacent clearings in lowlands of east and west, also occurring in diminishing numbers well up into subtropics on both slopes. Has been called Gray Potoo. Iris yellow, reflecting brilliant orange-red. **Normal morph** grayish brown to brown, variably mottled and vermiculated with buff and blackish, shoulders usually black and

Mostly below 1700 m

Mostly 1800–2300 m, occasionally (?) higher

often with small whitish patch on wing-coverts. *Almost always has an irregular patch of black spots on midbreast* and usually a *black malar streak*; tail banded grayish and dark brown. **Dark morph** dark brown, showing less pattern (especially below), and wings mainly blackish. Like most other potoos (but not Great), upstanding feathers above eyes often impart a horned effect. **Similar species:** *By far Ecuador's commonest and most frequently seen potoo*; can therefore be used as basis of comparison with others. **Habits:** By day difficult to spot, resting motionless on a bare vertical branch in woodland or forest canopy or borders (sometimes looking like extension of a broken stub), relying on cryptic coloration and lack of movement to avoid detection. Sometimes rests even on posts or poles fully in open, even in towns and cities. Eye is then usually held tightly shut. Becomes active soon after dusk, often flying out into adjacent clearings and then usually perching on a branch with a commanding view, sallying out after large flying insects, often repeatedly returning to same spot. **Voice:** Memorable and haunting song, heard especially on moonlit nights, a series of loud wailing notes that gradually descend in pitch, much louder at first (startlingly so if you are close) and then fading off, e.g., "u-wah, wah, woh, woh, wuh, wüü." What is probably ♀'s call, shorter and less loud, is often given quickly following ♂'s.

Andean Potoo, *Nyctibius maculosus*
Nictibio Andino   Plate 37(5)

38–40.5 cm (15–16"). *Rare and seemingly local in canopy and borders of subtropical forest on e. slope*, mainly at *higher elevations* than other potoos (but some overlap with Common). Formerly considered conspecific

with White-winged Potoo (*N. leucopterus*) of lowland e. South America. A *dark brown* potoo with much rufous spotting and mottling that resembles Common Potoo, especially Common's quite similar dark morph. Differs principally in having *considerable buffy whitish to white on lesser wing-coverts* (usually quite conspicuous, though apparently ♀♀ have less). Beware certain Commons which may also show white in wing-coverts, though these are usually (perhaps always) normal morph birds and thus would look generally paler and more streaked. Andean looks quite black on crown, nape, and breast. **Habits:** Similar to Common Potoo, often feeding low at forest edge and in pastures adjacent to forest. **Voice:** Far-carrying song a distinctive, rather high-pitched (for a potoo), and almost querulous wailing shriek, "kwaaaanh," given at intervals of 3–5 seconds.

Rufous Potoo, *Nyctibius bracteatus*
Nictibio Rufo   Plate 37(6)

25–26 cm (9¾–10¼"). *Very rare and local in lower and middle growth of seasonally flooded várzea forest and adjacent terra firme in lowlands of east. By far the smallest potoo*; easily recognized on that basis alone. Iris yellow, with an odd dark wedge in its lower

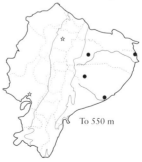

To 550 m

part. *Mostly cinnamon-rufous* with faint black vermiculations and *scattered large black-encircled white spots on shoulders, tertials, and breast and belly*; crissum feathers also tipped white. Tail rufous narrowly barred black. **Similar species:** Nearly unmistakable; no other potoo is anywhere near as small or rufous. Cf. much larger Oilbird. **Habits:** Not well known. Birds seen recently have been found in lower or middle growth inside seasonally flooded or várzea forest; species appears not to range in extensive terra firme. Seems not to emerge into clearings, even to feed. **Voice:** Song unusual for a potoo, a slightly descending musical series of evenly paced notes, "who-o-o-o-o-o-o-o-o-o," lasting about 3 seconds and usually given at quite long intervals (often a minute or more). The vocalization often (e.g., Hilty and Brown 1986) ascribed to this species was incorrect and is actually an alternate call of Great Potoo.

Nightjars and Nighthawks: Caprimulgidae (19)

Primarily nocturnal birds found virtually worldwide, nightjars and nighthawks roost by day on the ground where their *cryptic patterning of buffs, browns, and blacks* makes them virtually impossible to spot unless they flush. They have *small bills* with mouths that open wide into a cavernous gape; their *feet are small and weak*, and they are thus capable of only shuffling on the ground. Their plumage is loose and fluffy. There are two distinct groups, the more crepuscular aerial nighthawks with relatively pointed wings and shorter tails, and the strictly nocturnal typical nightjars with shorter and more rounded wings and longer tails. Identification distinctions are often subtle, and many species are known mainly through their *characteristic voices*. Nightjars and nighthawks are exclusively insectivorous. They make no real "nest," the eggs being laid directly on the ground or in a shallow scrape.

Lurocalis Nighthawks

Notably short-tailed nighthawks seen at dusk as, *bat-like*, they become active, feeding over forest canopy. The Short-tailed Nighthawk nests on treelimbs and is the only family member known not to nest on the ground. **Sexes are alike.**

Short-tailed Nighthawk
Lurocalis semitorquatus
Añapero Colicorto   Plate 38(2)

19 cm (7½"). Seemingly uncommon and local in *canopy and borders of humid forest in lowlands*, a few up into foothills; largely overlooked until recently. Formerly sometimes called Semicollared Nighthawk. A *very dark* nighthawk with *notably short square tail* and rather long, somewhat pointed wings (less so than in *Chordeiles*); *neither wings nor tail show any white.* Mainly blackish with rufous speckling; throat white, and some whitish marbling on tertails; belly and crissum more rufescent, coarsely barred with blackish. **Eastern birds** slightly less dark than those of west. **Similar species:** Rufous-bellied Nighthawk markedly larger with solid rufous belly; so far as known, the two species do not overlap. Common and Lesser Nighthawks have longer and slightly forked tails and more pointed wings with pale band across primaries. **Habits:** Generally seen at dawn and dusk as it feeds just above forest canopy, often coming out over rivers and adjacent clearings but never ranging at any distance from forest. Not known whether it continues to feed all through night. Usually seen singly or in pairs, rarely in small groups (up to 5–6 loosely associated individuals) but never in flocks. Flight erratic and shifting with bursts of shallow wingbeats followed by a glide, very bat-like—which is often what one first thinks it is. By day roosts on horizontal branches high in forest canopy, where exceptionally difficult to see. **Voice:** Most often silent, but flying birds at dawn and dusk occasionally give a sharp stacatto "cu-it," often repeated several times in series.

Rufous-bellied Nighthawk
Lurocalis rufiventris
Añapero Ventrirrufo   Plate 38(1)

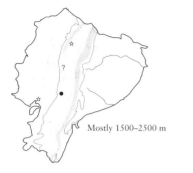

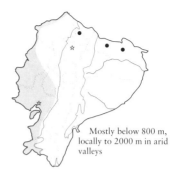

Mostly 1500–2500 m

Mostly below 800 m,
locally to 2000 m in arid
valleys

23 cm (9″). Uncommon in *canopy and borders of subtropical and lower temperate forest on both slopes*; largely overlooked until recently. Formerly often considered conspecific with Short-tailed Nighthawk. *Odd short-tailed shape* similar, but *markedly larger; belly and crissum contrastingly rufous* (and *unbarred*). **Similar species:** Not likely confused except with Short-tailed Nighthawk of lowlands. These two species are not known to occur together, but conceivably they could meet in lower subtropical zone on either slope of Andes. Actually seeing the rufous belly in the lighting conditions one normally views these birds is not easy, so size and vocalizations are the characters to be alert for. **Habits:** Similar to Short-tailed Nighthawk. **Voice:** Like Short-tailed, usually silent. Flying birds (mainly during breeding season?) give a rapidly delivered series of notes that gradually descend in pitch, e.g., "kwa-kwa-kwa-kwa-ko"; also (Hilty and Brown 1986) gives a pair of barks followed by a hiccup, "tor-ta-quírrt."

Chordeiles Nighthawks

Distinctive nightjars with *long, narrow, and pointed wings, Chordeiles* become active at dusk when they course gracefully through the air with light, easy wingstrokes; some species mainly feed over water. By day they roost on the ground, less often on a low tree limb.

Lesser Nighthawk, *Chordeiles acutipennis*
Añapero Menor   Plate 38(4)
20.5–21.5 cm (8–8½″). Locally fairly common in *semiopen scrub and grassy areas in more arid lowlands of west*, also in arid inter-montane valleys of north; a few records (status?) in ne. lowlands. ♂ blackish above mottled with gray, brown, and a little buff. Buffy whitish below with white throat patch, blackish-mottled chest, and blackish-barred breast and belly. *At rest wings*, on which white patch on primaries is usually visible, *extend to or slightly beyond tail*; slightly notched tail with buff barring and white sub-terminal band. In flight shows *pointed wings* and *wide white band across primaries*; under-wing-coverts and inner flight feathers (*including inner primaries*) with much buff spotting and barring. ♀ similar but with *wing-band buff*, buffier throat patch, and no white band on tail. **Similar species:** Closely resembles Common Nighthawk, and often cannot be distinguished; see discussion under that species. Otherwise Lesser Nighthawk readily recognized by slim pointed wingshape, primaries crossed by conspicuous white or (♀) buff wing-band. At rest *Chordeiles* nighthawks resemble other nightjars, though usually the nighthawks' relatively longer wings can be seen to extend at least to tip of tail. **Habits:** By day rests lengthwise on a branch near ground, most often where there is sparse cover; nests, however, are usually placed fully in open on bare or stony ground. Much more often seen after birds have begun to feed during very late afternoon when they course about erratically with shallow flutter-ing wingbeats and brief glides with wings held in a dihedral, generally remaining fairly low. Sometimes feeds (and even roosts) in loose flocks. **Voice:** Quiet in flight. Breeding birds give bursts of a soft low churring or trilling, "ur-r-r-r-r," while on ground, some-times repeated many times over several

minutes; also occasionally gives a bleating call.

Common Nighthawk, *Chordeiles minor*
Añapero Común   Plate 38(3)

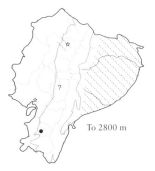

To 2800 m

Mostly below 300 m

23–24 cm (9–9½″). A boreal winter resident and transient, *mainly to lowlands of east*, but some records (most or all transients) from central valley and a few from west. *Usually seen in flight overhead.* Closely resembles Lesser Nighthawk, all differences being subtle; some nighthawks seen are only identifiable to genus. Common differs in its slightly larger size and somewhat darker overall coloration; *somewhat longer and even more pointed wings* (with outermost primary longest); *position of white wing-band somewhat closer to bend of wing* (and *wing-band white in both sexes*, though slightly narrower in ♀); and *underside of inner primaries uniformly blackish* (with no buff spotting or barring). **Habits:** By day rests lengthwise on tree limbs at varying heights (sometimes quite high), less often on ground; sometimes roosts with flock of Sand-colored Nighthawks. Much more apt to be seen when it starts to feed or migrate in late afternoon (sometimes earlier on cloudy days), then quickly gaining altitude and flying with an easy languid grace, at times gliding in a dihedral. May occur in loose flocks. **Voice:** In Ecuador usually silent, though its distinctive nasal and abrupt "peeeent" or "beezhnt" call is occasionally given during northward passage.

Sand-colored Nighthawk, *Chordeiles rupestris*
Añapero Arenizco   Plate 38(5)

20.5–21.5 cm (8–8½″). A small, boldly patterned nighthawk *with much white* found on sandbars along major rivers in lowlands of east. Above grayish to grayish brown speckled and vermiculated with blackish, wing-coverts mottled with white; there seems to be variation in overall dorsal coloration (perhaps ♂♂ grayer, ♀♀ and younger birds browner). *Below mostly white*, with band of dusky brownish spots across breast. *Quite deeply forked tail mostly white with blackish tip* and dusky central pair of feathers. In flight from above shows *conspicuous white band on flight feathers* (only outermost primaries being all black); from below *wings mainly white* with blackish outer primaries and trailing edge. **Similar species:** This attractive nighthawk is unlikely to be confused, at least not once it has taken wing. At rest, when striking pattern is obscured, it can be more confusing, though it is the only caprimulgid likely to be seen roosting in groups out in the open on sandbars. Cf. much larger Nacunda Nighthawk and ♂ Ladder-tailed Nightjar. At a great distance flying birds can even be confused with Yellow-billed Tern. **Habits:** Roosts by day in sometimes large groups (up to several hundred birds) on sandbars, occasionally around lake margins, frequently where jumbled piles of driftwood have accumulated. Commences feeding just before dusk, flying low over water and adjacent open areas with a fast and somewhat jerky flight; wingstrokes quite deep, recalling Yellow-billed Tern. Nests in scattered groups on open sandbars, often in close proximity to a tern colony, which presumably provides some protection from nest predators. **Voice:** Usually quiet, but sometimes (breeding ♂♂?) gives a low-pitched hollow "go-go-go-go-g-g-go" and other trilling calls.

Band-tailed Nighthawk, *Nyctiprogne leucopyga*
Añapero Colibandeado   Plate 38(7)

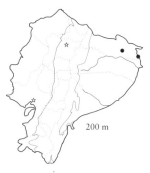

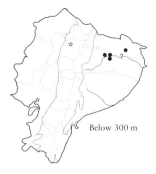

18–19 cm (7–7½″). A *small, dark* nighthawk found very locally around *blackwater lakes in lowlands of far northeast* (Río Lagarto and Cuyabeno). **Sexes alike.** Above dusky brown speckled with buff, scapulars mottled blackish and rufous. Below densely barred dusky brown and whitish or rufescent, with inconspicuous slash of white on either side of throat. In flight *wings appear entirely dark;* notched tail crossed by *conspicuous white band.* **Similar species:** Common Nighthawk larger with conspicuous white band across primaries; white on tail of Band-tailed is more conspicuous than Common's markings there. Short-tailed Nighthawk has similarly dark wings but has very different shape and widely divergent behavior. **Habits:** Not well known in Ecuador. Almost invariably seen as it emerges from low woodland—where it presumably roosts by day—fringing blackwater lakes to feed low over open water of lakes, sometimes with other nighthawks. Flight fast and erratic with shallow stiff wingstrokes interspersed with brief glides when wings are held in a shallow dihedral. Not known to be migratory. **Voice:** Usually quiet. Presumed breeding ♂♂ give a distinctive leisurely "kwoit . . . ku-woít-kwoit" repeated steadily from a low perch near water.

Nacunda Nighthawk, *Podager nacunda*
Añapero Nacunda   Plate 38(6)

28–29.5 cm (11–11½″). Apparently a *very rare* austral migrant (wanderer?) to *lowlands of northeast.* An unmistakable *large* and *boldly patterned* nighthawk with *comparatively rounded wings.* Above brown densely vermiculated with buff and blackish. Throat

and breast brown vermiculated paler with white crescent across lower throat; *underparts contrastingly white. Underwing-coverts white* and blackish primaries *crossed by wide white band;* tail barred dusky and buffy brown, ♂ with broad white tip. **Habits:** Not well known in Ecuador. Has been seen, once in a small group, flying at dusk over open terrain above and near Ríos Napo and Aguarico. Flight languid and graceful, often well above ground, looking more like an owl or raptor than a *Chordeiles* nighthawk. By day roosts on open ground (sometimes stumps) where hard to see until flushed. **Voice:** Most often silent, and at least so far not heard vocalizing in Ecuador. Elsewhere (only when breeding?) gives various clucking calls, sometimes in short series.

Pauraque, *Nyctidromus albicollis*
Pauraque   Plate 39(1)

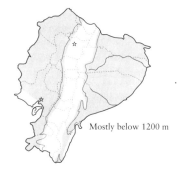

26.5–28 cm (10½–11″). *Widespread and generally common in second-growth and borders in lowlands and foothills* in east and west; less numerous in east, where it *avoids* extensive forest. Sometimes called Common Pauraque. *Tail comparatively long and rounded,*

extending well beyond wings at rest; wings rounded. Dimorphic. **Gray morph** has grayish crown and upper back *contrasting with rufescent cheeks*; otherwise grayish brown above with *"straps" of large black spots on scapulars* and *buff spots on wing-coverts*. Chin white, *large throat patch white* (flaring to sides), chest grayish; underparts buff narrowly barred dusky. **Rufous morph** similar but *ground color more cinnamon-rufous* (especially evident on crown and back, this resulting in *less* contrasting cheeks). ♂ has *bold white bar across black-ish primaries* and *white inner webs of outer tail feathers* (both flashing conspicuously in flight); ♀ has *narrower wing-band buff* and much reduced white in tail (only on tips of outer feathers). **Similar species:** This large, familiar, and attractive nightjar is proportionately longer-tailed than any *Caprimulgus*, so much so that it usually can be recognized on that basis alone; large scapular spots and pattern on wing-coverts, as well as plain face, are also distinctive. In subtropics cf. the smaller and shorter-tailed Band-winged Nightjar, in e. lowlands the Ladder-tailed Nightjar. **Habits:** Though nocturnal like other nightjars, in most areas Pauraque is much the most often encountered member of its family. It rests on little-traveled roads much more often than any *Caprimulgus*, its eyes reflecting a fiery red from great distances. Can sometimes be closely approached but at other times is wary. Hunts for food mainly from ground, less often from a low perch, flying up after large insects. Roosts by day on ground, relying on its cryptic pattern to avoid detection. **Voice:** Vocal much of year, with breeding birds calling through night, at other times especially around dusk and dawn. Most frequent song a hoarse "whe-wheeée-oo," sometimes preceded by a series of "bup" notes (occasionally given alone) or slurred into "por-weeéer."

Nyctiphrynus Poorwills
Dark-plumaged, forest-inhabiting nightjars, one species on either side of the Andes.

Ocellated Poorwill, *Nyctiphrynus ocellatus*
Chotacabras Ocelado   Plate 39(3)

21–22.5 cm (8¼–8¾"). Scarce and perhaps local (but likely overlooked) *inside terra firme forest in lowlands of east.* ♂ *brownish*

To 500 m

sooty with a few large black spots on sca-pulars. Below sooty with white crescent across lower throat and *white spots on belly.* Wings with narrow rufous barring on flight feathers; tail dark rufescent brown broadly barred dusky, *outer feathers broadly tipped white.* ♀ has *sooty replaced by rich rufous brown.* **Similar species:** A dark nightjar which in its range and forest habitat is likely confused only with Blackish Nightjar; Blackish differs in its blackish barred pattern. **Habits:** Usually inconspicuous and solitary, resting by day on forest floor, escaping detection through its cryptic, leaf-like coloration. Rarely emerges from forest, even to feed. **Voice:** Mainly recorded when vocalizing. ♂'s song a rather explosive mellow trill, "kwr'r'r'r'o," given from a low perch (usually) or from ground.

Chocó Poorwill, *Nyctiphrynus rosenbergi*
Chotacabras del Chocó   Plate 39(2)

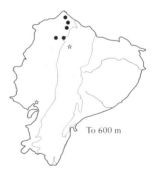

To 600 m

21–22.5 cm (8¼–8¾"). An *extremely dark* nightjar, seemingly local (overlooked?) in *humid forest and borders in lowlands and foothills of northwest* (south to nw. Pichin-cha). Formerly considered conspecific with

Ocellated Poorwill. **Sexes alike.** *Mainly blackish*, somewhat grayer on crown and with some rufescent vermiculation and spotting on wing-coverts and scapulars. Large white crescent across lower throat and some whitish flecking on belly. *Two (sometimes 3) conspicuous large white spots on inner secondary wing-coverts*; tail feathers narrowly fringed white. **Similar species:** No really similar nightjar exists in this species' restricted range and habitat. **Habits:** Poorly known. Calling birds may vocalize closer to forest edge than Ocellated Poorwill typically does (P. Coopmans). Foraging birds sometimes fly above canopy like a nighthawk, coming lower at edge (O. Jahn). **Voice:** Like Ocellated Poorwill, mainly recorded from vocalizing ♂♂. Song a steadily repeated resonant, whistled, rhythmic "kwor-kwor-kwor-kweeér," with each note higher pitched than the previous one. Also gives a variety of calls, some of them frog-like (or recalling Pauraque), e.g., "kwok," "kwi-kwok," and a sometimes doubled "klaw" (P. Coopmans).

Caprimulgus Nightjars

The "typical" nightjars, with relatively broad and rounded wings and rather long tails. They become active at dusk, and then are usually most vocal. Identification, especially of females, is often difficult on plumage characters alone; *voice is more important.* Flushed birds fly off with stiff wingbeats on bowed wings, all too briefly displaying their distinctive wing and tail patterns.

Band-winged Nightjar
Caprimulgus longirostris
Chotacabras Alifajeado   Plate 39(4)

21.5–23 cm (8½–9″). *Widespread in semi-open areas in highlands*, locally well down

Mostly 1800–3700 m

into subtropical zone on outside Andean slopes where clearings exist. ♂ *dark and coarsely marked*, blackish speckled with rufous, buff, and gray with rufous nuchal collar; *white crescent across lower throat* and belly buffier. Blackish primaries crossed by *broad white band* and *terminal half of outer tail feathers white* (both conspicuous in flight). ♀ similar overall but with *throat crescent and wing-band buff*, tail barred blackish and buff with no white. **Similar species:** Occurs at *higher elevations* than other *Caprimulgus*, overlapping mainly with the pair of *Uropsalis* nightjars, streamer-tailed ♂♂ of which differ strikingly though respective ♀♀ are similar to ♀ of smaller Band-winged. Both *Uropsalis* are darker overall, and neither has ♀ Band-winged's buff wing-band (this is usually obscure on resting birds, however); tails of both show more of a fork (this mainly evident in flight). ♀ Swallow-tailed differs further in its *lack* of rufous nuchal collar and more rufous-spotted crown and upperparts. ♀ Lyre-tailed is especially similar though its breast is more densely vermiculated. Proportionately longer-tailed Pauraque overlaps marginally in elevation with Band-winged but is not as dark and has plain rufescent cheeks and different pattern on scapulars and wing-coverts. **Habits:** Strictly nocturnal, feeding and resting on or near ground (regularly on roads), sallying out after passing insects; favors cliffs or rocky areas. Frequently tame, and often mesmerized by strong lights (as a result often found as a road casualty). Roosts by day on ground, sometimes under cover of a bush or small tree but often completely in the open. **Voice:** ♂'s song, usually delivered steadily from a low perch and given most persistently soon after dusk, a very high-pitched "psee-yeet" or "psee-ee-eyt." Sometimes sings from buildings in Quito (P. Coopmans).

White-tailed Nightjar
Caprimulgus cayennensis
Chotacabras Coliblanco   Plate 39(5)

19–20.5 cm (7½–8″). Locally numerous in *arid scrub* in *intermontane valleys of far north*, so far only at two sites in *Imbabura*. ♂ above brownish gray mottled and vermiculated with blackish, buff, and whitish; *frosted whitish brow* and *fairly prominent*

1400–2000 m

rufous nuchal collar. Throat and malar streak white; breast finely barred grayish brown and buff, *belly white*. Wings with rufous bars but apparently no (?) white wing-band (not even in ♂; ANSP specimen); *inner webs of four outer tail feathers white* (conspicuous in flight). ♀ browner above and buffier below with *buffyish throat and belly*; wings as in ♂, tail dusky barred buff (no white). **Similar species:** The only *small* nightjar in its restricted range; Pauraque is much larger and longer-tailed. Cf. Anthony's Nightjar (no overlap). **Habits:** Similar to Band-winged Nightjar, but less likely to rest or feed from roads, more often perching on a low branch or rock. Usually recorded when vocalizing. **Voice:** ♂'s song a distinctive high-pitched but slurred "pk-tseeeeeeur."

Anthony's Nightjar, *Caprimulgus anthonyi*
Chotacabras de Anthony   Plate 39(6)

To 650 m

18.5–19 cm (7¼–7½″). *Grassy areas, scrub, and adjacent low woodland in more arid lowlands of west.* Has been called Scrub Nightjar. ♂ above uniform brownish gray mottled and vermiculated with blackish, buff, and whitish. Chin dark brown, with

white crescent across lower throat; breast narrowly barred dusky brown and buff, becoming more extensively pale buff on belly. Wings with *broad white band across primaries*; inner webs of two outer tail feathers white. ♀ similar but browner above and with throat crescent buff; wings much as in ♂ (also with white wing-band, at least when adult), and tail with inner web of outermost tail feather (only) buffy whitish. **Similar species:** *The only small nightjar found in semiopen w. lowlands.* Cf. larger (and longer-tailed) Pauraque. **Habits:** Generally similar to Band-winged Nightjar, favoring open grassy or even barren areas when feeding (sometimes even seeming to concentrate at certain favorable sites), roosting in adjacent shrubby or wooded terrain by day. Nesting (and vocalizing) appears to be correlated with rain. **Voice:** ♂'s song a short and very simple "treeow" repeated steadily at intervals of 1–2 seconds from a low perch.

Spot-tailed Nightjar
Caprimulgus maculicaudus
Chotacabras Colipunteado   Plate 39(9)

350 m

19–20.5 cm (7½–8″). Apparently a *very rare* and local resident in *damp grassy areas in lowlands of northeast.* Only one record (specimen from near Lago Agrio); could increase? ♂ has *crown and face blackish* with *contrasting buff superciliary and malar stripe* and *fairly prominent cinnamon-rufous nuchal collar*; otherwise grayish brown above with *prominent buff spotting on scapulars and wing-coverts.* Throat buff, *breast dusky coarsely spotted buff*, belly cinnamon-buff with sparse blackish barring. Wings with cinnamon-rufous bars (but no white wingband); tail grayish barred black, *outer tail* feathers boldly tipped white (several large white spots on underside of tail, for which species named, almost never visible in life). ♀ similar but tail with no white. **Similar species:** Not known to occur with any other *small Caprimulgus* nightjar, and dark face on which buff brow stands out is, in any case, unique. **Habits:** Not known in Ecuador. Elsewhere favors pastures and open grassy areas, usually where at least damp, often where seasonally flooded. Usually recorded when vocalizing. **Voice:** ♂'s song a distinctive sharp and high-pitched "pt-sweeeét," given steadily from a low perch.

Blackish Nightjar, *Caprimulgus nigrescens*
Chotacabras Negruzco   Plate 39(7)

To 1200 m

19.5–21 cm (7¾–8¼"). A *very dark* nightjar found locally around *rocky or gravelly openings in terra firme forest in lowlands and foothills of east*. ♂ mostly blackish brown with some rufous dotting and grayish vermiculations. *Small white collar on lower throat, often mainly on sides*; underparts narrowly barred rufous-buff (but still looking *dark*). Wings with *short white band across three inner primaries*; tail dark grayish barred black with narrow whitish tipping on two next-to-outermost feathers. ♀ similar but lacking white on wings and tail. **Similar species:** This well-named nightjar is so dark that it is unlikely to be confused in range. Cf. Ocellated Poorwill. **Habits:** Often roosts by day on rocky substrates (sometimes roadcuts through forest), often fully in open and flushing only when almost trod upon. Sometimes feeds along roads. **Voice:** Unlike other Neotropical *Caprimulgus*, does not have a forceful loud song, and seems to sing relatively infrequently. ♂♂ have a soft "pr-r-r-r-

t" repeated several times in succession, often followed by long pause before another series is given.

Rufous Nightjar, *Caprimulgus rufus*
Chotacabras Rufo   Plate 39(8)

700–1100 m

25.5–28 cm (10–11"). A *large, uniformly dark rufescent brown* nightjar found in deciduous woodland *around Zumba in Río Marañón drainage of far southeast*. ♂ brown above with complex pattern of buff and blackish vermiculations and spotting. Throat buff barred with blackish, bordered below by narrow buffy whitish crescent of large spots; breast quite blackish, belly buffy whitish with blackish barring and vermiculations. Wings with *profuse even rufous barring*, but no white wing-band; tail grayish brown barred and vermiculated dusky, with *outer third of inner web of outer three feathers whitish, actual tip pale rufous*. ♀ similar but with only narrow rufous tip on rectrices. **Similar species:** This dark, relatively unpatterned nightjar is large enough that it likely will be confused only with Pauraque. Pauraque has a longer tail with a different pattern of white, prominent white (♂) or buff (♀) wing-band, and contrasting rufescent cheeks and spots on wing-coverts (both obvious on perched birds). **Habits:** Less often in open than most other nightjars, rarely leaving cover of woodland and only infrequently resting on roads. At night usually perches on branches a short distance above ground, and typically roosts in such situations. Usually recorded when vocalizing. **Voice:** ♂'s unmistakable and far-carrying song a fast "chuck, wick-wick-weeeo," given especially around dawn and dusk but can be repeated all night long during breeding season; reminiscent of song of Chuck-will's-widow (*C. carolinensis*) of North America.

Ladder-tailed Nightjar
Hydropsalis climacocerca
Chotacabras Coliescalera   Plate 39(10)

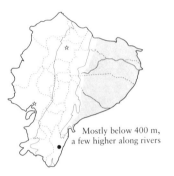

Mostly below 400 m, a few higher along rivers

♂ 25–26 cm (9¾–10¼"); ♀ 22.5–23.5 cm (8¾–9¼"). Widespread in *semiopen areas (especially islands) along larger rivers and lakes in lowlands of east*. ♂ *rather pale sandy grayish buff above* with little pattern, only sparse blackish vermiculation and streaking. Throat whitish, breast buffier finely barred dusky; belly white. Wings with broad white band across primaries; *strikingly patterned tail quite long and "double-notched," outer feathers longest and mostly white on inner web (flashing conspicuously in flight)*, central feathers grayish, *inner feathers shorter and also with much white*. ♀ much like ♂ above; *below buffyish with uniform dusky barring*. Wings have buff band across primaries (narrower than ♂'s); tail entirely grayish with dusky barring (no white). **Similar species:** This nightjar can usually be known by its restricted habitat, in Ecuador shared only by more robust Pauraque. **Habits:** By day roosts on ground near water (sometimes in small loose aggregations), occasionally in open but more often where there is some grassy cover or around piles of driftwood. Becomes active at dusk, sitting conspicuously near water's edge on either the ground or a low perch, often on branches protruding from the water. From there makes long graceful sallies after insects, generally staying low and flying on bowed wings, ♂ showing off its flashy tail to good advantage. **Voice:** For a nightjar not very vocal. Flying birds give a rather squeaky "chweeit;" perched birds (only ♂♂?) give a repeated "chup" call accompanied by bobbing.

Uropsalis Nightjars
Scarce, *montane* nightjars with dark plumage, the males most notable for their *extraordinary tails*, though the songs of both species are also wonderful.

Swallow-tailed Nightjar, *Uropsalis segmentata*
Chotacabras Tijereta   Plate 37(7)

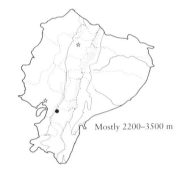

Mostly 2200–3500 m

21–23 cm (8¼–9"), *but ♂'s spectacular tail streamers up to 46–51 cm (18–20") long*. Rare and local at edge of *upper subtropical and temperate* forest and near cliffs up to near treeline on both slopes. ♂ *mainly blackish profusely spotted with rufous*; narrow crescent across lower throat buffy whitish, belly buffy with irregular blackish barring. *Wings dark* with no white or buff markings. *Outer tail feathers can be greatly elongated (up to 2–3 times body's length) into nearly straight "scissorlike" streamers with whitish shafts*, but these are frequently missing or broken off. ♀ similar, but tail "normal" (*lacking* tail streamers though outer rectrices longer than others, resulting in *forked shape*). **Similar species:** Both sexes likely to be confused only with Lyre-tailed Nightjar, but cf. also ♀ Band-winged Nightjar. Lyre-tailed occurs mainly at *lower elevations*, but the two do overlap at least locally. ♂ Lyre-tailed's tail streamers can be even longer than Swallow-tailed's, and usually their more flexible and somewhat curved ("lyre") shape is apparent; shafts of Lyre-tailed's streamers are dark, but tips whitish (when not abraded or broken off). Otherwise ♀ and streamer-less ♂♂ Lyre-taileds can be distinguished by their usually prominent rufous nuchal collar (lacking in Swallow-tailed) and lack of rufous spotting on dark crown. Cf. also ♀ Band-winged Nightjar. **Habits:** Roosts by day on open, often rocky and damp, ground near forest edge, sometimes under a bush but more frequently in recess of a roadcut or cliff. Becomes active at dusk, then regularly resting on roads or low perches, sallying low after insects. **Voice:** ♂'s unmistakable and beautiful but infrequently heard song a vibrating "wor-r-r-r-e-e-e-e-e-r," at first sliding up, then dropping down. It bears a considerable resemblance to Wattled Guan's song.

Lyre-tailed Nightjar, *Uropsalis lyra*
Chotacabras Colilira   Plate 37(8)

Mostly 800–2000 m, locally a little higher

23.5–25.5 cm (9¼–10"), *but ♂'s spectacular tail streamers up to 63.5–68.5 cm (25–27") long.* Uncommon and local at edge of *foothill and subtropical* forest and near cliffs and gorges on both slopes. ♂ mainly blackish with buff and grayish barring and spotting and *fairly prominent rufous nuchal collar.* Irregular crescent across lower throat rufescent; underparts buffyish with wavy blackish barring. Wings *dark* with no white or buff markings. *Outer tail feathers can be greatly elongated (up to 3–4 times body's length) into gracefully curving, "lyre-shaped" streamers with whitish tips,* but these are frequently missing or broken off. ♀ similar but tail "normal" (lacking tail streamers though outer rectrices longer than others, resulting in *forked shape*). **Similar species:** Cf. Swallow-tailed Nightjar of higher elevations. At lower edge of range, cf. also smaller Blackish Nightjar (with no nuchal collar, etc.). Cf. also ♀ Band-winged Nightjar. **Habits:** Roosts by day on ground, often on steep but moist rock

faces. Becomes active at dusk, then sallying from cliffs or prominent rocky perches, occasionally resting on roads. Usually near water, favoring rocky streams and rivers but also on dripping wet roadcuts and natural cliffs. **Voice:** ♂'s unmistakable rollicking song, usually given in flight and sometimes while chasing a ♀, a loud and musical "wor-pilly-o, wor-pilly-o, wor-pilly-o . . ." (up to 5–6 phrases) gradually rising in pitch; also gives a repeated, burrier "wor-worrow" or "wor-worrow-wo."

Apodiformes
Swifts: Apodidae (15)
Superficially swallow-like, swifts are *highly aerial,* wide-ranging birds with *long, narrow, and pointed stiff wings* and small bills that open wide; they eat only insects. Their small feet have short, sharp claws adapted for perching on vertical surfaces, but swifts cannot perch "normally." They are almost always seen in flight, often high overhead and sometimes several species together. *Accurate identification remains a challenge;* indeed unless lighting conditions are good, it often is impossible. Many species are closely similar; pay attention to size and overall shape (especially of wings) and the placement of paler areas on their otherwise blackish plumage. **Sexes are usually alike.** Swift voices may help in identification, but they remain poorly studied. Swifts nest on inaccessible cliff surfaces (sometimes behind waterfalls), in caves, and in tree hollows; nests are small cups attached to a vertical surface with saliva.

White-collared Swift, *Streptoprocne zonaris*
Vencejo Cuelliblanco   Plate 40(1)

To at least 4000 m

20.5–21.5 cm (8–8½″). A spectacular *large* swift with *slightly forked tail*; found widely in highlands, also often foraging out over lowlands as well. **Adult** blackish with *bold white collar completely encircling neck*, widest across upper chest. Birds nesting at higher elevations are larger. **Juvenile** has white collar more or less restricted to nape, with white on chest reduced to some faint scaling (often hard to see in field). **Similar species:** So much larger than other Ecuadorian swifts that it is generally recognizable on that basis alone; no other shows the white collar, but cf. rare White-chested Swift. Cf. also Bat Falcon (with surprisingly similar shape). **Habits:** The most wide-ranging swift, with very fast and powerful flight on sickle-shaped wings, wingstrokes deep and steady; can ascend to tremendous heights, sometimes to beyond where it is visible. White-collareds also often soar on stiff outstretched wings. They generally cruise around in flocks, sometimes compact, at other times dispersed; other swifts often accompany them. They roost and nest in colonies on cliffs, in caves, and behind waterfalls. **Voice:** Gives loud screeches both in flight and while resting on rock faces, also various chippers. The wings themselves also often produce a whooshing sound, sometimes loud.

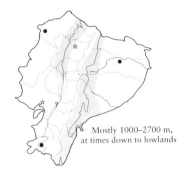

Mostly 1000–2700 m, at times down to lowlands

Cypseloides Swifts

Midsized swifts, two of them *hard to identify*; the distinctive Chestnut-collared is much the most numerous member of the genus in Ecuador. *Cypseloides* are larger than *Chaetura* and have longer and more swept-back wings and proportionately shorter, squared tails; their flight is very fast, with more frequent gliding than in *Chaetura*.

Chestnut-collared Swift, *Cypseloides rutilus*
Vencejo Cuellicastaño   Plate 40(2)

13–13.5 cm (5–5¼″). *Widespread in highlands*, sometimes foraging out over adjacent lowlands. Sometimes placed in genus *Streptoprocne*. **Adult** blackish to sooty brown with *contrasting rufous-chestnut collar*, broadest across chest and often extending up over throat; tail comparatively long, often looking *slightly notched*. Some ♀♀ lack collar entirely (younger birds?), in others it is partial. **Similar species:** Chestnut color unique among Ecuadorian swifts if it can be discerned (hard except in good light or against a dark background). Chestnut-collared is by far the most common *Cypseloides*; cf. its congeners. Compared to *Chaetura*, its wings are longer and more swept-back, and tail is slightly longer and usually shows a fork. **Habits:** Generally gregarious, occurring in high-flying groups numbering from a few to several dozen individuals, often with other species of swifts (especially White-collared and White-tipped). Flight resembles that of some *Chaetura* though Chestnut-collared tends to glide more (and flutter less), typically proceeding with several flaps followed by a glide; banking birds may spread tail widely, the usually apparent notch then disappearing. **Voice:** Flight calls include a variety of buzzy chatters, also single sharper "bzzt" notes.

White-chinned Swift, *Cypseloides cryptus*
Vencejo Barbiblanco   Plate 40(5)

15 cm (6″). *Apparently rare in foothills and adjacent lowlands; probably under-recorded.*

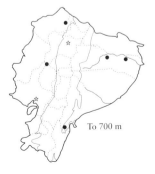

To 700 m

Quite large and heavy-bodied. **Adult** uniform blackish with a bit of whitish scaling on chin and sides of forehead (not visible in field, barely apparent even in specimens); *tail relatively short and squared*. **Juvenile** similar but shows some white scaling on belly and crissum. **Similar species:** This chunky swift is very difficult to identify with certainty. Spot-fronted Swift is almost identical, and one has to be very close to see that species' white facial markings; Spot-fronted is a little smaller and slighter than White-chinned, and a proportionately longer-tailed. Chestnut-collared Swifts lacking collar are also similar but differ in being smaller and more slightly built with a proportionately longer tail that usually looks notched. Chimney Swift is the most similar *Chaetura*, and it too is quite uniform-looking, differing in being browner and somewhat paler overall with pale grayish throat. **Habits:** Poorly known. In Ecuador birds believed to be this species have been noted in small groups flying with other swifts. **Voice:** Not certainly known.

Spot-fronted Swift, *Cypseloides cherriei*
Vencejo Frentipunteado   Plate 40(4)

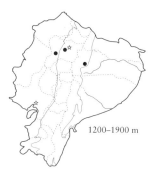

1200–1900 m

14 cm (5½″). *Poorly known.* Apparently rare in *subtropics of n. Ecuador* (Pichincha and w. Napo); probably under-recorded. **Adult** dull black above, slightly more brownish below, with *small white spots in front of and behind eye, also sometimes one on chin* (these visible only at very close range); *tail relatively long and squared*. **Juvenile** similar but white facial markings usually absent and with some white scaling on belly. **Similar species:** Cf. very similar White-chinned Swift. Chestnut-

collared Swifts lacking collar are also extremely similar, so much so that the two are probably not distinguishable unless Spot-fronted's facial white can be discerned. **Habits:** Similar to Chestnut-collared Swift, with comparable flight style. Has been found nesting behind a waterfall near Chiriboga road. **Voice:** Not certainly known.

White-chested Swift, *Cypseloides lemosi*
Vencejo Pechiblanco   Plate 40(3)

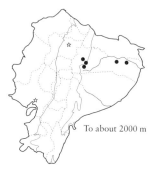

To about 2000 m

14 cm (5½″). *Poorly known.* Apparently rare in *subtropics and foothills on e. slope in north*, also foraging out over adjacent lowlands; perhaps under-recorded. **Adult ♂** blackish with *large and distinct white chest patch, tapering to a point*; tail long and *distinctly forked*. **Adult ♀** and **juvenile** similar but with chest patch smaller; tail apparently somewhat less forked. **Similar species:** Adults with white chest patch distinctive and readily recognized, at least once patch can be seen (it can be surprisingly hard to discern under some conditions). White-collared Swift much larger, has complete white collar; wings are proportionately longer and narrower. **Habits:** Has been seen with high-flying flocks of other swifts (especially White-collared and Chestnut-collared). **Voice:** Not certainly known.

Chaetura Swifts
Relatively small swifts, all species with *contrastingly paler rumps and uppertails (strikingly so in some)*, some also with *contrastingly paler throats*. *Chaetura* wingbeats are relatively fast, their typical flight consisting of repeated bursts of fluttery flapping; they glide much less than *Cypseloides*. As with most other swifts, some *Chaetura* are

very hard to identify; most must be studied closely under ideal conditions before one can identify them with confidence. Voices of some *Chaetura* are hard to distinguish; also, several species often fly together, making it hard to isolate one species' calls from another's.

Chimney Swift, *Chaetura pelagica*
Vencejo de Chimenea   Plate 40(6)

13 cm (5"). Apparently an *uncommon transient* (Oct.–Mar.) and boreal winter visitant, mainly in lowlands. A *large*, relatively heavy-bodied and uniform-looking *Chaetura. Sooty brownish gray*; rump and uppertail-coverts only slightly paler grayish, *hardly contrasting*; throat and upper chest pale grayish, *slightly* contrasting with rest of underparts. **Similar species:** Very rare Chapman's Swift is *closely* similar, barely distinguishable in field; see that species. Other *Chaetura* swifts show more contrast on rump. *Cypseloides* swifts larger and darker generally (more blackish); their wings are longer and they tend to fly differently, with deeper wingstrokes and more gliding, less fluttering. Cf. especially White-chinned Swift. **Habits:** Not well known, and probably under-recorded because of identification difficulties. Apparently often occurs in groups, sometimes associating with other *Chaetura*. Transients of this species are the only *Chaetura* likely to occur above the foothill zone in the Andes (though to date there are surprisingly few reports from so high). The species is not known to enter chimneys in Ecuador—nor, for that matter, is any other swift here. **Voice:** So far as known, silent or nearly so on its winter quarters.

[Chapman's Swift, *Chaetura chapmani*
Vencejo de Chapman]   Plate 40(7)

13 cm (5"). Known in Ecuador only from one (Jan.) sighting from lowlands of east

(Jatun Sacha); status uncertain. A *large* and relatively uniform-looking *Chaetura* that closely resembles Chimney Swift; often not distinguishable from that species. Differs in having *crown and back blacker* (hence the grayish rump and uppertail-coverts *contrast more*), but throat more or less concolor with remainder of underparts (not paler and slightly contrasting). **Similar species:** Gray-rumped Swift smaller with rump grayer and more contrasting. **Habits:** Similar to other *Chaetura* swifts. Elsewhere Chapman's often accompanyies more numerous Gray-rumped or Band-rumped Swifts.

Short-tailed Swift, *Chaetura brachyura*
Vencejo Colicorto   Plate 40(10)

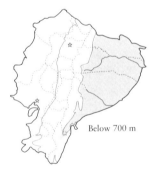

11 cm (4¼"). A distinctive, *strikingly short-tailed* swift, common over clearings, along rivers, and at forest borders and openings (especially where swampy) in *lowlands of east*. Sooty black above with *contrasting ashy brownish gray rump and uppertail-coverts* (latter completely covering the short tail). *Below uniform blackish*, crissum and under-tail pale brownish (somewhat contrasting). **In flight** inner primaries can be seen to be rather

long and secondaries relatively short, creating appearance of a "bulge" in rear margin of wing. **Similar species:** An easily recognized swift: contrasting pale hindquarters are obvious, as is very short tail (bird essentially looks "tail-less"). Other sympatric *Chaetura* longer-tailed, etc. Tumbes Swift occurs only west of Andes. **Habits:** Similar to other *Chaetura*, though wings are relatively broad and flight relatively loose and floppy. Often flies quite slowly, "rocking" back and forth, gliding only briefly. **Voice:** Very fast, high-pitched, run-together twitters are frequently uttered in flight.

Tumbes Swift, *Chaetura ocypetes*
Vencejo de Tumbes   Plate 40(11)

Below 1000 m

11 cm (4¼″). Rather local at edge of deciduous forest and woodland and over adjacent clearings in *lowlands of southwest*; the only *Chaetura* in this range. Formerly considered conspecific with Short-tailed Swift. Sooty black above with *contrasting ashy brownish gray rump and uppertail-coverts* (latter completely covering tail, which is longer than in Short-tailed). Below blackish, with *paler grayish throat and foreface* (showing some contrast); pale brownish crissum and undertail somewhat contrasting. **In flight** wings notably long and bowed, very different from Short-tailed. **Similar species:** Only other *Chaetura* found in Tumbes Swift's overall range—though ranging only in more humid habitats, mainly in foothills—is rather different Gray-rumped Swift; Gray-rumped has less contrasting rump that is pure gray, paler and grayer underparts, wings not as long, etc. **Habits:** Not often encountered, Tumbes Swift favors forest edge and is most often seen flying in pairs or small groups, usually not too high. Flight quite fluttery. **Voice:** One

flight call is a series of well-enunciated, somewhat descending notes, "chip-chip-chip-chip-chip-chip-chup."

Band-rumped Swift, *Chaetura spinicauda*
Vencejo Lomifajeado   Plate 40(9)

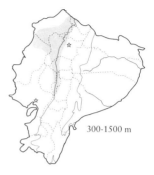

300-1500 m

11 cm (4¼″). A small *Chaetura* found over humid forest and adjacent clearings in *lowlands and foothills of northwest* (mainly south to w. Cotopaxi), a few ranging up into lower subtropics. *Tail relatively long.* Blackish above with *striking narrow whitish band across rump*, contrasting strongly. *Throat and upper chest pale brownish gray* contrasting with sooty brown of underparts. **Similar species:** Confusion most likely with western race of Gray-rumped Swift, which is similarly shaped and with which Band-rumped regularly flies, at least in some areas. Gray-rumped differs in its *much less contrasting gray rump* (the gray also encompasses a greater area), and more uniform grayish underparts (lacking Band-rumped's paler throat). **Habits:** Usually occurs in small to fair-sized flocks of up to 20–30 birds, sometimes associating with other swifts. Regularly flies quite high. Flight quite fluttery, gliding very little.

Gray-rumped Swift, *Chaetura cinereiventris*
Vencejo Lomigris   Plate 40(8)

11 cm (4¼″). Over humid forest and adjacent clearings in lowlands and foothills in east and west, smaller numbers up into lower subtropics especially in east. More numerous and widespread in east. *Tail relatively long.* **Eastern birds** blackish above with *contrasting gray rump and uppertail-coverts. Uniform gray below*, throat only slightly paler. **Western birds** similar but rump and uppertail-coverts *duller and less contrasting,*

To 1700 m (E),
to 1000 m (W)

underparts somewhat paler (but also looking quite uniform). **Similar species:** East of Andes, confusion likely only with larger Pale-rumped Swift, which if observed well can be seen to have conspicuously paler, almost whitish, rump and uppertail. West of Andes, cf. Band-rumped Swift, whose *narrow* whitish rump is quite different from pattern of this species. **Habits:** Similar to other *Chaetura*. Notably gregarious, often flocking with other swifts. Western birds scarcer, and seem more often to range in pairs and small groups; they tend to glide more on slightly wider wings than eastern birds.

Pale-rumped Swift, *Chaetura egregia*
Vencejo Lomipálido   Plate 40(12)

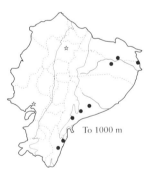

To 1000 m

13.5 cm (5¹/₄″). Scarce over humid forest and adjacent clearings in *lowlands and foothills of east*; so far recorded only Aug.–Dec., so not definitely a permanent resident in Ecuador. A large and heavy-bodied *Chaetura*. Above sooty black with *highly contrasting whitish to pale grayish rump and uppertail-coverts*. Sooty below, throat and upper chest grayer and contrastingly paler. **Similar**

species: Gray-rumped Swift notably smaller, further differs from Pale-rumped in its pure gray (not whitish) rump. Beware, however, Gray-rumpeds out in strong midday light: rumps of birds in such a situation can look very "pale" indeed. The two species often fly together, which should simplify matters if they are in reasonable range and light. **Habits:** Similar to other *Chaetura* swifts. Pale-rumped flies with deeper wingstrokes and glides more than Gray-rumped; wings are longer and broader, and appear more bowed.

White-tipped Swift, *Aeronautes montivagus*
Vencejo Filipunteado   Plate 40(14)

1300–2700 m

12 cm (4³/₄″). *Local* over semiopen terrain in *subtropical and lower temperate zones*, favoring more arid regions; most frequent in central and interandean valleys. Tail somewhat forked, but usually held closed so that it looks square or at most notched. ♂ sooty black above with whitsh spot in front of eyes; *outer tail feathers tipped white* (easier to see from above than below). *Throat and chest white*, contrasting with sooty black lower underparts; whitish band across lower belly. ♀ similar but browner overall and with *reduced* whitish tail tipping. **Similar species:** The only swift found in highlands showing a prominent white "bib." Lesser Swallow-tailed Swift occurs only in lowlands. **Habits:** A gregarious swift, usually flying in flocks of up to about 20 birds, sometimes moving with other swifts, e.g., Chestnut-collared. Flight exceptionally fast. Apparently nests colonially on cliff faces. **Voice:** Quite noisy, members of a flock giving near-continuous reeling trills.

Lesser Swallow-tailed Swift
Panyptila cayennensis
Vencejo Tijereta Menor   Plate 40(13)

To 900 m

Mostly below 500 m, locally higher

13.5 cm (5¼″). A striking *black and white* swift found in small numbers in *lowlands and foothills of east and west. Tail long and deeply forked* but *usually held closed in a point. Mostly black* with *contrasting white throat and upper chest, extending back as narrow nuchal collar*; white spot in front of eye and *quite conspicuous white patch on lower flanks*. In flight *wings very long, narrow, and swept-back*, with narrow white trailing edge to secondaries and inner primaries. Similar species: Boldly patterned and not apt to be confused. Cf. White-tipped Swift of highlands (the two species are unlikely ever to be together), and in e. lowlands the Neotropical Palm-Swift. Habits: Not as gregarious as other swifts, typically seen singly or in pairs (usually) or at most small groups. Flies very high, most often on its own though sometimes loosely associated with other swifts, especially *Chaetura*. Flight fast with shallow fluttery wingbeats. Breeds in solitary pairs, the beautiful nest being a long, cylindrical, downward-tapering cone up to 1 m long, made of plant down and attached to a tree trunk or wall, or hanging from a branch. Voice: Usually quiet, but flying birds give shrill, high-pitched, drawn-out twitters.

Neotropical Palm-Swift, *Tachornis squamata*
Vencejo de Morete   Plate 40(15)

13 cm (5″). A *small, slender* swift found locally—*usually near palms*—in lowlands of east, a few into foothills. Formerly called Fork-tailed Palm-Swift, and often placed in genus *Reinarda. Tail long and deeply forked* but *usually held closed in a point*. Blackish brown above, feathers of back narrowly edged pale gray. Below whitish, *mottled and scaled with dusky on sides and flanks*. In flight wings narrow and back-swept. Similar species: So much smaller and more lightly built than other Ecuadorian swifts that confusion unlikely. Cf. larger and much more boldly patterned Lesser Swallow-tailed Swift. Habits: Usually in small groups, often flying low around clearings and palm groves; occasionally also soars higher. Generally does not associate with other swifts for long. Flight fast and direct on rather stiff, very fast and shallow wingbeats. Nests are attached to underside of palm fronds; various palm species are used (*Mauritia, Bactris,* etc.). Voice: Distinctive flight call a thin, almost buzzy "dzeeee, dzeee-dit" or simply a long trill "dzee-ee-ee-ee-ee-ee."

Hummingbirds: Trochilidae (132)
A distinctive and diverse family of exclusively American birds, hummingbirds reach their maximum diversity in northwestern South America. In Ecuador they are especially numerous in the Andes. The family includes the world's smallest bird, traditionally considered to be the Bee Hummingbird (*Mellisuga helenae*) of Cuba, but several woodstars in Ecuador are at most only marginally "larger." Although a few hummingbirds have dull coloration and show no sexual dimorphism (notably most hermits), the family includes some of the world's most *brilliantly colored* and *ornamented* birds. Areas of *glittering iridescent coloration* are a feature, this produced by microscopic feather structure (not pigmentation) and thus dependent on light angle; at the "wrong" angle colors look black. Hummingbird bills are slender and pointed, and often proportion-

ately long. Bill length and shape are often important for identification (at least to genus level); bills can be presumed to be black unless otherwise indicated. It is for their *power of flight* that hummingbirds are most renowned. Most notable is their ability to rotate the entire wing at the shoulders, this permitting stationary hovering and even backward flight; hummingbirds are the only birds capable of the latter. Wingbeats in most species are so fast as to appear blurred. They feed mainly on nectar, and are important pollinators for many plants, but many small insects are also consumed. Most species aggressively defend their food sources, some attempting to defend not only against conspecifics but also other hummingbirds and even other small birds such as Bananaquits. Hummingbirds, particularly those occurring at high elevations, are capable of lowering their body temperature and entering a torpor-like state at night, thus conserving energy. Pairs are not formed, females raising the young alone with no assistance from males; nests are tiny neat cups of soft downy material, usually held together and attached to a branch or leaf with cobwebs. Males of some species—notably the various hermit genera—gather in leks to "sing" and display, but most males just advertise their presence through the constant repetion of a simple squeaky song. The voices of some species are so undistinctive that they are not mentioned here.

The recent installation of hummingbird feeders at an increasing number of eco-tourism facilities is proving to be a boon to those of us who are aficionados of these feathered gems (and who isn't?). We hope it continues, and that soon there will be hummingbird feeders everywhere. Being essentially fearless of us lumbering humans, hummingbirds become enchanting ambassadors of the natural world.

Note that the lengths given below are measured only from the *base* of the bill to the tip of the tail (thus differing from the lengths given for other species). Bill lengths are given separately, following bill curvature where this is appropriate.

Glaucis Hermits

Inconspicuous hermits *whose rounded tails show considerable rufous*. One species is found on either side of the Andes.

Rufous-breasted Hermit, *Glaucis hirsuta*
Ermitaño Pechicanelo   Plate 41(2)

10 cm (4"). Undergrowth of humid forest and woodland in *lowlands and foothills of east*, favoring vicinity of water and *Heliconia* thickets. *Bill long and decurved* (33 mm; 1.3"), *lower mandible mostly yellow*. Metallic green above, crown duller and duskier, cheeks dusky outlined buffy whitish below. *Dull cinnamon-rufous below. Tail rounded*, central pair bronzy green tipped white, others *rufous* with black subterminal band and white tip. ♀ slightly brighter below. **Similar species:** Bronzy Hermit occurs only west of Andes. Pale-tailed Barbthroat has little rufous on underparts, lacks rufous in tail. *Phaethornis* hermits have elongated white-tipped central tail feathers. **Habits:** Solitary, usually remaining low in vegetation where not often seen, sometimes spotted while dashing across a stream or opening, or feeding at *Heliconia* flowers or gleaning for insects from underside of leaves. **Voice:** Frequently heard flight call a sharp, thin, inflected "swyeep!" ♂♂ also have a fast and high-pitched territorial song, e.g., "tzee-tzee-tzi-tzi-tzit."

Bronzy Hermit, *Glaucis aenea*
Ermitaño Bronceado   Plate 41(1)

8.5 cm (3¼"). Local in undergrowth of humid forest and woodland in *lowlands of northwest. Bill long and decurved* (30 mm; 1.2"), *mainly blackish*. **Sexes alike.** *Bronzy to coppery green' above*, crown duller and duskier; cheeks dusky, outlined buffy whitish below. *Dull cinnamon-rufous below. Tail rounded*, central pair of feathers bronzy green tipped white, others *rufous* with black subterminal band and white tip. **Similar species:** Rufous-breasted Hermit occurs only

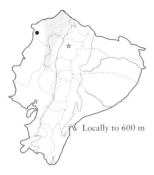

Locally to 600 m

east of Andes. Band-tailed Barbthroat has little rufous on underparts, lacks rufous in tail. *Phaethornis* hermits have elongated white-tipped central tail feathers. **Habits:** As in larger Rufous-breasted Hermit, though seems less tied to vicinity of water. **Voice:** Flight call a sharp "tzeet."

Threnetes Barbthroats
Hermit-like hummingbirds (their decurved bills are similar) whose rounded tails are strongly patterned. One species is found on either side of the Andes.

Pale-tailed Barbthroat, *Threnetes niger*
Barbita Colipálida   Plate 41(3)

Mostly below 1100 m

10 cm (4″). Undergrowth of humid forest and secondary woodland in *lowlands and foothills of east*, favoring vicinity of water and *Heliconia* thickets. Formerly named *T. leucurus*. *Bill long and decurved* (30 mm; 1.2″), lower mandible pale grayish. Metallic green above, cheeks blackish with whitish postocular and malar stripes. *Throat black* with *contrasting cinnamon*

band across chest; breast metallic green becoming grayish white on belly. Tail rounded, central feathers bronzy green, *others mainly buff* with white tips and some black in outer web. ♀ similar but with less extensive cinnamon on chest, less green on breast, more whitish belly. **Similar species:** In size and shape recalls Rufous-breasted Hermit (and the two species are often together), but has much more complex pattern on face and underparts and lacks rufous in tail. **Habits:** Usually solitary, occurring low inside heavy cover where often hard to see well. **Voice:** Flight call a thin hermit-like "tseep." Displaying ♂ ♂ sing a brief series of high-pitched notes.

Band-tailed Barbthroat, *Threnetes ruckeri*
Barbita Colibandeada   Plate 41(4)

To 900 m

10 cm (4″). Undergrowth of humid forest and (especially) secondary woodland and borders in *lowlands and foothills of west*, favoring vicinity of water and *Heliconia* thickets. *Bill long and decurved* (30 mm; 1.2″), *lower mandible yellow*. **Sexes alike. Adult** metallic green above, cheeks blackish with buff postocular stripe and white malar stripe. *Throat blackish* with *contrasting cinnamon band across chest*; remaining underparts grayish, some metallic green on sides of breast. Tail rounded, *mainly black with basal third and narrow tips white*. **Immature** has grayish throat and less cinnamon on chest. **Similar species:** Smaller Bronzy Hermit has bolder facial pattern, cinnamon-rufous underparts, considerable rufous in tail, etc. **Habits:** Much as in Pale-tailed Barbthroat. **Voice:** ♂'s song a short series of high thin notes, e.g., "tzi-tzi-tzí-titi-tzi." At least in Panama ♂ ♂

sometimes sing and display in small loose groups.

Phaethornis Hermits

A large but relatively uniform group of drab hummingbirds that show little or no sexual dimorphism, *Phaethornis* hermits are marked by their *long decurved bills* and *white-tipped tail feathers* with *central rectrices often much elongated*. They come in essentially two sizes: a large group with very long central rectrices, and a group of smaller species whose tails are more wedge-shaped. *Phaethornis* inhabit forest and woodland undergrowth, mainly in the lowlands with a few species on Andean slopes. Males of most species gather to display and "sing" in small groups at traditional lek sites. Their cone-shaped nests are attached to the underside of a large leaf (e.g., of a palm or *Heliconia*), which thus provides a roof.

White-whiskered Hermit, *Phaethornis yaruqui*
Ermitaña Bigotiblanco   Plate 41(5)

Mostly below 1300 m

12 cm (4¾″). A *large* and *dark* hermit, common in undergrowth of humid forest, woodland, and borders in *lowlands and foothills of west*. Bill very long and slightly decurved (45 mm; 1.8″), lower mandible mostly red. Crown coppery bronze; otherwise dark metallic green above, cheeks blackish with *prominent buff superciliary and buffy white malar streak*. Below dark metallic green, becoming grayer on belly with *conspicuous white crissum*. Graduated tail blue-black, somewhat elongated central feathers tipped white. ♀ with more pale grayish mottling on median underparts and broader white tail-tipping. **Similar species:** A dark hummingbird with contrasting white

crissum; in its western range really nothing very similar. Cf. Baron's Hermit (paler above, grayer below, longer tailed), which favors less humid habitats though with some overlap. **Habits:** Numerous and frequently seen, usually singly while checking out flowers in undergrowth or at edge. Can be curious, hovering momentarily in your face, then darting off abruptly, sometimes giving a sharp squeak at same time. **Voice:** Often gives a sharp "tseek!" in flight. Singing ♂ ♂ perch more or less solitarily, emitting a near-continuous stream of harsh "kree-u" notes accompanied by tail-wagging (P. Coopmans).

Green Hermit, *Phaethornis guy*
Ermitaño Verde   Plate 41(6)

Mostly 900–1800 m

11.5 cm (4½″). Undergrowth of montane forest in *foothills and subtropics on e. slope*; mainly at *lower* elevations than Tawny-bellied Hermit. Bill very long and decurved (42 mm; 1.7″), lower mandible mostly red. Dark metallic green above, slightly bronzier on crown and bluer on rump; cheeks blackish with *prominent buff superciliary and malar streak. Dark gray below with buff median throat*. Graduated tail black, elongated central feathers tipped white. ♀ with slightly longer central tail feathers. **Similar species:** Tawny-bellied Hermit occurs at higher elevations, White-bearded and Straight-billed only lower. **Habits:** Similar to White-whiskered Hermit, though Green forms leks (see below). **Voice:** ♂ ♂ gather to display and sing in leks, often large (12 or more birds), there emitting a distinctive nasal and metallic (almost frog-like) "kwee-u," lower pitched than vocalizations of other hermits, repeated endlessly at rate of about once a second and accompanied by tail-wagging.

Tawny-bellied Hermit
Phaethornis syrmatophorus
Ermitaño Ventrileonado   Plate 41(7)

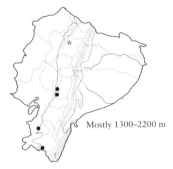

Mostly 1300–2200 m

13 cm (5"). Undergrowth of *subtropical forest on both slopes; occurs at higher elevations than other Ecuadorian hermits.* Bill very long and decurved (42 mm; 1.7"), lower mandible mostly red. **Sexes alike.** Metallic green above, duskier on crown and with *bright ochraceous rump and uppertail-coverts*; cheeks blackish bordered by buffy white superciliary and malar streak. *Ochraceous buff below*, on **west slope** more uniform, on **east slope** richer but with more white on median underparts. Graduated tail black, feathers tipped bright buff, greatly elongated central feathers broadly tipped white. **Similar species:** This brightly colored, attractive hermit of Andean forests is unlikely to be confused. **Habits:** Similar to White-whiskered Hermit, tending more to remain inside forest and less often at edge or in adjacent clearings. **Voice:** ♂♂ gather to display and sing in leks, usually quite small, there giving a repeated high-pitched "tsi-seét" note (sometimes varied to "tsí") accompanied by tail-wagging (P. Coopmans).

Baron's Hermit, *Phaethornis baroni*
Ermitaño de Baron   Plate 41(9)

13 cm (5"). Undergrowth of humid and deciduous forest, woodland, and borders in *lowlands and foothills of west.* Ecuador birds were formerly treated as a race of Long-tailed Hermit (*P. superciliosus*), now considered to range only in ne. South America. Bill long and decurved (41 mm; 1.7"), lower mandible

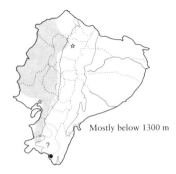

Mostly below 1300 m

mostly reddish orange. **Sexes alike.** Above dull metallic green, crown browner and with rump ochraceous scaled with blackish; cheeks blackish bordered by buff superciliary and white malar stripe. *Below dull grayish mottled with dusky, whiter on belly*, with buffyish median throat stripe. Graduated tail black, feathers narrowly tipped white, greatly elongated central feathers broadly tipped white. **Similar species:** White-whiskered Hermit favors more humid habitats (though the two overlap locally) and is much darker generally. Stripe-throated Hermit much smaller. **Habits:** Aside from lekking behavior, similar to White-whiskered Hermit. **Voice:** ♂♂ gather to display and sing in leks, usually not very large, rhythmically giving a "tchee" note at about half-second intervals.

Great-billed Hermit, *Phaethornis malaris*
Ermitaño Piquigrande   Plate 41(8)

Mostly below 1000 m

13 cm (5"). *Common* in undergrowth and borders of humid forest—*mainly terra firme*—in lowlands (especially) and foothills of *east.* Formerly considered a race of Long-tailed Hermit (*P. superciliosus*). Bill very long and decurved (42 mm; 1.8"), lower mandible

mostly orange-red. **Sexes alike.** Above dull metallic green, rump browner and scaled with blackish; cheeks blackish bordered by buffy whitish superciliary and malar stripe. *Below uniform dull buffyish.* Graduated tail black, feathers narrowly tipped white, greatly elongated central feathers broadly tipped white. **Similar species:** White-bearded Hermit grayer below with much more pronounced white "beard" on median throat; it favors várzea and riparian areas, not terra firme. Straight-billed Hermit *is* in terra firme but is essentially straight-billed. **Habits:** Much like other hermits. **Voice:** Flight call a sharp squeaky "skweep!" Lekking ♂♂ gather to display and sing, emitting a repeated, squeaky "skweeip" vocalization.

White-bearded Hermit, *Phaethornis hispidus*
Ermitaño Barbiblanco   Plate 41(10)

To 600 m

12 cm (4¹⁄₄"). Undergrowth of *várzea and riparian forest and woodland (including islands)* in *lowlands of east*. Bill long and decurved (31 mm; 1.2"), lower mandible mostly yellow. **Sexes alike.** Above dusty green, somewhat browner on crown, *rump and uppertail-coverts decidedly grayer*; cheeks blackish bordered by white malar streak and short superciliary. *Mostly gray below* fading to grayish white on belly, with *conspicuous median throat stripe white*. Graduated tail black, feathers narrowly tipped white, elongated central feathers broadly tipped white. **Similar species:** Great-billed Hermit buffier below with less prominent throat stripe, rump rufescent (not gray); it favors terra firme forest. **Habits:** Much like other hermits. **Voice:** ♂♂ gather to display and sing in small leks in dense

undergrowth, giving an incessant, rapidly repeated "tsip-tsip-tsip . . ." call.

Straight-billed Hermit, *Phaethornis bourcieri*
Ermitaño Piquirrecto   Plate 41(11)

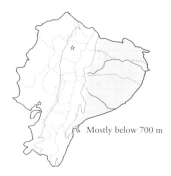

Mostly below 700 m

12 cm (4³⁄₄"). Undergrowth of terra firme forest in lowlands (especially) and lower foothills of east. *Bill long and virtually straight* (32 mm; 1.3"), lower mandible mostly orange-yellow. **Sexes alike.** Above dull metallic green, rump feathers slightly browner; cheeks dusky bordered by short buff superciliary and whitish malar stripe. *Dull pale grayish below* with faint whitish median throat stripe. Graduated tail black, feathers narrowly tipped white, elongated central tail feathers broadly tipped white. **Similar species:** A rather dull and faded-looking hermit, to be recognized by its terra firme habitat (normally the only other hermit there is Great-billed) and essentially straight bill. **Habits:** Much as in other hermits, though seems more retiring than most. **Voice:** ♂♂ gather in small leks inside forest, giving rather weak "tsiseé . . . tsiseé . . ." (J. Moore recording), characteristically doubled.

Reddish Hermit, *Phaethornis ruber*
Ermitaño Rojizo   Plate 41(12)

7.5 cm (3"). Apparently scarce and local in undergrowth of humid forest, secondary woodland, and borders in *lowlands of east*. Bill long and somewhat decurved (23 mm; 0.9"), lower mandible mostly orange-yellow. ♂ bronzy green above with *rufous rump*; cheeks blackish bordered by buffy white superciliary. *Uniform cinnamon-rufous below* with *narrow black band across breast*. Wedge-shaped tail bronzy green, feathers

To 400 m

narrowly tipped rufous-buff, central feathers tipped white. ♀ paler below, with black band reduced or lacking. **Similar species:** Black-throated Hermit slightly larger and has black streaking on throat. Cf. also very similar Gray-chinned Hermit of foothills (no known overlap). **Habits:** Usually found singly, darting and weaving among foliage, pausing to feed at flowers, frequently of *Heliconia*. **Voice:** Displaying ♂ ♂ seem to sing more or less solitarily, with song in Guyana descending characteristically into a jumble, "tsii-tsii-tsiitsiiteeteeteeu."

Gray-chinned Hermit
Phaethornis griseogularis
Ermitaño Barbigris   Plate 41(13)

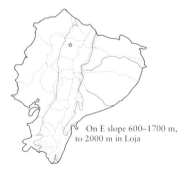

On E slope 600–1700 m,
to 2000 m in Loja

7.5–8 cm (3–3¼"). Generally uncommon and local in undergrowth and borders of *foothill and lower subtropical forest and woodland on e. slope*, also locally in *Loja*. Bill long and somewhat decurved (23 mm; 0.9"), lower mandible mainly yellow. On **east slope** metallic green above with *rufous rump*; cheeks blackish bordered by buff superciliary. Mainly cinnamon-rufous below, but with *chin and median throat grayish*. Wedge-

shaped tail bronzy green, feathers narrowly tipped rufous-buff, central feathers tipped white. ♀ slightly paler and duller below. In **Loja** slightly larger and *markedly paler buff below*, with *lateral tail feathers tipped whitish*. **Similar species:** On e. slope this species occurs *above* range of similar (especially in ♀ ♀) Reddish Hermit. Similar Stripe-throated Hermit not known to occur south of El Oro, and thus apparently does not overlap with the Loja population of Gray-chinned. **Habits:** Similar to Reddish Hermit. **Voice:** On e. slope displaying ♂ ♂ gather, sometimes 12 or more, to sing in leks situated in dense undergrowth; there they emit a series of high-pitched squeaky "swit-swit-sweeit . . ." notes.

Stripe-throated Hermit
Phaethornis striigularis
Ermitaño Golirrayado   Plate 41(15)

Mostly below 800 m

7.5 cm (3"). Undergrowth and borders of humid and deciduous forest and woodland in *lowlands (mainly) and foothills of west*. Formerly treated as a race of Little Hermit (*P. longuemareus*), now considered to range only in ne. South America. Bill long and somewhat decurved (23 mm; 0.9"), lower mandible mainly yellow. **Sexes alike.** Bronzy green above with rufous rump; cheeks blackish bordered by buff superciliary. *Throat and breast buffy grayish* with *median throat streaked dusky*; belly cinnamon-buff. Tail wedge-shaped, feathers tipped buffy whitish, central feathers tipped white. **Similar species:** *The only small hermit found in w. Ecuador* (except in Loja), and as such readily recognizable. Cf. similar Black-throated Hermit (east of Andes). **Habits:** Similar to Reddish Hermit. **Voice:** Displaying ♂ ♂ gather to sing in leks situated in dense growth close to ground, there interminably giving a series of high-pitched, thin, and squeaky "tsit" notes interspersed with a more tinkling complex phrase.

Black-throated Hermit
Phaethornis atrimentalis
Ermitaño Golinegro   Plate 41(14)

To 800 m

8.5 cm (3¼"). Scarce and local in undergrowth of humid forest and borders in *lowlands of east*. Formerly considered a race of Little Hermit (*P. longuemareus*). Bill long and somewhat decurved (26 mm; 1"), lower mandible mainly yellow. **Sexes alike.** Bronzy green above with rufous rump; cheeks blackish bordered by buffy whitish superciliary and malar stripe. Mostly cinnamon-buff below but with *extensive and contrasting blackish streaking on throat*. Tail wedge-shaped, feathers tipped white. **Similar species:** Reddish Hermit is even smaller (though these are both small hermits), lacks black on throat, and is more richly colored below. **Habits:** Not well known in Ecuador, but probably differs little if at all from other small hermits. **Voice:** ♂ ♂ at their small leks give repeated high-pitched "psss-psss-psss-psee-u" (G. Rivadeneira recording).

Eutoxeres Sicklebills
Heavy-bodied hummingbirds with *unmistakable very sharply decurved bills and streaked underparts*. They range in humid and lower montane forest undergrowth. *Sexes alike.*

White-tipped Sicklebill, *Eutoxeres aquila*
Pico de Hoz Puntiblanco   Plate 41(16)

12 cm (4¾"). Not uncommon but inconspicuous in undergrowth and borders of *foothill*

Mostly 400–1600 m

and lower subtropical forest on both slopes, locally down into lowlands in northwest (especially in Esmeraldas). *Very sharply decurved, sickle-shaped bill* (35 mm; 1.4"), lower mandible yellow. Dark shining green above, sootier on crown. *Below heavily streaked sooty and whitish. Graduated tail dark bronzy green, feathers tipped white* (broadly so on **east slope**). **Similar species:** Unmistakable on w. slope, provided bill is seen, where the only sicklebill. On e. slope, cf. Buff-tailed Sicklebill (mainly at lower elevations—though with some overlap—and showing prominent buff in tail). **Habits:** Generally remains within cover and hard to see. Feeds primarily by clinging with strong feet and sharp claws to *Heliconia* flowers, probing corollas for nectar, doubtless incidentally obtaining insects; also gleans insects from foliage and branches. Wingbeats slow and audible. **Voice:** Flight call a piercing sharp "tist!" E.-slope ♂ ♂ sing a very complex, jumbled series of high-pitched notes and squeaks (P. Coopmans); w.-slope ♂ ♂ sing a very different, simpler and rhythmic series of hermit-like phrases, e.g., "tsi-se-rík" (M. Lysinger and L. Navarrete recordings).

Buff-tailed Sicklebill, *Eutoxeres condamini*
Pico de Hoz Colihabano   Plate 41(17)

12 cm (4¾"). Uncommon and inconspicuous in undergrowth of humid *lowland (principally terra firme) and foothill forest and borders in east. Very sharply decurved, sickle-shaped bill* (35 mm; 1.4"), lower mandible yellow. Dark shining green above, sootier on crown, with patch of shining bluish green on sides of neck. Below heavily streaked sooty and buffy whitish. *Outer tail feathers conspicuously cinnamon-buff tipped white*, central feathers bronzy green. **Similar**

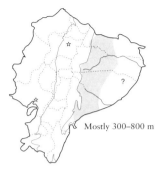

Mostly 300–800 m

species: White-tipped Sicklebill lacks buff in tail; it tends to occur at higher elevations, with Buff-tailed the only sickle-bill in actual lowlands. **Habits:** Similar to White-tipped Sicklebill. Buff-tailed favors vicinity of streams. **Voice:** Song a rhythmic series of loud, clear, hermit-like phrases, e.g., "sweee-swe-seék, sweee-swe-swík . . ." (P. Coopmans).

Tooth-billed Hummingbird
Androdon aequatorialis
Colibrí Piquidentado   Plate 41(18)

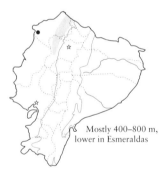

Mostly 400–800 m, lower in Esmeraldas

10 cm (4″). Generally scarce and local in lower and middle growth of humid lowland and foothill forest in northwest, *mainly in Esmeraldas, a few extending to n. Pichincha. Bill long and absolutely straight* (40 mm; 1.6″), lower mandible yellowish. ♂ metallic green above, *fore- and midcrown reddish coppery* and with *uppertail-coverts white* (forming a prominent band). *Below whitish broadly streaked with blackish.* Rounded tail grayish with blackish subterminal band and white tipping. ♀ lacks coppery on crown. **Similar species:** Nearly unmistakable in its

limited range, where it is the only humming-bird with combination of long straight bill and streaked underparts. **Habits:** Usually seen singly as it feeds at flowers at varying heights, regularly at epiphytic plants well above ground. Also hovers for insects. **Voice:** Calls include a series of very high-pitched notes, e.g., "tsit-tseé-tsu" or "tseé-tsu" (K. Berg recording).

Doryfera Lancebills
Dark hummingbirds with *long black straight bills*, *rounded tails*, and *glittering frontlets* ranging in foothill and lower subtropical forests, especially near streams.

Blue-fronted Lancebill, *Doryfera johannae*
Picolanza Frentiazul   Plate 41(23)

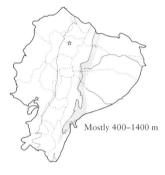

Mostly 400–1400 m

9 cm (3½″). Uncommon in undergrowth and borders of *foothill and lower subtropical forest on e. slope. Bill straight, almost upswept* (27 mm; 1.1″). ♂ *dark overall*, with *glittering violet forecrown* and small white postocular spot, somewhat coppery on nape; otherwise dark metallic green above, bluer on uppertail-coverts. *Below very dark, almost blackish blue-green. Tail rounded*, blue-black. ♀ has *smaller frontlet glittering blue-green*, much paler and grayer underparts, and gray-tipped tail feathers. **Similar species:** Dark ♂ quite distinctive, but ♀ readily confused with only slightly larger Green-fronted Lancebill; Green-fronted's bill proportionately longer, frontlet clearly green (not blue-green), and it shows more coppery on hindneck. **Habits:** Similar to Green-fronted Lancebill, likewise most often near water. **Voice:** Occasionally gives a high-pitched "tsit" note, especially in flight.

Green-fronted Lancebill, *Doryfera ludovicae*
Picolanza Frentiverde   Plate 41(22)

Mostly 1100–1700 m

Mostly 300–600 m

9.5 cm (3¾"). Uncommon in undergrowth and borders of *lower subtropical forest on both slopes. Bill long and straight, slightly upswept* (36 mm; 1.4"). ♂ with *glittering green forecrown, coppery rearcrown and nape*, and small white postocular spot; otherwise dark metallic green above, bluer on uppertail-coverts. Below dull grayish green. *Rounded tail* black tipped grayish. ♀ has smaller frontlet, grayer underparts. **Similar species:** Similar but slightly smaller Blue-fronted Lancebill has forecrown glittering violet and darker, almost bluish-black underparts. **Habits:** An inconspicuous hummingbird, usually found singly and favoring the vicinity of rushing mountain streams. Comes regularly to flowering shrubs and small trees at forest edge, locally together with Blue-fronted Lancebill.

Campylopterus Sabrewings
Quite large hummingbirds named for the adult males' "sabre-like" flattened shafts of the outer two primaries. Sabrewings are found in forests of the east, where they range from the lowlands (Gray-breasted) to the subtropics (Lazuline).

Gray-breasted Sabrewing
Campylopterus largipennis
Alasable Pechigris   Plate 43(1)

11.5 cm (4½"). Humid forest, woodland, and borders in *lowlands of east*. Bill slightly decurved (27 mm; 1"). *Large and relatively dull.* **Sexes alike.** Shining metallic green above with *prominent white postocular spot. Uniform gray below.* Central tail feathers bluish green above, others blackish, *outer*

feathers with broad white corners. **Similar species:** ♀ Fork-tailed Woodnymph considerably smaller, has much smaller white tail corners, lacks postocular spot. **Habits:** Forages at varying levels, most often low but can also be seen in forest subcanopy and canopy. Seems to favor vicinity of streams flowing through forest, there often sunning itself on logs or rocks. **Voice:** Not very vocal; ♂♂ (usually solitary, sometimes in small loose groups) give a repeated, sharp, tanager-like "tchip" note every 1–2 seconds.

Lazuline Sabrewing, *Campylopterus falcatus*
Alasable Lazulita   Plate 43(2)

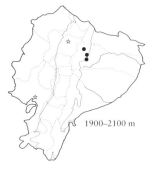

1900–2100 m

11 cm (4¼"). *Very rare and local* in canopy and borders of *subtropical* forest and adjacent clearings on *e. slope. Thus far known only from Baeza region. Bill markedly decurved* (25 mm; 0.9"). ♂ shining metallic green above, more glittering on hindcrown and nape, with small white postocular spot. *Throat and breast glittering violet-blue* becoming blue-green on belly. *Tail rufous-chestnut*, central feathers tipped or entirely blue-green. ♀ like ♂ but duller green above.

Mostly gray below, most birds with at least some glittering blue on throat outlined with whitish; some green on sides and flanks. *Tail as in ♂ but paler rufous* (not rufous-chestnut). **Similar species:** The only Ecuadorian hummer with combination of noticeably decurved bill and largely rufous tail. Cf. Napo Sabrewing (occurs at lower elevations, has blue-black tail, etc.). **Habits:** Barely known in Ecuador; a recently seen bird was in a garden. Elsewhere forages at varying heights, usually low and near cover but also in flowering trees. **Voice:** In Venezuela a variable sputtering has been recorded (Hilty and Brown 1986).

Napo Sabrewing
Campylopterus villaviscensio
Alasable del Napo   Plate 43(3)

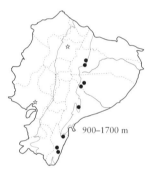

900–1700 m

11.5 cm (4½"). Local in lower growth and borders of *foothill and lower subtropical forest on e. slope*. Bill fairly long and essentially straight (28 mm; 1.2"). *Crown glittering emerald green*; otherwise shining green above with small white postocular spot. *Throat and breast glittering violet-blue*; belly dark gray with green disks. *Tail mostly steel blue*, central feathers metallic green. ♀ shining green above, more glittering on hindcrown and with small white postocular spot. *Below uniform gray*. Tail as in ♂, but outer feathers narrowly white-tipped. **Similar species:** ♂ White-tailed Hillstar has similar overall color pattern but shows considerable white in tail. ♀ resembles Gray-breasted Sabrewing of lowlands (they are not known to overlap), but Gray-breasted paler below, has large white tail-corners and more decurved bill. Cf. also Lazuline Sabrewing. ♀ Fork-tailed Woodnymph smaller, paler gray

below. **Habits:** Usually seen inside forest along streams or rivers, sometimes venturing to edge to feed at low flowering trees. Does not seem to forage high above ground.

White-necked Jacobin, *Florisuga mellivora*
Jacobino Nuquiblanco   Plate 43(6)

Mostly below 800 m

9.5 cm (3¾"). *Widespread* in canopy and borders of humid forest, woodland, and clearings in *lowlands of east and west*. Bill rather short and essentially straight (20 mm; 0.8"). ♂ has *entire head, neck, and chest bright shining blue* with *conspicuous white crescent across hindneck*; otherwise shining green above. Sides of breast shining green; *belly contrastingly white. Tail mostly white*, feathers black-tipped; central feathers shining green. ♀ shining green above. *Throat and breast dusky-green, feathers edged white imparting distinct scaly effect*; belly white, crissum dusky scaled white. Tail blue-green, feathers with black subterminal band and white tipping. Some ♀♀ assume varying degrees of ♂'s plumage, especially the blue on head and white on tail. **Similar species:** Beautiful ♂♂ essentially unmistakable, but cf. Purple-crowned and Black-eared Fairies. ♀'s obvious scaly (as opposed to *spotted*) pattern on underparts distinctive. **Habits:** Usually conspicuous and often occurring in open, sometimes surprisingly far from any real forest. Several may concentrate with other hummers at flowering trees; jacobins also are frequently seen hovering for protracted periods, often over water, darting to and fro as they catch minute insects. ♂♂ engage in an attractive swooping display flight, often at considerable heights, in which they may fan their tails in a near-full semicircle. **Voice:** Not especially vocal, though

♂♂ give a series of "tsip" notes, usually from twigs high in canopy.

Colibri Violetears

A trio of hummingbirds united by their *violet ear-patches*; one species is brown and dull, the other two green and more attractive. All three are *notably vocal*. *Sexes alike* or nearly so.

Brown Violetear, *Colibri delphinae*
Orejivioleta Parda   Plate 43(7)

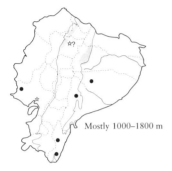

Mostly 1000–1800 m

9 cm (3½"). *Scarce and erratic* in subtropical forest and woodland borders and semiopen areas with scattered trees on both slopes. Bill quite short (17 mm; 0.7") and straight. *Mostly drab brown*, somewhat mottled or streaked whitish below, with *long glittering violet-blue ear-tuft on sides of neck*, *whitish malar streak*, and small glittering green and violet throat patch; *rump feathers edged cinnamon-tawny*, crissum also rufescent. Tail greenish bronze with dusky subterminal band and sometimes buff tipping. **Similar species:** A dull-plumaged hummer without much in the way of bright colors (and those it has are hard to see); best known by combination of short bill, drab overall coloration with contrasting dark ear-patch and whitish malar, rusty on rump. Bronzy and Brown Incas have much longer bills, etc. **Habits:** This wide-ranging violetear seems notably uncommon in Ecuador, where it has mainly been seen singly while feeding at flowering trees in semiopen, usually not too far from forest or woodland cover. Also captures insects while hovering. **Voice:** ♂'s often interminably continued song is delivered from a high prominent perch, usually at edge, often through heat of day. It is a rapidly delivered series of 5–10 sharp "tcheep" or "tsik" notes, then a pause of variable duration before the sequence is repeated.

Green Violetear, *Colibri thalassinus*
Orejivioleta Verde   Plate 43(8)

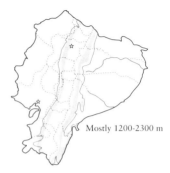

Mostly 1200-2300 m

9.5 cm (3¾"). Widespread but only infrequently very numerous in canopy and borders of *subtropical and lower temperate* forest borders, secondary scrub, and clearings on both slopes. Bill nearly straight (20 mm; 0.8"). Shining green above with *long glittering violet ear-patch on sides of neck*. Throat and chest somewhat more glittering green, belly shining green. Tail metallic blue-green, central feathers bronzier, with *prominent blackish subterminal band*. **Similar species:** Sparkling Violetear considerably larger with a more extensive violet ear-patch (especially in ♂♂) and violet patch on mid-belly (sometimes hard to see). **Habits:** Favors humid regions, and absent from the central valley (where Sparkling Violetear takes over); these two violetears sometimes, however, feed together at flowering *Inga* trees. Often seen in semiopen brushy areas away from extensive forest. **Voice:** Solitary ♂♂ sing, often tirelessly, from the same high exposed twigs day after day, giving a monotonously repeated sharp and dry "tsu-tzeek" (sometimes just a "tzeek" or "tsu-tz-tzeek") at a rate of about one call/second. Though usually fully in the open, they are sometimes surprisingly hard to locate.

Sparkling Violetear, *Colibri coruscans*
Orejivioleta Ventriazul   Plate 43(9)

12 cm (4¾"). *Widespread and often common* in semiopen and agricultural areas with scattered trees, gardens, and *subtropical and (especially) temperate woodland and forest*

Mostly 1000–3500 m

Mostly below 500 m

borders on both slopes and in central and interandean valleys. One of the few hummers found in areas with little or no native vegetation, regular even in Quito itself. Bill slightly decurved (25 mm; 1″). *Above shining green with long glittering violet ear-patch extending from sides of neck to chin.* Below mostly glittering green with *patch of glittering violet-blue on midbelly.* Tail metallic blue, central feathers greener, with dark subterminal band. ♀ shows white postocular spot lacking in ♂. **Similar species:** Green Violetear substantially smaller with a smaller violet ear-patch (not extending under bill as a "chin-strap"), less glitter below, and no violet patch on belly. **Habits:** Beautiful and conspicuous, this is one of most frequently encountered hummingbirds in semiopen and arid areas in the highlands; elsewhere it seems more irregular or perhaps seasonal. Regularly comes to hummingbird feeders. ♂♂ are very aggressive in territorial defense. **Voice:** ♂'s song, one of the characteristic bird sounds in many highland areas, an often interminably repeated "tik" note, given more rapidly than Green's and with a less sharp and mechanical quality. Singing birds usually perch on a high exposed twig. In an often-seen display flight they mount 5–10 m up from perch, give a quick song, then close wings and spread tail, plunging back to original perch.

Black-throated Mango
Anthracothorax nigricollis
Mango Gorjinegro   Plate 44(3)

11 cm (4¼″). *Semiopen areas, clearings, and woodland and forest borders* in lowlands of west and northeast, more numerous in west. Includes the west-Ecuadorian form formerly

considered a race of Green-breasted Mango (*A. prevostii*). *Bill slightly decurved* (23 mm; 0.9″). ♂ shining metallic green above. *Throat, breast, and median belly black,* throat and chest bordered by glittering blue and green, flanks green. *Tail purplish maroon,* feathers tipped black, central feathers blue-green. Nearly unmistakable ♀ like ♂ but with *white underparts setting off conspicuous black stripe down median underparts,* sides and flanks narrowly green; tail feathers tipped whitish. **Similar species:** ♂, which looks dark and unpatterned in poor light, recognized by combination of fairly large size, noticeably decurved bill, purplish tail, and black on underparts. ♀ relatively easy, but cf. very rare Fiery-tailed Awlbill. **Habits:** A nonforest hummingbird, foraging mainly at flowering trees in semiopen, less often closer to ground in plantations, etc. Also frequently seen capturing insects in air, often well above ground. **Voice:** Not especially vocal, but foraging birds give a "tsik" note.

Fiery-tailed Awlbill, *Avocettula recurvirostris*
Colibrí Piquipunzón   Plate 42(1)

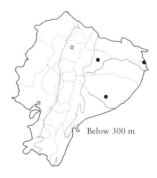

Below 300 m

7.5 cm (3"). *Very rare* in canopy and borders of humid forest in lowlands of east. Bill fairly short, *strongly upturned at tip (especially on lower mandible)*. ♂ above shining green. *Throat and breast glittering emerald green*, belly shining green with some black in center. Tail bronzy above, central pair of feathers greener, *underside glistening coppery*. ♀ above shining green. White below with *green throat extending down as conspicuous black median stripe*, green on sides and flanks. Tail bronzy above, central pair of feathers greener, *underside basally glistening coppery* and outer feathers with whitish tips. **Similar species:** Bill shape unique, but often not easy to discern in field. Birds in ♀ plumage seem usually to outnumber ♂♂, and with their mango-like stripe down underparts they are relatively easy to pick out (mangos themselves being, of course, very much larger). **Habits:** As poorly known in Ecuador as it is elsewhere across its range. Birds seen have usually been solitary, perching and feeding at moderate heights at edge of forest or in clearings.

Violet-headed Hummingbird, *Klais guimeti*
Colibrí Cabecivioleta   Plate 42(2)

Mostly 800–1700 m

7.5 cm (3"). Seasonally not uncommon in *foothill and lower subtropical forest, borders, and adjacent clearings on e. slope*. Bill short and straight (13 mm; 0.5"), *black*. ♂ has *head and throat violet-blue* with *conspicuous white postocular spot*; otherwise shining green above. Below grayish green. Tail bronzy green, lateral feathers with vague dusky subterminal band and whitish tip. ♀ much like ♂ but *only crown glittering violet-blue, entire underparts pale gray*, and wider white tail-tipping. **Similar species:** Both sexes of this small hummer can be known by all-

black bill (showing no red below) and obvious white postocular spot. Cf. various sapphires. **Habits:** Usually found singly, foraging at low to moderate heights at forest edge, usually feeding at relatively small flowers, sometimes with other hummingbirds. Often at flowering *Inga* trees. **Voice:** ♂♂ gather in loose singing assemblies where they perch on open dead twigs at mid-levels, usually just inside forest. Song a series of high-pitched notes, e.g., "tsi-titititi" or "tsi-ti-tí, tsi-ti-tí, tsi-ti-tí."

Lophornis Coquettes
Tiny hummingbirds, all of them rare and poorly known in Ecuador and sharing a *conspicuous white or buff rump band*. Males are *highly ornamented*.

Spangled Coquette, *Lophornis stictolophus*
Coqueta Lentejuelada   Plate 42(3)

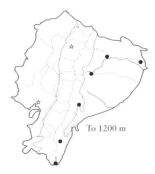

To 1200 m

7 cm (2¾"). *Rare* and local in forest borders and adjacent clearings *along e. base of Andes*. Bill very short (10 mm; 0.4"), reddish with black tip. *Tiny*. ♂ metallic green above with *very long, wide, bushy crest rufous with feathers tipped black* and *buffy whitish rump band*. Throat glittering green, some white showing at its lower edge and some lateral feathers tipped rufous; underparts metallic green. Tail mostly rufous, outer webs of feathers bronzy green. ♀ metallic green above with *rufous forecrown* and *buffy whitish rump band as in* ♂. Throat whitish with some rufous spotting and some dark spotting along lower edge; breast dull bronzy green, belly washed cinnamon. Tail bronzy green tipped rufous. **Similar species:** This tiny hummer with rufous crest (♂) or forecrown (♀) is not likely confused except with the ap-

parently very rare Rufous-crested Coquette (which see). **Habits:** Usually found singly, foraging at varying heights, sometimes high in flowering trees such as *Inga* and *Chimarrhis*, at other times lower at flowering hedges and shrubs. Perched birds often rest on high exposed dead twigs. Flight tends to be slow and weaving, not as fast and direct as in most other hummingbirds; hum of wings is sometimes audible. Feeding birds sometimes cock or wag their short tails.

[Rufous-crested Coquette, *Lophornis delattrei* Coqueta Crestirrufa] Plate 42(4)

7 cm (2¼"). *Seemingly very rare* (possibly overlooked, or confused with previous species) in forest borders and adjacent clearings *near e. base of Andes in Napo* (Jatun Sacha). Both sexes resemble more numerous Spangled Coquette. ♂ differs in its *somewhat longer and more pointed (not so bushy) rufous crest* whose feathers *lack* black tipping. ♀ differs in having *more or less rufous throat* in addition to rufous forecrown. **Habits:** As in Spangled Coquette.

Festive Coquette, *Lophornis chalybeus* Coqueta Festiva Plate 42(5)

7.5 cm (3"). Apparently very rare and local in canopy and borders of humid forest in *lowlands of east*. Bill short (13 mm; 0.5"), blackish. A *dark* coquette, not as minute as other Ecuadorian *Lophornis*, with fuller tail. ♂ has *frontlet and gorget glittering green*, extending back as *tuft of long white-tipped feathers on sides of neck* (usually held close to body); midcrown black, hindcrown dark bronzy green extending back as short crest (usually held down); otherwise metallic green above with *white rump band*. Below dark green.

To 500 m

Tail bronzy copper. ♀ lacks ornamentation: dark metallic green above with *white rump band. Chin buffy whitish extending back as malar streak*; underparts mottled dusky. **Similar species:** Both sexes lack rufous in crest and crown shown by the other two Ecuadorian coquettes. ♂ not likely confused, ♀ most likely mistaken for a ♀ thorntail though those have a white flank patch (it and all the ♀♀ thorntails have malar streaks) and more slender tail. **Habits:** Much as in Spangled Coquette, though from limited data at hand Festive seems to be more of a forest-based hummingbird. Has been seen feeding at flowering *Inga* and *Erythrina* trees.

Popelairia Thorntails

Tiny hummingbirds with a *conspicuous white rump band and flank patches*. Males have long and deeply forked tails, whereas females show bold patterning below. They are forest-based hummers that especially favor the foothills. The genus is sometimes merged into *Discosura*.

Wire-crested Thorntail, *Popelairia popelairii* Colicerda Crestuda Plate 42(6)

Mostly 600–1600 m

♂ 10 cm (4″); ♀ 7 cm (2¾″). Uncommon at borders of *foothill and lower subtropical* forest and in adjacent clearings on *e. slope.* Bill short (13 mm; 0.5″). ♂ has crown and throat glittering green with *long wispy wire-like crest springing from midcrown*; otherwise coppery green above with *conspicuous white rump band* extending to lower flanks. Underparts sooty blackish. *Tail extremely long and deeply forked*, black, outer feathers narrow and sharply pointed and with white shafts. ♀ *coppery green above* with *conspicuous white rump band* extending to lower flanks. Blackish below with *white malar streak and patch on flanks*. Slightly forked tail much shorter than ♂'s, black with outer feathers tipped white. **Similar species:** Cf. Black-bellied Thorntail, which mainly occurs at lower elevations; ♀♀ of the two are very similar (differing only in dorsal coloration) and usually cannot be distinguished in field. **Habits:** Usually found singly, foraging at varying heights though most often quite high in flowering trees, often with other hummingbirds and congregating at flowering *Inga* and *Erythrina* trees. Wasp-like flight is slow and weaving; hovering birds usually cock their tails, often steeply. Mainly perches high, often on twigs out in open.

Black-bellied Thorntail, *Popelairia langsdorffi*
Colicerda Ventrinegra   Plate 42(7)

Mostly below 400 m

♂ 12 cm (4¾″); ♀ 7 cm (2¾″). Rare in canopy and borders of humid forest (especially terra firme) in *lowlands of east*. Bill short (13 mm; 0.5″). ♂ much like ♂ Wire-crested Thorntail, differing in *lacking crest*, less coppery upperparts, and in having narrow glittering coppery red band below green gorget and *outer tail feathers gray with*

white shafts (breast band hard to see in field, but gray in tail can stand out). ♀ very similar to ♀ Wire-crested Thorntail, differing only in less coppery upperparts. **Similar species:** ♀ Festive Coquette is somewhat similar but lacks prominent white flank patch. **Habits:** As in Wire-crested Thorntail, though Black-bellied seems to be more of a forest-based bird, more often occurring in canopy of actual forest.

Green Thorntail, *Popelairia conversii*
Colicerda Verde   Plate 42(8)

Mostly 300–1000 m

♂ 9.5 cm (3¾″); ♀ 7 cm (2¾″). Canopy and borders of humid forest and adjacent clearings in *lowlands and foothills of west, where the only thorntail present.* Bill short (13 mm; 0.5″). ♂ mostly shining green with glittering green crown and nape and blue spot on chest; *conspicuous white rump band* extends to lower flanks. *Tail extremely long and deeply forked*, blue-black, outer feathers very narrow with white shafts. ♀ shining green above with *conspicuous white rump band* extending to lower flanks. Throat black bordered at sides by *prominent white malar streak*; underparts mixed green and black with *prominent white patch on flanks*. Slightly forked tail much shorter than ♀'s, blue-black with outer feathers tipped white. **Similar species:** The only thorntail on Pacific slope, so both sexes should be easily recognized. **Habits:** As in Wire-crested Thorntail.

Blue-chinned Sapphire, *Chlorestes notatus*
Zafiro Barbiazul   Plate 44(13)

8 cm (3¼″). *Rare* at borders of humid forest and shrubby clearings in *lowlands of northeast*. Bill essentially straight (18 mm; 0.7″),

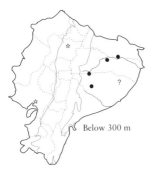

Below 300 m

To 750 m (N);
900–2600 m (S)

lower mandible red tipped black. ♂ shining green above. *Mainly glittering green below,* chin slightly bluer (but blue hard to see in field). Tail slightly rounded, blue-black. ♀ like ♂ above. Below dingy whitish with green spots on throat and breast. Tail as in ♂. **Similar species:** ♂ resembles ♂ of somewhat smaller Blue-tailed Emerald though that species has an all-black bill and more forked tail; ♀♀ of the two species are quite different. Cf. also Glittering-throated Emerald (with whitish median stripe on underparts, etc.). **Habits:** Usually seen singly at low to moderate heights, especially favoring borders of forest and just inside; seems more forest-based than *Amazilia*. **Voice:** Elsewhere ♂ gives a fast series of high-pitched notes, e.g., "tss-tss-tss."

Chlorostilbon Emeralds

Small hummingbirds with short bills found in semiopen terrain, one species on either side of the Andes. Males are *mainly glittering green* with forked tails, whereas females have a *distinctive facial pattern with a dusky mask and a white postocular stripe.*

Blue-tailed Emerald, *Chlorostilbon mellisugus*
Esmeralda Coliazul   Plate 44(23)

7 cm (2¾"). Scarce at borders of humid forest and in shrubby clearings, often near rivers, in *lowlands of northeast,* and at borders of foothill and lower subtropical forest on *e. slope of Andes in southeast (mainly Zamora-Chinchipe).* W.-slope populations, formerly considered conspecific, are now separated as a distinct species (following). *Bill short* (13 mm; 0.5"), straight, *black.* ♂ shining green above, *glittering green below and on fore-crown* (somewhat blue on chest in certain

lights). *Tail somewhat forked*, blue-black. ♀ shining green above, somewhat bronzier on crown and with *dusky ear-coverts surmounted by prominent white streak behind eye. Below uniform pale gray*, sides washed green. Tail as in ♂ but outer feathers tipped whitish. **Similar species:** Does not overlap with very similar Western Emerald. ♂ otherwise most likely confused with ♂ Blue-chinned Sapphire though sapphire has proportionately longer bill with mostly red lower mandible; ♀♀ of the two are easier (note especially emerald's "mask" and postocular stripe). ♀ of larger Fork-tailed Woodnymph is also uniform pale grayish below but lacks facial pattern. **Habits:** Usually seen singly, foraging rather low.

Western Emerald
Chlorostilbon melanorhynchus
Esmeralda Occidental   Plate 44(24)

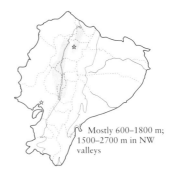

Mostly 600–1800 m;
1500–2700 m in NW
valleys

7 cm (2¾"). Fairly common in scrub and gardens in *arid intermontane valleys south to Quito region,* and on *w. slope from Pichincha to Guayas.* Formerly considered conspecific with Blue-tailed Emerald. Bill *short* (13 mm; 0.5"), straight, *black. Both sexes*

extremely similar to Blue-tailed Emerald, and best distinguished by range. ♂ differs subtly in having pure emerald green glitter to underparts (lacking any blue on chest) and more golden glitter on forecrown. **Habits:** Similar to Blue-tailed Emerald, though Western seems more numerous in Ecuador, and is far more likely to be found in gardens and disturbed areas provided adequate nectar sources are available. **Voice:** Not very vocal, but ♂♂ have weak twittering song, e.g., "tsit-trr, tsst-trr, tsit-trr . . ." (N. Krabbe recording).

Thalurania Woodnymphs
A trio of hummingbirds found in the lower growth of humid forest, one species in the east and two in the west. Colorful males have *deeply forked tails*, whereas much plainer females have *mainly or entirely gray underparts.*

Fork-tailed Woodnymph, *Thalurania furcata*
Ninfa Tijereta   Plate 44(21)

Mostly below 1000 m

♂ 9.5 cm (3¾"); ♀ 6.5 cm (3"). Generally numerous in lower growth and borders of humid forest in *lowlands and foothills of east.* Bill essentially straight (19 mm; 0.7"), *black.* ♂ shining green above. *Throat and chest glittering green, contrasting with glittering violet-blue lower underparts. Tail rather long and deeply forked,* blue-black. Notably smaller ♀ shining green above. *Below uniform pale grayish.* Somewhat forked tail blue-black, outer feathers tipped whitish. **Similar species:** Other woodnymphs occur west of Andes. Cf. ♀ Blue-tailed Emerald; in foothills cf. larger and much scarcer Napo Sabrewing. **Habits:** Usually seen singly inside forest or at edge, less often

out into adjacent clearings, then mainly to feed. Regularly forages at *Heliconia* flowers. Tends to remain in lower growth, only occasionally venturing up into subcanopy (then usually ♂♂). **Voice:** Generally quiet. ♂'s infrequently heard song a series of weak "tsip" notes.

Green-crowned Woodnymph
Thalurania fannyi
Ninfa Coroniverde   Plate 44(19)

Mostly below 800 m

♂ 9.5 cm (3¾"); ♀ 6.5 cm (3"). Generally numerous in lower growth and borders of humid forest and woodland in *lowlands and foothills of northwest (south to Manabí and Los Ríos).* Formerly considered conspecific with Crowned Woodnymph (*T. colombica*), of farther north in Middle America. Bill essentially straight (19 mm; 0.7"), *black.* ♂ above shining green with *glittering green crown* and some glittering violet on shoulders and sides of upper back. *Throat and chest glittering green, contrasting with glittering violet-blue underparts. Tail rather long and deeply forked,* blue-black. Notably smaller ♀ shining green above. *Throat and chest pale gray, contrasting with dark mixed green-and-gray lower underparts;* crissum whitish. Somewhat forked tail blue-black, outer feathers tipped whitish. **Similar species:** Emerald-bellied Woodnymph occurs south of this species; ♂ differs in having underparts entirely green (no violet-blue), ♀ in having uniform pale grayish underparts (not "two-toned" as in this species). ♂ Violet-bellied Hummingbird smaller and has reddish lower mandible and graduated tail, more extensive violet below. **Habits and Voice:** Much as in Fork-tailed Woodnymph.

Emerald-bellied Woodnymph
Thalurania hypochlora
Ninfa Ventriesmeralda   Plate 44(20)

To 1100 m

♂ 9.5 cm (3¾"); ♀ 6.5 cm (3"). Lower growth of humid forest and woodland in *lowlands and foothills of southwest (Guayas to w. Loja)*. Formerly considered conspecific with Crowned Woodnymph (*T. colombica*). Bill essentially straight (19 mm; 0.7"), *black*. ♂ resembles ♂ Green-crowned Woodnymph but has *underparts entirely glittering green*, and *lacks* white on crissum. ♀ like ♀ Green-crowned but *underparts uniform pale grayish* (*not* noticeably darker on belly). ♀ Violet-bellied Hummingbird smaller and has reddish lower mandible and graduated tail **Habits and Voice:** Much as in Fork-tailed Woodnymph.

Violet-bellied Hummingbird, *Damophila julie*
Colibrí Ventrivioleta   Plate 44(22)

To 1100 m

♂ 7.5 cm (3"); ♀ 7 cm (2¾"). Lower growth and borders of forest, woodland, and adjacent clearings in *more humid lowlands and foothills of west*. Bill short (13 mm; 0.5") and straight, *lower mandible mostly reddish*. ♂

shining green above, crown glittering green. Throat glittering green; *underparts glittering violet-blue. Tail rather long and graduated*, blue-black. ♀ shining green above. *Pale grayish below*, whiter on lower belly and with a few small green spots on breast. *Graduated tail as in* ♂ but slightly shorter, outer feathers tipped grayish. **Similar species:** Cf. Green-crowned and Emerald-bellied Woodnymphs, both of which are larger with all-black bills and have forked tails. ♂ Violet-bellied most resembles ♂ Green-crowned, ♀ Violet-bellied most resembles ♀ Emerald-bellied. **Habits:** Usually seen singly, generally not at any great height above ground though it sometimes ascends to feed in flowering trees with other hummingbirds. **Voice:** ♂'s song a thin series of high-pitched trilled "prrree" notes.

Hylocharis Sapphires
"Typical" hummingbirds showing quite strong sexual dimorphism, males marked by their *mainly coral red bills with a black tip* (sometimes in females as well). They range in a variety of forested or semiopen habitats, most species occurring in humid regions, a few in arid areas. Unlike *Amazilia*, virtually all species are rare in Ecuador.

Rufous-throated Sapphire
Hylocharis sapphirina
Zafiro Barbirrufo   Plate 44(17)

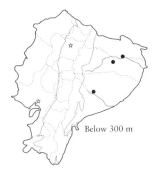

Below 300 m

9 cm (3½"). *Rare* in canopy and borders of humid forest and shrubby clearings in *lowlands of east*. Bill essentially straight (18 mm; 0.7"), ♂'s *coral red with black tip*, ♀'s black with lower mandible pinkish tipped dusky. ♂ shining green above with uppertail-coverts coppery rufous. *Rufous upper throat; lower*

throat and breast glittering violet-blue; lower underparts dark shining green. ♀ like ♂ above. *Upper throat pale rufous*; otherwise *whitish below* with *glittering blue-green spots on lower throat and chest* and *buff crissum*. Note that tail color of Ecuadorian birds remains uncertain; in the one extant specimen (♀) it is *bronzy green*, though in the rest of species' range it is a distinctly different coppery chestnut. **Similar species:** White-chinned Sapphire has blue-black tail in both sexes, etc. ♂ Golden-tailed Sapphire has red only on lower mandible, blue on entire head and neck, etc. **Habits:** Hardly known in Ecuador, where a few birds have been seen at borders of humid forest, both terra firme and várzea. Feeds at flowering trees and shrubs at varying heights. **Voice:** ♂♂ give weak song from perches high in subcanopy, e.g., "swit, swee-tit, swee-tit, swee-su"; also give a more gravelly "ch-cht."

White-chinned Sapphire, *Hylocharis cyanus*
Zafiro Barbiblanco   Plate 44(18)

250 m

9 cm (3½"). *Very rare* in canopy and borders of humid forest and adjacent shrubby clearings in *lowlands of southeast*; only one old specimen. Bill essentially straight (18 cm; 0.7"), ♂'s *coral red with black tip*, ♀'s black with lower mandible pinkish tipped dusky. ♂ has *entire head, throat, and chest glittering violet-blue*, chin white (hard to see in field); otherwise shining green above, uppertail-coverts more coppery. Underparts shining blue-green. Tail steel blue. ♀ shining green above, more coppery on uppertail-coverts. *Below grayish white* with a few glittering blue-green spots on sides of throat and chest. *Steel-blue tail* as in ♂, outer feathers tipped

whitish. **Similar species:** ♂ with all-blue head unlike any other hummer of e. lowlands, but cf. Golden-tailed Sapphire (with coppery bronze tail). ♀ can be more difficult. ♀ Blue-chinned Sapphire has more spotting on throat and chest; ♀ Blue-tailed Emerald shows more facial pattern; ♀ Fork-tailed Woodnymph has all-black bill, no coppery on uppertail-coverts, no spotting on its darker and grayer underparts. **Habits:** Unknown in Ecuador. Elsewhere a forest-based hummer, feeding at varying heights but inside forest usually remaining in subcanopy or above, coming lower in clearings but even there most often staying high. **Voice:** In the Guianas ♂♂ gather to sing in loose assemblies of 2–3 birds, most often at borders or associated with treefalls; they perch on open branches in subcanopy, where hard to spot. Song itself a jumbled series of high-pitched, somewhat insect-like (or Bananaquit-like) notes, e.g., "sweesee-see-see-seé."

Blue-headed Sapphire, *Hylocharis grayi*
Zafiro Cabeciazul   Plate 44(15)

1200–2200 m

9 cm (3½"). Local in arid scrub and gardens in *intermontane valleys of n. Ecuador*. Bill essentially straight (18 mm; 0.7"), *lower mandible coral pink with black tip*. ♂ shining green above with *head and upper throat glittering blue*. Lower throat and breast glittering green, belly grayish with green on sides. *Slightly forked tail blue-black.* ♀ shining green above. Grayish white below with green spotting on throat and breast, sides also green. *Blue-black tail* as in ♂ but outer feathers tipped whitish. **Similar species:** Cf. Humboldt's Sapphire of Esmeraldas coast. **Habits:** A fairly conspicuous hum-

mingbird, foraging at varying levels in flowering trees and shrubs; seems to be fond of *Hibiscus*. Regularly seen in gardens, often together with Western Emeralds. **Voice:** Gives a sharp "ts-tsrrrrr" call (P. Coopmans).

Humboldt's Sapphire, *Hylocharis humboldtii*
Zafiro de Humboldt   Plate 44(16)

9 cm (3½"). Apparently rare in mangroves and adjacent woodland and shrubby clearings in *coastal lowlands of n. Esmeraldas*. Formerly considered conspecific with Blue-headed Sapphire. Bill essentially straight (18 mm; 0.7"), *lower mandible coral pink with black tip*. ♂ has *head and throat glittering blue*; otherwise shining green above. Below glittering green, belly grayish. *Slightly forked tail dark green*. ♀ shining green above. *Pale grayish below* with some green on sides. *Dark green tail* as in ♂ but outer feathers tipped whitish. **Similar species:** Both sexes differ from Blue-headed Sapphire of highlands in their green (not blue-black) tail. ♂ Blue-headed further differs in less extensive blue on throat, ♀ Blue-headed in green spotting below. Andean Emerald also resembles ♀ Humboldt's, though differing in its whiter underparts and bronzier tail. **Habits:** Unknown in Ecuador. Birds seen in Panama were foraging at flowering trees near—sometimes immediately adjacent to—coast, often just back from mangroves.

Golden-tailed Sapphire, *Chrysuronia oenone*
Zafiro Colidorado   Plate 44(14)

9 cm (3½"). *Locally numerous at borders of humid and montane forest and in clearings in foothills along e. base of Andes*, also in decreasing numbers out into e. lowlands. Bill essentially straight (18 mm; 0.7"), lower

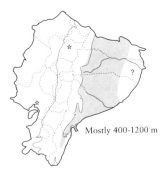

Mostly 400-1200 m

mandible pink with black tip. ♂ has *entire head, neck, and throat glittering violet-blue*. Otherwise shining emerald green (above and below); uppertail-coverts and crissum shining coppery bronze, *tail shining golden coppery*. ♀ shining green above. Pale grayish below, sides with glittering green spots. *Tail shining golden coppery*, outer feathers tipped grayish. **Similar species:** Shimmering coppery tail color of both sexes is conspicuous and generally precludes confusion. **Habits:** Similar to *Hylocharis* sapphires. Seems most numerous at forest borders and in adjacent clearings; at times several or even more will gather at certain flowering trees, often together with- different hummingbird species. **Voice:** Singing ♂ ♂ give a two-parted squeaky song, repeated steadily from an open twig.

Green-tailed Goldenthroat, *Polytmus theresiae*
Gorjioro Coliverde   Plate 96(17)

300 m

8.5 cm (3¼"). *Apparently very rare or local in shrubby areas near water in lowlands of southeast*; only one old specimen. *Bill slightly decurved* (20 mm; 0.8"), *lower mandible dull reddish*. ♂ shining green above with *small* white crescent in front of eye and a white postocular spot. Below glittering emerald green; crissum white. Slightly rounded tail entirely bright shining green. ♀ has upperparts and tail like ♂, tail feathers narrowly white-tipped. Below whitish thickly spotted with green except on lower belly (so thickly it can look solidly green). **Similar species:** No other Ecuadorian hummer combines mainly glittering green plumage with white around eye. Cf. Glittering-throated and Blue-tailed Emeralds, and Blue-chinned Sapphire. **Habits:** Unknown in Ecuador. In the Guianas favors shrubbery intermixed with tall grass along rivers, most often in areas where seasonally flooded. **Voice:** Distinctive song of ♂ in Guyana a fast series of high-pitched squeaky notes lasting 2–3 seconds and distinctly rising in pitch.

Many-spotted Hummingbird
Taphrospilus hypostictus
Colibrí Multipunteado   Plate 44(6)

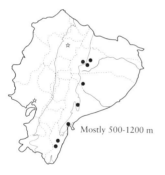

Mostly 500-1200 m

10 cm (4″). Scarce at borders of foothill and lower subtropical forest and adjacent clearings on e. slope. Bill fairly long (25 mm; 1″), somewhat decurved, lower mandible pinkish at base. **Sexes alike.** Shining green above with white postocular spot. White below thickly spotted with shining green except on median belly. Tail bluish green, outer feathers tipped dusky. **Similar species:** Combination of fairly large size and profuse spotting below should identify it. Cf. ♀ ♀ of various Heliodoxa brilliants, none of which is green-tailed, and also ♀ White-necked Jacobin. **Habits:** Not well known in Ecuador. Usually seen singly at flowering trees (including Inga), sometimes together with various other hummingbirds.

Leucippus Hummingbirds
Dull, faded-looking hummingbirds found in scrub and semiopen areas. They resemble Amazilia but have all-black bills.

Olive-spotted Hummingbird
Leucippus chlorocercus
Colibrí Olivipunteado   Plate 44(5)

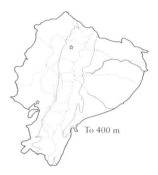

To 400 m

8 cm (3¼″). A notably dull hummingbird, locally not uncommon on islands in Río Napo where it favors semiopen areas and early-succession growth. Bill essentially straight (17 mm; 0.7″). **Sexes alike.** Dull metallic green above, crown slightly browner, with quite prominent white postocular spot. Whitish below, throat with a few inconspicuous grayish green spots, sides washed dull greenish. Tail green, outer feathers with grayish tips. **Similar species:** In its highly restricted habitat, confusion unlikely. Cf. Glittering-throated Emerald (which also occurs on river islands). **Habits:** Similar to various Amazilia. As it is usually in open, Olive-spotted is generally easy to see. **Voice:** Song of ♂ an insistent, piercing "tseéyip" repeated 4–7 times in succession, then a pause.

Tumbes Hummingbird, Leucippus baeri
Colibrí de Tumbes   Plate 41(26)
8 cm (3¼″). Local in arid scrub of s. Loja. Bill essentially straight (20 mm; 0.8″). **Sexes alike.** Very drab. Dusty green above, somewhat browner on crown with small white postocular spot. Below pale buffy grayish. Tail dull bronzy green, outer feathers grayish with broad black subterminal band. **Similar species:** In its range, where there are few if any similar hummingbirds, this notably drab

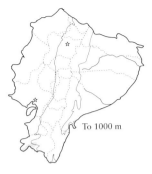

To 1000 m

species is unlikely to be confused. **Habits:** Usually seen singly, feeding on flowers close to ground; seems to come infrequently if at all to flowering trees.

Amazilia Hummingbirds and Emeralds
Medium-sized "typical" hummingbirds of uniform size found mainly in the lowlands where they range in a variety of habitats, with most being nonforest birds. Several species are numerous and rank among the more frequently seen hummingbirds in Ecuador's lowlands. Most have some red on the lower mandible, at least at its base. The genus is sometimes split apart, with the Ecuadorian species in the genera *Amazilia*, *Agyrtria*, and *Polyerata*.

Rufous-tailed Hummingbird, *Amazilia tzacatl*
Amazilia Colirrufa   Plate 44(10)

Mostly below 1500 m, locally (seasonally?) to 2500 m

9 cm (3½"). *Common and widespread* in clearings and gardens, secondary woodland, and forest borders in *more humid lowlands of west*, also ranging up in semiopen areas well into *subtropics on w. slope*. Bill essentially straight (21 cm; 0.9"), lower mandible reddish pink (sometimes base of upper mandible as

well). ♂ shining green above. Throat and breast glittering green, becoming dingy grayish on belly with some green on flanks. *Entire tail contrastingly rufous-chestnut.* ♀ similar to ♂ but throat and breast feathers edged grayish. **Similar species:** In most of its range no other hummer has such an obviously rufous tail. **Habits:** Similar to Glittering-throated Emerald, and like that species a *non-forest* hummingbird; often equally numerous. **Voice:** ♂'s song a weak high-pitched phrase, "tseép, tsi-ti" or "tsi-tsu, tseet"; both sexes also give other sputtering calls.

Amazilia Hummingbird, *Amazilia amazilia*
Amazilia Ventrirrufa   Plate 44(11)

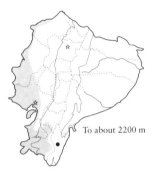

To about 2200 m

9 cm (3½"). *Often common* in desert scrub, deciduous woodland and borders, and gardens in *more arid lowlands of west*, in south also ranging up into *arid semiopen highlands*. Highland birds may represent a separate species, *A. alticola* (Loja Hummingbird). Bill essentially straight (21 mm; 0.9"), *reddish pink with black tip*. **Sexes alike.** **Western-lowland birds** shining to bronzy green above. Upper throat and sides of neck glittering green with *chest white*; *lower underparts mostly rufous*, somewhat variable in extent, lowermost belly and crissum white. Tail bronzy green. **Highland birds** similar but *tail mainly rufous*, central feathers bronzy green. **Southern Azuay birds** quite different, showing *much whiter underparts* (with little or no rufous), rufous of tail extending onto uppertail-coverts, and perhaps a blacker bill. **Similar species:** Rufous below is distinctive in this *Amazilia*. The similarly shaped and sized Rufous-tailed Hummingbird can occur with Amazilia, though they usually segregate by habitat (Rufous-tailed favoring more humid

regions); it lacks any white below. **Habits:** Similar to Rufous-tailed Hummingbird.

Andean Emerald, *Amazilia franciae*
Amazilia Andina   Plate 44(12)

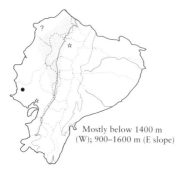

Mostly below 1400 m (W); 900–1600 m (E slope)

9 cm (3½"). Borders of humid and montane forest in *more humid lowlands of west*, ranging up into *foothills and subtropics on w. slope*, also in *foothills and lower subtropics on e. slope in Zamora-Chinchipe*. Bill essentially straight (21 mm; 0.9"), lower mandible reddish at base. **Western** ♂ shining green above with *glittering green crown. Snowy white below* with some green on sides. Tail bronzy green with dusky subterminal band, outer feathers tipped pale grayish. ♀ similar but lacking glitter on crown. **East-slope** ♂ similar to western ♂ but *most of crown and sides of neck glittering blue*, forehead duskier. ♀ lacks blue on crown. **Similar species:** Nearly unmarked, pure white underparts of this hummingbird are distinctive. Other ♀♀ hummers with white underparts show at least some spotting. **Habits:** Similar to other *Amazilia* though Andean appears to be more dependent on actual forest than many of them are. Also feeds regularly at flowering trees in adjacent clearings, often together with other hummingbirds. **Voice:** Song a rather complex series of fast and jumbled notes, repeated regularly from a song perch (P. Coopmans).

Glittering-throated Emerald
Amazilia fimbriata
Amazilia Gorjibrillante   Plate 44(7)

8 cm (3¼"). *Common and widespread in a variety of semiopen and edge habitats in lowlands (especially) and foothills of east*. Bill

To 1200 m

essentially straight (20 mm; 0.8"), lower mandible mostly pinkish. ♂ shining green above with small white postocular spot. *Throat, breast, and sides of neck glittering green,* flanks shining green, with *white stripe extending up from lower belly onto mid-breast*. Tail mostly blue-black, central feathers greener. ♀ similar but duller, with white median stripe extending up to throat, which shows some whitish. **Similar species:** As it is so frequently seen, this is a good species to learn well as a basis of comparison with other, scarcer, hummers in e. lowlands. White median stripe on underparts distinctive, but cf. very rare Sapphire-spangled Emerald. **Habits:** Perhaps the most frequently seen hummingbird in open and semiopen areas in e. lowlands; regular in gardens around houses. Usually does not forage very high above ground, often perching in open on low branches. Normally hovers when feeding at flowers, as do other members of genus. **Voice:** Most frequent call a simple repeated "j-dit," similar to various other *Amazilia*. Dawn song a "tsrr trr trr trr trr trr" phrase (P. Coopmans).

[Sapphire-spangled Emerald, *Amazilia lactea*
Amazilia Pechizafiro]   Plate 41(25)

9 cm (3½"). Known from *only one sighting* from lowlands of east. Bill essentially straight (20 mm; 0.8"), lower mandible mostly pinkish. **Sexes alike.** Shining green above. *Throat, breast, and sides of neck glittering violet-blue,* feathers often edged duskier; belly metallic green with *white stripe down median lower breast and belly*. Tail bronzy blue-black, outer feathers vaguely tipped grayish. **Similar species:** Very similar to the common Glittering-throated Emerald, differ-

300 m

ing in its extensive violet-blue on foreneck (obvious in decent light); beware, however, that in certain lights Glittering-throated's foreneck *can look quite blue*, though compared to Sapphire-spangled it is more of a turquoise blue-green, not such a deep violet-blue. **Habits:** As in Glittering-throated Emerald.

Blue-chested Hummingbird, *Amazilia amabilis*
Amazilia Pechiazul   Plate 44(8)

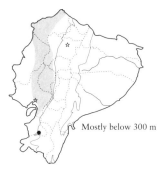

Mostly below 300 m

7.5 cm (3″). Lower growth of humid forest, woodland, and shrubby clearings in *more humid lowlands of west* (south mainly to Guayas). Bill essentially straight (18 mm; 0.7″), lower mandible pinkish. ♂ shining green above with *glittering green crown*. Throat dusky with some green glitter on sides, *chest glittering violet-blue*, lower underparts grayish with green on sides. Tail bronzy blackish. ♀ like ♂ above but lacking glitter on crown. Below pale grayish with extensive green spotting, the spotting more blue across chest. Tail bronzy blackish, outer feathers tipped whitish. **Similar species:** Purple-chested Hummingbird is very similar; for distinctions, see that species (bear in mind

that Blue-chested is much more wide-ranging). **Habits:** Much as in Glittering-throated Emerald, though more a forest-based species. **Voice:** ♂ ♂ gather in loose leks where they give a regularly spaced, evenly pitched, and squeaky "psee-psee-psee . . ." or "tsit-tsit-tsit . . ." from low perches in second-growth, often aggressively chasing each other around.

Purple-chested Hummingbird
Amazilia rosenbergi
Amazilia Pechimorada   Plate 44(9)

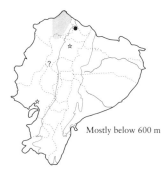

Mostly below 600 m

8 cm (3¼″). Lower growth of humid forest and borders in *lowlands of northwest*, mainly in *Esmeraldas*. Bill essentially straight (18 mm; 0.7″), lower mandible pinkish. ♂ shining green above. *Throat extensively glittering green, chest glittering violet-blue*; lower underparts grayish with green on sides and *white on extreme lower belly and crissum*. Tail bronzy blackish. ♀ like ♂ above. Below pale grayish, *extensively spotted green on throat and breast*; *lower belly and crissum white*. Tail bronzy blackish, outer feathers tipped whitish. **Similar species:** Closely resembles Blue-chested Hummingbird; despite their names, *color of glittering throat patch is the same*. Better characters to separate ♂ ♂ of these two similar species are Purple-chested's lack of glitter on crown, more extensive glitter on throat, and white on crissum; the last often is quite conspicuous and can be the best mark of all. ♀ Blue-chested shows some blue chest spotting (though often obscure) and lacks white on crissum. **Habits:** Much as in Blue-chested Hummingbird, though Purple-chested appears to be a more forest-based species and ranges more often inside actual forest. **Voice:** As noted by Hilty and Brown

(1986), and in contrast to Blue-chested Hummingbird, no leks of singing ♂♂ have been reported for this species. ♂'s song consists of 3 sharp, high-pitched notes, "tsip-tsu-tsrit" (P. Coopmans).

Chalybura Plumeleteers

Fairly large hummingbirds with *silky white crissums* that are often conspicuous in the field. The two species inhabit forest and woodland in western Ecuador, one (Bronze-tailed) in the extreme north, the other (White-vented) isolated in the far southwest.

White-vented Plumeleteer, *Chalybura buffonii*
Calzonario de Buffón   Plate 43(12)

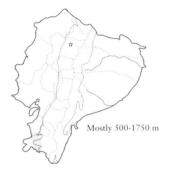

Mostly 500-1750 m

10 cm (4"). *Scarce and local in lower and middle growth of foothill and subtropical forest and woodland in El Oro and w. Loja.* May represent a separate species, *C. intermedia* (Ecuadorian Plumeleteer). Bill fairly long and slightly decurved (25 cm ; 1"), lower mandible dull pinkish, sometimes with dusky tip. ♂ above shining green. *Throat and chest glittering green, becoming somewhat more blue-green on breast*; belly grayish, with contrasting *white crissum. Rather long, slightly forked tail blue-black.* ♀ like ♂ above. *Below uniform gray, but crissum white as in ♂.* Tail blue-black as in ♂ though central feathers greener and outer feathers tipped whitish. **Similar species:** Really nothing very similar in its limited range. Rather similar Bronze-tailed Plumeleteer ranges far to north and has, true to its name, a bronzy colored (not blue-black) tail. ♀ Emerald-bellied Woodnymph considerably smaller, etc. ♀ White-necked Jacobin has obviously scaly pattern below. **Habits:** Not very conspicuous, tending to be retiring and to remain in shady cover, though

sometimes coming out to edge while feeding. **Voice:** Gives "chip" notes as it forages.

Bronze-tailed Plumeleteer
Chalybura urochrysia
Calzonario Patirrojo   Plate 43(13)

To 800 m

10 cm (4"). *Numerous in lower growth and borders of humid forest in lowlands and foothills of n. Esmeraldas.* Bill fairly long and slightly decurved (25 cm; 1"), lower mandible pinkish; *feet pink* (often surprisingly obvious in field). ♂ above shining green. *Throat and breast glittering green*, belly grayish, with *white crissum. Uppertail-coverts and tail bronzy.* ♀ like ♂ above. *Below uniform gray*, but *crissum white as in ♂. Tail bronzy as in ♂* but outer feathers tipped whitish. **Similar species:** White-vented Plumeleteer occurs far to south of this species' range; both sexes have blue-black tail, etc. ♀ Green-crowned Woodnymph is smaller, has distinctly two-toned gray underparts (darker on belly), no white on crissum. **Habits:** More often in understory of extensive forest than White-vented Plumeleteer, but behavior otherwise similar. **Voice:** Both sexes give loud "chup" and "chip" calls.

Speckled Hummingbird
Adelomyia melanogenys
Colibrí Jaspeado   Plate 41(24)

8.5 cm (3¼"). *Generally common and widespread* in undergrowth and borders of *subtropical and temperate* forest and woodland on both slopes, also locally on coastal cordillera in southwest. Bill short and straight (15 mm; 0.6"). **Sexes alike.** Shining green above; *cheeks blackish bordered above by whitish superciliary.* Below buffy whitish, buffiest on belly and *speckled dusky on*

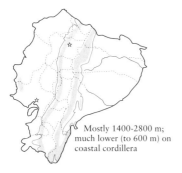

Mostly 1400-2800 m;
much lower (to 600 m) on
coastal cordillera

throat, chest, and sides. Tail bronzy brown, feathers tipped buffy whitish. **Similar species:** Hermit-like facial pattern—it also recalls a ♀ *Chlorostilbon* emerald—and buffy underparts of this numerous montane hummingbird are distinctive. Tail shape of all hermits distinctly different. **Habits:** Usually found singly as it feeds at flowers close to ground, generally clinging to flower or perching just to its side while probing for nectar. **Voice:** In flight both sexes give a gravelly and quite loud "trrt" call. ♂'s song a series of weak and high-pitched "tsit" notes. Also gives a high-pitched, somewhat descending series, e.g., "tsi-ti-tit-tseee-tseee-tseee, tseeeuw, tseeeuw."

Urosticte Whitetips

Inconspicuous hummingbirds found mainly in lower growth inside montane forest, one species on either side of the Andes (formerly sometimes considered conspecific). Males are marked by the *unmistakable positioning of the white in their tails*.

Purple-bibbed Whitetip, *Urosticte benjamini*
Puntiblanca Pechipúrpura   Plate 41(20)

Mostly 900-1600 m

♂ 9 cm (3½"); ♀ 7.5 cm (3"). Scarce in lower growth and borders of foothill and subtropical forest on *w. slope*. Bill straight (20 mm; 0.8"). ♂ mostly shining green, glittering green on gorget with *patch of glittering purple on chest*; white postocular spot prominent. Rather deeply forked tail bronzy black with *central two pairs of feathers broadly tipped white*. ♀ shining green above with white postocular spot. *White below, thickly spotted with glittering green especially on throat and breast*. Forked tail bronzy, outer feathers tipped white. **Similar species:** White in its tail being uniquely positioned, ♂ unlikely to be confused in range. ♀ can be confused with ♀ Booted Racket-tail though that species is smaller and shows much less green spangling below. Rufous-vented Whitetip occurs only on *e. slope*. **Habits:** Not often seen, usually remaining inside forest where it forages singly at varying heights though usually not very high; sometimes at flowering *Inga* trees.

Rufous-vented Whitetip, *Urosticte ruficrissa*
Puntiblanca Pechiverde   Plate 41(21)

1300-2300 m

♂ 9.5 cm (3¾"); ♀ 8 cm (3¼"). Scarce in lower growth and borders of subtropical forest on *e. slope*. Bill straight (20 mm; 0.8"). ♂ mostly shining green with white postocular spot and *large gorget glittering green*; crissum buffyish (hard to see in field). Rather deeply forked tail bronzy with *central two pairs of feathers tipped white*. ♀ shining green above with white postocular spot. *White below, thickly spotted with glittering green especially on throat and breast*. Forked tail bronzy, outer feathers tipped white. **Similar species:** As with Purple-bibbed Whitetip (found only on *w. slope* of Andes),

♂♂ of this species are best known by their prominent white tipping on central rectrices. ♀♀ whitetips on e. slope are even more likely to be confused with ♀♀ racket-tails because latter are there more thickly green-spangled on underparts than on w. slope (both species even show similar buff on crissum); whitetip, however, is larger and typically shows even more spangling. **Habits:** Similar to Purple-bibbed Whitetip, likewise seen only very infrequently.

Ecuadorian Piedtail
Phlogophilus hemileucurus
Colipunto Ecuatoriano   Plate 42(11)

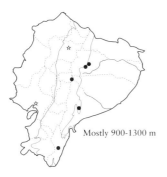

Mostly 900-1300 m

7.5 cm (3″). Scarce in *undergrowth of foothill and lower subtropical forest on e. slope.* Short bill (17 mm; 0.7″) with some brownish at base of lower mandible. **Sexes alike.** Above shining green with small white postocular spot. *Below white,* throat thickly spotted with dusky-green and *contrasting with white pectoral collar,* some green mottling on sides of chest and flanks. *Rounded tail* bronzy green with *diagonal white band at base and broad white tipping.* **Similar species:** White patterning in tail of this small hummer distinctive. ♀♀ of Booted Racket-tail and Rufous-vented Whitetip (both of them found with piedtail) are more profusely green-spotted below. **Habits:** Remains inside forest, feeding low in undergrowth where usually inconspicuous. ♂♂ display low in undergrowth, often several in fairly close proximity. **Voice:** Call of displaying ♂ a series of extremely high-pitched notes, e.g., "tzeee-tzeee-tzeee-ts-ts," then repeated and sometimes with a chipper at end (L. Navarrete recording).

Heliodoxa Brilliants
Fairly large, robust hummingbirds occurring mainly in foothill and subtropical forests; two species occur in the eastern lowlands. None is conspicuous or vocal, and several (especially Pink-throated) are scarce and local; they do, however, readily come to hummingbird feeders. Their *"flat" crowns,* with feathers protruding onto the upper part of the base of the bill, impart a distinct "tapered" facial expression. Most species—all but the Fawn-breasted—are sexually dimorphic, with males of many being exceptionally attractive.

Empress Brilliant, *Heliodoxa imperatrix*
Brillante Emperatriz   Plate 43(19)

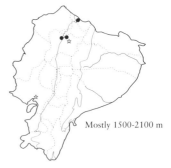

Mostly 1500-2100 m

♂ 13 cm (5″); ♀ 11.5 cm (4½″). *Scarce in lower growth and borders of subtropical forest on w. slope south to Pichincha.* Bill straight (25 mm; 1″). ♂ metallic green above with small white postocular spot, more glittering at base of bill. *Glittering green below, more golden on belly,* with inconspicuous glittering violet-purple patch on lower throat. *Tail long and very deeply forked, dark bronzy green.* ♀ like ♂ above, but with white malar streak. White below thickly spotted with glittering green. Tail much shorter and less deeply forked than ♂'s, outer feathers more blackish. **Immature** ♂ like ♀ but with rufous malar streak that is retained even when remainder of plumage has molted so as to resemble adult ♂. **Similar species:** Often confused with smaller Green-crowned Brilliant, though that species normally is found at lower elevations (there is some overlap). ♂ Green-crowned differs in lacking golden glitter so striking on Empress, and its blue-black tail is much less deeply forked.

♀ ♀ of the two are more difficult to separate, but Green-crowned's tail is less deeply forked and shows pale tipping absent in Empress. **Habits:** Spectacular adult ♂ ♂ are, unfortunately, in decided minority. Usually seen singly, feeding at flowers both inside forest and at edge, often hovering below them and probing upward.

Green-crowned Brilliant, *Heliodoxa jacula*
Brillante Coroniverde   Plate 43(16)

Mostly 500-1550 m

♂ 11.5 cm (4½″); ♀ 10 cm (4″). Undergrowth and borders of *foothill and lower subtropical forest on w. slope*, also ranging down into more humid lowlands and locally onto slopes of coastal cordillera. Bill nearly straight (25 mm; 1″). ♂ metallic green above with small white postocular spot and *glittering green forecrown*. Throat and breast glittering green with inconspicuous glittering violet-blue patch on lower throat, belly duller green. Rather long forked tail, blue-black. ♀ like ♂ above, but lacking glitter on forecrown and with *white malar streak. Below whitish thickly spotted with bright green*, more solid on sides. *Tail less deeply forked, blue-black* with central feathers bronzier, outer feathers tipped whitish. **Juveniles** of both sexes may show considerable rufous on malar and even face and chin; **immature** ♀ resembles adult but retains rufous m alar. **Similar species:** Cf. larger (and rarer) Empress Brilliant. Violet-fronted Brilliant occurs only on e. slope. Other hummers with such thickly green-spangled underparts are smaller. **Habits:** Often numerous and conspicuous, feeding both inside forest and in semiopen, sometimes even out to trees in cleared areas. Feeds both by hovering and by probing when perched on or next to a flower.

Violet-fronted Brilliant, *Heliodoxa leadbeateri*
Brillante Frentivioleta   Plate 43(15)

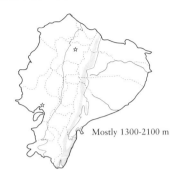

Mostly 1300-2100 m

♂ 11.5 cm (4½″); ♀ 11 cm (4¼″). Lower growth and borders of *subtropical forest on e. slope*. Bill nearly straight (25 mm; 1″). ♂ metallic green above, decidedly bronzier on head and nape, with small white postocular spot and *glittering violet-blue forecrown. Throat and breast glittering green*, belly metallic green. Rather long forked tail, blue-black. ♀ like ♂ above, but with *forecrown glittering pale blue, white malar streak*, and less bronzy head and neck. *Below whitish thickly spotted with bright green*, more solid on sides. *Less deeply forked tail blue-black*, central feathers bronzier, outer feathers tipped whitish. **Similar species:** Beautiful ♂ unlikely to be confused. ♀ of similar Green-crowned Brilliant occurs only on w. slope. Other hummers with such thickly green-spangled underparts are smaller; especially cf. rare Many-spotted Hummingbird (with green tail, etc.). **Habits:** Less conspicuous than Green-crowned Brilliant, less apt to venture into open. Forages, mainly solitarily, at flowering shrubs, low trees, and epiphytes; sometimes perches as it feeds.

Pink-throated Brilliant, *Heliodoxa gularis*
Brillante Gorjirrosado   Plate 43(18)

♂ 9.5 cm (3¾″); ♀ 9 cm (3½″). *Rare and local* in undergrowth and borders of *foothill forest on e. slope*. Bill almost straight (25 mm; 1″). ♂ shining green above with small white postocular spot and *glittering green forecrown*. Below mostly shining green with *large patch of glittering pink on lower throat*; belly grayish, contrasting with *white crissum*. Tail fairly long and forked, *bronzy green*. ♀ like ♂ above but with less glitter on crown,

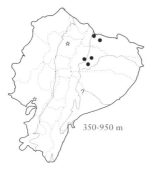

350-950 m

white malar streak. Below has *smaller glittering pink throat patch*, more green-spotted effect on chest, and whitish mid-belly; *crissum white* as in ♂. Tail as in ♂, feathers narrowly white-tipped. **Similar species:** Considerably smaller than the other brilliants; Fawn-breasted has similar glittering throat patch but is much buffier below, lacks white crissum. ♀ Rufous-vented Whitetip lacks malar streak and throat patch, has black tail with more white tipping. **Habits:** Very poorly known, and scarce throughout its (limited) range. Birds seen have been solitary, in lower growth.

Black-throated Brilliant, *Heliodoxa shreibersii*
Brillante Gorjinegro   Plate 43(17)

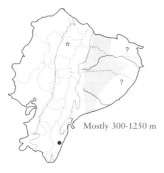

Mostly 300-1250 m

♂ 11.5 cm (4½″); ♀ 11 cm (4¼″). Scarce and seemingly local in lower growth inside humid forest (*especially terra firme*) in *lowlands of east*, locally also ranging up into *lower subtropics*. Bill nearly straight (23 mm; 0.9″). ♂ shining green above with small white postocular spot, glittering at base of bill. *Throat velvety black, bordered below by band of glittering purple and then a band of glittering green*; *lower underparts black*. Tail fairly long and forked, blue-black. ♀ like ♂ above but with *prominent whitish malar streak*. *Throat black* with *patch of glittering violet*

on upper chest; *remaining underparts mixed sooty and green*. **Juveniles** of both sexes show rufous on gape. **Similar species:** This large, dark hummingbird is so black below that confusion is unlikely; ♂♂ seen in good light—unfortunately not a frequent occurrence—are stunning. **Habits:** Seems mainly to remain inside forest, rarely venturing even briefly into nearby clearings; on rare occasions one does ascend to feed in subcanopy. **Voice:** ♂'s song a faint, extremely high-pitched—though descending—trill (J. Moore recording).

Fawn-breasted Brilliant, *Heliodoxa rubinoides*
Brillante Pechianteado   Plate 43(14)

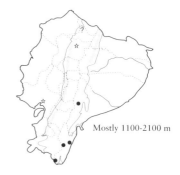

Mostly 1100-2100 m

♂ 11 cm (4¼″); ♀ 10 cm (4″). Local and not especially numerous in lower growth and borders of *subtropical forest* on both slopes. Bill nearly straight (25 mm; 1″). **Sexes alike.** Above shining green with small white postocular spot. *Dull buffy fawn below* with small green spots (especially on breast) and *patch of glittering pink on lower throat* (slightly smaller in ♀♀). Tail fairly long and forked, bronzy. **West-slope birds** show some coppery bronze on bend of wing and greater wing-coverts (greener on e.-slope birds). **Similar species:** No other brilliant has buff on underparts, and no other highland hummer combines mainly buff underparts with green upperparts. Cf. Buff-tailed Coronet (with buff in tail, shorter bill, etc.). **Habits:** Like other brilliants, Fawn-breasted is seen singly inside forest and at edge, foraging at low and middle levels; a few may congregate at flowering trees, sometimes even out in clearings. **Voice:** ♂'s song a simple series of emphasized "tchik" notes (J. Moore recording). Often-heard call a fast "swi-swi-swi-swu" (M. Lysinger recording).

Gould's Jewelfront, *Heliodoxa aurescens*
Brillante Frentijoya   Plate 44(4)

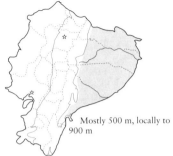

Mostly 500 m, locally to 900 m

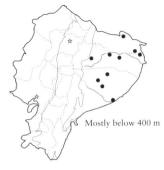

Mostly below 400 m

9.5 cm (3³/₄″). Uncommon and inconspicuous in lower growth and borders of humid forest (mainly *terra firme*) in *lowlands of east*. Formerly classified in the genus *Polyplancta*. Bill straight (18 m; 0.7″). ♂ shining green above with glittering violet stripe on median forecrown and small buffy white postocular spot. Upper throat black, lower throat and chest glittering green; *breast crossed by conspicuous orange-rufous band*; lower underparts green. *Tail mainly rufous-chestnut*, feathers tipped green, central feathers also green. ♀ duller than ♂, with forecrown stripe smaller and less glittering, buff below lores and on upper throat. **Similar species:** Both sexes are easily known by unique rufous chest-band (*non-iridescent*, so it shows well even in dim light). **Habits:** Usually seen singly inside heavy forest, most often near streams or other small openings; rarely leaves forest cover. On rare occasions a feeding bird does venture up into subcanopy.

Topaza Topazes
Splendid large, heavy-billed hummingbirds found locally in the eastern lowlands, mainly or entirely along forested streams. *Colorful males, with their elongated and crossed tail feathers*, are among the most spectacular of all the hummingbirds.

Fiery Topaz, *Topaza pyra*
Topacio Fuego   Plate 43(11)

♂ 19–19.5 cm (7¹/₂–7³/₄″); ♀ 13–13.5 cm (5–5¹/₄″). *Scarce and local in association with blackwater streams in lowlands of east. Heavy, rather short (25 mm; 1″) bill*, slightly decurved. ♂ stunning and—when with full tail—unmistakable. *Hood velvety black* surrounding *large glittering green gorget, golden at center*; *otherwise mostly fiery red*,

more glittering on breast and belly, uppertail-coverts and crissum glittering golden green; wings brownish, underwing-coverts rufous-chestnut. *Tail purplish*, with *next to central pair of feathers much elongated* (can be more than 6.5 cm [2¹/₂″] long) *and crossing halfway to tip*. Many ♂♂ lack full tails. ♀ shining green above; wings blackish, underwing-coverts rufous-chestnut. *Large gorget glittering coppery red*, underparts glittering green. Tail forked with no elongated feathers, mostly purplish black, outer web of outermost feather dull rufous. **Similar species:** Aside from Crimson Topaz—which apparently does not even occur in Ecuador—hardly to be confused. **Habits:** Usually seen singly, almost invariably along or near blackwater streams; usually remains low, but also forages in forest canopy. Often perches on snags protruding from water, or on branches overhanging water; also nests in such situations. Seems to catch many insects—it is rarely seen at flowers—procuring them either in a sally from perch (to which it may return repeatedly) or while hovering, often out over water; sometimes robs spider webs. **Voice:** A distinctive sharp "dzeeyp" call is given in flight.

[Crimson Topaz, *Topaza pella*
Topacio Carmesí]   Plate 43(10)

300 m (?)

♂ 19–19.5 cm (7¹/₂–7³/₄"); ♀ 13–13.5 cm (5–5¹/₄"). *Known only from old specimens supposedly from lowlands of northeast (Río Suno)*; recent evidence indicates they actually were taken in the Guianas, and that Crimson Topaz does not occur in Ecuador. Heavy, rather short (25 mm; 1") bill, slightly decurved. In both sexes resembles Fiery Topaz, differing in having *outer three tail feathers all rufous* (not dark, as in ♂ Fiery, or with rufous only on outer web of outermost feather, as in ♀ Fiery) and *white* (not black) *leg tufts.* **Habits and Voice:** As in Fiery Topaz.

Oreotrochilus Hillstars

Hefty hummingbirds *found in paramo at exceptionally high elevations*, one (Andean) occurring only marginally in Ecuador but the other being a stunning and nearly endemic resident of the country's high peaks.

Ecuadorian Hillstar, *Oreotrochilus chimborazo*
Estrella Ecuatoriana   Plate 45(1)

Mostly 3600–4600 m

11.5 cm (4¹/₂"). *High arid slopes above treeline* on both slopes south to Azuay. Has been called Chimborazo Hillstar. Bill slightly decurved (20 mm; 0.8"). ♂ in **most of range** shining olive green above with *glittering violet-purple hood* outlined on chest with black stripe. *Underparts white* with irregular black median belly stripe. *Tail mostly white* but central feathers shining blue-green and outer feathers with some dusky. On **Volcán Chimborazo** similar but *lower throat glittering green.* ♀ much duller. Above dusty olive green with small white postocular spot. *Throat whitish speckled with dull green*; *remaining underparts dingy pale grayish buff.* Tail shining blue-green, outer feathers *broadly tipped white.* **Similar species:** ♂♂ are dazzling, especially given their stark

windswept surroundings. Much drabber ♀♀ can be known by combination of large size and white in tail; Blue-mantled Thornbill is generally dark with no white in tail. In far south cf. Andean Hillstar. **Habits:** Often surprisingly inconspicuous given its open habitat, frequently just seen in low dashing flight, often disappearing before you can track it down. Hillstars often roost in holes and crevices of banks, and regularly perch on rocks and atop low shrubs. They are most easily located by watching for orange-flowered *Chuquiragua* shrubs at which they habitually feed. Check every stand of this plant for feeding hillstars. If one is not present, wait and often one will appear, usually a ♂ (they dominate ♀♀).

Andean Hillstar, *Oreotrochilus estella*
Estrella Andina   Plate 45(2)

3250–3500 m

11.5 cm (4¹/₂"). *Paramo and treeline woodland in extreme south at Cordillera Las Lagunillas.* Bill slightly decurved (20 mm; 0.8"). ♂ resembles ♂ Ecuadorian Hillstar but has *entire bib glittering green*; top of head shining olive green. ♀ very like ♀ Ecuadorian Hillstar. **Similar species:** ♂♂ Ecuadorian Hillstars (no overlap) have hood mainly or entirely violet. ♀ might carelessly be confused with ♀ Rainbow-bearded Thornbill. **Habits:** Similar to Ecuadorian Hillstar, though not seen to feed at *Chuquiragua* shrubs (which do not appear to be present at Lagunillas). Regularly perches atop trees at treeline, also on boulders.

White-tailed Hillstar, *Urochroa bougueri*
Estrella Coliblanca   Plate 45(3)

11.5 cm (4¹/₂"). Scarce in lower growth and borders of *subtropical forest* on both slopes

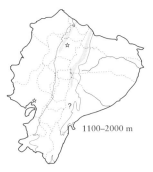

1100–2000 m

in n. Ecuador. *Bill long and straight* (30 mm; 1.2″). **Sexes alike** (♀♀ duller, especially below). On **west slope** *coppery bronze above* with *prominent rufous malar area* and small buff postocular spot. *Throat and breast glittering blue*; belly gray. Central and outer tail feathers dusky, *remaining rectrices white* with mainly dusky outer webs. On **east slope** differs in being shining green above (not bronzy) except for coppery rump and uppertail-coverts, lacking rufous malar, and in having *more white in tail* (especially outermost rectrix). **Similar species:** This flashy hummer is not likely confused, especially on w. slope where its conspicuous rufous malar mark is unique. On e. slope could be confused with ♂ Napo Sabrewing, though that species has *all-dark* tail. **Habits:** Most often (especially on w. slope) seen along or near rushing rocky torrents, sometimes hovering over water to catch insects. Also feeds at flowering trees, sometimes with other hummingbirds and usually dominating them. **Voice:** W.-slope birds give simple series of "tsit" calls (J. Moore recording).

Giant Hummingbird, *Patagona gigas*
Colibrí Gigante   Plate 45(4)

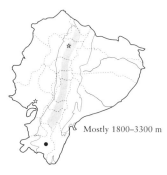

Mostly 1800–3300 m

16.5 cm (6½″). *By far the largest hummingbird*, easily recognized on that basis alone. *Widespread in semiopen scrub, agricultural areas, and gardens in arid regions of Andes south to Azuay.* Bill long and straight (40 mm; 1.5″). Above dusty brownish olive with *white rump* (very conspicuous in flight). *Below dull cinnamon-rufous*, spotted dusky on throat (especially) and breast; crissum whitish. *Long forked tail bronzy olive.* **Sexes nearly alike,** ♀♀ averaging paler below with somewhat more spotting. **Habits:** A conspicuous hummingbird, often perching in open (even on phone wires), and flying more like a swift or swallow than a hummer, with slow and erratic wingbeats interspersed with short glides. Hovers with deep and slow wingstrokes. In many areas feeds prefentially on inflorescences of *Agave*, but also visits many other flowers, often defending them aggressively against other visiting hummingbirds. **Voice:** Call a high-pitched "cwueet," frequently given in flight but also while perched.

Shining Sunbeam, *Aglaeactis cupripennis*
Rayito Brillante   Plate 45(5)

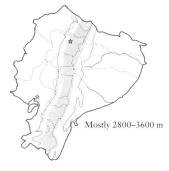

Mostly 2800–3600 m

11–11.5 cm (4¼–4½″), southern birds smaller. *Generally numerous and conspicuous in scrubby areas, woodland borders, and treeline shrubbery in temperate zone and paramo.* Bill short and straight (14–20 mm; 0.6–0.8″), southern birds proportionately shorter. ♂ *metallic dusky brown above*, dark on crown and ear-coverts, with area of glittering purple on lower back becoming coppery on rump and green on uppertail-coverts. *Face and underparts cinnamon-rufous*, often extending up as at least partial nuchal collar, sometimes with dusky throat flecking. Tail bronzy olive, lateral feathers with rufous on inner webs. ♀ similar but with little or no glitter on back or rump. Small and short-billed birds of **Azuay, El Oro, and Loja** have more richly colored underparts, more rufous in tail (olive on distal third). **Similar species:** No other hummingbird of high-elevation terrain is so extensively brown, rufous, and cinnamon. Rainbow Starfrontlet (of south only) has much longer bill, mainly green head, and rufous (not dark) tail. **Habits:** A characteristic bird of scrub and treeline habitat, where one of the more frequently seen hummers. Often perches fully in the open, holding wings aloft for an extended period after it settles on a twig, also often raising wings as it clings to a flower while feeding. **Voice:** Gives fast twitters when feeding and sharper single notes in flight.

Mountain Velvetbreast, *Lafresnaya lafresnayi*
Colibrí Terciopelo   Plate 46(1)

Mostly 2400–3500 m

9 cm (3½"). Widespread though typically not very numerous in *shrubby temperate forest borders and adjacent scrub and clearings on both slopes*. Slender bill strikingly decurved (25 mm; 1"). ♂ shining green above with small white postocular spot. *Throat and breast glittering green, belly velvety black. Tail mostly white, feathers tipped black,* central feathers bronzy green. ♀ has upperparts *and tail* as in ♂. Below whitish to buffy whitish (buffiest on throat) thickly spotted with green, almost solid on flanks. **Similar species:** Relatively small size, decurved bill, and extensive white in tail identify both sexes of this montane hummer. Beautiful fully adult ♂ ♂ seem to be in a decided minority. **Habits:** Remains low in shrubbery, hovering in front of flowers as it feeds, often spreading and closing tail (whose white then flashes conspicuously). Forehead often pale because of pollen.

Great Sapphirewing, *Pterophanes cyanopterus*
Alazafiro Grande   Plate 45(6)

Mostly 3000–3600 m

15.5 cm (6"). A *spectacular large and long-winged hummingbird* found in *shrubby temperate forest borders and treeline vegetation on both slopes*; occurs *only in humid regions*. Bill fairly long and straight, almost upswept (30 mm; 1.2"). ♂ dark shining green above with small white postocular spot; *wings, especially wing-coverts, shining blue*. Below uniform shining blue-green. *Tail long and deeply forked,* dark bronzy green. ♀ like ♂ but not so dark above, and with browner crown; wings show less blue (mainly just on coverts). *Cinnamon-rufous below* with green crissum and some green spots on sides and flanks. Tail as in ♂ but *outer web of outermost feather whitish* (conspicuous in flight). **Similar species:** Sapphirewing is normally the largest hummer in its habitat (the Giant favors more arid regions); the two have similar, characteristically *slow* wingbeats. No other hummingbird shows blue in wings, a color that is normally evident, even in the less flashy ♀ ♀. **Habits:** Direct flight very fast with some gliding; hovers with noticeably slow wingbeats. Feeds at flowers either while hovering or when perched, then often holding wings outstretched as if for balance.

Coeligena Incas and Starfrontlets
Rather large hummingbirds, most boldly patterned and all with long straight bills; perched birds hold the bill tilted slightly upward. *Coeligena* are found in montane forests and borders and fly very fast, sometimes seen zooming above the forest canopy or even across a valley. Most species trapline, visiting individual flowers at long intervals.

Bronzy Inca, *Coeligena coeligena*
Inca Bronceado   Plate 45(8)

Mostly 1400–2300 m

10 cm (4″). Fairly common in lower and middle growth of *subtropical* forest on *e. slope. Bill very long and straight* (32 mm; 1.3″). **Sexes alike.** *Dark bronzy brown above*, darkest on crown and greener on lower back and rump. *Throat and chest whitish streaked dusky*; lower underparts dusky-brown. Tail bronzy, slightly forked. **Similar species:** Combination of long straight bill and bronzy brown overall appearance is distinctive in range; Brown Inca occurs only on w. slope. Brown Violet-ear is much shorter-billed, etc. **Habits:** This relatively drab inca is generally found singly, and mostly remains inside forest (less frequent at borders). It especially favors long tubular red flowers, hovering below them while feeding. Sometimes quite tame. **Voice:** Song an emphatic but high-pitched "tze-tze-tze-tze" (M. Lysinger recording).

Brown Inca, *Coeligena wilsoni*
Inca Pardo   Plate 45(9)
10 cm (4″). Fairly common in lower and middle growth of *foothill and subtropical*

Mostly 800–2000 m

forest on *w. slope. Bill very long and straight* (32 mm; 1.3″). *Dark bronzy above* with small whitish postocular spot, greener on back and rump. *Dusky brown below* with inconspicuous glittering amethyst patch on lower throat and *conspicuous white patch on sides of neck*. Tail bronzy, slightly forked. **Sexes alike,** but ♂♂ slightly darker below. **Similar species:** Combination of long straight bill, bronzy brown overall coloration, and white chest patches distinctive in range. Bronzy Inca occurs only on *e.* slope. Brown Violet-ear is much shorter-billed, etc. **Habits:** Much as in Bronzy Inca. **Voice:** Most often heard is distinctive flight call, given as bird speeds through understory, a descending series of 4–5 "tseee" or "tsee-deee" high-pitched notes. Song a squeaky "tsik-tsee-uu-tsi-ik" (P. Coopmans).

Collared Inca, *Coeligena torquata*
Inca Collarejo   Plate 45(10)

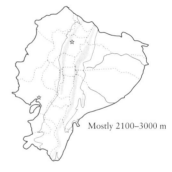

Mostly 2100–3000 m

11 cm (4¼″). Fairly common in *upper subtropical and temperate* forest and borders on both slopes. *Bill very long and straight* (33 mm; 1.3″). On **west slope,** ♂ *mostly black above*, lower back and rump dark shining green, with small patch on crown glittering blue and small white postocular spot. Throat glittering green with *large and conspicuous white shield across chest*; lower underparts black with green sheen. Central tail feathers greenish black, *others white with black tip*. On **east slope,** ♂ differs in having crown patch glittering violet and blacker throat and lower underparts. ♀ on both slopes similar and not as flashy as ♂ *though echoing its pattern*. Above shining green. Throat white spotted green, *white breast patch smaller but still conspicuous*; lower underparts gray with

green disks. Tail as in ♂. **Similar species:** No other Ecuadorian hummer combines highly contrasting white chest patch with white in tail. **Habits:** This stunning hummingbird of upper-elevation forests is conspicuous, often feeding at flowers in open at varying heights, regularly at epiphytes. **Voice:** Simple twittering calls are given during aerial chases.

Buff-winged Starfrontlet, *Coeligena lutetiae*
Frentiestrella Alianteada   Plate 45(11)

Mostly 2700–3500 m

11 cm (4¼″). Fairly common in *temperate forest and borders on both slopes. Bill very long and straight* (33 mm; 1.3″). Both sexes with *unique cinnamon-buff patch on secondaries and tertials*, conspicuous both at rest and in flight. ♂ *velvety black above* with glittering green frontlet and small white postocular spot, uppertail-coverts more coppery. Below dark glittering green with glittering violet-blue patch on lower throat. Tail dark bronzy. ♀ shining green above, glittering at base of bill. *Throat cinnamon-buff;* remaining underparts so densely spangled with golden green disks as to almost obscure the buff ground color. **Similar species:** Essentially unmistakable on account of the obvious buff wing patch. **Habits:** Much as in Collared Inca, like that species often flying long distances in the open, even dive-bombing down valleys well above canopy. **Voice:** Flight call a readily recognized short nasal "eernt" or "churt."

Rainbow Starfrontlet, *Coeligena iris*
Frentiestrella Arcoiris   Plate 45(12)
11.5 cm (4½″). Fairly common and habitat-tolerant in temperate forest borders, sec-

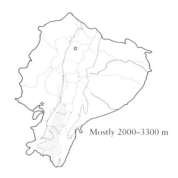

Mostly 2000–3300 m

ondary woodland, and shrubby areas in *highlands of south from Azuay and adjacent Chimborazo and Cañar southward.* Bill long and straight (30 mm; 1.2″). ♂ of **southern race** (mainly El Oro and Loja) dark green above with *crown glittering mixed gold, coppery, green, and blue* (a veritable "rainbow"); *lower back, wings, and tail rufous.* Throat and breast glittering green; *belly rufous.* ♀ similar but crown mainly glittering green and with some rufous showing through glittering green of throat. ♂ of **northern race** (Azuay northward) similar but *crown glittering coppery red mixed with purple* and rufous on underparts confined to crissum and lowermost belly. ♀ similar but with duller crown. **Similar species:** Both sexes are readily recognized by large size in conjunction with extensive rufous on wings, tail, and underparts. ♂♂ are positively dazzling when seen in good light. Shining Sunbeam is shorter-billed, more rufescent on head, and darker on tail (not bright rufous). **Habits:** Similar to other *Coeligena*, but less forest-based than others, more often out in disturbed scrub and gardens. **Voice:** Gives high-pitched trills and chips during aerial maneuvers.

Sword-billed Hummingbird, *Ensifera ensifera*
Colibrí Pico Espada   Plate 45(7)
13–13.5 cm (5–5¼″). Scarce and local (or erratic) in canopy and borders of *temperate* forest, secondary woodland, and shrubby areas on both slopes. Instantly recognizable on account of its *slightly upswept and extraordinarily long bill* (90–100 mm; 3½–4″). ♂ shining green above, somewhat bronzier on head and neck and with small white postocular spot. Throat black; sides of neck and

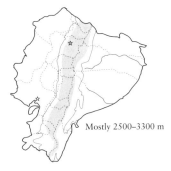

Mostly 2500–3300 m

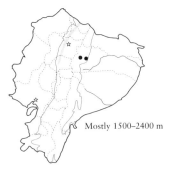

Mostly 1500–2400 m

chest dull glittering green; lower underparts mixed gray and shining green. Tail long and deeply forked, bronzy olive. ♀ above like ♂ but head more coppery bronze. Below whitish thickly spotted with green. Tail somewhat shorter than ♂'s and less deeply forked. **Habits:** This amazing hummingbird can never be seen often enough. All too frequently it is glimpsed just in fast direct flight (sometimes high overhead), the enormous bill being evident at extreme distances and always imparting a distinct and unusual appearance. Perched birds rest with the bill sharply upraised, as if to balance its excessive length. Feeds at a variety of flowers, usually with long corollas, most often hovering beneath them but also sometimes feeding while perched. Particularly favors *Datura* flowers. **Voice:** Not very vocal, but hum of flying (especially hovering) birds easily audible. Infrequently heard flight call a distinctive "toot."

Boissonneaua Coronets
Short-billed hummingbirds found in subcanopy and borders of montane forests and forest borders.

Buff-tailed Coronet, *Boissonneaua flavescens*
Coronita Colianteada   Plate 45(17)

11 cm (4¼"). Canopy and borders of *subtropical forest and adjacent clearings on both slopes*; in west known *south to Pichincha*, in east only from remote sites in Volcán Sumaco vicinity. *Bill short and straight* (16 mm; 0.6"). **Sexes alike.** Shining green above with small white postocular spot; bend of wing and *underwing-coverts buff* (latter prominent in flight). Throat glittering green, breast shining green, belly buffy grayish with green disks.

Central tail feathers bronzy green, *outer feathers buff* tipped bronze. **East-slope** birds similar but buff in tail slightly paler. **Similar species:** This short-billed, mainly green hummer can be known by buff in tail and under wing; both are prominent in the field. **Habits:** Can be locally numerous, especially above Mindo. Mainly arboreal, coming lower in clearings. Holds wings aloft for 1–2 seconds after alighting; also often extends wings as it clings to flowers while feeding. Several may gather with other hummers at flowering trees. Often quite pugnacious. **Voice:** ♂'s song a fast series of high-pitched "chip" notes given as it perches on an open branch in subcanopy, sometimes several birds within earshot of each other.

Chestnut-breasted Coronet
Boissonneaua matthewsii
Coronita Pechicastaña   Plate 45(18)

10.5 cm (4"). Canopy and borders of *upper subtropical and temperate forest and adjacent clearings on e. slope*, also locally on w. slope from Chimborazo southward; *most numerous in southeast. Bill short and straight*

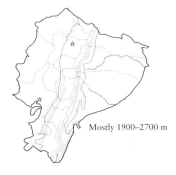

Mostly 1900–2700 m

(16 mm; 0.6"). ♂ shining green above, more glittering on head and with small buffy white postocular spot; bend of wing and *under-wing-coverts rufous* (latter prominent in flight). Throat glittering green; *remaining underparts contrastingly rufous-chestnut.* Central tail feathers coppery bronze, *outer feathers rufous* edged and tipped bronze. ♀ similar but buff shows through green disks on throat, and underparts somewhat paler. **Similar species:** No other montane hummer shows such extensively rich rufous under-parts. Cf. Fawn-breasted Brilliant (buff below, etc.) and Rainbow Starfrontlet (much longer-billed, etc.). **Habits:** Similar to Buff-tailed Coronet.

Velvet-purple Coronet, *Boissonneaua jardini*
Coronita Aterciopelada   Plate 45(19)

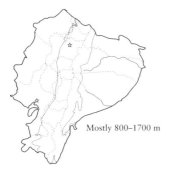

Mostly 800–1700 m

11 cm (4¼"). *Scarce and local* in canopy and borders of *foothill and subtropical forest on w. slope south to Pichincha.* Bill short and straight (18 mm; 0.7"). ♂ gorgeous in good light, but all too often just looks black. *Head, neck, and throat black* (like a hood) with glittering purple forecrown, also a little purple glitter on throat. Back glittering bluish green; *underwing-coverts rufous* (prominent in flight). *Breast and belly glittering royal purple.* Central tail feathers bronzy black, *outer feathers white edged and tipped black.* ♀ similar but duller: no glitter on crown, and underparts more grayish with glitter bluer and less evident. **Similar species:** White-tailed Hillstar larger and longer-billed, shows less glitter overall (especially above); it has rufous malar, shows no rufous under wing. More numerous Buff-tailed Coronet much greener overall with buff (not white) in tail; occurs at somewhat higher elevations. **Habits:** Not

well known, but probably differs little from Buff-tailed Coronet, though Velvet-purple never seems to be as numerous.

Heliangelus Sunangels
Midsized, rather short-billed hummingbirds with *striking, usually brightly colored gorgets* (at least in males); most species have a *white pectoral collar,* conspicuous in some. They inhabit montane forest borders and clearings, mainly in the temperate zone.

Amethyst-throated Sunangel
Heliangelus amethysticollis
Solángel Gorjiamatista   Plate 46(19)

Mostly 1900–2700 m

9.5 cm (3¾"). *Canopy and borders of sub-tropical and lower temperate forest on e. slope in s. Ecuador.* Bill short and straight (16 mm; 0.6"). ♂ shining green above with small white postocular spot and glittering blue-green frontlet. *Gorget glittering ame-thyst* bordered below by *broad white pec-toral collar;* lower underparts grayish, green on sides and flanks. Tail blue-black, central feathers bronzy green. ♀ similar but *throat rufous-buff,* often with some glittering violet disks; midbelly buffier. **Similar species:** Gor-geted Sunangel occurs only on w. slope. In its range not likely confused on account of its white collar, conspicuous in both sexes and not shared by any comparable hummers. **Habits:** Most frequent in shrubby clearings and forest edge. All sunangels, like coronets, briefly hold wings aloft after they have settled on a perch. Generally clings to flowers while feeding, often with wings outstretched; also hawks insects from a perch, or sometimes while hovering. **Voice:** Hovering birds some-times give a gravelly "trrr."

Gorgeted Sunangel, *Heliangelus strophianus*
Solángel de Gorguera   Plate 46(20)

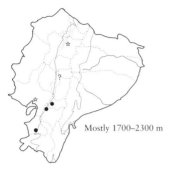

Mostly 1700–2300 m

9.5 cm (3³/₄″). Canopy and borders of *sub-tropical forest on w. slope*, locally or seasonally down into foothills (especially southward) and up into temperate zone. Bill short and straight (14 mm; 0.5″). Resembles Amethyst-throated Sunangel of e. slope (no overlap). There is only minimal sexual dimorphism. Gorgeted differs from ♂ Amethyst-throated in lacking glittering frontlet and in having dark shining green lower underparts and tail entirely blue-black. Overall Gorgeted is a very dark hummingbird whose white pectoral collar therefore stands out prominently. **Habits:** Similar to Amethyst-throated Sunangel.

Tourmaline Sunangel, *Heliangelus exortis*
Solángel Turmalina   Plate 46(21)

Mostly 2200–3100 m

8.5 cm (3¹/₄″). Shrubby lower growth at borders of *temperate forest on e. slope in the north* (south to nw. Morona-Santiago). Bill short and straight (15 mm; 0.6″). ♂ shining green above with glittering green frontlet and small white postocular spot. Chin glittering

violet-blue, *lower throat glittering rosy purple*; breast glittering green, belly gray, *crissum white*. Rather long forked tail mostly blue-black, central feathers bronzy green. ♀♀ variable below ("polychromatic"; R. Bleiweiss). Above like ♂♂. *Some ♀♀ have contrasting white throat*, remaining underparts mixed dusky and glittering green, with crissum white. *Others resemble ♂♂*. **Similar species:** Replaced southward by Flame-throated Sunangel (no overlap). White-throated ♀♀ are easily recognized; ♂♂ are dark hummers whose glittering colors are often hard to see, but the white crissum usually stands out. **Habits:** Similar to Amethyst-throated Sunangel.

Flame-throated Sunangel
Heliangelus micraster
Solángel Gorjidorado   Plate 46(22)

Mostly 2400–3100 m

8.5 cm (3¹/₄″). Shrubby lower growth at borders of *temperate forest on e. slope in the south* (north to along Gualaceo-Limón road). Formerly often considered conspecific with Tourmaline Sunangel. Bill short and straight (15 mm; 0.6″). ♂ resembles ♂ Tourmaline Sunangel, differing in its *glittering flame orange lower throat*. ♀ does not show the striking variation shown by ♀♀ Tourmalines, and it *never has full white throat*. It thus resembles ♂ but *throat mixed white, dusky-green, and glittering flame color*. In both sexes white crissum prominent (as it is in Tourmaline). **Habits:** Much as in Amethyst-throated Sunangel.

Purple-throated Sunangel, *Heliangelus viola*
Solángel Gorjipúrpura   Plate 46(23)

♂ 11.5 cm (4¹/₂″); ♀ 11 cm (4¹/₄″). *Numerous in scrub, shrubby areas, and forest borders in*

Mostly 1800–3300 m

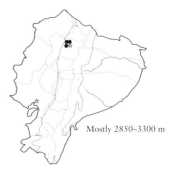

Mostly 2850–3300 m

highlands of s. Ecuador. Bill short and straight (14 mm; 0.6″). **Sexes much alike** (♀ ♀ duller and shorter-tailed). Shining green above with glittering blue-green forecrown. *Gorget glittering violet-purple* bordered below by band of glittering blue-green; lower underparts shining green with *crissum mainly buff. Tail long and deeply forked*, central feathers green, outer feathers black. **Similar species:** This beautiful hummer is unlikely to be confused in the semiopen habitats it favors. Rather different Flame-throated Sunagel is much more a forest-based bird; it is smaller with a shorter tail, white crissum in both sexes, flame-colored gorget in ♂, etc. **Habits:** Widespread and conspicuous, this sunangel is only member of its genus to occur in relatively arid habitats, where it is regular in gardens and other disturbed situations. Notably pugnacious, perched birds often chasing each other and other humming-bird species (especially smaller ones such as Green-tailed Trainbearers) for long distances.

Eriocnemis Pufflegs

Often beautiful hummingbirds (especially the males) found almost entirely at high eleva-tions (some species at or just above treeline) in the Andes, where they favor shrubby areas and forest borders. They are marked by the *downy "puffs" on their thighs, usually white* (black in one) and *sometimes very large and prominent.* Males especially have at least some glittering coloration. *Eriocnemis* usually perch while feeding. None is espe-cially vocal.

Black-breasted Puffleg, *Eriocnemis nigrivestis*
Zamarrito Pechinegro   Plate 46(2)

8.5 cm (3¼″). *Rare in temperate forest and borders on nw. slopes of Volcán Pichincha,*

mostly in remote areas. Bill short and straight (16 mm; 0.6″). ♂ *mostly black* with slight green sheen especially on crown and rump, small white postocular spot; uppertail-coverts blue. Small gorget glittering violet-blue, as is crissum. *Large leg-puffs white.* Tail blue-black, forked. ♀ dark shining green above, more coppery on neck and with short buffy malar streak. Golden green below with blue patch on midthroat; large leg-puffs white and crissum glittering violet-blue. **Similar species:** ♂ distinctive, but ♀ would be hard to distinguish from ♀ of even rarer Turquoise-throated Puffleg (which seemingly occurs at lower elevations). Black-breasted is smaller than other pufflegs occurring with it (Sapphire-vented, Golden-breasted). **Habits:** Not well known, but seems similar to other pufflegs, mainly feeding low in shrubbery at forest borders.

Glowing Puffleg, *Eriocnemis vestitus*
Zamarrito Luciente   Plate 46(4)

Mostly 2500–3500 m

8.5 cm (3¼″). Lower growth and borders of *temperate forest and adjacent shrubby clear-ings on e. slope,* locally up to treeline. Bill short and straight (17 mm; 0.7″). Aptly named ♂ shining green above, *glittering emerald green on rump*. Throat and chest dark green, *patch on lower throat glittering purple*; *breast and belly glittering green*, with *large leg-puffs white* and crissum glittering violet-blue. Tail forked, blue-black. ♀ like ♂ above and on tail, but with small buffy whitish postocular spot. *Throat and breast buff* spotted with glittering violet-blue on midthroat and green elsewhere (sometimes with effect of buff malar streak); lower underparts shining green with large white leg-puffs and glittering violet-blue crissum. **Similar species:** Sapphire-vented Puffleg larger and longer-tailed with inconspicuous blue on forecrown lacking in Glowing; both sexes of Sapphire-vented more uniform green below, lacking glittering purple gorget of ♂ Glowings, and buff on throat and breast of ♀ Glowings (Glowing is the only puffleg that shows any buff below). Cf. also Golden-breasted Puffleg. **Habits:** Tends to remain low in shrubby forest borders, several sometimes concentrating in areas where feeding opportunities are good. Often clings to flowers when feeding, and may hold wings up for 1–2 seconds.

Turquoise-throated Puffleg, *Eriocnemis godini*
Zamarrito Gorjiturquesa   Plate 46(3)

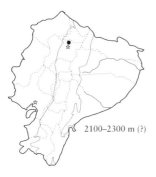

2100–2300 m (?)

8.5 cm (3¼″). *Status uncertain*. No definite recent records, only a few old specimens from "ravines" in *Río Guaillabamba drainage north of Volcán Pichincha*. Bill short and straight (17 mm; 0.7″). *Virtually identical to Glowing Puffleg*, and probably not safely identified in field, Glowing does not, so far as known, occur in supposed range of Turquoise-throated. ♂ differs from ♂ Glowing in having *patch on lower throat glittering blue* (not purple) and apparently in

being more glittering golden on throat and sides of neck. ♀ differs from ♀ Glowing in lacking cinnamon-buff below. **Similar species:** ♀ probably not safely distinguished from ♀ Black-breasted Puffleg (which also is rare), though Turquoise-throated apparently ranges at lower elevations; Black-breasted may be slightly shorter-billed. **Habits:** Unknown (similar to Glowing Puffleg?).

Sapphire-vented Puffleg, *Eriocnemis luciani*
Zamarrito Colilargo   Plate 46(5)

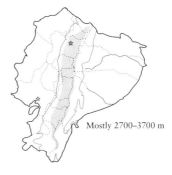

Mostly 2700–3700 m

11.5 cm (4½″). Locally numerous in temperate forest borders and shrubby areas in Andes south at least to Azuay, *mainly on slopes above central and interandean valleys*, locally up to near treeline. Bill straight (20 mm; 0.8″). **Sexes nearly alike.** Above shining green with forecrown indistinctly bluer and small white postocular spot. *Below glittering golden green*, with *large leg-puffs white* and *crissum glittering violet*. Tail long and deeply forked, blue-black. ♀ may show some white flecking on throat. **Similar species:** ♂ Glowing Puffleg is smaller with a shorter and much less deeply forked tail, has glittering purple on throat and green on rump; ♀ shows at least some buff on throat and breast (often quite extensive), never shown at all by Sapphire-vented. The two species occur together only marginally. Golden-breasted Puffleg is similarly sized but shows coppery across foreneck, dull crissum (no violet), and greener (not blue-black) tail. **Habits:** Feeds actively in semiopen shrubby areas, either clinging directly to flower at which it is feeding or perching nearby; in most areas seems less associated with actual forest than are other pufflegs.

Golden-breasted Puffleg
Eriocnemis mosquera
Zamarrito Pechidorado   Plate 46(6)

Mostly 3000–3600 m

11.5 cm (4½"). Local in *temperate forest, borders, and adjacent shrubby areas in the north*, south to Pichincha in west and Napo in east (a few to Morona-Santiago). Bill straight (20 mm; 0.8"). **Sexes nearly alike.** Shining green above, somewhat bronzier on neck, and with small white postocular spot. More glittering green below, *decidedly golden or coppery on sides of neck and across breast*; large leg-puffs white, crissum dusky (♂) or dull green (♀). *Tail long and deeply forked, dark bronzy green*. **Similar species:** Golden-breasted can occur with similarly sized Sapphire-vented Puffleg, the latter differing in lack of golden-coppery across breast, often conspicuous violet on crissum, and blue-black (not green) tail. **Habits:** More a forest-based puffleg than many of congeners, but with similar overall behavior.

Emerald-bellied Puffleg, *Eriocnemis alinae*
Zamarrito Pechiblanco   Plate 46(7)

7.5 cm (3"). A *rare*, poorly known puffleg recorded locally from *subtropical forest and borders on e. slope*. Bill straight (15 mm;

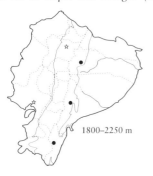

1800–2250 m

0.7"). *Very small*. **Sexes nearly alike.** Shining green above with small white postocular spot, uppertail-coverts brighter emerald green. *Mostly glittering green below* with *irregular patch on breast white with green spangles*; large leg-puffs white. Rather short tail somewhat forked, shining green. **Similar species:** By a considerable margin *the smallest puffleg*, and occurring at much lower elevations than other *Eriocnemis*. Cf. Greenish Puffleg. **Habits:** Not well known. Elsewhere seen singly inside montane forest and at edge, sometimes in low vegetation on ridges.

Black-thighed Puffleg, *Eriocnemis derbyi*
Zamarrito Muslinegro   Plate 46(8)

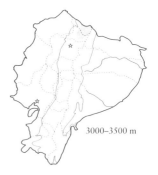

3000–3500 m

8 cm (3¼"). Uncommon and local in *temperate forest and borders in the north (Carchi and Imbabura)*. Bill straight (18 mm; 0.7"). ♂ shining green above, brightest on crown and more coppery on rump; *uppertail-coverts glittering emerald green*, contrasting sharply with *black of short, somewhat forked tail*, feathers obviously pointed. Below glittering golden green; *large leg-puffs black, crissum glittering emerald green*. ♀ like ♂ above but with small white postocular spot. Below white thickly spotted with glittering green; *large leg-puffs mixed black and white, crissum glittering green*. **Similar species:** Black leg-puffs are unique but can be hard to see, so more easily recognized by the short and black tail that contrasts sharply with brilliant glittering green of tail-coverts (both above and below). **Habits:** Forages at varying levels, both inside forest (mainly at openings) and at edge.

Haplophaedia Pufflegs
Much duller—compared to *Eriocnemis*—pufflegs with less prominent leg "puffs" than

in that genus. *Haplophaedia* are found inside subtropical forest, one species on either side of the Andes.

Greenish Puffleg, *Haplophaedia aureliae*
Zamarrito Verdoso   Plate 46(10)

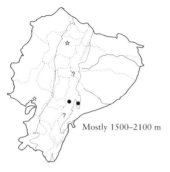

Mostly 1500–2100 m

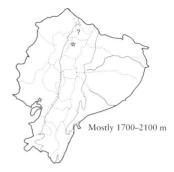

Mostly 1700–2100 m

9 cm (3½″). Local in lower and middle growth *inside subtropical forest on e. slope.* Bill straight (20 mm; 0.8″). **Sexes alike.** Relatively dull and nondescript, lacking obvious field marks. Above shining green, *head more coppery* and with small white postocular spot; uppertail-coverts coppery. Below green, *feathers variably scaled whitish*, becoming solidly whitish on midbelly; *small leg-puffs white* (often not apparent in field). Tail somewhat forked, blue-black. **Similar species:** Occurs at lower elevations than other pufflegs except for the rare (and much more brightly colored) Emerald-bellied. Hoary Puffleg occurs only on w. slope. **Habits:** A relatively inconspicuous hummer, usually seen singly; unlike other pufflegs it normally ranges inside forest or at borders, hardly ever venturing outside it. Feeds at flowering shrubs, small trees, and vines, also sometimes at bromeliads. **Voice:** Not very vocal. Males at a loose assembly in Colombia gave an interminable "tur-seet" at a rate of about one call/second (Hilty and Brown 1986).

Hoary Puffleg, *Haplophaedia lugens*
Zamarrito Canoso   Plate 46(9)
9 cm (3½″). Scarce in lower and middle growth inside *subtropical forest on w. slope in Pichincha* (northward?). Bill straight (20 mm; 0.8″). **Sexes alike.** Resembles Greenish Puffleg (found only on e. slope of Andes), differing in being *darker and decidedly grayer*

below with (as in Greenish) variable amount of whitish scaling. **Similar species:** The dingiest puffleg, occurring with no other. **Habits:** As in Greenish Puffleg. **Voice:** Foraging birds give a loud "tzik" (P. Coopmans).

Booted Racket-tail, *Ocreatus underwoodii*
Colaespátula Zamarrito   Plate 42(10)

Mostly 900–2200 m

♂ 11.5 cm (4½″); ♀ 7 cm (2¾″). Generally uncommon in lower growth and borders of *foothill and subtropical forest and adjacent clearings on both slopes*, more numerous in west. Bill fairly short and straight (12 mm; 0.5″). On **west slope**, ♂ bright shining green with glittering green throat and chest and small white postocular spot and *very large white leg puffs. Tail very long and deeply forked, outer feathers reduced to shaft distally and ending in large blue-black rackets.* ♀ shining green above with small white postocular spot and malar streak. *Mostly white below* with sparse green spotting on sides and flanks and white leg puffs (smaller than ♂'s, but still evident). Tail much shorter than ♂'s but still forked, mostly green, outer feathers blue-black with white tips. On **east slope**, ♂ differs from w.-slope ♂ in having *leg puffs* *rich buff.* ♀ differs from w.-slope ♀ in being more profusely spotted with green below and in having buff crissum and small puffs. **Similar species:** ♂♂ unmistakable; *no other Ecuadorian hummer has tail rackets.* ♀♀ can be more problematic, however, and especially resemble ♀♀ of the two whitetips, both of which are larger, longer-billed, and lack leg puffs. On w. slope, ♀ Purple-bibbed more green-spotted below than ♀ racket-tail; on e. slope they are more similar, but ♀ Rufous-vented shows even more spotting below. **Habits:** Feeds at varying levels, depending on where there are flowers, from near ground to quite high in forest canopy. ♂♂ usually hold their fancy tails somewhat elevated. **Voice:** In flight both sexes often give a descending series of semimusical notes, almost a trill.

Lesbia Trainbearers
Small-bodied and short-billed hummingbirds with *very long tails* in males, *Lesbia* are found in shrubby areas in the Andes, the Black-tailed up into paramo edges.

Black-tailed Trainbearer, *Lesbia victoriae*
Colacintillo Colinegro   Plate 45(13)

Mostly 2500–3800 m

♂ up to 24 cm (9½″); ♀ 13.5–14.5 cm (5¼–5¾″). *Common and widespread in semiopen and shrubby areas in temperate zone and in shrubby paramo*, mainly in and above central and interandean valleys. Bill fairly short (13–15 mm; 0.5–0.6″), *slightly decurved.* ♂ with *strikingly long and deeply forked tail, mostly black*, upperside with all but the longest pair of feathers tipped green. Shining green above with small white postocular spot. *Throat and chest glittering golden green, lower edge ending in point*; underparts buff with thick green spotting. ♀

lacks ♂'s extremely elongated black outer tail feathers but *still is quite long-tailed* with outer web of outermost pair whitish. Like ♂ above; below whitish to buffy white thickly spotted with green. Birds from extreme s. Loja shorter-billed. **Similar species:** Both sexes of Green-tailed Trainbearer brighter green generally and have straight bill. ♂ Black-tailed so long-tailed as to be essentially unmistakable. **Habits:** A numerous and familiar bird in much of the highlands, regularly occurring in gardens of towns and cities (even downtrown Quito). Favors arid areas, with Green-tailed tending to take over in more humid regions. For its small size—aside from tail—an aggressive hummer that feeds at a variety of flowers. Males have a spectacular aerial display in which they mount high into sky with widely spread tail feathers, descending with a surprisingly rough ripping sound. **Voice:** Most often heard is a descending and accelerating chipper, slowing at end, e.g., "tseee, tseee, tseee-tsee-tsi-tititsi-tsik-tsik" (P. Coopmans).

Green-tailed Trainbearer, *Lesbia nuna*
Colacintillo Coliverde   Plate 45(14)

Mostly 1900–3000 m

♂ up to 16.5 cm (6½″); ♀ 11 cm (4¼″). Local and erratic on *shrubby slopes and in forest and woodland borders on both slopes and in interandean valleys, more numerous southward.* Bill short (10 mm; 0.4″) and *straight.* ♂ with *very long and deeply forked tail, all but longest pair of feathers mostly bright emerald green.* Above bright emerald green with small white postocular spot. Throat and chest glittering emerald green, *lower edge rounded*; underparts bright green. ♀ *lacks* ♂'s elongated outer tail feathers, but *still quite long-tailed* with outer web of outermost pair whitish. *Bright green above* with small white postocular spot. Whitish below thickly spotted with bright green, glittering on throat and chest. **Similar species:** Black-tailed Trainbearer larger and heavier-bodied, has slightly decurved (not straight) bill, and both sexes are less brilliant green generally; glittering bib of ♂ Black-tailed larger and pointed. **Habits:** Similar to Black-tailed Trainbearer, but tends to fly more like a woodstar (slowly and less direct). Hovers at flowers, ♂♂ with tail sometimes gently wagged up and down, usually not clinging. **Voice:** Regularly gives a buzzy "bzzzt."

Purple-backed Thornbill
Ramphomicron microrhynchum
Picoespina Dorsipúrpura   Plate 42(9)

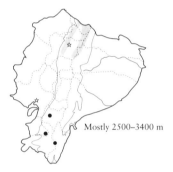

Mostly 2500–3400 m

8 cm (3¼″). *Generally scarce* (but sporadic, and can be temporarily more numerous) in canopy and borders of *temperate* forest and shrubby clearings on both slopes, especially in n. Ecuador. *Bill extremely short* (5 mm; 0.2″), the shortest of any hummingbird. Beautiful ♂ has *unique shining purple upperparts* with small white postocular spot. *Gorget glittering golden green*; underparts shining green. *Long tail blackish.* ♀ much duller, metallic green above with small white postocular spot, and sometimes showing white stripe on lower back; *whitish below with profuse green spotting.* Fairly long tail blackish, outer feathers tipped white. **Similar species:** Stunning ♂ unmistakable in decent light. ♀ can be more difficult, though its almost absurdedly short bill should identify her; no other hummer combines such a short bill with such thickly spotted underparts. Mountain Avocetbill is considerably larger

with distinctly longer bill; underparts greener. **Habits:** Not often encountered in Ecuador, typically found alone at forest borders though rarely several may gather, sometimes with other hummers, to feed at flowering shrubs and trees. Tends to perch atop flower umbels, sometimes actually walking on them, probing blossoms. Flight usually slow and not direct; hovering birds do not wag their rather long tails.

Metallura Metaltails
Small hummingbirds with *short bills* found in shrubby areas and forest borders at high elevations in the Andes; none, however, goes far out into open paramo. *Their distinctive tail colors change according to the angle of light*; in three species this is basically green, whereas in the common Tyrian it is coppery, at times almost appearing rufous.

Viridian Metaltail, *Metallura williami*
Metalura Verde   Plate 46(13)

Mostly 3000–3700 m

8 cm (3¼″). Borders of *forest and woodland and in treeline and paramo shrubbery on e. slope*, on w. slope locally in far north. Bill short and straight (13 mm; 0.5″). ♂ shining bronzy green above and below with small white postocular spot, throat and chest more glittering. *Tail dark bronzy green to bronzy purplish above, bright shining green below.* ♀ above as in ♂. *Below buff densely spotted with green, unmarked crissum buff. Tail as in ♂.* **Southward** (north to w. Morona-Santiago), ♂ similar but with *black patch on lower throat.* **Similar species:** Tyrian Metaltail is often sympatric with Viridian—and almost everywhere is more numerous—but differs in its obviously coppery tail, ♀♀ in buff on throat and chest (not crissum), etc.

Does not show glittering colors or white leg-puffs of Glowing Puffleg, a hummer with which it often occurs. **Habits:** Usually seen singly, remaining close to ground and sometimes actually on it. Often perches in the open on low twigs. Clings to flowers when feeding. **Voice:** Song a fast descending series of "zee" notes (usually 4–5), often followed by a jumbled part (P. Coopmans).

Violet-throated Metaltail, *Metallura baroni*
Metalura Gorjivioleta   Plate 46(12)

Mostly 3100–3700 m

8 cm (3¼"). Borders of patches of *Polylepis* woodland and in adjacent shrubby areas *near treeline and in shrubby paramo* in *limited area of w. Azuay* (Cajas area). Bill short and straight (13 mm; 0.5"). ♂ dark shining bronzy green above and below with small white postocular spot. *Throat and chest glittering violet* (sometimes obscured by dusky flecking). *Tail purplish to bluish bronzy above, shining green below.* ♀ like ♂ but more scaled with buff below, and showing less violet on throat. **Similar species:** *Note very limited range* and generally dark coloration. Tyrian Metaltail has an obviously coppery tail, and birds in ♀ plumage—which usually are what is seen—have throat and chest solid buff. Viridian Metaltail shows no violet on throat. **Habits:** Similar to Viridian Metaltail.

Neblina Metaltail, *Metallura odomae*
Metalura Neblina   Plate 46(15)

9 cm (3½"). Locally numerous in patchy *treeline* woodland and adjacent shrubby paramo in far south *from Podocarpus National Park southward.* Bill short and straight (15 mm; 0.6"). ♂ dark shining

Mostly 2950–3400 m

bronzy green above with small white postocular spot. *Throat glittering reddish purple;* underparts dull bronzy green, feathers often scaled buff, feathers of crissum edged rufous. *Tail bronzy bluish green above, bright shining green below.* ♂♂ in fully adult plumage seem always to be in minority. ♀ like ♂ above, but upperside of tail more coppery (at least in some lights). *Below much like ♂ but feathers usually extensively scaled whitish or buff.* **Similar species:** *Note very limited range.* Cf. Flame-throated Sunangel and Tyrian Metaltail. **Habits:** Similar to Viridian and Tyrian Metaltails. ♂♂ in fully adult plumage seem to range at higher elevations than those in ♀ plumage. **Voice:** Similar to Viridian Metaltail (N. Krabbe).

Tyrian Metaltail, *Metallura tyrianthina*
Metalura Tiria   Plate 46(14)

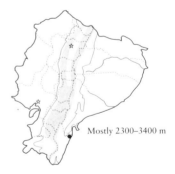

Mostly 2300–3400 m

7.5 cm (3"). *Easily the most numerous metaltail. Widespread at shrubby borders of temperate forest and woodland and in adjacent clearings on both slopes*, and on slopes above central and interandean valleys. Bill very short and straight (11 mm; 0.4"). ♂ above shining bronzy green with white postocular spot. Throat patch glittering green; underparts dull bronzy green. *Tail shining coppery, more purplish below. ♂ ♂ in fully adult plumage seem always to be in minority. ♀ like ♂ above. Throat and chest rufous-buff* with a few small dark spots; remaining underparts buffy whitish with green speckling on sides and flanks. *Tail as in ♂.* **Similar species:** Cf. other metaltails, all of which have darker bronzier tails showing green below (never Tyrian's coppery effect). In far south, cf. also similar (but much rarer) ♀ Rufous-capped Thornbill. Learn this small metaltail well: you will see plenty, and then can use it as basis of comparison with scarcer species. **Habits:** Most often in semiopen, favoring shrubby growth at forest edge and on roadcuts and landslides. Generally feeds low, and only infrequently enters actual forest. Usually clings to flowers while feeding, often hanging upside-down. **Voice:** Emits a variety of short, high-pitched notes, sometimes a fast jumble. Singing ♂ ♂ give a repeated weak "tiz-tiz-tiz. . . ."

Chalcostigma Thornbills

Similar to the metaltails, *Chalcostigma* thornbills are usually larger; they have *very short bills*, even finer and shorter than in *Metallura*. Males have *elongated and pointed iridescent gorgets.* Two species are found in shrubbery at and above treeline; the atypical Rufous-capped ranges in the se. subtropics. None is especially vocal.

Rufous-capped Thornbill
Chalcostigma ruficeps
Picoespina Gorrirrufa   Plate 46(16)

9.5 cm (3¾"). *Rare* in shrubby clearings and upper subtropical and temperate forest borders on e. slope *in far south. Bill tiny, very*

2100–2700 m

short, and straight (12 mm; 0.5"). ♂ has *crown rufous;* otherwise metallic green above with small white postocular spot. *Elongated and pointed throat patch glittering green;* otherwise dull buff below with obscure green spotting. *Tail light bronzy green,* bronzier below. ♀ entirely metallic green above, *lacking ♂'s rufous crown. Below mostly rufous-buff,* spotted with green on throat and sides. **Similar species:** Rainbow-bearded Thornbill is larger, inhabits treeline shrubbery at higher elevations than Rufous-capped, and both sexes have white tail corners (especially evident in flight). ♂ Rufous-capped is distinctive enough, but ♀ ♀ resemble ♀ ♀ of much commoner Tyrian Metaltail, with similar short bills and buff underparts; the metaltail is smaller with a shorter tail that is coppery (not bronzy). **Habits:** This scarce hummer generally forages low, and seems fond of early-successional vegetation on roadcuts and landslides. It clings to flowers while feeding.

Rainbow-bearded Thornbill
Chalcostigma herrani
Picoespina Arcoiris   Plate 46(18)

Mostly 2800–3700 m

10 cm (4"). Scarce and local in shrubby clearings and at *temperate* forest and woodland borders (*often around treeline*) on both slopes. *Bill tiny, very short,* and straight (1.2 mm; 0.5"). ♂ dark bronzy green above with *rich rufous median crown stripe accented by black border* and small white postocular spot; rump reddish coppery. *Elongated and pointed throat patch glittering green becoming glittering orange and tapering to fiery red point on chest;* underparts dark greenish gray, crissum dull buff. *Tail dark purple, outer feathers broadly tipped*

white. ♀ much like ♂ but *rufous crown stripe* less defined and not black-outlined, and it lacks glittering beard. **Similar species:** When seen well, ♂ is one of Ecuador's most dazzling hummingbirds, not to be confused. ♀♀ are duller, though normally they show enough rufous on crown to be recognized; their white tail corners are conspicuous in flight, as is coppery on rump contrasting with upper tail's royal purple. **Habits:** Favors shrubby areas around rocky slopes, cliffs, and boulder fields. Feeds while clinging to flowers, often hanging upside-down.

Blue-mantled Thornbill, *Chalcostigma stanleyi*
Picoespina Dorsiazul   Plate 46(17)

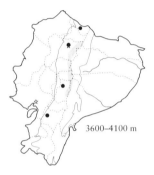

3600–4100 m

10–11.5 cm (4–4½″). A *dark and long-tailed* hummingbird of *shrubby paramo and borders of woodland near treeline.* Bill tiny, *very short*, and straight (11 mm; 0.4″). ♂ *mainly sooty brown*, nearly black on face and sides of neck and with purplish blue gloss on back. *Tail long and deeply forked, steel blue. Elongated and pointed throat patch glittering green becoming glittering purple toward lower tip.* ♀ similar but shorter-tailed, lacking gloss on back, and without glittering throat patch. **Similar species:** Not likely confused in its high-elevation paramo habitat. Ranges at higher elevations than any other hummer except Ecuadorian Hillstar. **Habits:** Feeds while clinging to flowers, often fluttering wings for balance (or to counteract wind); sometimes these flowers are nearly prostrate, and the hummer almost seems to hop on ground itself. Also gleans tiny insects from leaves, or hawks them from air.

Mountain Avocetbill, *Opisthoprora euryptera*
Piquiavoceta   Plate 46(11)

Mostly 2400–3200 m

10 cm (4″). *Rare* and apparently local in lower growth and borders of *temperate forest on e. slope.* Bill short (13 mm; 0.5″), *distinctly upturned at tip.* **Sexes alike.** Above shining green, *head and neck much more coppery* and with small white postocular spot. Below whitish densely spotted with green, *giving somewhat streaked effect on throat and chest*, becoming rufous-buff on lower belly and crissum. Tail rather short and broad, blue-black with narrow whitish tips, central feathers bronzy. **Similar species:** Heavier-bodied than a metaltail, with a more prominent postocular spot than they show. The upturned bill can be hard to discern in field, but the streaked effect below (not spotted) is obvious. **Habits:** Generally inconspicuous, tending to remain inside cover more than many other hummers and at times even seeming rather inactive. Feeds primarily while clinging to flowers, especially of *Centropogon* (whose corollas it sometimes even pierces; N. Krabbe).

Aglaiocercus Sylphs
Distinctive hummingbirds with short bills found in montane forest borders and undergrowth. Males *are exceptionally beautiful with very long, deeply forked, and colorful tails;* females have *distinctive rufous lower underparts.*

Long-tailed Sylph, *Aglaiocercus kingi*
Silfo Colilargo   Plate 45(15)

♂ up to 18.5 cm (7¼″); ♀ 9.5–10 cm (3¾–4″). Lower growth and borders of *subtropical and lower temperate* forest on e. slope and in

Mostly 1600–2600 m

Mostly 800–1950 m

northwest. Bill short and straight (13 mm; 0.5″). On **east slope**, *gorgeous* ♂ mostly shining green, somewhat duller below; *crown glittering green (bluer at certain angles) and throat patch glittering violet-blue. Tail very long and extremely deeply forked, upperside shimmering green (bluer at certain angles).* ♀ shining green above, *more glittering on crown* and with small white postocular spot. *Throat white spotted with green; remaining underparts contrastingly cinnamon-buff*, some green on sides. Notched tail much shorter than ♂'s, blue-green with outer feathers tipped white. **West-slope** ♂ has *no* glittering throat patch; ♀ slightly richer below. **Similar species:** On e. slope easily recognized; trainbearers are smaller and narrower-tailed. On w. slope can be confused with Violet-tailed Sylph, which mainly occurs at lower elevations (though there is some overlap). ♂♂ differ in tail color, shimmering violet in Violet-tailed (green in w.-slope Long-taileds; remember that it can look blue at certain angles, though never the intense violet shown by Violet-tailed); ♂ Violet-tailed has violet-blue throat patch. ♀ Violet-tailed similar but it has glittering blue (not green) crown. **Habits:** Forages at varying heights, usually in semi-open, sometimes gathering with other hummingbirds at flowering trees, even high in their crowns. Usually clings to flowers while feeding, sometimes piercing corollas. Perched ♂♂ often move their spectacular long tails rhythmically. **Voice:** Foraging birds frequently give a sharp, throaty "jeeyp."

Violet-tailed Sylph, *Aglaiocercus coelestis*
Silfo Colivioleta   Plate 45(16)

♂ up to 18.5 cm (7¼″); ♀ 9.5–10 cm (3¾–4″). Lower growth of *foothill and sub-*

tropical forest on w. slope. Bill short and straight (13 mm; 0.5″). In **north**, spectacular ♂ like w.-slope ♂ Long-tailed Sylph above, but *upperside of equally long and deeply forked tail contrastingly shimmering violet-blue*, extending up onto uppertail-coverts. *Throat patch glittering violet-blue*; underparts bronzy green. ♀ resembles ♀ w.-slope Long-tailed Sylph, but differs in its *glittering blue crown* (not green), *unspotted white chest*, and *deeper rufous lower underparts*. In **south**, ♂ differs in lacking glittering throat patch; ♀♀ similar. **Similar species:** Generally found at lower elevations than Long-tailed Sylph; ♂ Long-tailed may show blue on upperside of tail, but never the intense violet of Violet-tailed. **Habits:** Similar to Long-tailed Sylph, though tending to remain more in lower growth and even inside forest, rarely or never venturing up into canopy. **Voice:** Much as in Long-tailed Sylph.

Wedge-billed Hummingbird
Schistes geoffroyi
Colibrí Piquicuña   Plate 41(19)

Mostly 800–2000 m

8 cm (3¼"). Scarce and inconspicuous in undergrowth and borders of *foothill and subtropical forest* on both slopes. *Bill short and sharply pointed*, longer on w. slope (15–18 mm; 0.6–0.7"). On **west slope**, ♂ shining green above with glittering green forecrown and short white postocular stripe. Gorget glittering green with *patch of glittering blue and magenta-violet on sides of chest, bordered below by patch of white*; lower underparts bronzy green. Rounded tail bronzy green, bluer below with broad blue-black subterminal band. ♀ like ♂ but lacking glittering forecrown, *entire throat white* with smaller patches on sides mainly blue, and whitish tail fringing. On **east slope**, ♂ differs in lacking glittering forecrown and in having less white across chest, blackish ear-coverts, extensive coppery from lower back to uppertail coverts, and whitish tail fringing. ♀ differs in having green-spangled throat. **Similar species:** W.-slope ♀ ♀ with white throats easy to recognize, but otherwise this infrequently encountered small hummer can be a bit confusing; distinctive glittering areas in ♂ ♂ are beautiful when visible, but angle has to be just right (the white is easier to see). **Habits:** Inconspicuous and solitary, usually remaining in cover. Hovers at flowers. **Voice:** On e. slope gives a simple, regularly spaced series of "tsit" notes (P. Coopmans); on w. slope a more complex series of "tsit" notes interspersed with longer and higher-pitched "tseeet" notes (L. Navarrete recording).

Heliothryx Fairies

Lovely hummingbirds with *gleaming white underparts and flashing white in the tail*. They range in lowland forests, one species on either side of the Andes.

Purple-crowned Fairy, *Heliothryx barroti*
Hada Coronipúrpura   Plate 43(5)

9–9.5 cm (3½–3¾"). Humid forest and woodland in *lowlands of west*. Bill fairly short and straight (18 mm; 0.7"). ♂ above bright shining green with *glittering purple forecrown* and *black mask through eyes* ending in a violet tuft and bordered below by glittering green malar area. *Immaculate white below. Tail long and graduated, mostly white*, central feathers blue-black. ♀ similar

To 800 m

but lacking glittering forecrown and malar area; tail somewhat longer. **Similar species:** Black-eared Fairy occurs east of Andes. Otherwise not likely confused, but cf. ♂ White-necked Jacobin. **Habits:** This exquisite hummer generally keeps to mid-levels and subcanopy of forest, though sometimes coming lower in clearings. Quite active, with graceful darting flight; often hovers with tail held partially cocked, and also often flashes mainly white tail open and shut. Regularly captures insects as it hovers, also gleaning them from leaves. **Voice:** Not very vocal.

Black-eared Fairy, *Heliothryx aurita*
Hada Orejinegra   Plate 43(4)

To 1200 m

9–9.5 cm (3½–3¾"). Canopy and borders of humid forest and woodland in *lowlands of east*. Bill short and straight (15 mm; 0.6"). Resembles Purple-crowned Fairly (found west of Andes). ♂ differs in having crown glittering green (with no violet). ♀ differs in having gray spotting on throat and breast. **Similar species:** Not likely confused. Purple-crowned Fairy occurs west of Andes. Cf. ♂ White-necked Jacobin. **Habits and Voice:** As in Purple-crowned Fairy.

Heliomaster Starthroats
Notably long and straight-billed humming-birds found in semiopen areas in the lowlands, one of them only an accidental.

Long-billed Starthroat
Heliomaster longirostris
Heliomaster Piquilargo   Plate 44(1)

Mostly below 700 m, but to 1500 m (S)

9.5 cm (3¾″). Uncommon at borders of forest and woodland and in clearings in lowlands of east and west, more numerous in west. *Bill very long and straight* (35 mm; 1¼″). ♂ shining green above with *glittering pale blue crown*, white postocular spot, and partially concealed white stripe on lower back and rump. *Gorget glittering reddish purple* bordered by *white malar streak*; underparts pale grayish with some green on sides and sometimes showing white patch on flanks. Tail bronzy green, outer feathers tipped white. ♀ like ♂ but lacking blue crown and with gorget smaller and duller, often scaled grayish, with wider white malar streak. **Similar species:** Not likely confused; no other regularly occurring lowland hummer has such a strikingly long and straight bill. **Habits:** Usually found in semiopen, often perched high on a dead branch. Feeds at flowering trees, regularly congregating with other hummers. Also sometimes captures tiny insects, usually while hovering in open.

[Blue-tufted Starthroat, *Heliomaster furcifer*
Heliomaster Barbado]   Plate 44(2)
11 cm (4¼″). *Very rare vagrant* (status uncertain) in *lowlands of northeast*. Bill long and essentially straight (30 mm; 1.2″). Beautiful ♂ shining bronzy green above with glittering bluish green crown. *Gorget glittering violet-magenta; entire underparts and long tuft on*

250 m

sides of neck glittering blue. Tail deeply forked, bronzy green. ♀ bronzy green above with small white postocular spot. *Dingy pale grayish below,* whitest on narrow malar streak and median breast and belly. Tail forked, bronzy green, outer feathers white-tipped. **Similar species:** Full-plumaged ♂♂ resemble no other hummingbird. Much drabber ♀♀ can be confused with several other species, though relatively large size in conjunction with quite long bill and essentially uniform pale grayish underparts should identify them. **Habits:** Unknown in Ecuador, where the one bird seen was perched at edge of a clearing. Elsewhere more a bird of scrub, low woodland, and gardens than Long-billed Starthroat, regularly occurring in arid regions.

[Peruvian Sheartail, *Thaumastura cora*
Colifina Peruana]   Plate 45(20)

2350 m

♂ up to 14 cm (5½″); ♀ 7.5 cm (3″). *Apparently very rare* (one report from *montane scrub in s. Loja*). In Peru also regular in gardens. *Bill very short* and straight (12 mm; 0.5″). ♂ pale shining green above. *Gorget glittering rosy magenta,* somewhat elongated at sides; *underparts grayish white* with some green mottling on sides. *Tail very long, next to central pair by far the longest and mostly white*, other feathers dark brown. ♀ pale shining green above. *Below uniform buffy whitish*. Tail mostly black, feathers with white tips, central feathers green. **Similar species:** ♂ with its elongated white rectrices unique, but in many individuals these are molted or broken off. ♀ resembles ♀ Purple-collared Woodstar, but sheartail has considerably shorter and straighter bill, somewhat longer and more pointed tail, and lacks whitish postocular stripe. **Habits:** Hardly known in Ecuador, where the one bird seen was feeding with Purple-collared Woodstars at flowering shrubs in montane scrub. In Peru often erratic in its appearances, but can be locally and seasonally numerous.

Calliphlox Woodstars
A pair of similar woodstars, one occurring on either side of the Andes. Although closely resembling woodstars in other genera, males are marked by their *long and deeply forked tails*, often wagged while they are feeding, females by the *rich rufous on their lower underparts*. *Flight is deliberate and bee-like*; foraging birds often feed relatively unmolested by other more aggressive hummingbirds. Note that all the woodstars except the Short-tailed have a *white patch on the sides of the back* that is sometimes partially hidden behind the wing.

Purple-throated Woodstar
Calliphlox mitchellii
Estrellita Gorjipúrpura   Plate 42(12)

♂ 7 cm (2¾″); ♀ 6.5 cm (2½″). Canopy and borders of *foothill and subtropical forest and*

adjacent clearings on w. slope. Bill straight (13 mm; 0.5″). ♂ metallic green above with small white patch on sides of back extending down to lower flanks. Gorget glittering violet-purple bordered below by *broad white pectoral collar extending up onto sides of neck* and almost connecting to white postocular spot; lower underparts dusky green with some rufous on lower flanks and crissum. *Tail long and deeply forked*, dark bronzy purple. ♀ like ♂ above. *Throat buffy whitish* with "echo" of ♂'s white pectoral collar arching up to white postocular stripe; *lower underparts rich rufous*, whiter on midbelly with bronzy green at least on sides of chest (sometimes all the way across). Tail shorter and less forked than ♂'s, mostly rufous with broad black subterminal band. **Similar species:** ♂ of very similar Amethyst Woodstar occurs only east of Andes. ♂ looks substantially longer-tailed than other sympatric woodstars (White-bellied and Gorgeted, possibly Little). ♀ White-bellied Woodstar has extensive white on lower underparts; ♀ Gorgeted has nearly uniform buff underparts. **Habits:** Perched birds usually are at considerable heights, most often fully in open on an exposed branch but also on wires. Regularly seen at flowering trees, where several birds may gather (often with other hummers); occasionally feeds closer to ground. Foraging birds usually hold tail partially cocked. **Voice:** Usually silent, though wings of flying birds produce an audible humming noise. Feeding birds give an occasional soft "chit" or "chrrt."

Amethyst Woodstar, *Calliphlox amethystina*
Estrellita Amatista   Plate 42(13)

♂ 6.5 cm (2½″); ♀ 6 cm (2¼″). Scarce in canopy and borders of *foothill forest and*

Mostly 800–1800 m

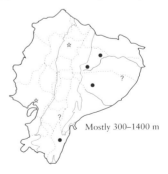

Mostly 300–1400 m

adjacent clearings on e. slope, in smaller numbers out into adjacent lowlands. Bill straight (13 mm; 0.5″). ♂ *closely resembles ♂ Purple-throated Woodstar (no overlap)*, differing in its slightly bronzier upperparts and more pinkish violet gorget. ♀ also resembles ♀ Purple-throated, differing in having *throat speckling of glittering violet mixed with green*, some white on median belly. **Similar species:** In its range, long-tailed ♂ unlikely to be confused. ♀ can be more confusing; cf. especially ♀ White-bellied Woodstar (whiter below, etc.). **Habits:** Very similar to Purple-throated Woodstar. Displaying ♂ arcs back and forth, pendulum-like, over perched ♀.

Purple-collared Woodstar, *Myrtis fanny*
Estrellita Gargantillada   Plate 42(14)

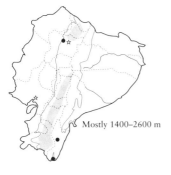

Mostly 1400–2600 m

♂ 7 cm (2¾″); ♀ 6.5 cm (2½″). Local in *scrub, woodland, gardens, and grassy areas in arid intermontane valleys of highlands* (also apparently prone to wandering). Bill somewhat decurved (18 mm; 0.7″). ♂ above bronzy green with small white patch on sides of back extending down to lower flanks. *Gorget glittering aquamarine blue bordered below by pinkish violet*; underparts whitish washed with green on flanks. Tail long and forked, bronzy green. ♀ like ♂ above. *Pale buff below*, with some white on median belly. Tail shorter than ♂'s, central feathers bronzy green, outer feathers black *with prominent white tipping*. **Similar species:** This is the woodstar most likely to be found in arid montane valleys; fully plumaged adult ♂♂ are only infrequently seen. White-bellied can occur with it, though its extensive white below (both sexes) is quite different. In extreme south also cf. the very rare Peruvian

Sheartail. **Habits:** Favors semiopen areas and gardens, usually not perching very high. ♂♂ often have regularly used territorial perches. Flight faster and less bee-like than in other woodstars, with tail neither cocked nor wagged. Displaying ♂♂ have U-shaped flight in which they rise 10 m or more (L. Jost). **Voice:** Displaying ♂♂ give a twitter, whereas perched ♂♂ occasionally emit a soft clicking or gurgling "song" (L. Jost). Flying birds also give an un-hummingbird-like "néh-neh-nuh" (P. Coopmans).

Short-tailed Woodstar, *Myrmia micrura*
Estrellita Colicorta   Plate 42(19)

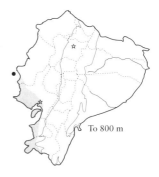

To 800 m

6 cm (2¼″). A *minute* woodstar found commonly in *desert scrub, shrubby areas, and gardens in arid lowlands of southwest*. Bill slightly decurved (13 mm; 0.6″). ♂ *above dusty pale shining green* with small whitish patch on sides of lower back extending down to lower flanks. *Gorget glittering violet*, bordered at sides by *white malar streak* and below by white pectoral collar extending up onto sides of neck; underparts whitish. *Tail very short*, black (so short it almost is covered by uppertail-coverts). ♀ like ♂ above but showing little or no whitish on lower back. *Below uniform pale buffy whitish. Tail as in ♂* but feathers white-tipped. **Similar species:** The only woodstar in most of its range, with small size normally precluding confusion. Cf. ♀ Little Woodstar (with richer buff underparts, etc.). **Habits:** Usually feeds close to ground, and often attracted to flowers planted around houses.

Chaetocercus Woodstars
Similar to the other woodstars, but males with tail feathers sharply pointed; in most

species the tail is also quite deeply forked. They range in forested habitats, some montane whereas others occur in the western lowlands. As with *Calliphlox*, *flight is slow and bee-like*. None is especially vocal. Some species were formerly placed in the genus *Acestrura*.

White-bellied Woodstar
Chaetocercus mulsant
Estrellita Ventriblanca   Plate 42(15)

1100–3500 m

♂ 7 cm (2¾″); ♀ 6.5 cm (2½″). *The most widespread and generally most numerous woodstar in highlands*, inhabiting a variety of habitats from montane forest borders to shrubby clearings and gardens. Bill essentially straight (18 mm; 0.7″). ♂ shining green above with *large* white patch on sides of lower back extending down to flanks. Gorget glittering pinkish violet; *underparts mainly white* with pectoral collar outlining gorget and arching up onto sides of neck and connecting to white postocular stripe; *sides contrastingly dark green*, creating a distinctive "vested" look. *Rather short deeply forked tail with outer feathers sharply pointed*, black. ♀ bronzier green above than ♂, with more prominent white postocular stripe. Mostly white below, including "echo" of ♂'s pectoral collar, with *contrasting rufous sides and flanks*. Unforked tail shorter than ♂'s, mostly rufous with black subterminal band. **Similar species:** A *chunky* woodstar, shorter-tailed than Purple-throated or Amethyst, with very prominent lower back/flank patch in both sexes. **Habits:** Basically a nonforest woodstar, most often seen feeding at flowering trees in semiopen and in gardens. Feeding birds often slowly wag tail.

Little Woodstar, *Chaetocercus bombus*
Estrellita Chica   Plate 42(17)

Mostly below 1200 m, locally (seasonally?) higher

6.5 cm (2½″). Now *seemingly scarce and local* at borders of humid and deciduous forest and woodland and in clearings in *lowlands and foothills of west—mainly the southwest—* ranging locally (or seasonally?) up into subtropics. Bill straight (13 mm; 0.5″). ♂ shining green above, bronzier on crown, with white patch on sides of lower back extending to flanks. Gorget glittering pinkish violet, *bordered by prominent buff pectoral collar arching up onto sides of neck* and reaching buffy white postocular stripe; underparts bronzy green. Fairly long deeply forked tail with outer feathers narrow and spiky, brownish black. ♀ like ♂ above. *Below uniform cinnamon-buff*, this color extending up onto sides of neck. Unforked tail shorter than ♂'s, outer feathers cinnamon-buff with broad black subterminal band. **Similar species:** ♂ ♂, which seem to be infrequent, are easily recognized (all other woodstars having a white pectoral collar). ♀ ♀ closely resemble ♀ Gorgeted Woodstar (though the two do not normally occur together); cf. also ♀ of very rare and local Esmeraldas Woodstar (with mainly whitish underparts). **Habits:** Similar to White-bellied Woodstar, though Little is seen much less often. Often flies slowly, seeming to float in air.

Gorgeted Woodstar, *Chaetocercus heliodor*
Estrellita de Gorguera   Plate 42(16)
6 cm (2¼″). *Rare* in canopy and borders of *foothill and subtropical forest on both slopes.* Bill straight (13 mm; 0.5″). ♂ dark shining green above with short white postocular

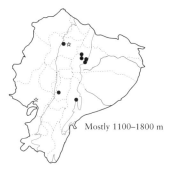

Mostly 1100–1800 m

stripe and white patch on sides of lower back extending to lower flanks. Gorget glittering pinkish violet, *elongated and pointed at sides*, with white pectoral collar less evident than in other woodstars; breast grayish, belly blue-green. Fairly short forked tail, outer feathers narrow and "spiky." ♀ closely resembles ♀ Little Woodstar. **Similar species:** A *tiny* woodstar, infrequently seen ♂♂ *dark overall* with distinctive *pointed* gorget, ♀♀ so similar to ♀ Little Woodstar as to not be distinguishable in field. The two barely overlap (if at all), however, and ♀ Gorgeted is the only montane woodstar with *uniform rufous-buff underparts*. **Habits:** Similar to White-bellied Woodstar, though more of a forest-based species.

Esmeraldas Woodstar
Chaetocercus berlepschi
Estrellita Esmeraldeña   Plate 42(18)

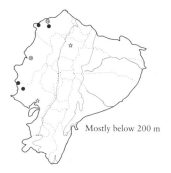

Mostly below 200 m

♂ 6.5 cm (2½″); ♀ 6 cm (2¼″). Now *rare and very local* in canopy and borders of semihumid forest and woodland in *lowlands of west*, seemingly occurring only on or near slopes of coastal cordillera. Bill straight (13 mm; 0.5″). ♂ above dark shining green with *prominent white postocular stripe* and small white patch on sides of lower back extending to flanks. Gorget glittering pinkish violet, somewhat flared and pointed on sides; *mainly white below* with some green on flanks (but showing no pectoral collar effect). Fairly long deeply forked tail, outer feathers narrow and spiky, brownish black. ♀ like ♂ above, postocular stripe buffier. *Throat pale buff; underparts whitish* with a little green on flanks. Unforked tail shorter than ♂'s, outer feathers cinnamon-buff with broad black subterminal band. **Similar species:** Another *minute* woodstar, most likely confused with Little Woodstar (the two can occur together), though both sexes of Little show conspicuous buff below (♂ on pectoral collar, ♀ on entire underparts). **Habits:** Most often seen at forest borders where both sexes, but especially ♂♂, have regularly used perches on dead twigs.

Trogoniformes
Trogons and Quetzals: Trogonidae (15)
A pantropical family of beautiful birds reaching its highest diversity in the Neotropics. They are widespread in Ecuador's humid forests, with the most species in the eastern lowlands. Trogons and quetzals have a soft lax plumage that in males is *brilliantly colored*, mainly green with contrasting lower underparts (either red or yellow); females have much the same patterns but are duller, and are often gray or brown above. Bills are short and stout, and *tails are long and squared off*; often the color and/or pattern of the tail's underside is important for identification. Trogons and quetzals *perch erectly with tail hanging downward*, and they may remain motionless and quiet for protracted periods, easily overlooked. Males' *far-carrying and hollow songs* attract attention, and though generally similar, they are useful in species discrimination; *many more will be heard than seen*. They eat both fruit and larger insects, and nest in natural cavities, holes dug by woodpeckers, or (certain trogons) holes dug into termitaries or arboreal wasp nests.

Pharomachrus Quetzals

Quetzals (especially females) are characterized by their *elongated wing-coverts and uppertail-coverts*, though the latter are not nearly as long as in Middle America's Resplendent Quetzal (*P. mocinno*). Quetzals are larger than typical trogons. All are forest dwellers, two species in the Andes with the Pavonine in the eastern lowlands. Quetzals are mainly frugivorous, fruits being taken in a swooping flight and quick flutter.

Crested Quetzal, *Pharomachrus antisianus*
Quetzal Crestado   Plate 48(7)

Mostly 1500–2500 m

33–34 cm (13–13½″). Uncommon in subcanopy and mid-levels of *subtropical and lower temperate forest and borders* on both slopes. *Iris red*; ♂'s bill yellow, ♀'s black. ♂ *bright shimmering emerald green above* with *frontal crest protruding out over bill* (sometimes almost obscuring it); *elongated scapulars* protrude over black wings, and elongated uppertail-coverts cover upperside of tail; *underside of outer three tail feathers white (from below, tail looks essentially white)*. Throat and chest bright shimmering green contrasting with bright red lower underparts. ♀ has *grayish brown head* contrasting with emerald green upperparts; scapulars and uppertail-coverts elongated but less so than in ♂. Underside of tail black, *outer webs of outer feathers with conspicuous white barring*. Below pale brown with some green on chest; belly and crissum red. **Similar species:** ♂ Golden-headed Quetzal similar but lacks frontal crest (so bill appears to protrude more), head more coppery-golden, and undertail all black (not with white). ♀ Golden-headed is likewise similar but with bronzier head and all-black tail

showing no barring. **Habits:** Solitary or in pairs—though several may gather in a fruiting tree—tending to perch high in trees, usually on larger branches. Despite their bright coloration, quetzals are not very conspicuous as they often rest motionless for long periods. Flight undulating. **Voice:** ♂'s characteristic song a loud and far-carrying "kweep-kwao" repeated over and over (5–10 or more times) at 3- to 4-second intervals. Calls of both sexes, given especially in flight or when agitated, consist of a variable series of cackling notes, e.g., a loud "ká-kára-kakára-kaká."

Golden-headed Quetzal
Pharomachrus auriceps
Quetzal Cabecidorado   Plate 48(8)

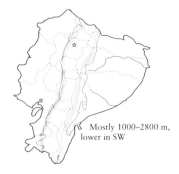

Mostly 1000–2800 m, lower in SW

33.5–35.5 cm (13¼–13¾″). Uncommon to locally fairly common in subcanopy and mid-levels of *subtropical and temperate forest and borders* on both slopes. Iris brown; ♂'s bill yellow, ♀'s dusky. ♂ *bright shimmering emerald green above* with *head more coppery-golden*; *elongated scapulars* protrude over black wings, and elongated uppertail-coverts cover upperside of tail; *underside of tail black*. Throat and chest bright shimmering green contrasting with bright red lower underparts. ♀ has *coppery bronze head* contrasting with emerald green upperparts; scapulars and uppertail-coverts elongated but less so than in ♂; *underside of tail entirely black*. Throat and breast dusky-brown with some green on chest; belly and crissum red. **Similar species:** Occurs with similar but usually less numerous Crested Quetzal; for differences, see that species.

Habits: Similar to Crested Quetzal; Golden-headed generally more numerous at lower elevations. On rare occasions the two species can be heard together, or may even feed at same fruiting tree. **Voice:** ♂'s unmistakable song a fast-paced "ka, ka-kweeéo, ka-kweeéo, ka-kweeéo, ka-kweeéo" with a somewhat querulous or reedy quality; there may be up to 6–8 "ka-kweeéo" phrases. Both sexes also give cackling calls, e.g., a descending whinny, "whídi-di-di-di-dr."

Pavonine Quetzal, *Pharomachrus pavoninus*
Quetzal Pavonino   Plate 48(9)

To 600 m

33–34 cm (13–13½"). Scarce (and local?) in subcanopy and mid-levels of *terra firme forest in lowlands of east, where the only quetzal.* ♂'s bill salmon red, ♀'s dusky reddish. ♂ *bright shimmering emerald green above; elongated scapulars* protrude over black wings, and elongated uppertail-coverts cover upperside of tail; underside of tail black. Throat and chest bright shimmering green contrasting with bright red lower underparts. ♀ emerald green above, head more bronzy; *scapulars and uppertail-coverts elongated* but less so than in ♂; underside of tail black, outer feathers narrowly tipped white. Throat and breast brownish, chest greener; belly and crissum red. **Similar species:** Should not be confused in its lowland range; cf. Black-tailed Trogon (smaller, etc.). **Habits:** Usually in well-separated pairs that are hard to see, even after tape playback. Behavior similar to montane quetzals. **Voice:** ♂'s song a distinctive, far-carrying slurred "kweeeooo-kúk" slowly repeated about 3–5 times. Both sexes have cackles like other quetzals.

Trogon **Trogons**
Almost as lovely as the quetzals, male trogons are *shining green or blue above with contrasting red or yellow lower underparts; females are more subdued* but share in their males' colored underparts. Many species have *brightly colored eye-rings* and *densely vermiculated (black and white) wing-coverts;* their *black and white undertail patterns* are often important in species recognition. Trogons mainly inhabit humid forests, with diversity being greatest in the lowlands though several species extend up into montane regions. Despite their often bright coloration, trogons—like quetzals—are often surprisingly inconspicuous, perching motionless and quiet for long periods, broad tails hanging straight down. Their songs are characteristic, and most species are quite tape responsive. Larger trogons are mainly frugivorous, smaller ones also taking many insects.

Black-tailed Trogon, *Trogon melanurus*
Trogón Colinegro   Plate 47(2)

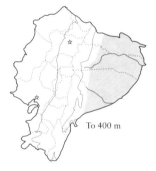

To 400 m

30.5–32 cm (12–12½"). Humid forest and borders (both terra firme and várzea) in *lowlands of east.* Western birds are now considered a separate species. ♂'s *bill bright yellow,* ♀'s *black above with yellowish base and yellow below;* ♂ with red eye-ring. ♂ shining bluish green above, bluest on rump and upperside of tail, with black-and-white vermiculated wing-coverts; underside of tail black. Face and upper throat black, lower throat and chest shining green, bordered below by narrow white band; *lower underparts bright red.* ♀ uniform gray above and on throat and breast, *with contrasting bright red belly;* a few (juveniles?) show white edging to outer tail feathers. **Similar species:** *The only large, red-bellied trogon in e. lowlands.* Ecuadorian Trogon occurs only west of Andes. **Habits:** A relatively phlegmatic trogon that tends to remain well above ground where heard much more often than seen. Usually in pairs, perching on larger limbs and often remaining motionless for protracted periods, then hurtling off to pluck a fruit (sometimes in a hover-glean) or to pick off a large insect, continuing on to another perch. Sometimes gathers in small groups, periodically displacing and chasing each other, ♂♂ singing and ♀♀ calling softly. **Voice:** ♂'s song an often long-continued series of up to 20–30 resonant "cow" notes that starts softly, e.g., "cuh-cuh-cuh-cuh-cow-cow-ców-ców-ców. . . ."

more apt to be confused with similar Chocó Trogon, *which like Ecuadorian is white-eyed and yellow-billed.* ♂ Chocó differs in its bluer tone to upperparts (especially notable on tail), and it *lacks* Ecuadorian's white band separating green chest from red underparts; it also does not have a red eye-ring. ♀♀ of the two are very similar; see Chocó. **Habits:** Similar to Black-tailed Trogon, though Ecuadorian more often ranges out to forest and woodland borders, and hence is more conspicuous and often seen. Ecuadorian favors somewhat less wet regions than the Chocó Trogon, and in northwest it is not found in foothill areas. **Voice:** ♂'s song a slow, short series of "cow" notes that often starts softly and builds in strength, e.g., "cuh-cuh-cuh-cuh-cow-cow-ców-ców-ców."

Ecuadorian Trogon, *Trogon mesurus*
Trogón Ecuatoriano   Plate 47(3)

Mostly below 800 m, locally up to 2000 m in Loja

Chocó Trogon, *Trogon comptus*
Trogón del Chocó   Plate 47(4)

300–800 m

30.5–32 cm (12–12½"). Deciduous and semihumid forest and woodland in *lowlands of west*, up into subtropics in southwest. Formerly considered conspecific with Black-tailed Trogon. ♂'s *bill bright yellow*, ♀ *black above with yellowish base and yellow below*; ♂ with *red eye-ring. Iris whitish in both sexes.* ♂ shining green above with black-and-white vermiculated wing-coverts; underside of tail black. Face and upper throat black, lower throat and chest shining green, *bordered below by narrow white band*; *lower underparts bright red.* ♀ uniform gray above and on throat and breast, with *contrasting red belly*, sometimes with a *narrow white band separating the two*; a few (juveniles?) show white edging to outer tail feathers. **Similar species:** Slaty-tailed Trogon occurs only in n. Esmeraldas, and both sexes have reddish bills and dark eyes. Ecuadorian is

30.5–32 cm (12–12½"). Mid-levels and subcanopy of very humid forest and borders in *foothills and adjacent lowlands of northwest.* Formerly called Blue-tailed (or White-eyed) Trogon. *Iris whitish;* ♂'s *bill bright yellow*, ♀'s *black above with yellowish base and yellow below.* ♂ shining bluish green above with black-and-white vermiculated wing-coverts; *rump and upperside of tail shining greenish blue*, underside black. Face and upper throat black; lower throat and chest shining green, contrasting with bright red lower underparts. ♀ uniform gray above and on throat and breast; underside of tail blackish. Belly contrastingly bright red. Juveniles may show whitish tipping to inner flight feathers and outer tail feathers. **Similar species:** Cf. rare Slaty-tailed Trogon (with red on bill, dark iris, etc.). Chocó is more apt to be confused with Ecuadorian Trogon of lowlands; it is *also white-eyed and yellow-billed*. ♂ Ecuadorian differs in its purer green tone to upperparts, and in having white band—sometimes indistinct—separating green and red on its underparts and a red eye-ring (lacking in Chocó). ♀♀ are very similar, but ♀ Chocó never seems to show narrow white band that separates gray and red on Ecuadorian's underparts (on which it can be indistinct, though normally some shows). **Habits:** Much as in Black-tailed Trogon. **Voice:** ♂'s steadily delivered song a slow repetition of 7–15 "cow" notes, higher pitched than Ecuadorian Trogon's song. Call a fast "krr-krr-krr."

Slaty-tailed Trogon, *Trogon massena*
Trogón Colipizarro   Plate 47(1)

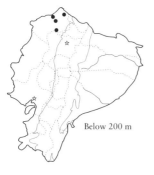

Below 200 m

32–33 cm (12½–13″). Apparently rare (but perhaps just local?) in humid forest in *lowlands of n. Esmeraldas*. ♂'s bill *salmon red*, ♀'s *blackish above, salmon red below*; iris dark, ♂ with salmon red eye-ring. ♂ shining green above with black-and-white vermiculated wing-coverts and black wings; underside of tail black. Face and upper throat black; lower throat and chest metallic green, contrasting with bright red lower underparts. ♀ uniform gray above and on throat and breast; lower underparts red; underside of tail black (sometimes a bit of whitish tipping on outer feathers). **Similar species:** A *large* trogon with *restricted Ecuadorian range*. Resembles the more numerous Black-tailed and Chocó Trogons, but the three species are at least mainly allopatric. Irides of both Black-tailed and Chocó are *pale* and bills yellow (♂♂) or yellowish (♀♀). **Habits:** Hardly known in Ecuador, but from be-

havior elsewhere presumed similar to Black-tailed Trogon. **Voice:** In Panama, ♂'s song a fast series of well-enunciated and rather nasal "cah" notes repeated with steady tempo (though often accelerating at beginning). Several birds may gather in what appears to be a loose singing assembly.

Amazonian White-tailed Trogon, *Trogon viridis*
Trogón Coliblanco Amazónico   Plate 47(5)

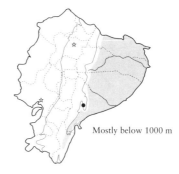

Mostly below 1000 m

28–29 cm (11–11½″). Common in mid-levels and subcanopy of humid forest and borders (both terra firme and várzea) in *lowlands of east*. Western birds are now considered a separate species. ♂'s bill bluish gray, ♀'s bluish gray with dusky culmen; *pale blue eye-ring* in both sexes. ♂ mostly shining bluish green above with more violet-blue hindcrown and nape; forecrown, face, and throat black; underside of tail black, *outer feathers very broadly tipped white (giving a "blocky" effect)*. Breast violet-blue; lower underparts orange-yellow. ♀ uniform gray above and on throat and breast, with some faint white vermiculations on wing-coverts and barring on outer webs of primaries. Underside of tail blackish, *outer feathers tipped and barred white*. Lower underparts orange-yellow. **Similar species:** Western White-tailed Trogon occurs only west of Andes. Both sexes of Amazonian White-tailed show more white on underside of tail than any other trogon in Amazonia. ♂ Black-throated Trogon is smaller, greener on upperparts and foreneck, etc. ♀'s undertail pattern resembles that of smaller Amazonian Violaceous, but latter differs in its whitish eye-crescents and whitish band separating gray and yellow on underparts. **Habits:** Often in pairs, usually remaining well above ground but coming lower at edge, when they can be tame (much like other trogons). Small groups may gather during courtship, raising tails and calling. **Voice:** ♂'s song a fast, fairly even series of 15–20 "cow" or "cowp" notes, higher pitched than in Black-tailed. Both sexes also give soft "chuk" notes and a nasal scolding, e.g., "kwa kwa kwo-kwo-kwo-kwo-kwo," often accompanied by raising and lowering of tail.

Western White-tailed Trogon
Trogon chionurus
Trogón Coliblanco Transandino   Plate 47(6)

Mostly below 500 m

28–29 cm (11–11½″). Mid-levels and sub-canopy of humid forest and borders in *lowlands of west*. Formerly considered conspecific with Amazonian White-tailed Trogon (and then called simply White-tailed Trogon), but songs differ markedly. ♂'s bill bluish gray, ♀'s bluish gray with dusky culmen; *pale blue eye-ring* in both sexes. ♂ similar to Amazonian White-tailed but with bluer rump and *outer tail feathers entirely white* (such that *tail appears all white from below*). ♀ also similar, differing in having *outer tail feathers more broadly tipped and barred with white*. **Similar species:** Amazonian White-tailed Trogon occurs only east of Andes. Both sexes show much more white on underside of tail than any other trogon west of Andes. ♀'s undertail pattern most resembles that of smaller Northern Violaceous Trogon, though that differs in its whitish eye-crescents and whitish band separating gray and yellow below. **Habits:** Similar to Amazonian White-tailed, though Western rarely seems as numerous as that species often is, and seems more often to occur closer to ground. **Voice:** ♂'s song a very fast series of 15–20 "cow" or "cowp" notes with characteristic acceler-

ation toward end, when it also drops in pitch. Both sexes give soft "chuk" notes and a nasal scolding, often accompanied by raising and lowering of tail.

Collared Trogon, *Trogon collaris*
Trogón Collarejo   Plate 47(10)

Mostly below 1300 m

24–15.5 cm (9½–10″). Mid-levels of humid forest and mature woodland in lowlands, ranging up on both slopes into lower subtropics. In e. lowlands favors várzea, in w. lowlands locally also in more deciduous forest. Bill yellow (with black culmen in ♀); ♂ has narrow red eye-ring, ♀ feathered white crescents in front and behind. ♂ *shining green above*, more golden on back, wing-coverts vermiculated black and white; forehead, face, and throat black; underside of tail black, outer feathers evenly barred white and with broad white tips. *Breast shining green, prominent white band* separating that from *red belly and crissum*. ♀ *brown above and on throat and breast*, more rufescent on crown and rufous-chestnut on upperside of black-tipped tail; *underside of tail whitish freckled and mottled with dusky*. Lower underparts red, with white band separating that from brown breast. **Western birds** have more contrasting blackish face. **Similar species:** In e. lowlands ♂ most likely confused with Blue-crowned Trogon, but that differs in its blue crown and breast (not green), yellow eye-ring, and fainter white breast band; ♀ Blue-crowned is gray where Collared is brown, and underside of tail shows white barring on outer webs only. In Andes, most likely confused with Masked Trogon (though that species occus at higher elevations); both sexes of Masked have barring on underside of tail *narrower* than in Collared. **Habits:** Usually in pairs, notably phlegmatic even for a trogon.

Voice: Both sexes give a descending "churrr," often accompanied by quickly raising and then slowly lowering tail. ♂'s song a short "karow-ców-ców-ców," sometimes up to 5 "ców"s; it seems not to vary geographically within Ecuador.

Masked Trogon, *Trogon personatus*
Trogón Enmascarado   Plate 47(11)

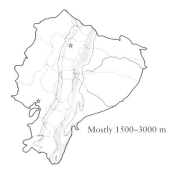

Mostly 1500–3000 m

25–26 cm (9¾–10¼"). Lower growth and mid-levels of *subtropical and temperate forest* on both slopes. *Bill bright yellow in both sexes*; ♂ has narrow orange-red eye-ring, ♀ feathered white crescents in front of and—especially—behind eye. ♂ **on west slope** shining bronzy green above, wing-coverts vermiculated black and white; forehead, face, and throat black; underside of tail black, outer feathers *very narrowly* barred white and with broad white tips. *Breast shining green, prominent white band* separating that from *red lower underparts.* **East-slope ♂** at lower elevations similar, but **east-slope ♂ at higher elevations** differs in *notably smaller bill*, darker green upperparts (less golden or bronzy) with *purer green upperside of tail*, and *nearly obsolete white barring on underside of tail.* ♀♀, aside from bill-size difference, similar: *brown above and on breast* with *rather sharply defined blackish face and throat*; upperside of black-tipped tail more rufous-chestnut, *underside blackish with narrow white barring and broad tips.* Lower underparts red, white band separating that from brown breast. **Similar species:** ♂ Collared Trogon has broader white tail barring; ♀ Collared has no barred pattern on tail, more contrasting black "mask." **Habits:** Similar to Collared Trogon. **Voice:** Upper-elevation ♂♂ on e. slope give fast "kowp,

kow-kow-kow" (sometimes an extra 1–2 "kow"s). Lower-elevation birds give a notably slower-paced and even "kwow, kwow, kwow," again sometimes with an extra note; song of w.-slope birds identical to this. Both sexes also give a descending "churrr."

Black-throated Trogon, *Trogon rufus*
Trogón Golinegro   Plate 47(7)

To 700 m

25–26 cm (9¾–10¼"). *Lower and middle growth inside humid forest in lowlands of east and northwest.* ♂'s bill greenish yellow to yellow, ♀'s dull bluish gray with dusky culmen. *Eye-ring yellow in ♂, yellowish in ♀.* ♂ shining green above, wing-coverts vermiculated black and white; forehead, face, and throat black; upperside of tail shining bronzy green (east of Andes) or olive green (west of Andes), underside as in ♂ Collared Trogon. *Breast shining green,* bordered below by diffused white band; *lower underparts yellow.* ♀ *brown above and on throat and breast,* wing-coverts finely vermiculated buff and blackish; upperside of black tail more rufous-chestnut. *Lower underparts as in ♂.* **Similar species:** ♂ is only Ecuadorian trogon combining green breast and yellow underparts (breast blue in the others that have the yellow underparts). ♀ is the only basically brown trogon with yellow underparts (red in others). Note that in Ecuadorian birds eye-ring is not blue, as it is in many other parts of species' range. **Habits:** Similar to Collared and Masked Trogons, but even more likely to remain inside forest (less at borders); favors vicinity of streams. **Voice:** ♂'s song a very slow "cuh, cwuh-cwuh," sometimes with extra note or two added; in w.-slope birds there may be up to 10 or even more "cwuh" notes. Both sexes give a "churrr" call.

Blue-crowned Trogon, *Trogon curucui*
Trogón Coroniazul   Plate 47(12)

To 1100 m

24–25.5 cm (9½–10″). Mid-levels and sub-canopy of humid forest and (especially) borders in *lowlands and foothills of east*. ♂'s bill greenish or bluish gray, ♀'s blackish above and pale grayish below. ♂ has yellow to orange-yellow eye-ring, ♀ feathered white crescents in front and behind. ♂ shining green above, more golden on back, with *crown and nape shining dark blue*; wing-coverts vermiculated black and white; forehead, face, and throat black; underside of tail as in ♂ Collared Trogon. *Breast shining blue*, bordered below by diffused white band. Lower underparts red. ♀ uniform gray above and on throat and breast, with white vermiculations on wing-coverts and barring on outer webs of primaries; underside of tail black, *outer webs of outer feathers barred and tipped white*. Lower underparts red, separated from breast by diffused white band. **Similar species:** ♂ Collared Trogon has green (not blue) crown and breast; ♀ Collared is predominantly brown (not gray). ♀ Black-tailed Trogon, also gray with red belly, differs in lacking any white on tail underside. **Habits:** Much like Collared Trogon, though more often in forest edge situations. **Voice:** ♂'s song a fast, evenly paced repetition of same "kow" note, lasting about 4–5 seconds and ending abruptly; higher pitched than Amazonian White-tailed's. Both sexes also give a "churrr" call much like other smaller trogons.

Amazonian Violaceous Trogon
Trogon violaceus
Trogón Violáceo Amazónico   Plate 47(8)

To about 500 m

22.5–23 cm (8¾–9″). Mid-levels and sub-canopy of humid forest (terra firme and várzea) in *lowlands of east*. Western birds are now considered a separate species. Bill pale bluish gray, ♀ with blackish cul-men. ♂ has *orange-yellow eye-ring*, ♀ *feathered white crescents in front and behind*. ♂ shining bluish green above with *crown and nape shining violet-blue*; forehead, face, and throat black; underside of tail evenly barred black and white, outer feathers broadly tipped white. A sometimes indistinct white band separates shining *violet-blue breast* from orange-yellow lower underparts. ♀ uniform gray above and on throat and breast, with some faint white vermiculations on wing-coverts and barring on outer webs of primaries. *Underside of tail blackish, outer webs of outer feathers barred and tipped white*. Belly and crissum orange-yellow. **Similar species:** Northern Violaceous Trogon occurs only west of Andes. Amazonian Violaceous most likely confused with larger Amazonian White-tailed Trogon, both sexes of which differ in their blue eye-ring, more white on undertail (especially in ♂♂). ♂ Black-throated Trogon has green foreneck, etc.; ♀ Black-throated is predominantly brown (not gray). Cf. also Blue-crowned Trogon. **Habits:** Similar to the two White-tailed Trogons. **Voice:** ♂'s song a fast but relatively short series of clipped "cow" notes, the notes often becoming doubled ("cadow-cadow-cadow . . .").

Northern Violaceous Trogon, *Trogon caligatus*
Trogón Violáceo Norteño   Plate 47(9)

To 900 m

22.5–23 cm (8¼–9″). Mid-levels and sub-canopy of humid forest, secondary woodland, and (especially) borders in *lowlands of west*. Formerly considered conspecific with Amazonian Violaceous Trogon (and then called simply Violaceous Trogon), but songs differ markedly. Bill pale bluish gray, ♀ with blackish culmen. ♂ has *orange-yellow eye-ring*, ♀ *feathered white crescents in front and behind*. ♂ resembles ♂ Amazian Violacous Trogon but has *crown black* (bluer on nape). ♀ much as in Amazonian Violaceous Trogon. **Similar species:** Amazonian Violaceous Trogon occurs only east of Andes. Western White-tailed Trogon is larger, and both sexes have complete pale blue eye-rings and considerably more white on underside of tails. **Habits:** Similar to Western White-tailed Trogon, though favors secondary and edge habitats and more often closer to ground. **Voice:** ♂'s song an even, rather fast, and long series of relatively high-pitched "ca" notes steadily repeated without a break, often 20 or more notes in a song.

Coraciiformes
Kingfishers: Alcedinidae (6)
A large and cosmopolitan group of primarily fish-eating birds with powerful bills, in Ecuador closely associated with freshwater. In Ecuador there is a pair of species (one very rare) with blue-gray upperparts, and four with dark oily green upperparts. They nest in burrows dug into banks, usually near water, and mainly eat fish.

Megaceryle Kingfishers
Large, bushy-crested kingfishers with *blue-gray upperparts*. They are mainly associated with larger watercourses. Both species are sometimes placed in the genus *Ceryle*.

Ringed Kingfisher, *Megaceryle torquata*
Martín Pescador Grande   Plate 49(1)

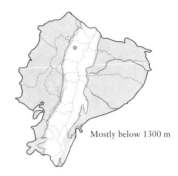

Mostly below 1300 m

38–40.5 cm (15–16″). *Widespread* along rivers, largers streams, and lakes in lowlands and foothills of east and west. *By far Ecuador's largest kingfisher*, with *distinctive bushy crest*. *Very heavy bill* mostly black, greenish horn toward base. ♂ *blue-gray above* with wide nuchal collar white; tail feathers blackish edged gray, and with sparse white barring. Throat white; *underparts chestnut-rufous*, some blue-gray protruding onto sides of chest. White patch in primaries evident in flight. ♀ similar but a *blue-gray band* separates white throat and rufous underparts. **Similar species:** Nearly unmistakable, other Ecuadorian kingfishers (aside from the accidental Belted) being green above; none is anywhere near as large. **Habits:** Widespread along rivers and streams—sometimes even where surprisingly small—and around edge of lakes and ponds; less frequent on salt water. Perches at varying levels, sometimes raising and lowering tail; more often high above ground than other kingfishers, sometimes even perching on phone wires. Plunges for fish from perch, often from considerable heights. Nests in burrows dug into banks, usually close to water; generally solitary or in pairs, but locally in loose colonies. Ringed is the only Ecuadorian kingfisher that flies high above ground, and attention is then often drawn to it by its loud calls. **Voice:** Has a variety of vocalizations, including a harsh "krek!" (the call normally uttered by high-flying birds), a very loud fast rattle (given especially after one has been flushed), and other sharp chatters.

Belted Kingfisher, *Megaceryle alcyon*
Martín Pescador Norteño   Plate 49(2)

30.5–32 cm (12–12½"). An *accidental* boreal winter visitant to near coast (a Dec. sighting from Manabí/Guayas border). Ragged crest, often looking "double-peaked." Heavy bill black. ♂ *Blue-gray above* with white nuchal collar and white spot in front of eye; tail with some white barring. *White below, chest crossed by single wide blue-gray band.* White patch in primaries evident in flight. ♀ similar but with *additional rufous band across breast*, extending irregularly down flanks. **Similar species:** Larger Ringed Kingfisher mainly rufous below, etc. **Habits:** Similar to Ringed Kingfisher, but much more likely to hover while feeding. **Voice:** Though loud, Belted's commonest call, a machine-gun-like rattle, is less harsh than Ringed's.

Chloroceryle Kingfishers
Four kingfishers of progressively smaller size—one is tiny—united by their *dark green upperparts.* Found in lowlands in close association with freshwater, the various species varying in the degree they are in the open.

Amazon Kingfisher, *Chloroceryle amazona*
Martín Pescador Amazónico   Plate 49(3)
28–29 cm (11–11½"). Along rivers, larger streams, and larger lakes and ponds in *lowlands and foothills of east.* The *largest*

To 1000 m

"green" kingfisher; with *very heavy blackish bill.* ♂ *dark, shiny, oily green above* with narrow white nuchal collar; tail green above, outer feathers with some white banding. *White below* with *broad rufous chest band* and some green streaks down flanks. ♀ similar but a *broken band of dark green* replaces rufous. **Similar species:** Green Kingfisher much smaller with proportionately slighter bill; has obvious white wing spotting. **Habits:** Usually seen singly, most often perching in open on low branches. Flight fast and direct low over water, unlike Ringed never flying high overhead. Plunges for fishes from perches, less often after hovering. **Voice:** Gives a loud "cak!" or "chat!," sometimes doubled, and a descending series of sputtering or squeaky notes that can end in a rattle.

Green Kingfisher, *Chloroceryle americana*
Martín Pescador Verde   Plate 49(4)

To at least 1300 m

18.5–20.5 cm (7¼–8"). *Widespread* along rivers, streams, and around margins of lakes and ponds in lowlands and lower subtropics of both east and west. Bill black. ♂ *dark, shiny, oily green above* with narrow white nuchal collar and *numerous small white spots on wings*; *outer tail feathers mainly white* (flashing in flight). White below with broad rufous chest band and green streaking down flanks. ♀ similar but a *pair of green-spotted chest bands* replaces ♂'s rufous. **Western birds** substantially larger than those in east. **Similar species:** Markedly smaller than similarly plumaged Amazon Kingfisher, particularly in e. lowlands where both species occur. Green differs further in showing white on wings of perched birds, and in tail on birds in flight. Cf. also much smaller American Pygmy Kingfisher. **Habits:** Occurs more often along small and rapidly flowing streams than does Amazon Kingfisher, and much more apt to be found in nonforest situations. More often perches on rocks than other Ecuadorian kingfishers. Flight fast and direct, usually low over water. Dives for fish from low perches, occasionally first hovering. **Voice:** Flight call a raspy "dzeet" or "treet," often doubled or trebled, much like two pebbles being struck together.

Green-and-rufous Kingfisher
Chloroceryle inda
Martín Pescador Verdirrufo   Plate 49(5)

Mostly below 400 m

21.5–23 cm (8½–9″). *Uncommon and inconspicuous along sluggish forested streams*, shady lake margins, and flooded várzea forest in lowlands of east and northwest (mainly Esmeraldas); quite rare in west. *Bill proportionately heavy*, black. ♂ dark shiny green above with buff streak above lores; wings and tail lightly speckled white or pale buff. *Collar on sides of neck and entire underparts rich orange-rufous*, somewhat paler on throat. ♀ similar but with *mixed green and white chest band*. **Similar species:** American Pygmy Kingfisher, though similarly colored,

is *much* smaller with proportionately slighter bill; its midbelly is white. **Habits:** Unobtrusive and usually solitary, perching on twigs and branches low over water, generally remaining inside cover and hard to see. Dives directly into water without hovering. Flight swift and direct, usually low over surface. **Voice:** Flight call a sharp, grating "dreet" or "dzreet," often trebled.

American Pygmy Kingfisher
Chloroceryle aenea
Martín Pescador Pigmeo   Plate 49(6)

Mostly below 400 m

13 cm (5″). *Inconspicuous* along small, usually sluggish streams and in swampy backwater areas in lowlands of east and west; quite rare in west. *By far Ecuador's smallest kingfisher.* ♂ dark metallic green above with rufous streak above lores. *Collar on sides of neck and underparts rich orange-rufous*, with *white median belly and crissum.* ♀ similar but with narrow mixed green and white chest band. **Similar species:** Similarly plumaged Green-and-rufous Kingfisher is substantially larger (though in fast flight confusion is possible), as is Green Kingfisher. **Habits:** Found singly, generally perching close to surface of shallow water, sometimes even feeding at stagnant pools. Flight low and darting, so fast that flying birds are hard to follow to their next perch. Reported feeding on insects is apparently in error, though Pygmies may eat some tadpoles in addition to their normal diet of small fish. **Voice:** Flight call a sharp but rather weak "tzit" or "tyeet." Perched birds give a dry "tik" note.

Motmots: Momotidae (4)
Fairly large but surprisingly inconspicuous—heard more often than seen—long-tailed

birds found in forest and woodland, mainly in lowlands. Motmots are clad mainly in shades of green, brown, and rufous and are known for the racket-shaped tips to the central rectrices found in most species; the barbs near the tips quickly fall off, leaving the terminal rackets. They feed mainly on large insects, to a lesser extent on fruit and small vertebrates, and nest in burrows dug into banks. **Sexes are alike.**

Broad-billed Motmot, *Electron platyrhynchum*
Momoto Piquiancho   Plate 49(7)

Mostly below 1000 m

33–35.5 cm (13–14″). Lower and middle growth of humid forest and forest borders in *lowlands and foothills of east and west. Bill broad and flat with keeled culmen.* Tail long and slender, **in west** *usually with terminal rackets* (sometimes worn or broken off), but **in east** *lacking. Head, neck, and breast rufous* with broad black mask through eyes and *large* black spot on breast. Above otherwise green; tail blue-green above, black below. *Belly bluish green*; some individuals also have bluish green chin. **Western birds** somewhat larger with heavier bill. **Similar species:** Rufous Motmot is substantially larger with violet-blue on primaries, smaller black breast-spot, and rufous on underparts extending farther down (to upper belly). **Habits:** Found singly or in pairs, perching vertically, most often on an open branch or liana, occasionally switching tail from side to side. Makes abrupt sallies in pursuit of prey—mainly large insects—snatching them from branches and leaves. **Voice:** Frequently heard call, given mainly around dawn (often in predawn darkness), a nasal "cwaah" or "cwahnk," usually repeated at long intervals

but occasionally in a short faster series; it is quite ventriloquial.

Rufous Motmot, *Baryphthengus martii*
Momoto Rufo   Plate 49(8)

Mostly below 900 m

43–46 cm (17–18″). Lower growth of humid forest and borders in *lowlands and foothills of east and west.* Formerly considered conspecific with *B. ruficapillus* (Rufous-capped Motmot) of se. South America. Bill heavy, strongly serrated. Tail long and slender, *in west usually with terminal rackets* (sometimes worn or broken off), but *rackets lacking* in **east-slope birds.** *Head, neck, and underparts rufous* with broad black mask through eyes and *small* black spot on breast. Above otherwise green, with *violet-blue edging on primaries*; tail blue-green above, black below. *Lower belly blue-green.* **East-slope birds** have mantle somewhat more olive, lower belly less bluish. **Similar species:** Superficially much like smaller and less robust Broad-billed Motmot, east of Andes both species even lacking tail rackets. Apart from size, Broad-billed differs most notably in its wider and flatter bill, more extensive green on belly, larger black chest-spot, and absence of contrasting color on primaries. Vocalizations also differ dramatically. **Habits:** A beautifully colored motmot, often shyer than Broad-billed but otherwise resembling it in general behavior. Tail is swung back and forth, pendulum-like, even more. Generally in pairs, occasionally small groups. Though usually perching low, foraging birds may range higher; one occasionally attends a swarm of army ants. **Voice:** West of Andes most common call, heard especially at dawn and dusk (sometime even when quite dark), a loud resonant hooting, e.g., "hooó-doo-doo," sometimes accelerated into a roll ("hoor-r-r-ooo, hooó-doo-doo"). Eastern birds more often give a simple "hó-du," very similar to Blue-crowned Motmot but (fide P. Coopmans) with first note slightly shorter. Also gives a more "rolling" song.

Momotus Motmots
A pair of beautiful motmots, both sporting a distinctive and lovely *blue "diadem" on the crown*. They range in forest and woodland undergrowth.

Blue-crowned Motmot, *Momotus momota*
Momoto Coroniazul   Plate 49(9)

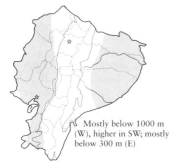

Mostly below 1000 m (W), higher in SW; mostly below 300 m (E)

39–41 cm (15½–16″). Lower growth of humid forest and borders in lowlands of east; lower growth of semihumid and deciduous forest and woodland in lowlands of west, also ranging into adjacent clearings. Bill heavy. Iris red. Tail long and slender, usually showing terminal rackets. **Eastern birds** have *blue crown encircling black midcrown patch, turquoise in front, deeper and more violet to rear*; black mask through eyes. Above green, bronzier on upper back, wings edged blue-green; flight feathers edged blue-green. Below somewhat bronzy olive green with black spot on chest. **Western birds** have more turquoise blue on rearcrown (less violet), are paler and purer (less bronzy) green below. **Similar species:** Broad-billed and Rufous Motmots have extensive rufous on foreparts, no blue on crown. Higher on e. slope, cf. Highland Motmot (no overlap). **Habits:** Found singly or in pairs, perching quietly in shady lower growth of forest and woodland though western birds can be more conspicuous, perching more in open especially in early morning (when occasionally even on phone wires). Especially when disturbed, often switches long tail back and forth. Feeds both on larger insects and small vertebrates, e.g., lizards and snakes, and fruit, prey being captured in a sally to a branch or foliage, sometimes dropping to ground. **Voice:** Most frequent call of eastern birds—given especially at dawn and dusk but also periodically through day—a fast, hollow "hooo-do," similar to call of Rufous Motmot but with first note longer. Also gives a rolling series of less tremulous hoots. Western birds usually give a less separated "whoooop," sometimes doubled.

Highland Motmot, *Momotus aequatorialis*
Momoto Montañero   Plate 49(10)

1000–2100 m

46–48 cm (18–19″). Lower growth and borders of *foothill and subtropical forest on e. slope*. Sometimes considered conspecific with Blue-crowned Motmot of lowlands. Bill heavy. Tail long and slender, usually showing terminal rackets. Resembles Blue-crowned Motmot (especially its geographically distant western race) but is *notably larger*. Crown coloration resembles western birds more than those from east, despite its occurring much closer to latter; color of underparts also resembles western birds. Highland Motmot *does not overlap with Blue-crowned*, and is only motmot found in montane areas on e. slope. **Habits:** Similar to Blue-crowned Motmot, though seems not as numerous. **Voice:** Call a fast "hó-doo," closely similar to comparable call of e.-slope Rufous Motmot.

Piciformes
Jacamars: Galbulidae (9)
Attractive slender birds found only in the Neotropics, jacamars have long graduated tails, weak small feet, and most have a *dis-*

tinctive shimmering green plumage and *long, thin, straight bills.* They are found mainly in lowland forest, most occurring east of the Andes; only two species range up into the lower subtropics. Jacamars sally gracefully after flying insects (butterflies, bees, wasps, etc.); bee and wasp stingers are removed before the insect is swallowed. Their loud vocalizations, often shrill and piercing, attract attention. Most species nest in burrows dug into banks, a few using arboreal termitaries or old wasp nests.

White-eared Jacamar
Galbalcyrhynchus leucotis
Jacamar Orejiblanco   Plate 50(1)

19–20 cm (7½–8″). A *stocky, short-tailed* jacamar with a *heavy and startlingly pink bill* found somewhat locally in *várzea forest borders and around lake margins* in lowlands of east. Formerly called Chestnut Jacamar. **Sexes alike.** Iris red; eye-ring pink, as are legs. *Mostly dark chestnut,* blackish on crown, wings, and tail; *ear-coverts contrastingly white.* **Similar species:** This conspicuous jacamar with its bubblegum-pink bill is unlikely to be confused; it looks vaguely kingfisher-like. **Habits:** Found in pairs or small groups, but many seemingly suitable areas appear inexplicably to be without them. This cute and ultradistinctive jacamar generally perches fully in open, not too high, making quick fast sallies into air, oft as not returning to same branch time and again. **Voice:** Most frequent calls include a sharp "kweeyp!" and an accelerating and shrill chatter, rising in pitch and somewhat woodcreeper-like (very different from other jacamars).

Brown Jacamar, *Brachygalba lugubris*
Jacamar Pardo   Plate 50(2)

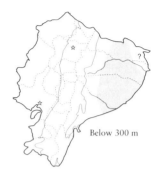

16–17 cm (6¼–6¾″). Generally local and scarce in *borders and canopy of várzea and riparian forest and woodland* in lowlands of east. *Long and slender black bill. Mostly sooty brown,* somewhat freckled and streaked white on face and throat; wings and *rather short tail* glossy bluish black. *Belly contrastingly paler, buff to buffy whitish.* ♂ somewhat richer brown and less mottled on throat and breast. **Similar species:** Smaller, shorter-tailed, and duller-plumaged than other Ecuadorian jacamars, and more arboreal than most. Silhouette is actually quite hummingbird-like. **Habits:** Often occurs in small (family?) groups, usually perching in semiopen on twigs and small branches, making long sallies into air after passing insects. **Voice:** Calls shrill and piercing, a single sharp "piii" or "peeey," also a thin, somewhat descending and slowing "pidi-dideedeedee-dee-dee-dew." It slightly recalls song of Dusky-tailed Flatbill.

Galbula Jacamars
The "classic" jacamars, with *shimmering plumage* and *strongly graduated tails.* All but one species range east of the Andes. Although inhabiting forest, most are fairly conspicuous birds, perching on open branches with rapier-like bills angled upward.

Yellow-billed Jacamar, *Galbula albirostris*
Jacamar Piquiamarillo   Plate 50(3)
19 cm (7½″). *Undergrowth inside terra firme forest and woodland* in lowlands of east. Typical birds have maxilla black, *mandible*

To 400 m

yellow (but in some the bill is entirely yellow, in others only basal half of mandible is yellow); eye-ring and legs also yellow. ♂ shining metallic golden green above, crown more bronzy purple; outer tail feathers rufous, upperside of central feathers metallic green. Chin buff, lower throat white; *remaining underparts rufous*, darkest and richest across breast. ♀ similar but *lacking* white on throat. **Similar species:** *The only jacamar with yellow on bill.* No other Ecuadorian jacamar is as apt to be found low inside forest (the others either occur mainly at borders or higher above ground). **Habits:** Found in pairs, perching on open branches in understory with bill typically held angled upward; looks around alertly and periodically sallies out after insects. Often rather tame. **Voice:** Most commonly heard song a distinctive, rising "wheee, wheee, whee, whee-whee-ee-ee-ee-ee-ee-ee" ending in a trill, fairly similar to White-chinned Jacamar's song. Also gives a slower series of drawn-out "peeeek" notes and a fast series of short "keek" notes.

White-chinned Jacamar, *Galbula tombacea*
Jacamar Barbiblanco   Plate 50(4)

?

To 400 m

23.5 cm (9¼"). Lower growth of humid forest, *especially in várzea and stream borders*, in lowlands of *northeast* (mainly or entirely north of Río Napo). Bill long and slender. ♂ shining metallic golden green above, *crown dusky brown* but somewhat bluer to rear; upperside of tail green, outer feathers rufous-chestnut (such that underside of tail looks rufous-chestnut). *Chin whitish, throat and breast shining green*; belly contrastingly rufous-chestnut. A minority of ♂♂ are more coppery above (individual variation?). ♀ similar to ♂, but belly and underside of tail paler, more cinnamon-rufous. **Similar species:** Purplish Jacamar has no rufous on underside of tail; ♂ has white throat patch, purplish bronze breast, and whitish on belly (no rufous), ♀ has white replaced by buff. It is much more a terra firme bird. **Habits:** Typically found in pairs that perch, often side by side, on fairly open branches and look around alertly. They make long sallies into air in pursuit of flying insects, often returning to same perch but if disturbed sometimes moving to a more hidden one. **Voice:** Most common call a loud and arresting, somewhat querulous "peeyk," often repeated several times. Song a series of "pee" notes that gradually accelerate and ascend in pitch, ending in a fast chipper.

Coppery-chested Jacamar, *Galbula pastazae*
Jacamar Pechicobrizo   Plate 50(5)

750–1500 m

24 cm (9½"). Local in lower growth and borders of *foothill and lower subtropical forest on e. slope*, occurring at higher elevations than any other *Galbula* in Ecuador. Bill very long and slender. *Eye-ring orange-yellow*, sometimes conspicuous though on

other birds it can be hard to see. ♂ above shining green, *bluer on crown*, and more bronzy on upperside of tail; outer tail feathers rufous (such that underside of tail is rufous). Throat and breast shining green; belly contrastingly rufous-chestnut. ♀ differs in having *large throat patch rufous-chestnut*. **Similar species:** Not known to occur with any other *Galbula* jacamar. ♂ White-chinned is most similar but differs in crown color, etc. **Habits:** Usually in pairs, sometimes well separated, that perch on branches in lower growth where they favor openings such as those along streams, trails, or around treefalls. **Voice:** Song a series of gradually rising "pee" notes that seem (unlike many other *Galbula*) usually not to end in a chipper. Also gives a sharper "peeyk" call.

Rufous-tailed Jacamar, *Galbula ruficauda*
Jacamar Colirrufo   Plate 50(6)

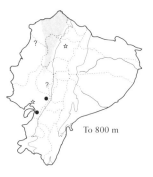

To 800 m

24 cm (9½"). Lower growth of humid forest and woodland borders and openings in *lowlands and foothills of west*, where the only "typical" jacamar. *Bill very long and slender.* ♂ *shining metallic golden to coppery green above; upperside of tail green*, outer feathers rufous (such that underside of tail is rufous). Chin blackish, throat white, and chest shining metallic golden to coppery green; *lower underparts rich rufous.* ♀ similar but throat buff, lower underparts less richly colored and somewhat paler. **Similar species:** Only other jacamar west of Andes is the very different and rarer Great (with much heavier and shorter bill, etc.). **Habits:** Similar to White-chinned Jacamar, though not tied to vicinity of water. **Voice:** Most frequent call, given by both sexes and often attracting attention, is a sharp "peeyeek!," sometimes repeated several

times in quick succession (beware similarity to Pacific Royal-Flycatcher's call). Song a long, high-pitched, and ascending series of "pee" notes ending in a trill.

Purplish Jacamar, *Galbula chalcothorax*
Jacamar Purpúreo   Plate 50(7)

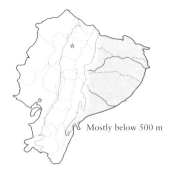

Mostly below 500 m

23.5 cm (9¼"). Somewhat local in *lower and middle growth of terra firme forest and borders* in lowlands of east. Formerly considered conspecific with *G. leucogastra* (Bronzy Jacamar) of ne. South America. Bill long and slender. ♂ *purplish coppery bronze above*, more bluish green on crown and tail; *underside of tail dusky, feathers edged whitish*. Chin black, large patch on lower throat white; *breast contrastingly purplish bronze; belly mixed white and blackish.* ♀ similar though not quite so bright generally, and *white on throat and belly replaced by buff.* **Similar species:** Much less green (more "purplish") than other *Galbula*, and showing no rufous on tail. Cf. White-chinned Jacamar. **Habits:** Similar to other *Galbula* (see White-chinned), though more a bird of forest interior than most others, tending to range higher above ground than Yellow-billed. **Voice:** Calls somewhat more chattering than many other jacamars'. Song a rising series of inflected notes, often doubled, e.g., "weeee weeee wi-deee wi-deee wi-deee wi-deee," sometimes speeding up into a trill or chipper (P. Coopmans). Call an occasional "weeee," recalling call of Dusky-capped Flycatcher.

Paradise Jacamar, *Galbula dea*
Jacamar Paraíso   Plate 50(8)

28.5–30.5 cm (11¼–12"). A nearly unmistakable large jacamar with *extremely long slim tail, rare and local in canopy of terra*

Below 250 m

firme forest in lowlands of east. Bill very long and slender. **Sexes much alike.** *Mostly dark bluish black*, wings and tail more bronzy green; underside of tail blackish, feathers tipped whitish. *Large throat patch contrastingly white.* ♂ apparently has crown mottled brownish, this color darker in ♀. **Similar species:** No other jacamar is as long-tailed or as dark overall. **Habits:** Usually in pairs that perch high in canopy, frequently on exposed branches from which they sally out into air, often for long distances, after passing insects. Easiest to see at forest borders. **Voice:** Call a sharp "pik!" or "peeyk!," sometimes given in a short series. Song (in Guyana) a rather slow series of 10–12 well-enunciated notes that gradually descend in pitch, e.g., "peeyr-peeyr-peeyr-peer-peer-peer-pur-pur-pur-pr."

Great Jacamar, *Jacamerops aureus*
Jacamar Grande   Plate 50(9)

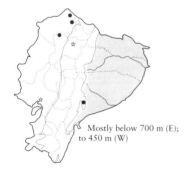

Mostly below 700 m (E);
to 450 m (W)

29.5–30.5 cm (11½–12″). A gorgeous, *large, and heavy-bodied jacamar* of mid-levels and subcanopy of humid forest in lowlands and foothills of east, also locally in far northwest. *Bill heavy and slightly decurved*, very different from the slender bills of all other jaca-

mars. ♂ *above shimmering metallic golden green* with coppery overtones on back and sides of neck, crown somewhat bluer; underside of tail blue-black. Upper throat metallic bluish green, patch on lower throat white (often hard to see); *underparts rich tawny-rufous.* ♀ like ♂ but lacks white throat patch, and slightly paler below. **Similar species:** Larger than other jacamars, and with a very different, heavier bill. **Habits:** Found singly or in pairs, surprisingly inconspicuous, perching quietly on open branches where it often does not move for long periods, then abruptly sallying out to capture an insect from a branch or leaf (unlike other jacamars *not* flying out into air). **Voice:** Distinctive song an eerie and mournful whistle that fades away, "kleeeeeee-enhhhhh," slurred and somewhat hawk-like in quality. Bird often sounds farther away than it actually is. Agitated birds give several other strange-sounding calls, including a querulous, cat-like meowing, "wir-owwhh, kwo-o-o-o."

Puffbirds: Bucconidae (19)
A Neotropical family of *chunky* birds with *large heads and short necks, stout hooked bills,* and small weak feet. Puffbirds are found primarily in humid lowland forests, a few ranging up into the subtropics. Their plumage is lax and soft, and coloration is subdued with brown, rufous, black, and gray predominating. Most puffbirds are lethargic, infrequently encountered birds that are easily overlooked unless vocalizing; nunbirds and the Swallow-winged Puffbird are exceptions. Puffbirds feed on large insects and even small vertebrates such as lizards. They nest in burrows dug into banks, a few species in termitaries. **Sexes are usually alike.**

Notharchus Puffbirds
Essentially black and white puffbirds found primarily in the subcanopy and borders of humid lowland forest.

White-necked Puffbird
Notharchus macrorhynchos
Buco Cuelliblanco   Plate 51(1)

25–25.5 cm (9¾–10″). Subcanopy and borders of humid and deciduous forest and woodland in lowlands of east and west. *Broad and heavy bill.* Black above with

To 400 m

prominent white forecrown and *broad white nuchal collar*. White below with *wide black breast band* and black barring on flanks. **Similar species:** In far northwest, cf. Black-breasted Puffbird. Otherwise this large, boldly patterned puffbird is unlikely to be confused; cf. smaller Pied Puffbird. **Habits:** Generally solitary, in early morning often perching quietly for long periods on high exposed branches. From time to time makes an abrupt sally out to capture large insects from leaves and branches, often grabbing prey with an audible snap and beating it against a branch before swallowing. **Voice:** Not very vocal. Infrequently heard song an evenly pitched monotonous trill that lasts 3–5 seconds, sometimes given by both members of a pair.

Black-breasted Puffbird, *Notharchus pectoralis*
Buco Pechinegro   Plate 51(2)

Below 200 m

20.5–21 cm (8–8¼″). Subcanopy and borders of humid forest in *lowlands of far northwest*. Heavy bill. Glossy blue-black above with *large white patch on ear-coverts* extending back as narrow nuchal collar; some narrow white scaling on wing-coverts. *Throat patch*

white surrounded by blue-black sides of neck and *broad breast band*; lower underparts white with black barring on flanks. **Similar species:** White-necked Puffbird larger with prominent white on forecrown and much more white on sides of neck and chest. Cf. also smaller Pied Puffbird. **Habits:** Much like White-necked Puffbird, though less often perching on high exposed branches; perches in the open primarily during first few hours of morning, at later hours apt to remain in forest cover. Sometimes one is seen in attendance at a swarm of army ants. **Voice:** Presence often made known by distinctive loud song, an often protracted series of whistled notes that usually ends with 3 drawling descending couplets, e.g., "kweee-kweee-kweee-kweee-kweee-kweee, kweee-a, kwey-a, kyoo-a" (there may be up to 30 "kweee" notes).

Pied Puffbird, *Notharchus tectus*
Buco Pinto   Plate 51(3)

To 500 m

14.5–17 cm (5¾–6¾″). A *small* puffbird of subcanopy and borders of humid forest and woodland in lowlands of east and west, more numerous in west. **Western birds** black above with a few small white spots on forecrown and narrow white superciliary; *white stripe on scapulars*, some white tipping on tail feathers. White below with *narrow black breast band* and some black barring on flanks. **Eastern birds** *substantially larger*, and have *larger and more profuse white crown spotting* and much broader breast band. **Similar species:** So much smaller than other "black and white" puffbirds that confusion is unlikely, even in east. White-necked Puffbird much larger with white forecrown and no spotting, no white scapular stripe, and no white tail tipping. **Habits:** Usually in pairs, often perched on open branches where relatively easy to see when at forest edge (but much harder in continuous canopy). Like other puffbirds, often perches motionless for long periods, then abruptly darts off after insect prey. **Voice:** Relatively vocal, with frequently heard song a series of high-pitched and thin whistled notes, "wheee, wheee, wheee wheedeedee-dee-dee, pee-pee-pee-pee-pee-peedi-peedi-peedi-peedi," somewhat variable but always with a distinctive shrill piping quality. It tends to speed up in the middle, then slow down again.

Bucco Puffbirds
A diverse trio of *very inconspicuous* puffbirds found only in humid forests in *lowlands of the east*. All are *boldly and attractively patterned* with brown, rufous, and black.

Chestnut-capped Puffbird
Bucco macrodactylus
Buco Gorricastaño   Plate 51(4)

To 600 m

16–16.5 cm (6¼–6½"). A *small* puffbird, scarce and unobtrusive in shrubby borders of humid forest and undergrowth of secondary woodland and várzea forest in lowlands of east. Iris red. *Crown rufous-chestnut*, narrow superciliary white, *face black* bordered below by white malar stripe; otherwise brown above with narrow orange-buff nuchal collar. Upper throat buff, bordered below by *black band across lower throat extending onto sides of neck*; underparts whitish with indistinct wavy brown barring. **Similar species:** Cf. larger and much rarer Spotted Puffbird. *Nonnula* nunlets are much less patterned and differently shaped. **Habits:** Almost always solitary (pairs seem not to forage together),

this small and phlegmatic puffbird favors tangled, densely vegetated situations and doubtless is often overlooked. It may remain motionless for long periods, then abruptly fly off or sally to a leaf after prey. **Voice:** Almost always quiet. Song in Peru described as basically a series of "wee-a" or "peee" notes (Hilty and Brown 1986). Call a plaintive "weeeeooo," easily mistaken for Dusky-capped Flycatcher (P. Coopmans).

Spotted Puffbird, *Bucco tamatia*
Buco Moteado   Plate 51(5)

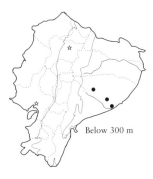

Below 300 m

18–18.5 cm (7–7¼"). *Very rare* in lower and middle growth of várzea forest in *lowlands of southeast*; few records. Iris red. Mostly brown above with *orange-rufous forehead and short superciliary*; white malar streak extending back as narrow nuchal collar and bordered below by *large black patch on sides of neck. Throat and upper chest orange-rufous*; underparts white with *irregular coarse black spotting*. **Similar species:** Cf. considerably smaller and unspotted Chestnut-capped Puffbird. Otherwise this boldly patterned puffbird is unlikely to be confused. **Habits:** Poorly known in Ecuador. Elsewhere stolid in demeanor, perching for long periods without moving, sometimes fully in the open on an unobstructed branch but usually hard to spot because of lack of motion. Mainly solitary, less often in pairs. **Voice:** Though usually quiet, the distinctive song—usually given in early morning—quite loud and far-carrying and can reveal this species' presence in areas where its existence had been unsuspected. Song a long series of monotonous and inflected "kueeép" notes that start softly and become louder, continuing 10–15 seconds.

Collared Puffbird, *Bucco capensis*
Buco Collarejo   Plate 51(6)

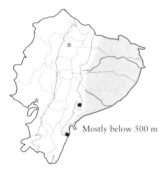

Mostly below 500 m

Mostly below 1000 m, higher around Mindo

18.5–19 cm (7¼–7½″). An unmistakable, *mainly orange-rufous* puffbird found at low densities in lower and middle growth inside humid forest in lowlands of east. *Bill bright orange* with black culmen; iris orange to orange-red; legs orange-yellow. *Head bright orange-rufous*, crown with wavy blackish barring; otherwise rufous above with wavy black barring, *narrow orange-rufous nuchal collar bordered below by black*; tail orange-rufous with narrow black barring. Throat white bordered below by *conspicuous black chest band*; lower underparts yellowish buff. **Habits:** Mainly solitary, perching quietly and unobtrusively inside forest, often in or near viny tangles where—despite its bright coloration—it is hard to spot. Occasionally one accompanies a mixed flock. **Voice:** Usually quiet, especially during day. At dawn, and sometimes in predawn darkness, far-carrying and highly distinctive song is given, a somewhat hoarse rhythmic phrase, "cua-will-kú, cua-will-kú, cua-will-kú . . . ," sometimes with "kú" omitted. This can be repeated steadily for long periods, a minute or even more.

Nystalus Puffbirds
Barred and streaked puffbirds with *buff nuchal collars*, one species on either side of the Andes. Both are very vocal.

Barred Puffbird, *Nystalus radiatus*
Buco Barreteado   Plate 51(7)

20.5–21.5 cm (8–8½″). Subcanopy and borders of humid forest and woodland in *lowlands and foothills of west*. Bill greenish

to yellowish gray; iris pale yellow. *Cinnamon-rufous above with conspicuous coarse black barring* and prominent buff nuchal collar. Throat white; underparts buff *with narrow black barring*, especially across breast and down flanks. **Similar species:** Striolated Puffbird occurs only east of Andes. Only possible confusion otherwise is with ♀ Fasciated Antshrike which is smaller with solid rufous crown, no buff nuchal collar, etc. **Habits:** Found singly or in pairs, perching stolidly on often rather open branches (sometimes even on wires), quietly surveying surroundings, occasionally flicking tail sideways. As it moves so infrequently, often rather hard to spot. Usually not with flocks. **Voice:** Heard more often than seen; soft but far-carrying vocalization readily recognized as a slowly rendered wolf whistle: "wheeee-eet? . . . wheeeee-urr." Rufous Mourner's comparable call is less drawn-out, with second note higher pitched.

Striolated Puffbird, *Nystalus striolatus*
Buco Estriolado   Plate 51(8)

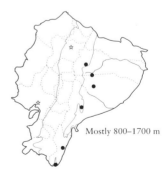

Mostly 800–1700 m

20–21 cm (7³/₄–8¹/₄″). Scarce and local in sub-canopy (especially) and borders of *foothill and lower subtropical forest on e. slope.* Bill yellowish green with dark tip; iris pale yellow to buff. Above dark brown spotted and edged with rufous buff and with whitish lores and *cinnamon-buff nuchal collar*; tail dusky barred cinnamon-buff. Upper throat and belly white, breast buff, *underparts narrowly streaked with black.* **Similar species:** Though rather drab and unmarked, this arboreal puffbird is unlikely to be confused. White-chested Puffbird ranges only in forest undergrowth; it is darker generally (especially below), lacks nuchal collar, etc. **Habits:** Similar to Barred Puffbird, though Striolated seems less often than that species to range near ground, and rarely occurs in edge situations. **Voice:** Heard much more often than seen. Soft but far-carrying call a melancholy whistled "whip, whi-wheeu, wheeeeeuu" with characteristic cadence.

Malacoptila Puffbirds
Inconspicuous puffbirds found in *under-growth* of humid lowland forest and charac-terized by their *stiff, usually white, loral feathers.* Each has a sombre plumage with much pale streaking.

White-chested Puffbird, *Malacoptila fusca*
Buco Pechiblanco   Plate 51(10)

Mostly below 900 m

18–18.5 cm (7–7¹/₄″). Undergrowth inside *terra firme forest in lowlands and foothills of east.* Bill *orange* with black tip and culmen. Above dark brown *boldly streaked with buff* except on tail, and with *white lores and at base of bill* and buff feathers spring-ing from base of bill. *Throat and breast con-spicuously streaked blackish, buff, and white,*

with white crescent across chest (often obscure in field); belly whitish and more or less unstreaked. **Similar species:** The only *Malacoptila* puffbird known from e. low-lands. Black-streaked Puffbird is more mon-tane in distribution (though they could overlap locally); it has black bill, buff on foreneck, etc. **Habits:** A stolid and incon-spicuous puffbird, seemingly even more so than its congeners; rarely seen apart from mist-net captures. Mainly solitary (less often in pairs), perching more or less immobile and close to ground; sometimes accompanies mixed understory flocks. Sallies abruptly and swiftly for prey, either to low branches and leaves or to ground, sometimes returning to same perch but more often moving on. **Voice:** Call an infrequently heard (per-haps mainly just overlooked), high-pitched single "pseeeeu." Less frequently given song a prolonged, high-pitched, descending "tsrrrrrrrrrrrrr" repeated at long intervals.

Black-streaked Puffbird
Malacoptila fulvogularis
Buco Negrilistado   Plate 51(9)

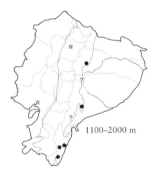

1100–2000 m

18.5–19 cm (7¹/₄–7¹/₂″). Undergrowth inside *foothill and subtropical forest on e. slope.* *Bill black*; iris red. Head blackish, upperparts otherwise wood brown, both narrowly streaked buff except on wings and tail (streaking most prominent on head and neck), and with whitish and brown feathers springing from lores and base of bill. *Midthroat and upper chest uniform buff* (unstreaked); underparts coarsely streaked blackish brown and whitish. **Similar species:** The only *Malacoptila* puffbird in its *montane* range. White-chested Puffbird has mainly orange bill, no solid buff area on foreparts, and is more heavily streaked on mantle. **Habits:** Similar to White-chested Puffbird, though more apt to be seen at forest edge; sometimes noted while accompanying a mixed flock. **Voice:** Infrequently heard song a single drawn-out, high-pitched, and rising note, "pseeeuueeé," steadily repeated at intervals of 2–4 seconds.

White-whiskered Puffbird
Malacoptila panamensis
Buco Bigotiblanco   Plate 51(12)

To 900 m

18.5–19 cm (7¼–7½″). Undergrowth and borders of humid forest and secondary woodland in *lowlands and foothills of west.* Maxilla blackish, lower mandible dull yellowish green; iris red. ♂ brown above lightly spotted with buff across mantle, and with buff and whitish feathers springing from lores and base of bill. *Throat and breast orange-rufous; lower underparts coarsely streaked blackish and buffy whitish.* ♀ similar to ♂ but more grayish above and with reduced orange-rufous below, the blackish on sides of neck protruding onto upper throat. **Similar species:** The only *Malacoptila* puffbird west of Andes and as such unlikely to be confused. Confusion possible with Moustached Puffbird (*M. mystacalis*; see Plate 51 [11]) of Venezuelan and Colombian Andes, and known from immediately adjacent Nariño, Colombia (possibly also in Ecuador?). It differs from White-whiskered mainly in its gray (not yellowish) lower mandible and plain rufescent underparts *with little or no streaking.* **Habits:** Similar to White-chested Puffbird, but considerably easier to observe; pairs are regularly noted accompanying mixed flocks at various sites. **Voice:** Most frequent call a simple, sibilant

"pseeeu," sometimes repeated at intervals. Infrequently given song a high-pitched descending trill similar to but much shorter than White-chested Puffbird's trill and usually with an emphasized note at end, e.g., "tssiirrrrr-tsít" (P. Coopmans).

Lanceolated Monklet
Micromonacha lanceolata
Monjecito Lanceolado   Plate 51(13)

Mostly below 1100 m

13.5 cm (5¼″). A *tiny* puffbird found locally in humid forest and borders in *lowlands and foothills of east and west.* Heavy arched bill black. Brown above and on sides of neck with *conspicuous white frontal band, lores, and base of bill,* white outlined with black above and on sides; tail with inconspicuous blackish subterminal band. White below *profusely streaked with black.* **Similar species:** Small size, white about bill, and streaked underparts of this infrequently encountered puffbird should preclude confusion. White-whiskered and White-chested Puffbirds are much larger, etc. **Habits:** Generally scarce and inconspicuous, the lethargic monklet is usually not difficult to observe once it has been discovered. Often perches in open on horizontal branches up to 10–20 m above ground, periodically making long sallies to branches and leaves in pursuit of large insects (especially katydids and cicadas) which are partially dismembered before being swallowed. Found singly or in pairs; usually not with mixed flocks. **Voice:** Infrequently heard song a short series of quick high-pitched notes (usually 4–6, sometimes more) with a rising inflection, faint at first but then gradually increasing in tempo and strength.

Nonnula Nunlets

Very small, basically brown puffbirds that are *very inconspicuous* in lower growth of humid forest in *lowlands of the east*.

Brown Nunlet, *Nonnula brunnea*
Nonula Parda   Plate 51(15)

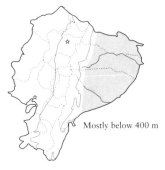

Mostly below 400 m

Below 250 m

14 cm (5½″). Scarce and retiring in lower and middle growth of humid forest and borders in lowlands of east, favoring thick treefall vegetation. Rather long, slender, slightly decurved bill gray with black culmen and tip; *eye-ring pink*. Uniform brown above and on sides of neck; *loral spot rufous-buff. Cinnamon-rufous below, paling to cinnamon-buff on belly*. **Similar** species: Cf. much rarer Rusty-breasted Nunlet. Otherwise its uniform, unpatterned plumage makes it unlikely to be confused, though it could carelessly be mistaken for ♀ Cinereous Antshrike or other antbird. **Habits:** Notably lethargic, Brown Nunlet is almost always found singly, perching upright on a slender stem or branch, often in a viny tangle. It does not move very much and therefore is not easy to spot—but once discovered can be quite tame. One or two sometimes accompany mixed understory flocks of antwrens, etc. **Voice:** Infrequently heard song a steadily repeated series of 20–25 "treeu" notes that commence softly but gradually become louder before fading off at end. It recalls Black Bushbird's song.

Rusty-breasted Nunlet, *Nonnula rubecula*
Nonula Pechirrojiza   Plate 51(14)

14 cm (5½″). *Very rare and local* in lower and middle growth of humid forest in lowlands of *northeast*, occurring at least at one site

with more numerous Brown Nunlet. Rather long, slender, and slightly decurved bill gray with more blackish culmen and tip; *eye-ring white or bluish white*. Resembles Brown Nunlet, differing in its *more contrasting white* (not pink) *eye-ring*, whiter loral spot, and duller and less rufescent underparts with more contrasting and whiter belly. **Habits:** Apparently much like better-known—at least in Ecuador—Brown Nunlet.

White-faced Nunbird, *Hapaloptila castanea*
Monja Cariblanca   Plate 51(16)

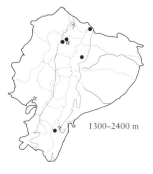

1300–2400 m

23–24 cm (9–9½″). A *scarce and inconspicuous* nunbird found *very locally* in *subtropical forest subcanopy, borders, and adjacent clearings on both slopes* (mainly in Pichincha and w. Napo). Heavy black bill; iris red. Above grayish olive, grayest on crown and duskier on wings and tail; *prominent white lores and frontal band*, bordered above by black. Upper throat white; *underparts otherwise rich chestnut-rufous*. **Similar** species: The only montane nunbird, and unique in having rufous in plumage. **Habits:** This attractive, chunky nunbird is only rarely encountered and apparently everywhere occurs at very low densities. It ranges in pairs or small groups, foraging at varying levels but sometimes surprisingly low; it usually is very sluggish and stolid, remaining perched on the same branch for long periods. Tends to hunch forward like a puffbird, less often perching upright as do *Monasa* nunbirds. **Voice:** Infrequently heard song a slowly repeated series of rising notes, "kwoah ... kwoah ... kwoah ..." (M. Lysinger recording).

Monasa Nunbirds

Very distinctive *gray and black puffbirds* found in *lowlands of the east*; their *somewhat decurved bills are brightly colored*. They are *very vocal* and, for puffbirds, are unusually conspicuous and gregarious. Nunbirds nest in J-shaped tunnels dug into more or less level ground.

Black-fronted Nunbird, *Monasa nigrifrons*

Monja Frentinegra   Plate 51(17)

To 400 m

26–27.5 cm (10¼–10¾″). Common and conspicuous in *várzea and riparian forest and woodland* in lowlands of east, most frequent at edge and also regular on river islands. *Bill coral red. Entirely slaty gray*, darker on foreparts and black on forehead and upper throat. **Similar species:** White-fronted Nunbird is found strictly in terra firme forest, not near water as this nunbird almost invariably is. In any case, Black-fronted is a darker bird generally that lacks *any* white on foreface. **Habits:** A familiar bird, sometimes seeming almost fearless, this svelte nunbird usually occurs in groups of up to 4–6 individuals, perching upright often fully in the open on horizontal branches or looping lianas. Rests quietly, then sallies to foliage or

branches after prey, generally continuing on to a new perch. Descends to ground less often, even more rarely pursuing insects in the air. Flight slow, a few shallow flaps and then a glide. Other birds regularly flock with it. **Voice:** Though capable of being very noisy, foraging flocks often move along almost noiselessly, giving an occasional soft or querulous note. At intervals, however, members of a group will suddenly break into a great gabbling that may continue for several minutes. This rollicking chorus is most often given by two birds (a pair?) that usually perch side by side, often facing in opposite directions, sometimes swiveling tails sideways; the chorus is more "jumbled" than in White-fronted Nunbird (P. Coopmans).

White-fronted Nunbird, *Monasa morphoeus*

Monja Frentiblanca   Plate 51(18)

Mostly below 1000 m

25–26 cm (9¾–10¼″). Mid-levels and subcanopy of *terra firme forest and borders* in lowlands and foothills of east. *Bill coral red. Mostly dark gray*, palest on belly and blacker on face and especially throat; *forecrown and chin contrastingly white*. **Similar species:** Likely only confused with Black-fronted Nunbird, which lacks facial white and is restricted to areas near water, with White-fronted replacing it in upland forests. Cf. also the all-gray Screaming Piha. **Habits:** Similar to Black-fronted Nunbird, though generally less easy to see; comes down to near ground less often, and groups are almost always smaller (most often just in pairs, less often small family groups). Flocks often seem to coalesce around them. **Voice:** Similar to Black-fronted Nunbird but less jumbled, a loud gabbling chorus given together by a pair of birds (occasionally several).

Yellow-billed Nunbird, *Monasa flavirostris*
Monja Piquiamarilla   Plate 51(19)

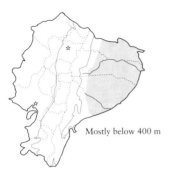

Mostly below 400 m

24–25.5 cm (9½–10″). *Relatively scarce and local* in canopy and borders of humid forest and secondary woodland in lowlands of east. *Bill pale lemon yellow. Slaty black* with *white scapulars and lesser wing-coverts* (white sometimes hidden or partially obscured). **Similar species:** Other nunbirds have red bills and show no white on wing. **Habits:** Tends to perch more often on high exposed branches at forest edge than other nunbirds, and—unlike them—usually does not occur with mixed flocks. Has same upright posture. Sallies more often to air than larger nunbirds. Occurs mainly in pairs, less often small groups. **Voice:** Yellow-billed tends to be less noisy than its larger congeners, but it does have a protracted rollicking gabble much like others (though perhaps less loud), with a frequently repeated phrase being "wheekit-wheeyk, wheekit-wheeyk. . . ."

Swallow-winged Puffbird
Chelidoptera tenebrosa
Buco Golondrina   Plate 51(20)

To 400 m

16.5 cm (6″). A chunky, *short-tailed* puffbird that is *conspicuous* in forest and woodland borders, especially along rivers, in *lowlands of east. Perches on high open branches, sallying into air.* Sometimes called simply Swallow-wing. Short black bill. Dull glossy blue-black above, with *white patch on lower back and rump* (obvious in flight, but usually hidden at rest); underwing-coverts white. Throat and breast dull black, *contrasting with cinnamon-rufous belly*; crissum gray. **Similar species:** In flight this species' very broad wings and short tail impart an unmistakable silhouette. Perched birds can look vaguely like a martin, though martins are not so short-tailed; this puffbird's square-headed shape even vaguely recalls a parrot. **Habits:** Pairs or small groups perch in the open even in the heat of a sunny midday, from there making long sallies after insect prey; they fly out rapidly and directly, then swoop back to the same perch with a slower long glide. **Voice:** Generally silent, but occasionally gives a weak twittering.

New World Barbets: Capitonidae (7)
Chunky, colorful birds found in the canopy and borders of humid and montane forests, the barbets of the New World are now considered to represent a family distinct from Old World barbets. (Megalaimidae) and African Barbets (Lybiidae). They appear to be closely related to the Toucans (Ramphastidae), and likewise are mainly frugivorous. Most species are sexually dimorphic, some strongly so. Nests, so far as known, are placed in tree holes and cavities.

Capito Barbets
Large barbets with heavy stout bills, found mainly in lowland forests. Most species are very vocal.

Scarlet-crowned Barbet, *Capito aurovirens*
Barbudo Coronirrojo   Plate 50(11)

18–19 cm (7–7½″). Fairly common and conspicuous in canopy and borders of *várzea and riparian forest and woodland, lake margins, and river islands* in *lowlands of east.* Iris red; bill mainly blackish, lower mandible bluish basally. ♂ has *scarlet crown and nape* contrasting with plain dusky-olive upperparts. *Throat and breast yellow-orange*; belly con-

To 400 m

trastingly olive. ♀ similar but *crown "frosty" white*. **Similar species:** Both sexes (especially ♀ ♀) of Gilded Barbet more boldly streaked or spotted generally with an "old gold" (not red or white) crown; Gilded Barbet occurs more widely, not being so restricted to areas near water as Scarlet-crowned. **Habits:** Most often in pairs, sometimes small groups, frequently perching stolidly in semiopen for protracted periods. When feeding clambers about in foliage or sits quietly munching fruit (often *Cecropia* catkins). Most often not with mixed flocks. **Voice:** Frequently heard call a mellow, rolling "crrrow, crrow, crrow..." (or "crrrr"), repeated up to 10–12 times. Resembles Lemon-throated Barbet's call but is more slowly paced.

Orange-fronted Barbet, *Capito squamatus*
Barbudo Frentinaranja   Plate 50(12)

Mostly below 800 m

17–18 cm (6³/₄–7″). Locally numerous in canopy and borders of humid forest and woodland, also in adjacent clearings with scattered trees, in *lowlands and foothills of west*. Iris red; bill bluish with black tip. ♂ has *reddish orange forecrown* with *rest of crown white*; *otherwise glossy blue-black above*, tertials broadly edged white. *White*

below washed with creamy yellow especially across breast. ♀ like ♂ above but with narrow white scaling on feathers of mantle. *Throat and breast black, contrasting sharply with creamy white belly*. **Similar species:** In most of w. lowlands this strongly patterned barbet is the only member of its family; in n. Esmeraldas, cf. Five-colored Barbet. **Habits:** Most often seen in pairs, often accompanying mixed flocks dominated by various other frugivores, especially tanagers. Forages at varying levels, lowest in fruiting trees out in clearings. **Voice:** Not very vocal. Nasal and guttural "aark" notes, sometimes delivered in an irregular series, are occasionally given. Easily overlooked song a low-volume, deep-pitched "rrrrrrrrrrrrrrrrrrrrrrrrrrrrrrrrrrrr," recalling a distant motorcycle (P. Coopmans).

Five-colored Barbet, *Capito quinticolor*
Barbudo Cinco Colores   Plate 50(10)

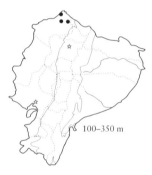

100–350 m

17–18 cm (6³/₄–7″). Apparently not uncommon in *canopy and borders of very humid forest in lowlands of n. Esmeraldas*. Iris brown; bill mostly black, grayish basally. ♂ mostly black above with *midcrown to nape contrastingly red*; *yellow stripe on sides of back forms an irregular V*, also a *single broad yellow wing-bar and yellow edging on tertials*; tail dusky-olive. Throat and breast white becoming orange-yellow on belly; streaking on flanks black. Rather different ♀ black above *narrowly streaked with yellow*; plain tail dusky-olive. Throat and breast white becoming yellow on belly, with *entire underparts profusely spotted with black* (streakier on lower flanks). **Similar species:** Orange-fronted Barbet has orange and white on crown, lacks yellow markings on upperparts, and ♀ is obviously bicolored below with no spotting. **Habits:** Not well known, but probably similar to Orange-fronted Barbet; perhaps somewhat more forest-based, occurring less often in adjacent clearings than Orange-fronted. **Voice:** Song a series of 10–17 deep hollow "oohp" or "oohng" notes that start and end abruptly (O. Jahn recording); ♀'s vocalization somewhat higher pitched and more bisyllabic. Also gives "aark" calls.

Gilded Barbet, *Capito auratus*
Barbudo Filigrana   Plate 50(13)

Mostly below 1200 m

17–18 cm (6³/₄–7″). A *colorful and strongly patterned* barbet, numerous and conspicuous in canopy and borders of humid forest and woodland in *lowlands (especially) and foothills of east.* Formerly considered conspecific with Black-spotted Barbet (*C. niger*) of ne. South America. Iris red; bill black, bluish basally. ♂ mainly black above, *crown "old gold"* becoming duskier to rear; *long superciliary, stripe on sides of back, wing-bar, and tertial edging golden yellow*; tail dusky-olive. *Throat and chest intense orange*, becoming yellow on remaining underparts; black spotting on sides and flanks. ♀ like ♂ above but *streaking on mantle and wings finer. Boldly and extensively spotted with black below*; ground color of throat and chest orange, yellow elsewhere. **Similar species:** Not likely confused in range, where both sexes are only barbet with streaking above, ♀ the only one with spotting below. **Habits:** Basically arboreal, foraging at varying levels (lower at edge and in clearings), often accompanying mixed flocks and gathering with other species at fruiting trees. Can seem rather clumsy as it hops about in foliage and along branches; tail often

held slightly cocked. **Voice:** Distinctive song a measured, repeated "whoo-boop, whoo-boop, whoo-boop" that is frequently heard but rather hard to track to source. Also gives "aark" calls.

Eubucco Barbets
Somewhat smaller than *Capito* barbets, with less stout and more pointed bills. They tend to be less vocal than *Capito*.

Lemon-throated Barbet, *Eubucco richardsoni*
Barbudo Golilimón   Plate 50(15)

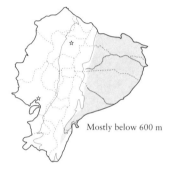

Mostly below 600 m

14.5–15 cm (5³/₄–6″). Uncommon in *canopy and borders of terra firme forest in lowlands of east.* Iris red to reddish brown; ♂'s bill olive yellow, ♀'s duller with culmen blackish. Both sexes *boldly patterned. Colorful* ♂ has *head and chin spot deep velvety red* contrasting with *grayish blue nuchal band*; otherwise *uniform green above.* Throat and chest yellow, with *reddish orange band across breast*; belly coarsely streaked green and pale yellowish. ♀ *green above* with gray forehead extending back as vague superciliary; *mask black* bordered behind by vague orange-yellow area. *Throat pale gray with orange band across chest*; breast dull pale olive and belly pale yellowish, latter streaked olive. **Similar species:** The *Capito* barbets are larger. Gilded is apt to occur with Lemon-throated, sometimes in the same flock. Cf. ♀ Red-headed Barbet of foothills and subtropics (ranging almost entirely above where Lemon-throated is found). **Habits:** Usually seen in pairs, foraging with mixed flocks mostly in canopy and subcanopy, sometimes coming lower at edge. At times quite acrobatic, clinging to and even entering curled dead leaves in search of insect prey; also eats much fruit.

Voice: Rather soft call a very rapidly paced "crrruu-crrruu-crrruu . . ." (usually about 10–12 "crrruu" notes). It is ventriloquial and seems to carry well.

Red-headed Barbet, *Eubucco bourcierii*
Barbudo Cabecirrojo   Plate 50(14)

Mostly 800–1900 m, lower in west

15.5–16 cm (6–6¼″). Canopy and borders of *foothill and subtropical forest and woodland on both slopes*, in west also locally out into more humid lowlands and on slopes of coastal cordillera. Iris red (west) or reddish brown (east); ♂'s bill bright greenish yellow, ♀'s (at least in east) duller with dusky culmen. Colorful ♂ has *entire head, neck, throat, and breast bright red* with bill outlined black and a narrow pale blue nuchal collar. Otherwise uniform green above; belly streaked green and yellow. **Western** ♂ has red below somewhat more extensive, contrasting more with bright yellow upper belly. ♀ has forehead and around eye black, crown golden ochraceous, and *sides of head blue bordered behind by golden ochraceous bar*; otherwise uniform green above. Chin black; *otherwise greenish yellow below* with *diffused orange band across chest* and some green streaking on flanks. **Eastern** ♀ similar but with blue border behind black forehead. **Similar species:** ♂ hardly to be confused, but cf. Red-hooded Tanager. More subtle ♀ also distinctive, but cf. ♀ Lemon-throated Barbet of e. lowlands (with black mask instead of blue on sides of head, etc.). **Habits:** Usually in pairs, often accompanying mixed canopy flocks; forages at varying levels, coming lower principally at edge and in adjacent clearings, especially at fruiting trees. Also

consumes many insects, and pulls apart or even climbs inside curled dead leaves. **Voice:** Usually silent. Western ♂ ♂'s short song a soft, low-pitched, and resonant "o-o-o-o-o-o-o-o" with quality of Scaled Antpitta or even a toad; it is typically delivered as bird bows forward, somewhat raising tail. E.-slope birds give rather different soft, churring "tor-rrrrrrrrrrrrrrrrr" (P. Coopmans).

Toucan Barbet, *Semnornis ramphastinus*
Barbudo Tucán   Plate 50(16)

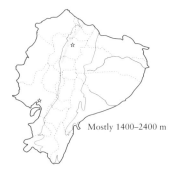

Mostly 1400–2400 m

21.5–23 cm (8½–9″). A *colorful* and *hefty* barbet found in canopy and borders of *subtropical forest, woodland, and adjacent clearings* in *northwest*. **Sexes are much alike,** ♀ slightly duller. Iris red; *bill very heavy* with maxilla yellow, mandible pale green, both tipped black. *Crown, foreface, and narrow nuchal collar black*, feathers of hindcrown elongated; *conspicuous white postocular stripe*; mantle rich golden brown becoming yellow on rump; wings and tail gray. *Throat, chest, and sides of neck bluish gray*; *breast and median belly red*; lower underparts greenish yellow. **Similar species:** Hardly to be confused. **Habits:** Most often in pairs or small groups that may perch stolidly for protracted periods, and then are sometimes hard to see though they often are actually out in the open. Though usually perching on larger horizontal branches, feeding birds can be quite acrobatic and energetic in their efforts to obtain fruit; *Cecropia* catkins are especially favored. Toucan Barbets generally move independently of mixed flocks, though sometimes aggregating with tanagers and other frugivores. They fly on rapidly beating and rather noisy wings. Remains tolerably numerous in Mindo and Tanadayapa region, one of this fine bird's strongholds. **Voice:** Unmistakable song a strange, far-carrying duet of loud, sonorous, honking "honh" notes on different pitches (given by the two sexes), given either in syncopation or—more often—not. Also regularly clacks bill.

Toucans: Ramphastidae (19)

Toucans are spectacular, fairly large frugivorous birds with *unmistakable long and laterally compressed, usually colorful bills.* Despite its size, the bill is actually quite light, being mainly hollow. Most toucans are boldly patterned and brightly colored, often with bare colored facial skin. They range in humid and montane forests. Most are quite vocal, giving a variety of croaking, grunting, yelping, or even squeaky sounds. As noted, they eat mainly fruit, but this is supplemented by some invertebrate and vertebrate prey, and they also take eggs and nestlings of other birds. Toucans nest in holes in trees. Roosting toucans have the curious capability of folding their tails flat onto the back.

Aulacorhynchus Toucanets

Relatively small, *mainly green* toucans found in montane forests. **Sexes are much alike** aside from females having shorter bills.

Emerald Toucanet, *Aulacorhynchus prasinus*
Tucanete Esmeralda   Plate 52(3)

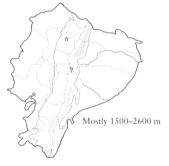

Mostly 1500–2600 m

33–34 cm (13–13¼"). Fairly common in canopy and borders of *subtropical and lower temperate* forest and adjacent clearings on *e. slope.* Two distinctly different forms: one south to w. Napo, the other north to nw. Morona-Santiago. Iris brown, bare facial skin buff. Bill 6.5–7.5 cm (2½–3"); **northern birds** have *bill black with tip and culmen yellow* and base outlined in white; **southern**

birds have *only tip of bill yellow,* and base of only mandible outlined in white (base of maxilla outlined in yellow). *Green,* somewhat paler below, with chestnut crissum and tips to tail feathers; southern birds similar, but yellower on flanks. The two forms differ most strikingly in throat color: *white in northern birds, dull blue in southern birds.* **Similar species:** Cf. less numerous Chestnut-tipped Toucanet (usually at lower elevations). Crimson-rumped Toucanet occurs only on w. slope. **Habits:** Ranges through forest in pairs or small groups of up to 5–6 birds, foraging at varying levels but usually at mid-levels or higher, coming lower at edge and in clearings. Rather nervous and excitable, peering about alertly and often cocking tail at a jaunty angle. Flight direct and "buzzy" on fast wingbeats, ending with brief glide before landing. **Voice:** Most frequent call a persistent and fast "rek-rek-rek-rek . . ." or "rr-rek, rr-rek, rr-rek . . . ," often with a barking quality; it can be continued 10–20 or more seconds, rarely a minute or more. Also gives a variety of other sharp squawks or croaks, mainly in aggressive encounters or in alarm.

Chestnut-tipped Toucanet
Aulacorhynchus derbianus
Tucanete Filicastaño   Plate 52(2)

800–1800 m

35–36 cm (13¾–14¼"). Scarce and local in canopy and borders of *foothill and lower subtropical* forest on *e. slope,* generally *below* elevations of the more numerous Emerald Toucanet. Iris reddish brown, bare facial skin buff. Bill 7–9 cm (2¾–3½"); *black with some dull reddish at base of maxilla and culmen,* and base outlined in white. *Green* with some whitish above eye and bluish on nape and below lores; *central tail feathers tipped chestnut.* **Similar species:** Emerald Toucanet has distinctly white (northward) or blue (southward) throat, at least some yellow on bill (more northward), and chestnut crissum and *more* chestnut on tail (*all* feathers tipped, not just central pair). **Habits:** Similar to Emerald Toucanet, but less numerous and rarely occurring in more than pairs. **Voice:** Most frequent call a series of honking or croaking notes delivered at a much slower pace than Emerald Toucanet, e.g., "gwak, gwak, gwak, gwak . . ." or "rok, rok, rok, rok. . . ."

Crimson-rumped Toucanet
Aulacorhynchus haematopygus
Tucanete Lomirrojo   Plate 52(1)

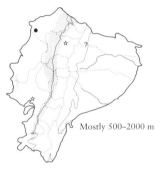

Mostly 500–2000 m

34.5–35.5 cm (13½–14″). Canopy and borders of *foothill and subtropical* forest, secondary woodland, and adjacent clearings on *w. slope*, ranging out into more humid lowlands and on slopes of coastal cordillera. Iris red, bare facial skin dull reddish or buff. Bill 6.5–7.5 cm (2½–3″); *dark red* with culmen and middle portion of mandible black, and base outlined in white. *Green*, with *narrow band on rump red* (often hidden when bird is at rest); some bluish below lores and across breast (usually not noticeable in field, but in a few [older?] individuals it can be more evident); tail feathers tipped chestnut. **Similar species:** The only "green" toucanet occurring on w. slope. **Habits:** Similar to Emerald Toucanet, though seems more tolerant of habitat disturbance and more often emerges from forest to feed around houses in clearings. **Voice:** Most frequent call a repetition of a rather high-pitched, almost nasal note, "rah, rah, rah, rah . . ." that may continue 10–20 seconds or more.

Selenidera Toucanets
Midsized toucans with ornate and colorful patterns found in humid lowland and foothill forests. Males of both species are marked by their striking golden yellow ear-tufts.

Yellow-eared Toucanet, *Selenidera spectabilis*
Tucancillo Orejiamarillo   Plate 52(5)

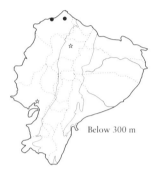

Below 300 m

37–38 cm (14½–15″). *Very rare* in canopy and borders of very humid forest of *n. Esmeraldas lowlands*. Iris dark red; bare ocular area mainly green, bluer above eye and yellow below it. Bill 9–10 cm (3½–4″); *black with upper half of maxilla greenish yellow.* ♂ has *head, neck, and underparts black* with *conspicuous tuft of bright lemon yellow feathers on ear-coverts* and patch of yellow on flanks; crissum red. Upperparts otherwise olive green, tail dusky. ♀ similar but lacking ear-tuft and with *crown and hindneck rich maroon-chestnut.* **Similar species:** Not likely confused in its very limited Ecuadorian range. **Habits:** Unknown in Ecuador. Elsewhere (e.g., Panama) a rather inconspicuous toucan that is almost always found singly or in pairs, usually ranging well up in subcanopy where generally remaining within concealment of foliage. Unlike many other toucans, rarely perches in open. **Voice:** In Panama gives a dry, rhythmic "t-krrrk, t-krrrk, t-krrrk . . . ," tossing bill sideways with each note.

Golden-collared Toucanet
Selenidera reinwardtii
Tucancillo Collaridorado   Plate 52(4)

30.5–32 cm (12–12½″). Subcanopy and mid-levels of *terra firme forest in lowlands (especially) and foothills of east.* Iris yellow,

Mostly below 800 m

tree. Groups often roost together in woodpecker holes.

Pale-mandibled Araçari
Pteroglossus erythropygius
Arasari Piquipálido   Plate 52(6)

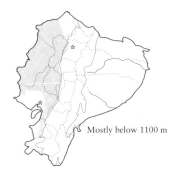

Mostly below 1100 m

with horizontally oriented pupil imparting an unusual look; bare ocular area mainly aquamarine blue. Bill 6–6.5 cm (2¼–2½″); *carmine with culmen and terminal third black*. ♂ has *head, neck, and most of underparts black* with *conspicuous tuft of golden yellow feathers on ear-coverts* and yellow nuchal collar. Otherwise olive green above, tail duskier with central two pairs of feathers tipped rufous. Belly dusky-olive, flank patch mixed yellow and rufous, crissum red. ♀ patterned like ♂ but *black replaced by rufous*, with ear-tufts bronzy olive. **Similar species:** This ornately patterned small toucan is unlikely to be confused in range. **Habits:** Inconspicuous, tending to remain within concealment of foliage and rarely perching in open. Usually occurs in pairs, less often small (family?) groups. **Voice:** Unique call, usually given by both members of pair, a low-pitched guttural growling, almost frog-like, "groww-groww-groww-groww . . . ," repeated at a rate of about one note/second for 8–10 seconds; calling birds often seesaw up and down in a comical fashion, bowing head and raising tail up over back.

Pteroglossus Araçaris
Midsized but quite slender and elongated-looking toucans with rather long bills and *long, graduated tails*, araçaris are found in lowland forests, smaller numbers of some species also ranging up into foothills. They can be recognized by their often *striking bill patterns* and the *pattern of banding on the underparts*. Araçaris rove through the forest canopy in small groups, but rarely does more than one species flock together, though occasionally several (together with other toucans) may feed at a fruiting

40.5–43 cm (16–17″). Canopy and borders of humid forest and secondary woodland in lowlands (especially) and foothills of *west* from w. *Esmeraldas and Pichincha southward*. **Sexes alike.** Iris yellow; ocular skin bright red, eye-ring and area in front of eye dark blue; base outlined in white. Bill 11.5–12.5 cm (4½–5″); *bill mostly creamy yellow*, maxilla tip yellow and black on sides of maxilla, mandible tip black; base outlined in white. Greenish black above with red rump (mainly hidden at rest). Throat black; underparts yellow, breast somewhat stained with red, and *with spot of black on breast and band of mixed black and red across upper belly*; thighs brown. **Similar species:** *The only araçari in most of w. Ecuador*. Cf. Stripe-billed Araçari (of far northwest). **Habits:** Usually in small groups, sometimes up to 6–8 or more birds, that forage in canopy, subcanopy, and borders, hopping on larger branches. Often perches in the open early in morning, but this is much less frequent at other times. Feeds mainly on fruit but some insects and even small lizards, eggs, and nestlings are consumed. Flight level on rapidly beating wings, ending with short glide before landing; often a group straggles along single-file, following much the same flight path across a clearing. **Voice:** Most frequent call a loud, arresting, high-pitched, and squeaky "ksísik" or "ksiyík!"

Stripe-billed Araçari, *Pteroglossus sanguineus*
Arasari Piquirrayado   Plate 52(7)

To 800 m

40.5–43 cm (16–17″). Canopy and borders of humid forest and trees in adjacent clearings in lowlands and foothills of *far northwest*. Sexes alike. Iris yellow; ocular skin red, eye-ring and area in front of eye dark blue. Bill 11.5–12.5 cm (4½–5″); maxilla pale yellow with black culmen and stripe on sides; *mandible black*; base outlined in white. Plumage as in Pale-mandibled Araçari. Similar species: Cf. Pale-mandibled Araçari, which occurs widely southward in w. Ecuador. Pale-mandibled's lower mandible is creamy yellow. The two (closely related) species are not known to occur together, but they may intergrade at least locally. Habits and Voice: As in Pale-mandibled Araçari.

Chestnut-eared Araçari
Pteroglossus castanotis
Arasari Orejicastaño   Plate 52(10)
43–45.5 cm (17–18″). Canopy and borders of *várzea and riparian forest and woodland* in lowlands and foothills of *east*. Sexes alike.

To about 1000 m

Iris white, bare ocular area bright blue, darker in front of eye. Bill 11.5–12.5 cm (4½–5″); maxilla orange-yellow deepening to rich brown basally, with yellow serrations and black culmen; mandible black; base outlined in yellow. Dark olive above with red rump (hidden at rest) and black crown; sides of head, throat, and nuchal collar maroon-chestnut. Chest black; underparts yellow *crossed by single broad red band*; thighs brown. Similar species: The only araçari whose underparts are crossed by only *one* band (very conspicuous). Confusion most likely with Many-banded, which has *two* bands; these two species generally segregate by habitat, Many-banded being more or less confined to terra firme, Chestnut-eared to low-lying areas near water. Habits: Similar to Stripe-billed Araçari. Voice: Call a harsh and querulous "skreeeyup."

Many-banded Araçari
Pteroglossus pluricinctus
Arasari Bifajeado   Plate 52(8)

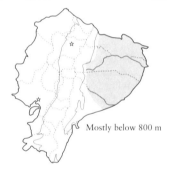

Mostly below 800 m

40.5–43 cm (16–17″). Canopy and borders of humid forest (*mainly terra firme*) in lowlands (especially) and foothills of *east*. Sexes alike. Iris yellow, ocular skin bright aquamarine blue. Bill 11–12.5 cm (4¼–5″); basal half of maxilla yellow, terminal half white, black at base and on culmen and with reddish tip; *mandible black*; base outlined yellow. Very dark slaty green above (often looks black) with red rump (hidden at rest) and black head, neck, and throat. Below yellow, *underparts crossed by two bands*, upper one black, lower one black or black mixed with red; thighs brown. Similar species: The only araçari whose lower underparts are crossed by two dark bands, easy to see in field; Chestnut-eared has only one (red) band,

Lettered and Ivory-billed none. **Habits:** Similar to Stripe-billed Araçari. Generally does not flock with other araçari species, though occasionally several will gather in same fruiting tree; Many-banded's flock size seems often to be larger (up to 10–12 birds). **Voice:** Call a rather weak and squeaky "kyseek" or "kyeek," often repeated several times in succession.

Ivory-billed Araçari, *Pteroglossus azara*
Arasari Piquimarfíl   Plate 52(9)

To 900 m

33–35.5 cm (13–14″). Uncommon in canopy and borders of *terra firme forest* in lowlands (especially) and foothills of *east*. Formerly often called *P. flavirostris*. Iris dark red, ocular skin red, eye-ring and area in front of eye blackish. Bill 8–9 cm (3¼–3½″); *ivory white to creamy yellow* with black tomium and *brown stripe on sides of mandible*. ♂ dark olive green above with black crown, reddish maroon hindneck and nape, and red rump (hidden at rest). Throat deep chestnut brown, *bordered below by bright red chest band, then a black band across breast*; belly yellow, with thighs olive. ♀ similar but black of crown extends back over nape (no reddish chestnut). **Similar species:** Easily distinguished from other Amazonian araçaris on basis of its mainly pale bill and the solidly dark continuum from brown to red to black on underparts, with yellow *only* on belly. **Habits:** Similar to Stripe-billed Araçari, though group size tends to be smaller, typically no more than 3–6 birds moving together. **Voice:** Calls rather different from those of other Ecuadorian araçaris. Gives a variety of high-pitched and querulous yelps or screams, e.g., "kweeeark?," sometimes given in series, or interspersed with "krr"

grunts; overall effect can be reminiscent of a mountain-toucan.

Lettered Araçari, *Pteroglossus inscriptus*
Arasari Letreado   Plate 52(11)

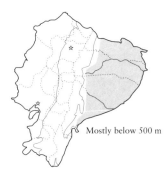

Mostly below 500 m

33–35.5 cm (13–14″). Fairly common in canopy and borders of humid forest, secondary woodland, and borders in *lowlands of east*. Iris dark red, ocular skin bright turquoise blue above eye, dark blue below eye, and red behind. Bill 7.5 cm (3″); *maxilla brownish yellow* with black culmen, tip, and *vertical "tooth" marks (the "letters") along tomium*; mandible black; base outlined in yellow. ♂ very dark green above with black head, neck, and throat and red rump (hidden at rest). *Underparts entirely pale yellow* (with no bands) but often somewhat stained reddish brown; thighs mainly brown. ♀ similar but with most of head and throat deep chestnut brown (only crown black). **Similar species:** *The only Ecuadorian araçari with no bands across underparts.* **Habits:** Similar to Stripe-billed Araçari. **Voice:** Rather quiet for an araçari, with call consisting of an often long-continued series of guttural "cha" notes.

Andigena Mountain-Toucans
Splendid, fairly large toucans with blue-gray underparts and colorful bill patterns found in *Andean forests*. Compared to other toucans their plumage is lax and almost hair-like (Haffer 1974). The **sexes are alike**, females with bills slightly shorter.

Plate-billed Mountain-Toucan
Andigena laminirostris
Tucán Andino Piquilaminado   Plate 52(12)
42–44.5 cm (16½–17½″). Locally fairly common in canopy and borders of *subtropi-*

1600–2600 m

2500–3300 m

cal and temperate forest in northwest. Iris dark red; ocular area turquoise green or pale blue above eye, bright yellow below it. Bill 8–10 cm (3¼–4″); outer half black, *inner half mostly red* with *raised yellow "plate" on maxilla.* Crown and nape black; upperparts otherwise bronzy olive with yellow band on rump; tail black with chestnut tip. *Grayish blue below* with contrasting yellow patch on flanks; crissum red and thighs chestnut. **Similar species:** Unmistakable in range. Somewhat similar Gray-breasted Mountain-Toucan occurs only on e. slope. **Habits:** Ranges mainly in pairs, less often small groups, occasionally mingling with aggregations of other birds, particularly at fruiting trees. Seems more numerous and more conspicuous than other two mountain-toucans. **Voice:** The most vocal *Andigena.* Most frequent call a loud and far-carrying nasal and querulous "quuuah" or "kwu-u-u-ah" often repeated rapidly many times, and sometimes interspersed with a grating bill rattle; several birds may give this at once. May call from an open perch like a *Ramphastos* toucan, but at least as often remains hidden.

Gray-breasted Mountain-Toucan
Andigena hypoglauca
Tucán Andino Pechigris   Plate 52(13)

43–45 cm (17–17¾″). Canopy and borders of *temperate forest on e. slope.* occurring *above* elevation range of Black-billed Mountain-Toucan. Two distinctly different forms occur, one ranging south to w. Napo, the other north to nw. Morona-Santiago. **Northern birds** have iris reddish brown, **southern birds** pale olive or yellow; small bare ocular area black. Bill 8–9 cm (3¼–3½″); **northern birds** with *mainly orange outer half of maxilla,*

southern birds with *that area pink*; maxilla otherwise mainly yellow with black at base; outer half of mandible black, then a band of yellow, then a band of black, with base again yellow; bill outlined with blue stripe. Head black with *pale grayish blue nuchal band*; otherwise bronzy olive brown above, greener on wings, with yellow band on rump and blackish tail tipped chestnut. *Below bluish gray* with red crissum and chestnut thighs. **Similar species:** Plate-billed Mountain-Toucan, occurs only on w. slope. Black-billed Mountain-Toucan has an all-dark bill (*no yellow*), white throat and sides of head, etc. **Habits:** Similar to Plate-billed Mountain-Toucan, though seems more secretive and less vocal. **Voice:** Most frequent call a whining, querulous, slowly rising "kwu-u-u-aaaanh?" usually given at several-second intervals though at times pace quickens; resembles main call of Plate-billed, though typically each note is more drawn out. Also gives various cackles and bill rattles.

Black-billed Mountain-Toucan
Andigena nigrirostris
Tucán Andino Piquinegro   Plate 52(14)

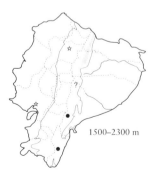

1500–2300 m

42–44.5 cm (16½–17½″). Scarce and local in canopy and borders of *subtropical forest on e. slope*, occurring *below* elevation of Gray-breasted Mountain-Toucan. Iris reddish brown, bare ocular area pale blue in front of eye, yellow behind it. Bill 8–10 cm (3¼–4″); *mainly black with dark red at base of maxilla*. Crown and nape black; upperparts otherwise bronzy olive with yellow band on rump; tail slaty black tipped chestnut. *Sides of neck and throat white*, becoming *pale grayish blue on underparts* with red crissum and chestnut thighs. **Similar species:** Not likely confused, its white throat and lovely "powder blue" underparts being conspicuous and very different from those of other mountain-toucans; cf. darker Gray-breasted Mountain-Toucan of higher elevations (with more colorful bill, pale nuchal collar, etc.). **Habits:** Similar to Plate-billed Mountain-Toucan, though at least in Ecuador the Black-billed tends to be less numerous and less vocal. **Voice:** Most frequent call a loud, nasal "kwuuak?" or "kwuuák?" that is repeated steadily, sometimes for fairly long periods. Also has various cackles and bill rattles.

Ramphastos Toucans

The "classic" toucans: big, showy, and conspicuous. They mainly range in humid lowland forests, one (Black-mandibled) in east-slope foothills. The commoner species can be notably gregarious. There are *two closely similar species with white bibs in the east*, and *two closely similar species with yellow bibs in the west*; members of both pairs are often best distinguished by their *distinctive voices*. The first two species described below (Channel-billed and Chocó) have shorter and somewhat "keeled" bills, and they *croak*; the last three (Chestnut-mandibled, Black-mandibled, and White-throated) have longer bills, and they *yelp*. **Sexes are alike**, though females have shorter bills, notably so in some species.

Channel-billed Toucan, *Ramphastos vitellinus*
Tucán Piquiacanalado   Plate 52(16)

43–46 cm (17–18″). Canopy and borders of humid forest in *lowlands (especially) and foothills of east*. Formerly often considered a separate species, Yellow-ridged Toucan (*R. culminatus*) ranging in w. Amazonia. Bare

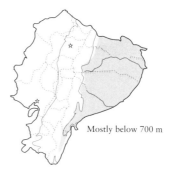

Mostly below 700 m

ocular area pale blue. *Bill 13–14 cm (5–5½″)* and "keeled" (slightly protruding ridge along culmen); mainly black with yellow tip, culmen, and base of maxilla; base of mandible pale blue. Mostly black with yellow rump and red crissum. *Throat and chest white*, bordered below by red band (usually inconspicuous). **Similar species:** Identical in plumage and bill coloration to larger White-throated Toucan, and the two species often occur together; they are best distinguished by voice, but bill length and shape also can help, bill of White-throated looking substantially longer, and smoother over culmen (with no keel). **Habits:** Usually in pairs, less often small groups, foraging at all levels in forest, most often staying high. Hops about in canopy and subcanopy with springy bounds, and surprisingly agile while feeding, using the long bill to good advantage when reaching for fruits. Sometimes accompanies groups of larger birds. Flight typically undulating and often seems weak (though birds can actually traverse fairly long distances, crossing rivers and other openings with relative ease); it usually consists of several quick flaps and then a glide, and often birds seem to gradually be losing altitude. **Voice:** Oft-heard call a rapidly repeated frog-like croaking, "kreeek, kreeek, kreeek . . . ," with each note often accompanied by an upward toss of head. Calling birds sometimes take to high exposed perches, though on the whole White-throated Toucans seem more likely to do this.

Chocó Toucan, *Ramphastos brevis*
Tucán del Chocó   Plate 52(18)

43–45.5 cm (17–18″). Local in canopy and borders of humid forest in *lowlands and*

Mostly below 900 m

foothills of west. Bare ocular area yellowish green. Bill 14–16.5 cm (5½–6½″) and "keeled" (slightly protruding ridge along culmen); most of maxilla yellow, *angled base of maxilla and entire mandible black.* Mostly black with white rump and red crissum. Throat and chest yellow, bordered below by red band (usually inconspicuous). **Similar species:** Identical to larger and usually more numerous Chestnut-mandibled Toucan in plumage. Though best identified by their strikingly different voices, with care the two species can be distinguished by size and bill shape (bill of Chestnut-mandibled considerably longer and therefore appearing thinner; it also is not keeled). In good light, the dark chestnut on Chestnut-mandibled's bill is also apparent. **Habits:** As in Channel-billed Toucan. **Voice:** Call a steadily repeated series of croaking "kreeork" notes, sometimes speeded up into a "kriik" but always very different from Chestnut-mandibled's yelping.

Chestnut-mandibled Toucan
Ramphastos swainsonii
Tucán de Swainson   Plate 52(17)

53.5–56 cm (21–22″). Local in canopy and borders of humid forest in *lowlands and*

To 1000 m

foothills of west. Bare ocular area yellowish green. Bill 16–18 cm (6¼–7″); most of maxilla yellow, *angled base of maxilla and entire mandible dark chestnut* (but can look black). Mostly black with white rump and red crissum. Throat and chest yellow, bordered below by red band (usually inconspicuous). **Similar species:** Resembles smaller Chocó Toucan; aside from size and voice differences, note Choco's often short-billed appearance (especially in ♀♀) and "keeled" bill with black (not chestnut). **Habits:** Similar to Channel-billed Toucan. **Voice:** Call a loud and far-carrying yelping that can be paraphrased as "keyeeer, te-deo, te-deo," sometimes just "keyeeeer" alone.

Black-mandibled Toucan
Ramphastos ambiguus
Tucán Mandíbula Negra   Plate 52(19)

1000–1600 m

53.5–56 cm (21–22″). *Decidedly scarce and local* in canopy and borders of *foothill and lower subtropical forest on e. slope.* Bare ocular area yellowish green. Bill 16–18 cm (6¼–7″); most of maxilla yellow, *angled base of maxilla and entire mandible black.* Mostly black with white rump and red crissum. *Throat and chest yellow*, bordered below by red band (usually inconspicuous). **Similar species:** *The only yellow-bibbed toucan east of Andes* and as such easily identified. **Habits:** Similar to Channel-billed Toucan, though Black-mandibled seems much warier. **Voice:** Identical to Chestnut-mandibled Toucan.

White-throated Toucan, *Ramphastos tucanus*
Tucán Goliblanco   Plate 52(15)

53.5–57 cm (21–22½″). Canopy and borders of humid forest in *lowlands (especially) and foothills of east.* Formerly often considered a

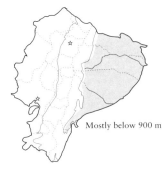

Mostly below 900 m

separate species, Cuvier's Toucan (*R. cuvieri*), ranging in w. Amazonia. Bare ocular area pale blue. *Bill very long, 18–21 cm (7–8¼")*; mainly black with yellow tip, culmen, and base of maxilla; base of mandible pale blue. Mostly black with yellow rump and red crissum; *throat and chest white*, bordered below by red band (usually inconspicuous). **Similar species:** Identical in plumage and bill coloration to smaller Channel-billed Toucan. The two are most easily distinguished by their very different voices; difference in size is most apparent when the two species are together (as happens not infrequently). With care, bill length can be useful even when looking at individual birds, especially when a ♂ White-throated is involved (its bill can look strikingly long). **Habits:** Similar to Channel-billed Toucan. In general more numerous than that species, the two often occurring together. **Voice:** This toucan's far-carrying call is one of most characteristic bird sounds of the Oriente. It consists of a loud yelping phrase, "keeo-keh-keh," sometimes just "keeo" or "keh-keh." Calling birds usually perch high in canopy, sometimes on an open branch, swinging head and bill from side to side with each call.

Woodpeckers and Piculets: Picidae (35)

A nearly cosmopolitan group—none occurs in Australasia or on remote oceanic islands—*adapted for climbing in trees*. Woodpeckers have chisel-like straight and pointed bills, and most (not piculets) have *stiffened central tail feathers* used for bracing against trunks and branches. **In most species the sexes are much alike** aside from minor head-pattern differences, males frequently having more red on the crown and moustachial region. Woodpeckers mainly feed by extracting insects and especially larvae from bark and wood with

their very long and extensible tongues; some species also eat fruit, a few eat ants, and several sometimes even flycatch. Their flight is distinctly undulating. Most woodpeckers "drum," a loud and fast hammering on an often-hollow branch or trunk that proclaims their presence on a territory; though they sound similar, with practice these sounds can be told apart, at least to genus. Most species give loud vocal calls as well. They nest (and sleep) in holes dug into trunks and branches, both live and dead.

Picumnus Piculets

Distinctive, *tiny* woodpeckers with *finely dotted crowns* (usually red in males, white in females) and *short black tails* (the feathers white-edged) that are generally *not* used for support as the birds tap for insects in dead twigs and smaller branches. They are found in a variety of forested and wooded habitats, principally in the lowlands; though often confiding, they generally remain quite inconspicuous.

Rufous-breasted Piculet, *Picumnus rufiventris*
Picolete Pechirrufo   Plate 54(1)

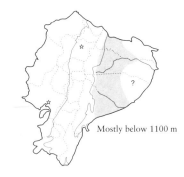

Mostly below 1100 m

9 cm (3½"). A distinctive piculet with *unique rufous underparts*, scarce and inconspicuous in *lower growth* of humid forest borders, secondary woodland, and regenerating clearings in lowlands and (especially) foothills of east. ♂ mainly olive above; crown black with red spots, spots tiny and buff on nape. *Below uniform rufous.* ♀ similar but crown with white dots. **Similar species:** Lafresnaye's Piculet is barred below. **Habits:** Inconspicuous in the dense lower growth of thickets, hopping about and industriously tapping on twigs, both dead and alive. Ranges both

singly and in pairs, often accompanying mixed flocks; Lafresnaye's Piculet almost always forages higher above ground. **Voice:** Seems very quiet, but occasionally gives a thin high-pitched "tseeyt-tseeyt-tsit" call, each note a little lower-pitched than previous one (P. Coopmans recording).

[Plain-breasted Piculet, *Picumnus castelnau*
Picolete Pechillano]   Plate 54(2)

8 cm (3¼"). Riparian and várzea forest and woodland in lowlands of northeast; known only from old specimens; *perhaps does not occur in present Ecuador territory.* ♂ olive above, *crown black conspicuously dotted with orange-red;* sides of neck and nape finely barred olive-gray and white; inner flight feathers edged yellow. *Below uniform yellowish white.* ♀ similar, but *crown all black.* **Similar species:** In the event this well-named piculet is relocated in Ecuador, it should be easily recognized on the basis of its unmarked underparts. **Habits:** In Peru usually seen in pairs, foraging at varying levels, mainly by tapping on dead twigs and branches, often working the same one for a long period; favors semiopen woodland. Regularly accompanies small mixed flocks. **Voice:** Has a weak, high-pitched, descending trill that fades off toward end.

Lafresnaye's Piculet, *Picumnus lafresnayi*
Picolete de Lafresnaye   Plate 54(4)
9 cm (3½"). A *coarsely barred* piculet found in humid forest, secondary woodland, and trees in adjacent clearings in *lowlands and foothills of east.* Formerly considered conspecific with Bar-breasted, or Gold-fronted Piculet (*P. aurifrons*) of s. Amazonia. ♂ olive

Mostly below 1400 m

above *barred with yellowish,* crown brown dotted with orange on forecrown, white on rearcrown; inner flight feathers edged yellow. Below yellowish white *conspicuously barred with black.* ♀ similar but entire crown dotted white. **Similar species:** *The only prominently barred piculet in Ecuador;* occurs only with very dissimilar Rufous-breasted Piculet. Cf. various xenops. **Habits:** Forages at varying levels (though rarely near the ground inside forest), coming lower at edge, hitching along smaller branches and on twigs. Frequently accompanies mixed flocks. **Voice:** Rather quiet, but occasionally gives a pair of high-pitched notes, "tseeyt, tsit."

Olivaceous Piculet, *Picumnus olivaceus*
Picolete Oliváceo   Plate 54(3)

To about 900 m

9 cm (3½"). A *rather dull* piculet of forest borders, woodland, and shrubby clearings in *more humid lowlands and foothills of west.* ♂ olive above with black crown dotted in front with orange and to rear with white; inner flight feathers edged olive-yellow. Throat whitish scaled black, *breast plain brownish olive,* belly buffy yellowish vaguely streaked olive. ♀ similar but entire crown dotted white. **Similar species:** Ecuadorian

Piculet favors more arid habitats, is grayer generally with much more prominently marked underparts. Cf. Plain and Streaked Xenops. **Habits:** Similar to other piculets, actively climbing along smaller branches and twigs, often upside-down, rapidly tapping on dead wood. Often with mixed flocks. **Voice:** Call a high thin chippering trill, often descending in pitch.

Ecuadorian Piculet, *Picumnus sclateri*

Picolete Ecuatoriano   Plate 54(5)

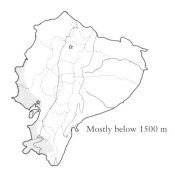

Mostly below 1500 m

9 cm (3½″). *Deciduous woodland and scrub in lowlands and foothills of southwest*, in s. Loja (at least) also ranging into more humid montane forest and woodland. ♂ **in Manabí and Guayas** brownish gray above; crown contrastingly black spotted in front with yellow and to rear with white. *Whitish below, throat and breast prominently scaled blackish, belly streaked blackish*. ♀ similar but crown entirely spotted with white. ♂ **in El Oro and Loja** similar but *more heavily marked below* (hence appearing darker). **Similar species:** This and Olivaceous Piculet tend to segregate by habitat, with Olivaceous replacing Ecuadorian in more humid habitats and regions. Separating the two should not pose any problems, Olivaceous being a plainer and more olive bird that *lacks* dark markings below. **Habits:** Similar to Olivaceous Piculet. **Voice:** Rather quiet, but gives a high-pitched "tseee-tsut" or "tseeet," latter sometimes doubled (P. Coopmans).

Andean Flicker, *Colaptes rupicola*

Picatierra Andino   Plate 53(13)

32–33 cm (12½–13″). An unmistakable *large* and *partially terrestrial* woodpecker found in *rocky paramo* and at edge of woodland

3100–3350 m

patches in *extreme south* (Cordillera Las Lagunillas). Bill long and slender, black; iris yellow. *Crown and malar stripe gray*, contrasting with *rich buff face and throat; above otherwise boldly banded black and buffy whitish*, except for *bright yellow rump* (conspicuous in flight); tail black, outer pair of feathers barred yellow. *Below cinnamon-buff*, becoming yellower on belly and especially crissum; chest neatly barred with black. **Sexes nearly alike,** ♂ with red spot at end of malar stripe. **Habits:** Favors areas strewn with boulders, often perching atop them. Feeds mainly on ground, shuffling ahead and probing into loose earth with long bill. Often wary. Roosts in holes dug into cliffs or road-cuts. **Voice:** Gives various loud calls, the most frequent being a piercing and inflected whistled "kweeir!" sometimes given in series, or "kli-kli-kli." Also gives a far-carrying, rather musical rattle (P. Coopmans). Several birds sometimes call together, raising heads high and flaring wings.

Spot-breasted Woodpecker
Chrysoptilus punctigula

Carpintero Pechipunteado   Plate 54(6)

Mostly below 1200 m

20.5 cm (8″). Fairly common in várzea and riparian woodland and trees in clearings in *lowlands and foothills of east*, now also following clearings up Andean slopes. Sometimes placed in genus *Colaptes*. *Boldly patterned.* ♂ has *forecrown black*, rearcrown red, both contrasting with *white face*; above otherwise yellowish olive *boldly barred with black*. Throat checkered black and white, bordered above by dark red malar stripe; breast brownish olive becoming yellowish olive on belly, *entire underparts spotted black.* ♀ like ♂ but lacking red malar stripe. **Similar species:** Head pattern of Golden-olive Woodpecker similar (cheeks, though pale, are not so white), but that mainly *montane* species *lacks* barring above and is barred (not spotted) below. The two overlap locally in lower subtropics. **Habits:** This handsome woodpecker tends to be conspicuous, in part because it favors semiopen terrain and edge. On rare occasions descends to ground to feed on ants, but typically it is arboreal like most other woodpeckers. **Voice:** Common call a series of 10–12 ringing notes, "kah-kah-kah . . ." or "keeh-keeh-keeh . . ."

Piculus Woodpeckers

Midsized woodpeckers, most—aside from the atypical and very distinctive Crimson-mantled—with *olive upperparts*, *bold facial patterns* (often helpful in species recognition), and *barred or banded underparts*. They range primarily in the subcanopy of lowland forests, though two species (Crimson-mantled and Golden-olive) are more montane.

Crimson-mantled Woodpecker, *Piculus rivolii*
Carpintero Dorsicarmesí   Plate 53(1)

Mostly 2000–3300 m

24–25.5 cm (9½–10″). A handsome woodpecker with *mainly red upperparts* found in *upper subtropical and temperate* forest and woodland on both slopes, also regular at borders and even out into trees in clearings. ♂ has *crown and most of upperparts shining crimson* with contrasting yellowish white face; tail black. Throat black bordered by crimson malar stripe; chest densely scaled red, black, and white; remaining underparts yellow, boldly scaled black across breast and down flanks. ♀ similar but crown and malar streak black. **Similar species:** No other montane woodpecker is extensively red above. Scarlet-backed Woodpecker of w. lowlands is much smaller, etc. **Habits:** Usually seen singly or in pairs, often accompanying mixed flocks. Forages at varying levels but usually remaining rather high, often in the open and therefore conspicuous. Mainly inspects trunks and larger limbs, probing into moss and other epiphytes. Does not often seem to drum. **Voice:** Rather quiet, occasionally giving a sharp and inflected "kreíp," sometimes in a short series; also a rolling "churrr-r-r" (Fjeldså and Krabbe 1990).

Golden-olive Woodpecker, *Piculus rubiginosus*
Carpintero Olividorado   Plate 53(2)

To at least 2100 m (W); 800–2300 m (E slope)

21.5–22 cm (8½–9″). *Widespread and fairly common in west*, there occupying a range of habitats (*both humid and arid*) from *lowlands up into lower subtropics*; *less numerous in subtropical forest and borders on e. slope.* In **west**, ♂ has crown and nape crimson (usually at least somewhat intermixed with gray) with *contrasting whitish face*; *otherwise golden-olive above*, rump yellowish barred olive; tail dusky-olive, outer feathers yellower. Throat black, finely speckled white on lower throat, and bordered by red malar streak; *underparts closely barred dusky-olive and yellowish.* ♀ similar but with most of crown gray (only nape crimson), lacking red malar streak, and entire throat finely speckled white. **East-slope birds** somewhat larger, and northward they are more richly colored above. **Similar species:** *The only midsized olive-backed woodpecker in much of its range.* In humid far northwest, cf. Lita Woodpecker. In lower subtropics on e. slope, cf. Spot-breasted Woodpecker (not barred below). Golden-green Woodpecker occurs only in e. *lowlands,* far below range of Golden-olive. **Habits:** Usually seen singly or in loosely associated pairs, foraging at varying levels but most often from mid-levels up; conspicuous and easy to see. Forages mainly on trunks and larger horizontal branches, tapping and probing; in arid terrain also regularly feeds on cactus, sometimes even fence posts and the like. Often accompanies mixed flocks. **Voice:** Loud call a ringing and strident "tree-tree-tree-tree-tree-tree" lasting 2–3 seconds, usually given from an exposed perch; also has various sharp "keep" calls and a loud, harsh rattle (similar to certain *Veniliornis,* e.g., Scarlet-backed and Yellow-vented).

Yellow-throated Woodpecker, *Piculus flavigula*
Carpintero Goliamarillo Plate 53(3)

Below 300 m

19–20 cm (7½–8″). Canopy and mid-levels of humid forest in *lowlands of east,* most often in terra firme. ♂ has crown and nape bright red *contrasting with equally bright yellow face and throat;* otherwise bright olive above; inner webs of primaries basally rufous (hard to see in field). Below coarsely barred dark

olive and whitish (often more spotted on chest, always barred lower down). ♀ similar to ♂ but *crown olive gold* (red only on nape). **Similar species:** Of the other two sympatric *Piculus* woodpeckers (White-throated and Golden-green), neither shows this species' *solid* yellow on face and throat. **Habits:** Usually seen singly or in well-separated pairs, sometimes moving with mixed flocks in canopy. Forages mainly on larger limbs, probing and flaking off pieces of bark. **Voice:** Most frequent call an abrupt, far-carrying "shreeyr!" with hissing quality, sometimes repeated but often then not given again for a long time.

White-throated Woodpecker
Piculus leucolaemus
Carpintero Goliblanco Plate 53(4)

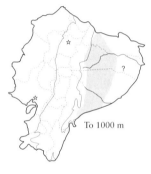

To 1000 m

18–19 cm (7–7½″). Canopy and mid-levels of humid forest in *lowlands and foothills of east,* mainly in terra firme. ♂ has crown and nape, as well as broad malar stripe, bright red; *face olive,* separated from malar stripe by *bright yellow stripe;* otherwise bright olive above; inner webs of primaries basally rufous (hard to see in field). *Throat white;* underparts coarsely barred olive and whitish, breast more olive and spotted with whitish. ♀ similar to ♂ but crown bright olive (only nape is red). **Similar species:** Lita Woodpecker occurs only west of Andes. Yellow-throated Woodpecker has an entirely yellow face and throat (both sexes); Golden-green Woodpecker is neatly and evenly barred below (lacking white throat). **Habits:** Similar to Yellow-throated Woodpecker. **Voice:** Infrequently heard call a loud and abrupt "shreeyr" with hissing quality similar to call of Yellow-throated Woodpecker.

Lita Woodpecker, *Piculus litae*
Carpintero de Lita   Plate 53(5)

16.5–18 cm (6½–7″). Canopy and mid-levels of humid forest in *lowlands and foothills of far northwest.* Formerly considered conspecific with White-throated Woodpecker, found on other side of Andes. Differs in its smaller size, *much more extensive yellow on sides of neck,* dark speckling on whitish throat, and more extensively dark olive breast (with only sparse whitish spotting or streaking). ♂'s red on crown and malar streak darker, more carmine than in White-throated. ♀ shows only a little red on nape. **Similar species:** In its limited range, nearly unmistakable. Golden-olive Woodpecker is larger, lacks yellow stripe above malar and on sides of neck, etc. Cf. also smaller Chocó Woodpecker. **Habits and Voice:** Similar to Yellow-throated and White-throated Woodpeckers.

Golden-green Woodpecker
Piculus chrysochloros
Carpintero Verdidorado   Plate 53(6)

20–21.5 cm (8–8½″). Scarce and local in subcanopy and borders of humid forest in *low-*

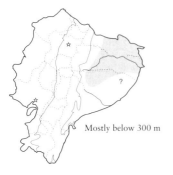

lands of east. Iris pale blue. ♂ has crown and nape bright red, face olive with *long bright yellow streak from lores across lower cheeks.* Above olive; inner webs of primaries basally rufous (hard to see in field). Throat whitish obscurely barred olive; *underparts boldly banded yellowish white and dark olive.* ♀ as in ♂ but lacking red on head. **Similar species:** Other *Piculus* with which Golden-green is sympatric (Yellow- and White-throated) are not so neatly and evenly banded below; Yellow-throated shows bright yellow across face, ♂ White-throated shows broad red moustache lacking in Golden-green. **Habits:** Similar to Yellow-throated and White-throated Woodpeckers, though more often foraging lower and in semiopen. Like them, Golden-green particularly relishes ants and termites, sometimes methodically feeding on them for long periods at their nests. **Voice:** Infrequently given call a shrill "shreeyr," sometimes doubled or tripled.

Celeus Woodpeckers
Handsome, *bushy crested* (often looking "hammer-headed"), *yellowish-billed* woodpeckers found primarily in the *eastern lowlands;* only one species (Cinnamon) occurs in the west. Most occur in humid forest, principally in the subcanopy where—aside from their distinctive vocalizations—they are generally inconspicuous. All except the unmistakable Cream-colored are *predominantly some shade of chestnut, rufous, or cinnamon,* often with bold black patterning.

Chestnut Woodpecker, *Celeus elegans*
Carpintero Castaño   Plate 53(7)

26.5–28 cm (10½–11″). Fairly common in humid forest in *lowlands of east,* where gen-

erally the most numerous and widespread *Celeus*. Iris dark red; bill ivory yellowish. *Obvious bushy pointed crest.* ♂ has *head and underparts plain chestnut*, becoming paler and more rufous on belly, with crimson malar streak (lacking in ♀). Upperparts rufous, *rump yellowish buff* (conspicuous in flight), tail dusky brown. **Similar species:** Scale-breasted Woodpecker is similarly colored but markedly smaller, and both sexes have black chevrons on much of underparts. Cf. also more boldly patterned Ringed Woodpecker. **Habits:** Forages at varying levels, more often low inside forest than most other *Celeus* woodpeckers. Climbs mainly on larger branches, gleaning from bark surfaces and crevices, also regularly probing termitaries; also eats considerable fruit, sometimes hanging upside-down to get at it. Usually found singly or in pairs, regularly accompanying mixed flocks. **Voice:** Has a variety of calls, including a rough and raspy "wahrrik, wahk-wahk-wahk-wahk" and a "wah-jeer." Also gives a nasal "kyeenh" (P. Coopmans).

Scale-breasted Woodpecker
Celeus grammicus
Carpintero Pechiescamado   Plate 53(8)

To 500 m

20.5–21 cm (8–8½"). Subcanopy and borders of humid forest, *mainly terra firme*, in *lowlands of east*. Iris dark red; bill greenish or grayish ivory. Short bushy pointed crest. ♂ *mainly rufous-chestnut*, paler on mantle and darker on head and below, with crimson malar streak (lacking in ♀); tail dusky-brown. *Underparts densely marked with black chevrons*, as are wing-coverts. Some birds also have sparse black markings on back and inner flight feathers. **Similar species:**

Can be confused with Chestnut Woodpecker, though that species is substantially larger and lacks any "scaly" pattern below or on wings. **Habits:** Similar to Chestnut Woodpecker, though generally remains higher and on the whole is less conspicuous and less often seen. **Voice:** Easily recognized and quite loud call, identical to that of Waved Woodpecker (*C. undatus*) of ne. South America, an abrupt and distinctly enunciated "kuwee? kuuu" given at long intervals. Has been aptly paraphrased as "silly boy" (M. and A. Hedemark).

Cinnamon Woodpecker, *Celeus loricatus*
Carpintero Canelo   Plate 53(9)

To 800 m

19–20.5 cm (7½–8"). Subcanopy and borders of humid forest in *lowlands and foothills of west*, the only *Celeus* found west of Andes. Iris dark red; bill pale greenish horn. Short bushy crest. ♂ *cinnamon-rufous above*, brightest on crest, sparsely barred and flecked with black; tail dusky with buff bars. Lower face and throat red; underparts whitish *densely marked with black chevrons*. ♀ as in ♂ but lower face and throat cinnamon-rufous (lacking red). **Similar species:** This attractive woodpecker is the only "cinnamon-brown" woodpecker west of Andes. **Habits:** Usually inconspicuous, tending to remain in forest canopy and heard much more often than seen. Most often seems to move independently of mixed flocks. **Voice:** Distinctive call a loud and far-carrying "wheeét!-wheeét-wheet-it," sometimes with an introductory "chuweeo."

Cream-colored Woodpecker, *Celeus flavus*
Carpintero Flavo   Plate 53(10)

25.5–26.5 cm (10–10½"). An unmistakable *creamy yellow* woodpecker found in canopy

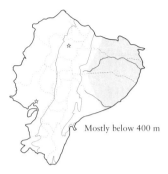

Mostly below 400 m

and borders of humid forest and woodland in *lowlands of east*. Iris dark red; bill yellow. Obvious bushy pointed crest. ♂ *yellow to creamy yellow* with red malar streak (lacking in ♀); *wings contrastingly dusky brown*, coverts with yellowish edging and some individuals with extensive cinnamon-rufous in flight feathers (reduced or lacking in others); tail dusky. **Habits:** Similar to other *Celeus*, though often more conspicuous, foraging more in open. Feeds especially by breaking open arboreal ant nests or termitaria, often lingering for protracted periods at them. **Voice:** Most frequent call a loud, ringing, and descending "peeyr, peeyr, peeyr, puh"; Ringed Woodpecker's similar call is evenly pitched. Also gives a throaty "whajeer" similar to Chestnut Woodpecker (P. Coopmans).

Rufous-headed Woodpecker
Celeus spectabilis
Carpintero Cabecirrufo   Plate 53(11)

25.5–26.5 cm (10–10½"). *Rare* in *lower and middle growth of riparian forest and woodland* in lowlands of east, favoring areas with abundant *Cecropia* trees and understory of *Gynerium* cane. Iris reddish brown; bill olive horn. Obvious bushy pointed crest. ♂ has

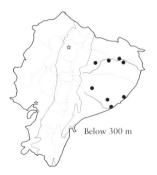

Below 300 m

rich rufous head with red slash in crest and red malar streak (red lacking in ♀); *otherwise above (including wing-coverts) yellowish buff with bold black spotting and barring*, rump unmarked cinnamon-buff; flight feathers extensively rufous, *tail uniform blackish*. Chest black; lower underparts cinnamon-buff, breast boldly scaled and barred with black, a few spots and scales on belly. **Similar species:** Unlikely to be confused, but cf. Ringed Woodpecker (*which looks much darker above*, etc.); note Rufous-headed's narrow habitat requirements. **Habits:** Less arboreal than other *Celeus*, and generally not as conspicuous. Forages singly or in separated pairs, moving through lower growth, independent of mixed flocks. Feeds by probing trunks and branches of *Cecropia*, apparently extracting ants. **Voice:** Distinctive call commences with a loud squeal followed by a bubbly phrase, "squeeah! kluh-kluh-kluh-kluh-kluh-kluh."

Ringed Woodpecker, *Celeus torquatus*
Carpintero Fajeado   Plate 53(12)

Below 300 m

26.5–28 cm (10½–11"). *Scarce* in canopy and borders of humid forest (both terra firme and várzea) in *lowlands of east*. Iris dark red; bill grayish. Obvious bushy pointed crest. ♂ has *head and throat cinnamon contrasting with black breast and nuchal collar*, and red malar streak (lacking in ♀); *above otherwise rufous-chestnut barred with black*; tail blackish banded rufous-chestnut. Lower underparts boldly banded pale ochraceous and black. **Similar species:** Chestnut Woodpecker much plainer chestnut, lacking this species' black patterning and black breast shield; Ringed's head conspicuously *paler* than rest of body. The rare Rufous-headed Woodpecker also has a black breast patch but is markedly paler above; its black markings thus contrast more. The two also segregate by foraging, Rufous-headed remaining relatively close to ground. **Habits:** Arboreal, usually remaining high in forest canopy and more often heard than seen. Found singly or in pairs, generally apart from mixed flocks. **Voice:** Far-carrying call a series of loud, clear, ringing notes, "kleee-kleee-kleee-kleee," evenly spaced and sometimes with only 3 or up to 5 notes. This differs from Cream-colored's similar call in being evenly pitched and not descending.

Lineated Woodpecker, *Dryocopus lineatus*
Carpintero Lineado   Plate 48(1)

To at least 1200 m

33–35.5 cm (13–14″). A *large* woodpecker, fairly common and widespread in humid and deciduous forest and woodland and adjacent clearings in lowlands and foothills of east and west; more numerous in west. Iris white to pale yellow; *bill blackish*, sometimes paler below. Conspicuous pointed crest. **Western** ♂ brownish black above with crown, crest, and malar streak bright red and *narrow white stripe from base of bill across lower face and down sides of neck*; *two parallel white stripes down sides of back*. Throat and chest blackish, lower underparts pale buffy brownish with irregular dark barring and spotting. ♀ similar but with *black forehead and malar streak*. **Eastern** ♂ **and** ♀ differ in being larger; they are glossier black above and on throat and chest, and have prominent blackish barring on lower underparts. **Similar species:** Narrow white facial and neck stripe of this strikingly patterned woodpecker distinctive, as are its back stripes that do *not* meet; other equal-sized, sympatric woodpeckers have simpler facial patterns (cf. especially ♀ Crimson-crested). In west, most likely confused with Guayaquil Woodpecker, though that is paler-billed; ♂ ♂ Guayaquils

differ in their all-red head, ♀ ♀ in their red (not black) forehead and broader white stripe down lower face (no black malar). In east, confusion most likely with Crimson-crested Woodpecker, ♂ ♂ of which also differ in their all-red head, ♀ ♀ in their black along entire front part of crest; in both sexes white back stripes converge on lower back. **Habits:** Found singly or in pairs, foraging at all levels, most often on trunks and larger limbs; though forest-based, Lineateds regularly fly out to isolated trees in clearings. Flight deeply undulating. Pries off pieces of bark and pecks deeply into rotting wood searching for beetles and larvae; also takes many ants and also consumes some fruit. **Voice:** Common calls include a "wik-wik-wik-wik-wik" (often longer, up to 15–20 "wik"s) that starts softly but quickly becomes very loud and far-carrying, and a "keép-grrrr." Also gives a loud drum of 6–8 notes.

Melanerpes Woodpeckers
Conspicuous, attractive, and *noisy* woodpeckers found in the canopy and—especially—at the edge of humid lowland forests and woodlands, one species on either side of the Andes.

Yellow-tufted Woodpecker
Melanerpes cruentatus
Carpintero Penachiamarillo   Plate 54(16)

18–19 cm (7–7½″). A *beautiful* woodpecker, *common and conspicuous* in canopy and borders of humid forest and in clearings in *lowlands and foothills of east*. Iris yellow. ♂ *mainly black* with obvious pale yellow eye-ring extending back as a *whitish postocular stripe which reaches a narrow golden yellow nuchal band*; center of crown red (white in ♀). *Rump white* (obvious in flight); median breast and belly red, flanks and crissum

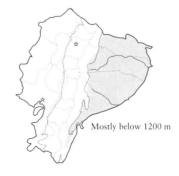

Mostly below 1200 m

barred black and whitish. **Similar species:** Gaudy and unlikely to be confused, though when back-lit it can look essentially black. *No other Ecuadorian woodpecker is so fond of dead trees and snags.* **Habits:** Very social, often occurring in groups of 3–5 birds, occasionally up to 12 or even more. Usually perches high, most often on dead snags and fully in open, even in the torrid heat of noonday sun. Feeds by probing like other woodpeckers, but also sallies for aerial insects and eats considerable fruit. Upon alighting, Yellow-tufteds almost invariably hold wings outstretched for a moment, and calling birds also frequently flare wings. **Voice:** Noisy, with distinctive and most frequent call being a "krr-rr-rr-rr-krénh-krénh" with variants but always with rolled beginning; sometimes several birds call simultaneously or in synchrony, wings flaring and heads bowing. Also often gives a fast "kedididí kedididí kedididí."

Black-cheeked Woodpecker
Melanerpes pucherani
Carpintero Carinegro   Plate 54(15)

Mostly below 800 m

18–19 cm (7–7½″). A *colorful* woodpecker, rather common in canopy and borders of more humid forest and woodland, also ranging freely into trees of planatations and gardens (sometimes far from actual forest), in *lowlands and foothills of west*. ♂ *mainly black above* with *yellow frontlet*, red crown, and white spot behind eye; rump white, back narrowly barred white, and flight feathers spotted white. Throat whitish, breast and belly grayish olive, *belly barred with black and with red patch on median belly*. ♀ similar but with midcrown black. **Similar species:** Nothing really resembles it in its

western range. **Habits:** Usually perches high in trees, often resting on dead snags. Gleans and probes for insects on branches and trunks, but also eats much fruit and sallies after flying insects. **Voice:** Usual call a "churrr," sometimes repeated 3–4 times.

Veniliornis Woodpeckers
Small, usually inconspicuous woodpeckers found in a variety of forested and wooded habitats, ranging both in lowlands and montane areas. Most species are *some shade of olive above* (often stained red or gold, sometimes with a golden nuchal collar) and show *coarse barring below*; the distinctive Scarlet-backed and plain Smoky-brown are exceptions.

Smoky-brown Woodpecker
Veniliornis fumigatus
Carpintero Pardo   Plate 54(13)

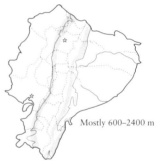

Mostly 600–2400 m

18–18.5 cm (7–7¼″). A *dark, uniform-looking* woodpecker, widespread but rather inconspicuous in lower and middle growth of *foothill and subtropical* forest, woodland, and borders on both slopes. ♂ *uniform olive-brown* with red crown and nape and usually a paler area below eyes; some individuals show a stain of gold on midback; tail blackish. ♀ similar but crown brown. Birds of El Oro and w. Loja darker and browner. **Similar species:** Other vaguely similar *Veniliornis* woodpeckers show barring on underparts. **Habits:** Found singly or in pairs, usually not too high above ground, often accompanying mixed flocks. Forages mostly on branches (not trunks), methodically tapping and probing into both live and dead wood. **Voice:** Usually quiet, but gives a short "chuk" and ocassionally a loud, fast, raspy "chk-skwiza-zazazah."

Little Woodpecker, *Veniliornis passerinus*
Carpintero Chico   Plate 54(9)

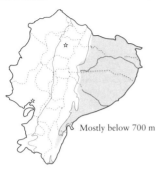

Mostly below 700 m

15.5 cm (6″). *Várzea and riparian* forest and woodland, clearings with scattered trees, and *river islands* in *lowlands of east*, ranging up in major river valleys to base of Andes. ♂ fairly bright yellowish olive above with red crown and nape, *whitish postocular and malar stripes*, and dusky ear-coverts; a few small yellowish spots on wing-coverts; tail dusky. *Below dull olive narrowly and obscurely banded with yellowish white.* ♀ similar, but crown olive-brown. **Similar species:** Red-stained Woodpecker, also found in e. lowlands, has golden-yellow nape and lacks facial stripes; it inhabits humid forest, not the semiopen wooded habitats of Little. **Habits:** Found singly or in pairs, foraging at varying levels; often in semiopen and easy to see. **Voice:** Call a series of "wik" notes, starting slowly, often given from prominent perch.

Red-stained Woodpecker, *Veniliornis affinis*
Carpintero Rojoteñido   Plate 54(10)

16.5–18 cm (6½–7″). Canopy and borders of *humid forest*, primarily in terra firme, in *lowlands of east*. ♂ fairly bright yellowish olive above with brownish olive forehead, red

To 600 m

crown (some brownish intermixed), and *yellow nuchal collar*; tail dusky with some paler barring; some individuals have some red staining on wing-coverts and back. Below coarsely barred olive and buffy whitish. ♀ similar, but crown brown. **Similar species:** Little Woodpecker is, as its name implies, smaller, but is more easily distinguished on basis of whitish facial stripes (not present in Red-stained) and lack of yellow collar. Red staining on upperparts is often not apparent, at least not in Ecuadorian birds. **Habits:** Found singly or in pairs, generally remaining quite high above ground and therefore not very conspicuous (less so than Little). Regularly accompanies mixed flocks. **Voice:** Not terribly vocal, but infrequently gives a fast series of up to 12–14 nasal, high-pitched "kih" notes.

Chocó Woodpecker, *Veniliornis chocoensis*
Carpintero del Chocó   Plate 54(11)

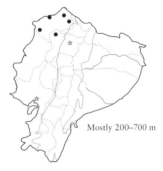

Mostly 200–700 m

15.5–16 cm (6–6¼″). Scarce and local in canopy and borders of humid forest in *lowlands and foothills of far northwest*. Formerly considered conspecific with Red-stained Woodpecker or—earlier—with Golden-collared Woodpecker (*V. cassini*) of ne. South America. ♂ yellowish olive above with sooty brown forehead, red crown (some dusky intermixed), and *yellow nuchal collar*; tail dusky with some paler barring. *Below boldly barred and scaled blackish and buffy whitish.* ♀ similar, but crown dusky. **Similar species:** Red-stained Woodpecker occurs only east of Andes; it is larger and markedly paler overall (especially below). Red-rumped Woodpecker, which occurs to south of Chocó in w. Ecuador (favoring less wet areas, but with limited overlap?), has whitish throat, red rump (often hidden), and paler (less bold) barring below. **Habits:** Similar to Red-stained Woodpecker, but seems more confined to actual forest. Red-rumped Woodpecker is more a bird of semihumid forest and woodland.

Red-rumped Woodpecker, *Veniliornis kirkii*
Carpintero Lomirrojo   Plate 54(12)

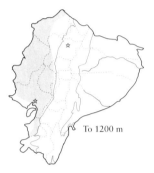

To 1200 m

15.5–16 cm (6–6¹⁄₄″). Widespread but rarely numerous in lower and middle growth of *humid and deciduous forest and woodland and adjacent plantations* in *lowlands and foothills of west*. ♂ fairly bright yellowish olive above with sooty brown forehead, red crown (some sooty intermixed), and *golden-yellow nuchal collar*; back and wing-coverts often stained red; *rump red*, tail dusky. *Throat whitish*; *underparts densely and evenly barred buffy whitish and brown*. ♀ similar, but crown dusky. **Similar species:** Red-rumped is only small woodpecker with barring below occurring in most of the west; red rump is unique, but note that this color is hard to see on perched birds. In far northwest, cf. scarce Chocó Woodpecker, which favors very wet situations. Scarlet-backed Woodpecker is much more extensively red above, whitish with only faint barring below. **Habits:** Similar to other *Veniliornis* woodpeckers though somewhat easier to see than many, at least in part because it favors more open habitats. **Voice:** Not very vocal. Most frequent vocalization a rather slow series of nasal and emphatic calls, "kénh kenh kenh kenh" (P. Coopmans); occasionally also gives an abrupt "kwik!"

Yellow-vented Woodpecker, *Veniliornis dignus*
Carpintero Ventriamarillo   Plate 54(8)

16–16.5 cm (6¹⁄₄–6¹⁄₂″). Uncommon in *subtropical and lower temperate forest and*

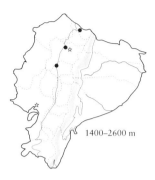

1400–2600 m

forest borders on e. slope; on w. slope only in northwest. ♂ yellowish olive above with a few yellow spots on wing-coverts and red crown and nape, *whitish postocular and malar stripes*, and blackish cheeks; tail blackish, outer feathers barred yellowish. Throat dusky, underparts densely barred dusky-olive and yellowish, *becoming plain pale yellow on belly*. ♀ similar but *crown black*, only nape red. **Similar species:** A small *Veniliornis* of the subtropics; its only sympatric congener is much plainer and browner Smoky-brown Woodpecker (which shows no barring below, etc.). At higher elevations, cf. larger Bar-bellied Woodpecker, with which Yellow-vented may occasionally overlap. **Habits:** Similar to those of other *Veniliornis*; on the whole, an inconspicuous and quiet woodpecker, not too often seen. Single birds or pairs sometimes accompany mixed flocks, foraging at varying levels though usually not near ground. **Voice:** Infrequently heard call a fast, rattled "krrrrrrrrrrrrrr" (P. Coopmans), resembling call of Golden-olive Woodpecker.

Bar-bellied Woodpecker, *Veniliornis nigriceps*
Carpintero Ventribarrado   Plate 54(7)

16.5–18 cm (6¹⁄₂–7″). Scarce in *temperate forest and woodland* on both slopes, occurring up to treeline and in *Polylepis* groves. ♂ olive above (back sometimes with a little red staining) with red crown and nape, *whitish postocular and malar stripes*, and blackish cheeks; tail blackish, outer feathers barred whitish. Throat dusky; *underparts densely and evenly barred blackish and yellowish white*. ♀ similar but *red on crown and nape replaced by black*, some birds showing a little red on nape; barring below more dusky-olive. **Similar species:** A rather large *Veniliornis* of

Mostly 2800–3500 m

higher elevations; no congener occurs as high. Confusion is most likely with smaller Yellow-vented, though that species has an unmarked (not barred) and obviously yellow belly. Their facial patterns are not dissimilar, though ♀ Yellow-vented has obvious red on nape, lacking in ♀ Bar-bellied. **Habits:** Similar to those of other *Veniliornis*, in particular Yellow-vented, though Bar-bellied seems more often to forage close to ground. **Voice:** Infrequently heard song a series of up to about 25 "kee" notes, at first ascending and louder, usually descending at end (P. Coopmans and N. Krabbe); also gives a "chik" call.

Scarlet-backed Woodpecker
Veniliornis callonotus

Carpintero Dorsiescarlata   Plate 54(14)

14–14.5 cm (5½–5¾"). An unmistakable *small, red-backed* woodpecker of deciduous and semihumid forest and woodland as well as partially cleared areas and arid scrub in *lowlands and foothills of west*. Bill dusky ivory. ♂ *mostly shiny red above*, some black showing through on crown; cheeks and sides of neck brownish; tail blackish, outer feathers buff barred dusky. *Below whitish*, with some blackish scaling on chest and flanks. ♀

Mostly below 1000 m,
to 1800 m in Loja

similar but *crown and nape black*. Birds from **El Oro and Loja** differ in having a whitish area separating crown from brownish on cheeks, and in having—on average—more dark scaling on underparts. **Habits:** More conspicuous that other *Veniliornis*, in part doubtless because its favored habitat tends to be much less dense. Often in pairs, foraging at varying levels in trees, even on very thin branches. **Voice:** Most frequent call a rattle lasting 1–2 seconds (P. Coopmans); also gives a sharp "ki-dik," sometimes quickly repeated in a short series.

Campephilus Woodpeckers

Large and spectacular woodpeckers with *obvious pointed crests* and that superficially resemble the somewhat smaller Lineated Woodpecker (whose calls differ strikingly). **Sexes nearly alike,** though males have somewhat more red on the head. They are found widely in forest and woodland, mainly in the humid lowlands.

Crimson-crested Woodpecker
Campephilus melanoleucos

Carpintero Crestirrojo   Plate 48(2)

Mostly below 900 m

33.5–35.5 cm (13¼–14"). Fairly common in humid forest and borders in *lowlands and foothills of east*. Iris yellow; bill mainly dark horn. Conspicuous pointed crest. ♂ mainly black above with *head largely bright red; whitish patch at base of bill* and another smaller black and white spot on ear-coverts; white stripe extends down sides of neck onto sides of back and *almost coverges into a V on lower back*. Throat and chest black; breast and belly coarsely barred blackish and buff. ♀ similar but has *forehead and front of crest black*, some black around and behind eye, and *white neck stripe extends forward to bill as broad stripe across lower face.* **Similar species:** Both sexes of Lineated Woodpecker differ in head pattern, neither sex showing as much red as ♂ Crimson-crested, whereas ♀ Lineated's white facial stripe is much narrower; its back stripes do not converge. **Habits:** Not dissimilar from Lineated Woodpecker, though more of a forest-based bird and less often out in large clearings. Forages in pairs, occasionally in small (family?) groups, hitching up trunks and larger branches at all levels; often feeds for protracted periods in same tree or snag, whacking off pieces of bark and chiseling deeply in its quest for beetles and larvae. **Voice:** Most often heard is a loud, very far-carrying drumming that consists of a very loud and forceful rap followed by several weaker strokes (at a distance often just the first two can be heard); drums of other *Campephilus* woodpeckers (other than Guayaquil) are only 2-noted. Also gives several calls, most frequently a slightly nasal and fast "ski-zi-zik" or "skik-skik-ski-zi-zik," also a downslurred "kiarrh."

Guayaquil Woodpecker
Campephilus gayaquilensis
Carpintero Guayaquileño   Plate 48(3)

33–35 cm (13–13¾"). Fairly common but now somewhat local in humid and deciduous forest and woodland in *lowlands and foothills of west*. Resembles Crimson-crested Woodpecker (found only east of Andes). ♂ differs from ♂ Crimson-crested in lacking whitish patch at base of bill and in having variable amount of buff barring on lower back and rump. ♀ differs in having no black on forehead, front of crest, or around eye (hence head is mainly red, though retaining broad white stripe across lower face). Both

sexes have brownish tinge to all black areas of plumage. **Similar species:** Both sexes of Lineated Woodpecker have different facial patterns with much more black showing. **Habits and Voice:** Similar to closely related Crimson-crested Woodpecker.

Red-necked Woodpecker
Campephilus rubricollis
Carpintero Cuellirrojo   Plate 48(4)

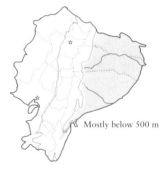

Mostly below 500 m

33.5–35.4 cm (13¼–14"). Scarce *inside terra firme forest* in *lowlands of east*. Bill greenish or bluish horn; iris yellow. Conspicuous pointed crest. ♂ has *head, neck, and chest bright crimson,* becoming *rufous on remaining underparts*; a small black and white spot on lower ear-coverts. *Upperparts otherwise contrastingly black,* with *rufous patch in primaries* conspicuous in flight and also often visible on perched birds; underwing-coverts also rufous. ♀ resembles ♂ but lacks tiny ear-spot, this being "replaced" by *broad white malar stripe* narrowly bordered with black. **Similar species:** Not likely confused, this splendid large woodpecker *lacks* the prominent white neck and back stripes shown by Crimson-crested and Lineated Woodpeckers. **Habits:** Usually found in wide-ranging pairs, tending to feed on trunks and larger branches of taller trees, often rather low; infrequent at edge, and hardly ever entering or crossing clearings. **Voice:** Gives a far-carrying, 2-noted rap with first stroke louder than second. Call a loud, nasal "kiahh."

Powerful Woodpecker, *Campephilus pollens*
Carpintero Poderoso   Plate 48(6)
33.5–35.4 cm (13¼–14"). Scarce in *subtropical and temperate forest and borders* on both slopes, *occurring at higher elevations than*

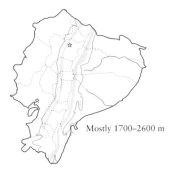

Mostly 1700–2600 m

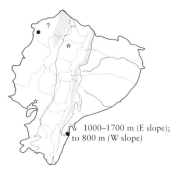

1000–1700 m (E slope);
to 800 m (W slope)

any other Campephilus. Bill blackish; iris golden to orange-yellow. Conspicuous pointed crest. ♂ mainly black above with *bright red crown and crest* and white stripe from base of bill across lower face and down sides of neck, connecting to pair of white stripes on sides of back *that converge on white lower back and rump*; primaries tipped whitish. Throat and chest black; breast and belly coarsely barred blackish *and rich buff.* ♀ looks rather different, lacking all red on head, *this replaced by black.* **Similar species:** Not known to occur with Crimson-crested Woodpecker of e. lowlands, ♂♂ of which have head mainly red, ♀♀ of which lack white rump and are not so richly colored below. ♀ Powerful, having mainly black head and neck (no red), is essentially unmistakable. Cf. also Lineated Woodpecker, which likewise occurs at *lower* elevations than Powerful. **Habits:** Similar to other *Campephilus* woodpeckers, though Powerful's home range seems exceptionally large and as a result species is encountered only infrequently. Most often forages low on trunks. **Voice:** Strong double-rap similar to Red-necked's. Most frequent call a loud nasal "kyaaah!," often repeated several times in succession or accelerated—most often while flying—into a fast "kikikikikah!" Excited birds also give a descending "kikikikik-keh-keh-keh-kah."

Crimson-bellied Woodpecker
Campephilus haematogaster
Carpintero Carminoso   Plate 48(5)

33–35 cm (13–13¾″). Scarce and local in lower growth of *foothill and subtropical forest on both slopes*, south only to Pichincha in west. Conspicuous crest, but less pointed than in other *Campephilus*. Bill black; iris reddish brown. On **east slope**, ♂

has head and neck mainly bright red with black mask *bordered above by buff postocular stripe and below by broad buff malar stripe*; otherwise mainly black above with red lower back and rump and *bold buffy whitish or buff barring on flight feathers* (most evident in flight; underwing-coverts same color). Throat and midchest black; *underparts mainly dark crimson*, some blackish showing through. ♀ similar but *buff malar stripe extends down sides of neck.* **West-slope birds** differ in having black restricted to throat (none on chest); they also have some narrow blackish barring below (*though underparts still look red*). **Similar species:** Not likely confused. Crimson-bellied is not known to occur with Red-necked Woodpecker of e. lowlands (which, in any case, has almost entirely red head and neck). **Habits:** This spectacular but only rarely encountered woodpecker ranges inside forest, foraging mainly close to ground on larger trunks, sometimes on buttresses themselves. It generally moves about in loosely associated pairs that keep in contact through calling. **Voice:** Call of e.-slope birds a loud and strident "stk! st-kr-r-r-r-r-r!" lasting about 2 seconds, with drum a fast series of 3–4 loud raps sounding like a machine-gun burst (M. B. Robbins recordings). In northwest gives a strong double-rap much as in Red-necked and Powerful Woodpeckers, and a loud "stk."

Passeriformes
Ovenbirds: Furnariidae (78)

A large and diverse family of relatively plain, brown and rufous birds found exclusively in the Neotropics. A few are boldly patterned, but in many genera plumage distinctions between species are slight, which leads to identification difficulties. The woodcreepers are closely related and have been considered as part of the same family. Although furnariids are found throughout Ecuador, their diversity is greatest in forests of the eastern lowlands and on Andean slopes. Vocalizations are often distinctive and, especially for the more skulking and less often seen species, are often the best indication of their presence in an area. **Sexes are alike.** Nests vary dramatically, though in all species it is essentially a closed structure (of varying types, usually either in a burrow or made of sticks) with a side entrance.

times given from an elevated perch, e.g., a boulder. Ecuador birds give a usually accelerating series of "keek" notes, e.g., "kyeek keekkeek kek kekkek ke-ke-ke-keke-ke . . ."; flight call a more nasal "kyeenh" (N. Krabbe recordings).

Cinclodes Cinclodes
Plain furnariids found in *open areas at high elevations*. In flight they show a *characteristic rufous wingstripe and tail-corners*. Nests are placed at the end of a burrow or hole dug into a bank, wall, or even an old building.

Slender-billed Miner, *Geositta tenuirostris*
Minero Piquitenue   Plate 59(1)

3350–4000 m

Bar-winged Cinclodes, *Cinclodes fuscus*
Cinclodes Alifranjeado   Plate 59(3)

Mostly 3200–4300 m

18cm (7″). Rare and local in *open arid paramo* and adjacent agricultural fields in *highlands of w. Cotopaxi and w. Chimborazo. Bill long, thin, and somewhat decurved.* Above pale grayish brown with narrow buff superciliary; in flight shows *mainly rufous flight feathers* and *mostly rufous tail* (with dusky terminal band and central pair of feathers). Below buffy whitish with *profuse brownish streaking on breast.* **Similar species:** In Ecuador, nothing really similar. Both cinclodes have markedly shorter and heavier bills, longer tails; they lack breast streaking, and have rufous wing *stripe* and rufous on tail only on *corners.* **Habits:** Mainly terrestrial, found singly or in pairs, walking or running about with waddling gait reminisent of a hornero. Can be quite tame, but flies strongly, and when flushed apt to fly off a considerable distance. **Voice:** During flight display ♂ circles and hovers above ground, pouring forth its simple and repetitive but quite musical song; this song is also some-

18cm (7″). *Numerous and widespread in paramo, grassy areas, and adjacent agricultural fields in highlands*, favoring areas near water. *Short, fine bill black.* Brown above with buff to whitish superciliary; in flight shows rufous wing-band and tail-corners. Throat and chest white with dusky brown scaling; underparts pale dingy grayish brown. **Similar species:** Stout-billed Cinclodes, often found with this species, is considerably larger with a heavier and more arched bill, more extensive scaling on breast. The two Ecuadorian cinclodes have *similar* wing-bars. **Habits:** Mainly terrestrial, most often occurring in pairs and very confiding; regularly forages on or along roads, often around water (e.g., in drainage ditches) but also sometimes on drier fields and grassy areas. Flight swift, usually low over ground; tail sometimes held cocked, especially soon after bird alights, but while feeding it is usually depressed. Walks on ground, picking at or into moist soil or animal droppings. **Voice:**

♂'s song a brief, high-pitched trill, most often given from an exposed perch with wings outstretched and flapped exuberantly; also sometimes given in a display flight. Call, given especially in flight, a quick "tsip" or "tseep."

Stout-billed Cinclodes, *Cinclodes excelsior*
Cinclodes Piquigrueso   Plate 59(2)

3300–4500 m

20.5 cm (8″). Paramo, open shrubby woodland, and edges of *Polylepis* woodland in highlands south to Azuay. *Heavy bill rather long, markedly decurved*. Above dark brown with whitish superciliary; in flight shows rufous-buff wing-band and dull buff tail-corners. Throat whitish faintly scaled dusky; underparts dull buffy whitish, brownest down sides and flanks, with *usually prominent brownish scaling across breast*. **Similar species:** Bar-winged Cinclodes markedly smaller (though size difference often not apparent except in direct comparison) with finer, shorter, straighter bill, and shows less scaling below. **Habits:** Similar to Bar-winged Cinclodes, though seems less tied to presence of water, and more apt to be found in areas with shrubs and low trees (on which it sometimes perches); seems more numerous at higher elevations. Feeding birds probe deeply into loose or moist soil. **Voice:** ♂'s song a rising and swelling trill, "tr-r-r-r-r-reeet," usually uttered while giving a wing-flapping display from an exposed perch; not as thin as trills of Bar-winged Cinclodes, and somewhat resembles White-chinned Thistletail's song (P. Coopmans). Call a sharp "keeu."

Furnarius Horneros
A distinct group of chunky, thrush-like furnariids with *notably short tails, long legs,* and *fairly long slender bills* that range in open and semiopen areas. Rufous and whitish predominate in their plumages. Horneros are best known for their remarkable mud nests that are shaped much like an old-fashioned oven (hence their English name; *horno* means "oven" in Spanish, *hornero* "baker"); these are typically placed on posts or atop a horizontal limb.

Pacific Hornero, *Furnarius cinnamomeus*
Hornero del Pacífico   Plate 59(4)

Mainly below 1500 m, up to 1800–2300 m in Loja

19 cm (7½″). *Common and conspicuous in a variety of open and semiopen habitats (including agricultural areas and even towns) in lowlands of west*, also ranging well up into subtropics in Loja; tends to avoid very humid and very arid regions, but overall range expanding. Formerly considered conspecific with cis-Andean Pale-legged Hornero (*F. leucopus*). Iris straw yellow to hazel; legs pale brownish gray. *Bright orange-rufous above* with contrasting gray crown, *conspicuous long white superciliary*, and brownish cheeks; primaries blackish with rufous wingstripe showing in flight. Throat white; *underparts pale cinnamon-buff*. **Similar species:** *The only hornero throughout its range*, thus easily known. **Habits:** Familiar wherever it occurs, Pacific Hornero often struts about in open, frequently on dirt roads, pausing to pick at or probe ground and also flick leaves aside to expose hidden insects. Though primarily terrestrial, also perches freely in trees and on houses, and regularly rests on fence posts. **Voice:** Frequently heard song an arresting—at times almost raucous—and fast series of loud piercing notes that gradually slows and drops in pitch; sometimes given more or less in unison by both

members of a pair, usually as they perch close together, heads tilted back. Often-heard call a loud and clear "kyeek."

[Bay Hornero, *Furnarius torridus*
Hornero Castaño]   Plate 59(5)

18.5 cm (7¼"). *Perhaps only a casual wanderer to river islands and margins in lowlands of far northeast.* Sometimes called Pale-billed Hornero. Iris brown; *rather long bill pale pinkish*; legs pinkish. *Above uniform rich and dark rufous-chestnut* with long and broad whitish superciliary; primaries blackish (but shows no pale wing-bar in flight, fide A. Whittaker). Throat white; *underparts mainly rufescent brown.* **Similar species:** Only other hornero in this species' limited Ecuadorian range is diminutive Lesser Hornero which, in addition to much smaller size, differs in markedly paler overall coloration and grayish crown. **Habits:** Hardly known in Ecuador. Elsewhere less conspicuous than Pacific Hornero, walking about on ground and mud inside riparian and várzea forest, often on islands.

Lesser Hornero, *Furnarius minor*
Hornero Menor   Plate 59(6)

15 cm (6"). A *small* hornero, *scarce on or near ground in low woodland and early-succession scrub on islands in Río Napo in lowlands of northeast.* Iris brown; bill blackish, grayish horn at base of mandible; legs dark gray. Above dull rufous with brownish gray crown, whitish superciliary, and dusky cheeks. Throat white; underparts dull buffyish. **Similar species:** Only hornero known to occur on Río Napo islands, Lesser is much smaller and duller than Ecuadorian congeners. Cf. in particular rare Bay Hornero.

Habits: An inconspicuous hornero, walking about on ground, usually remaining in dense low cover though occasionally emerging out to edge. **Voice:** ♂'s song a fast and descending series of relatively—compared to other horneros—high-pitched and shrill "kee" notes. Call a sharp and scratchy "krik."

Andean Tit-Spinetail, *Leptasthenura andicola*
Tijeral Andino   Plate 57(1)

16.5–17 cm (6½–6¾"). A distinctive, *very long-tailed* and *streaky* furnariid found in shrubby paramo, *Polylepis* woodland patches, and low woodland near treeline in highlands mainly from Carchi to Azuay. Crown black streaked rufous and with *conspicuous white superciliary and narrow frontlet*; otherwise dark brown above, back streaked white; tail dusky-brown, *feathers graduated and very pointed, tips of central pair protruding as a "double point."* Chin white; underparts brown *boldly and extensively streaked white.* **Similar species:** This attractive and acrobatic spinetail is not likely confused, but cf. often sympatric Many-striped Canastero (with much shorter tail, rufous in wings and tail, etc.). Very differently shaped ♀ Plumbeous Sierra-Finch also has a generally streaked pattern. **Habits:** Found in small groups (also pairs) that forage restlessly, moving frequently from bush to bush, sometimes hanging upside-down as they creep about in foliage inspecting leaves, branches, and flowers. They may accompany loose mixed flocks. If you can position yourself at right spot, this charming tit-spinetail may become quite confiding, feeding unconcernedly at close range. **Voice:** Apparent song a hesitating series of high-pitched short trills, e.g., "trrrr . . . trrrr . . ."; also gives various "tzik" or "tzi-dik" call notes.

Synallaxis Spinetails

A large group of confusing small furnariids with rather long double-pointed tails, *Synallaxis* typically skulk in dense lower growth but are often persistently vocal. Some species inhabit forests (either lowland or montane), but many others are found in more open shrubby terrain; many have quite narrow habitat requirements and thus are necessarily local though they may be numerous where found. Identification can be difficult, especially as they are so hard to see well; *often voice provides the best clue*. Nests are globular or ball-shaped structures made of grass with a side entrance.

Azara's Spinetail, *Synallaxis azarae*
Colaespina de Azara   Plate 56(1)

Mostly 1500–3000 m, locally to 900 m or even lower

17–17.5 cm (6¾–7″). *Generally common and widespread* in forest borders, lighter woodland, shrubby clearings, and hedgerows in *subtropical and temperate zones*, locally down into *foothills in s. Ecuador*. The most *numerous montane spinetail*, occurring in both humid and fairly arid regions. Above

olive brown with *contrasting rufous crown* and brown frontlet; *wings and rather long tail also rufous*. Throat black variably scaled with white; underparts gray, whiter on mid-belly and brownish on flanks. **Southwestern birds** paler gray below and may show vague pale superciliary. **Similar species:** Only other sympatric *Synallaxis* with rufous on crown, wings, and tail is much darker Slaty of w. slope; these two species differ markedly in voice. *Cranioleuca* spinetails are more arboreal, etc. **Habits:** Furtive and hard to see, though its oft-heard voice draws attention. Occurs singly or in pairs, creeping about in dense vegetation close to ground; most often not with mixed flocks. Even when singing, only rarely comes fully into open. **Voice:** Frequently heard song, given throughout day, an often endlessly repeated, sharp "ka-kweeék." Southwestern birds' song similar but higher pitched. Less often gives a very different, *Scytalopus* tapaculo-like series of rapidly uttered notes, "kakakakakaka . . ." continuing 3–5 seconds. Also gives a short trill or churring while foraging, "trrt."

Dusky Spinetail, *Synallaxis moesta*
Colaespina Oscura   Plate 56(2)

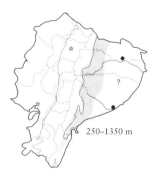

250–1350 m

15.5 cm (6″). A *dark and obscure* spinetail, *scarce and local in dense undergrowth of foothill forest, borders, and secondary woodland along e. base of Andes*, also sparingly out into lowlands. Above dark grayish brown with *rufous crown* and dusky frontlet, mainly rufous wings, and *short, often frayed-looking rufous-chestnut tail*. Throat mixed silvery gray and black; *underparts dark grayish brown*. **Similar species:** More numerous Dark-breasted Spinetail is grayer generally (not so brown), and its longer tail is brownish (not rufous-chestnut); it favors grassy clearings and scrub. Cf. also Marañón Spinetail. **Habits:** Even more furtive and skulking than other spinetails, creeping and hopping about in tangles near ground. Usually in pairs. In some areas favors patches of bamboo. **Voice:** Gives a low-pitched nasal chattering or churring, "rha-a-a-a-a-a-a."

Slaty Spinetail, *Synallaxis brachyura*
Colaespina Pizarrosa   Plate 56(3)

Mostly below 1400 m

15.5–16 cm (6–6¼"). *Common in shrubby forest and woodland borders, clearings, and gardens in lowlands and foothills of west.* Above olive brown with *rufous crown* and dusky-brown frontlet; *wing-coverts also rufous*; tail dusky-brown. Upper throat white flecked with black, lower throat blackish (depending on angle, sometimes with silvery effect); *underparts uniform gray.* Southwestern birds (especially in El Oro) have midbelly whiter, flanks browner. **Similar species:** In most of its range the only *Synallaxis* present, and thus easily recognized on basis of contrasting rufous crown and wing-coverts. Azara's Spinetail occurs primarily at higher elevations, overlapping only locally with Slaty; it has a much longer rufous tail and mainly rufous wings, and the two differ markedly in voice. **Habits:** Somewhat less skulking and easier to see than other *Synallaxis*, more often foraging higher above ground and even occasionally leaving dense cover. Like the others, however, it usually remains in tangled growth. **Voice:** Song a low-pitched, throaty churring often introduced by a few notes, e.g., "ch-ch-chirrrr"; often just "chirrrr" is given. ♀'s churring slightly higher pitched. Also gives a "chk" call while foraging.

Dark-breasted Spinetail, *Synallaxis albigularis*
Colaespina Pechioscura   Plate 56(4)

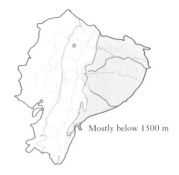

Mostly below 1500 m

15.5 cm (6"). *Common* in grassy pastures, shrubby clearings and borders, and early-succession woodland (including river islands, where favors *Gynerium* cane stands) in *lowlands of east*, also following clearings up Andes. Above olive brown with rufous crown and dusky frontlet; wing-coverts also rufous; *rather short, "spiky" tail grayish brown.* Upper throat white, lower throat white scaled black; underparts gray (darker northward) with midbelly whitish and flanks browner. **Similar species:** Dusky Spinetail darker generally, more uniform below, and has rufous-chestnut tail; it is more a forest-based bird. Slaty Spinetail occurs only west of Andes. Azara's Spinetail ranges in Andes, and its much longer tail is rufous. **Habits:** Similar to other *Synallaxis*. As attested to by its frequent vocalizing, Dark-breasted Spinetail is numerous and—as a result of forest destruction—increasing, but it is often hard to see well; occasionally a singing bird will perch in the open in a grass clump or low shrub. **Voice:** Very vocal, with song an oft-repeated, fast "whít, di-di-di," sometimes with an extra "di." Often vocalizes during heat of day. Excited birds give an accelerating whinny, "neeh-neeh-neeh-neeh-neh-neh-neh" (P. Coopmans).

Plain-crowned Spinetail
Synallaxis gujanensis
Colaespina Coroniparda   Plate 256(6)

16–16.5 cm (6¼–6½"). *Undergrowth of riparian woodland and scrub on islands in Ríos Napo and Aguarico in lowlands of northeast.* Head grayish brown with slightly darker crown and dingy pale lores, becoming

To 400 m

olive brown on back; *wings and tail contrastingly rufous. Below dingy buff,* whiter on throat. **Similar species:** *Lacks* rufous on crown and black on throat shown by many other *Synallaxis,* including several species that occur with it on river islands. White-bellied Spinetail has black throat patch and gray breast. Parker's Spinetail has upperparts *entirely* rufous. **Habits:** Very skulking, foraging on or near ground, and favoring areas with extensive undergrowth of *Gynerium* cane (sometimes in *Cecropia*-dominated woodland). Usually in pairs, keeping in contact with each other through frequent calling. Generally not with flocks. **Voice:** Often heard and distinctive call a leisurely "keé, kuh" repeated at several-second intervals and given by both sexes. Often vocalizes even during heat of day.

Marañón Spinetail, *Synallaxis maranonica*
Colaespina de Marañón   Plate 56(5)

650–1200 m

15.5 cm (6″). *Undergrowth of deciduous and semihumid forest and woodland near Zumba in Río Marañon drainage of far southeast.* Formerly considered a race of Plain-crowned Spinetail. Head brownish gray, becoming dull brown on back; *wings and tail contrastingly rufous. Below uniform gray,* slightly whiter on upper throat and browner on lower flanks. **Similar species:** Easily recognized in its limited range; note *lack* of rufous on head and of black on throat. **Habits:** Usually in pairs, hopping on or near ground and often hard to see as it tends to remain in cover. Usually not with flocks. **Voice:** Call, given by both sexes, a very slow-paced, somewhat nasal "kieeuuw . . . keeeu," often given with interval of at least 5–10 seconds between phrases.

White-bellied Spinetail, *Synallaxis propinqua*
Colaespina Ventriblanca   Plate 56(7)

Mostly below 300 m

16 cm (6¼″). Local and inconspicuous (except by voice) in *early-succession scrub on islands in larger rivers in lowlands of east.* Above grayish brown, grayest on crown, with *contrasting rufous wings and tail,* tail feathers very pointed. Chin silvery gray with *large black patch on lower throat* (depending on angle, can be quite conspicuous); *breast gray,* becoming white on midbelly and brownish on flanks. **Similar species:** Plain-crowned Spinetail, which regularly occurs with this species though favoring undergrowth in more mature woodland, differs in lacking black on throat and in its drab buff underparts (no gray). **Habits:** Favors areas with a dense, often almost impenetrable growth of young *Gynerium* cane and scattered bushes. Single birds or pairs creep about on or near ground, rarely leaving cover and hard to see without tape playback. **Voice:** Quite vocal. Unmistakable song a strange, low-pitched, and nasal churring, "ch-r-r-r-r-r-r-r-r." Also gives a slower and scratchy "krreenh-kreeenh-kre-kre-kre-kre-kre," agi-

tated birds sometimes accelerating this into a *Laterallus*-like churr. Call a doubled "kr-krreenh."

Blackish-headed Spinetail, *Synallaxis tithys*
Colaespina Cabecinegruzca   Plate 56(8)

To 1100 m

14.5 cm (5¾″). *Local in undergrowth of deciduous forest and woodland in lowlands and foothills of southwest*. Head and neck dark gray, *becoming black on foreface*; otherwise olivaceous gray above, *wing-coverts contrastingly bright cinnamon-rufous*; tail sooty. Throat black, somewhat grizzled with white along malar; underparts gray, paler on midbelly and slightly more olivaceous on lower flanks. **Similar species:** An attractive *Synallaxis*, not likely confused in its limited range (where the only other typical *Synallaxis* is the rather different Slaty, a species favoring more humid regions). Cf. also the different-looking and more arboreal Necklaced Spinetail. **Habits:** Usually in pairs and typically inconspicuous, hopping about on or near ground; favors dense tangled situations. Attention is usually drawn to it by its distinctive song. **Voice:** Song a short, dry, ascending trill, "t-t-t-t-t-trit," repeated every few seconds. Excited birds can give a "weé-di weé-di weé-di ..." series (P. Coopmans).

Rufous Spinetail, *Synallaxis unirufa*
Colaespina Rufa   Plate 56(9)

17–18 cm (6¾–7″). Undergrowth in *upper subtropical and temperate forest and borders* on both slopes. *Uniform bright rufous*, somewhat darker and more chestnut above, with contrasting black lores. **Juvenile** paler and browner. **Similar species:** Closely resembles Rufous Wren, though the wren differs in

Mostly 2200–3200 m

showing faint dark barring on wings and tail, and its tail shape is different (more rounded whereas spinetail's is frayed and double-pointed). The wren tends to be more gregarious than the spinetail, traveling about in groups rather than just in pairs. Also cf. Sepia-brown Wren. Ruddy Spinetail occurs only in lowlands. **Habits:** Favors stands of *Chusquea* bamboo. Rather skulking, tending to remain in dense cover, and hard to see unless vocalizing. Though sometimes accompanying mixed flocks, at least as often a pair forages independently. **Voice:** ♂'s song a simple, rather shrill "kweeík" or "kueék" or—less frequently—"kuh-kweeík" with querulous upslurred effect, often repeated steadily every 1–2 seconds for long periods.

Ruddy Spinetail, *Synallaxis rutilans*
Colaespina Rojiza   Plate 56(10)

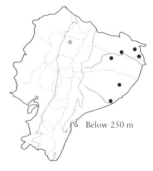

Below 250 m

14.5–15 cm (5¾–6″). A *dark* and *richly colored* spinetail, *scarce and local in dense undergrowth of terra firme forest in lowlands of east*. Mostly rich rufous-chestnut with *contrasting black lores* and *black throat patch*, wings duskier; rather short and often frayed tail black; belly brownish gray. **Similar**

species: Even rarer Chestnut-throated Spinetail has browner upperparts and rufous
throat and breast that contrast with very
dark belly. Chestnut-throated favors more
secondary habitats (in Ecuador the two
species have not been found together); they
have markedly different vocalizations.
Rufous Spinetail occurs only in Andes.
Habits: Usually found in pairs that forage on
or near ground, inspecting tangles and leaf
litter, often in thick growth around treefalls.
Sometimes accompanies understory flocks,
but generally forages apart. **Voice:** Song a
rapidly repeated and insistent repetition of a
"keé-kawów" or "keé-kow" phrase, at times
continued interminably. More often heard
are single nasal call notes.

Chestnut-throated Spinetail
Synallaxis cherriei
Colaespina Golicastaña   Plate 56(11)

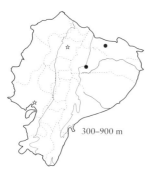

300–900 m

14 cm (5½″). *Very rare and local in undergrowth of secondary woodland and forest
borders in foothills and along e. base of
Andes* (w. Sucumbíos and w. Napo). Above
rich rufescent brown with dusky lores, wings
and rump also duskier; rather short tail
black. *Throat and breast rufous* contrasting
with *dark gray belly*. **Similar species:** Ruddy
Spinetail has a black throat patch (often not
easy to see in field), more rufous upperparts,
and shows less contrast on underparts.
Habits: Not well known in Ecuador.
Behavior similar to Ruddy Spinetail, though
Chestnut-throated is much more a bird of
secondary growth and borders. Why such a
bird should be so rare remains a mystery.
Voice: ♂'s song a rapidly repeated, almost
frog-like "trrrr tuuít, trrrr tuuít . . . ," often
continued for long periods.

Necklaced Spinetail, *Synallaxis stictothorax*
Colaespina Collareja   Plate 56(12)

Below 200 m

12.5 cm (5″). *Arid scrub and borders of deciduous woodland in lowlands of southwest.*
Guayas and Manabí birds have forehead
streaked black and white, becoming grayish
brown on crown and upper back, brown on
back, and rufous on rump; *long narrow superciliary white*; wings rufous with outer flight
feathers dusky; tail rufous with inner web of
central pair of feathers blackish, *producing
quite marked bicolored effect.* Below white,
snowiest on throat, with *band of fine dusky
streaking across breast* and buff on flanks.
Southwestern Loja birds (s. El Oro too?) differ
in having tail almost entirely rufous. **Similar
species:** Not likely confused in its restricted
range and habitat. Can look vaguely wren-like
(e.g., Superciliated). **Habits:** Usually in pairs,
gleaning in foliage and more arboreal than
other *Synallaxis,* easier to observe and often
not at all shy. Perhaps more closely allied to
Cranioleuca. **Voice:** Most frequent song a
series of sputtering notes that commences
loudly and then gradually slows and trails off,
e.g., "ch-ch-chéh-chéh-chéh-cheh-cheh-ch-
ch-ch, ch, chch." At times only "ch" or
"kyeek" notes are given in a series, sometimes
long. Also gives a "tr-r t-rík t-rík t-rík!" (P.
Coopmans).

White-browed Spinetail, *Hellmayrea gularis*
Colaespina Cejiblanca   Plate 56(13)
13–13.5 cm (5–5¼″). *A small, short-tailed*
spinetail found in *undergrowth of temperate
forest on both slopes.* Formerly sometimes
placed in genus *Synallaxis.* Above rufous
brown, most rufous on tail, with *white lores
and narrow white superciliary. Small throat
patch white* bordered with dusky; underparts

2500–3700 m

Mostly 900–1700 m

uniform buffy brown. **Similar species:** Can be confused with Mountain Wren, which is similarly colored and also short-tailed; the wren lacks, however, any white on face. Rufous Spinetail has a much longer tail, also lacks white on face. **Habits:** Found singly or in pairs, generally not accompanying mixed flocks; an acrobatic and energetic feeder that probes into moss, dead leaves, and other detritus. Though it favors dense growth, once located this attractive little spinetail can be rather unwary and may continue foraging at close range. **Voice:** Song a series of *Cranioleuca*-like, high-pitched notes ending in a trill, e.g., "chiyt-chit-chit-chit-chi-chi-chichichichichichi." Also gives repeated single "chiyt" or "tseet" notes.

Cranioleuca Spinetails

Rather plain, small furnariids with rufous wings and tails, most *Cranioleuca* are arboreal inhabitants of montane forests, though two species (Parker's and Speckled) favor shrubby lower growth. They differ from *Synallaxis* spinetails in their shorter tails; *Cranioleuca* tend to be less vocal. Nests are oval or ball-shaped structures, often composed primarily of moss and usually attached toward the outer tip of a limb.

Ash-browed Spinetail, *Cranioleuca curtata*
Colaespina Cejiceniza   Plate 56(15)

14.5 cm (5¾"). Canopy and borders of *foothill and lower subtropical forest and woodland on e. slope. Crown rufous-chestnut* with dusky on forecrown and *indistinct grayish superciliary*; above olive brown, with contrasting rufous-chestnut wings and tail. Throat whitish scaled with dusky; underparts dull brownish olive with some mottling on breast. **Immature** rather different, above much like adult but *superciliary, sides of head*

and neck, and most of underparts orange-ochraceous. This plumage was formerly thought to represent a separate species, Fork-tailed Spinetail (*C. furcata*). **Similar species:** Line-cheeked Spinetail's range comes fairly close, though it never reaches actual e. slope where Ash-browed is found; Line-cheeked has bolder and whiter superciliary. Cf. also Montane Foliage-gleaner. **Habits:** Found singly or in pairs, foraging actively with mixed flocks, usually remaining well above ground. Hitches along branches, sometimes even hanging upside-down, also probes into bark crevices and rummages in epiphytes and tangles; like other *Cranioleuca*, rarely gleans from leaves. **Voice:** Song a fast and spritely series of shrill notes that usually ends in a trill and fades in intensity.

Red-faced Spinetail, *Cranioleuca erythrops*
Colaespina Carirroja   Plate 56(14)

14 cm (5½"). *Canopy and borders of foothill and lower subtropical forest and woodland on w. slope* (south to nw. Azuay), also locally on coastal cordillera. **Adult** has *crown and face entirely rufous*; otherwise olive brown above with contrasting rufous wings and tail. Throat whitish; underparts dull brownish

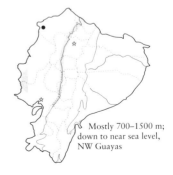

Mostly 700–1500 m; down to near sea level, NW Guayas

olive (some, however, are grayer below). **Juvenile** lacks rufous on face but shows narrow buff superciliary and some ochraceous on underparts. **Immature** seems to acquire rufous first on crown, and may then retain juvenile's buff superciliary. **Similar species:** Line-cheeked Spinetail shows a clean-cut rufous crown and bolder, whiter superciliary—but beware younger birds of both species that lack rufous on head. **Habits:** Similar to Ash-browed Spinetail. **Voice:** As in Ash-browed Spinetail. Call a "chi-tik, chi-ti-chik" (P. Coopmans).

Line-cheeked Spinetail
Cranioleuca antisiensis
Colaespina Cachetilineada   Plate 56(16)

Mostly 1000–2500 m

14.5 cm (5¾″). *Montane forest, woodland, and scrub as well as in agricultural land in subtropics and temperate zone of southwest*, north to Azuay highlands. *Crown rufous bordered below by narrow white superciliary*; lores buff, cheeks indistinctly streaked with buff; above olivaceous brown with contrasting rufous wings and tail. Throat whitish; underparts dull buffy brownish. **Similar species:** Distinctive in range, but at its northern periphery confusion possible with Red-faced Spinetail, mainly among young birds of both species; if brow is white, it is Line-cheeked. **Habits:** Similar to Ash-browed Spinetail, but Line-cheeked is more tolerant of habitat disturbance, and regularly persists in scrubby and agricultural areas where extensive forest is a fading memory. Also seems more often to forage in small groups. **Voice:** Has a variety of chippering and scolding calls, e.g., "tsi-chík," used as contact notes. Song a fast series of loud shrill notes that usually ends in a trill and fades in intensity.

Parker's Spinetail, *Cranioleuca vulpecula*
Colaespina de Parker   Plate 56(17)

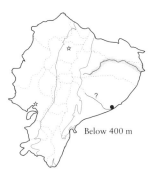

Below 400 m

14 cm (5½″). Fairly common in *undergrowth of riparian woodland and in early-succession scrub on river islands in lowlands of east*. Formerly considered conspecific with Rusty-backed Spinetail (*C. vulpina*). *Uniform rufous above* with *narrow whitish superciliary* and grayish cheeks with fine pale streaking. *Throat white; underparts whitish* with faint grayish spotting, lower belly and crissum dull grayish buff. **Similar species:** No other spinetail on the river islands where this species occurs is so uniformly rufous above or so white below. **Habits:** Usually in pairs that forage actively in shrubbery and dense undergrowth where they often are hard to see well or for very long. Much less arboreal than other *Cranioleuca* in Ecuador. **Voice:** Vocal, giving a variety of vocalizations including an accelerating and descending series of nasal notes that ends in a chortle, e.g., "tew-tew-tew-tew-trrrrrr," both parts sometimes prolonged; also a sharp fast "chut-chut," sometimes tripled or given singly.

Speckled Spinetail, *Cranioleuca gutturata*
Colaespina Jaspeada   Plate 56(18)

14.5 cm (5¾″). Scarce and apparently local *in lower growth and mid-levels of humid forest and borders in lowlands of east*; mainly in terra firme. Dark olive brown above with rufous-chestnut crown and narrow buff superciliary; wings and tail also rufous-chestnut. Chin yellowish; *underparts dull pale buff thickly speckled with blackish on breast*, speckles becoming more obscure on belly, flanks washed olivaceous brown. **Similar species:** Easily recognized among Ecuadorian spinetails by unique speckled or spotted underparts. Cf. rare Plain Softtail (much more

Mostly below 400 m

uniform, and lacks obvious spotting below). **Habits:** Found singly or in pairs, often accompanying mixed understory flocks composed of various antwrens and other birds. Forages by hopping along larger branches and trunks and into vine tangles, probing into vegetation and dead leaf clusters. **Voice:** For a spinetail not very vocal. Song a short series of high piercing notes, "tsee-tsee-tsee-tsee-tsee-tsee," somewhat reminiscent of a hummingbird or Slender-billed Xenops.

Schizoeaca Thistletails
Small plump furnariids with *notably long tails* (in freshly molted birds the tail is longer than the body itself) that *usually look frayed.* They occur in *shrubbery near treeline.*

White-chinned Thistletail
Schizoeaca fuliginosa
Colicardo Barbiblanco   Plate 57(4)

Mostly 2800–3500 m

18.5–19 cm (7¼–7½"). Undergrowth of shrubby woodland near treeline, and in patches of *Polylepis* woodland, in highlands of *n. and cen. Ecuador* (south to Cotopaxi and nw. Morona-Santiago). *Chestnut-brown above* with narrow white eye-ring and short pale grayish superciliary; *very long tail chest-*

nut-rufous. *Uniform gray below* with *whitish chin patch.* **Similar species:** In s. Ecuador, cf. Mouse-colored Thistletail (no overlap). Both Ecuadorian canasteros are obviously streaked. Cf. also Rufous Spinetail. **Habits:** Found singly or in pairs, most often foraging apart from mixed flocks; methodically hops and flutters, at times acrobatically, through dense vegetation, gleaning insects from foliage. Can be quite confiding. Long tail usually held raised, and wings often flicked. Flights usually brief and weak, on notably short stubby wings. **Voice:** Songs include a trill that lasts about 3 seconds, a descending series of somewhat higher-pitched notes that accelerates into a trill, and a slightly rising series of tripled notes, "tididit tididit, tididit!" (P. Coopmans and N. Krabbe recordings). Also gives a sharp "pyeek" or "chink" call note.

Mouse-colored Thistletail
Schizoeaca griseomurina
Colicardo Murino   Plate 57(5)

Mostly 2800–4000 m

18.5–19 cm (7¼–7½"). Undergrowth of shrubby woodland near treeline, and in patches of *Polylepis* woodland, in highlands of *s. Ecuador* (north to Azuay and w. Morona-Santiago). Olive brown above with *conspicuous white eye-ring* and faint gray postocular stripe. Grayish below with whitish chin patch. **Similar species:** White-chinned Thistletail (which replaces this species northward) is much more rufescent above and has a more prominent superciliary. **Habits:** As in White-chinned Thistletail. **Voice:** Song a series of notes that accelerates into a trill, the first notes inflected "sweeí, sweeí, sweeí, swi, ti-ti-titi-trrrrr" (P. Coopmans). Call a high-pitched but descending "pseeeuw."

Asthenes Canasteros

Small and fairly long-tailed furnariids, canasteros are relatively shy denizens of *paramo and shrubby grassland*. Both species are prominently streaked and show a small orangey chin patch. Nests are fairly large structures made of sticks and with a side entrance; *canastero* means "basket maker" in Spanish.

Streak-backed Canastero, *Asthenes wyatti*

Canastero Dorsilistado   Plate 57(3)

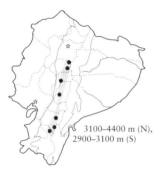

3100–4400 m (N),
2900–3100 m (S)

16–18 cm (6¼–7″). *Rather scarce and local in shrubby paramo and grassy scrub, especially in more arid regions*, in highlands from Pichincha south to Chimborazo; also in a small area of s. Azuay, n. Loja, and nw. Zamora-Chinchipe. **Northern birds** grayish brown above *with rather prominent black streaking* and narrow buff superciliary; wings with small patch of rufous at base of flight feathers; tail dusky with outer three pairs of feathers rufous. Chin patch dull orange-buff; *underparts plain dull buffy grayish*. **Southern birds** somewhat larger with a little more rufous in wings and tail, and buffier (less grayish) underparts. **Similar species:** More widespread Many-striped Canastero is boldly streaked below (not plain and dingy), has much more conspicuous ochraceous streaking on mantle, shows less rufous on tail; it tends to favor more humid regions. Cf. also ♀ *Catamenia* seedeaters (with very different conical bills) and Paramo Pipit (with very different tail). **Habits:** Generally inconspicuous and mainly terrestrial, scampering rapidly between clumps of grass. Even where vegetation is sparse, this canastero can be frustrat-

ingly adept at hiding. More apt to be seen when vocalizing, as it then may perch in the open atop a boulder, shrub, or grass clump. **Voice:** ♂'s song a very fast trill that lasts several seconds, usually accelerating and slightly rising in pitch; songs of the two races are similar (N. Krabbe). Call a doubled or tripled short trill.

Many-striped Canastero, *Asthenes flammulata*

Canastero Multilistado   Plate 57(2)

Mostly 3200–4200 m

16.5 cm (6½″). *Fairly common and widespread in grassy and shrubby paramo in highlands*. Blackish brown above with narrow tawny streaking on crown, *broader ochraceous streaking on mantle*, and narrow pale buff superciliary; *wings mainly rufous-chestnut*; tail dark brown, feathers sharply pointed and margined with rufous. Chin patch orange-buff; *underparts whitish prominently streaked dusky-brown*. **Similar species:** Despite its name, Streak-backed Canastero is much less streaked generally. Cf. Andean Tit-Spinetail (with no rufous on wing, white mantle streaking, more prominent white superciliary). **Habits:** Hops about on or near ground, often sneaky and remaining hidden amongst tussocks of grass and *Espeletia*, sometimes cocking or elevating its tail. Perches more often in the open than Streak-backed Canastero, and when conditions are calm will at times rest atop a grass clump or shrub for protracted periods, quietly surveying its territory. **Voice:** Song a fast and accelerating series of trilled "trree" notes that usually culminate in a chipper, e.g., "trree-trree-trree-trreetrreetreetritritritrititititi."

Plain Softtail, *Thripophaga fusciceps*
Colasuave Sencillo   Plate 57(14)

Below 400 m

16.5 cm (6½″). *Dingy and plain-looking; rare and local in mid-levels and canopy of várzea forest, borders, and woodland in lowlands of east.* Bill bluish horn; iris hazel. *Drab olivaceous brown*, slightly darker above than below, with indistinct pale frontlet and superciliary; wings and tail rufous. ♀ tends to have frontlet and underparts paler. **Similar species:** Note this species' *lack of obvious field marks*. It somewhat recalls a foliage-gleaner but is smaller and less patterned, showing no streaking. **Habits:** Favors vine tangles and thick vegetation at forest edge and in treefall openings. Usually in pairs or small groups, generally not accompanying mixed flocks; clambers about rather actively, with general comportment reminiscent of a thornbird. **Voice:** Song a sharp, loud, and descending churring, often given more or less simultaneously by both members of a pair.

Rufous-fronted Thornbird
Phacellodomus rufifrons
Espinero Frentirrufo   Plate 57(10)

16.5 cm (6½″). Fairly common in secondary woodland and scrub as well as clearings

650–1500 m

with scattered trees *around Zumba in Río Marañón drainage of far southeast.* Has been called Common Thornbird. Drab brown above with *contrasting rufous forecrown* and whitish lores and superciliary. *Below whitish*, tinged grayish on sides and buff on flanks and crissum. **Similar species:** A nondescript bird lacking obvious field marks, but basically bicolored (brownish above, whitish below) with distinctive rufous on crown. **Habits:** Arboreal and often quite conspicuous, hopping about in foliage; usually forages in semiopen, and sometimes drops to ground. Often remains near its large stick nest, attached near tip of drooping branches of a tree in semiopen, usually not too high above ground. **Voice:** Vocal, often giving a loud and abrupt series of "cheh" or "chit" notes that often start slowly but gradually accelerate before slowing and descending at end. Pairs often duet.

Spectacled Prickletail, *Siptornis striaticollis*
Colapúa Frontino   Plate 57(15)

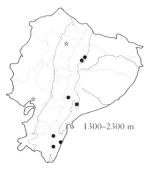

1300–2300 m

12 cm (4¾″). *Scarce and local in canopy and borders of subtropical forest on e. slope.* Rufous brown above with rich chestnut crown and a *short bold white postocular stripe*; wing-coverts and tail rufous-chestnut. Below drab brownish gray with *whitish streaking on throat and breast.* **Similar species:** Streaked Xenops has an obviously upturned lower mandible and silvery white malar streak, as well as pale streaking on crown and upper back. Cf. also much grayer Equatorial Graytail. **Habits:** Found singly or in pairs, foraging quite actively and often accompanying mixed flocks. Usually remains at mid-levels or higher, hitching along larger moss-covered limbs, probing in crevices or

into epiphytic plants; sometimes softly taps into dead wood. **Voice:** A high-pitched trill has been heard (J. W. Eley).

Xenerpestes Graytails

Obscure and warbler-like *grayish* furnariids with rounded tails. The two graytails are arboreal birds found in the *canopy of wet foothill forests*, one species on either side of the Andes.

Equatorial Graytail, *Xenerpestes singularis*
Colagris Ecuatorial   Plate 57(12)

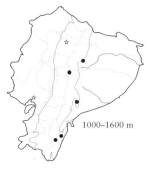

1000–1600 m

11.5 cm (4½″). *Scarce and local in canopy and borders of foothill and lower subtropical forest on e. slope. Olive gray above* with *rufous forecrown* (somewhat "streaky") and narrow white superciliary; wings and tail duskier. Below creamy whitish with *conspicuous but blurry gray streaking*, crissum buffier. **Similar species:** Other vaguely similar sympatric furnariids (e.g., Ash-browed Spinetail, Montane Foliage-gleaner) are larger and basically brown above (not gray). Streaking below immediately distinguishes graytail from Gray-mantled Wren (which is species most likely to be confused with graytail; even their overall behavior is similar) and Yellow-breasted Antwren; both species sometimes forage with graytail. Because of its small size, graytail can also be confused with a warbler or greenlet. **Habits:** Seen singly or in pairs, usually foraging with a mixed flock; generally remains in canopy of very tall trees, and therefore hard to see well. Gleans from leaves, twigs, and small branches, sometimes clinging briefly to undersides; occasionally one sidles along a branch, much like Gray-mantled Wren. **Voice:** Song a long and dry, almost insect-like and somewhat reeling trill that lasts 5 or more seconds, "tzzzzzzzzzzzzzzzz" (P. Coopmans recording). Also gives dry "tsit" calls.

Double-banded Graytail, *Xenerpestes minlosi*
Colagris Alibandeado   Plate 57(13)

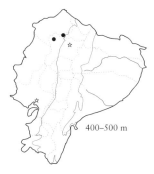

400–500 m

11 cm (4¼″). *Rare and very local in canopy and borders of forest in lower foothills of northwest* (nw. Pichincha and adjacent Imbabura). *Olive gray above* with *blackish forecrown* and *narrow white superciliary*; wings duskier with *two bold white wingbars*. Below creamy whitish, some gray mottling on sides and grayish on crissum. **Similar species:** Distinctive in its very limited range. Overall pattern reminiscent of certain nonbreeding boreal migrant warblers. Equatorial Graytail occurs only on e. slope. **Habits:** Behavior similar to Equatorial Graytail's, and equally hard to see well. In Panama favors mid-level viny tangles. **Voice:** Dry, reeling, trilled song very similar to Equatorial Graytail's (P. Coopmans and M. Lysinger).

Orange-fronted Plushcrown
Metopothrix aurantiacus
Coronifelpa Frentidorada   Plate 57(11)

11.5 cm (4½″). *Clearings and gardens with scattered trees, secondary woodland, and forest borders in lowlands of east*; a nonforest bird. *Small and warbler-like*, very unlike other furnariids. *Legs orange. Forehead bright orange* (feathers plushlike, but this usually not evident), becoming *bright yellow on foreface and throat*; otherwise grayish olive above; wings dusky, coverts edged yellowish. Underparts pale yellowish. **Immature** has reduced orange and yellow on face, but *legs already orange*. **Similar species:**

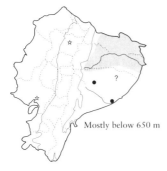

Mostly below 650 m

Not likely confused. Perhaps most resembles Orange-headed Tanager or ♀ Yellow Warbler. **Habits:** Most often ranges in small (family?) groups, generally independent of mixed flocks. Gleans actively and often acrobatically, sometimes hanging upside-down, in foliage and on twigs; also feeds on fruit and at flowers. Often seen around its large and conspicuous stick nests. **Voice:** Not very vocal. Occasionally gives high-pitched sibilant notes, at times in a variable short series, usually well enunciated (e.g., "tswit-tsweét" or "tsweet-tsweet") but sometimes more run together.

Pseudocolaptes Tuftedcheeks

Large and handsome furnariids with a *unique and obvious pale tuft on the sides of the neck*, ranging in the canopy of montane forests. Bills of females are somewhat longer than those of males. Nests are ball-shaped structures with a tubular entrance below, placed in a hole or crevice.

Streaked Tuftedcheek
Pseudocolaptes boisonneautii
Barbablanca Rayada   Plate 59(8)

21–21.5 cm (8¼–8½″). A *striking*, *large* arboreal furnariid of canopy and borders of

Mostly 1800–3100 m

subtropical and temperate forest on both slopes. Brown above, duskier on crown and with narrow buff superciliary, *crown and back streaked buff* (more broadly on back); wing-coverts edged rufous; rump and tail bright rufous. *Throat white, feathers on sides of neck lengthened and flaring back to form conspicuous snowy white tuft*; breast whitish with brown scaling, becoming fulvous on belly and rufous on crissum. **Immature** has blacker crown with little or no streaking, bolder blackish scaling on breast, and more rufous on belly. **Similar species:** Aside from Pacific Tuftedcheek of w. slope (which see), unmistakable. **Habits:** Found singly or in pairs, often moving with mixed flocks, generally remaining well above ground. Forages mainly by working along larger horizontal limbs, probing into bromeliads and other epiphytes, sometimes propping itself up with tail and forcefully hammering or rummaging about. **Voice:** Not terribly vocal. Foraging birds give a loud "chink!" or "cheeyk!" Song an infrequently heard combination of these notes and others that are more trilled, often (fide P. Coopmans) increasing in volume and slowing toward end.

Pacific Tuftedcheek, *Pseudocolaptes johnsoni*
Barbablanca del Pacífico   Plate 59(9)

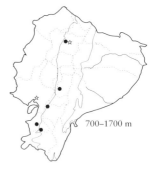

700–1700 m

20.5 cm (8″). *Very local in canopy and borders of foothill and lower subtropical forest on w. slope; mainly in wet, mossy cloud forest.* Formerly considered conspecific with Buffy Tuftedcheek (*P. lawrencii*) of Costa Rica and Panama. This scarce species occurs *below* elevational range of similar and more numerous Streaked Tuftedcheek, with marginal overlap above Mindo. Differs from that species in having *back unstreaked and rufous-chestnut*, *breast darker with white chevrons* (lacking Streaked's scaled effect),

and *buff-tinged tuft* with *no white throat.*
Habits: Similar to Streaked Tuftedcheek.
Voice: As in Streaked Tuftedcheek, but
tending to be higher pitched.

Point-tailed Palmcreeper, *Berlepschia rikeri*
Palmero   Plate 59(7)

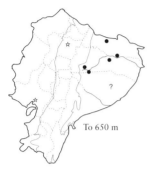

To 650 m

21.5 cm (8½″). An *attractively patterned
large* furnariid, found locally in stands of
palms (especially *Mauritia*) in lowlands of
northeast. Bill long, straight, and pointed.
Unmistakable. *Head, neck, and underparts
black conspicuously streaked with white;
mantle, wings, and tail contrastingly bright
rufous-chestnut.* **Habits:** Strictly arboreal
and, unless vocalizing, surprisingly inconspicuous as it rummages about toward the
bases of large, fan-shaped palm fronds.
Occurs as widely dispersed pairs, rarely if
ever associating with other birds. **Voice:** ♂'s
song an unmistakable and far-carrying series
of fast and very loud ringing notes that
continues 3–5 seconds, "dedede-kee!-kee!-
kee!-kee!-kee!-kee!-kee!" Birds vocalize
infrequently, sometimes while perched sideways on a palm's tall, spike-like growing
stalk. Responsive to tape playback, but even
then often hard to see well.

Margarornis Treerunners
Attractive furnariids of Andean forests,
treerunners creep up trunks and along lateral
branches much like woodcreepers. Nests are
small, ball-shaped structures made of moss
and with a side entrance.

Pearled Treerunner, *Margarornis squamiger*
Subepalo Perlado   Plate 57(6)

15 cm (6″). A *beautifully patterned* furnariid,
widespread in *upper subtropical and temperate forest and woodland on both slopes.*

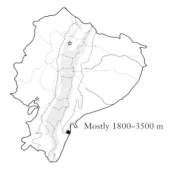

Mostly 1800–3500 m

Bright rufous-chestnut above, duller and
browner on head with *bold white superciliary.* Throat snowy white; underparts brown
*profusely marked with large tear-shaped
white, black-edged spots.* **Similar species:**
Montane Woodcreeper has somewhat similar
overall pattern but lacks superciliary, is
streaked below, and has decurved bill.
Habits: Found singly or in pairs, frequently
accompanying mixed flocks and generally
conspicuous and easy to watch. Hitches
along mossy branches and up trunks,
often using tail for support much like a
woodcreeper; sometimes moves out onto
smaller terminal twigs. **Voice:** Not especially
vocal. Foraging birds give thin, high-pitched
"tsit" contact calls, sometimes in a quick
series.

Star-chested Treerunner, *Margarornis stellatus*
Subepalo Pechiestrellado   Plate 57(7)

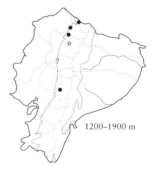

1200–1900 m

15 cm (6″). *Very rare and local* in mid-levels
and subcanopy of *lower subtropical forest on
w. slope; perhaps confined to wet, mossy
cloud forest.* Formerly called Fulvous-dotted
Treerunner. *Uniform bright chestnut above*
with indistinct pale superciliary. *Throat contrastingly white,* feathers of lower throat
black-edged; underparts rufous-chestnut

slightly mottled paler, *chest with small but conspicuous white "stars" edged with black.* **Similar species:** Far more numerous Pearled Treerunner is much more profusely spotted below, has obvious white superciliary. Cf. also Wedge-billed Woodcreeper. **Habits:** Not well known. General behavior appears to resemble Pearled Treerunner's. **Voice:** Not known; apparently very quiet.

Spotted Barbtail, *Premnoplex brunnescens*
Subepalo Moteado   Plate 57(9)

Mostly 900–2500 m

13.5 cm (5¼"). A *small, dark,* and *inconspicuous* furnariid of *shady foothill, subtropical, and lower temperate forest and woodland on both slopes. Dark brown above* with indistinct buff superciliary; tail brownish black with protruding spines. *Throat tawny-buff;* underparts dark brown *profusely marked with large oval buff, black-edged spots.* **Similar species:** Less numerous Rusty-winged Barbtail, often found with this species, has rufous wings and tail and looks more streaked (not so spotted) below. Pearled Treerunner much brighter overall and has bold white superciliary. Cf. also Wedge-billed Woodcreeper (similar overall coloration but very different behavior). **Habits:** Quiet and unobtrusive, not often seen despite being fairly common. Usually found singly as it hops and creeps on mossy branches and trunks, generally not using its tail for support (despite protruding spines); sometimes accompanies mixed flocks of understory birds. **Voice:** Not very vocal. Infrequently heard song a short, descending trill, "pseerrr," sometimes preceded by several emphatic higher-pitched notes. Resembles harsher trill of Rufous-headed Pygmy-Tyrant.

More often heard is a sharp "teep!" or "teeyk!" call, often given as bird flies from one tree to the next.

Rusty-winged Barbtail, *Premnornis guttuligera*
Subepalo Alirrojizo   Plate 57(8)

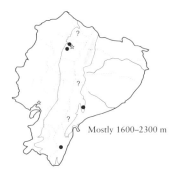

Mostly 1600–2300 m

14.5 cm (5¾"). An uncommon, *nondescript* furnariid found in lower growth of *subtropical* forest, *mainly on e. slope.* Brown above with vague buff superciliary, sparse buff back streaking, and more prominent streaking on sides of neck; wings and tail rufous, wing-coverts indistinctly tipped buff. Throat buffy whitish; underparts brown *with conspicuous buff-scalloped streaking.* **Similar species:** Resembles certain foliage-gleaners, though this barbtail is considerably smaller. The even smaller and darker Spotted Barbtail lacks rufous on wings and tail, and its throat is deep buff. **Habits:** Usually found singly, less often in pairs, generally as it accompanies a mixed flock of understory birds. Forages by clambering about actively in dense vegetation, often where viny or tangled, sometimes probing or even entering clumps of moss or dead leaves. Usually does not hitch up limbs or trunks as Spotted Barbtail habitually does. **Voice:** Not very vocal. Foraging birds occasionally give a sharp "tseep" or "tsip" call, sometimes run together into an emphatic series, "tsip-tsip-tsip-tsip-tsip" (J. Moore recording). Also gives an accelerating and very fast "tsi-tsi-tsi-si-si-sisisisisi."

Syndactyla Foliage-gleaners
"Typical" midsized foliage-gleaners found in the understory of montane forest. Aside from their *contrasting and unstreaked pale throats,* all three species are prominently streaked

below. Nests are placed at the end of burrows dug into banks.

Lineated Foliage-gleaner
Syndactyla subalaris
Limpiafronda Lineada   Plate 58(4)

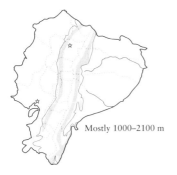

Mostly 1000–2100 m

18–18.5 cm (7–7¼"). Undergrowth and mid-levels of *foothill and subtropical forest* on both slopes. **East-slope birds** brown above, more blackish on crown and nape, with indistinct buff postocular streak and *narrow buff streaking from crown to back*; wings more rufescent, tail rufous. *Throat plain yellowish buff*; underparts brown extensively streaked with yellowish buff, diminishing on lower belly. **West-slope birds** have browner crown and are less streaked (*above often more or less confined to band on nape*). **Juvenile** much more rufescent generally, with orange-ochraceous postocular streak as well as streaking on back and breast. **Similar species:** Potentially confusing. Of the *Thripadectes* treehunters, Striped and Uniform are the most similar. Striped especially resembles e.-slope Lineateds (which are extensively streaked), though treehunter is a heftier bird with heavier bill and streaking on its buff throat. Uniform differs from w.-slope Lineateds in its stouter bill and in lacking all streaking above (which on Lineated occurs mainly on nape); below, treehunter has streaking only on throat. Also resembles the two woodhaunters: Eastern's buff streaking is blurrier and less extensive than in Lineated, whereas Western is nearly unstreaked above. **Habits:** Seen singly or in pairs, often accompanying a mixed understory flock; hops and clambers on limbs and in tangles, and generally hard to see well or for very long. **Voice:** ♂'s frequently heard song a distinctive accel-

erating series of harsh nasal notes, sputtering at first, "anh, anh, anh-anh-anh-anhanhan-hanh." Call a very harsh, abrup "skanh!" or "kr-rk," sometimes given in a short series.

Buff-browed Foliage-Gleaner
Syndactyla rufosuperciliata
Limpiafronda Cejianteada   Plate 58(5)

1700–1900 m

18 cm (7"). Montane forest in lower growth at higher elevations on *remote Cordillera del Cóndor in extreme se. Zamora-Chinchipe. Above uniform brownish olive* (with no streaking) with *prominent buff superciliary*; wings more rufescent, tail rufous. *Throat buffy whitish*; underparts brownish olive with *prominent yellowish buff streaking and spotting*. **Similar species:** Lineated Foliage-gleaner less olive above and obviously streaked there; it has less obvious superciliary and buffier throat. Buff-browed's overall pattern and coloration recall Olive-backed Woodcreeper (whose behavior is very different). **Habits:** As in Lineated Foliage-gleaner, sometimes foraging with it in the same flock; Buff-browed tends to be a little less furtive. **Voice:** ♂'s frequently heard song a fast series of harsh notes that recalls Lineated's though its quality is less nasal, e.g., "kuh-kuh-kuh-kihkihkihkikikikiku."

Rufous-necked Foliage-gleaner
Syndactyla ruficollis
Limpiafronda Cuellirrufa   Plate 58(6)

18 cm (7"). *Local in undergrowth and mid-levels of foothill and subtropical forest and woodland in Loja.* Formerly placed in genus *Automolus.* Above rufescent brown with *superciliary and sides of neck contrasting orange-rufous*; tail rufous. *Throat cinnamon-buff* (brightest at sides); underparts olive

Mostly 1300–2300 m

brown, broadly streaked buff on breast. **Similar species:** Not likely confused in its limited range, where few other foliage-gleaners (or similar furnariids generally) occur. **Habits:** Found singly or in pairs, often accompanying small mixed flocks. Forages mainly by hitching along larger horizontal limbs and on trunks, inspecting moss, epiphytic plants, and tangles; easier to see than most other foliage-gleaners. **Voice:** ♂'s frequently heard song similar to Lineated's, a series of harsh, nasal, ratchetty notes that start slowly and then speed up, sometimes almost ending in a roll. Foraging birds often give a sharp nasal "ank" call.

Anabacerthia Foliage-gleaners
Relatively small and slender foliage-gleaners, more arboreal and easier to see than many other foliage-gleaners. One species is found on either side of the Andes.

Scaly-throated Foliage-gleaner
Anabacerthia variegaticeps
Limpiafronda Goliescamosa   Plate 58(7)

16.5 cm (6½″). *Fairly common in subcanopy and borders of foothill and lower subtropical*

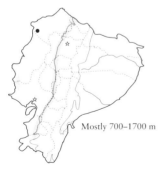

Mostly 700–1700 m

forest and woodland on w. slope, also locally on coastal cordillera. Formerly sometimes called Spectacled Foliage-gleaner. Crown dusky with faint olivaceous streaking, *contrasting with wide, bright ochraceous postocular stripe and eye-ring*, ear-coverts dusky; *otherwise rufous brown above* with rufous-chestnut tail. Throat yellowish white, *feathers edged dusky resulting in a distinct scaly look; breast with blurry ochraceous and brownish olive streaking*; belly olive brown. **Similar species:** Handsome and relatively boldly marked, unlikely to be confused in its limited range. Montane Foliage-gleaner occurs only on e. slope. Cf. Buff-fronted Foliage-gleaner. **Habits:** Found singly or in pairs, frequently accompanying mixed flocks; forages actively by moving along horizontal branches, peering around to their undersides like some *Tangara* tanagers; sometimes proceeds all the way out onto terminal twigs. Often in the open and relatively easy to observe. **Voice:** ♂'s infrequently given song a fast-paced, evenly pitched series of up to 15–20 piercing and harsh "skee" or "tjik" notes. More frequent call a single "skeeyh" or "skek" note with similar sharp, dry quality.

Montane Foliage-gleaner
Anabacerthia striaticollis
Limpiafronda Montana   Plate 58(8)

Mostly 1000–1800 m

16 cm (6¼″). *Fairly common in subcanopy and borders of foothill and subtropical forest on e. slope.* Uniform brown above with *conspicuous buffy whitish eye-ring and narrow postocular streak*; wings more rufescent, tail contrastingly rufous. Throat yellowish white faintly *scaled olivaceous; underparts uniform dull olivaceous brown with sparse buffy*

whitish streaking on breast. **Similar species:** A drab foliage-gleaner that looks distinctly spectacled. Rufous-rumped Foliage-gleaner overlaps with Montane in foothills; it has a bolder brow, more contrasty and ochraceous throat that lacks scaling, and shows no streaking on breast. Scaly-throated Foliage-gleaner occurs only on w. slope. **Habits:** Similar to Scaly-throated Foliage-gleaner. **Voice:** Similar to Scaly-throated's, but ♂'s song seems more irregularly paced and is less shrill.

Hyloctistes Woodhaunters

Obscure foliage-gleaners of forest lower growth. They were formerly considered conspecific but differ strikingly in voice. One species occurs on either side of the Andes.

Eastern Woodhaunter, *Hyloctistes subulatus*
Rondamusgos Oriental Plate 58(1)

17 cm (6¾″). Inconspicuous in lower growth of humid forest and woodland in *lowlands and foothills of east.* This and the following species were formerly considered conspecific, under the name of Striped Woodhaunter. Olive brown above, duskier on crown, with *blurry buff streaking on crown, neck, and mantle*; wings more rufescent, tail rufous-chestnut. Throat pale buffyish; underparts dull olivaceous brown, *breast somewhat flammulated with buff.* **Similar species:** Western Woodhaunter occurs only west of Andes. Lineated Foliage-gleaner (more montane in distribution, but with some overlap) is more crisply and extensively streaked with buff both above and below; its vocalizations are notably different. Buff-throated Foliage-gleaner east of Andes is less streaked above and shows more of

an eye-ring. **Habits:** Usually found singly in lower growth, often accompanying a mixed flock and foraging much like an *Automolus* foliage-gleaner, hopping and rummaging in tangled vegetation and epiphytes. Seems to be able to remain hidden from view much of time. **Voice:** ♂'s distinctive song a loud, ringing "teeu-teeu" (sometimes 3–4 "teeu" notes), often followed by a softer and lower-pitched rattling, "tr-r-r-r-r," effect similar to Chestnut-winged Hookbill but not ascending as usually is the case in hookbill. Call a sharp "squirp!"

Western Woodhaunter, *Hyloctistes virgatus*
Rondamusgos Occidental Plate 58(2)

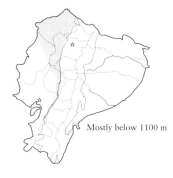

17 cm (6¾″). Inconspicuous in lower growth of humid forest and woodland in *lowlands and foothills of west.* Formerly considered conspecific with previous species. Similar to Eastern Woodhaunter but darker above with *streaking restricted to small faint streaks on crown; throat more ochraceous*, and underparts slightly browner (less olivaceous) with *less* flammulation on breast. **Similar species:** Uniform Treehunter darker generally with shorter and stouter bill, and its throat is nearly uniform with rest of underparts (not notably paler, as in woodhaunter). Lineated Foliage-gleaner west of Andes has distinct band of crisp buff streaking on nape. Buff-throated Foliage-gleaner west of Andes is whitish-throated. **Habits:** Similar to Eastern Woodhaunter. **Voice:** ♂'s distinctive song, very different from Eastern Woodhaunter, a series of sharp nasal notes, "keeu-keeu-keeu-keeu . . . ," evenly pitched and paced, sometimes continued for protracted periods. Call a sharp "squirp!"

Chestnut-winged Hookbill
Ancistrops strigilatus
Picogancho Alicastaño   Plate 58(3)

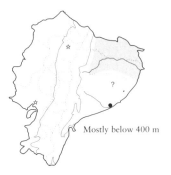

Mostly below 400 m

19 cm (7½″). *Mid-levels and subcanopy of terra firme forest in lowlands of east.* Despite its impressive-sounding name, the fairly heavy bill of this species is not much more hooked than in other foliage-gleaners. Above dark olive brown *prominently streaked with yellowish buff* and with narrow yellowish buff superciliary; wings and tail contrastingly rufous. Below yellowish buff *narrowly but conspicuously streaked with dusky-olive.* **Similar species:** Less robust Chestnut-winged Foliage-gleaner is unstreaked and has relatively bright and contrasting orange-ochraceous throat; the two species can occur in the same flock. Otherwise this "streaky" and arboreal foliage-gleaner is unlikely to be confused. **Habits:** Found singly or in pairs, most often while accompanying a mixed canopy flock; hookbill often is with birds such as nunbirds and woodcreepers. Forages mainly along larger limbs and in vine tangles, often lingering in semiopen and thus not too hard to see. **Voice:** ♂'s song an often protracted trill that may extend for 30 or more seconds, sometimes ascending a bit. A frequently heard call is a much shorter ascending trill, similar to song of Rufous-tailed Xenops (J. Moore and P. Coopmans).

Philydor Foliage-gleaners
A uniform group of relatively slender foliage-gleaners found mainly in humid lowland forests, where most species are arboreal, a few others favoring lower growth. They are generally easier to see than the more robust *Automolus* foliage-gleaners, though they tend to vocalize less. *Philydor* are relatively strongly patterned, many species having a

bold superciliary. Nests are placed in holes dug, depending on the species, into snags or banks.

Chestnut-winged Foliage-gleaner
Philydor erythropterus
Limpiafronda Alicastaña   Plate 58(14)

Mostly below 400 m

18.5 cm (7¼″). *Uncommon in mid-levels and subcanopy of terra firme forest in lowlands of east.* Olive grayish above *with lores and throat pale ochraceous orange*, narrow buff superciliary, and narrow buffy whitish streaking on ear-coverts; *wings and tail contrastingly rufous-chestnut.* Underparts pale dingy buffyish with some olivaceous shading. **Similar species:** Rather striking and easily known by its *lack* of streaking, contrasting rufous wings, and conspicuous orangey throat. Chestnut-winged Hookbill is a heavier bird with a stouter bill and, besides being prominently streaked, it *lacks* orangey throat. Rufous-rumped and Rufous-tailed Foliage-gleaners have wings concolor with back, and their throats are only slightly ochraceous, contrasting much less than in Chestnut-winged. **Habits:** Seen singly, less often in pairs, often accompanying mixed flocks of canopy birds. Usually remains well above ground, coming lower to forage in vine tangles at edge or in treefall clearings; often inspects suspended large dead leaves. **Voice:** ♂'s rather infrequently heard song a trill that descends slightly in pitch and lasts 2–3 seconds.

Slaty-winged Foliage-gleaner
Philydor fuscipennis
Limpiafronda Alipizarrosa   Plate 58(10)

17 cm (6¾″). *Scarce and local in lower growth and mid-levels of humid forest and woodland in lowlands of west* (s. Pichincha

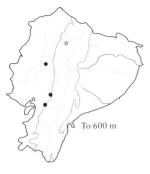

To 600 m

to nw. Azuay). Formerly considered conspecific with Rufous-rumped Foliage-gleaner. Rufescent brown above, duskier on head with *bold cinnamon-buff superciliary* and *cinnamon-rufous sides of neck; wings contrastingly dusky*; rump and tail rufous. *Underparts uniform buffy-ochraceous.* **Similar species:** Nothing really similar to this boldly patterned foliage-gleaner occurs west of Andes; Cinnamon-rumped Foliage-gleaner ranges east of Andes. **Habits:** Usually found singly or in pairs (less often small groups), often accompanying mixed flocks; nervous and fast-moving, often hard to observe for any length of time though not especially skulking. **Voice:** Foraging birds give a sharp "chef!" at infrequent intervals.

Cinnamon-rumped Foliage-gleaner
Philydor pyrrhodes
Limpiafronda Lomicanela   Plate 58(11)

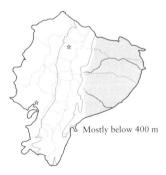

Mostly below 400 m

17 cm (6¾"). *Scarce in lower growth of humid forest in lowlands of east.* Rufescent brown above with *cinnamon lores and superciliary; wings contrastingly slaty*; rump and tail bright cinnamon-rufous. *Entire underparts rich orange-ochraceous.* **Similar species:** A handsome foliage-gleaner, hard to confuse

in its range. Slaty-winged Foliage-gleaner, with similar overall pattern, occurs only west of Andes. **Habits:** Found singly or in pairs which, unlike so many other foliage-gleaners, most often forage independently of mixed flocks. Active and rather furtive, remaining mainly in heavy foliage and often hard to see well or for very long, inspecting tangles and hanging dead leaves and other debris. Seems to favor the vicinity of forest streams, often where there is a palm understory. **Voice:** ♂'s very distinctive song often two-parted. It commences with a long low reeling trill and gradually becomes a little louder, then suddenly breaks out into much louder trill that slides upward and rises to a crescendo, then ends abruptly. There is some variation; some versions sound vaguely like Plumbeous Antbird. Foraging birds occasionally give a "chak!" or "chakit!" call.

Rufous-rumped Foliage-gleaner
Philydor erythrocercus
Limpiafronda Lomirrufa   Plate 58(9)

To 1300 m

17 cm (6¾"). Fairly common in lower growth to mid-levels of humid forest (mainly terra firme) in *lowlands and foothills of east*. Olive brown above with *quite prominent buff lores and superciliary*; uppertail-coverts tinged rufous (but this is virtually impossible to see in the field, being hard to discern even in specimens; other races of the species, not occurring in Ecuador, show more rufous on rump), tail rufous. Throat yellowish white; *underparts uniform dingy olivaceous buff*, sometimes tinged ochraceous on belly. **Similar species:** Extremely similar to rarer Rufous-tailed Foliage-gleaner; see that species. Montane Foliage-gleaner is smaller with obvious spectacled look and shows fine streaking on breast. **Habits:** A wide-ranging

and (unlike Rufous-tailed) fairly often seen foliage-gleaner in Ecuador; one or two often accompany mixed flocks moving through lower and mid-levels. Favors viny tangles, and usually not too hard to observe. **Voice:** Not particularly vocal, but gives an occasional abrupt and shrill "wheeeeyk!" (J. Moore recording) and other sharp "cheeyu" or "chak" calls.

Rufous-tailed Foliage-gleaner
Philydor ruficaudatus
Limpiafronda Colirrufa   Plate 58(13)

17 cm (6¾"). *Apparently rare* in *mid-levels and subcanopy* of terra firme forest in lowlands of northeast. *Greatly outnumbered by very similar Rufous-rumped Foliage-gleaner*; the two are frequently confused, and many sightings are suspect. Rufous-tailed may occur *only in w. Napo and w. Sucumbíos*, prior records to the contrary. Rufous-tailed differs (subtly) in having no rufous tinge on uppertail-coverts (but this absence is almost impossible to discern under normal field conditions) and in showing *dull olivaceous mottling or flammulation on breast* (in Rufous-rumped, underparts look relatively smooth and uniform). Yellowish white throat color of the two species in Ecuador is about the same. **Habits:** As noted above, this species appears to be more arboreal than Rufousrumped. It moves more with flocks that may also contain, for instance, Chestnut-winged Foliage-gleaners and Chestnut-winged Hookbills (thus, as it tends to occur higher above ground, is hard to see well); Rufous-rumpeds accompany understory flocks along with antwrens and Olive-backed Foliage-gleaners. **Voice:** Distinctive song (in se. Peru) a staccato series of 5–10 evenly pitched notes that drop in pitch and accelerate at end, e.g., "te-te-te-

te-te-te-te-te-t-t-t-r" (P. Coopmans); this has not been heard in Ecuador.

Buff-fronted Foliage-gleaner, *Philydor rufus*
Limpiafronda Frentianteada   Plate 58(12)

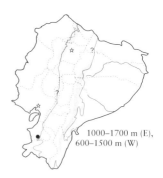

1000–1700 m (E),
600–1500 m (W)

18.5–19 cm (7¼–7½"). *Subcanopy and borders of foothill and lower subtropical forest on both slopes.* Bill blackish above, pale grayish below (extensively so in w.-slope birds). **East-slope birds** olive brown above, somewhat duskier on crown and with *rufescent forehead and buff superciliary*; tail more rufescent, wings extensively rufous. *Throat bright ochraceous buff*; underparts duller ochraceous. **West-slope birds** similar but darker overall, with more rufous tail and more olivaceous underparts. **Similar species:** Buff-fronted Foliage-gleaners in Ecuador lack the obvious "buff front" that is so conspicuous in much of the rest of the species' range, but they can nonetheless be known by their ochraceous underparts (brightly so on throat). Cf. Russet Antshrike (stockier and shorter-tailed, with heavier bill). **Habits:** Seen singly or in pairs, usually accompanying a mixed flock in canopy; often forages in semiopen, hopping and twisting along larger horizontal limbs, sometimes even hanging upside-down in terminal foliage. **Voice:** ♂'s song a fast descending series of sharp, metallic, almost woodpecker-like notes, "whi-ki-ki-ki-ke-ke-ke-kuh-kuh."

Bamboo Foliage-gleaner
Anabazenops dorsalis
Rascahojas de Bambú   Plate 58(18)
18.5 cm (7¼"). *Rare and local in bamboo-dominated undergrowth of forest borders and secondary woodland in foothills on e.*

Locally to 1300 m

Olive-backed Foliage-gleaner
Automolus infuscatus
Rascahojas Dorsiolivácea   Plate 58(15)

To 700 m

slope; also occurs in *Gynerium* cane-domi-
nated riparian areas in lowlands of east. Formerly placed in genus *Automolus* and called
Crested, or Dusky-cheeked, Foliage-gleaner.
Bill rather stout. *Above uniform rufescent
brown* with *narrow buffy whitish superciliary*, faint eye-ring, and *dusky cheeks*; rump
and tail rufous-chestnut. *Throat creamy
whitish* (sometimes puffed out); underparts
pale grayish, browner on lower flanks.
Similar species: Much more numerous and
widespread Olive-backed Foliage-gleaner is
more olivaceous (less rufescent) brown
above, lacks any obvious superciliary, and has
cheeks that are about same color as crown
(not duskier); it occurs in terra firme forest.
Habits: Found singly or in pairs, generally
keeping in dense cover (often inside bamboo
thickets) and thus difficult to more than
glimpse. Sometimes accompanies mixed
understory flocks. Most often found through
its vocalizations. **Voice:** ♂'s song a measured
"tcho-tcho-tcho-tcho-tcho . . ." (number of
notes varying) with quality and tempo similar
to that of Ferruginous Pygmy-Owl (though
lower pitched). Agitated birds give a protracted rattling that may continue for surprisingly long periods (30 seconds or more).

Automolus Foliage-gleaners
Fairly large, drab furnariids ranging in lower
growth of forest; most of the generally smaller
and more slender *Philydor* foliage-gleaners
are more arboreal. Some *Automolus* are noto-
rious skulkers, heard many times for each time
they are seen. Partly because seeing them well
is often so difficult, species identification can
be a problem; note especially iris and throat
color, and the presence or absence of an eye-
ring or short superciliary. Nests are placed at
the end of a burrow dug into a bank.

19 cm (7½"). Fairly common in lower growth
of humid forest in lowlands of east. *Uniform
brownish olive above* with *indistinct whitish
eye-ring* and narrow streaking on ear-coverts;
rump and tail rufous-chestnut. *Throat white*
(often puffed out); underparts uniform
pale drab buffy grayish, slightly darker
on sides and flanks. **Similar species:** Much
rarer Bamboo Foliage-gleaner more rufescent above, has prominent superciliary and
duskier ear-coverts; it occurs in different
habitat. Buff-throated Foliage-gleaners in
east have throat obviously buff, also buffier
underparts with flammulations on breast. Of
the *Philydor* foliage-gleaners, Olive-backed is
most apt to be confused with Rufous-rumped
Foliage-gleaner, which has bold superciliary
and less contrasting throat. **Habits:** Seen
singly or in pairs, most often while accompanying mixed flocks of understory birds,
especially antbirds such as *Myrmotherula*
antwrens and *Thamnomanes* antshrikes.
Clambers about rather actively in dense
tangled habitat, often hanging upside-down
while probing into epiphytes and suspended
dead leaves (which it sometimes crawls
inside). **Voice:** ♂'s song a fast, loud, evenly
pitched staccato rattle, "ch-r-r-r-r-r-r-r-r."
Similar song of Chestnut-crowned Foliage-
gleaner higher pitched and usually descends
toward end. Call, often given while foraging,
a sharp "chíkah."

Buff-throated Foliage-gleaner
Automolus ochrolaemus
Rascahojas Golipálida   Plate 58(19)

18.5–19 cm (7¼–7½"). *Undergrowth of
humid forest in lowlands of east and west,*

Mostly below 800 m

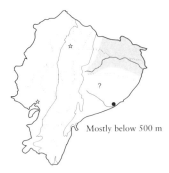

Mostly below 500 m

in east mainly in várzea and near streams. Iris brown. **Eastern birds** olive brown above with *prominent buff eye-ring*, indistinct superciliary, and narrow streaking on ear-coverts; rump and tail rufous-chestnut. *Throat pale buff*; underparts dull ochraceous brown, *flammulated with pale buff on breast*. **Western birds** have *white throat* and less flammulation on breast. **Similar species:** Olive-backed Foliage-gleaner differs from eastern Buff-throateds in having a white throat and whitish eye-ring, and it lacks Buff-throated's breast flammulations. Chestnut-crowned and Brown-rumped Foliage-gleaners have buff to ochre throats much like sympatric Buff-throateds, but differ in their orangey eyes, showing no eye-ring, and lacking breast flammulation. No similar foliage-gleaner occurs west of Andes. **Habits:** Similar to Olive-backed Foliage-gleaner, though often more furtive; in east occasionally occurs in same flocks as that species. Mostly recorded through its far-carrying and oft-given vocalizations. **Voice:** ♂'s distinctive song (similar west and east of Andes), heard especially at dawn and dusk, a short descending series of well-enunciated notes, e.g., "kee-kee-ke-krr" or "ki, ki, ki-ki-ke-ke-krr."

Chestnut-crowned Foliage-gleaner
Automolus rufipileatus
Rascahojas Coronicastaña   Plate 58(16)

19 cm (7½″). *Undergrowth and borders of várzea forest and woodland, also on river islands, in lowlands of east.* Iris bright yellow-orange. *Uniform rufescent brown above* with *slightly contrasting rufous crown*; rump and tail rufous-chestnut. Throat pale buff; underparts pale drab olivaceous brown. **Similar species:** Brown-rumped Foliage-gleaner also has orange eye but differs in lacking this species' chestnut crown and in

having a brighter, more ochraceous throat (especially on sides). Sympatric Buff-throated Foliage-gleaner (also buff-throated) is dark-eyed, more olivaceous above with buff eye-ring but no rufous on crown. Neither of these species normally occurs in Chestnut-crowned's usual várzea and riparian habitats. **Habits:** Even more skulking than other *Automolus* foliage-gleaners (except Ruddy), and the dense nature of its favored habitat doesn't help. Rarely joins mixed flocks. Heard much more often than seen. **Voice:** ♂'s oft-heard song a run-together series of sharp, stacatto notes that drop in pitch, "d-r-r-r-r-r-r-r-r." It resembles Olive-backed's song but is faster and higher pitched, though descending toward end. Foraging birds also give a low-pitched, almost sneezing "cheeu!"

Brown-rumped Foliage-gleaner
Automolus melanopezus
Rascahojas Lomiparda   Plate 58(20)

Mostly below 400 m

18.5 cm (7¼″). *Scarce and apparently local in dense tangled undergrowth of terra firme forest in lowlands of east, favoring vicinity of streams or swampy places.* Iris orange (sometimes reddish orange); bill rather short and heavy. Uniform dark rufescent brown above; tail rufous-chestnut. *Throat ochraceous orange, brightest on sides*; underparts pale drab olivaceous brown. **Similar species:** Buff-throated Foliage-gleaner differs in its dark eye, more olivaceous upperparts with buff eye-ring and faint superciliary, and breast flammulations. Chestnut-crowned Foliage-gleaner has contrasting chestnut crown, markedly paler throat; it favors várzea and riparian habitats, where Brown-rumped does not occur. **Habits:** A shy and reclusive foliage-gleaner, tending to skulk inside heavy viny cover and only infrequently observed. Sometimes one is seen as it accompanies a mixed understory flock. **Voice:** ♂'s song a fast and rhythmic "whit-whit-whidididit-wrrrrrr" with distinctive cadence.

Ruddy Foliage-gleaner, *Automolus rubiginosus*
Rascahojas Rojiza   Plate 58(17)

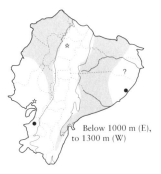

Below 1000 m (E),
to 1300 m (W)

18.5 cm (7¼"). *Generally scarce and local in dense undergrowth and borders of humid and foothill forest in east and west*, most numerous in foothills. *Very dark overall.* **Eastern birds** *uniform dark rufescent brown above*; tail rufous-chestnut. *Throat and upper chest rich rufous*; remaining underparts rufescent brown. **Birds from Sucumbíos** paler and less rufescent below, so rufous throat and upper chest stand out more. **Western birds** similar but have *black tail* and underparts more olivaceous brown. **Similar species:** This foliage-gleaner is so dark it can be confused with a *Sclerurus* leaftosser, though latter's chunky and short-tailed shape is quite different. In east, Brown-rumped Foliage-gleaner is most similar, though it differs in its orange eye and brighter, more contrasting orange-ochraceous throat. Cf. also the two woodhaunters. **Habits:** Usually in pairs, foraging on or close to ground in dense vegetation; very skulking and hard to see, especially without tape playback. Rarely accompanies mixed flocks. Heard much more often than seen. **Voice:** Persistent call, apparently given by both sexes and similar on either side of Andes, a querulous and nasal, upslurred "kweeeeahhhh," vaguely recalling a call of Smooth-billed Ani.

Henna-hooded Foliage-gleaner
Hylocryptus erythrocephalus
Rascahojas Capuchirrufa   Plate 58(21)

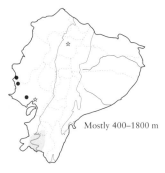

Mostly 400–1800 m

21 cm (8¼"). A *handsome and boldly patterned* foliage-gleaner, *now scarce and local on or near ground in deciduous and semihumid forest, woodland, and borders in lowlands and (especially) foothills of southwest. Iris orangey brown to hazel. Head, neck, wings, rump, and tail orange-rufous* ("henna"); back contrastingly brownish olive. *Throat pale orange-rufous*; underparts pale brownish gray, tinged olive brown on lower flanks; crissum rufous. **Similar species:** Unmistakable in its limited range, where one of the most striking and distinctive endemic birds. Cf. Rufous-necked Foliage-gleaner (which really is very different). **Habits:** Occurs singly or in pairs, foraging on or near ground, frequently accompanying small mixed flocks. Often quite noisy when feeding, flicking aside dry leaves with bill and at times creating quite a commotion; though hardly obvious, one can sometimes be tracked down by following up this noise. Heard more often than seen, vocalizing especially during its Jan.–May breeding season. **Voice:** Far-carrying and distinctive song a persistent, staccato churring, "kree-kruh-kruh-kruh-kruh-kruh-kruh-kurr," with odd, mechanical-sounding quality.

Thripadectes Treehunters
Large and robust furnariids with *heavy black bills* found in the undergrowth of Andean forests, some species favoring a bamboo understory. Treehunters are notably furtive and difficult to see, and the various species are hard to distinguish. Nests are placed at the end of burrows dug into banks.

Flammulated Treehunter
Thripadectes flammulatus
Trepamusgos Flamulado   Plate 59(10)

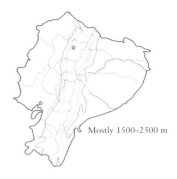

Mostly 1500–2500 m

Mostly 2200–3500 m

24 cm (9½"). Uncommon in undergrowth of *upper subtropical and temperate forest on both slopes*, favoring areas with extensive *Chusquea* bamboo. *Mainly blackish above and below* with *conspicuous buff striping on head, mantle, and underparts*, becoming browner on belly; wings, rump, and tail rufous-chestnut. **Similar species:** *The most "contrasty" and boldly patterned treehunter*, mainly because its basic ground color is *blackish*. Smaller Striped Treehunter has much the same overall pattern, but its ground colors are dusky and brownish, and streaking is thus much less prominent (especially below). **Habits:** Furtive and infrequently seen, then usually as a solitary bird foraging independently of a mixed flock. Tends to remain in heavy cover. **Voice:** Infrequently heard song a fast staccato trill of harsh and evenly pitched notes that lasts about 2 seconds, lacking the descending effect of Striped Treehunter; after tape playback this can be prolonged considerably. Call a single sharp "chek."

Striped Treehunter, *Thripadectes holostictus*
Trepamusgos Listado   Plate 59(11)
21 cm (8¼"). Undergrowth of *subtropical and lower temperate forest on both slopes*,

favoring areas with extensive *Chusquea* bamboo. *Above dusky brown prominently streaked with buff*; wings more rufescent, rump and tail rufous-chestnut. Brown below *with buff streaking, especially on throat and breast*. **Similar species:** Flammulated Treehunter considerably larger and more boldly patterned. Striped Treehunter more likely to be confused with Streak-capped and Black-billed Treehunters, though both of these show virtually no streaking on underparts. Cf. also smaller and less robust Lineated Foliage-gleaner, especially on e. slope (where it is more extensively streaked), the foliage-gleaner differing in its unmarked pale buff throat. **Habits:** Similar to Flammulated Treehunter. The two species can occur together, though on the whole Striped ranges at lower elevations. **Voice:** Song similar to Flammulated Treehunter's but faster and somewhat higher pitched, descending toward end; when a bird is excited it can extend longer. Call a sharp, fast "kwi-di-dik!" (P. Coopmans recording).

Streak-capped Treehunter
Thripadectes virgaticeps
Trepamusgos Gorrirrayado   Plate 59(13)

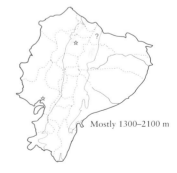

Mostly 1300–2100 m

21.5 cm (8½″). Undergrowth of *subtropical forest on both slopes in n. Ecuador*. Above dark brown, *duskier on head and nape with narrow buff streaking*; wings rufescent, rump and tail rufous-chestnut. *Throat and upper chest ochraceous-buff streaked with dusky*; underparts plain ochraceous brown with no streaking. **Similar species:** Much less streaked than Striped Treehunter. On e. slope, most resembles Black-billed Treehunter (which tends to occur at lower elevations, though with overlap), but somewhat smaller Black-billed differs in having streaking on back and a more streaked (less scaly) pattern on throat; it also tends to be more ochraceous below. On w. slope, Streak-capped most resembles Uniform Treehunter though latter is smaller with a proportionately stouter bill, shows no streaking at all on upperparts, and is browner (less ochraceous) below. **Habits:** Similar to other treehunters (see Flammulated). **Voice:** Song a short and evenly pitched series of emphatic and well-enunciated notes, "chup, cheyp-cheyp-cheyp-cheyp-cheyp." Call a fast, sharp "chidik."

Black-billed Treehunter
Thripadectes melanorhynchus
Trepamusgos Piquinegro   Plate 59(12)

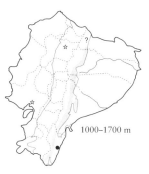

20.5 cm (8″). Undergrowth of *subtropical forest and secondary woodland on e. slope*. Above dark brown, duskier on crown, *crown and back narrowly streaked with buff*; wings more rufescent, rump and tail rufous-chestnut. *Throat quite bright ochraceous, feathers edged with black giving a distinct scaly appearance*; underparts plain brown with virtually no streaking. **Similar species:** Streak-capped Treehunter somewhat larger, un-streaked on back, and has streaky (not

scaly) pattern on its less ochraceous throat. **Habits:** Similar to other treehunters (see Flammulated). **Voice:** Song a short series of sharp, loud "kyip" notes, sometimes paired.

Uniform Treehunter, *Thripadectes ignobilis*
Trepamusgos Uniforme   Plate 59(14)

19 cm (7½″). *Undergrowth of foothill and lower subtropical forest on w. slope. Notably short and stout bill*. Above dark rufescent brown *with no streaking* aside from *short, broken buff postocular streak*; wings more rufescent, tail rufous-chestnut. *Below dull brown*, throat with buff streaking extending down more sparsely onto chest. **Similar species:** Streak-capped Treehunter larger with longer bill; it has streaking on crown and nape and is more ochraceous below. Western Woodhaunter has longer and more slender bill, and throat is distinctly buff (contrastingly paler than rest of underparts). **Habits:** Similar to other treehunters (see Flammulated), but Uniform tends to be less shy and furtive, more often foraging up into midlevels and more likely to accompany mixed understory flocks. **Voice:** Song a series of 6–8 sharp "kik" or "kyip" notes, higher pitched and much faster than that of Streak-capped Treehunter.

Xenops Xenops
Small arboreal furnariids with laterally compressed bills, most species with the *lower mandible obviously upturned*; most also show a *unique silvery malar streak*. Xenops occur primarily in humid lowland forests, one species (Streaked) ranging more widely; they are frequent flock members. Nests are placed in small holes dug into rotten wood.

Streaked Xenops, *Xenops rutilans*
Xenops Rayado Plate 57(18)

To about 2000 m (W);
800–2000 m (E slope)

12 cm (4¾″). Locally fairly common in canopy and borders of *foothill and subtropical forest and woodland on both slopes, also ranging widely in lowlands of west* (where also in *more deciduous* habitats). *Lower mandible strongly upturned.* Rufous brown above, duskier on crown, *lightly streaked with buff on crown and upper back*; superciliary buffy whitish and with *prominent silvery white malar streak*; wings rufous with some black in flight feathers (rufous wing-band shows in flight); rump and tail rufous, inner webs of some inner tail feathers with some black. Throat whitish; *underparts olive brown extensively streaked with whitish.* **Similar species:** *The only montane xenops,* occurring at elevations well above others (but overlapping with Plain in west). Slender-billed Xenops is extremely similar but occurs only in e. lowlands with at most limited overlap with Streaked; for distinctions, see that species. Plain Xenops generally is much less streaked, showing no streaking at all above, and below only a little on chest. On e. slope cf. also Spectacled Prickletail. **Habits:** Found singly or in pairs, often accompanying mixed flocks, foraging at various levels though usually not in lower growth inside forest; does come lower at borders. Works along or beneath slender branches and in vine tangles, swiveling from side to side and pausing to tap at dead wood or to flake off small bark pieces. **Voice:** Song a short series, first ascending and then descending, of 4–7 shrill notes, e.g., "swee-swee-swee-swee-swee."

Slender-billed Xenops, *Xenops tenuirostris*
Xenops Picofino Plate 57(17)

Mostly below 600 m

11.5 cm (4½″). Scarce in canopy and borders of humid forest in *lowlands of east. Closely resembles more numerous Streaked Xenops,* which does not occur in e. lowlands (if it did, the two would be very difficult to distinguish). Slender-billed differs in having bill longer and slightly more slender; tail slightly shorter and shows more black (black often visible in field, whereas in Streaked it generally is not); and streaking below somewhat sparser. **Habits:** Similar to other xenops (see Streaked). Slender-billed almost always forages well above ground as it accompanies canopy flocks. **Voice:** Song a simple series of shrill, evenly pitched notes, "tsip-tsip-tsip-tsip." Streaked Xenops's song is slightly faster and lower-pitched, ascending at first and then descending.

Plain Xenops, *Xenops minutus*
Xenops Dorsillano Plate 57(19)

11.5 cm (4½″). Widespread in subcanopy and borders of humid forest and woodland in *lowlands of east and west,* more numerous in

Mostly below 900 m

west. *By far the least streaked xenops. Lower mandible strongly upturned.* Above olive brown with pale buff superciliary and *prominent silvery white malar streak*; wings mainly rufous, with considerable black on flight feathers (cinnamon-rufous wing-band shows in flight); rump and tail rufous, tail with black on lateral feathers. Throat whitish; underparts pale dull brown with some whitish chest streaking. **Western birds** have more extensive white on throat and more chest streaking. **Similar species:** All other xenops are more streaked, this especially noticeable on their underparts; note, however, that at a distance their streaking can be hard to see. Cf. also Wedge-billed Woodcreeper (though that lacks malar streak, etc., and behaves very differently). **Habits:** Similar to other xenops (see Streaked), though Plain forages more frequently at lower levels, especially in east where it is the only xenops normally occurring with understory flocks of antwrens, antshrikes, and other species. **Voice:** Song east of Andes similar to that of Streaked Xenops, a series of shrill notes, first ascending and then descending, e.g., "swee-swee-swee-swee-swee." West of Andes song a faster (almost trilled), a mostly ascending series of notes, e.g., "ts-tsi-tsi-tsi-tsi-tsi." Also gives a sharp "peeyk" call while foraging.

Rufous-tailed Xenops, *Xenops milleri*
Xenops Colirrufo   Plate 57(16)

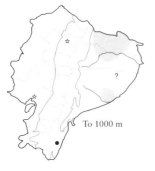

To 1000 m

11 cm (4¼"). *Scarce and apparently local* in canopy and borders of humid forest in *lowlands of east*. Differs from other xenops in its *essentially straight bill* and in *lacking a white malar streak*. Crown dusky narrowly streaked with pale buff and with pale buff superciliary; otherwise brown above,

streaked with pale buff on back; wings rufous except for mainly blackish primaries; rump and *entire tail rufous*. Throat buffy whitish streaked olive; underparts brownish olive with buffy whitish streaking. **Similar species:** The plain face of this xenops is distinctive (other xenops have obvious white malar streak); its all-rufous tail is often spread and can be surprisingly apparent on foraging birds. **Habits:** Similar to other xenops (see Streaked). Like Slender-billed, Rufous-tailed generally forages well above ground with canopy flocks. **Voice:** Song (in se. Peru) a short (less than 2-second), ascending trill similar to short trill of Chestnut-winged Hookbill.

Sclerurus **Leaftossers**
A uniform group of *dark-plumaged, cryptic* furnariids with short black tails that range solitarily on the ground inside humid forests, mainly in lowlands and foothills. Their legs are short, and in most species the bills are quite long and slender. Nests are placed at the end of long burrows dug into banks.

Tawny-throated Leaftosser
Sclerurus mexicanus
Tirahojas Golianteado   Plate 59(16)

To 1500 m

16.5 cm (6½"). *Widespread* but scarce on or near ground inside *humid and montane forest in lowlands, foothills, and lower subtropics of east and west*. Bill long and slender, slightly drooped at tip. Dark brown above with rufous to rufous-chestnut rump and black tail. *Throat and chest rich tawny-rufous*, becoming dark brown on remaining underparts. **Similar species:** Short-billed Leaftosser has considerably shorter bill, throat paler (buff) and not as rich, and shows a vague pale eye-ring and short superciliary. Black-tailed and Scaly-throated Leaftossers have whitish throats. **Habits:** A furtive and inconspicuous bird, mainly terrestrial and for the most part solitary; never with mixed flocks. Favors damp places and shady hill-sides where it hops and shuffles on ground, flicking aside leaves and other debris with bill (not feet), also probing ground. Not espe-cially wary, and may allow a close approach though more often you are not even aware of its presence until it suddenly flushes, giving a sharp "tseeeét" as it goes. A startled bird sometimes will perch on a low open branch, where it may remain motionless for several minutes, occasionally flicking wings. **Voice:** Song a descending series of 4–5 high-pitched wheezy notes, each progressively a bit shorter, e.g., "peéeeee-peéeee-peéee-peee," often ending in a chattered "chrrrr" when excited.

Gray-throated Leaftosser, *Sclerurus albigularis*
Tirahojas Goligris   Plate 59(15)

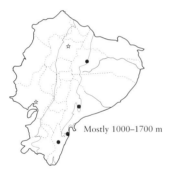

Mostly 1000–1700 m

18 cm (7"). *Rare* on or near ground inside *foothill and lower subtropical forest on e. slope.* Bill long. Above dark brown with rufous-chestnut rump and black tail. *Chin white, becoming pale ashy gray on lower throat*, with *contrasting rufous chest band*; lower underparts dull grayish brown. **Similar species:** Tawny-throated Leaftosser has entire throat and chest tawny-rufous (not a con-trastingly paler throat). **Habits:** Similar to other leaftossers (see Tawny-throated). **Voice:** Song a series of 4–6 rather querulous notes, each higher pitched than previous, e.g., "kwu-kwu-kwe-kwe-kwi-kwi?" (P. Coop-mans); excited birds may add trills and chat-ters at end.

Short-billed Leaftosser, *Sclerurus rufigularis*
Tirahojas Piquicorto   Plate 59(17)

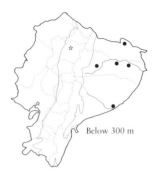

Below 300 m

16 cm (6¼"). *Rare and perhaps local* on or near ground inside terra firme forest in *low-lands of east. Bill relatively short for genus.* Dark brown above with *buffyish lores and partial eye-ring* (also sometimes the sugges-tion of a short superciliary); rump rufous-chestnut, tail black. *Throat cinnamon-buff*; underparts dark brown, chest variably mottled with buffyish. **Similar species:** Easily confused with Tawny-throated Leaftosser, but Tawny-throated differs in its longer bill, more deeply and richly colored throat and chest, and lack of any buff on face. **Habits:** Similar to other leaftossers (see Tawny-throated). **Voice:** Song a fast series of shrill and high-pitched notes that descend at first, then ascend and speed up, level out, and slow down again. Also gives a sharp "suip!" call.

Black-tailed Leaftosser, *Sclerurus caudacutus*
Tirahojas Colinegro   Plate 59(19)

18.5 cm (7¼"). On or near ground inside terra firme forest in *lowlands of east.* Bill long and straight. Brown above, rump slightly more chestnut; tail black. *Throat white,*

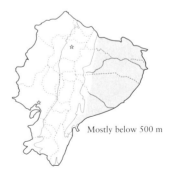

Mostly below 500 m

feathers scaled darker; underparts dark brown. **Similar species:** *The only leaftosser east of Andes with white on throat* (though this can be hard to discern in the dim light of forest interior); Black-tailed is also larger than other leaftossers there. Scaly-throated Leaftosser occurs only west of Andes. **Habits:** Similar to other leaftossers (see Tawny-throated). **Voice:** Song a series of loud, emphatic, ringing notes that steadily drop in pitch; sometimes faster and ending with brief trill. Call a sharp "skweeup!"

Scaly-throated Leaftosser
Sclerurus guatemalensis
Tirahojas Goliescamoso   Plate 59(18)

To 800 m

18 cm (7"). Scarce and local on or near ground inside humid forest in *lowlands and foothills of west*. Bill long and straight. Dark brown above; tail black. *Throat white, feathers scaled darker*; chest rufescent brown with some buff shaft streaking; underparts dark brown. **Similar species:** Only other leaftosser found with this species is Tawny-throated, which has an obvious tawny-rufous throat and chest and rufous-chestnut on rump. **Habits:** Similar to other leaftossers (see Tawny-throated). **Voice:** Song a fast series of 10–12 sharp, clear whistled notes, first few dropping in pitch, last few ascending and speeding up, the series often repeated numerous times in fast succession (P. Coopmans). Call a sharp "pik!"

Sharp-tailed Streamcreeper
Lochmias nematura
Riachuelero   Plate 59(20)

15 cm (6"). *Scarce and local on or near rocky streams in foothill and lower subtropical forest and woodland on e. slope.* Bill long

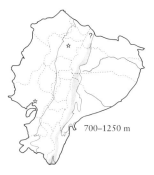

700–1250 m

and slender, slightly decurved. Uniform dark brown above, somewhat more chestnut on mantle; tail black. Below dark brown *conspicuously spotted with white*. **Similar species:** Leaftosser-like in shape (though smaller than any), but differing immediately in its bold white spotting on underparts. **Habits:** Hops on or near ground, with behavior similar to leaftossers; equally hard to see. Probes into damp soil, also flicks leaves aside with bill. **Voice:** Song a series of dry unmusical notes that starts slowly, often with a single sharply accented note, and then gradually accelerates into a run-together chipper.

Woodcreepers: Dendrocolaptidae (28)
A uniform group of scansorial birds with stiff tails whose exposed shafts protrude and curve sharply inward. Woodcreepers range primarily in humid or montane forest, with few or none occurring in semiopen areas; maximum diversity occurs in the eastern lowlands. They are predominantly some shade of brown to rufescent brown, usually with some buff streaking or spotting; wings and tail are rufous-chestnut. Bill shape varies substantially among the different genera. **Sexes are alike**, though in a few species males are notably larger. The identification of some species can present a challenge. Woodcreepers are quite vocal, collectively forming one of the more conspicuous components of avian choruses in tropical forests, especially at dusk. Their songs often assist in species identification.

Dendrocincla Woodcreepers
Midsized to fairly large woodcreepers with straight bills and *relatively uniform, plain patterns* found in humid forests, primarily in the lowlands (though the Tyrannine is exclu-

sively montane). Lowland species *frequently attend army antswarms. Dendrocincla* often ruffle their crown feathers.

Tyrannine Woodcreeper
Dendrocincla tyrannina
Trepatroncos Tiranino   Plate 55(1)

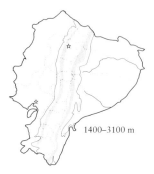

1400–3100 m

24–26.5 cm (9½–10½″). A *large* and *uniform-looking* woodcreeper that is *generally scarce in subtropical and temperate forest and borders on both slopes*. Iris brownish to bluish gray. ♂♂ average larger than ♀♀. *Essentially uniform olive brown*, throat slightly paler and with faint buff streaking on forecrown and throat, in some individuals extending down over chest. **Similar species:** Other *Dendrocincla* woodcreepers, which are equally plain in appearance, all occur at lower elevations. Montane Woodcreeper is smaller with slender decurved bill and extensively streaked. **Habits:** Usually found singly, often while moving with a mixed flock. Forages by hitching up trunks and along larger lateral branches, at varying heights though usually not very high. At least to date has not been found at antswarms. **Voice:** Song a long stuttered rattle that gradually increases in pitch and volume before trailing off and slowing toward end; it lasts 5–10 seconds. Call a fast phrase of 3–6 sharp abrupt notes, e.g., "di-di-di-di-dik!," with quality similar to Long-tailed Antbird (P. Coopmans).

Plain-brown Woodcreeper
Dendrocincla fuliginosa
Trepatroncos Pardo   Plate 55(2)

19.5–21 cm (7¾–8¼″). A *widespread* and *plain* (well-named!) woodcreeper found in lower and middle growth of humid forest in

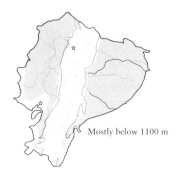

Mostly below 1100 m

lowlands of east and west, in west also ranging into deciduous forest. Iris brownish gray. *Essentially uniform brown* with *paler grayish lores and ear-coverts* and *fairly obvious dusky malar stripe*; flight feathers and tail rufous-chestnut. **Eastern birds** generally more rufescent, **western birds** more olivaceous. **Similar species:** The most uniformly brown woodcreeper in lowlands. In ne. lowlands, cf. rare White-chinned Woodcreeper (with blue iris and contrasting white throat). **Habits:** Though routinely seen foraging singly or in pairs while alone or accompanying mixed flocks, most often seen while attending army antswarms; if these are large, 6 or more birds may gather. Perches on trunks and branches like other woodcreepers, but also regularly sits "normally" across branches. **Voice:** Typical song a descending series of rattled notes that slows toward the end, lasting 2–4 seconds. Less often heard is a protracted series of "keé" or "keh" notes that can continue 30 or more seconds. In west also often gives a sharp "peeyk" call.

White-chinned Woodcreeper
Dendrocincla merula
Trepatroncos Barbiblanco   Plate 55(3)

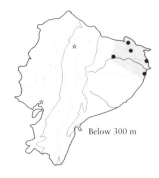

Below 300 m

19–19.5 cm (7½–7¾″). *Rare and apparently local* in lower growth of humid forest (both terra firme and várzea) in *lowlands of northeast. Iris bluish gray to blue.* Uniform rufescent brown above; wings and tail rufous-chestnut. *Small but contrasting white throat patch*; underparts uniform olivaceous brown, with crissum rufous. **Similar species:** Plain-brown Woodcreeper lacks white throat and blue eye, and shows stronger face pattern (White-chinned's face looks unmarked and plain); Plain-brown's throat can appear whitish, but it never forms as discrete a white patch as in this species. **Habits:** An inveterate follower of army ants, only infrequently seen away from them. Behavior at swarms similar to Plain-brown Woodcreeper, though White-chinned tends to remain closer to ground. **Voice:** Seems unrecorded in Ecuador.

Deconychura Woodcreepers
Obscure woodcreepers found *at low densities* inside humid lowland and subtropical forests in the east. Both species have *notably long tails* and show *striking size dimorphism*, males being larger.

Long-tailed Woodcreeper
Deconychura longicauda
Trepatroncos Colilargo   Plate 55(4)

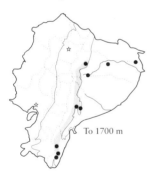

To 1700 m

19–21 cm (7½–8¼″). *Rare and local* in lower and middle growth inside montane and humid forest in *lower subtropics and foothills on e. slope, and in lowlands of east*; in lowlands favors terra firme. Bill fairly long, straight, and slender. ♂ considerably larger than ♀. **Foothill/subtropical birds** brown above with faint buff streaks on crown and sides of head and *indistinct buff postocu-*

lar stripe; wings, uppertail-coverts, and tail rufous-chestnut, *tail proportionately longer than in other woodcreepers* (except Spot-throated). Throat dull buff with faint dusky streaking; underparts dull olivaceous brown, *breast with buff chevrons or spots.* **Lowland birds** similar but with *more streaked pattern on breast.* **Similar species:** A confusing bird, difficult to identify and often not seen very well. *Slim shape, accentuated by long tail, helps.* Spot-throated Woodcreeper averages smaller, though large ♂♂ Spot-throateds approach ♀♀ Long-taileds in length. Spot-throated differs in its more extensively rufous wings, rufous rump (not just on uppertail-coverts), more sparsely spotted pattern on breast (recall that lowland Long-taileds have streaky pattern), and shorter and more slender bill. No *Xiphorhynchus* woodcreeper shows such an obvious postocular, though the more olivaceous Olive-backed may show indistinct eye-ring and postocular. Wedge-billed Woodcreeper is much smaller with differently shaped bill. **Habits:** Unobtrusive, not often encountered anywhere in Ecuador; when seen, usually with a mixed flock inside forest. Forages mainly on trunks, generally at mid-levels. **Voice:** Rather quiet for a woodcreeper. Song distinctive when heard, a strongly descending series of 8–12 well-separated, clear, penetrating whistled notes, almost with effect of a *Microcerculus* wren; very different from other woodcreeper songs.

Spot-throated Woodcreeper
Deconychura stictolaema
Trepatroncos Golipunteado   Plate 55(5)

16.5–17.5 cm (6½–7″). *Rare and local (overlooked?) in lower growth inside terra firme*

Below 350 m

forest in lowlands of northeast. Bill straight and rather slender. ♂ considerably larger than ♀. Brown above with indistinct buff postocular stripe and streaking on sides of head; inner flight feathers (only) rufous-chestnut; tail rufous-chestnut, *this color extending up over rump, tail proportionately longer than in other woodcreepers* (except Long-tailed). Dull olivaceous brown below, *throat and breast with small chevron-shaped spots.* **Similar species:** Cf. similar Long-tailed Woodcreeper (the two species do occur together, though *only Long-tailed occurs above lowlands*). Spot-throated is a small, obscure woodcreeper, most likely confused with the much more numerous Wedge-billed Woodcreeper; that species is smaller, and though similar in overall color and pattern, has a much shorter and wedge-shaped bill. **Habits:** Not well known, but unobtrusive behavior seems similar to Long-tailed. Usually found singly, foraging with mixed flocks, most often at lower levels than Long-tailed. **Voice:** Song a simple, colorless, and fast trill, descending at first, then rising toward end, and lasting about 2 seconds (P. Donahue and N. Krabbe recordings).

Wedge-billed Woodcreeper
Glyphorynchus spirurus
Trepatroncos Piquicuña   Plate 55(6)

Mostly below 1700 m

14–14.5 cm (5½–5¾″). *Generally numerous and widespread* in lower and middle growth of humid forest and woodland in *lowlands of east and west*, smaller numbers well up into subtropics on both slopes. A *small* woodcreeper with *distinctive short, wedge-shaped bill.* Above rufescent brown with indistinct buff postocular stripe and narrow streaking on sides of head; wings somewhat more rufescent (buff wing-stripe shows in flight); rump and tail rufous, tail with *very long protruding spines* (proportionately the longest of any woodcreeper). Throat buff; underparts olivaceous brown, breast with a few buffy whitish streaks. **Similar species:** In e. lowlands, cf. much rarer Spot-throated Woodcreeper. Plain Xenops has similarly shaped bill but differs markedly in behavior, etc. **Habits:** Usually found singly, less often in pairs, sometimes accompanying mixed flocks of understory birds but also often alone. Forages principally by hitching up trunks of larger trees, usually not on lateral branches. **Voice:** Song a fast and ascending series of upslurred, semimusical notes, e.g., "tuee-tuee-tuee-tuee-teeé-tueé-tueé?," often shriller at end. Often-given call an abrupt, sneezing "cheeyf!"

Olivaceous Woodcreeper
Sittasomus griseicapillus
Trepatroncos Oliváceo   Plate 55(7)

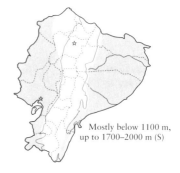

Mostly below 1100 m, up to 1700–2000 m (S)

14.5–16 cm (5¾–6¼″). *Numerous and widespread in deciduous and semihumid forest and woodland in lowlands and subtropics of west; much less numerous in east,* there mainly in várzea and second-growth. A *small, unstreaked* woodcreeper with short and quite slender bill. **Western birds** have *head, neck, and underparts uniform grayish olive,* back more rufescent; flight feathers and tail cinnamon-rufous (buff stripe on flight feathers is exposed when wing is spread). **Eastern birds** larger and have *head, neck, and underparts darker and more grayish,* flight feathers and tail rufous. **Similar species:** *The only small and unstreaked woodcreeper.* **Habits:** Seen singly or in pairs, hitching along open trunks and larger branches at varying levels though most often at mid-levels and in subcanopy. Sometimes accompanies mixed flocks, but at least as often alone. **Voice:** Vocalizations differ strikingly on either side of Andes. Western birds give a fast, rolling, semimusical trill, "tr-r-r-r-r-r-r-r-r-r-r-r-r-r-eu," that lasts about 3 seconds. Eastern birds give a very different, 3- to 4-second-long series of 6–14 successively higher-pitched and gradually louder notes, "pu-pu-pew-pew-peh-peh-peé-peh," with slight drop at end.

Long-billed Woodcreeper, *Nasica longirostris*
Trepatroncos Piquilargo   Plate 55(24)

To 400 m

35–36 cm (13¾–14¼″). *Spectacular and unmistakable*, easily the *largest* woodcreeper in Ecuador; can look small-headed. Found in mid-levels, subcanopy, and borders of humid forest in *lowlands of east, favoring várzea* but also in terra firme borders. *Very long and nearly straight bill ivory to creamy white.* Crown and upper cheeks blackish narrowly streaked buff, and separated by white postocular stripe; *above otherwise bright rufous-chestnut. Throat snowy white*, underparts brown, with broad black-edged white lanceolate streaks on sides of neck and breast. **Habits:** Found singly or in pairs, often foraging in semiopen along edge of lakes and streams, but not terribly conspicuous; generally not with flocks. Probes into bromeliads and inspects bark crevices. Rarely descends to near ground or water. **Voice:** Loud and far-carrying song an easily recognized series of 3–4 eerie and plaintive whistles, e.g., "twooooooóoo . . . twooooooóoo . . . twooooóoo." There usually is a long pause between songs. A faster version (recalling Fasciated Antshrike) is also sometimes given. Birds may respond strongly to tape playback

and whistled imitations, flying in uttering various chuckled calls as well as the song.

Cinnamon-throated Woodcreeper
Dendrexetastes rufigula
Trepatroncos Golicanelo   Plate 55(8)

Mostly below 500 m

25 cm (9¾″). Generally uncommon in canopy and especially borders of humid forest in *lowlands of east. Rather heavy bill horn-colored to greenish horn*; iris red. Uniform brown, *more cinnamon-buff on throat* and with *band of narrow white, black-edged streaks across breast*. **Similar species:** A large and rather plain-looking woodcreeper whose bill is contrastingly paler; note that the breast streaking can be hard to see in field. **Habits:** Usually found singly, less often in pairs; sometimes accompanies mixed flocks but at least as often alone. Hitches along trunks and on larger branches like so many other woodcreepers, but also regularly clambers about, foliage-gleaner-like, in leafy or twiggy vegetation (sometimes even rummaging amongst palm fronds). Heard more often than seen. **Voice:** Distinctive song a fast series of loud rattled notes, ascending at first and descending and trailing off toward end; may start with a sputter and always ends with a distinctive lower-pitched "tchew" or "trreew" note. This song is often one of first to be given in the predawn darkness and is also heard at dusk.

Strong-billed Woodcreeper
Xiphocolaptes promeropirhynchus
Trepatroncos Piquifuerte   Plate 55(9)

28–30.5 cm (11–12″). A *very large* woodcreeper found in *subtropical and temperate forest* on both slopes, and also (as a separate

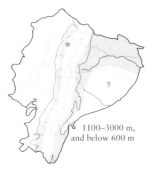

1100–3000 m,
and below 600 m

population) in humid forest in *lowlands of northeast*. Widespread but never very numerous. *Massive, somewhat decurved, bill* blackish or dusky to horn-colored (tending to be longer and paler in lowland birds); iris brown to reddish brown (redder in lowland birds). **Highland birds** brown above with narrow buffy whitish streaking on crown and head and *buffy whitish lores and postocular and supramalar stripes*; rump, wings, and tail rufous-chestnut. Throat whitish with some brown streaking and *bordered by a usually prominent blackish malar stripe*; underparts brown, streaked buffy whitish on breast and usually irregularly barred with blackish on belly. In **El Oro and Loja** similar but smaller, and with unstreaked whitish throat. **Lowland** birds differ in more blackish crown, less obvious pale supramalar stripe, and more rufescent plumage (especially below). **Similar species:** Can usually be known on basis of strikingly large, heavy-set appearance. In highlands, cf. rare Greater Scythebill (with longer, narrower, and pale bill; also its dark throat bordered by contrasting whitish malar). In lowlands most apt to be confused with commoner Buff-throated Woodcreeper, though that is smaller with less heavy bill, lacks dark malar stripe and streaking on throat, and never shows belly barring. Cf. also Black-banded Woodcreeper. **Habits:** Found singly or in pairs, foraging at all levels though usually not too high above ground; regularly accompanies mixed flocks, and sometimes attracted to antswarms, where generally dominant over other birds present. Perched birds grasp trunk with feet splayed widely outward. **Voice:** Distinctive and far-carrying song a series of 3–5 paired notes, each pair at a slightly lower pitch than preceding, "pt-teeu, pt-teeu, pt-teeu, pt-teuu."

At a distance, initial "pt" may not be audible, and entire vocalization may be overlaid with a soft squealing. Songs of lowland birds appear to be faster (N. Krabbe recordings). Agitated birds give a weird, drawn-out nasal squeal that may end in a "sneeze."

Dendrocolaptes Woodcreepers

Fairly large woodcreepers with strong straight bills and showing *fairly complex streaked and barred patterns*, found mainly in humid lowland forests.

Amazonian Barred-Woodcreeper
Dendrocolaptes certhia

Trepatroncos Barreteado Amazónico Plate 55(11)

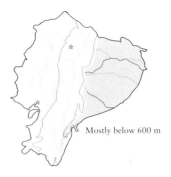

Mostly below 600 m

27–28 cm (10½–11″). Lower growth of humid forest in *lowlands of east*. Birds from west of Andes are now considered a separate species, their songs differing strikingly. Bill reddish brown to brown. *Prominently and uniformly barred*. Buffy brown *evenly barred with blackish across back and on entire underparts*, upper throat whitish; rump, wings, and tail rufous-chestnut. **Similar species:** Black-banded Woodcreeper similarly barred on lower underparts but differs in being *streaked* on foreparts and (sparsely) on back. Northern Barred-Woodcreeper occurs only west of Andes; it differs in its blacker bill, blackish lores, and denser blackish barring (especially below). **Habits:** Rather inconspicuous, foraging mainly at antswarms where it tends to perch close to ground and is dominant over other smaller woodcreepers present. Less often encountered as it forages, typically alone, on trunks and larger branches; then may be quite stolid. **Voice:** Song, given especially at dawn and dusk, a fast and descending series of run-together whistled notes that fade away toward end, e.g., "tew-tew-tew-tew-tew-tew-tew-tew-tu-tu, tu tu, tu"; has somewhat of a laughing quality. Various snarls are given while feeding, especially at antswarms.

Northern Barred-Woodcreeper
Dendrocolaptes sanctithomae
Trepatroncos Barreteado Norteño   Plate 55(12)

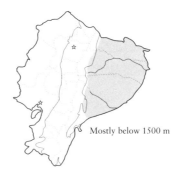

Mostly below 1500 m

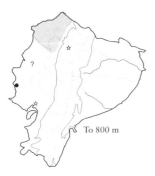

To 800 m

27–28 cm (10½–11″). Lower growth of humid forest in *lowlands and foothills of northwest*. Now considered a separate species from Amazonian Barred-Woodcreeper. Bill blackish. *Prominently and uniformly barred.* Rufescent brown above (most rufescent on crown) and buffy brown below, *evenly and narrowly barred with blackish across back and entire underparts*, lores blackish; rump, wings, and tail rufous-chestnut. **Similar species:** West of Andes this large woodcreeper is the only one that shows any barring. **Habits:** Similar to Amazonian Barred-Woodcreeper, and equally apt to be attracted to swarms of army ants. **Voice:** Song, given especially at dawn and dusk, an excited-sounding and somewhat rising series of forceful clear whistled notes that gradually become much louder, e.g., "oowít, oowít, oowít, OOWIT, OOWIT!" Gives snarling calls while feeding at antswarms.

Black-banded Woodcreeper
Dendrocolaptes picumnus
Trepatroncos Ventribandeado   Plate 55(10)

27.5–28 cm (10¾–11″). Generally scarce in lower growth of humid forest in *lowlands and lower subtropics of east*. Bill blackish above, grayish below. Above brown, darker and duskier on crown, streaked with buff on head and, more sparsely, on back; rump, wings, and tail rufous-chestnut. Throat pale buff streaked with brown; breast brown with prominent buff streaking, *lower underparts boldly barred buff and blackish*. **Similar species:** A large woodcreeper with distinctive combination of streaking on foreparts, barring on lower underparts. Buff-throated Woodcreeper is superficially similar but tends to be more arboreal and lacks barring below. Cf. also even larger and heavier-billed Strong-billed Woodcreeper. **Habits:** Similar to Amazonian Barred-Woodcreeper. **Voice:** Song a fast and slightly descending series of liquid-sounding "winh" notes, usually lasting 2–4 seconds. Various whines and chatters are given when agitated.

Xiphorhynchus Woodcreepers
The most confusing group of woodcreepers: midsized to fairly large species that range primarily in lowland forests, foraging at varying levels. They reach their maximum diversity in the Oriente. All Ecuadorian species are streaked or spotted to some degree; their bills are more decurved than in *Dendrocolaptes* but are stouter and less decurved than in *Lepidocolaptes*.

Straight-billed Woodcreeper
Xiphorhynchus picus
Trepatroncos Piquirrecto   Plate 55(13)

21 cm (8¼″). *Numerous* in *várzea and riparian forest, woodland, and borders* in *lowlands of east*. Bill straight and dagger-shaped, whitish to ivory. Above rufous, crown and sides of head contrastingly dusky with narrow buff streaks extending to upper back,

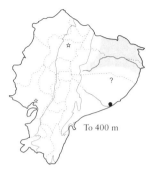

and indistinct whitish superciliary; wings and tail rufous-chestnut. Throat buffy whitish with faint dusky scaling, *breast with large black-edged pale buff squamate spots*; lower underparts brown with very faint narrow buff streaking. **Similar species:** Less numerous Striped Woodcreeper has a somewhat darker and more decurved bill and is more extensively streaked, especially below but also on back; it is less rufescent, more olivaceous, overall. Cf. also Ocellated Woodcreeper. **Habits:** Forages singly or in pairs and, for a woodcreeper, often quite conspicuous and tame, sometimes foraging fully in the open, low at woodland edge. Hitches up trunks and along larger branches, mainly at low and mid-levels; often accompanies mixed flocks. **Voice:** Song a descending trill, though often with an upturn at end. Unlike most other woodcreepers, does not sing primarily at dawn and dusk, rather giving voice at intervals through day.

Striped Woodcreeper
Xiphorhynchus obsoletus
Trepatroncos Listado   Plate 55(17)

20.5 cm (8″). *Várzea forest and woodland* in *lowlands of east*. Though the two species are

often together, Striped is less numerous than Straight-billed and is *more confined to várzea* (not being found on river islands). Slightly decurved bill grayish horn, duskier toward base. Above brown, duskier on crown, with *prominent black-edged buff streaks extending from crown down over back*; rump, wings, and tail rufous-chestnut. Throat buff, feathers faintly scaled dusky; underparts dull brown *prominently streaked with buffy whitish* except on belly. **Similar species:** Straight-billed Woodcreeper differs in its straighter and whiter bill, less extensive back streaking, more ocellated effect on chest (not streaked), and overall more rufescent tone. Lineated Woodcreeper has similar pattern below (though its streaking is narrower) but differs in its finer and more decurved bill and lack of streaking on back; it forages higher, mainly in canopy. **Habits:** Similar to Straight-billed Woodcreeper, though much less apt to be in open. **Voice:** Song a rather harsh and staccato trill that distinctly ascends in pitch (Straight-billed's descends).

Ocellated Woodcreeper
Xiphorhynchus ocellatus
Trepatroncos Ocelado   Plate 55(15)

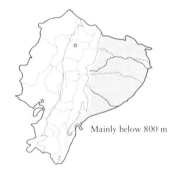

21.5 cm (8½″). Lower growth inside humid forest (especially terra firme) in *lowlands and foothills of east*. Bill blackish above, gray below. Brown above, duskier on crown and nape, crown and nape with guttate buff spots, back with sparse and fine buff streaking (at a distance often looking uniform); rump, wings, and tail rufous-chestnut. Throat buff, *feathers of lower throat distinctly scaled blackish*; underparts brown, *chest with large squamate black-edged buff spots*, lower underparts obscurely streaked buffyish. **Similar species:** Cf. much rarer Spix's Woodcreeper. Buff-throated Woodcreeper larger with heavier bill, and its plain buff throat *lacks* any scaling. Striped Woodcreeper is paler-billed and more streaked; it does not range in terra firme forest that Ocellated favors. **Habits:** Found singly or in pairs, hitching up trunks and larger branches, probing into crevices and epiphytes. Almost always found *inside* forest (not at edge), usually accompanying mixed understory flocks; on the whole, rather inconspicuous. **Voice:** Song, heard mainly at dawn and dusk (though a shortened version may be given while foraging), a fast series of nasal notes with descending effect that ends with several sharply emphasized notes, e.g., "whe-whe-whe-whe-whe-chéchécheow." Sometimes only part of song is given. It seemingly is heard relatively infrequently.

Spix's Woodcreeper, *Xiphorhynchus spixii*
Trepatroncos de Spix   Plate 55(16)

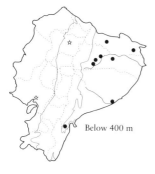

Below 400 m

21.5 cm (8½"). *Rare and apparently local* in lower growth of *várzea forest* (apparently especially in blackwater drainages) in *lowlands of northeast. Frequently confused with much more numerous Ocellated Woodcreeper*; records, especially sight reports, are hopelessly confused. Ecuadorian birds have been considered as part of a separate species, (Elegant Woodcreeper, *X. elegans*). Bill bluish gray, often duskier above or toward base. Differs from Ocellated in having *wider black-edged buff streaking on back* (back streaking in Ocellated is typically fainter, sometimes lacking altogether but in other birds about equally extensive as in Ocellated), more whitish throat, and somewhat more extensive guttate buff spotting on breast. Note that

there still exists substantial confusion and disagreement concerning plumage (and also vocal) characters separating Ocellated and Spix's Woodcreepers. For present, the best one can say is that vast majority of Ecuadorian specimens in various museums have been identified as Ocellateds. **Habits:** Much as in Ocellated Woodcreeper. **Voice:** Song differs from Ocellated's in having a clearer, more musical quality though still descending in pitch, e.g., "tchip-tchip-tchip-tchip-tchup-tchup, tchweu, tchweu." Sometimes this may continue as a longer series of notes, and may slide back up in pitch at end.

Buff-throated Woodcreeper
Xiphorhynchus guttatus
Trepatroncos Golianteado   Plate 55(14)

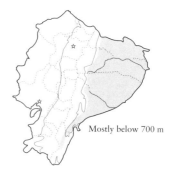

Mostly below 700 m

25.5–26 cm (10–10¼"). A *large* woodcreeper, *numerous* in humid forest and borders in *lowlands and foothills of east. Bill long,* dusky to grayish horn, darkest on maxilla. Above brown, duskier on crown and nape, with guttate buff spotting on crown and buff streaking on nape and upper back; rump, wings, and tail rufous-chestnut. *Throat unmarked pale buff*; underparts brown with buff streaking, becoming plain on belly, mid-belly sometimes tinged rufescent. **Similar species:** Other *Xiphorhynchus* woodcreepers are noticeably smaller with less heavy bills. Black-banded Woodcreeper has streaked foreneck and barring on belly. Strong-billed Woodcreeper is much larger and even heavier-billed, though it and Buff-throated can be confused in a brief or poor view. **Habits:** Rather conspicuous, foraging with mixed flocks at varying levels but often hitching up trunks and larger branches at mid-levels, regularly higher above ground than Ocellated Woodcreeper. Often rummages in palm fronds and dead leaves. **Voice:** Very vocal. Most frequent song, given periodically throughout day (though especially at dawn and dusk), a series of evenly paced, loud, and ringing whistled notes that start slowly and become louder. Also gives a shorter, fast series of "laughing" notes that descend more in pitch, e.g., "wheeyer, wheep-wheep-wheep-wheep-whip," and a doubled "wheeyer, wheeyer." An often-heard call is a loud and descending "kyoow!"

Black-striped Woodcreeper
Xiphorhynchus lachrymosus
Trepatroncos Pinto   Plate 55(18)

24 cm (9½"). A *boldly and handsomely patterned* woodcreeper found in humid forest and borders in *lowlands of far northwest*. Bill black above, gray below. *Head and mantle black, head streaked with pale buff, mantle and scapulars boldly striped with pale buff*; rump and wings rufous, tail rufous-chestnut. Throat pale buff; *underparts boldly streaked pale buff and blackish*, becoming more mottled on belly. **Similar species:** Not likely confused in its restricted Ecuadorian range; cf. much duller Spotted Wood-creeper. **Habits:** Similar to Buff-throated Woodcreeper, though even more likely to forage well above ground, and only rarely in understory. **Voice:** Frequently heard call loud and distinctive, a brief and fast series of 3–4 notes with laughing quality, e.g., "whee-hew-hew." Less often heard is actual song, a rapid and descending whinnying series of at least 10 notes. Another call is an inflected "toooo-ít?" (O. Jahn recording).

Spotted Woodcreeper
Xiphorhynchus erythropygius
Trepatroncos Manchado   Plate 55(19)

Mostly below 1400 m, but up to 2000 m (S)

23 cm (9"). *Numerous in humid forest, secondary woodland, and borders in lowlands and subtropics on w. slope*. Bill black above, pale grayish below. *Above brownish olive*, somewhat duskier on crown (forecrown with a little buff spotting), and with indistinct buff eye-ring and postocular stripe; back with fine and sparse buff streaking; rump, wings, and tail rufous. Throat buff *spotted with dusky; underparts olivaceous boldly spotted with dull buff*. **Similar species:** Olive-backed Woodcreeper occurs only on e. slope. Otherwise not likely confused; cf. Montane Woodcreeper. **Habits:** Found singly or in pairs, often accompanying mixed flocks, hitching up trunks and along larger branches at various levels. **Voice:** Rather vocal, even at times during midday. Most frequent song a far-carrying series of rather high pitched but descending whinnies (each lower pitched than previous) with distinctive reedy quality and drawn-out effect, e.g., "d-d-d-r-rreeuw, d-d-d-r-rreeuw, d-d-d-r-rreeuw," sometimes with 1–2 clipped notes at end. Also gives a sharp descending "jeeu" call.

Olive-backed Woodcreeper
Xiphorhynchus triangularis
Trepatroncos Dorsioliváceo   Plate 55(20)

23 cm (9"). *Foothill and subtropical forest and woodland on e. slope*. Bill blackish above, bluish gray below. *Above brownish olive*, duskier and lightly spotted with yellowish buff on crown, and with indistinct buffy whitish eye-ring and postocular stripe; wings and tail rufous. *Throat dull buff pro-*

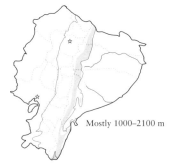

Mostly 1000–2100 m

minently scaled with dusky; underparts olivaceous boldly spotted with buffy whitish. **Similar species:** Spotted Woodcreeper occurs only in west. The rare Long-tailed Woodcreeper is much more rufescent overall, more slender and longer-tailed, and lacks such extensive spotting below. Cf. Montane Woodcreeper. **Habits:** Similar to Spotted Woodcreeper, though Olive-backed seems quieter. **Voice:** Call a rather sharp and piercing, strongly downslurred "keeeyur," at times interspersed with a run-together series of semimusical notes (M. Lysinger recording).

Lepidocolaptes Woodcreepers

Midsized woodcreepers with distinctive slender and slightly decurved bills.

Streak-headed Woodcreeper
Lepidocolaptes souleyetii

Trepatroncos Cabecirraydo   Plate 55(22)

20 cm (8″). Widespread in deciduous and semihumid forest, woodland, and borders as well as plantations and locally even in arid scrub in lowlands and foothills of west. Bill rather long, slender, and decurved, pale grayish horn. Rufescent brown above, crown

Mostly below 800 m, but locally up to 1800 m in Loja

and nape duskier with distinct buff streaking, and with fairly prominent broken whitish superciliary and streaking on sides of head; rump, wings, and tail rufous. Throat buffy whitish; underparts brown with broad black-edged buffy whitish streaking. **Similar species:** Montane Woodcreeper—a highland bird that only marginally overlaps with Streak-headed—is spotted (not streaked) on crown, and streaking on its underparts is distinctly narrower and "crisper." Otherwise there is no other woodcreeper in west with such a slender, decurved bill. **Habits:** Forages singly or in pairs, mainly on trunks and larger limbs (often their undersides), ranging more often in semiopen than most other woodcreepers; can be confiding. Sometimes even feeds on columns of cactus. **Voice:** Song a clear musical descending trill that lasts 1.5–3 seconds. Call a short "trrew, trrew."

Montane Woodcreeper
Lepidocolaptes lacrymiger

Trepatroncos Montano   Plate 55(23)

20 cm (8″). Widespread in subtropical and temperate forest and borders on both slopes.

Mostly 1500–3000 m

Formerly considered conspecific with Spot-crowned Woodcreeper (L. affinis) of Middle America. Bill slender and decurved, dark horn to grayish. Rufescent brown above, crown duskier with distinct buff spotting and broken whitish superciliary and streaking on sides of head; rump, wings, and tail rufous. Throat whitish, feathers scaled and edged black; underparts brown with bold black-edged buffy whitish streaking. **Similar species:** The slender decurved bill shape in this species' highland range is normally distinctive; other sympatric woodcreepers have heavier and straighter bills. Tyrannine

Woodcreeper larger, plainer, and unstreaked; Olive-backed Woodcreeper dull and olivaceous with spotting below. Cf. also superficially similar Pearled Treerunner; its short bill is, however, distinctly different, and it is much brighter rufous above with a bold white brow. **Habits:** Forages in typical woodcreeper fashion, hitching up trunks and along larger limbs (most often on their underside), probing into crevices and clumps of moss. Frequently accompanies mixed flocks. Generally remains at moderate heights or higher, rarely close to ground. **Voice:** Song an accelerating series of downslurred whistled notes with distinctive quality and rhythm, e.g., "tseu-tseu, tsip-tsip, tsee-tsee-tsee-tsee-tsee," vaguely fruiteater-like in quality.

Lineated Woodcreeper
Lepidocolaptes albolineatus
Trepatroncos Lineado   Plate 55(21)

Mainly below 600 m

19 cm (7½"). Scarce in *canopy and mid-levels of terra firme forest* in *lowlands of east. Bill slender and decurved*, pinkish horn to brownish. Above uniform brown, *including crown (which has no streaks or spots)*; rump, wings, and tail rufous. Throat buffy whitish; underparts brown with *conspicuous crisp black-edged buff to whitish streaking*. **Similar species:** The only *Lepidocolaptes* in e. lowlands, and as such readily identified on basis of distinctive bill shape. Striped is most similar of *Xiphorhynchus* woodcreepers, but its bill is heavier and less decurved, and it shows streaking on head and back as well as broader blurrier streaking below; it favors várzea forest, never ranging into terra firme canopy. **Habits:** Usually remains well above ground (where easily overlooked), hitching up larger branches or on upper trunks.

Regularly accompanies mixed flocks. **Voice:** Pretty song a soft series of notes with becard-like quality that gradually drops in pitch and speeds up, e.g., "ti, ti, ti-ti-tee-tee-teh-teh-tutututututu."

Campylorhamphus Scythebills
Although scythebills are easily recognized as a group by their *striking long and decurved bills*, identification to the species level can be problematic. Note that despite their English names, *they cannot be distinguished on the basis of bill color or shape*. The Red-billed is easily the most numerous and widespread species in Ecuador. They range inside humid or montane forest.

Greater Scythebill
Campylorhamphus pucherani
Picoguadaña Grande   Plate 54(20)

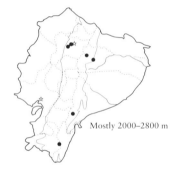

Mostly 2000–2800 m

29 cm (11½"). *Very rare* in *upper subtropical and temperate forest and borders* on both slopes (in west known only from Pichincha). *By far the largest scythebill*, recognizable on that basis alone. *Bill long (6.5 cm; 2½") and strikingly decurved*, mostly dull pinkish horn. *Essentially uniform rufescent brown* with *narrow white superciliary and somewhat broader malar streak* and faint narrow buff streaking on head and neck; wings and tail rufous. **Similar species:** Other scythebills are smaller, have proportionately longer bills, and are more streaked; none occurs at elevations as high as this species (Brown-billed coming closest). Strong-billed Woodcreeepr has darker and more massive bill and shows prominent breast streaking. **Habits:** An enigmatic and rare bird, still poorly known. On very infrequent occasions solitary birds have been seen accompanying large mixed flocks,

hitching up the trunks of larger trees. **Voice:** Song a rather weak and nasal, ascending "ee-ee-ee-ee-ee-énh" (G. Rosenberg recording), very different from other scythebills.

Red-billed Scythebill
Campylorhamphus trochilirostris
Picoguadaña Piquirrojo Plate 54(17)

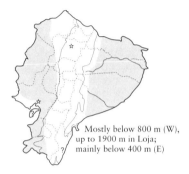

Mostly below 800 m (W), up to 1900 m in Loja; mainly below 400 m (E)

23.5–24 cm (9¼–9½"). Uncommon in humid and (locally) deciduous forest and woodland in *lowlands and lower subtropics in west*; rare in humid forest and woodland in *lowlands of east*. Bill very long (6.5–7.5 cm; 2½–3") *and decurved*, slightly shorter in east, brownish to reddish brown (not very "red"). Brown above, somewhat duskier on crown, with head and back narrowly but prominently streaked with buff; rump, wings, and tail rufous-chestnut. Throat whitish, feathers scaled dusky; underparts brown to rufescent brown with blackish-edged buff streaking on breast and upper belly. **Similar species:** Brown-billed Scythebill favors more humid and montane situations (it and Red-billed are not known to occur together, though they come close); it differs in being darker and less streaked generally with throat buff (not whitish). *Their bill colors do not appreciably differ.* Cf. also very similar, but range-restricted, Curve-billed Scythebill. **Habits:** Despite its spectacular long and sickle-shaped bill, Red-billed Scythebill usually feeds much like other woodcreepers, hitching up trunks and out along larger lateral branches, pausing to probe into bark crevices and into moss and epiphytic plants. One or two often accompany mixed flocks. **Voice:** Song a series of quite musical notes that have rather an antbird-like quality, variable in phraseology,

e.g., a descending and gradually slowing down series of upslurred notes, e.g., "tuwee-tuwee-toowa-tew-tew," sometimes with trill at start. Agitated birds also give a loud semi-musical chipper.

Curve-billed Scythebill
Campylorhamphus procurvoides
Picoguadaña Piquicurvo Plate 54(18)

Below 250 m

23 cm (9"). *Very rare and local in terra firme forest in lowlands of northeast* (Cuyabeno). *Closely resembles Red-billed Scythebill*, which is slightly larger. Bill length similar, as is color (which is somewhat variable in both species). Curve-billed differs primarily in having *back essentially unstreaked* (but beware certain Red-billeds on which back streaking is faint or virtually lacking). Curve-billed is more olivaceous (less rufescent) brown below, and its streaking there is less extensive; in the hand these streaks can be seen to lack faint blackish edging seen in Red-billed. Many birds are probably not safely identified in field, and indeed what appear to be Red-billed Scythebills have been seen to respond to tape recordings of Curve-billeds. **Habits:** As in Red-billed Scythebill. **Voice:** Similar to Red-billed Scythebill, but songs elsewhere tend to be more evenly pitched or ascending (not sliding down) and to be introduced by a single longer note.

Brown-billed Scythebill
Campylorhamphus pusillus
Picoguadaña Piquipardo Plate 54(19)

23.5–24 cm (9¼–9½"). *Foothill and lower subtropical forest* on both slopes, *strictly where conditions are humid* (unlike Red-billed). *Bill very long* (6.5 cm; 2½") *and decurved*, dull reddish brown to dusky-

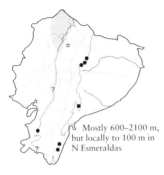

Mostly 600–2100 m, but locally to 100 m in N Esmeraldas

brown. Dark brown above, duskier on crown, with head narrowly streaked buff (can look somewhat spotted), back sparsely streaked deep buff; rump, wings, and tail rufous-chestnut. Throat buff; underparts dark brown with sparse buff streaking. **Similar species:** Red-billed Scythebill has somewhat more extensive streaking above and below and more whitish (not so buff) throat. **Habits:** Much as in Red-billed Scythebill. Often probes into moss. **Voice:** Sweet but variable song has tremulous quality; it consists of a fast series of "tuwee" and "teeur" notes that either rise or fall in pitch and are often intermixed with trills, e.g., "teeurrrrr, teeur-teeur-tututu-tututu."

Typical Antbirds: Thamnophilidae (94)

A large and complex group of small to mid-sized passerine birds whose name ("antbird") is derived from the fact that some of the first species seen and described by naturalists habitually follow swarms of army ants. Despite the fact that none actually eats ants (except by mistake; rather, they capture insects and other animals attempting to flee the ants), the name has stuck. Certain other groups were named (e.g., antshrikes, antvireos, antwrens) for their supposed similarity to other birds more familiar to the individuals naming them; these names too have stuck. Exclusively Neotropical in distribution, antbirds range in a variety of mainly lowland habitats, with *species diversity being greatest in Amazonian forests*; relatively few occur on Andean slopes. Recent research has demonstrated that what was once considered an even larger and more diverse family of antbirds (Formicariidae) is better divided, into the mainly arboreal and gleaning Thamnophilidae (Typical Antbirds; note that

a few species *are* mainly terrestrial) and the almost entirely terrestrial Formicariidae (Antthrushes and Antpittas, or "ground" antbirds).

A large majority of typical antbirds show *sexual dimorphism* in plumage. Shades of gray, black, and white predominate in males, brown, buff, and rufous in females. All have *hooked bills*, markedly so in some species. Many *habitually join the mixed flocks* that are so typical of lowland forests and woodlands. As they tend to be shy, and to favor dense growth, most typical antbirds are inconspicuous and difficult to see, with many species being heard far more often than seen; it is thus important to learn their *often distinctive voices*.

Fasciated Antshrike, *Cymbilaimus lineatus*
Batará Lineado   Plate 60(1)

To 1000 m

17–18 cm (6¾–7″). Widespread in *tangled borders of humid forest and secondary woodland in lowlands* of east and west, a few up into foothills. *Heavy hooked bill*, base of lower mandible pale; *iris bright red.* ♂ *black above narrowly barred with white* with crown essentially solid black (with variable amount of white barring in birds *west of Andes*). *Below narrowly barred black and white.* ♀ *blackish above narrowly barred with pale buff* except for *unmarked rufous-chestnut crown*, forehead barred buff and black. *Below buff narrowly barred with black.* **Similar species:** Much more of a forest bird than any of the "barred" *Thamnophilus* antshrikes. In east, cf. much scarcer and larger Undulated Antshrike. **Habits:** Favors borders and tangled openings such as around treefalls where pairs forage deliberately at low and (especially) middle levels. Generally remains within dense cover and hard to see, though frequently heard; sometimes one or two accompany mixed understory flocks. **Voice:** Song a series of 6–8 steadily repeated, soft whistles with ventriloquial and plaintive quality, "cü-ü, cü-ü, cü-ü . . . ," the first gradually higher in pitch. Calls include a complaining "teeeou"; also gives stacatto chattering calls.

Undulated Antshrike, *Frederickena unduligera*
Batará Ondulado   Plate 60(2)

To 700 m

23 cm (9″). A *large* and slightly crested antshrike, *rare and apparently local in undergrowth inside terra firme forest in lowlands of east*. Bill *very heavy and hooked*, lower mandible bluish at base. Iris brown to amber or orange-brown. ♂ *black with very narrow wavy grayish white barring* (the "undulations") except for solid black throat and upper chest. ♀ *above evenly barred rufous-buff and black* (with wavy pattern as in ♂), more solidly rufous-chestnut on crown; tail black barred with gray. *Below rich rufous-buff with narrow wavy black barring.* Immature ♂♂, black with variable amount of rufous-buff to white wavy barring, seem relatively frequent. **Similar species:** Larger than any other sympatric antshrike. Cf. especially smaller Fasciated Antshrike, both sexes of which are not so dark overall and have *red eyes* and *more even* (not so wavy) barring. **Habits:** Skulking, usually found singly or in pairs, favoring areas with dense tangled growth such as what springs up around treefalls. Much less often encountered than most other antshrikes in e. lowlands. Generally does

not accompany mixed flocks, and does not seem as vocal as many other antbirds. **Voice:** ♂'s song a steadily repeated series of whistled notes, "uué, uué, uué . . . ," somewhat reminiscent of Fasciated Antshrike but higher pitched and considerably faster. Singing birds sometimes raise and lower crest while singing. Call, given by both sexes, a rather nasal "squehhh"; also gives a long, high-pitched, and descending "keeeeeeeeyur" (J. Moore recording).

Great Antshrike, *Taraba major*
Batará Mayor   Plate 60(3)

Mostly below 1000 m, higher in Loja

20 cm (8″). A *bicolored* antshrike, *widespread in undergrowth of clearings, secondary woodland, and forest borders in lowlands of east and west*, in southwest also up into lower subtropics. In west occurs in both humid and deciduous situations. Heavy hooked bill blackish; *iris bright red*. Slight shaggy crest, somewhat expressive. ♂ *black above* with white wing-bars; *white below*, tinged grayish on flanks and crissum. ♀ similarly patterned, but *rufous replaces ♂'s black*, flanks and crissum tinged buff; wings have no white. **Similar species:** Nearly unmistakable, no other antshrike being as boldly black (or rufous) and white. **Habits:** Usually in pairs that hop through thick undergrowth where—though not particularly shy—they are usually hard to see because it is so dense. Sometimes accompany mixed flocks. Heard much more often than seen. **Voice:** Song an accelerating series of hoots ending with a bouncing-ball effect, somewhat trogon-like aside from distinctive snarled "nyaah" ending. Call a gravelly "chrr-krr-krr-krr-krr" (P. Coopmans).

Collared Antshrike, *Sakesphorus bernardi*
Batará Collarejo   Plate 60(4)

Mostly below 1500 m

16.5–17 cm (6½–6¾"). *Common and—for an antshrike—conspicuous in lower growth of deciduous woodland and forest, shrubby second-growth, and even desert scrub in lowlands of southwest,* in El Oro and Loja also up into subtropics. *Avoids* humid regions. *Almost continually wags tail* and has *expressive bushy crest.* Blackish hooked bill, paler at base of lower mandible; iris dark brown. ♂ has *head, throat, and midchest black* with some white scaling on face and throat; *nuchal collar, sides of chest, and lower underparts contrastingly white.* Back brown to rufous brown; wings dusky with white spotting on coverts, two white wing-bars, and white and rufous flight-feather edging; tail black, feathers tipped white. ♀ *lacks* ♂*'s black foreparts:* crown rufous with buffyish forehead, *sides of head black speckled white, contrasting with ochraceous buff nuchal collar and underparts.* Back rufous brown; wings dusky with buff spotting on coverts, two buff to whitish wing-bars, and rufous flight-feather edging; *tail rufous.* **Similar species:** This engaging and attractive antshrike is distinctive in range. In the Loja highlands, cf. ♀ Chapman's Antshrike. **Habits:** Bold and— mainly as a result of its relatively open habitat—easily observed. Occurs mainly in pairs that forage in lower and (less often) middle growth. Sometimes accompany loose mixed flocks. **Voice:** Most frequent song a distinctive "ánk, ar-r-r-r-r"; both sexes gave an "ank," sometimes repeated slowly, also other calls.

Thamnophilus Antshrikes
A diverse group of midsized antbirds with *hooked bills* found primarily in lower growth of lowland forests; a few species range in more open and deciduous habitats, and one (Uniform) in montane areas. The first three species show *at least some barring* (prominent especially in males), whereas in the others males are *predominantly black or gray* with females usually *some shade of rufous or chestnut to brown.* Notably vocal, all antshrikes are heard more often than seen, and voice is often helpful in identification.

Lined Antshrike, *Thamnophilus tenuepunctatus*
Batará Listado   Plate 60(7)

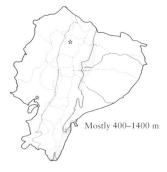

Mostly 400–1400 m

16.5 cm (6½"). Quite numerous in shrubby clearings, secondary woodland, and forest borders in *foothills and lower subtropics on e. slope;* does not range far east out onto lowlands. Now usually considered a separate species from Chestnut-backed Antshrike (*T. palliatus*) of s. Amazonia and e. Brazil. Expressive loose crest. Iris yellow. ♂ *black above with narrow white barring,* except that crown is solid black. *Below evenly barred black and white,* except streaked on throat. ♀ *bright rufous-chestnut above* except *sides of head and hindneck streaked black and white. Below evenly barred black and white* aside from throat, which is streaked; flanks tinged buff. **Similar species:** ♂ resembles ♂ Barred Antshrike but is blacker generally with only very narrow white barring above; ♀♀ differ markedly. The two species do not occur together in Ecuador. **Habits:** Ranges in pairs that tend to skulk in vegetation but are very vocal. Generally do not accompany mixed flocks, at least not for long. **Voice:** Frequently heard song, given by both sexes (♀ echoing ♂'s louder effort), a fast accelerating series of nasal notes with strongly emphasized and lower-pitched final note, "hah-hah-ha-ha-hahahahahahaha-hánh." Also gives several other growling or guttural calls including a short nasal "nah!"

Barred Antshrike, *Thamnophilus doliatus*
Batará Barreteado   Plate 60(5)

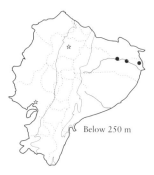

Below 250 m

Mostly 800–2000 m

16–16.5 cm (6¼–6½"). *Local in dense thickets on islands in Ríos Napo and Aguarico in lowlands of northeast.* Expressive loose crest. Iris yellow. ♂ *above black coarsely barred with white* aside from all-black crown (semiconcealed white shows when bird is excited); sides of head and hindneck more streaked. *Below white evenly barred with black* aside from more streaked throat. ♀ *bright cinnamon-rufous above,* crown somewhat darker; *sides of head and hindneck streaked buffy whitish and black. Below uniform deep ochraceous buff.* **Similar species:** Easily recognized in its limited range and habitat. Lined Antshrike does not occur in e. lowlands. **Habits:** A familiar bird elsewhere in Neotropics, in Ecuador the Barred Antshrike is of very limited distribution and not very numerous. Occurs in pairs that usually remain concealed inside thick vegetation. **Voice:** Similar to Lined Antshrike's, though song falls in pitch toward end (except for emphasized final note).

Chapman's Antshrike, *Thamnophilus zarumae*
Batará de Chapman   Plate 60(6)

15.5 cm (6"). Undergrowth of secondary woodland, overgrown clearings, and borders of semihumid and montane forest in *foothills and subtropical zone of southwest in e. El Oro and much of Loja.* Formerly sometimes considered conspecific with Barred Antshrike, of which it is essentially a *pallid* version. ♂ above much like ♂ Barred Antshrike but back mixed with gray and some buff on rump. *Black barring below faint and restricted to breast; flanks and lower belly buff.* ♀ differs from ♀ Barred in having grayer sides of head and hindneck, and is *nowhere near as deep ochraceous-buff below*; it also has *faint dusky speckling on throat and breast.* **Similar species:** Collared is only other antshrike occurring with Chapman's. ♂ Collared very different; ♀ Collared has bold spotting and streaking on wings (wings plain in ♀ Chapman's), brighter underparts, etc. Fasciated Wren has vaguely similar pattern but very different shape, etc. **Habits:** Similar to Lined and Barred Antshrikes, though given the more open nature of its habitats, Chapman's is usually easier to see. **Voice:** Song a fast series of at least 8–10 "chup" notes that end with several distinctly higher-pitched and more nasal notes. Thus song is rather different from Lined and Barred Antshrikes, being obviously two-parted and lacking their characteristic final accented note. Calls include a nasal "nah" like Lined Antshrike.

Cocha Antshrike, *Thamnophilus praecox*
Batará de Cocha   Plate 60(8)

16 cm (6¼"). Local in lower growth of várzea forest, *principally in thickets along small blackwater streams,* in *lowlands of northeast.* ♂ *entirely deep black;* underwing-coverts white (but this normally not visible in field). ♀

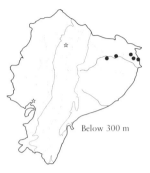

Below 300 m

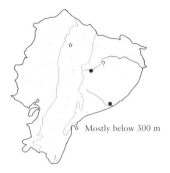

Mostly below 300 m

has *head, throat, and chest black* with faint white shaft streaks on throat in some individuals. *Above otherwise bright cinnamon-rufous; lower underparts somewhat paler cinnamon-rufous.* **Similar species:** Both sexes uncannily resemble respective sexes of much more common White-shouldered Antbird; the antbird is larger, and both sexes show some bare blue skin around eyes (lacking in antshrike). ♂ White-shouldered—also black—differs further in having white at bend of wing (this usually apparent, and never shown by ♂ Cocha). ♀ White-shouldered has much the same color pattern as ♀ Cocha but is somewhat less brightly colored overall. **Habits:** Usually in pairs, foraging in dense tangles where generally hard to see; rarely noted unless vocalizing, and ♂♂ seen more often. Moves close to water, favoring terrain that is flooded much of year; though sometimes accompanied by other antbirds such as the Black-chinned, generally does not accompany mixed flocks. **Voice:** ♂'s song a hollow, evenly paced "ko-ko-ko-ko-ko-ko-ko-ko-ko-ko," given as it perches motionless aside from its vibrating, often partially spread tail; ♀ sometimes follows with a slightly higher-pitched, shorter version of same song. Both sexes also give a mellow "pwow-pwow" and a more trilled "krrrrrr" call. Curiously, and unlike most antbirds, it does not seem to vocalize much before midmorning.

Castelnau's Antshrike
Thamnophilus cryptoleucus
Batará de Castelnau   Plate 60(9)

17–18 cm (6³/₄–7"). *Lower and middle growth of riparian forest and more mature woodland found on river islands in lowlands of east.* A *large, heavy-billed* antshrike. ♂

entirely deep lustrous black with semiconcealed white dorsal patch (exposed mainly when excited); *outer scapulars, bend of wing, and wing-coverts tipped white with fringed effect.* ♀ similar but *lacks* white on closed wing, though like ♂ it has white dorsal patch and underwing-coverts. **Similar species:** Will probably not be mistaken in its limited habitat, being *strictly confined to river islands.* The all-black ♀ Castelnau's is more apt to be confusing than ♂ (with its obvious white wing-fringing): cf. ♂ White-shouldered Antbird (which shows some bare blue skin around eye and white at bend of wing) and ♂ Cocha Antshrike (which occurs in different microhabitat and has smaller bill). ♂ White-shouldered Antshrike is strictly confined to terra firme forest. **Habits:** Usually in pairs that forage deliberately inside better-developed riparian woodland on some river islands (those supporting only early-succesion habitats do not have this species), often slowly wagging tail. Does not seem to join flocks. **Voice:** ♂'s song a short, fast, accelerating "keoh, keoh, kuh-kuh-kuhkuhkuhkuhkuh" with nasal, bouncing-ball quality. Both sexes also give a drawn-out "kawh" call note, sometimes doubled or in a slow series; also a "kowah, kr-r-r-r."

White-shouldered Antshrike
Thamnophilus aethiops
Batará Hombriblanco   Plate 60(10)

15.5–16 cm (6–6¹/₄"). *Scarce and local in undergrowth inside terra firme and foothill forest on e. slope,* not ranging far out into e. lowlands. Bill heavy; *iris red (♂) or reddish brown (♀).* ♂ *uniform lustrous black,* relieved only by a few small white spots on wing-coverts and some white on bend of

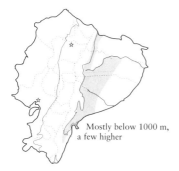

Mostly below 1000 m, a few higher

wing and underwing-coverts. ♀ *uniform rufous-chestnut*, somewhat richer above, somewhat paler below. **Similar species:** Plain-winged Antshrike is smaller with slighter bill; ♂ is uniform gray (not black), ♀ nowhere near as richly colored as ♀ White-shouldered. **Habits:** An inconspicuous and generally infrequently encountered antshrike that favors dense shady tangled areas, where it appears to be quite sedentary, rarely following mixed flocks for long. **Voice:** ♂'s distinctive song a series of evenly and slowly delivered nasal notes, "anh . . . anh . . . anh . . . anh . . . anh" (about one "anh"/ second) almost with effect of Barred Forest-Falcon (though faster). Call, given by both sexes, a slurred "keyurr."

Uniform Antshrike, *Thamnophilus unicolor*
Batará Unicolor   Plate 60(11)

Mostly 1000–2000 m

15.5–16 cm (6–6¼″). *Uncommon in lower growth inside foothill and subtropical forest on both slopes*; more numerous in west, on e. slope known only from southeast. *Iris gray. ♂ uniform slaty gray.* ♀ rufous brown above, somewhat brighter on crown, which *contrasts with gray face and chin.* Below

uniform ochraceous brown. **Similar species:** Nothing really similar in its *montane* range. Smaller Plain-winged Antshrike occurs in e. lowlands, overlapping only slightly with Uniform; Plain-winged differs in iris color (reddish in both sexes), and in everywhere but extreme south ♂ Plain-winged has fairly obvious black crown. Cf. also White-streaked and very rare Bicolored Antvireos. **Habits:** Like so many other antshrikes, Unicolored mainly occurs in pairs; it tends to be sluggish and inconspicuous in forest undergrowth, generally not following mixed flocks. **Voice:** Rather soft song a simple short series of nasal notes, each note sometimes with rising inflection, "anh, anh, anh, anh" (sometimes 3 or 5 notes). Both sexes give a rattled "kar'r'r'r" call as well.

Plain-winged Antshrike
Thamnophilus schistaceus
Batará Alillano   Plate 60(12)

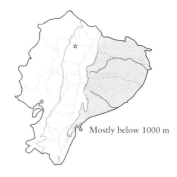

Mostly below 1000 m

14 cm (5½″). *Widespread and numerous in lower and middle growth inside humid forest, especially terra firme, in lowlands of east* (smaller numbers up into foothills), where one of the more common antshrikes. Formerly often called Black-capped Antshrike. *Iris reddish brown to red.* ♂ uniform gray, slightly paler below; in most of its Ecuadorian range shows a *fairly contrasting black crown*, but around Zamora black much less apparent. ♀ olivaceous brown above, somewhat grayer on face and more rufescent on wings and tail; fairly contrasting *rufous crown.* Below uniform drab olivaceous buff. **Similar species:** Both sexes (especially ♀ ♀) resemble Mouse-colored Antshrike, with which locally sympatric in terra firme. Both sexes of Mouse-colored

differ in their gray to pale hazel iris; ♂ differs in having white tipping on wing-coverts (wings plain in Plain-winged), whereas ♀ is whiter below (lacking Plain-winged's ochraceous or buff tone). Especially in south, cf. also ♂ Cinereous Antshrike. **Habits:** Usually found in pairs that hop in tangled lower and middle growth, somewhat lethargic and often quite unsuspicious, allowing a close approach. Though sometimes joining a mixed flock, they usually forage independently. In some areas a pair of Mouse-coloreds may be close by. Heard more often than seen. **Voice:** ♂'s far-carrying song is one of the more frequently heard bird vocalizations in Amaz. forests, and often continues at intervals through middle of day, when most other birds have fallen silent. ♂'s song a series of rapidly uttered nasal notes, "anh-anh-anh-anh-anh-anh-anh-anhanh," with distinctive doubled (and lower-pitched) note at end; sometimes ♀ chimes in, midway through ♂, with her higher-pitched and briefer version. Number of notes and speed of delivery vary, causing potential confusion with Mouse-colored Antshrike. Both sexes, but mainly ♂, also give a slow "arr . . . arr . . . arr . . ." with barking effect quite like Barred Forest-Falcon. Also often gives a nasal "nyeenh."

Mouse-colored Antshrike
Thamnophilus murinus
Batará Murino   Plate 60(13)

To 450 m

14 cm (5½"). Uncommon in lower and middle growth inside terra firme forest in lowlands of east, especially in areas with some relief, *mainly or entirely south of Río Napo. Iris gray to pale hazel. Both sexes resemble more numerous Plain-winged Antshrike*, but differ in eye color (red or

reddish in Plain-winged). ♂ further differs in having *narrow white tipping on wing-coverts* and whiter median belly. ♀ differs in its marginally less rufous crown, and *whiter median lower underparts* (in ♀ Plain-winged, this area decidedly more buff or ochraceous). **Habits:** Similar to Plain-winged Antshrike, and the two species regularly occur in close proximity (though rarely actually together), Mouse-colored favoring better-drained hilly ridges, Plain-winged more in intervening valleys. Mouse-colored seems even less inclined to join mixed flocks. **Voice:** ♂'s song resembles that of Plain-colored but is shorter, higher pitched, and delivered more slowly; some songs, however, especially of excited individuals, can be quite similar. Mouse-colored also gives an abrupt *Micrastur*-like call.

Western Slaty-Antshrike
Thamnophilus atrinucha
Batará Pizarroso Occidental   Plate 60(14)

Mostly below 1100 m

14.5–15 cm (5¾–6"). *Common in lower growth of humid and semideciduous forest and woodland in lowlands and foothills of west.* Formerly considered conspecific with *T. punctatus*, now treated as a complex of species, ranging locally east of Andes in e. South America; species was then simply called Slaty Antshrike. ♂ *gray above* with *black crown,* feathers on face edged black giving a scaly or grizzled look, back mixed black and gray with semiconcealed white dorsal patch. Wings black with *scapulars, wing-coverts, and flight feathers boldly edged and spotted white;* tail and uppertail-coverts black, feathers tipped white. *Below uniform gray.* ♀ olive brown above with dull rufous crown, face with scaly or grizzled look much as in ♂, dorsal patch as in ♂. Wings blackish with *scapulars, wing-coverts, and flight feathers boldly edged and spotted buff*; tail brown, feathers tipped white. Below pale olivaceous buff. **Similar species:** No other *Thamnophilus* occurs in lowlands west of Andes. Cf. ♂ Dusky Antbird. **Habits:** Wide-ranging and often numerous, this antshrike seems capable of persisting in small, degraded, and fragmented forest patches. It is easier to observe than many other *Thamnophilus*, hopping about deliberately in lower growth. Regularly accompanies mixed understory flocks of *Myrmotherula* antwrens, etc., and on occasion even attends swarms of army ants. **Voice:** ♂'s frequently heard song a fast, rolling "anhanhanhanhanhanhanhanhanhánh" with distinctive higher-pitched final note.

Marañón Slaty-Antshrike
Thamnophilus leucogaster
Batará Pizarroso del Marañón   Plate 96(3)

14.5–15 cm (5³/₄–6″). *Apparently rare in lower growth of deciduous woodland in Río Marañón drainage around Zumba.* Formerly considered a race of Slaty or Eastern Slaty-Antshrike (*T. punctatus*); these are now generally regarded as a complex of allospecies. Iris gray. ♂ resembles ♂ of much better known Western Slaty-Antshrike (ranges of the two are widely disjunct) but *lacks scaly or grizzled effect on face*, and *median belly considerably whiter*. ♀ likewise lacks scaly/grizzled effect on face; it differs from ♀ Western Slaty in having *white* wing markings and *much whiter underparts* (lacking any buff tone). **Similar species:** No other antshrike occurs in the very limited Ecuadorian range of this species. **Habits:** Not well known, but

appears to be similar to other *Thamnophilus* antshrikes. Has characteristic habit of frequently wagging or quivering tail. **Voice:** ♂'s song an accelerating series of well-enunciated nasal notes, "anh-anh-anh-anh-ah-ah-ahahah," accompanied by vibrating tail.

Amazonian Antshrike
Thamnophilus amazonicus
Batará Amazónico   Plate 96(2)

14 cm (5½″). *Local in lower growth of black-water várzea woodland in lowlands of far northeast* (Río Lagarto). ♂ gray above with slight admixture of black on back and a semiconcealed white dorsal patch. Wings black with scapulars, wing-coverts, and flight feathers boldly edged and spotted white; tail black, feathers tipped white. Below gray, somewhat paler than upperparts. Pretty ♀ differs dramatically from ♀♀ of other *Thamnophilus*: *head, neck, and underparts orange-rufous*, fading to buff on belly; back and rump contrastingly olive brown; wings and tail as in ♂. **Similar species:** Can normally be known by its very restricted range and habitat; brightly colored ♀ is in any case easily recognized. **Habits:** In its limited Ecuadorian range pairs have been seen primarily in flooded areas, foraging within a few meters of water; elsewhere they have been seen higher up. Seems not to range with mixed flocks (but species diversity is in any case low in its microhabitat). **Voice:** ♂'s song a fast and accelerating series of trogon-like notes with a nasal quality, fading a bit toward end, "kuh, kuh, kuh-kuh-kuh-kuhkuhkuh-kunh," first rising and then descending; ♀ sometimes echoes with her higher-pitched version. Also gives a querulous, nasal "keeunh" call.

Pearly Antshrike, *Megastictus margaritatus*
Batará Perlado   Plate 60(16)

Below 300 m

Mostly below 400 m

13 cm (5¼"). *Rare and local in lower growth inside terra firme forest in lowlands of east.* Iris gray. ♂ *bluish gray above*; wings and tail black, *wing-coverts and tips of tertials with very large round white spots*, uppertail-coverts and tail feathers broadly tipped white. ♀ brown above, somewhat duskier on crown; *wings and tail marked as in ♂, but spotting bright buff.* Below uniform ochraceous-buff, somewhat paler on throat. **Similar species:** Though many other antshrikes have spots on wing-coverts, none has spots anywhere near as large as the Pearly. Note too its tertial spotting, unique among antshrikes. **Habits:** Rarely encountered in Ecuador, this attractive and easily recognized antshrike seems to favor somewhat hilly areas. Usually forages in pairs that do not associate with mixed flocks, hopping from branch to branch and gleaning from leaves. **Voice:** ♂'s unmistakable song distinctly two-parted: several querulous notes followed by a fast series of lower-pitched and more raspy notes, e.g., "whee? whee? whee? jrr-jrr-jrr-jrr-jrr-jrr."

Spot-winged Antshrike, *Pygiptila stellaris*
Batará Alimoteado   Plate 60(15)

13.5 cm (5¼"). A *very short-tailed*, bull-headed antshrike found in *mid-levels and subcanopy* of humid forest and woodland in *lowlands of east.* Bill *notably heavy for size of bird.* ♂ mainly gray above with *black crown* and some black intermixed with gray on back and a semiconcealed white dorsal patch; wing-coverts with *small but conspicuous white spots.* Below uniform gray, somewhat

paler than upperparts. ♀ gray above with *wings contrastingly rufous brown* (with no spots). Foreface, sides of neck, and underparts uniform pale dull ochraceous. **Similar species:** This *arboreal* antshrike is often best recognized by its stocky and short-tailed shape; ♂ is further known by wing spots, ♀ by plain rufescent brown wings. **Habits:** Favors viny tangles, often quite high above ground. Usually ranges in pairs that often accompany mixed flocks of various birds, frequently foraging in terminal branches making it comparatively easy to see. **Voice:** ♂'s distinctive but brief song a sharp and piercing "t-t-t-t-t-t-teéuw" repeated at several-second intervals. Calls include a sharp "chet!," sometimes followed by a "keeeuw." Excited birds give a repeated querulous "tu-di-dit?" (from one member of pair) and a fast raspy "kr-kr-kr-kr-kr-kr-krrreeet-kr-kr," (from the other; P. Coopmans).

Russet Antshrike, *Thamnistes anabatinus*
Batará Rojizo   Plate 60(19)

14.5 cm (5¾"). An *arboreal* antshrike found in *foothill and lower subtropical forest and forest borders on both slopes*, and locally on

Mostly 400–1300 m, lower in Esmeraldas

coastal cordillera. *Heavy hooked bill.* **Sexes alike**, aside from ♂'s semiconcealed orange-rufous dorsal patch. Above rufescent brown (**west slope**) to olivaceous brown (**east slope**) with *yellowish buff superciliary*; wings and tail rufous. Throat and chest ochraceous, lower underparts dull olivaceous. **Similar species:** Overall coloration and pattern more resemble a *Philydor* foliage-gleaner than most antshrikes. Cf. especially Buff-fronted and Rufous-rumped, the two *Philydor* most likely to be found with it; Russet has heavier bill and shorter tail. Of the antshrikes, ♀ Spot-winged is most similar, but it occurs exclusively in e. lowlands (at most limited overlap with Russet). **Habits:** Found singly or in pairs, foraging at various levels though tending to move higher than most other antshrikes. Frequently accompanies mixed flocks comprising various arboreal birds, foraging quite actively, inspecting branches, limbs, and vine tangles, peering at leaves and also sometimes probing clusters of dead leaves. **Voice:** Infrequently heard song a rather loud and penetrating "teeeu, tseu!-tseu!-tseu!-tseu!," sometimes given repeatedly; pace faster on e. than on w. slope. Call a much thinner and more sibilant "wee-tsip."

Dysithamnus Antvireos

Small, chunky, and short-tailed antbirds found in lower growth of humid and montane forest, one species (Plain) also ranging into more deciduous situations. Unusual among the antbirds, no antvireo is found in Amazonian lowlands. Antvireos are larger and heavier-billed than *Myrmotherula* antwrens, and they are shorter tailed than *Thamnophilus* antshrikes (which they resemble in their sluggish foraging behavior).

Plain Antvireo, *Dysithamnus mentalis*
Batarito Cabecigris   Plate 61(1)

11.5 cm (4½"). *Common and widespread in lower growth of remaining humid and deciduous forest and woodland in lowlands and foothills of west; less numerous in foothill and lower subtropical forest on e. slope.* In **west-slope birds**, ♂ olive grayish above, grayest on head and neck and with *contrasting dusky auriculars*; wing-coverts very narrowly tipped whitish. Throat grayish white,

To 1500 m (W slope);
700–1700 m (E slope)

breast gray, *belly pale yellow* suffused with olive on flanks. ♀ like ♂ above but with *contrasting rufous crown* and whitish eye-ring. Below much like ♂, but breast more clouded with olive. On **east slope**, ♂ differs in being more uniformly gray above and more grayish below (lacking yellow), only a tinge of olive on lower flanks. ♀ more brownish olive above with less contrasting auriculars, and drab buffy-olive below (lacking yellow). **Similar species:** This chunky antvireo is an important bird to learn well, especially in the west where it can be so numerous. Both sexes' contrasting dusky auriculars are a good mark, as is ♀'s rufous on crown; no other similar-looking antbird shows either character. *Myrmotherula* antwrens, which regularly forage with this species, are smaller and more active; *Thamnophilus* antshrikes are larger and longer-tailed. **Habits:** Most often in pairs, foraging rather lethargically in lower growth, often perching quietly and peering about for protracted periods. Often accompanies understory flocks. **Voice:** ♂'s song a brief series of rapidly repeated semimusical notes that accelerate into a descending roll with almost a bouncing-ball effect. Both sexes frequently give a soft "ert" call, sometimes interminably repeated at 1- to 2-second intervals; also a more abrupt and nasal "nyah."

Spot-crowned Antvireo
Dysithamnus puncticeps
Batarito Coronipunteado   Plate 61(2)

11.5 cm (4½"). *Lower growth inside humid forest in lowlands and foothills of northwest,* now mainly in Esmeraldas. *Iris pale gray.* ♂ *gray above, crown vaguely streaked with black*; wing-coverts tipped white. Whitish

To 800 m

below, *throat and breast with blurry gray streaking*, sides more mottled with gray, lower belly tinged yellowish. ♀ olive brown above, *crown vaguely streaked dusky and dull rufous*; wing-coverts tipped buff. *Below pale buffy ochraceous*, with *blurry dusky streaking on throat and chest*, flanks more olivaceous. **Similar species:** Plain Antvireo basically replaces this species southward (the two have never actually been found in same forest, though they come close). Both sexes of Plain differ in their dark eyes, dusky auriculars, a plain crown that lacks streaks, and underparts without streaking. **Habits:** Much as in Plain Antvireo. **Voice:** ♂'s song a rather long series of soft notes, longer and with faster but more even cadence and less abrupt delivery than Plain Antvireo. Also gives a descending trill (P. Coopmans).

White-streaked Antvireo
Dysithamnus leucostictus
Batarito Albirrayado   Plate 60(20)

12.5 cm (5"). *Uncommon and local in lower growth inside subtropical forest on e. slope.* Formerly considered conspecific with *D. plumbeus* (Plumbeous Antvireo) of se. Brazil. ♂ *uniform slaty gray*, slightly blacker on

Mostly 1300–1800 m

crown and chest, with semiconcealed white dorsal patch; bend of wing white, wing-coverts with small white spots. ♀ *uniform rufous brown above* aside from *rufous crown. Sides of head and neck and entire underparts gray boldly streaked with white.* **Similar species:** Cf. rare Bicolored Antvireo (mainly ranging at higher elevations). ♀ White-streaked is more easily recognized than its blackish mate. Compared to latter, ♂ Plain Antvireo is smaller and not so black, has contrasting dark auriculars, etc.; the two species can occur together. ♂ Uniform Antshrike is larger and more uniform gray (showing no black); it has pale iris. **Habits:** Usually found in pairs, gleaning quietly and methodically in lower growth, most often accompanying mixed flocks of understory birds. **Voice:** ♂'s song a well-enunciated and descending series of 7–8 soft whistled notes.

Bicolored Antvireo, *Dysithamnus occidentalis*
Batarito Bicolor   Plate 96(4)

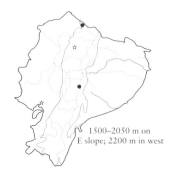

1500–2050 m on E slope; 2200 m in west

13.5 cm (5½"). *Rare, local, and poorly known in lower growth inside subtropical forest and woodland on e. slope* (mainly w. Napo); *also a recent record from w. slope in extreme north.* Formerly called Western Antshrike and placed in genus *Thamnomanes.* ♂ *uniform sooty*, slightly paler below and with semiconcealed white dorsal patch; wing-coverts with small white spots, primaries edged browner. ♀ has *chestnut crown; upperparts otherwise dark chestnut brown*; wing-coverts with small buffy whitish spots. *Sides of head and underparts dull gray with sparse whitish shaft streaks, especially on throat; lower belly umber brown.* **Similar species:** ♂ White-streaked Antvireo, aside from its smaller size, is quite similar though showing more contrast between black bib and gray belly; ♀♀ of the two species are, however, quite different, White-streaked being much more prominently streaked below and brighter and paler rufous above. White-streaked tends to occur at lower elevations, though there is a little overlap. Cf. also ♂ White-shouldered Antshrike (larger, with red iris, etc.). **Habits:** Found singly or in pairs, usually moving about independent of mixed flocks and gleaning much like other antvireos. **Voice:** Most common call a distinctive fast throaty scold, "jeér-deer-dur"; also heard are clear "peeu" calls and (M. Lysinger recording) a fast ascending "pu-pu-pooyeh?"

Thamnomanes Antshrikes

Rather plain antshrikes found in forests of the Oriente, where they are frequent members of understory flocks.

Dusky-throated Antshrike
Thamnomanes ardesiacus
Batará Golioscuro   Plate 60(18)

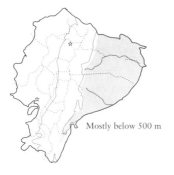

Mostly below 500 m

14 cm (5½"). Fairly common in lower growth inside humid forest, especially terra firme, in *lowlands of east*. ♂ *uniform gray*, somewhat paler below (especially on belly), *often with some black showing on throat* (though in some individuals little or none shows); semiconcealed white dorsal patch small, sometimes not present at all; tail feathers very narrowly tipped white. ♀ olive brown above, face vaguely mottled with buffy whitish, dorsal patch small or absent as in ♂; wings (especially) and tail more rufescent brown. Mostly buffy ochraceous below, mottled with olivaceous on breast, whitish on upper throat. **Similar species:** Both sexes resemble respective sexes of widely sympatric Cinere-

ous Antshrike; Cinereous is slightly larger, has longer tail, and tends to perch more vertically. ♂ Cinereous never shows any black on throat (but some Dusky-throateds don't either), nor does it ever have any white tail-tipping (but this is so narrow on Dusky-throated as to be invisible under normal field conditions; in the hand it usually can be seen). ♂ Cinereous also is more uniform below (not somewhat paler on belly); this may be best mark of all. ♀ Cinereous is easier with its rich cinnamon-rufous lower underparts (much deeper than in duller ♀ Dusky-throated, which can look quite flycatcher-like). **Habits:** Usually occurs in pairs, less often in small (family?) groups, generally as they accompany mixed flocks of understory birds (often including Cinereous Antshrikes). Less conspicuous than Cinereous, tending to perch lower and not as often in open; gleans directly from foliage and branches rather than sallying. **Voice:** ♂'s song a series of raspy but musical notes that obviously accelerate and rise in pitch before (often but not always) ending in a drawn-out growl, "grr, grr, grr-grr-gee-gee-gee-geegeegeegigigi greeeyr." Calls include a sharp, raspy "greeyr" and a sneezing "tchif!"

Cinereous Antshrike, *Thamnomanes caesius*
Batará Cinéreo   Plate 60(17)

Mostly below 600 m

14.5 cm (5¾"). Common in lower growth inside humid forest, especially terra firme, in *lowlands of east*. ♂ *uniform slaty gray*. ♀ olivaceous brown above, somewhat more grayish on face and usually showing an indistinct buff eye-ring and lores; wings and tail more rufescent. Throat dull whitish, chest grayish olive; *remaining underparts rich cinnamon-rufous*. **Similar species:** Both sexes resemble respective sexes of Dusky-throated Antshrike, and the two species regularly forage together in the same understory flocks. For distinguishing characters, see that species; often the two are best separated by posture (more vertical in Cinereous) and voice (see below). ♀ Cinereous can look quite flycatcher-like. **Habits:** A numerous bird in understory of Amaz. forests; it is often around Cinereous Antshrikes that small flocks of understory birds form. Usually occurs in pairs or small family groups, perching erectly and in the open on horizontal limbs, scanning nearby foliage for prey, abruptly sallying out to catch an insect, sometimes one flushed by another bird. **Voice:** ♂'s distinctive song starts slowly with several shrill whistled notes (almost with quality of a piping-guan), then rapidly accelerates before ending in bubbling trill, "whee? whee? whee-whee-whee-wheep-wheep-whip-whipwhip-p-p-p-p-p-p-prrrrr." Both sexes often give a staccato "wer-chicory" or "wu-chidididik" call.

Myrmotherula Antwrens

Small, short-tailed antbirds found primarily in lowland forests (*especially east of the Andes*) where they form an important component of understory flocks. A few species range up into foothills and lower subtropics. Six species (the "Pygmy/Streaked" group) comprise a more arboreal group that favors viny tangles in the subcanopy. On the whole *Myrmotherula* are difficult to identify, with many species differing only subtly; in some cases field separation is best made by voice or behavioral characters. Their tendency to forage actively and to remain in thick foliage only compounds the problem. Points to watch for include:

1. overall coloration (whether streaked or essentially brownish, gray, or black);
2. whether a black bib is present (in ♂♂);
3. whether the throat is checkered with black and white;
4. the pattern on the wing-coverts (whether plain or marked; if the latter, whether with fringed or spotted effect); and
5. whether there is rufous on the back, rump, or tail.

Note that, though to some extent it varies interspecifically, iris color is usually not a useful character, in part as it is so hard to ascertain clearly.

Pygmy Antwren, *Myrmotherula brachyura*
Hormiguerito Pigmeo   Plate 61(25)

Mostly below 600 m

8.5 cm (3¼"). *Numerous and widespread in mid-levels and subcanopy of humid forest in lowlands of east.* A *tiny* antwren with *very short* tail. ♂ *above black streaked with white*, with pale auriculars and semiconcealed white dorsal patch; wings black with two white wing-bars. *Throat white* bordered by *narrow black malar stripe*; *remaining underparts pale yellow* with a few black streaks on sides of chest. ♀ like ♂ but with buff streaking on crown and buff tinge on face; throat and chest often tinged buff as well. **Similar species:** Both sexes of Short-billed Antwren are blacker above with a wider—and hence more conspicuous—black malar stripe. **Habits:** Usually moves about in pairs, favoring dense viny tangles at forest edge and around treefalls. Sometimes accompanies mixed flocks, but at least as often alone. Heard more often than seen, and usually first located through its vocalizations. **Voice:** ♂'s song a fast and accelerating series of slightly husky chippers, "chree-chree-chree-chee-chee-ee-ee-ee-rrr," rising at first and then descending, ♀ sometimes chiming in or following with her shorter version. Both sexes also give various trilled contact calls.

Griscom's Antwren, *Myrmotherula ignota*
Hormiguerito de Griscom   Plate 96(5)

7.5 cm (3"). Uncommon and local (perhaps overlooked) in mid-levels and subcanopy of

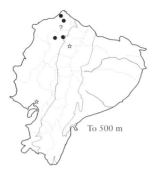

To 500 m

humid forest in *lowlands and lower foothills of northwest*. Formerly considered conspecific with Pygmy Antwren. **Both sexes** resemble respective sexes of that species, differing in their slightly smaller size and *wider black malar stripe*. **Similar species:** Unique in its limited range. Not known to occur with Pacific Antwren; the very similar Pygmy and Short-billed Antwrens do not range west of Andes. **Habits:** Similar to Pygmy Antwren, but seems even less inclined to accompany mixed flocks. **Voice:** ♂'s song reminiscent of Pygmy Antwren, differing in being more moderately paced with less acceleration, the notes clearer and semimusical, lacking Pygmy's "rolled" end; it also closely resembles Short-billed Antwren's song. Can be confused with Dot-winged Antwren's vocalizations (O. Jahn).

Short-billed Antwren, *Myrmotherula obscura*
Hormiguerito Piquicorto   Plate 61(26)

To about 600 m

7.5 cm (3″). *Subcanopy and borders of humid forest (mainly terra firme) in lowlands of east.* **Both sexes** resembles respective sexes of Pygmy Antwren, but differ in being *substantially blacker above* (white streaking narrower, hence showing much less) and in

having a *wider and more conspicuous black malar stripe*. ♀ differs further in having throat and chest buff to orange-buff (but can nearly be equalled in this respect by some Pygmies). **Habits:** Similar to Pygmy Antwren, but seems even less inclined to accompany mixed flocks. The two species can occur together, though in general Short-billed is more confined to terra firme, especially where hilly. **Voice:** ♂'s song similar to Pygmy Antwren's but slower and less run-together, notes with somewhat more musical quality; calls also similar. Dugand's Antwren's more staccato song can further confuse the situation.

Amazonian Streaked-Antwren
Myrmotherula multostriata
Hormiguerito Rayado Amazónico   Plate 61(23)

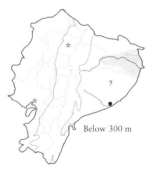

Below 300 m

9.5 cm (3¼″). Uncommon and local in *shrubby growth along margins of lakes and streams in lowlands of east; invariably near water*. Formerly considered conspecific with what is now called Pacific Antwren, found on other side of Andes, and the expanded species was then called Streaked Antwren (*M. surinamensis*). ♂ *black above streaked with white*, with semiconcealed white dorsal patch; wings black with two white wing-bars. *White below streaked with black.* ♀ has *crown and nape orange-rufous streaked with black*; otherwise like ♂ above. *Below pale ochraceous with extensive fine black streaking* (especially across breast), whiter on belly. **Similar species:** Somewhat larger Stripe-chested Antwren occurs along e. base of Andes, not overlapping range of Amazonian Streaked; in any case, its ♂ has streaking below only on breast, whereas ♀ is unstreaked below. **Habits:** Usually in pairs or small groups that forage low in bushes and low trees close to water, often where vegetation is periodically submerged by fluctuating water levels. Most often not with flocks, though sometimes joining a few other small antbirds. **Voice:** Vocalizations include an evenly pitched dry trill, "dr-r-r-r-r-r-r," and a distinctive and more lilting and musical song, e.g., "pur-pur-peé-peé-peé-pur," with unusual cadence. Both sexes also give a White-flanked Antwren-like "chee-pu" contact note.

Pacific Antwren, *Myrmotherula pacifica*
Hormiguerito del Pacifico   Plate 61(22)

Mostly below 800 m

9.5 cm (3¾"). Shrubby humid forest and woodland borders and adjacent clearings and gardens in *lowlands and foothills of west.* Formerly considered conspecific with Amazonian Streaked-Antwren, found east of Andes. Somewhat longer-billed than that species. ♂ similar to ♂ Amazonian Streaked-Antwren. ♀ has *head and neck rather bright orange-rufous* with blackish streaking only on hindcrown, *underparts plain ochraceous*; otherwise as in ♀ Amazonian Streaked. **Similar species:** Nothing really similar on west side of Andes. Black-and-white Warbler has vaguely similar color pattern but very different shape and behavior. **Habits:** Compared to similar-looking Amazonian Streaked-Antwren, Pacific is much more apt to forage higher above ground *and is not tied to water.* **Voice:** ♂'s song a fast, spritely chipper that rises slightly in pitch, e.g., "chee-chee-chi-chich-ch-ch-ch-ch-ch-ch"; somewhat recalls song of Pygmy Antwren. Both sexes also give "chee-pu" and "chee-cher" calls. Also gives a strident, evenly pitched "chrreee-chrreee-chrreee-chrreee!" (P. Coopmans).

Stripe-chested Antwren
Mymotherula longicauda
Hormiguerito Pechilistado   Plate 61(24)

Mostly 400–1000 m

10 cm (4"). Locally not uncommon in subcanopy and mid-levels of secondary woodland and forest borders in *foothills and lower subtropics on e. slope.* ♂ *black above streaked with white*; wings black with two white wing-bars. *Below white with broad band of black streaking across breast.* ♀ *black above broadly streaked with buff*; wings black with two buff wing-bars. *Below ochraceous buff* (with no streaking), belly white. **Similar species:** Likely confused only with Amazonian Streaked-Antwren, which ranges much farther out in e. lowlands in a different habitat; in any case, both sexes differ in being uniformly black-streaked below. Cf. also smaller Pygmy and Short-billed Antwrens (with pale yellow underparts, etc.). **Habits:** Usually in pairs that are essentially arboreal, tending to remain higher above ground than Amazonian Streaked-Antwren. Generally forages independently of mixed flocks. **Voice:** ♂'s distinctive song a fast repetition of a musical phrase, "chidu-chidu-chidu-chidu . . . ," with up to 12 or so notes. Call a doubled note followed by a short descending trill, "chiwi-chrrrrrrrt" (P. Coopmans).

Plain-throated Antwren
Myrmotherula hauxwelli
Hormiguerito Golillano   Plate 61(21)

10 cm (4"). *On or near ground* inside humid forest (mainly terra firme) in lowlands of east. *Notably short tail.* ♂ *uniform gray*, only slightly paler below, with a semiconcealed

Mostly below 400 m

Mainly below 900 m

white dorsal patch. Wings blackish with two wing-bars and *tipping on tertials white*; uppertail-coverts and tail feathers tipped white. ♀ olive brown above, with dorsal patch as in ♂; *wing and tail pattern as in ♂, but buff replaces white. Below bright cinnamon-rufous*, lower belly more olivaceous. **Similar species:** Other *Myrmotherula* do not habitually remain so close to ground, and none shows conspicuous pale tertial tipping. ♂ most resembles ♂ Scale-backed Antbird, even to its habitat preferences and songs, but latter is considerably larger, has scaly pattern on back, etc. **Habits:** Most often in pairs, hopping about near ground, frequently near streams or swampy spots; usually not with mixed flocks. Foraging behavior reminiscent of *Hylophylax* antbirds, like them often clinging to slender vertical stems. **Voice:** ♂'s song a series of 6–10 high-pitched and penetrating "chwee" notes that usually start slowly and increase in volume. Contact and alarm calls include a repeated, sharp "chik!" and a stuttered "ch-ch-ch-ch-ch-ch-ch."

Checker-throated Antwren
Myrmotherula fulviventris
Hormiguerito Ventrifulvo   Plate 61(20)

10 cm (4″). Lower growth inside humid forest and woodland in *lowlands and foothills of west. Iris pale*, buff or hazel to grayish white. ♂ olive brown above; wing-coverts dusky *boldly tipped buff forming two spotted wing-bars. Throat conspicuously checkered black and white*; remaining underparts uniform fulvous brown. ♀ above like ♂. *Uniform fulvous brown*, throat sometimes with a few dusky streaks. **Similar species:** *West of*

Andes, there are few other antwrens with which to confuse this species. ♂ is, in any case, the only one there with a checkered throat pattern. Obscure ♀ can be more confusing. ♀ White-flanked is less uniform below, with whitish throat and white flank plumes. ♀ Slaty Antwren has plain wings (no wing-bars). **Habits:** Usually in pairs, less often small (family?) groups that often accompany mixed flocks with other antwrens (White-flanked, Dot-winged, and Slaty) and other birds. Gleans in foliage, also has frequent habit of inspecting curled-up dead leaves, often where these have been hung up in dense thickets or viny areas. **Voice:** ♂'s song a descending series of high-pitched notes, "seee, seee, seeu, seeu." Displaying ♂♂ sometimes posture at each other a meter or so apart, puffing out throats and singing repeatedly. Both sexes also give a fast rattle and a "peeyk" note.

Stipple-throated Antwren
Myrmotherula haematonota
Hormiguerito Golipunteado   Plate 61(18)

11 cm (4¼″). *Undergrowth inside terra firme forest in lowlands of far northeast* (Tigre Playa). *Iris grayish white.* ♂ brown above with *rufous-chestnut back and rump*; wing-

Below 250 m

coverts blackish tipped white forming two spotted wing-bars. *Throat black spotted white*; face and remaining underparts gray, browner on lower flanks and crissum. ♀ much like ♂ above, *including rufous-chestnut back* (only faintly shown in some individuals); wing-coverts tipped buff. *Sides of head and underparts uniform ochraceous, usually with some flammulation on throat.* **Similar species:** Newly described Yasuní Antwren occurs only south of Río Napo; in both sexes the back is brown (not rufous). Both sexes of Ornate Antwren have rufous-chestnut back and rump similar to Stipple-throated's; ♂ differs in its gray head and neck and solid black throat, ♀ in its contrasting black throat with white spots. Foothill Antwren occurs only at higher elevations; it lacks rufous on back, etc. ♀ Rufous-tailed Antwren is quite similar to ♀ Stipple-throated aside from latter's rufous (not brown) tail. **Habits:** Usually in pairs or small (family?) groups, almost invariably foraging with mixed understory flocks. Gleans in foliage and on stems; also frequently inspects curled-up dead leaves. **Voice:** Song a high-pitched and thin "zee-ee-ee-ee-ee-ee" that somewhat recalls certain *Picumnus* piculets. Calls include a sharp rattle.

Yasuní Antwren, *Myrmotherula fjeldsaai*
Hormiguerito del Yasuní   Plate 61(17)

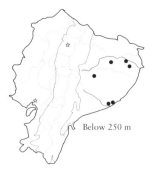

Below 250 m

11 cm (4¼"). Scarce and local in undergrowth inside terra firme forest in *lowlands of east* (*south of Río Napo*), and was confused with White-eyed Antwren (*M. leucophthalma*). A recently described species has been called Brown-backed Antwren. *Iris grayish brown.* ♂ *brown above*, darker on tail; *wing-coverts blackish tipped buff* forming two spotted wing-bars. Throat black spotted white; face

and underparts gray, browner on lower flanks and crissum. ♀ like ♀ Stipple-throated Antwren, differing in iris color, *brown back* (with no rufous), and *whitish throat with small black streaks.* **Similar species:** Stipple-throated Antwren is found only in far northeast, with no overlap with Yasuní; both sexes have prominent rufous back. Cf. also Rufous-tailed Antwren. **Habits:** Similar to Stipple-throated Antwren, foraging usually below eye level with mixed flocks inside tangled areas in terra firme. Forages lower than Rufous-tailed Antwren, which in other ways it rather resembles. **Voice:** Similar to Stipple-throated Antwren.

Foothill Antwren, *Myrmotherula spodionota*
Hormiguerito Tropandino   Plate 61(19)

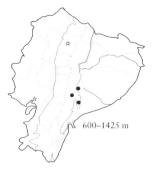

600–1425 m

11 cm (4¼"). *Lower growth inside foothill forest on e. slope.* Formerly often considered a race of Stipple-throated Antwren. Iris hazel to pale grayish. ♂ *olivaceous gray above*, browner on crown; wing-coverts dusky tipped white forming two spotted wing-bars. *Throat black spotted white*; face and remaining underparts gray, browner on lower flanks and crissum. ♀ olive brown above; wing-coverts dusky *tipped buff forming two spotted wing-bars. Sides of head and underparts uniform ochraceous, usually with some flammulation on throat.* **Similar species:** Occurs above range of most similar *Myrmotherula*; Stipple-throated and Yasuní Antwrens occur exclusively *in the lowlands.* Ornate Antwren has rufous on back and contrasting black on throat (solid in ♂, checkered in ♀). Cf. also ♀ Slaty Antwren. **Habits:** Much like Stipple-throated and Yasuní Antwrens; Foothill regularly flocks with Slaty Antwren. **Voice:** Song much as in Stipple-

throated and Yasuní Antwrens. Call a short harsh rattle (N. Krabbe recording).

Ornate Antwren, *Myrmotherula ornata*
Hormiguerito Adornado   Plate 61(16)

To 1200 m

11 cm (4¼″). *Scarce and seemingly local* in lower growth inside humid forest and secondary woodland in lowlands and foothills of east, *favoring vine tangles (in lowlands) or stands of bamboo (in foothills)*. Iris brown. ♂ gray above with *chestnut lower back and rump*; wings blackish, coverts tipped white forming two spotted wing-bars. *Throat black*, contrasting sharply with *gray remaining underparts*. ♀ like ♂ above, but olive brown replaces gray. *Throat black boldly spotted white*, sharply set off from fulvous remaining underparts. **Similar species:** Smartly patterned, in Ecuador the Ornate Antwren should not be confused. No other combines a chestnut lower back with the contrasting black throat patch. **Habits:** Usually in pairs, foraging mainly with mixed understory flocks; like other members of Stipple-throated/Yasuní group, frequently searches for prey in hanging dead leaves. **Voice:** ♂'s song a thin, high-pitched chipper that fades away, "tsee-tsee-tsi-tsi-tsitsitsi."

Rufous-tailed Antwren
Myrmotherula erythrura
Hormiguerito Colirrufo   Plate 61(15)

11.5 cm (4½″). *Lower and middle growth inside terra firme forest in lowlands of east.* Iris red to orange. Somewhat longer-tailed than other *Myrmotherula*. ♂ olive brown above with *rufous back* and *rufous tail*; wing-coverts tipped buffy whitish forming two spotted wing-bars. *Throat and breast gray*

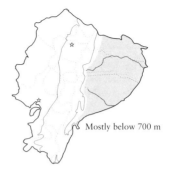

Mostly below 700 m

(some individuals with a little black scaling on throat), becoming olive brown on belly. ♀ like ♂ above. *Throat and chest rather bright ochraceous buff*, somewhat duller on lower underparts. **Similar species:** ♂ is only comparable *Myrmotherula without* a contrasting throat patch; rufous on back is usually obvious, though that of tail often is not. ♀ Stipple-throated Antwren (very limited range in Ecuador) differs in its slightly longer *brown* (not rufous) tail. **Habits:** Usually in pairs or small groups, with behavior similar to previous several species (likewise investigating curled-up dead leaves), though tending to forage higher above ground. **Voice:** ♂'s song a high-pitched "swee, swee-swi-swi-seeseeseesr" with squeaky, almost hummingbird-like quality.

White-flanked Antwren, *Myrmotherula axillaris*
Hormiguerito Flanquiblanco   Plate 61(14)

To 900 m

10–10.5 cm (4–4¼″). *Numerous and widespread* in lower and middle growth inside humid forest and woodland in *lowlands of east and west*. ♂ *blackish above*; wing-coverts tipped white forming two spotted wing-bars, tail feathers also tipped white.

Below also blackish, with axillars and *long silky plumes on flanks white* (often quite conspicuous, but can be hidden underneath wing). ♀ olive brown above, wings more rufescent with two rather faint buff-dotted wing-bars. Ochraceous below with whiter throat and *long silky plumes on flanks as in ♂* (also sometimes concealed). **Similar species:** No other antwren shows white on flanks which, though sometimes partially hidden, usually protrudes from under wings and is often exposed as bird flicks wings. ♀ Long-winged Antwren similarly colored but more uniform ochraceous below (lacking any white). ♀ Slaty Antwren grayer and plainer above with nearly unmarked wing-coverts. **Habits:** Ranges in pairs and small groups, often the numerically dominant member of understory flocks. Gleans actively in foliage and viny tangles, often flicking wings. **Voice:** ♂'s song a distinctly descending series of well-enunciated whistled notes, e.g., "pyii, pii, pee, pey, peh, puh, pu." Frequently heard call, given by both sexes, a fast "chee-du" or "chee-doo."

more brightly and richly colored below. **Similar species:** Occurring at higher elevations than most other *Myrmotherula*, Slaty can often be known on that basis alone. Long-winged Antwren ranges at lower elevations; ♂ Long-winged is notably paler gray than ♂ Slaty (hence its black bib contrasts more), but ♀ ♀ of the two would be hard to distinguish where Long-winged is ochraceous below (behavioral characters would help more). Río Suno Antwren, though smaller, is quite similar to Slaty in plumage; it occurs, so far as known, only at lower elevations. Cf. also rare Plain-winged Antwren. ♀ Checker-throated Antwren is similar but has rather prominent buff wing-bars; these two species regularly occur together. **Habits:** Usually in pairs, gleaning from foliage and tangled vegetation; often accompanies mixed understory flocks. **Voice:** ♂'s relatively infrequently heard song on w. slope an upward-inflected "wheeyp," often doubled or tripled (P. Coopmans recording). Both sexes frequently give a nasal complaining scold, e.g., "skeeeur" or "skeeuh-skur."

Slaty Antwren, *Myrmotherula schisticolor*
Hormiguerito Pizarroso   Plate 61(12)

Mostly 400–1450 (W),
900–1700 m (E slope)

Long-winged Antwren
Myrmotherula longipennis
Hormiguerito Alilargo   Plate 61(11)

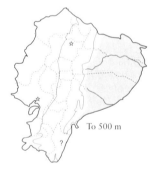

To 500 m

10 cm (4″). Lower growth inside *foothill and lower subtropical* forest and woodland on both slopes, in west also ranging out locally into humid lowlands and on slopes of coastal cordillera. ♂ *mostly dark gray* with *black bib from throat down over median breast*; wing-coverts black tipped with white forming two wing-bars. ♀ **on west slope** *uniform grayish olive above* with *nearly unmarked wing-coverts* (only vague rufescent tipping). Below uniform drab ochraceous buff. On **east slope** differs in being *pure bluish gray above*, and

10 cm (4″). Lower and middle growth inside terra firme forest and secondary woodland in *lowlands of east*. ♂ mostly gray, somewhat paler on belly, with *contrasting black bib from throat down over median chest*. Scapular fringing white; wing-coverts black tipped or fringed with white forming two wing-bars; tail feathers narrowly tipped white. ♀ **in most of range** *uniform bluish gray above* with nearly unmarked wing-coverts (only vague rufescent tipping). Below uniform

ochraceous buff. In **extreme northeast** very different: *brown above*, wings slightly more rufescent with some tipping on coverts; throat and chest pale ochraceous, *median breast and belly contrastingly whitish*, flanks tinged drab olivaceous. **Similar species:** Cf. much rarer Río Suno Antwren. Slaty Antwren occurs in foothills and lower subtropics, *above* range of Long-winged (no known overlap). Otherwise Long-winged is most apt to be confused with often sympatric Gray Antwren. ♂ Gray differs in lacking black bib, but ♀♀ of the two in most of their Ecuadorian range are very similar, ♀ Gray being somewhat purer blue-gray above and more intensely colored below. Behavior can be the most help: *Long-winged flicks its wings*, whereas *Gray twitches its tail sideways*. The very different brown-backed and white-bellied ♀ Long-wingeds of extreme ne. Ecuador are more apt to be confused with ♀ White-flanked Antwren, though latter is more uniform below and usually shows white flank tufts. **Habits:** Usually seen in pairs as they forage with mixed understory flocks, often together with several other antwren species; gleans from foliage, sometimes while hovering. As noted above, often flicks or shivers wings (like a White-flanked). **Voice:** ♂'s song a rather harsh "chuwey-chuwey-chuwey-chuwee-chuwee-chuwee" that gradually increases in strength and intensity before abruptly ending. Call similar to White-flanked Antwren, but often 3-noted.

Río Suno Antwren, *Myrmotherula sunensis*
Hormiguerito del Suno   Plate 61(10)

9 cm (3½"). Apparently *rare and local* in undergrowth inside terra firme forest in *lowlands of east*. Resembles much more numerous Long-winged Antwren, but

To 500 m

smaller with *proportionately shorter tail*. ♂ differs in *darker gray plumage* (about same as in ♂ Slaty, so black bib contrasts less), and its *white tipping on wing-coverts gives effect of spotting* (in Long-winged more one of fringing or barring). ♀ *notably drab*, with olive grayish upperparts and drab ochraceous underparts. **Similar species:** ♀ Long-winged Antwren (most of range) similar apart from size difference but is purer gray above and less drab below; ♀ Long-wingeds of far northeast, with their brown backs and white bellies, are relatively distinct. **Habits:** Similar to Long-winged Antwren, though Río Suno apparently forages mainly closer to ground. **Voice:** ♂'s song a clear, melodic "wi-weedy-weedy-weedy" (P. Coopmans recording).

Plain-winged Antwren, *Myrmotherula behni*
Hormiguerito Alillano   Plate 61(13)

Mostly 800–1600 m

9.5 cm (3¾"). *Rare and local in lower growth inside foothill and lower subtropical forest on e. slope*. ♂ *uniform gray* with *contrasting black bib from throat down over chest*. ♀ olivaceous brown above, slightly duskier on tail, with *plain* wing-coverts. Drab olivaceous buff below, throat more whitish. **Similar species:** ♂ distinctive. ♀ resembles ♀ Slaty Antwren (also plain-winged) but is notably drabber overall (not as gray above or as ochraceous below). **Habits:** Similar to Slaty Antwren; the two species regularly forage together in the same flocks. **Voice:** Calls a sharp "sweeík" and a more nasal "kyunh" (N. Krabbe recordings).

Gray Antwren, *Myrmotherula menetriesii*
Hormiguerito Gris   Plate 61(9)

10 cm (4"). *Middle growth and subcanopy inside terra firme forest in lowlands of east,*

Mostly below 600 m

Mostly below 500 m

smaller numbers up into foothills. ♂ *uniform pale gray*; wing-coverts gray, feathers with black subterminal band and white tip, *forming three parallel bars*; tail slaty, narrowly tipped white. ♀ *gray above* with *wings unmarked. Below uniform and rather bright ochraceous.* **Similar species:** ♂ Long-winged Antwren is about same gray tonality but has contrasting black bib lacking in Gray. ♀♀ of the two species are quite similar, though ♀ Long-winged is less richly colored below (in far northeast, ♀ Long-wingeds with brown backs and white bellies are easy). Gray's tail is often twitched from side to side, providing a useful point of distinction (Long-winged flicks its wings). **Habits:** Behavior similar to other antwrens, though tending to forage *higher above ground* than other "non-streaked" *Myrmotherula*; sometimes accompanies subcanopy flocks with a different species composition. **Voice:** Thin song a wavering series of 10–12 "ree" or "shree" notes that rise in pitch and accelerate a bit; reminiscent of Scale-backed Antbird's song. Contact call a spritely "chir, whi-whi-whi-whi, chik."

Dot-winged Antwren, *Microrhopias quixensis*
Hormiguerito Alipunteado   Plate 61(5)
11.5–12.5 cm (4½–5″). Lower and middle growth and borders of humid forest and secondary woodland (often in bamboo thickets) in lowlands of east and west. *More numerous in west*, where birds are *noticeably smaller.* ♂ *in west uniform glossy black* with semiconcealed but large white dorsal patch, *white spotting on wing-coverts, one broad white wing-bar*, and *broad white tipping on tail feathers.* ♀ **in west** patterned

like ♂ above, but black duller and sootier. *Below uniform rufous-chestnut.* ♂ in east similar, but ♀ differs in having *contrasting black throat.* **Similar species:** This attractive antwren with its flashy white in wings and tail is unlikely to be confused. It often accompanies understory flocks with *Myrmotherula* antwrens, of which the most similar is ♂ White-flanked. **Habits:** Wide-ranging in west, where it seems often to forage rather high above ground, sometimes even up into subcanopy; in east favors viny tangles and bamboo stands. Regularly cocks and spreads its rather long tail, as if to show off white. Forages actively, mainly gleaning in foliage; for an antwren, easy to observe. **Voice:** ♂'s song an accelerating and descending series of 5–10 semimusical whistled notes, e.g., "wee, tsee-tsi-tsi-tsi-tu-tu", sometimes with rougher "zhait" or "zheeeit" notes mixed in. These latter notes, sometimes more drawn out, are also given independently, by both sexes. In east also gives a harsh, metallic "di-duk" (P. Coopmans), in west a quite different and softer "cheuw" (O. Jahn recording).

Herpsilochmus Antwrens
Rather long-tailed and strongly patterned antwrens found in the canopy and borders of humid forest, two species (Dugand's and Ancient) in the lowlands and two (Yellow-breasted and Rufous-winged) in the foothills and lower subtropics. They are inconspicuous aside from their vocalizations. Both sexes of all species show a *bold eyebrow* and *conspicuous white tipping to the tail feathers.*

Dugand's Antwren, *Herpsilochmus dugandi*
Hormiguerito de Dugand Plate 61(8)

Mostly below 450 m

11 cm (4¼″). *Subcanopy and borders of terra firme forest in lowlands of east.* Formerly sometimes considered conspecific with Spot-tailed Antwren (*H. sticturus*) of ne. South America. ♂ has *black crown* with inconspicuous small white spots on forehead, *long white superciliary*, black postocular line, and grayish ear-coverts; back gray with large but usually concealed white dorsal patch; wings black with white scapular line and bold white wing-bars; tail black, *feathers broadly white-tipped* (visible mainly from below) and central feathers with white spots on inner webs (visible only from above). *Below uniform grayish white.* ♀ has *crown uniform rufous*; otherwise above much like ♂ except more brownish tinged. Below uniform dingy buffy whitish, buffiest across breast. **Similar species:** The only *Herpsilochmus* antwren in most of the e. lowlands, and as such not difficult to identify because generic characters can be used. Note both sexes' white tail tipping (often conspicuous from below), ♂'s bold black crown and white superciliary, ♀'s rufous crown. In far southeast, cf. rare Ancient Antwren. **Habits:** Usually in pairs that accompany canopy flocks of other insectivorous birds; generally hard to see well from ground, though that task is easier from canopy "towers" that have been built at many lodges. Gleans in foliage, often along outer branches. **Voice:** Heard much more often than seen. ♂'s song, usually given while rapidly shivering or vibrating its tail, an accelerating series of fast chippered semimusical notes that drop slightly in pitch, e.g., "ch, ch, ch-ch-chchchchchchchch." ♀ often follows with a shorter version of its own. Both sexes give a contact call, a distinctively doubled or tripled, "chut-chut" or "tu-tuk."

Ancient Antwren, *Herpsilochmus gentryi*
Hormiguerito Antiguo Plate 96(7)

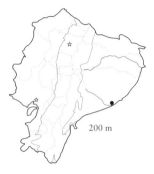

200 m

11.5 cm (4½″). *Subcanopy and borders of terra firme forest in lowlands of far southeast.* A recently described species. ♂ has *crown black, long superciliary and ear-coverts pale yellow* with black postocular line; back gray with large but usually concealed white dorsal patch, and some black mottling; wings black with white scapular line and bold white wing-bars; tail black, *feathers broadly white-tipped* (visible mainly from below). *Below pale clear yellow*, clouded olive on sides and flanks. ♀ much like ♂ but *crown spotted with yellowish white*, white dorsal patch smaller, and with *more ochraceous tinge to chest.* **Similar species:** Occurs sympatrically with Dugand's Antwren, though apparently not in precisely the same forest types (see below). Both sexes of Dugand's differ strikingly in their whitish underparts as well as other characters; voices also differ. Yellow-breasted Antwren occurs only on lower Andean slopes, is paler yellow below, etc. **Habits:** Behavior similar to Dugand's Antwren, likewise usually foraging high above ground in terra firme forest, but favors forest areas where subsurface soils are sandier. **Voice:** ♂'s song a series of chippered notes that slow markedly in pace and fall slightly in pitch, e.g., "chedidididi-di-di-deh-deh-deh." ♀ often follows with a shorter and higher-pitched version.

Yellow-breasted Antwren
Herpsilochmus axillaris
Hormiguerito Pechiamarillo   Plate 61(7)

800–1700 m

600–1300 m (E slope);
below 200 m (W)

11.5 cm (4½"). Canopy and borders of
*foothill and lower subtropical forest on e.
slope*. ♂ has *crown black spotted with white*,
long white superciliary composed of white
spots, ear-coverts blackish with white speckling; back uniform grayish olive; wings black
with bold white wing-bars and grayish olive
edging on flight feathers; tail blackish, feathers broadly tipped white (visible mainly from
below). *Below uniform pale clear yellow*,
clouded olive on sides. ♀ like ♂, but *crown
uniform dull rufous* and upperparts slightly
browner. **Similar species:** Both sexes of
Rufous-winged Antwren show obvious
rufous in wings. Otherwise not likely confused, but cf. Rufous-rumped Antwren and
Ecuadorian Graytail (both of which can
occur in flocks with this species). **Habits:**
Similar to Dugand's Antwren, likewise
usually with canopy flocks high above the
ground, and heard more often than seen.
Voice: ♂'s song a chippered trill that
descends evenly in pitch, "tree-ee-ee-ee-ee-ee-
ew." ♀ often follows with her briefer version.

Rufous-winged Antwren
Herpsilochmus rufimarginatus
Hormiguerito Alirrufo   Plate 61(6)

11.5 cm (4½"). Local in canopy and borders
of *foothill and lower subtropical forest on e.
slope*, and *very local in lowlands of west*.
Both sexes have *distinctive rufous edging on
flight feathers*, forming an almost solid patch.
♂ with *black crown*, long white superciliary,
and black postocular line; back mixed gray
and black; wings black with bold white wing-

bars and rufous edging. *Below pale creamy
yellowish*, throat whiter. ♀ like ♂ but *crown
rufous-chestnut*, postocular line dusky,
and back brownish olive. **Similar species:**
Nearly unmistakable on account of rufous
wing-edging (lacking in otherwise somewhat
similar Yellow-breasted Antwren, which
see). Cf. Rufous-winged Tyrannulet (with
rather similar rufous in wing). **Habits:**
Similar to Dugand's Antwren, but more apt
to be at edge, sometimes even foraging in isolated trees out in clearings adjacent to forest.
Voice: ♂'s song a fast, descending, and accelerating series of nasal, almost gravelly, notes,
"chu, chu, chu-chu-chu-ch-ch-chchch-rrr-
chúp," with accented final note; its mate
often follows with softer, shorter version.

Drymophila Antbirds
Small, streaky antbirds with *long, narrow,
and graduated tails* that are found in
bamboo-dominated undergrowth of montane (Long-tailed) or lowland (the rare Striated) forest.

Long-tailed Antbird, *Drymophila caudata*
Hormiguero Colilargo   Plate 62(2)

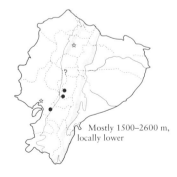

Mostly 1500–2600 m,
locally lower

15 cm (6″). A small, *long-tailed*, and *profusely streaked* antbird found in *bamboo-dominated undergrowth and borders of subtropical and lower temperate forest on both slopes*. ♂ has *head and back black streaked with white*, becoming *rufous-chestnut on rump*; wing-coverts black with two white-spotted wing-bars, flight feathers edged buff; tail dusky-olive, feathers broadly white-tipped. *Throat and breast white with black streaking*, becoming *bright rufous on flanks and crissum*, white on median belly. ♀ with similar pattern, but *upperparts streaked black and cinnamon-buff*, streaking below somewhat finer, and entire underparts tinged buff. **Similar species:** Warbling Antbird has much the same pattern but is markedly chunkier in shape, shorter tailed, etc.; it occurs at lower elevations (with marginal overlap). Cf. also much rarer Striated Antbird. **Habits:** Usually in pairs that forage together, hopping about in lower growth where often hard to locate except through its frequent vocalizing. Usually does not accompany mixed flocks. **Voice:** ♂'s song a distinctive raspy "cheeyt-cheeyt, wheeyz-wheeyz-wheeyz"; sometimes ♀ chimes in with a few "cheet" calls. Both sexes give higher-pitched "peedik" call.

Striated Antbird, *Drymophila devillei*
Hormiguero Estriado   Plate 62(1)

300–750 m

14 cm (5½″). *Very rare and local* in stands of bamboo in *lowlands of northeast*. Resembles much more numerous and *larger and longer-tailed* Long-tailed Antbird. **Both sexes** differ in having *sparser black streaking below* (where essentially restricted to sides), less extensive and paler rufous on sides and flanks, and *large white spots on middle tail*

feathers (these visible from above; uppertail unmarked in Long-tailed). **Habits:** Poorly known in Ecuador. Elsewhere occurs in pairs or small groups, hopping about in lower and middle growth and gleaning from foliage and nodes of bamboo; tends to range higher above ground than Long-tailed. **Voice:** In Peru and Brazil, ♂'s oft-heard song a series of 4–5 wheezy "dzzrrip" notes, last ones so fast as to almost form a trill, ♀ often echoing with softer and shorter version. Both sexes give soft "chit" contact calls.

Terenura Antwrens
Small, somewhat warbler-like antwrens found in the subcanopy of humid and montane forests; the three species in Ecuador segregate by range. They are inconspicuous except by voice—which is *essentially identical in all three species*—and one can actually sometimes follow canopy flocks around by listening for the males' oft-given song.

Rufous-rumped Antwren, *Terenura callinota*
Hormiguerito Lomirrufo   Plate 61(4)

900–1800 m

11 cm (4¼″). Uncommon in canopy and borders of *foothill and lower subtropical forest* on both slopes. ♂ has *black crown*, gray face and sides of neck, and blackish postocular line; upper back olive *contrasting with rufous lower back and rump*; wings dusky with *bright yellow shoulders*, wing-coverts black with two pale yellowish wing-bars, and olive edging on flight feathers; tail dusky. Throat and chest pale grayish, *becoming pale yellow on breast and belly*. ♀ like ♂ but crown grayish olive barely contrasting with back, superciliary faint, no yellow on shoulders, and duskier wing-coverts. **Similar species:** With its *montane* distribution,

Rufous-rumped not known to occur with any other *Terenura*. This is just as well, for ♀♀ of it and Chestnut-shouldered would be hard to distinguish; ♂♂ differ in shoulder color (admittedly often hard to see in field). Ash-winged Antwren has whitish underparts. Overall shape and posture somewhat resemble those of various small tyrannulets, though none of latter shows a rufous rump. **Habits:** Found in pairs, generally as they accompany a mixed canopy flock well above ground (and thus easy to overlook). Gleans in foliage, often in outer branches and in semiopen, sometimes turning upside-down to inspect the underside of leaves, the contrasting rufous rump color then flashing out momentarily. Heard more often than seen. **Voice:** ♂'s frequently given song a rapidly uttered, high-pitched "tsii-tsii-tsi-tsi-titititititititi" that accelerates into a fast chipper or trill.

Chestnut-shouldered Antwren
Terenura humeralis
Hormiguerito Hombricastaño   Plate 61(3)

To 600 m

11 cm (4¼"). Canopy of terra firme forest in *lowlands of east*, apparently ranging entirely *south of Río Napo*. Resembles Rufous-rumped Antwren of Andean slopes (no overlap with Chestnut-shouldered). ♂ differs in its *chestnut shoulders* (not yellow), darker and more rufous-chestnut rump, and *whitish median belly* (with pale yellow only on flanks and crissum). ♀ closely resembles ♀ Rufous-rumped, differing in its slightly browner crown and deeper rufous on rump; some individuals have rufous on shoulders. **Similar species:** Ash-winged Antwren occurs only north of Río Napo. Otherwise not likely confused in its *lowland* range. Note that the several greenlet species that occur with it—

often in same flock—lack wing-bars. **Habits and Voice:** As in Rufous-rumped Antwren, and equally hard to see well.

[Ash-winged Antwren, *Terenura spodioptila*
Hormiguerito Alicinéreo]   Plate 96(6)

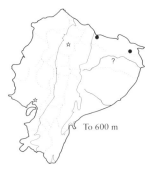

To 600 m

10 cm (4"). Canopy of terra firme forest in *lowlands of northeast*, so far recorded only *north of Río Aguarico*. ♂ has *black crown*, gray face and sides of neck, and blackish postocular line; upper back ashy gray contrasting with *rufous lower back and rump*; wings and tail blackish, wings with two white wing-bars. *Below uniform grayish white.* ♀ has crown rufescent brown with faint buffyish superciliary; upper back olivaceous brown contrasting with *rufous lower back and rump*; wings and tail as in ♂. Throat and breast dingy buffy whitish, belly whitish. **Similar species:** Chestnut-shouldered Antwren apparently occurs only *south of* Río Napo (no overlap); ♀♀ in particular could be confused, but Chestnut-shouldered is yellower below (though yellow rather pale). Rufous-rumped Antwren of montane forests (no overlap) is even yellower below, etc. Cf. somewhat similarly shaped greenlets, none of which has wing-bars, etc. **Habits and Voice:** As in Rufous-rumped Antwren.

Cercomacra Antbirds
Slender and *plain*, midsized antbirds with *fairly long, graduated tails* found in dense undergrowth of forest borders and secondary woodland in lowlands. One species (Gray) differs, ranging in viny tangles of subcanopy. On the whole *Cercomacra* are sneaky birds much addicted to staying out of sight, but they are vocal and tape-responsive.

Gray Antbird, *Cercomacra cinerascens*
Hormiguero Gris   Plate 62(5)

Mostly below 700 m

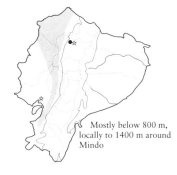

Mostly below 800 m, locally to 1400 m around Mindo

15 cm (6″). *Numerous in viny tangles of sub-canopy and borders of terra firme forest in lowlands of east.* ♂ uniform gray, marginally paler below, with usually concealed white dorsal patch and a variable amount of white spotting on wing-coverts (prominent in some individuals, completely absent in others); *tail feathers with broad white tipping. Very drab* ♀ olive brown above, grayer on rump and tail; *tail feathers with broad white tipping. Dull ochraceous below,* slightly more olivaceous on belly. **Similar species:** This species ranges *higher above ground* than other *Cercomacra* in Ecuador and can normally be identified on that basis alone. Its broad white tail-tipping is usually apparent, even when bird is seen from directly below. Cf. Plain-winged Antshrike (which lacks tail-tipping). **Habits:** Usually found in pairs, often creeping about in dense viny tangles; only rarely approaches ground or appears in open for long. Though sometimes with mixed canopy flocks, more often it remains independent of them, or moves in loose association with, for instance, a pair of Pygmy or Short-billed Antwrens. Heard more often than seen. **Voice:** ♂'s distinctive gravelly song, frequently heard through heat of day, a measured, repeated "ch-krr, ch-krr, ch-krr . . ." (up to 7–8 "ch-krr"s), somewhat hiccup-like. Both sexes also give a nasal but sharp "keeyr" call, sometimes repeated steadily, and a fast growling "kr-kr-kr-kr-kr."

Dusky Antbird, *Cercomacra tyrannina*
Hormiguero Oscuro   Plate 62(6)

14 cm (5½″). *Undergrowth of humid and semihumid forest borders and secondary woodland in lowlands of west.* ♂ uniform gray, somewhat paler below, with rather large semiconcealed white dorsal patch; blacker *wing-coverts narrowly fringed with white; tail feathers narrowly tipped with white.* ♀ olive brown above with white dorsal patch somewhat smaller; wing-coverts very narrowly fringed buff, tail very narrowly tipped buff (both barely showing in field). *Below uniform and quite bright ochraceous tawny,* duller and more olivaceous on flanks. **Similar species:** Given its *western* range, where there are few similar-appearing antbirds, not likely confused. Cf. Western Slaty-Antshrike (with which Dusky often occurs). Jet Antbird tends to occur in less humid areas. **Habits:** Usually forages in pairs, often remaining in dense undergrowth where it can be hard to see clearly, though really not all that shy. Sometimes forages with small mixed flocks, but at least as often alone. **Voice:** ♂'s distinctive and often-heard song a series of whistled notes that start slowly but then speed up and usually rise in pitch, e.g., "pü, pü, pee-pee-pipipi?"; often ♀ chimes in with softer and higher-pitched version. Calls given by both sexes include a "dididit" and a "wheeerrr."

Blackish Antbird, *Cercomacra nigrescens*
Hormiguero Negruzco   Plate 62(7)

15 cm (6″). Occurs in two *distinctly different* habitats: undergrowth of *foothill and lower subtropical forest borders and secondary woodland on e. slope,* and *secondary and riparian woodland and borders in lowlands of east.* ♂ *uniform slaty gray to blackish* (somewhat blacker above) with rather large semiconcealed white dorsal patch; bend of wing white, also with small white spots or

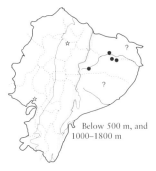

Below 500 m, and
1000–1800 m

To 1300 m

fringes to wing-coverts. ♀ somewhat rufescent brown above with semiconcealed white dorsal patch; *forehead, sides of head, and entire underparts deep orange-rufous,* lower flanks more brownish. **Similar species:** *Easily confused* with Black Antbird; even their voices are readily confounded. ♂ Black differs only in being somewhat blacker below; ♀ Black differs in being more olivaceous (less rufescent) above with less rufous on forehead (especially) and face. **Habits:** Usually in pairs, foraging in dense undergrowth, most often in thickets at borders. As with most other *Cercomacra,* generally does not accompany mixed flocks. Often vocal. **Voice:** Songs differ strikingly in the two regions inhabited by this species (which actually may be two species). In upland areas, ♂'s common song a fast and mainly falling "wor, chíh-chih-cheh-cheh-cheh-cheh," with ♀ often following with a clearly enunciated series of 4–5 rising notes, "pur, pu-puh-peh-pih-pi?" In riparian areas of lowlands, ♂ sings a rather different, loud and drawn-out "wor-cheéyr," often given independently though ♀ sometimes follows with a rising series similar to that of upland ♀♀.

Black Antbird, *Cercomacra serva*
Hormiguero Negro   Plate 62(8)

15 cm (6"). *Undergrowth of forest borders and secondary woodland in lowlands and foothills of east.* ♂ *uniform blackish* with rather large semiconcealed white dorsal patch; bend of wing white, also with small white spots or fringes to wing-coverts. ♀ *olivaceous brown above* with semiconcealed white dorsal patch; *lower face and entire underparts deep orange-rufous,* lower flanks more brownish. **Similar species:** Cf. closely similar Blackish Antbird; differences are sum-

marized under that species. **Habits:** Similar to Blackish Antbird, but in e. lowlands not in riparian woodland (unlike that species). **Voice:** ♂'s song a distinctly rising series of loud and rather harsh notes, given deliberately though speeding up toward end, "wor, chur, cheh-cheh-che-che-chi-chi-chi?"; sometimes ♀ chimes in with a softer and usually shorter version. Call an accelerating "drrr-drr-dr-dr-d'd'd'd" (P. Coopmans).

Jet Antbird, *Cercomacra nigricans*
Hormiguero Azabache   Plate 62(9)

Below 500 m

15 cm (6"). *Local in tangled, viny undergrowth of semihumid and deciduous forest borders and secondary woodland in lowlands of west.* ♂ *deep lustrous black with large but semiconcealed white dorsal patch; bend of wing and prominent fringing on wing-coverts white; tail feathers broadly tipped white.* ♀ slaty gray; *throat and breast with fine white streaking; wings and tail as in* ♂. Some individuals, perhaps immatures, resemble ♀♀ but are more extensively streaked and scaled with white below. **Similar species:** ♀ Jet somewhat resembles ♂ Dusky Antbird, but latter is much less marked with white on wings and tail and shows no streaking below;

♀ Dusky, with ochraceous underparts, is very different. Dusky Antbird favors more humid regions than Jet, but there is some overlap. ♂ Western Slaty-Antshrike has different shape (shorter tailed, etc.) and is predominantly gray (not black, and not showing any streaking), whereas ♀ is brownish. **Habits:** Usually in pairs that skulk in dense undergrowth and are shy and hard to see unless vocalizing. Generally not with mixed flocks. **Voice:** ♂'s song a fairly loud, measured series of 4–5 (occasionally more) harsh paired "tch-ker" notes, the second lower-pitched. Also gives an even and emphatic series, "chak chak chak chak chak chak" (P. Coopmans).

Myrmoborus **Antbirds**
Plain but attractively plumaged antbirds with *short tails* and *chunky shapes*. Despite all being found in forest and woodland in the east, they segregate by habitat and in Ecuador are rarely or never found together.

White-browed Antbird
Myrmoborus leucophrys
Hormiguero Cejiblanco   Plate 62(17)

To 1100 m

13.5 cm (5¼"). Undergrowth in *secondary woodland, regenerating clearings, and borders* of terra firme forest in *foothills on e. slope and adjacent lowlands*. ♂ has *broad snowy white superciliary extending back from forehead; otherwise uniform dark bluish gray*, with black face and throat and *unmarked* wing-coverts. ♀ has *broad cinnamon-buff superciliary* that *contrasts sharply with black mask*; otherwise brown above, tinged rufescent on crown and wings, and with buff tipping on wing-coverts. *Below mainly white.* **Similar species:** No other *Myrmoborus* (few other antbirds, for that matter)

have as bold and conspicuous a brow as that shown by both sexes of White-browed. Both sexes of Black-faced Antbird have conspicuous white fringing on wing-coverts and a much weaker eyebrow. Note that White-browed does not occur in ne. lowlands, rather ranging mainly along e. base of Andes. **Habits:** Usually occurs in pairs, less often in small family groups, foraging close to ground in dense younger growth, often along streams; generally does not range in areas with extensive unbroken forest, or at least scarce and local in such situations. Often perches on slender vertical saplings, hopping and sallying short distances. Most often does not move with mixed flocks. **Voice:** ♂'s song a very fast and descending series of loud, ringing notes that at first increase in volume, then slowly fade away, "pipipipipipipip-ipipip'p'p'p'p'p'rr," usually lasting 3–4 seconds. Both sexes give a "jeeyr" call, relatively undistinctive.

Ash-breasted Antbird, *Myrmoborus lugubris*
Hormiguero Pechicinéreo   Plate 96(8)

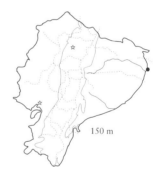

150 m

13.5 cm (5¼"). Known only from undergrowth of *riparian forest and woodland on one island in Río Napo near Peruvian border*. Iris red (♂) or *more orange* (♀). ♂ bluish gray above, paler on forehead, with *contrasting black sides of head and throat; wings plain*. Below paler gray. ♀ rufescent brown above with *contrasting black mask through eyes; wings virtually plain* (no obvious bars or spots). Throat white, bordered below by partial necklace of black spots; underparts whitish, sides and flanks washed olive brown. **Similar species:** Not likely confused in its restricted range and habitat; Ash-breasted does not occur with the other two *Myrmoborus* antbirds. **Habits:** Similar to White-browed Antbird, favoring dense undergrowth, often where there are extensive thickets of *Heliconia*. Likewise can be hard to see. **Voice:** ♂'s song resembles White-browed Antbird's but slower. Calls, given by both sexes, include a "peeyr" and a "peeyr-pur" (not as harsh as White-browed's).

Black-faced Antbird, *Myrmoborus myotherinus*
Hormiguero Carinegro   Plate 62(16)

Mostly below 700 m, a few locally to 1300 m

13.5 cm (5¼"). Often numerous in undergrowth inside humid forest in lowlands of east, *mainly in terra firme*. Iris dark red. ♂ bluish gray above with *contrasting black face and throat* outlined above and behind by *whitish border* and with semiconcealed white dorsal patch; *wing-coverts black fringed with white forming three obvious wing-bars*. Below paler gray. ♀ olive brown above with *contrasting black mask* and semiconcealed white dorsal patch; *wing-coverts black fringed with buff forming three obvious wing-bars. Throat white, contrasting with rather bright ochraceous-buff underparts*; a few blackish spots along throat's lower margin form partial necklace. **Similar species:** White-browed and rare Ash-breasted Antbirds both have *plain* wings, etc.; neither is found inside extensive terra firme forest. **Habits:** Similar to White-browed Antbird, though Black-faced usually much easier to observe, in part as it favors forests with more open, less tangled understory. **Voice:** ♂'s song a loud, descending, and fairly fast series of raspy notes, slightly descending, e.g., "dree-dree-dree-dree-dree-dree-dree-drew"; sometimes ♀ replies with briefer and shriller version. Both sexes give various strident

scolds, e.g., a sharp "jeeeyr!"; also gives a short, sneezing "tchif!" (P. Coopmans).

Hypocnemis Antbirds
Small, chunky, and short-tailed antbirds found in Amazonian forests, both species with *attractive streaked plumage patterns*.

Warbling Antbird, *Hypocnemis cantator*
Hormiguero Gorjeador   Plate 62(3)

Mostly below 600 m

12 cm (4¾"). *Numerous in lower growth of forest borders and openings, and in secondary woodland in lowlands of east*. Bill black above, pale grayish to whitish below. ♂ has *black head with white streaking and white superciliary*; back mixed black, grayish brown, and white, with semiconcealed white dorsal patch, becoming rufescent brown on rump; wing-coverts black tipped white forming three bold wing-bars; tail brown narrowly tipped buff. Throat and breast white, *feathers scalloped with black especially on sides*; *flanks contrastingly bright rufous*, median belly whitish. ♀ like ♂ but streaking above and wing-bars buffyish, and dorsal patch reduced or lacking. **Similar species:** Less familiar Yellow-browed Antbird has yellow superciliary and underparts, and lacks rufous on flanks; it occurs strictly in terra firme forest. *Herpsilochmus* antwrens, though somewhat similarly patterned, inhabit the subcanopy; in any case, none has contrasting rufous flanks. Also cf. very rare Striated Antbird. **Habits:** Usually in pairs that forage mainly in lower growth but sometimes hop higher, especially in dense tangles; accompanies small mixed flocks, but usually moves about independent of them. Gleans in foliage, frequently picking prey from underside of leaves. **Voice:** ♂'s song (not at all

"warbling") a raspy, almost snarling "peér, peer-peer-peer-peer-pur-pur-pyur" with descending effect; sometimes, about half-way through ♂'s delivery, ♀ chimes in with shorter, higher-pitched version. Both sexes often give a distinctive "wur-cheeé" or "wur-cheeé-cheeé" call.

Yellow-browed Antbird
Hypocnemis hypoxantha
Hormiguero Cejiamarillo   Plate 62(4)

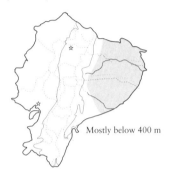

12 cm (4¾"). Undergrowth inside *terra firme forest in lowlands of east*. Bill black. ♂ has black crown with white streaks in midcrown, *long bright yellow superciliary*, and *olive back* with sparse black streaking; wing-coverts black with bold white tipping forming three wing-bars; tail dusky tipped whitish. *Below bright yellow*, sides of breast variably streaked with black, flanks with some olive. ♀ like ♂ but midcrown streaks pale yellow. **Similar species:** This pretty antbird with its *bright* yellow is unlikely to be confused. Warbling Antbird is patterned in black *and white*, has contrasting rufous flanks. **Habits:** Similar to better-known Warbling Antbird, but perhaps more apt to forage with understory flocks. Favors areas with a fairly open understory, often on ridges. **Voice:** ♂'s song similar to Warbling Antbird's, but somewhat less raspy and with a slower, more evenly paced tempo. Calls include a fast "dree-pu" or "dree-pu-pu"; also a scratchy "kreeéuk" (P. Coopmans).

Black-chinned Antbird
Hypocnemoides melanopogon
Hormiguero Barbinegro   Plate 62(15)

11.5 cm (4½"). Locally fairly common in undergrowth of *várzea forest in lowlands of*

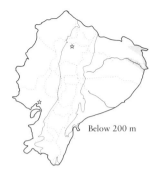

Below 200 m

far northeast. Rather long bill; *iris pale to bluish gray*. ♂ gray, somewhat paler below, with *black throat patch*; wing-coverts black fringed with white forming 2–3 wing-bars; *short tail black narrowly tipped white*. ♀ like ♂ above; below whitish *mottled with grayish across breast and down flanks, throat often scaled gray*. **Similar species:** A *small* antbird that hops about near water's edge, regularly in same habitat as Silvered Antbird; ♀ Black-chinned vaguely resembles ♂ Silvered, but Silvered is larger with dark eye and long pink (not grayish) legs, whiter underparts, small white *spots* on wing-coverts, and *no* white tail-tipping. Black-chinned is so small it can even be confused with a *Myrmotherula* antwren. **Habits:** Usually found in pairs that hop on or near ground and in tangled undergrowth *near water*, often in areas that are seasonally inundated; typically not shy. Sometimes accompanies the small parties of bird that forage together in such situations. Tail may be held somewhat elevated. **Voice:** ♂'s song a loud series that gradually accelerates and becomes raspier, "cheé-chee-chi-chi-chichichichichichechechechez," descending toward end.

Hylophylax Antbirds
Small, chunky antbirds with short tails and attractive (even ornate) plumages, found in undergrowth of humid lowland forests.

Spotted Antbird, *Hylophylax naevioides*
Hormiguero Moteado   Plate 63(14)

11.5 cm (4½"). Undergrowth inside humid forest and secondary woodland in *lowlands of northwest* (now mainly Esmeraldas). Iris dark gray; legs pinkish gray. ♂ has *head ashy gray* contrasting with *rufous-chestnut back*;

Mostly below 300 m

Mostly below 700 m, small numbers up to over 1000 m

semiconcealed white dorsal patch; wings black with white spots on lesser coverts and *two broad rufous wing-bars and large tertial tips*; tail olive brown with blackish subterminal band and buff tip. Throat black; underparts white with *band of large black spots across breast*, flanks washed gray. ♀ duller *but patterned much as in* ♂, with head brown, underparts buff-tinged with no black on throat and a less distinct band of dusky spots across breast, and spots on lesser wing-coverts buff. **Similar species:** Nothing really similar in its range west of Andes; Spot-backed Antbird occurs east of Andes. **Habits:** Usually in pairs, foraging close to ground inside forest, frequently clinging to slender vertical stems. Often spreads tail feathers, and flicks tail upward. Though often found foraging independently, small groups of Spotted Antbirds are also frequently found at army antswarms. **Voice:** ♂'s song a descending series of high-pitched wheezy notes that gradually fade off, e.g., "peezee, wheezee, wheezee, wheezee, wheeya." Both sexes also give soft churring calls as well as sharper "pseek" calls when disturbed or alarmed.

Spot-backed Antbird, *Hylophylax naevia*
Hormiguero Dorsipunteado   Plate 63(15)

11.5 cm (4½"). Undergrowth inside humid forest (both terra firme and várzea) in *lowlands of east*. Iris gray; legs pink. ♂ has head and upper back gray; *midback black with large buff tear-shaped spots*, rump plain brown; wing-coverts black prominently tipped white or buffy white forming three wing-bars, and with buff tertial tipping; tail brown with blackish subterminal band and tipped buff or white. Throat black; under-

parts white with *band of large black spots across breast*, flanks and lower belly buff. ♀ like ♂ above but crown tinged brown and wing markings ochraceous-buff. Throat white bordered by a prominent black malar stripe; *underparts ochraceous buff*, deepest on belly, with *band of large black spots across breast*. **Similar species:** Cf. much scarcer Dot-backed Antbird. Spotted Antbird ranges only west of Andes. Banded Antbird has rump *band* (not spots). **Habits:** Much as in Spotted Antbird, though unlike that species Spot-backed generally does not forage at army antswarms. **Voice:** ♂'s song a fast, high-pitched, and somewhat wheezy "wur, weépur-weépur-weépur-weépur-weépur-weépur-weépur-weépur" with distinctive doubled notes, loudest in the middle and fading at end. Both sexes give a sharp "beet" or "beet-bit" call.

Dot-backed Antbird, *Hylophylax punctulata*
Hormiguero Lomipunteado   Plate 63(16)

Below 300 m

11 cm (4¼"). *Scarce and local in undergrowth of várzea forest and woodland, usually near streams and lakes, in lowlands of east*, mainly in *blackwater* drainages. Iris

brown; *legs gray.* Resembles much more numerous Spot-backed Antbird; the two species routinely occur together. Both sexes of Dot-backed differ in their somewhat shorter tail, different eye and leg colors, *whitish lower face* (not gray), *white* (not buff) *spots on back smaller and less tear-shaped* and *extending down over rump,* whiter underparts (even ♀ shows only a little buff), and black tail (not brown). ♂ and ♀ Dot-backed are alike aside from ♀ having ♂'s solid black throat reduced to *very wide black malar stripe* (more prominent than in ♀ Spot-backed). **Habits:** Usually occurs in pairs, foraging close to ground and almost always independent of mixed flocks. Does not seem to attend army antswarms. **Voice:** ♂'s song a distinctive leisurely series of well-spaced and emphatic phrases, "whee-beéyr, whee-beéyr, whee-beéyr . . ."; often very responsive to tape playback, though—unlike most antbirds—it may fly in and then remain motionless and silent, therefore hard to see. Both sexes give a sharp, downslurred "peéyr" call.

Scale-backed Antbird, *Hylophylax poicilinota*
Hormiguero Dorsiescamado   Plate 63(13)

Mostly below 700 m, in small numbers to 1100 m

13 cm (5"). Undergrowth inside humid forest (especially terra firme) in *lowlands of east.* ♂ *uniform gray* with midback and wing-coverts black, *feathers prominently tipped white resulting in conspicuous scaled effect;* semi-concealed white dorsal patch; tail black, feathers with large white spots toward base and tipped white. ♀ rufescent brown above (more strongly rufous on face and forecrown), dorsal patch and *conspicuous scaled pattern on midback and wing-coverts* as in ♂; throat cinnamon-buff, underparts

ochraceous brown. **Similar species:** No other similar antbird shows this species' obvious scaly back pattern. **Habits:** Usually in pairs, foraging on or close to ground, often hopping from one vertical stem to another, capturing prey by quickly dropping to ground or sallying to nearby foliage. Pairs regularly attend army antswarms, multiple individuals sometimes gathering at large and active swarms. Can be charmingly unsuspicious. **Voice:** ♂'s distinctive song a leisurely series of 5–6 piercing and upslurred notes, each succeeding note higher in pitch and a little louder, "teeuw, tuweeé? tuweeé? tuweeé? tuweeé?" Calls of both sexes include a thin rattle, a sneezing "tchef," and nasal scolds.

Banded Antbird, *Dichrozona cincta*
Hormiguero Bandeado   Plate 63(17)

To 450 m

10 cm (4"). *Scarce on ground inside terra firme forest in lowlands of east,* favoring *areas with a fairly open understory such as on ridges.* Tiny *and short-tailed,* with long slender bill. ♂ has crown and back chestnut brown with indistinct narrow whitish superciliary and grayish face; lower back and rump black, *rump crossed by conspicuous white band;* wings black, lesser-coverts with white spotting and with *two wide and conspicuous buff wing-bars;* outer tail feathers white. *Below white* with *conspicuous wide band of black spots across breast,* sides and flanks washed grayish. ♀ similar but shoulder spots and rump band buff, underparts slightly buff-tinged, and with somewhat less chest spotting. **Similar species:** Overall pattern of this unique little antbird vaguely recalls Spot-backed Antbird, though latter is obviously spotted above and lacks rump band. **Habits:**

More terrestrial than most other small antbirds, the cute Banded Antbird *habitually walks on ground*, often wagging and spreading its short tail, exposing lateral white. Usually found singly, less often in pairs; does not accompany mixed flocks. **Voice:** ♂'s song a long series of up to 15 or so loud "pueeeée" notes steadily delivered at rate of about one note/second, with an odd ringing and piercing quality and slight crescendo effect. Song's quality somewhat recalls that of Scale-backed Antbird, though Banded's has more notes, and they are longer and more evenly pitched (and Scale-backed's individual notes slur upward). Call a gravelly rattle, descending distinctly (rattles of most other antbirds do not descend).

Black-and-white Antbird
Myrmochanes hemileucus
Hormiguero Negriblanco   Plate 62(18)

Below 300 m

11.5 cm (4½"). A distinctive *small, black and white* antbird found in *early-succession growth on islands in Río Napo* in lowlands of northeast. *Long slender bill* black, grayish below in ♀. ♂ *black above* with large semi-concealed white dorsal patch (exposed prominently when bird is agitated), gray on rump; wing-coverts spotted with white; tail feathers tipped white. *White below.* ♀ similar, but with a little white on lores and tinged buff on flanks. **Similar species:** Not likely confused in its restricted range and habitat. ♂ Great Antshrike is much larger with heavy hooked bill. Cf. ♂ Black-and-white Tody-Tyrant. **Habits:** Favors low growth of the shrub *Tessaria* and young willows, also ranging into lower growth beneath a canopy of *Cecropia* trees. Usually in pairs that glean actively in foliage and for

an antbird are usually easy to see. **Voice:** ♂'s frequently given song a fast "tu-tu-u-u-u-u-u," first several notes at a lower pitch; its mate often replies with an inflected "toot!" (sometimes doubled or tripled). Call a slurred rattle.

Schistocichla Antbirds
Infrequently seen and inconspicuous antbirds found in the undergrowth of terra firme forest in Amazonian lowlands. Both species were formerly often placed in the genus *Percnostola*.

Spot-winged Antbird
Schistocichla leucostigma
Hormiguero Alimoteado   Plate 62(13)

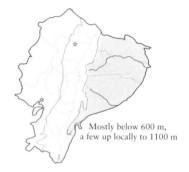

Mostly below 600 m, a few up locally to 1100 m

15 cm (6"). Scarce in undergrowth *inside terra firme forest in lowlands of east.* Favors vicinity of forest streams. Iris brown; lower mandible and legs bluish gray. ♂ *uniform dark gray*, slightly paler below, darkest on wings and tail; *wing-coverts with small white dots.* ♀ has *head dark gray* that *contrasts with rufous brown upperparts*; wing-coverts with buff spots (larger than ♂'s white dots); tail dusky. *Below uniform deep orange-rufous.* **Similar species:** In far north, cf. Slate-colored Antbird. Both sexes of larger and more heavily built Plumbeous Antbird have conspicuous bare blue skin around eye. **Habits:** An inconspicuous antbird of deep forest, shy and hard to see well. Pairs and small (family?) groups range in thick shrubby vegetation along forested streams; does not associate with mixed flocks or attend army antswarms. **Voice:** ♂'s song a loud fast series of somewhat musical, chippered notes that descend and fade a bit toward end and last 2–3 seconds, similar to White-browed Antbird's song but less harsh. Both sexes give

a sharp scold, "cht-t-t-t-t," a whining "keeeyu," and a rattle.

Slate-colored Antbird
Schistocichla schistacea
Hormiguero Pizarroso   Plate 62(14)

Below 250 m

To 450 m

14.5 cm (5³/₄″). Local in undergrowth inside terra firme forest in *lowlands of far northeast. Bill all black in ♂*, lower mandible paler gray in ♀; *iris grayish*; legs bluish gray. *♂ virtually identical to ♂ of more numerous and widespread Spot-winged Antbird*; its gray is slightly more bluish-toned. They are best distinguished by soft-part colors: Spot-winged's iris is brown (not pale gray), and its lower mandible pale bluish gray (not with all-black bill); both characters can be seen in field, given a decent view. ♀ more distinctive: *crown rufescent brown with blurry rufous shaft streaks*; mantle rufescent brown, wing-coverts with buff spots; tail dusky. *Below uniform deep orange-rufous.* **Similar species:** ♀ Slate-colored lacks contrasting gray on head of ♀ Spot-winged Antbird. **Habits:** Not well known, but apparently similar to Spot-winged Antbird. **Voice:** ♂'s song, distinctly different from Spot-winged's more run-together song, a simple series of penetrating but semimusical notes, "peeyr-peeyr-peeyr-peeyr-peeyr," similar to Sooty Antbird's song.

Silvered Antbird, *Sclateria naevia*
Hormiguero Plateado   Plate 62(19)

14–14.5 cm (5¹/₂–5³/₄″). *Undergrowth of várzea forest and woodland and along swampy margins of lakes and streams in lowlands of east. Long bill black (pale below in ♀); long legs pink to flesh. ♂ gray above,* wings and tail blackish, *wing-coverts with small but conspicuous white spots. White below* with some gray mottling on sides and flanks. *♀ dark brown above; wing-coverts with small buff spots*, tail blackish. White below with *sides, flanks, and crissum extensively orange-rufous.* **Similar species:** Compare ♂ Silvered to ♀ Black-chinned Antbird, somewhat similar but notably smaller. Black-chinned occurs only in far northeast; here the two species can forage in close proximity. **Habits:** Usually found in pairs, hopping on or near wet ground or in vegetation along the margins of lakes and sluggish streams; generally not too shy. Tail may be held somewhat elevated. **Voice:** ♂'s song a loud and ringing "jyíp, ji-ji-ji-ji-ji-jíjíjíjíjí-ji-ji-jrrr" that gradually accelerates and reaches a crescendo in middle, then fades a bit; *initial well-separated and accented note is especially distinctive.* Often-heard alarm call "tik chik" or "ti-tik" distinctive (P. Coopmans).

Black Bushbird, *Neoctantes niger*
Arbustero Negro   Plate 62(11)

16 cm (6¹/₄″). *Scarce* in undergrowth of humid forest and woodland, perhaps favor-

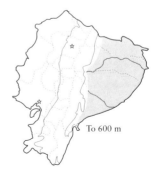

To 600 m

ing areas around treefalls and at borders, in *lowlands of east*. Bill *with lower mandible strongly upturned*; bill black above, bluish gray below. ♂ *entirely deep black*; large semi-concealed dorsal patch white. ♀ as in ♂ (though black is somewhat sootier) but *broad area across breast contrastingly rufous-chestnut*. **Similar species:** Several other all-black antbirds occur with this species, though none shares bushbird's conspicuously upswept bill; further, many of these show some bare blue skin around eye (lacking in bushbird). ♀'s broad cummerbund unique among vaguely similar antbirds. **Habits:** Rather skulking and hard to see, in part because of the dense nature of its favored habitat. Found singly or (more often) in pairs, hopping near ground or sometimes on it. Has been seen probing into rotting logs (S. Hilty), but whether bushbird does this on a regular basis remains unknown. **Voice:** Not especially vocal. ♂'s distinctive song a long-continued and often slightly rising series of semimusical "werk" notes given at a rate of a little faster than 1/second; this can go on for a minute or more and slightly resembles Brown Nunlet's song. Also gives nasal "kyoo" calls (P. Coopmans).

White-backed Fire-eye, *Pyriglena leuconota*
Ojo-de-Fuego Dorsiblanco   Plate 62(10)

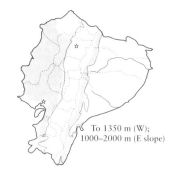

To 1350 m (W);
1000–2000 m (E slope)

17.5–18 cm (6¾–7″). Undergrowth and borders of *deciduous and humid forest and woodland in lowlands and foothills of west*, and *foothill and subtropical forest on e. slope. Iris bright red.* **Western birds** slightly longer-billed and shorter-tailed. ♂ *entirely glossy black* with large but semiconcealed

dorsal patch white. **Western** ♀ *dull and uniform*: brown above with dorsal patch as in ♂ and dusky tail; *drab grayish buff below.* **East-slope** ♀ rather different: mostly sooty black (somewhat duller than ♂) with *mantle contrastingly chestnut-brown*; dorsal patch as in ♂. **Similar species:** In west, compare ♂ fire-eye to ♂ Immaculate Antbird (also black, but with dark iris and blue skin around eye); ♀ fire-eye of west is dull-plumaged but easily recognized by conspicuous red eye. On e. slope no similarly shaped black or mainly black antbird has such a staring red eye. **Habits:** Usually in pairs that range through lower growth, pounding tail downward when nervous or agitated. Especially in west, groups of up to 4–6 birds regularly gather at army antswarms, often together with other ant-following birds. They take prey from foliage, branches, and ground. **Voice:** ♂'s often-heard song a far-carrying series of rapidly delivered notes, "peer-peer-peer-peer-peer-peer-peer-peer-peer-peer" (sometimes more "peer"s), fading and descending a bit toward end; sometimes ♀ echoes with a shorter, softer song. Song recalls Immaculate Antbird's song though pace is much faster. Calls include a loud "chik" or "chi-djik," when excited a "chi-dji-djik" (P. Coopmans). Song and calls seem similar on both slopes.

Myrmeciza Antbirds

A *diverse* group of midsized to moderately large antbirds that reach their *maximum diversity in forests of the Amazonian lowlands*, though there are also several species in the lowlands west of the Andes. Only one, an aberrant one (Gray-headed, probably not a "real" *Myrmeciza*), is strictly montane. The genus is so heterogeneous as to make generalizations difficult, and it may ultimately be broken up so as to more accurately reflect actual relationships. After the Gray-headed, we present two small species (Chestnut-tailed and Black-throated) of Amazonia; then four large and robust species with heavy bills (Plumbeous, White-shouldered, Sooty, and Immaculate); and finally three smaller species found in western forests (Chestnut-backed, Esmeraldas, and Stub-tailed).

Gray-headed Antbird, *Myrmeciza griseiceps*
Hormiguero Cabecigris   Plate 62(12)

600–2500 m

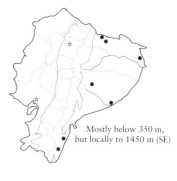

Mostly below 350 m,
but locally to 1450 m (SE)

13.5 cm (5¼"). *Now rare to uncommon and local in undergrowth and borders of subtropical forest and secondary woodland in far southwest.* ♂ has *head and neck gray;* back olive brown with semiconcealed but usually large white dorsal patch; wing-coverts black with white fringing; graduated tail dusky, *feathers narrowly tipped white.* Throat gray, *midbreast black;* remaining underparts gray, becoming olive brown on flanks and crissum. ♀ like ♂ above but head and neck paler gray and dorsal patch smaller. *Throat and breast pale gray with some mottled whitish streaking* (some individuals have some black on breast as well), becoming olive brown on flanks and crissum. **Similar species:** Unlikely to be confused in its very limited range, where in fact there are no small antbirds any more similar than the quite different Plain Antvireo. Cf. also Speckle-breasted Wren and Azara's Spinetail. **Habits:** Found singly or in pairs, foraging through dense undergrowth, especially where there is dense understory of bamboo. Sometimes accompanies small mixed flocks of other understory birds, but generally hard to see well unless vocalizing. Responds readily to tape playback. **Voice:** ♂'s song a short and clearly descending trill that lasts about a second, "trrrrrrrrrr." Foraging birds of both sexes often give a nasal, somewhat querulous contact call, "skrree-squirt," steadily repeated every 2–5 seconds.

Chestnut-tailed Antbird
Myrmeciza hemimelaena
Hormiguero Colicastaño   Plate 63(3)

12 cm (4¾"). *Rare and local* in undergrowth of terra firme forest in *lowlands and foothills*

of east. *Tail notably short.* ♂ has *head and neck dark gray* (feathers with black centers, resulting in faint scaly look); otherwise reddish brown above with semiconcealed white dorsal patch, becoming *rufous-chestnut on tail;* wing-coverts black tipped buff or white. *Throat and breast black,* becoming gray on sides and brown on lower flanks and crissum, with variable amount of white on median belly. ♀ has brownish gray head and neck, brown on back, more rufescent on rump; *tail rufous-chestnut. Throat and breast cinnamon-buff to orange-rufous, belly buffy white* with lower flanks tinged brownish. **Similar species:** This small and short-tailed antbird of forest interior is unlikely to be confused; similar species lack rufous-chestnut tail. ♀'s obviously two-toned underparts are distinctive. **Habits:** Little known in Ecuador. Forages singly or in pairs, hopping on or near ground, often in dense undergrowth near treefalls. Rarely accompanies mixed flocks, and seldom attends antswarms. **Voice:** ♂'s song an ascending and only slightly accelerating series of clear and rather high-pitched notes, e.g., "teeeee-teee-tee-te-tit?" (P. Coopmans). Chestnut-tailed Antbirds found south of Río Marañón in Peru sound very different, and likely represent a separate species.

Black-throated Antbird, *Myrmeciza atrothorax*
Hormiguero Golinegro   Plate 63(2)

14 cm (5½"). *Scarce and local* in undergrowth of forest borders, secondary woodland, and riparian growth in lowlands of east; *favors swampy situations.* ♂ *essentially uniform black* with small semiconcealed white dorsal patch; wing-coverts with small white dots

To 400 m

Below 300 m

(hardly noticeable in field). ♀ brown above, more rufescent on back and rump, with dorsal patch as in ♂; wing-coverts with small buff dots; *tail blackish. Throat white, breast orange-rufous* becoming paler on midbelly, olivaceous on flanks. **Similar species:** ♂ in Ecuador much blacker than in most of the rest of species' range, so most likely confused with ♂ of Black or Blackish Antbird (though voices very different); those show more obvious white fringing on wing-coverts. ♀♀ differ markedly. ♀ Spot-winged Antbird is more uniformly orange-rufous below. **Habits:** Usually in pairs, foraging close to ground in dense swampy growth; usually not with flocks, and rarely if ever attends antswarms. Mainly recorded when vocalizing. **Voice:** ♂'s incisive song a fast and ascending series of sharp, high-pitched notes, "chee-ch-chee, chi-chi-chi-chí-chí" (sometimes sounding like peeping of baby chicks); sometimes ♀ answers with its more evenly pitched song. Both sexes give various scolds and chatters and a "cheeyt" call.

Plumbeous Antbird, *Myrmeciza hyperythra*
Hormiguero Plomizo   Plate 63(4)

17–18 cm (6¾–7″). Numerous in under-growth and borders of *várzea and floodplain forest in lowlands of northeast. Extensive bare blue skin around eye* (essentially an elongated tear-shaped patch behind eye). ♂ *uniform slaty gray*, more blackish on wings and tail; *wing-coverts with small but conspicuous white spots.* ♀ like ♂ above (*including wing-spots*); *below uniform rich orange-rufous.* **Similar species:** ♂ Spot-winged and Slate-colored Antbirds are similar to ♂ Plumbeous but have no bare blue skin around eye, and their wing-spotting

is less prominent; ♀ Spot-winged likewise similar in basic color pattern to ♀ of heftier Plumbeous. ♂ White-shouldered and Sooty Antbirds are blacker than ♂ Plumbeous and lack wing-spotting. **Habits:** Usually seen in pairs, less often small groups, hopping through swampy lower growth; rather unsuspicious and, for an antbird, relatively easy to see. Usually not with mixed flocks, and rarely attends antswarms. Pounds tail downward, especially when disturbed. **Voice:** Distinctive song, given by both sexes, a slightly rising series of very fast notes that accelerate into a rattle, "wo-wu-wu-wu-wu-wu-wu-wrrrrrrrrr," lasting about 3 seconds and with an odd chortling or ringing quality; one of the more characteristic bird sounds at lake edges and in várzea forest in the Río Napo drainage. Calls include a "wo-púr" or "klo-kú." Also gives a fast chattering "chrr-trr-trr-trr-trr-trr-trr" (P. Coopmans).

White-shouldered Antbird
Myrmeciza melanoceps
Hormiguero Hombriblanco   Plate 63(5)

18.5 cm (7¼″). *Numerous* (especially as revealed by voice) in lower growth of várzea and riparian forest and woodland, and borders of terra firme, in *lowlands of east. Small* area of dull bare blue skin around eye. ♂ *uniform lustrous black* with white on shoulders and bend of wing (white usually hard to see). ♀ has *head, throat, and chest black* in striking contrast to *rufous upperparts* and *cinnamon-rufous underparts.* **Similar species:** ♂ resembles ♂ Sooty Antbird though latter is duller black and has more extensive and brighter blue around eye; ♀♀ of the two species are very different. Strikingly patterned ♀ unmistakable aside

To 500 m

from ♀ of localized Cocha Antshrike; latter is smaller with a less heavy bill and no bare blue skin around eye. ♂♂ of these two species also similar, but ♂ antshrike differs in *lacking* white on wing, and blue skin around eye. **Habits:** Usually in pairs that hop through lower growth, often where dense and viny, at times ranging up to 5–8 m above ground. Sometimes accompanies mixed flocks, and occasionally attends antswarms. Pounds tail downward. Heard much more often than seen. **Voice:** ♂'s distinctive song a loud and far-carrying "pur, pee-ur pee-ur pee-ur pee-ur" with ringing quality; sometimes ♀ answers with a soft, short version of its own. Agitated birds also give an abrupt "cheedo-cheeo-cheeo-cheeo-cheeyo" that can sound nunbird-like. Call a loud clear "kluk!," sometimes given in a fast series.

Sooty Antbird, *Myrmeciza fortis*
Hormiguero Tiznado   Plate 63(6)

18.5 cm (7¼"). Undergrowth *inside terra firme forest in lowlands of east*. A persistent antswarm follower. *Extensive bare blue skin around eye*. ♂ *uniform sooty gray*, slightly blacker on crown and foreneck; white along

Mostly below 600 m

bend of wing (usually hard to see). ♀ has *crown rufous-chestnut*; otherwise brown above, somewhat grayer on upper back and more rufescent on wings and rufous-chestnut on tail; white along bend of wing as in ♂. *Sides of head, neck, and underparts uniform gray*, brown on flanks. **Similar species:** ♂ resembles ♂ White-shouldered Antbird, but latter is blacker with less blue around eye and slightly more white shows on wing; it inhabits edge situations, not the deep forest interior favored by Sooty. ♀ ♀ of the two species very different. Immaculate Antbird occurs only west of Andes. **Habits:** A shy antbird of heavy forest, most often seen at army antswarms, when sometimes a bit bolder. Otherwise forages as pairs, generally independent of understory flocks but sometimes with them. Pounds tail downward, especially when nervous. **Voice:** ♂'s song a loud and penetrating "teeuw-teeuw-teeuw-teeuw-teeuw-teeuw-teeuw-teeuw-teeuw," slightly ascending and lasting 2–4 seconds. Also gives a loud, low-pitched rattle. Seems much less vocal than White-shouldered or Immaculate Antbird.

Immaculate Antbird, *Myrmeciza immaculata*
Hormiguero Inmaculado   Plate 63(7)

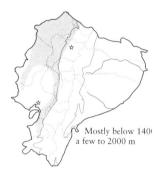

Mostly below 140(
a few to 2000 m

18.5 cm (7¼"). Undergrowth of humid forest and woodland in *lowlands and foothills of west, where the only large Myrmeciza. Extensive bare blue skin around eye* (paler, sometimes whitish, behind eye). ♂ *uniform lustrous black* with white on shoulders (usually hard to see). ♀ *uniform rich dark brown*, marginally paler below with *somewhat contrasting blackish face and upper throat*; tail blackish. **Similar species:** Cf. smaller Chestnut-backed Antbird (which also has bare blue skin around eye). **Habits:** A shy antbird, heard much more often than seen; seems to persist in fragmented habitat better than many other antbirds. Though a persistent follower of army antswarms, the Immaculate also regularly forages as independent pairs. Pounds tail downward, especially when disturbed. **Voice:** ♂'s rapidly delivered song a loud ringing and slightly descending series of clear whistled notes, "peer-peer-peer-peer-peer-peer-peer-peer," slowing a bit toward end. Both sexes also give an explosive "cheek!" call and a fast scolding "jee-jee-jit."

Chestnut-backed Antbird, *Myrmeciza exsul*
Hormiguero Dorsicastaño   Plate 63(1)

Mostly below 900 m, a few to 1500 m around Mindo

13.5 cm (5¼"). *Numerous* in undergrowth inside humid forest and secondary woodland in *lowlands and foothills of west*. Extensive *bare blue skin around eye*; iris dark brown. ♂ has *head, neck, and underparts slaty black* contrasting with *dark chestnut back, wings, and tail*. Wing-coverts with numerous white spots; flanks and crissum brown. ♀ like ♂ above but duller, and spotting on wing-coverts buff. Upper throat slaty; *underparts orange-rufous*, flanks and crissum brown. **Similar species:** Cf. scarcer Esmeraldas Antbird. Otherwise not likely confused in its *western* range; Chestnut-backed does often occur with larger Immaculate Antbird. **Habits:** Usually in pairs, foraging close to ground, sometimes in areas with a fairly open understory but also frequents denser growth found in ravines, along streams, and treefall gaps. Sometimes attracted to army antswarms, but not a persistent follower. Pounds tail downward when alarmed. Heard more often than seen. **Voice:** ♂'s song an easily recognized and imitated set of 2–3 whistled notes, "peh, peeea" or "peh, peh, peeéa" (sometimes paraphrased as "come . . . here" or "come . . . right . . . heéar"); ♀'s song similar but higher pitched. Calls include a soft nasal churring, "kreeuyr," and a sharper, fast "whit-it."

Esmeraldas Antbird, *Myrmeciza nigricauda*
Hormiguero Esmeraldeño   Plate 62(20)

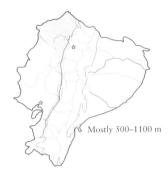

Mostly 500–1100 m

14 cm (5½"). *Undergrowth of humid lowland and (especially) foothill forest and secondary woodland in west*. Formerly named *Sipia rosenbergi*. Iris bright red. ♂ *dark leaden gray* with semiconcealed white dorsal patch; wing-coverts blacker with small but conspicuous white dots. ♀ like ♂ but back, rump, and wings dark chestnut brown with spotting on wing-coverts usually buff; *throat lightly spotted or scaled with white*, flanks and lower belly dark brown. **Similar species:** ♂ Chestnut-backed Antbird resembles ♀ Esmeraldas, though differing in its dark brown iris, bare blue skin around eye, and *lack* of throat flecking; however, ♀ Chestnut-backed, with orange-rufous underparts, looks very different. Cf. also Stub-tailed Antbird. **Habits:** Similar to Chestnut-backed Antbird, and sometimes with it. Favors undergrowth on damp slopes and near shady streams. Hops about in pairs, sometimes attending small antswarms. Pounds tail downward. **Voice:** ♂'s song a short series of very high-pitched, thin, and sharp notes, well enunciated but not very farcarrying, "psee-pseé-psi-psi-psi-pseé," usually with second and always last note higher pitched and emphasized. ♀ sometimes echoes with a short version. Both sexes give a sharp but nasal and falling "skweeyr" or "sk-kweeyr."

Stub-tailed Antbird, *Myrmeciza berlepschi*
Hormiguero Colimocho   Plate 62(21)

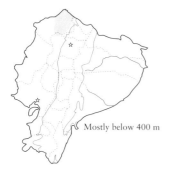

Mostly below 400 m

Mostly below 600 m,
a few to 1100 m

13.5 cm (5¼"). Undergrowth of humid forest, secondary woodland, and borders in *lowlands of far northwest*. Formerly placed in genus *Sipia*. Iris reddish brown. ♂ *entirely black*, relieved only by semiconcealed white dorsal patch. ♀ as in ♂, but wing-coverts with sparse white spotting, and *throat and breast with conspicuous white spotting.* **Similar species:** Both sexes of Esmeraldas Antbird have an obvious bright red eye; ♂ Esmeraldas is grayer with white wing-spotting, ♀ Esmeraldas is gray and brown with white flecking below only on throat. **Habits:** Usually in pairs that forage close to ground in dense undergrowth, favoring areas of secondary growth and around treefall gaps. Pounds tail downward. **Voice:** ♂'s song a series of downslurred notes that first drop and then rise in pitch, e.g., "chi-chu-chu-chu-chew-chéw-chéw-chéw." Calls include a sharp "chit" and a "ch-dit."

White-plumed Antbird, *Pithys albifrons*
Hormiguero Cuerniblanco   Plate 63(8)

12 cm (4¾"). An unmistakable, *ornately plumed* little antbird found in undergrowth *inside terra firme forest in lowlands of east. A persistent antswarm follower.* Legs yellow-orange. **Sexes alike.** *Conspicuous long white plumes on either side of forehead held up in a bifurcated point,* and *shorter white plumes on chin form "beard"*; head and throat black, mantle and wings dark blue-gray. *Nuchal collar, underparts, rump, and tail chestnut.* **Juvenile** duller with white plumes reduced or absent, and no rufous collar. **Similar species:** Only possible confusion would be with rare

and little known White-masked Antbird (*Pithys castanea*; see Plate 63[9]), known from only one specimen taken just over border in Peru near Río Pastaza and perhaps a hybrid between White-plumed and some other antbird (White-shouldered?). It resembles White-plumed but is larger (14 cm; 5½") and lacks white plumes; mostly chestnut with black head and throat, white face and chin, no gray mantle. **Habits:** The classic (and original) "antbird," only infrequently seen away from army antswarms, where 12 or more individuals may gather. Even there usually wary, retreating to dense cover if disturbed, churring in alarm. Typically clings to slender vertical stems, dropping quickly to ground in pursuit of prey, then continuing on to another branch. **Voice:** Utters a thin listless "tseeee" note, sometimes interspersed with "chip" notes, and a descending "chyurrr" (latter especially when at antswarms). Curiously, White-plumed seems to have no loud territorial song.

Gymnopithys **Antbirds**
Plump and short-tailed antbirds found in undergrowth of humid forest. The Bicolored is one of the more numerous "professional" attendants at army antswarms.

Bicolored Antbird, *Gymnopithys leucaspis*
Hormiguero Bicolor   Plate 63(11)

14–14.5 cm (5½–5¾"). Widespread in undergrowth inside humid forest and mature woodland in *lowlands of both east and west. Often at antswarms.* Sometimes treated as two species: White-cheeked Antbird (*G. leucaspis*) east of Andes, Bicolored Antbird (*G. bicolor*) west of them. *Bare ocular area pale bluish* (and therefore striking) *east of*

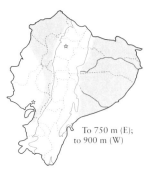

To 750 m (E);
to 900 m (W)

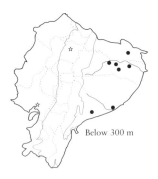

Below 300 m

Andes, but *dusky* (and less conspicuous) *west of Andes*; legs gray. **Eastern birds** *uniform chestnut brown above*. *Below white*, the white extending up to include lower cheeks; a black band extends from face down sides of neck and breast to flanks, where mixed with brown. ♀ like ♂, but with semiconcealed cinnamon-rufous dorsal patch. **Western birds** similar, differing in having more rufous crown and *gray border above black* (not white) *cheeks*. ♀ lacks dorsal patch. **Similar species:** This well-named antbird, brown above and white below, is hard to confuse, especially when at antswarms it so habitually frequents. **Habits:** Almost always found at army antswarms, where often one of the more numerous species present; 12 or more may attend big swarms. Like other small ant-following antbirds, Bicolored frequently perches on slender vertical stems, dropping quickly to the ground to pursue prey flushed by the ants. Though usually shy, at times it can be relatively bold, especially when at a swarm. **Voice:** Rather noisy; Bicolored's calls are often the first indication of the presence of an antswarm. ♂'s song a series of whistled notes, at first rising and semimusical, then descending and more nasal, characteristically ending with a snarl or "chrrr." Both sexes give a "chrrr" call.

Lunulated Antbird, *Gymnopithys lunulata*
Hormiguero Lunado   Plate 63(10)

14.5 cm (5¾″). *Rare and local in undergrowth of várzea forest in lowlands of east.* ♂ uniform gray with *contrasting white throat*; tail more blackish. ♀ mainly olive brown, *supraloral stripe and throat contrastingly white*; *feathers of back and wing-*

coverts with black subterminal band and buff tip, imparting an obvious banded effect; tail dusky with three whitish bars on inner webs of feathers. **Similar species:** *Prominent contrasting white throat of both sexes* makes this scarce antbird virtually impossible to confuse. **Habits:** Infrequently encountered, this antbird remains one of the least known in Ecuador. Pairs and small groups have been seen at army antswarms. **Voice:** ♂'s song a fast series of evenly pitched notes, then slowing into several consecutively lower-pitched notes; it has much the same quality and pattern as Bicolored Antbird though lacking the rise in middle of song (J. Moore recording). Both sexes also give various "chip" and "churr" notes, especially when agitated.

Hairy-crested Antbird
Rhegmatorhina melanosticta
Hormiguero Cresticanoso   Plate 63(12)

15 cm (6″). *Scarce in undergrowth inside terra firme forest in lowlands of east. Often at antswarms. Wide bare ocular area pale bluish to whitish ("goggle-like"); crown feathers filamentous and hair-like*, sometimes

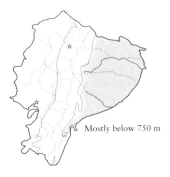

Mostly below 750 m

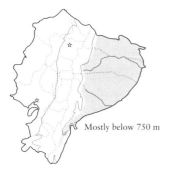

Mostly below 750 m

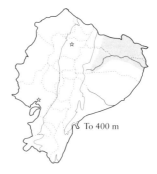

To 400 m

raised as bushy crest. ♂ has *pale smoky gray crown* and *black face and upper throat*; otherwise brown above, more rufescent on wings; tail blackish. Underparts uniform brown. ♀ like ♂ but *feathers of back and wing-coverts with wide black subterminal band and very narrow buff tip*, imparting irregular spotted or scaly effect. **Similar species:** No other Ecuadorian antbird has nearly as wide and round a bare ocular area. **Habits:** Typically rather shy, foraging primarily at army antswarms, mainly in hilly terra firme well away from larger rivers. Clings to vertical stems and branches close to ground, dropping briefly to snap up flushed prey; rarely stays on ground for very long. Flicks tail upward. **Voice:** ♂'s rather slow song a short series of wheezy, somewhat nasal whistled notes, e.g., "wheeeyr, wheer-wheer-wheer-wheer" with descending effect; sometimes there are several snarling or churring notes at end, or these may be given independently.

Phlegopsis Bare-eyes

Spectacular, large antbirds with *extensive bare red ocular skin* found in undergrowth of humid forest in the eastern lowlands. They tend to segregate by habitat, Black-spotted in várzea and riparian areas, Reddish-winged in terra firme.

Black-spotted Bare-eye
Phlegopsis nigromaculata
Carirrosa Negripunteada   Plate 63(18)

18.5 cm (7¼"). A stunning *large* antbird found in undergrowth inside *várzea and floodplain forest and woodland in lowlands of northeast*. Large bare ocular area bright red (darker in juveniles). **Sexes alike.** *Head,*

neck, and underparts black, flanks and crissum brown. Back and wing-coverts olive brown *with scattered large tear-like black spots encircled with buff*; flight feathers and tail rufous-chestnut. **Habits:** Almost invariably found when following army antswarms, where it is dominant over any other antbirds present; at large swarms upward of 12 birds can be in attendance. On rare—and very special—occasions both species of bare-eyes are found foraging at the same swarm. **Voice:** ♂'s distinctive and slow song a simple raspy "zhweé, zhwu" or "zhweé, zhwu, zhwu." Both sexes also give, especially at antswarms or when alarmed, a rough and drawn-out "zhheeeuw."

Reddish-winged Bare-eye
Phlegopsis erythroptera
Carirrosa Alirrojiza   Plate 63(19)

To 750 m

18.5 cm (7¼"). A handsome *large* antbird, *scarce* in undergrowth inside *terra firme forest in lowlands of east*. Large bare ocular area bright red in ♂ but *much reduced in* ♀ (little more than a small triangle behind eye). ♂ unmistakable: *mostly black* with *feathers of back, wing-coverts, and rump with narrow white fringes*, imparting a scaly effect; *wings with bold rufous markings* (two broad wing-bars, tipping on tertials, and large patch on flight feathers). ♀ dark rufescent brown above with blackish wings and tail, *wings with two bold bands on coverts and another across flight feathers. Below rich rufous*, becoming duller and browner on belly. **Similar species:** ♀ readily known by combination of large size, rich rufous coloration, and prominent buff wing-banding. **Habits:** Usually in pairs that forage in dense undergrowth and typically are shy and hard to see well. Most often found when following a swarm of army ants, where it is dominant over other passerine birds present except larger woodcreepers. Wary and quick to retreat to cover even at such swarms, returning only slowly. **Voice:** ♂'s song a short descending series of some 4–6 harsh and piercing notes that drop in strength; Black-spotted's similar song has fewer notes and is more slowly delivered. Both sexes give a snarling, downslurred "skíyarrr" at antswarms.

Ocellated Antbird, *Phaenostictus mcleannani*
Hormiguero Ocelado   Plate 63(20)

Mostly below 400 m,
a few to 700 m

19.5 cm (7¾"). *Scarce* in undergrowth of humid forest in *lowlands of far northwest. Unmistakable. Very large area of bare bright blue skin around eye.* **Sexes alike.** Crown grayish; otherwise olive brown above, *back and wing-coverts with large buff-rimmed black spots*; tail blackish. Ear-coverts, throat, and chest black; *nape, sides of neck, and underparts rufous-chestnut with large buff-rimmed black spots on breast and upper belly*, lower belly brown. **Habits:** When this spectacular antbird is found—never often enough—it is usually in pairs that forage

mainly at antswarms, where they are dominant over other antbirds present (most often Immaculate, Bicolored, and Spotted). Tail is jerked upward abruptly, then slowly lowered. **Voice:** ♂'s infrequently heard song a series of high-pitched, penetrating whistled notes that rise rapidly, then drop at end, e.g., "peee-peee-pee-peepee-ee-ee-ee-ee-ee-ee-ee-eer-eer." A nasal "dzurrr" or "dzeerr" call is often given at antswarms.

Wing-banded Antbird, *Myrmornis torquata*
Hormiguero Alifranjeado   Plate 63(21)

Below 400 m

15 cm (6"). *Rare and local inside hilly terra firme forest in lowlands of east.* An odd-looking ("dumpy") *terrestrial* antbird with *short legs, short tail*, and long bill. Orbital area grayish blue. ♂ brown above mottled with chestnut and dusky, and with small semi-concealed white dorsal patch; wings blackish, coverts and outer flight feathers edged buff; tail rufous-chestnut. *Throat and chest black* bordered by *wide area of black and white scaling extending from behind eye down sides of neck to sides of chest*; remaining underparts gray, crissum rufous. ♀ similar but with *throat and upper chest rufous*, only malar area black. **Similar species:** This chunky terrestrial antbird is so distinctively shaped that confusion is improbable; though short-tailed like an antpitta, it has much shorter legs than any member of that group, and its behavior is much more like that of various "typical" antbirds. **Habits:** Poorly known in Ecuador, from whence there is only one recent record. Elsewhere it ranges mainly as pairs, hopping or shuffling (not walking) in leaf litter, often tame for an antbird. Forages by probing into ground or flicking aside leaves with bill. Rarely or never with flocks or at antswarms.

Voice: ♂'s infrequently heard song, often delivered from a perch 3–6 m above ground, a long series of insistent emphatic whistled notes that gradually ascend in pitch and characteristically increase in intensity, e.g., "tueee-tueee-tueee-tueee-tueee . . . tueee!-tueee!-tueee!" Both sexes also regularly give a nasal "chirr" or "churr" call, especially when nervous or startled.

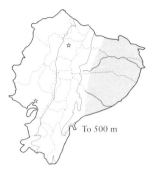

To 500 m

Antthrushes and Antpittas: Formicariidae (30)

Although formerly united with the Typical Antbirds (Thamnophilidae), the Antthrushes and Antpittas (sometimes called "ground antbirds") are now accorded family rank. As befits birds of the forest floor, they are somberly hued in shades of brown, rufous, and gray, though the patterns of many species are attractive. Their legs are long and bills often quite heavy. Antthushes are reminiscent of certain rails, and their tails are often held somewhat cocked; antpittas, on the other hand, appear virtually tail-less. Antthrushes tend to walk, antpittas to hop. Shy and elusive, members of this family are all too infrequently seen, though many species have loud songs that at least reveal their presence.

Formicarius Antthrushes

Dark and plainly attired antbirds that walk on the floor of humid lowland and montane forests, usually with their *tail cocked up jauntily*. Shy and inconspicuous birds, they vocalize often and can be quite responsive to tape playback.

Rufous-capped Antthrush, *Formicarius colma*
Formicario Gorrirrufo   Plate 64(13)

18 cm (7"). On or near ground *inside terra firme forest in lowlands of east*. **Sexes alike.** Forecrown and face black, *hindcrown rufous*; upperparts otherwise uniform olive brown; tail blackish. *Throat and breast sooty black*, becoming dull grayish on belly. **Juveniles** (especially ♀ ♀ ?) have throat white, usually speckled with black. **Similar species:** Black-faced Antthrush, which tends *not* to occur in extensive terra firme, differs in its brown crown (with no rufous) and black on throat only (not extending onto face and sides of neck, nor down over breast). Rufous-breasted Antthrush occurs only in montane

forests; its breast is extensively rufous. Rufous-capped occurs in same terre firme forests as Striated Antthrush, which differs in its larger size and shorter tail; Striated shows scalloped pattern below. **Habits:** Usually seen alone, walking slowly and deliberately on forest floor, generally with tail cocked up like a little rail, occasionally pausing to sing. Turns leaves over with bill, or flicks them aside, searching for insect prey in leaf litter. On rare occasions one is seen in attendance at an army antswarm. Heard much more often than seen. **Voice:** ♂'s lovely song a fast series of high-pitched musical notes which at first falter and drop a little in pitch, then gradually rise; usually lasts 4–6 seconds. Also given, by both sexes, is a sharp and piercing "kyew!" or "tchew!" alarm call (J. Moore recording), very different from other *Formicarius*.

Black-faced Antthrush, *Formicarius analis*
Formicario Carinegro   Plate 64(14)

18 cm (7"). On or near ground inside humid forest and woodland in *lowlands of east*, where more *widespread* (ranging in various forest types, even in more mature secondary

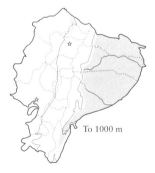

To 1000 m

growth) and *numerous* than Rufous-capped Antthrush. Bare ocular area bluish white, widest in front of and behind eye. **Sexes alike.** Uniform brown above, more rufescent on wings and rump, and with small white loral spot; tail blackish. *Lower cheeks and throat black*; breast gray becoming paler grayish on belly, somewhat browner on flanks; crissum rufous. **Juvenile** similar, but throat whitish flecked or scaled with dusky. **Similar species:** Only possible confusion is with more boldly marked Rufous-capped Antthrush (with contrasting rufous hindcrown, black on face and down over breast, etc.). **Habits:** Similar to Rufous-capped Antthrush. Like that species, heard more often than seen. **Voice:** ♂'s far-carrying and musical song consists of an emphasized drawn-out note followed by a distinct pause, then a fast series of shorter notes, first ascending and becoming louder, then descending, slowing, and fading away, e.g., "tüüü, ti-ti-tí-tí-tí-ti-te-te-tu-tu-tu-tu." Sometimes also gives a slower descending series of more evenly spaced notes. Alarm call, given by both sexes, an abrupt "churlew!"

Black-headed Antthrush
Formicarius nigricapillus
Formicario Cabecinegro　　　　　Plate 64(12)

Mostly below 900 m

18 cm (7″). On or near ground inside *humid lowland and foothill forest in west*. Bare ocular area bluish white, widest in front of and behind eye. **Sexes nearly alike.** *Entire head, neck, throat, and chest black*, becoming rich dark brown on upperparts, and shading into slaty gray on breast and slightly paler gray on belly; uppertail-coverts and crissum rufous-chestnut. ♀ has belly tinged olivaceous brown. **Similar species:** The only *Formicarius* antthrush in most of its

western range; may overlap very locally with more montane Rufous-breasted Antthrush, but for the most part these two species replace each other altitudinally. **Habits:** Similar to Rufous-capped Antthrush though even harder to see, mainly because of its generally more thickly vegetated habitat and more uniform, dark plumage. Heard much more often than seen. **Voice:** ♂'s distinctive song a loud and resonant series of 15–30 short whistled notes, the first few slower, then rising a little in pitch before evening out, the last notes slower and a bit louder, ending abruptly. Alarm call similar to Black-faced Antthrush's.

Rufous-breasted Antthrush
Formicarius rufipectus
Formicario Pechirrufo　　　　　Plate 64(15)

Mostly 1100–2000 m, locally lower on W slope

19 cm (7½″). On or near ground in *foothill and (especially) subtropical forest and woodland on both slopes*. Bare ocular area bluish white, broadest in front of and behind eye. **Sexes alike. West-slope birds** have *entire crown and nape chestnut* contrasting with *black face and throat*; otherwise dark brown above, more rufescent on uppertail-coverts; tail blackish. *Breast rich rufous-chestnut*, becoming olivaceous gray on flanks; crissum also rufous-chestnut. **East-slope birds** similar but with crown blackish (contrasting little or not at all with black face) and browner on flanks. **Juvenile** duller, with whitish throat. **Similar species:** Not likely confused in its *montane* range; easily recognized by the rufous breast, unique in genus. Cf. various *Grallaria* antpittas (differently shaped, etc.). **Habits:** Similar to Rufous-capped Antthrush, though seems shyer; the hardest *Formicarius* to see, doubtless in part because of its steep and densely vegetated habitat. Heard much

more often than seen. **Voice:** ♂'s distinctive song a simple pair of whistled notes, rapidly delivered, "hü-hü," with second note either a semitone above first (usually) or on same pitch. Yellow-breasted Antpitta can sound similar, especially at a distance when its first note cannot be heard. Alarm call similar to Black-faced Antthrush's, but sometimes given in a short series.

Chamaeza Antthrushes

Fairly large, terrestrial antbirds found inside humid and montane forests, *Chamaeza* antthrushes resemble *Formicarius* but are plumper, shorter billed, and have very different, boldly patterned underparts. **Sexes are alike.** Even shyer than *Formicarius*, *Chamaeza* antthrushes are also heard much more often than seen.

Short-tailed Antthrush
Chamaeza campanisona
Chamaeza Colicorto   Plate 64(10)

950–1700 m

19 cm (7½"). On or near ground inside *foothill and lower subtropical forest on e. slope.* Lower mandible pale grayish pink. *Olivaceous brown above* with *whitish loral spot, postocular streak, and patch on sides of neck*; tail with blackish subterminal band and narrow whitish tip. Below whitish (tinged buff across chest and on lower belly) *coarsely streaked blackish brown* except on throat (which is only faintly speckled) and median belly (where streaking sparser); crissum buff with sparse black markings. **Similar species:** Resembles Striated Antthrush in plumage, but latter is considerably larger, more rufescent above, and much whiter on throat and median lower underparts; Striated occurs in lowlands, *below* elevation range of Short-tailed (no known overlap). **Habits:** Very shy

and hard to see, encountered singly or in pairs as they slowly walk along on forest floor, often pumping their somewhat cocked tail and looking a little like a bantam hen. Singing birds often take a somewhat elevated perch such as a horizontal branch, standing high with head back and neck arched. Heard much more often than seen. **Voice:** ♂'s beautiful two-parted song a series of hollow musical "cow" notes that start slowly but quickly accelerate and become louder, then abruptly shift into descending series of 4–6 lower-pitched "wo" or "wop" notes that gradually become weaker and fade away. Alarm call a mellifluous "ku-it."

Striated Antthrush, *Chamaeza nobilis*
Chamaeza Noble   Plate 64(9)

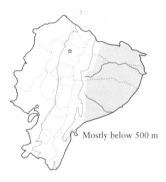

Mostly below 500 m

22.5 cm (8¾"). On or near ground inside *terra firme forest in lowlands of east.* Sometimes called Noble Antthrush. Base of lower mandible whitish. *Rufescent brown above* with *white loral spot, postocular streak, and patch on sides of neck*; tail with blackish subterminal band and narrow whitish tip. *White below* (no buff tinge) with *bold blackish scalloping across breast, down flanks, and on crissum*. **Similar species:** Short-tailed Antthrush has similar pattern but is decidedly smaller and less white below (this especially marked on Striated's throat and midbelly), and its pattern below is more one of streaking (not scalloping); the two species are not known to occur together, Short-tailed replacing Striated on lower slopes. **Habits:** Much as in Short-tailed Antthrush, but this splendid bird seems even shyer and harder to see, even after tape playback often remaining difficult. Heard much more often than seen. **Voice:** ♂'s beautiful song similar to Short-tailed Antthrush's, but typically longer and lower in pitch, delivered more rapidly, and often with longer series of trailing "woo" or "wooop" notes. Alarm call a loud, frog-like, upward-inflected "kowep?" often given as bird paces back and forth agitatedly, sometimes atop a fallen log but more often on ground. Also gives a loud ringing "wak-wak-wak-wak-wak . . ." (upward of 20 "wak"s).

Barred Antthrush, *Chamaeza mollissima*
Chamaeza Barreteado   Plate 64(11)

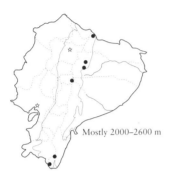

Mostly 2000–2600 m

20.5 cm (8″). *Rare on or near ground inside subtropical and temperate forest on e. slope.* Above rich chestnut brown with buffy whitish loral spot and *postocular stripe and stripe on sides of neck closely barred dusky-brown and white. Below densely barred dusky-brown and white.* Similar species: Other *Chamaeza* antthrushes are streaked or scalloped below; none ranges at nearly such high elevations. Several *Grallaria* antpittas are also barred below, but these are very differently shaped. **Habits:** Much as in Short-tailed Antthrush, though this superb antthrush is even more secretive and harder to see. Heard much more often than seen. **Voice:** ♂'s beautiful song a long, ascending, and fast series of musical "cuh" notes that become increasingly loud before abruptly ending (unlike other *Chamaeza*, has no descending terminal notes), lasting 15–22 seconds. Alarm call a fast "whi-whik!" (M. Lysinger recording).

Rufous-crowned Antpitta
Pittasoma rufopileatum
Pitasoma Coronirrufa   Plate 64(5)

16.5 cm (6½″). On or near ground *inside humid lowland and foothill forest in north-*

Mostly 200–700 m

west (mainly Esmeraldas). Long straight bill black; long legs gray. Unmistakable. ♂ with *rufous-chestnut crown and nape* and *long broad black superciliary that extends back to nape*; back olive brown with broad black striping; wings more rufescent, wing-coverts and tertials spotted whitish. *Cheeks, sides of neck, and throat ochraceous* sparsely dotted with black; *underparts evenly and boldly barred black and white.* ♀ has black superciliary spotted with whitish, and *underparts ochraceous with only sparse and irregular black spotting and speckling.* **Habits:** Found singly or in pairs, bounding along rapidly on long legs, then pausing and freezing for extended periods. A startled bird may flush up onto a low branch. Apparently feeds regularly at army antswarms, and then can be surprisingly bold and even tame (more so than most other ant-following antbirds), hopping about unconcernedly only a few meters away. **Voice:** Song a piercing whistled "keeee-yurh" (almost with quality of Great Jacamar), repeated steadily at several-second intervals (P. Coopmans; in sw. Colombia); sometimes varied to an inflected "tyuuee" (O. Jahn recording). Calls include a loud and emphatic "tche-tchik!" and a harsh and guttural "kuk kuk kuk kuk kuk" (O. Jahn recordings), latter much as in extralimital Black-crowned Antpitta (*P. michleri*).

Grallaria Antpittas
A wonderful group of plump and round antbirds whose feathers are often fluffed up, making them look even more rotund; they have stout bills, very short tails, and very long bluish gray legs (pinkish in Watkins's). Although none is really colorful, antpittas are attractively patterned in shades of brown, rufous, and gray, and they often show some

scaling, barring, or streaking (especially below). **Sexes are alike.** Antpittas are essentially terrestrial birds found inside humid and montane forests; considering how dense their habitat is, they are capable of hopping or bounding, kangaroo-like, with astonishing rapidity. Although vocal, most species are shy and very infrequently seen (Tawny being an exception); singing birds often perch off the ground.

Giant Antpitta, *Grallaria gigantea*
Gralaria Gigante   Plate 65(2)

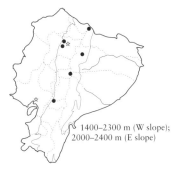

1400–2300 m (W slope);
2000–2400 m (E slope)

24 cm (9½″). *Rare and seeminly local on or near ground in subtropical forest and borders on both slopes,* occasionally into secondary growth; apparently only in n. Ecuador. *Heavy bill,* black above and horn to pale dusky below. **West-slope birds** have *rufous forehead* grading into gray crown and nape, latter contrasting with olive brown upperparts. *Sides of head and neck and entire underparts rich orange-rufous with narrow wavy black barring.* **East-slope birds** similar but *ground color on underparts paler and more ochraceous buff.* **Similar species:** Well named, easily the largest antpitta in Ecuador. Undulated Antpitta is smaller (though hardly a small bird), and further differs in its prominent blackish submalar stripe and lack of rufous on forehead (showing loral spot instead); it occurs at higher elevations than Giant. Undulated and e.-slope Giants have about same ventral ground color. Cf. also Moustached Antpitta. **Habits:** Favors wet muddy places. Usually found singly, hopping with great springing bounds on ground, fallen logs, and through low undergrowth. Feeds mostly on ground, probing in muddy soil and leaf litter; may feed primarily on

large earthworms. On infrequent occasions, the normally elusive Giant Antpitta comes out into wet pastures immediately adjacent to forest, this perhaps especially in early morning. **Voice:** W.-slope ♂'s song, usually given from a low perch 1–4 m above ground, a fast quavering hollow trill that lasts about 5 seconds and gradually increases in strength before ending in a crescendo (overall effect rather owl-like); e.-slope song similar but slightly higher pitched and typically lacking a strongly accented ending. It closely resembles Undulated Antpitta's song. Western birds also give a much shorter (0.5-second) hollow trill, "hohohohohohohoho" (F. Sornoza recording).

Undulated Antpitta, *Grallaria squamigera*
Gralaria Ondulada   Plate 65(1)

2200–3700 m

21.5 cm (8½″). On or near ground inside *upper subtropical and temperate forest and woodland on both slopes,* also above central and interandean valleys. Bill black above, horn below; legs grayish flesh. Crown and nape gray with buffyish loral spot; upperparts grayish olive. *Sides of head and neck, and most of underparts, ochraceous with coarse wavy black barring*; midthroat white bordered by *prominent black submalar stripe.* **Southeastern birds** (north to Morona-Santiago) have entirely gray upperparts and whitish loral area. **Similar species:** A *large* antpitta, usually readily recognizable on that basis alone. Giant Antpitta is even bigger, and has a more massive bill, rufous forehead, and no malar stripe. **Habits:** Shy and retiring, infrequently seen even in perfect habitat; occasionally, most often in early morning, one may hop along a forest trail or come out to forest borders (and then can be confiding).

Voice: ♂'s song, usually given from a somewhat elevated perch inside forest or woodland, a fast hollow quavering trill that slightly ascends in pitch and lasts 3–4 seconds, e.g., "hohohohohohohohohohohoho," with last few notes more enunciated. Overall effect is rather like a screech-owl, and as the antpitta often sings in darkness before dawn or after dusk, it easily can be mistaken for one. It closely resembles Giant Antpitta's song. Undulated's singing season seems notably short, about Nov.–Jan. Rarely heard call a hollow "rrhooh-rrhooh-rrhooh" (P. Coopmans).

Scaled Antpitta, *Grallaria guatimalensis*
Gralaria Escamada   Plate 65(3)

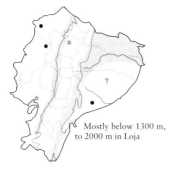

Mostly below 1300 m,
to 2000 m in Loja

16 cm (6¼"). On or near ground *inside humid forest and woodland in lowlands and foothills of east and west.* Bill blackish above, grayish below; legs grayish pink. Above olive brown with grayer crown and nape, *feathers edged black imparting a scaly look* (obvious in fresh plumage, at other times less so); lores whitish. Throat and chest brownish olive with *semiconcealed white crescent across upper chest* and *buffyish to whitish malar stripe; underparts rich rufous to tawny-buff.* Some individuals show white streaking on breast. **Similar species:** Cf. closely similar Moustached Antpitta (which in the north replaces Scaled at higher elevations). Plain-backed Antpitta has white patch on lower throat (though lacking Scaled's crescent) and shows little or no scaly pattern on upperparts. **Habits:** Shy, secretive, and hard to see. Generally found singly, hopping quickly on forest floor, pausing to flick aside leaves with bill and to probe into moist soil. Soon after dawn one may emerge to feed along damp

trails or even at edge of little-traveled roads. Startled birds sometimes flush up to a perch at some height above ground. Heard more often than seen. **Voice:** ♂'s song a low-pitched, hollow, and resonant trill that gradually increases in pitch and volume, characteristically slowing in middle before accelerating again; ♀ may answer with shorter trill. Notes are not quite as rapidly delivered as in Giant and Undulated Antpittas. Often sings from an elevated perch (at times to 6–8 m above ground).

Moustached Antpitta, *Grallaria alleni*
Gralaria Bigotuda   Plate 65(4)

1850–2200 m

16.5 cm (6½"). On or near ground inside *subtropical forest* on both slopes in *n. Ecuador* (thus far only in *w. Pichincha and w. Napo*). Ranges *above* range of very similar Scaled Antpitta. Differs from Scaled in its *creamy whitish belly* (not ochraceous), darker upperparts, uniformly dark brown cheeks, and black scaling in white malar stripe. **Habits:** Not well known; only in mid-1990s was it realized that Moustached Antpitta even occurred in Ecuador. It resembles Scaled Antpitta in overall behavior. **Voice:** ♂'s song a slightly ascending series of hollow notes that gradually become louder; higher pitched and slower paced than Scaled Antpitta's song.

Plain-backed Antpitta, *Grallaria haplonota*
Gralaria Dorsillana   Plate 65(5)

16 cm (6¼"). Local on or near ground inside *foothill and subtropical* forest on both slopes. Bill blackish above, grayish below; legs grayish pink. **West-slope birds** *uniform olive brown above* with whitish to pale buffyish lores; tail rufescent. *Midthroat white* bor-

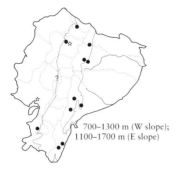

700–1300 m (W slope);
1100–1700 m (E slope)

dered by *dusky submalar stripe* and *pale buff malar stripe*; *remaining underparts ochraceous*, deeper on breast. **East-slope birds** similar but faintly scaled with blackish above, and not so richly colored below with more olivaceous mottling on breast. **Similar species:** Recalls Scaled Antpitta, but brighter and more uniformly ochraceous below (with no white chest crescent), and never as "scaly" as that species (not even on e. slope). **Habits:** Similar to Scaled Antpitta, but even more secretive (the hardest antpitta actually to see). **Voice:** ♂'s song, often delivered from slightly elevated perch, a series of 10–18 low, hollow, mournful notes that gradually become louder and rise slightly in pitch, then fall at end. Thrush-like Antpitta's song is similar in quality but with fewer notes.

Chestnut-crowned Antpitta
Grallaria ruficapilla
Gralaria Coronicastaña   Plate 65(6)

18.5 cm (7¼″). *Numerous and widespread on or near ground in subtropical and temperate forest, woodland, and borders on both slopes. Legs grayish blue. Head and nape orange-rufous*; otherwise olive brown above. Throat white; *underparts white with bold*

Mostly 1900–3100 m

blackish brown streaking, mainly on sides and flanks. **El Oro and Loja** birds similar but more pallid generally with whitish lores, some whitish streaking on ear-coverts, and less streaking below. **Similar species:** This attractive montane antpitta is unlikely to be confused in most of its Ecuadorian range, where *the only antpitta with extensive streaking below.* In southwest, cf. Watkins's Antpitta. **Habits:** Though typically shy and secretive like other *Grallaria*, Chestnut-crowned also hops in the semiopen reasonably often, though never straying too far from cover. Most often ranges into open at and soon after dawn. The species tolerates disturbed conditions, persisting even in mainly agricultural areas so long as a few woodland patches and thickly vegetated hedgerows remain. **Voice:** ♂'s frequently heard song, often delivered from a slightly elevated perch (though it also sings from ground, sometimes even out in open) a loud whistled "wheee whuuu wheuu" with distinctive cadence (has been aptly paraphrased as "com-pra pan" or even "can't-see-me"). Alarm call, given by both sexes, a loud and abrupt "keeeuw," sometimes burrier.

Watkins's Antpitta, *Grallaria watkinsi*
Gralaria de Watkins   Plate 65(7)

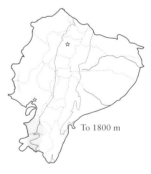

To 1800 m

18 cm (7″). Numerous on or near ground in deciduous and montane forest, woodland, borders, and locally even regenerating scrub in *lowlands and lower subtropics of southwest.* Formerly considered conspecific with slightly larger Chestnut-crowned Antpitta. *Legs pinkish to pale horn.* Watkins's replaces similar Chestnut-crowned at lower elevations; their strikingly different vocalizations can sometimes be heard from same spot.

Watkins's differs in leg color (those of Chestnut-crowned being bluish or grayish), *more pallid and less extensive rufous on crown and nape* with more whitish shaft streaking and more white streaking on ear-coverts. Most often the two are distinguished by voice. **Habits:** Similar to Chestnut-crowned Antpitta, likewise more apt to be in semiopen than most other antpittas, though at times Watkins's will skulk like any other. Often responds strongly to tape playback. **Voice:** ♂'s distinctive and often-heard song a series of 4–7 well-enunciated and emphatic whistled notes, the first set all similar but the last longer and sharply upslurred, e.g., "keeu, kew-kew-kew k-wheeeei?" Also gives various shorter calls consisting of fewer initial notes plus the last slurred one, or just the slurred one alone.

Jocotoco Antpitta, *Grallaria ridgelyi*
Gralaria Jocotoco   Plate 96(9)

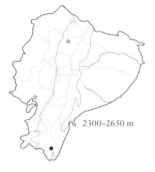

2300–2650 m

23 cm (9″). *Uncommon and extremely local on or near ground inside temperate forest with extensive bamboo on e. slope in s. Zamora-Chinchipe* (mainly at Quebrada Honda/Tapichalaca Reserve). A recently described species, *unmistakable* and *very different from any other antpitta. Crown glossy black* contrasting with *broad snowy white malar stripe that starts at lores* and is outlined by *black submalar stripe* and ear-coverts; otherwise rich olive brown above, back variably suffused with black; wings, especially flight feathers, more rufescent. *Throat snowy white*; underparts white, variably suffused and mottled with gray, especially across breast and down flanks; crissum dusky. **Similar species:** No other antpitta is patterned anything like this very large species. **Habits:** Poorly known, but seems

similar to other antpittas. Very difficult to observe, in part because of the steep and heavily vegetated terrain it favors, in part because it appears genuinely shy and wary. Ranges in pairs, mainly on steep slopes near streams, at times responding strongly to tape-recordings of its voice, sometimes even audibly crashing through undergrowth; agitated birds often run rapidly back and forth on horizontal branches, bobbing their head and occasionally pausing to sing. Pairs seem highly sedentary. **Voice:** ♂'s unmistakable song—very different from other antpittas'— a series, sometimes long continued (for a minute or more, especially in response to tape playback), of low-pitched hooting "hoo" notes repeated steadily at 1- to 2-second intervals; singing birds arch head back and pump the short tail with each hoot. Other calls, given by both sexes, include a doubled "hoo-coo" and, more infrequently, a more guttural "hoó-krrr." Natural singing is most frequent around dawn and dusk, but may occur at other times of day when light intensity is low, especially in light rain and fog.

Chestnut-naped Antpitta, *Grallaria nuchalis*
Gralaria Nuquicastaña   Plate 65(8)

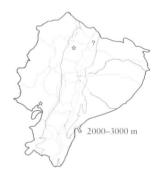

2000–3000 m

19.5 cm (7¼″). On or near ground *inside temperate forest, mainly in extensive bamboo, on e. slope*; on w. slope *scarcer,* ranging south only to Pichincha. Iris gray, with triangular patch of bare whitish skin behind eye; legs leaden gray. **East-slope birds** have *crown, nape, and sides of head rufous-chestnut* (brightest on nape, darker on ear-coverts), becoming uniform reddish brown on upperparts. *Below uniform dark gray,* slightly blacker on throat. **West-slope birds** darker above (chestnut-rufous only on nape), and *much darker and sootier below*. **Similar species:** This handsome antpitta is easily recognized on the basis of its large size and gray underparts; no other Ecuadorian antpitta much resembles it. **Habits:** Favors thick, often impenetrable thickets of *Chusquea* bamboo and therefore difficult to see: even with tape playback, usually remains hidden. Most likely seen hopping along forest trails in early morning, then sometimes tame. Heard much more often than seen. **Voice:** ♂'s song on e. slope a distinctive and far-carrying series of musical but somewhat metallic notes that hesitate at first, then gradually accelerate before ending in a short series of rapidly rising tinkling notes, e.g., "tew; tew, tew, tew-tew-tew-teh-te-ti-ti-titititi?" On w. slope, rarely heard song similar in quality but with a different pattern, lacking initial hesitation and starting with fast phrase, e.g., "tew-te-te-tew, tew-tew-tew-tew-tew-titititi?" (L. Navarrete recording). At least on e. slope also gives an unexpectedly different and strange vocalization, sometimes in response to tape playback but also spontaneously, a repetition of a much higher-pitched note with almost a hummingbird-like quality, e.g., "tsi-tsi-tsi-tséw-tséw-tsi-tsi-tsi."

Bicolored Antpitta, *Grallaria rufocinerea*
Gralaria Bicolor   Not illustrated

15.5 cm (6″). On or near ground in *temperate forest and borders on e. slope in nw. Sucumbíos*. Simply patterned: *rufous brown above and on throat*, with *remaining underparts contrastingly gray*. Some birds show an admixture of gray feathers on face and throat. **Similar species:** Could only be confused with smaller Chestnut-naped Antpitta, which is much less rufescent above and has

black throat. **Habits:** Not well known, but reclusive behavior probably differs little from other montane *Grallaria* such as Chestnut-naped. **Voice:** Song a high clear whistled "treeeee" or more slurred "treeeeeaaaa," given at 2.5- to 3-second intervals (Hilty and Brown 1986).

White-bellied Antpitta, *Grallaria hypoleuca*
Gralaria Ventriblanca   Plate 65(9)

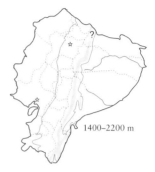

1400–2200 m

17 cm (6¾″). On or near ground in *subtropical forest borders and secondary woodland on e. slope. Above uniform rufous brown*, brightest on cheeks and sides of neck and slightly blacker on forecrown and lores. Throat pure white; *underparts pale gray*, lower belly and crissum tinged buff. **Similar species:** This simply patterned and basically bicolored antpitta (rufescent above, gray below) should be easily recognized. The larger Chestnut-naped Antpitta is much darker below, blackest on throat (instead of having throat white); it occurs at higher elevations. Yellow-breasted Antpitta occurs only on w. slope. **Habits:** Similar to other montane forest *Grallaria* antpittas though White-bellied seems more one of second-growth and borders, persisting in areas with degraded and fragmented habitat. Heard much more often than seen. **Voice:** ♂'s simple and far-carrying song a fast "too, téw-téw," given at rather long intervals (often 10 or more seconds). Also gives a strikingly pygmy-owl-like vocalization, "too, too, too, too . . ." (M. Lysinger recording).

Yellow-breasted Antpitta, *Grallaria flavotincta*
Gralaria Pechiamarillenta   Plate 65(10)

17 cm (6¾″). On or near ground *in subtropical forest and forest borders on w. slope*

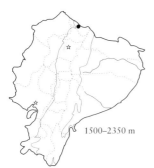

1500–2350 m

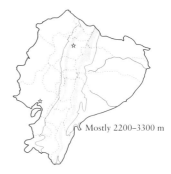

Mostly 2200–3300 m

(south to Pichincha). Formerly often considered conspecific with *G. hypoleuca* (which then was called Bay-backed Antpitta). *Above uniform rufous-brown*, more grayish on lores and darker on cheeks. *Below pale yellowish*; sides, flanks, and crissum mottled with rufous brown. **Similar species:** Not likely confused in its w.-slope range, where there are no similar *Grallaria* antpittas. White-bellied Antpitta ranges only on e. slope; it is much grayer below and lacks rufous on sides. **Habits:** Similar to other montane forest-based antpittas; seems more forest-based than White-bellied Antpitta. Usually found singly, most often hopping on ground. Heard much more often than seen. **Voice:** ♂'s song a fast, musical whistled "pu-püüü-puuh," with first note so quick and soft as to be almost inaudible. When agitated, such as after tape playback, may give a drawn-out shrill and piercing "eeeeeeeeee-yk" (M. Lysinger recording).

Rufous Antpitta, *Grallaria rufula*
Gralaria Rufa   Plate 65(11)

14.5 cm (5¼"). Widespread on or near ground in upper *subtropical and temperate forest and borders, especially in bamboo, on both slopes. Uniform and rather rich rufous*, slightly paler below (especially on belly), and with indistinct pale buffyish eye-ring (widest to rear). **Similar species:** Easily recognized on basis of small size and uniform rufous coloration, unique among *Grallaria* antpittas in Ecuador. **Habits:** Similar to other montane forest-based antpittas, though Rufous seems a little easier to see than others. Hops singly on forest floor and inside *Chusquea* bamboo thickets, especially favoring damp spots or the vicinity of streams. Heard more often

than seen. **Voice:** Has two vocalizations, a series of "tu" notes given so rapidly as almost to be run together into a 1- to 4-second-long trill, and a clear ringing "píh, pipee" or "peé, pipipee." Usually vocalizes from low perch.

Tawny Antpitta, *Grallaria quitensis*
Gralaria Leonada   Plate 65(12)

Mostly 3000–4500 m

16.5 cm (6½"). *Numerous* and—for an antpitta—*conspicuous and easy to see* in *woodland, scrub, and borders in upper temperate zone and paramo on both slopes and above central and interandean valleys;* relatively tolerant of habitat disturbance, and frequent in mainly agricultural areas. *Uniform dull olive brown above* with *whitish lores and eye-ring. Below dull buffy ochraceous,* often somewhat flammulated with olive, whiter on throat and midbelly. Really not "tawny" at all. **Similar species:** Though dull-plumaged, this antpitta is not likely to be confused, so dramatically does it differ in behavior from the others. *No other Ecuadorian antpitta ever emerges from forest depths the way this species so habitually does.* **Habits:** Usually seen singly, often hopping about in open (though rarely far from cover), sometimes—especially in early morning—perching along roadsides or atop a shrub or low tree. Often flicks wings and tail, and bobs up and down, almost comically, on long legs. However, even this antpitta is heard more often than seen. **Voice:** ♂'s often-heard song a loud and far-carrying "took, tu-tu" with slightly hollow ring; unlike other antpittas, it may sing from a fairly exposed perch, throwing head and neck back and puffing out throat. Both sexes also give a very loud and penetrating "keeyurr!" call, reminiscent of one of Great Thrush's calls.

Ochre-striped Antpitta, *Grallaria dignissima*
Gralaria Ocrelistada   Plate 65(13)

Below 450 m

19 cm (7½"). *On or near ground inside terra firme forest in lowlands of east.* Bill black above, horn below; long legs bluish gray. Above brown, grayer on crown and with pale buffyish lores; long plumes on lower back and rump with white shaft streaks. *Throat and chest rich orange-ochraceous,* chest feathers with white shaft streaks, becoming whiter on lower underparts (*with long plumes on flanks*), *sides and flanks broadly striped black and white.* **Similar species:** Nothing else really resembles this spectacular and all-too-rarely seen antpitta. Scaled Antpitta occurs in same hilly terra firme forests. **Habits:** Favors areas near shady forest streams in relatively hilly or at least broken terrain. Ranges singly or in pairs, usually shy and hard to see. Almost exclusively terrestrial, hopping or bounding along rapidly on the ground. Heard much more often than seen. **Voice:** ♂'s characteristic song a far-carrying and mournful "whü, wheeeow," second note slurred downward,

repeated slowly at 5- to 10-second intervals, most often from low hidden perch.

Hylopezus Antpittas
Fairly small antpittas found in lowland forests, one on either side of the Andes, *both species with streaking on their underparts.* Sexes are alike.

Streak-chested Antpitta
Hylopezus perspicillatus
Tororoi Pechirrayado   Plate 64(6)

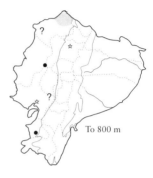

To 800 m

14 cm (5½"). Scarce on or near ground inside humid forest in *lowlands and foothills of northwest.* Formerly sometimes called Spectacled Antpitta. Crown and nape gray with *bold ochraceous eye-ring* and buff lores; otherwise olive brown above, back with a little narrow buff streaking; wing-coverts tipped buff. White below with black malar streak and *extensive blackish streaking across breast and down flanks.* **Similar species:** Only other antpittas in nw. *lowlands* are larger and dissimilar Rufous-crowned and Scaled. **Habits:** A solitary terrestrial bird of deep forest that hops on ground; may run for a short distance, then pause to flick leaves aside with bill. Elsewhere known occasionally to attend antswarms. Surprised birds may flush a short distance to low perch, pausing there for a period before hopping or flying back to ground and (usually) running off. Nervous or agitated birds often flick wings. Heard far more often than seen. **Voice:** ♂'s song, usually given from slightly elevated perch (often a fallen log), a slowly delivered series of melancholy whistled notes, at first slightly rising in pitch, then characteristically fading away, "poh, po-po-po-po-po-po-peu-peu-peu." Singing birds often rock from side

to side. Alarm note a sharp and piercing "keeuw."

White-lored Antpitta, *Hylopezus fulviventris*
Tororoi Loriblanco   Plate 64(7)

14.5 cm (5³⁄₄"). *Uncommon in very dense thickets and undergrowth at borders of humid forest and woodland, and in regenerating clearings in lowlands of east.* Formerly considered conspecific with Fulvous-bellied, or Thicket, Antpitta (*H. dives*) of Honduras to sw. Colombia. Olive above, *darker and slatier on head and nape* with *prominent whitish lores* and small bare white triangle behind eye. Throat and partial nuchal collar white; underparts white tinged buff, especially across chest and down sides and flanks, and with coarse dusky streaking across breast and down flanks; lower flanks and crissum ochraceous buff. Similar species: Thrush-like Antpitta browner and more uniform above, lacks whitish lores and buff on underparts. Habits: Very secretive and hard to see, in large part because of its often virtually impenetrable habitat. Hops through thick growth, frequently just above ground; usually seen singly. Heard much more often than seen. Voice: ♂'s song a short slow series of 3–4 abrupt and hollow notes, e.g., "kwoh-kwoh-kwoh-kwoh," with first note soft and inaudible at a distance. Also gives a faster and accelerating series of shorter notes, "kow-kow-kow-kow-ko-ko-ko-ko-ko-ko-ko"; this resembles Cocha Antshrike's song but is considerably lower pitched (P. Coopmans).

Thrush-like Antpitta
Myrmothera campanisona
Tororoi Campanero   Plate 64(8)

14.5 cm (5³⁄₄"). *Numerous and widespread in dense thickets on or near ground in humid*

forest and borders in lowlands and foothills of east. Sexes alike. *Above uniform rufescent brown* with grayish lores and small bare white triangle behind eye. Below white *with extensive blurry grayish brown streaking,* throat and midbelly unmarked. Similar species: Cf. White-lored Antpitta (with distinctly gray head, white lores, and buff on underparts). Habits: Favors areas around treefalls and along streams where undergrowth is especially thick. Found singly or in pairs, and seems notably sedentary, often vocalizing from the same small thicket day after day. Shy and very hard to see, heard much more often; usually not tape-responsive. Voice: ♂'s song a series of 4–6 hollow whistled notes, delivered quite quickly, "whoh-whoh-whoh-whoh-whoh." May vocalize for protracted periods while—aside from puffing its throat—remaining motionless. Agitated birds give a semimusical trill, e.g., "t-r-r-r-r-r-r-r-r-r-r-r," often while flicking wings.

Grallaricula Antpittas
Easily the smallest of the antpittas, *Grallaricula* are attractive, round little birds inhabiting montane forest undergrowth; several species appear to be genuinely rare and local. All are little known, retiring, and difficult to observe, though tape playback helps.

Ochre-breasted Antpitta
Grallaricula flavirostris
Gralarita Ocrácea   Plate 64(3)

10 cm (4"). Uncommon and apparently local (overlooked?) in lower growth of *foothill and subtropical forest and dense overgrowth borders on both slopes,* occurring at *lower elevations* than other *Grallaricula*. Individually variable to an unusual extent. *Bill usually bicolored, dark above and yellow below,*

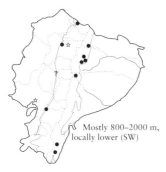

Mostly 800–2000 m,
locally lower (SW)

2000–2900 m

latter sometimes mixed with brown, but entirely dark in a few birds from e. slope, and entirely yellow in most birds from the southwest (Azuay and El Oro), though bicolored in a few. **Sexes alike.** Olive brown above with *prominent ochraceous eye-ring and lores. Throat and breast ochraceous*, belly creamy whitish, *breast and flanks with usually extensive blackish streaking.* Some birds from southwest are uniform ochraceous on throat and breast *with little or no streaking.* **Similar species:** Slate-crowned Antpitta darker and more richly colored below with no streaking; it occurs at high elevations. Cf. rare Peruvian Antpitta. **Habits:** Inconspicuous and difficult to see in dense lower growth it favors. Solitary individuals are occasionally encountered as they hop through undergrowth, holding motionless for a period and then continuing on, periodically flicking wings (especially when nervous). Unlike larger antpittas it only infrequently drops to ground. Does not associate with flocks. **Voice:** Seems not very vocal, less so than at least some other *Grallaricula.* One vocalization is a simple "weeeu" repeated steadily at 8- to 10-second intervals. In El Oro also gives a rapid series of piping notes on even pitch (N. Krabbe recording).

Slate-crowned Antpitta, *Grallaricula nana*
Gralarita Coronipizarrosa   Plate 64(2)

11 cm (4¼"). Undergrowth inside *upper subtropical and lower temperate forest on e. slope*, principally in extensive stands of *Chusquea* bamboo. Bill mainly dark. **Sexes alike.** *Crown slaty gray* with lores and eye-ring buffy ochraceous; otherwise olive brown above. *Below uniform rich orange-rufous*, whiter on midbelly. **Similar species:** Other *Grallaricula* on e. slope all show streaking on underparts, and none is as rufous below as

Slate-crowned. **Habits:** Similar to other *Grallaricula* (see Ochre-breasted), and equally difficult to observe without aid of tape playback. **Voice:** ♂'s often heard song a short, pretty, rather high-pitched series of 14–18 notes that fade and descend slightly, e.g., "we-e-e-e-e-e-e-e-e-e-e-e-ew." Call a short and abrupt "tchew" (N. Krabbe recording).

Peruvian Antpitta, *Grallaricula peruviana*
Gralarita Peruana   Plate 64(4)

1750–2100 m

10 cm (4"). *Rare and local in undergrowth of subtropical forest on e. slope in s. Ecuador; few records.* Bill blackish above, creamy whitish below. ♂ with *crown and nape rich rufous*, buff lores and partial eyering (widest in front of and behind eye); otherwise brown above. *White below* with broad black submalar streak and *extensive heavy black scalloping or streaking across breast and down flanks.* ♀ similar but with concolor brown crown and blackish on forecrown. **Similar species:** Ochre-breasted Antpitta shows at least some ochraceous below. **Habits:** Nearly unknown in life, but presumably similar to other *Grallaricula.* Most Ecuador records have involved mistnetted birds. **Voice:** Unknown.

Crescent-faced Antpitta, *Grallaricula lineifrons*
Gralarita Carilunada   Plate 64(1)

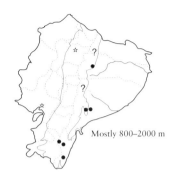

11.5 cm (4½″). A *strikingly patterned, unde-niably "cute"* antpitta found locally inside *temperate forest and woodland on e. slope.* **Sexes alike.** Bill all black. *Head dark slaty,* blacker on auriculars, with *conspicuous white crescent in front of eye* that becomes ochraceous on its lower part, white posto-cular spot, and *ochraceous patch on sides of neck*; otherwise brownish olive above. Midthroat white bordered by broad black submalar streak; *underparts heavily streaked black and ochraceous buff,* whiter on midbelly, and becoming brown on flanks with some whitish streaking. **Similar species:** No other antpitta has such fancy facial pattern. **Habits:** Similar to other *Grallaricula* (see Ochre-breasted), and equally hard to see without aid of tape playback. Heard more often than seen, at least during its apparently brief song period (ca. Jan.–Apr.). **Voice:** ♂'s song an ascending series of piping notes, last several rather shrill, e.g., "pu-pu-pe-pe-pee-pee-pi-pi-pi?" (M. B. Robbins recording).

Gnateaters: Conopophagidae (3)
Cute and round, the gnateaters are plump, short-tailed, and long-legged birds found in tangled forest undergrowth. They are elusive birds that occur at low densities.

Chestnut-crowned Gnateater
Conopophaga castaneiceps
Jejenero Coronicastaño   Plate 66(1)

13–13.5 cm (5–5¼″). Uncommon, local, and inconspicuous in undergrowth of montane forest in *foothills and subtropical zone on e. slope,* mainly in s. Ecuador. *Lower mandible*

pale; legs bluish gray. ♂ has *rufous crown* becoming more *chestnut on hindcrown* and *long silvery white postocular tuft*; otherwise olive brown above. *Sides of neck and under-parts dark slaty gray,* paler gray on midbreast and whitish on midbelly. ♀ has *rufous-chestnut crown* (brighter orange-rufous on forecrown) with *postocular tuft as in ♂*; oth-erwise rufescent brown above (more oliva-ceous northward). *Throat and breast orange-rufous,* becoming grayish olive on belly, whiter in middle. **Similar species:** Larger than other gnateaters, and the only one occurring on Andean slopes; only very local overlap with Ash-throated, both sexes of which have buff spotting on wing-coverts and prominent scaly pattern on back. **Habits:** Found singly or in pairs, favoring the dense tangles that spring up around treefalls. Often perches on vertical saplings, low but rarely actually on ground, hopping or jumping short distances. Does not follow mixed flocks. Infrequently seen, though not espe-cially shy. **Voice:** Song a distinctive ascending series of rattled notes, "chrrr, chrr-chrr-chrr-chrr-chrr-chrrít" (P. Coopmans). Call a sharp and abrupt "zhweeík" or "tsink" similar to other gnateaters.

Ash-throated Gnateater
Conopophaga peruviana
Jejenero Golicinéreo   Plate 66(2)

11.5–12 cm (4½–4¾″). Uncommon and inconspicuous in terra firme forest under-growth in *lowlands of east, apparently only south of Río Napo.* Bill black; legs pinkish to horn. ♂ has crown dark brown with grayish lores and *conspicuous long silvery white pos-tocular tuft*; otherwise brownish gray above, *feathers of back conspicuously margined*

To 600 m

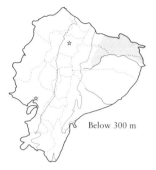

Below 300 m

with black; wings and tail chestnut brown, *wing-coverts and inner flight feathers tipped buff. Below gray*, whiter on throat and midbelly, browner on lower flanks. ♀ *above much like ♂* but browner generally and with rufous crown. Throat whitish, *sides of neck and breast orange-rufous*, midbelly whitish, flanks brown. **Similar species:** Note range: apparently does not occur with Chestnut-belted Gnateater. In any case, ♀ of that species differs from ♀ Ash-throated in its nearly plain back (with little or no black scaling) and wings (no obvious buff dots). **Habits:** Found singly or in pairs, favoring dense tangled habitat such as around treefalls or in viny areas on well-drained ridges. Generally hard to see, but often—unlike many antbirds—rather unwary when located. **Voice:** Song a loud and inflected "zhweeík" repeated at well-spaced but regular intervals. Both sexes also give a rather soft and low-pitched call, "shreff."

Chestnut-belted Gnateater
Conopophaga aurita
Jejenero Fajicastaño   Plate 66(3)

11.5–12 cm (4½–4¾"). Uncommon and inconspicuous in terra firme forest undergrowth in *lowlands of northeast, apparently only north of Río Napo.* Bill black; legs pale bluish. ♂ has chestnut crown with *conspicuous long silvery white postocular tuft*; otherwise brown above, back feathers faintly scaled black. *Forehead, sides of head, and throat black* contrasting with rufous sides of neck and breast; lower underparts pale olivaceous brown, whiter on midbelly. ♀ like ♂ above, *including postocular tuft*, but crown concolor. Sides of neck, throat, and breast orange-rufous; lower underparts pale oliva-

ceous brown, whiter on midbelly. **Similar species:** Apparently does not occur with Ash-throated Gnateater. Dapper ♂ can hardly be confused, but ♀ resembles ♀ Ash-throated aside from its plainer upperparts (with less black scaling and no buff dots on wings). **Habits:** Similar to Ash-throated Gnateater. **Voice:** Song a loud and rather harsh rattling trill that slightly ascends and then levels in pitch.

Tapaculos: Rhinocryptidae (14)
An exclusively Neotropical family of obscure birds reaching its *maximum diversity in the Andes*, mainly because of rapid speciation in the genus *Scytalopus*; most of its larger and more spectacular members occur in far southern South America. Their bills are usually short and heavy, the nostrils covered by a movable flap (the operculum); the feet are strong and well developed, as befits mainly terrestrial birds. Tapaculos fly very little, and when they do, flights are weak and short. They are *notably vocal*, and this typically reveals the presence of these skulking birds.

Rusty-belted Tapaculo, *Liosceles thoracicus*
Tapaculo Fajirrojizo   Plate 66(7)

19–19.5 cm (7½–7¾"). A fairly large tapaculo found *on or near ground inside terra firme forest in lowlands of east.* Iris dark brown; bill black above, creamy white below. **Sexes alike.** Head and neck gray with *narrow white superciliary*; otherwise dark rufescent brown above, wing-coverts with some elongated buff spots. *Throat and breast contrastingly white*, with band of orange-rufous across chest (variable in extent); belly heavily barred blackish, brown, and white. **Similar species:**

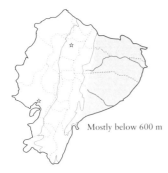

Mostly below 600 m

To about 2300 m

Not likely confused, in part because this tapaculo is usually seen in response to tape playback. Overall pattern is vaguely wren-like (Coraya being the most similar), and it could conceivably be confused with certain terrestrial antbirds as well. **Habits:** Forages singly while walking or hopping on forest floor, usually where the vegetation is dense and showing a special predilection for fallen logs. Rather shy and furtive, even after tape playback often not easy to see, sneaking in with head and tail held low and rarely pausing long in open. **Voice:** Oft-heard song a series of low, mellow, whistled notes on a nearly even pitch, "pü-pü-pü-pü-pu-pu-pupupu," accelerating slightly and trailing off at end. Alarm call a somewhat nasal and abrupt "squeah!," often in series of 2–3; when disturbed also gives thrush-like clucks.

Melanopareia Crescentchests

Attractive and boldly patterned tapaculos that—other than their skulking behavior—bear little resemblance to other members of the family. They occur in scrub in the s. and w. Ecuador.

Elegant Crescentchest, *Melanopareia elegans*
Pecholuna Elegante   Plate 66(4)

14.5 cm (5¼"). A *well-named* tapaculo, not uncommon (but skulking) in *dense scrub and woodland undergrowth in more arid lowlands of southwest*, ranging up into subtropics in El Oro and Loja. ♂ has *head and neck black* with *long buffy white superciliary*; back grayish olive. Wing-coverts and inner flight feathers broadly edged rufous, primary-coverts and outer primaries edged silvery; tail blackish, outer web of outermost rectrix whitish. *Throat buffy white*, contrasting sharply with *black crescent-shaped pectoral band across chest*, bordered below by a chestnut band that blends into cinnamon-buff lower underparts. ♀ similar but duller above, with sooty brown crown and *lacking chestnut* below its narrower black pectoral band; lower underparts slightly paler. **Similar species:** This handsome and boldly patterned bird is not likely confused; it does not occur with range-restricted Marañón Crescentchest. **Habits:** Forages singly low in dense vegetation, sometimes hopping on ground. Furtive, even when singing rarely perching in the open for very long, but quite responsive to tape playback. **Voice:** Distinctive and far-carrying song a measured, chortling "cho-cho-cho-cho-cho-cho-cho-cho," sounding vaguely frog- or insect-like. Seems to sing at intervals throughout day, and vocal more or less through year. Alarm call a dry "churr" (N. Krabbe).

[Marañón Crescentchest
Melanopareia maranonica
Pecholuna del Marañón]   Plate 66(5)

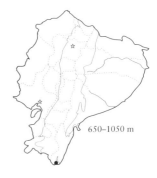

650–1050 m

16 cm (6¹⁄₄"). Scrub in *Zumba region of Río Marañón drainage in extreme s. Zamora-Chinchipe*. Resembles Elegant Crescentchest (no overlap) but *larger*. Both sexes differ further in having *conspicuous silvery edging to most of wing feathers* (which show *no* rufous edging) and more deeply colored underparts; in addition, ♀'s black pectoral band is wider. **Similar species:** In its restricted range, nearly unmistakable. **Habits and Voice:** Much as in Elegant Crescentchest.

Ash-colored Tapaculo, *Myornis senilis*
Tapaculo Cenizo   Plate 66(8)

Mostly 2300–3500 m

14–14.5 cm (5¹⁄₂–5³⁄₄"). Undergrowth and borders of *temperate and upper subtropical forest* on both slopes (often most numerous just below treeline), also locally on in-terandean slopes. *Comparatively long-tailed.* Sexes alike. *Essentially uniform ashy gray*, slightly paler below, with at least a tinge of cinnamon on median lower belly and crissum. **Juvenile** very different, rufous brown above and buffy ochraceous below with faint dusky barring on wings and tail (little or none elsewhere). **Similar species:** Various *Scytalopus* tapaculos occur with Ash-colored, but all are markedly shorter tailed; their voices also differ. **Habits:** Favors dense stands of *Chusquea* bamboo where it creeps and hops about through dense low undergrowth and is unlikely to be noticed unless singing. Long tail often held partially cocked. **Voice:** Song a distinctive long mechanical-sounding trill or churr that may last a minute or more (and sometimes is given as a series of such trills) and is nearly always introduced by a series of sharp single or doubled "chef!" or "chedef!"

notes that are gradually given at a faster pace. Sometimes the introductory notes or long trill are given alone. Alarm call a short chirring or sharp "chit!"

Scytalopus Tapaculos
One of the most complex Neotropical bird genera, *Scytalopus* tapaculos are secretive, mouse-like little birds that skulk in montane forest and woodland undergrowth, hardly flying and rarely seen except in response to tape playback. They are closely similar, and many species are indistinguishable on any plumage character; some are hard to tell apart even in the hand! *To differentiate the various species one must rely on their vocalizations; distribution and elevation also help.* Fortunately not only are these tapaculos quite vocal, but their primary songs are reasonably distinctive (N. Krabbe's assistance in clarifying certain points is gratefully acknowledged). In recent years a concerted effort has been made by field workers—notably N. Krabbe and T. Schulenberg—to work out the complex systematics of the genus, and this recently culminated work (Krabbe and Schulenberg 1997) has resulted in a much improved understanding of their taxonomy, as well as in the description of no fewer than three new Ecuadorian species. Note that all *Scytalopus* have a variable, browner juvenal plumage, often with extensive rufous barring below; this is not described in the species accounts.

Unicolored Tapaculo, *Scytalopus unicolor*
Tapaculo Unicolor   Plate 66(9)

12–12.5 cm (4³⁄₄–5"). *Fairly common to common and widespread in undergrowth of subtropical and temperate forest and wood-*

Mostly 2300–3500 m,
lower in SW; 1900–2450 m
(E slope)

land (locally even where low in stature) on both slopes and above interandean valleys; less numerous and more local on actual e. slope. In **most of range**, both sexes *uniform blackish gray*, ♀ ♀ slightly paler. On **east slope** and in the **southwest** (north to Azuay), ♂ *uniform black*, but ♀ paler and grayer (in southwest sometimes distinctly so) with some brown on lower flanks and uppertail-coverts. **Similar species:** Try to learn to recognize—by both voice and appearance—this relatively numerous tapaculo. In most of its range it is distinctly blacker and more uniform than any other *Scytalopus* in Ecuador. Near treeline on e. slope, cf. Paramo Tapaculo, ♂ ♂ of which are uniform gray (paler than Unicolored); its voice differs notably. In southwest, cf. very local El Oro Tapaculo, which appears to occur only at lower elevations than Unicolored ever reaches. **Habits:** Forages solitarily in dense vegetation, usually close to ground though where undergrowth is very dense it may creep somewhat higher. As with other *Scytalopus*, Unicolored is noted almost entirely through its vocalizations, and this mouse-like bird is rarely seen unless vocalizing, even then most often after tape playback. **Voice:** Song in most of range a rapidly repeated series of "pir" notes that may continue 15 or more seconds. Frequently heard call in most of range a distinctly doubled and rising "huir-huir." Song in subtropics on e. slope a fast series of somewhat sharper "pur" or thrush-like "puk" notes that continue steadily.

Equatorial Rufous-vented Tapaculo
Scytalopus micropterus
Tapaculo Ventrirrufo Equatorial   Plate 66(10)

13.5 cm (5¼"). Undergrowth of *subtropical forest, woodland, and borders on e. slope.*

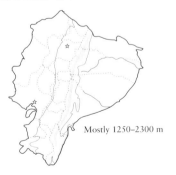

Mostly 1250–2300 m

Formerly included in Rufous-vented Tapaculo (*S. femoralis*), which now is split into a number of species, including Northern White-crowned Tapaculo (below). **Sexes alike.** Mostly slaty gray, somewhat darker above with rump more rufescent; lower flanks and crissum rufous with wavy black barring. **Similar species:** Closely resembles Spillmann's Tapaculo (northward) and Chusquea Tapaculo (southward), so much as to not be safely separated in field on basis of appearance, but Equatorial Rufous-vented is somewhat longer tailed than either, and tends to be darker below. The similar Nariño Tapaculo occurs only on w. slope. As with other *Scytalopus*, best identified by voice. **Habits:** Secretive behavior similar to other *Scytalopus* (see Unicolored). **Voice:** Song a long series of notes that starts slowly but then quickly accelerates, "chu-dok; chu-dok; chudók, chudók, chudók, chudók-chudók-chudók-chudók . . . ," often continuing a half-minute or more.

Northern White-crowned Tapaculo
Scytalopus atratus
Tapaculo Coroniblanco Norteño   Plate 66(16)

850–1650 m

12.5 cm (5"). Undergrowth and borders of *foothill and lower subtropical forest on e. slope.* Formerly included in Rufous-vented Tapaculo (*S. femoralis*), which now is split into a number of species, including Equatorial Rufous-vented Tapaculo (above). **Sexes alike.** Mostly slaty gray, somewhat darker above with rump more rufescent and with *small but distinct white patch on midcrown;* lower flanks and crissum rufous with wavy dark barring. **Similar species:** Though resembling Equatorial Rufous-vented Tapaculo of somewhat higher elevations, Northern

White-crowned can—almost uniquely among *Scytalopus* in Ecuador—be recognized on a plumage character, the white crown patch; unfortunately this is small and often hard to discern in the dim light this furtive little bird favors. Like other *Scytalopus*, it is almost always located and recognized by voice. **Habits:** Secretive behavior similar to other *Scytalopus* (see Unicolored), though this species seems to be the most skulking of all. **Voice:** Song a fast series of strikingly frog-like notes—easily passed over as not belonging to a bird—"wr-wr-wr-wr-wr" or "wrt, wr-wr-wr-wr."

Nariño Tapaculo, *Scytalopus vicinior*
Tapaculo de Nariño   Plate 66(11)

Mostly 1250–2000 m

12.5 cm (5"). Undergrowth of *subtropical forest on w. slope south to nw. Cotopaxi.* **Sexes alike.** Mostly slaty gray, somewhat darker above with rump more rufescent; lower flanks and crissum rufous with wavy black barring. **Similar species:** Closely resembles Spillmann's Tapaculo, and probably not safely distinguished on basis of appearance; Nariño tends to occur at lower elevations (with some overlap, however), and is proportionately slightly longer tailed. **Habits:** Secretive behavior similar to other *Scytalopus* (see Unicolored). **Voice:** Song a fast series of well-enunciated, ringing notes that starts with a brief stutter but then may go on for 15–30 seconds, "pididi-ü-ü-ü-ü-ü-ü-ü-ü-ü-ü. . . ." Also has a single-noted call.

Chocó Tapaculo, *Scytalopus chocoensis*
Tapaculo del Chocó   Plate 66(12)

11.5 cm (4½"). Local in undergrowth in *foothill forest of far northwest.* A recently described species. **Sexes alike.** Mostly slaty

350–950 m

gray, somewhat darker above with rump more rufescent; lower flanks and crissum rufous with wavy black barring. **Similar species:** Identical in appearance to El Oro Tapaculo (no overlap). Chocó is the only tapaculo occurring *at such low elevations in the northwest.* Nariño Tapculo occurs at higher elevations, perhaps with a slight elevation overlap; it is larger, has less heavy bill, and differs in voice. **Habits:** Secretive behavior similar to other *Scytalopus* (see Unicolored). **Voice:** Song a series of sharp, high-pitched, and well-enunciated notes introduced by a stutter, "p-d-d-d-pi-pi-pi-pi-pi-pi-pi-pi . . ." lasting some 15–25 seconds. Scold a sharp, high-pitched 3- to 8-noted "chiu-chiu-chiu . . ." (N. Krabbe).

El Oro Tapaculo, *Scytalopus robbinsi*
Tapaculo de El Oro   Plate 66(13)

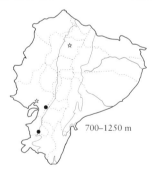

700–1250 m

11.5 cm (4½"). Local in undergrowth of *foothill and lower subtropical forest of southwest.* A recently described species. **Sexes alike.** Mostly slaty gray, somewhat darker above with rump more rufescent; lower flanks and crissum rufous with wavy black barring. **Similar species:** Identical in appearance to Chocó Tapaculo (no overlap).

El Oro is only tapaculo occurring *at such low elevations in southwest*. Unicolored Tapaculo replaces it at somewhat higher elevations. **Habits:** Secretive behavior similar to other *Scytalopus* (see Unicolored). **Voice:** Song similar to Chocó Tapaculo's but individual notes are given at a faster rate, often seeming doubled. Call a short "quik?" (N. Krabbe).

Spillmann's Tapaculo, *Scytalopus spillmanni*
Tapaculo de Spillmann   Plate 66(14)

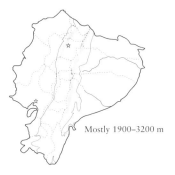

Mostly 1900–3200 m

12.5 cm (5″). Undergrowth and borders of subtropical and temperate forest on *both slopes*, but *only in n. Ecuador* (on w. slope south to nw. Cotopaxi, on e. slope south to Azuay/Morona-Santiago border). Formerly treated as a race of Brown-rumped Tapaculo (*S. latebricola*), now considered to range only on Colombia's Santa Marta Mtns. Mostly slaty gray, somewhat darker above with rump more rufescent; lower flanks and crissum rufous with wavy black barring. ♀ similar but with belly and flanks paler and brighter rufous, and less barred. **Similar species:** This wide-ranging and usually numerous tapaculo closely resembles several other species in plumage and is best identified by voice. It overlaps with Nariño Tapaculo on w. slope, with Equatorial Rufous-vented Tapaculo on e. slope, and is replaced by Chusquea Tapaculo southward on e. slope. **Habits:** Secretive behavior similar to other *Scytalopus* (see Unicolored). **Voice:** Song a long, very fast, and relatively high-pitched trill that rises slightly in pitch and continues some 10–15 seconds, the trill generally being introduced by a few slower notes. Also gives a short rising trill (like rubbing a comb's tines) and a "keekeekee-

kee" scold much as in Nariño Tapaculo but higher pitched.

Chusquea Tapaculo, *Scytalopus parkeri*
Tapaculo de Chusquea   Plate 16(15)

2250–3150 m

12.5 cm (5″). Understory of dense stands of *Chusquea* bamboo in upper subtropical and temperate forest on *e. slope north to nw. Morona-Santiago*. A recently described species, formerly considered part of Brown-rumped Tapaculo (*S. latebricola*) complex. **Sexes alike.** Mostly slaty gray, somewhat darker above with rump more rufescent; lower flanks and crissum rufous with wavy black barring. **Similar species:** Essentially identical in plumage to Spillmann's Tapaculo (especially ♀), but the two do not overlap; they differ in voice (see below). Overlaps with Equatorial Rufous-vented Tapaculo, though Chusquea generally occurs at higher elevations. **Habits:** Secretive behavior similar to other *Scytalopus* (see Unicolored); true to its name, however, this species' distribution seems quite closely tied to stands of bamboo. **Voice:** Dawn song a trill, initially descending, lower pitched and somewhat slower paced than in Spillman's. Day song a series of relatively lower-pitched trills, overall similar to song of Spillmann's Tapaculo but differing in its repeated breaks (thus not as evenly paced). Also gives various shorter calls.

Paramo Tapaculo, *Scytalopus canus*
Tapaculo Paramero   Plate 66(17)

11.5 cm (4½″). Local in undergrowth of *temperate forest borders and woodland on e. slope, mainly near treeline* and sometimes in *Polylepis*. Formerly considered conspecific

3050–4000 m

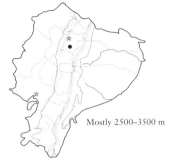

Mostly 2500–3500 m

with Andean Tapaculo (*S. magellanicus* or, with two austral species split off, *S. grisei-collis*). ♂ *uniform gray*, lower flanks (especially) and rump often with rufous brown barring. ♀ similar but more tinged with brown above, and more prominently barred rufous brown on flanks. **Similar species:** Unicolored Tapaculo (in zone of overlap) is slightly larger, blacker generally, and only young birds show much rufous flank barring. Because of its small size and limited range and habitat, Paramo is one *Scytalopus* that be identified with some confidence on basis of appearance alone. **Habits:** Secretive behavior similar to other *Scytalopus* (see Unicolored), but on the whole Paramo is an easier bird to see. **Voice:** Song a fast dry trill lasting 5–10 seconds, "trrrrrrrrrrr." ♂ may sing while ♀ gives a descending series of high-pitched notes. Call a "kee-kee-kee-kee," but in s. Zamora-Chinchipe gives a short churr reminiscent of song (N. Krabbe).

Ocellated Tapaculo, *Acropternis orthonyx*
Tapaculo Ocelado   Plate 66(6)

21.5–22 cm (8½–8¾″). An unmistakable *large* and *ornately patterned* tapaculo found in *undergrowth of upper subtropical and temperate forest on both slopes*, also locally above central and interandean valleys. Furtive like other tapaculos, heard far more often than seen. **Sexes alike.** *Mostly black to blackish with large round white spots*, the spots on hindcrown buffier, and tail unspotted. *Forehead, face, and throat contrastingly cinnamon-rufous*; rump, uppertail-coverts, and extreme lower flanks rich rufous. **Habits:** Ranges singly (usually) or in well-separated pairs, in many regions favoring areas with extensive stands of *Chusquea* bamboo; nor-

mally shy and hard to see unless vocalizing (then usually only after tape playback). Walks, runs, and hops through dense undergrowth, perhaps dropping to ground mainly to feed; sometimes scratches with both feet at once (F. Sornoza), but the function of the long hindclaw remains obscure (N. Krabbe). Scratching birds can make a fair bit of noise (S. Howell). **Voice:** Most frequently heard song a distinctive loud and far-carrying jay-like "keeeuw!" repeated at roughly 2- to 4-second intervals, faster when bird is agitated (as after playback). Also gives a less penetrating—but still quite loud—"queeu-queeu-queeu-queeu," or sometimes a long-continued slow repetition of same "queeu" call.

Tyrant Flycatchers: Tyrannidae (208)
A huge and diverse family of American birds; there are more species of flycatchers than than there are in any other family of birds found only in the New World. Although some tyrannids have distributions that reach either the northern or the southern temperate zones, virtually all of these "retreat" to the tropics during their respective winters, and the family reaches by far its highest diversity in the Neotropics. Flycatchers have radiated into every terrestrial habitat in Ecuador. Although they are most diverse and numerous in humid lowland forests, there is also a good range of species at higher elevations in the Andes, and a few even occur up into paramo. It is hard to generalize. Most have somewhat flattened bills, often with a hook at the tip, and many have a semiconcealed coronal patch. They tend to be plain, drab birds, olives or browns usually predominating—but there are some notable exceptions, including one of the most vividly colored of

all birds, the male Vermilion Flycatcher. The sexes are usually alike, however.

Some tyrannids are among the most notoriously difficult of Neotropical birds to identify, with various members of certain genera (notably *Elaenia*, also various tyrannulets) being virtually impossible to distinguish from each other except by voice. A knowledge of vocalizations is thus vital for getting a "handle" on many of the more obscure groups. Although North Americans may be familiar with what to them are "typical" sallying flycatchers, a substantial majority of the Neotropical species do not sally, rather gleaning in foliage for their primarily insectivorous fare. Many also eat a great deal of fruit; most consume at least some, especially when not breeding. A few tyrannids are among Ecuador's most numerous and ubiquituous birds, but many others are scarce or inconspicuous, and some are genuinely rare or have extremely restricted ranges or habitats. Nest form and placement vary tremendously and are described under many generic headings.

Phyllomyias Tyrannulets

Obscure, short-billed tyrannulets found primarily in Andean forests and borders though one species (Sooty-crowned) is more a bird of clearings. Compare them especially to *Zimmerius* (which lack wing-bars but have crisp, well-marked yellow wing-edging and usually cock their tails), *Mecocerculus* (with a bold superciliary and even bolder wing-bars), and *Phylloscartes* (with longer bills and longer tails).

White-fronted Tyrannulet
Phyllomyias zeledoni
Tiranolete Frentiblanco   Plate 67(9)

11.5 cm (4½"). *Rare and local* (overlooked?) in canopy and borders of *foothill and lower*

subtropical forest on both slopes. *P. zeledoni* is considered a species separate from *P. burmeisteri* (Rough-legged Tyrannulet); formerly sometimes placed in the genus *Acrochordopus*. Fairly heavy stubby bill, *lower mandible pale grayish or pinkish*. Olive above with *slaty crown* and *white superciliary that broadens in front of eye and across forehead*; narrow line through eye dusky, lower face grizzled gray and white; wings dusky with two broad yellowish wing-bars. Throat whitish; underparts pale yellow, vaguely flammulated olive on breast. **Similar species:** Obscure and visually hard to identify with certainty, especially as it so habitually remains high above ground. *Lacks* the dark ear-patch present in several other similar tyrannulets (e.g., Plumbeous-crowned, Ashy-headed); Plumbeous-crowned lacks white "front" and occurs at higher elevations. Ecuadorian Tyrannulet has a longer and all-black bill and *lacks* white across forehead. **Habits:** Not well known. Usually seen singly, foraging actively in mid-levels and subcanopy, often accompanying mixed flocks. Usually perches horizontally, but does not cock tail; calling birds may perch more upright. Occasionally a wing may be flicked upward briefly. seconds. **Voice:** Song a high-pitched and piercing "tzeeee" or "sweeeu," either given as a protracted series of single notes (with 2- to 4-second interval), sometimes in a descending series of up to 5–7 notes.

Sooty-headed Tyrannulet
Phyllomyias griseiceps
Tiranolete Coronitiznado   Plate 67(10)

10 cm (4"). A *small, plain* tyrannulet found in humid forest borders, secondary woodland, and clearings with scattered trees in *lowlands and foothills of west* (where more numerous) *and east* (in latter not found far from Andes).

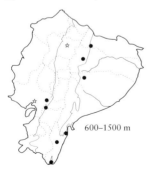

600–1500 m

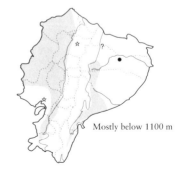

Mostly below 1100 m

Though found only in humid regions, *basically a nonforest tyrannulet*. *Crown sooty brownish*, becoming grayer on sides of head, and with narrow white supraloral streak; otherwise olive above, wings and tail duskier, *wings with narrow whitish edging (but with no evident wing-bars)*. Throat grayish white; underparts pale yellow, breast clouded with olive. **Similar species:** All other *Phyllomyias* tyrannulets have obvious wing-bars; *Zimmerius* tyrannulets lack wing-bars but have very sharp wing-edging (much more evident than in Sooty-headed). Similarly patterned Greenish Elaenia is much larger. Yellow-crowned Tyrannulet often occurs with this species, and has similar overall comportment, but differs obviously in having bold wing-bars (as well as a very different voice). **Habits:** Usually in pairs, sometimes well separated, that perch vertically and almost always forage independently of mixed flocks. Sometimes comes to fruiting trees, but eats mainly small insects. Inconspicuous and apt to be overlooked until its characteristic voice is learned. **Voice:** Readily recognized and often-given song a rather loud, bright, and rhythmic "whip, whip-dip-tiríp" or "whit, whit-típ"; song of eastern birds faster than in west. Distinctive cadence is reminiscent of Yellow Tyrannulet's song.

Plumbeous-crowned Tyrannulet
Phyllomyias plumbeiceps
Tiranolete Coroniplomizo   Plate 67(7)

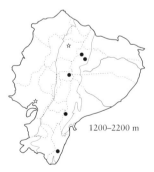

1200–2200 m

11.5 cm (4½″). *Scarce* (but easy to overlook, and doubtless underrecorded) in mid-levels and subcanopy of *subtropical forest on e. slope*. Formerly in genus *Oreotriccus*. Short, all-black bill. *Crown gray with white superciliary* bordered below by dusky streak through eye; *sides of head whitish with dusky

crescent on ear-coverts; back bright olive; wings and tail dusky, wings with *two prominent pale yellowish wing-bars*. Throat grayish white; underparts yellow, brightest on belly and clouded olive on breast. **Similar species:** Ecuadorian Tyrannulet similar but a bit smaller with longer bill and longer tail, and lacks any paler area behind dark ear-crescent; its voice differs, and it occurs mainly at lower elevations (though with some overlap). Ashy-headed Tyrannulet differs in its bluer crown, blacker ear-crescent, and distinctly streaky effect on breast. Cf. also Marble-faced Bristle-Tyrant and Slaty-capped Flycatcher, both of which perch vertically (not more or less horizontally as does Plumbeous-crowned). **Habits:** Found singly or in pairs, usually while foraging with mixed flocks of canopy birds. Sallies to foliage and twigs, but also sometimes remains motionless for protracted periods. Occasionally lifts a wing up over back. **Voice:** Song a series of 5–8 short hard notes, with quality of a furnariid (e.g., Black-billed Treehunter) but higher pitched, "pik pik pik pik pik"; it is given at relatively long intervals (B. Whitney and P. Coopmans).

Black-capped Tyrannulet
Phyllomyias nigrocapillus
Tiranolete Gorrinegro   Plate 67(11)

2300–3300 m

11 cm (4¼″). Borders of *upper subtropical and temperate forest and woodland on both slopes*, often most numerous near and just below *treeline*. This and the next two species were formerly in genus *Tyranniscus*. Short, all-black bill. *Crown black* with narrow white superciliary; otherwise dark olive above; wings blackish with *two bold yellowish white wing-bars*; tail dusky. Throat grayish; underparts yellow, breast heavily clouded with olive. **Similar species:** Tawny-rumped Tyrannulet is browner above with

buffier wing-bars and extensive tawny on rump, much grayer and whiter below (not as bright yellow). **Habits:** Seen singly or in pairs, actively gleaning in foliage at varying levels (though rarely inside actual forest), often nervously twitching its wings. Frequently accompanies mixed flocks. **Voice:** Song a thin and high-pitched "tzi-tzi-tzrrr," often with distinctive double-noted effect, varied to "tzi-tzi-tzrrr, tzi-tzrrr" (P. Coopmans and M. Lysinger recordings).

Ashy-headed Tyrannulet
Phyllomyias cinereiceps
Tiranolete Cabecicinéreo   Plate 67(8)

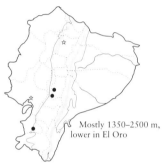

Mostly 1350–2500 m, lower in El Oro

11 cm (4¼"). Mid-levels, subcanopy, and borders of *subtropical forest on both slopes.* An *attractive* tyrannulet, more brightly patterned than most others. Short, all-black bill; iris dark red. *Crown bluish gray, contrasting with bright olive back;* lores and area around eyes white grizzled with black; sides of head yellowish white with *large black crescent on ear-coverts;* wings blackish with *two yellowish white wing-bars* and edging on flight feathers (but not on coverts). Throat whitish; *breast finely streaked yellowish white and olive;* belly bright yellow. **Similar species:** Ashy-headed's pattern and coloration recall that of Plumbeous-crowned Tyrannulet, Marble-faced Bristle-Tyrant, and even larger Slaty-capped Flycatcher; however, it differs notably in bluer tone to its crown (quite striking in good light) and the finely streaked effect on breast. **Habits:** Found singly or in pairs, often foraging with mixed flocks, sometimes coming quite low at borders. Perches somewhat more vertically than congeners, and occasionally lifts a wing up over back. **Voice:** Song a high-pitched, sibilant "sweeeee, see-ee-ee-ee-ee."

Tawny-rumped Tyrannulet
Phyllomyias uropygialis
Tiranolete Lomileonado   Plate 67(12)

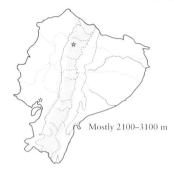

Mostly 2100–3100 m

11.5 cm (4½"). *Borders of subtropical and temperate forest and woodland,* and *adjacent clearings with scattered trees,* on both slopes. Mainly a *nonforest* tyrannulet, less tied to extensive forest than other montane *Phyllomyias.* Short, all-black bill. *Crown dark sepia brown* with narrow white superciliary; *back olive brown,* shading into *tawny on rump and uppertail-coverts;* wings blackish with *two buff wing-bars;* tail dusky. *Throat and breast grayish,* becoming yellowish white on belly. **Similar species:** The tawny rump is unique when it can be seen. Black-capped Tyrannulet is much yellower below and more olive above with no tawny on rump; their crown colors are fairly similar, Tawny-rumped's being so dark as to often appear blackish. Neither White-banded nor White-tailed Tyrannulet is as brown above, and they have bolder white superciliaries. **Habits:** Found singly, sometimes in pairs, and often accompanying mixed flocks though also forages alone. Gleans actively in foliage, frequently hovering while inspecting leaf surfaces for insects, the distinctive tawny rump then often being visible. **Voice:** Infrequently heard call a sharp and sibilant "pseee-psít," sometimes repeated several times in rather quick succesion.

Zimmerius Tyrannulets
A group of confusing tyrannulets united by a common *wing pattern in which the feathers are sharply edged with yellow,* but there are no actual wing-bars. They range in the canopy and borders of humid forest and are notable for eating considerable fruit; some, perhaps all, frequently eat mistletoe berries. All

members of the genus frequently perch in the open atop leaves. All were formerly in genus *Tyranniscus*.

Golden-faced Tyrannulet, *Zimmerius chrysops*
Tiranolete Caridorado   Plate 67(23)

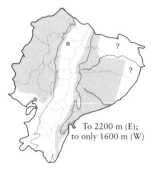

To 2200 m (E); to only 1600 m (W)

11 cm (4¹⁄₄"). *Widespread and often common* in canopy and borders of foothill and subtropical forest and woodland and in adjacent clearings on both slopes, and in lowlands of east and west (in latter only in more humid regions, and south to Guayas); most numerous in west. Here split from *Z. viridiflavus* (Peruvian Tyrannulet). *Distinctive golden yellow on face.* Olive above with *narrowfrontlet, broad supraloral, and lower eyelid yellow*; wings and tail dusky, *wing-coverts and flight feathers crisply edged yellow.* Throat yellowish white; breast grayish, becoming whitish on belly. **West-slope birds** whiter below, **east-slope birds** yellower. **Similar species:** An important tyrannulet to learn to recognize, as in many areas it will be seen frequently. Key points are yellow on face and prominent yellow edging on wing feathers. In southwest, replaced by similar Loja Tyrannulet. In e. lowlands, cf. Slender-footed Tyrannulet. **Habits:** Generally an active, conspicuous, and widespread little tyrannulet that should soon become familiar; however, it is less easy to see in e. lowlands, where largely confined to forest canopy well above ground. Gleans in outer foliage, often perching fully in open; usually perches horizontally, often with tail partially cocked but head erect. Sometimes accompanies mixed flocks, but at least as often found away from them. Heard more often than seen; in some areas one of most frequently heard bird sounds. **Voice:** On e. slope the most frequent call is a simple clear "cleeuw" or "peeur,"

sometimes in a quick series; also gives a more spritely and varied "teeu, te tititi?" On w. slope gives a rather different and querulous, ascending "treeu, tree-ree-ree-ree?" (most frequent around dawn) and a simple "cheli" call repeated over and over.

Loja Tyrannulet, *Zimmerius flavidifrons*
Tiranolete de Loja   Plate 67(24)

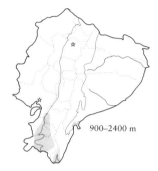

900–2400 m

11 cm (4¹⁄₄"). Common in canopy and borders of *foothill and subtropical* forest and woodland and adjacent clearings in *southwest* (se. Chimborazo to Loja) and *extreme southeast* (Zumba region). Formerly considered conspecific with Golden-faced Tyrannulet, which it closely resembles. Differs in having less yellow on face; on some individuals (perhaps ♀♀?), virtually none is apparent. **Habits:** Similar to Golden-faced Tyrannulet. **Voice:** Strikingly different from Golden-faced; Loja Tyrannulet's frequently heard call a loud and sharp, drawn-out "truuu-eeé." Song, given mainly around dawn, a fast "ti tuueé!" (P. Coopmans).

Slender-footed Tyrannulet
Zimmerius gracilipes
Tiranolete Patidelgado   Plate 67(22)

10.5 cm (4"). Canopy and borders of humid forest in *lowlands of northeast* (*mainly north of Río Napo*). *Iris pale grayish.* Above olive with grayer crown, *short whitish superciliary*, and grizzled gray and white lores; wings and tail dusky, *wing-coverts and flight feathers sharply edged yellow.* Throat grayish white, becoming grayish olive on breast and flanks and clear pale yellow on belly. **Similar species:** Often confused with Golden-faced Tyrannulet (which, though primarily montane, *also occurs widely in lowlands east of*

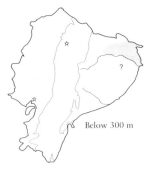

Below 300 m

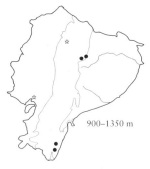

900–1350 m

Andes). Golden-faced differs in its dark eye, yellow on face, and whitish underparts (with no yellow on belly); their calls differ. Also cf. rare Red-billed Tyrannulet (not known to occur with Slender-footed). Sooty-headed Tyrannulet differs especially in its much plainer wing; their calls are very different. Forest Elaenia somewhat larger and has fairly well marked wing-bars, blurry breast streaking, and coronal patch; its call also differs strikingly. **Habits:** Tends to remain in forest canopy well above ground, where hard to see well except from tourist lodge "towers" and platforms. Often in pairs, perching more or less horizontally and often holding tail "half-cocked." Sometimes with mixed flocks. Heard more often than seen. **Voice:** Song (given mainly around dawn) a soft, querulous, semimusical "peeu, tri-ri-ri" (with somewhat becard-like quality) that is repeated steadily; Golden-faced's higher-pitched song is similar, with more drawn-out initial note. Also gives an inflected "tuwee?" repeated slowly at 2- to 3-second intervals (J. Moore recordings).

Red-billed Tyrannulet
Zimmerius cinereicapillus
Tiranolete Piquirrojo   Plate 67(21)

12 cm (4½"). *Apparently rare and local* (overlooked?) in canopy and borders of *foothill and lower subtropical forest on e. slope*. Iris *straw yellow*; bill blackish above, purplish flesh below (hard to see). Above olive with grayer crown and *relatively plain face*; wings and tail dusky, *wing-coverts and flight feathers sharply edged yellow*. Throat grayish white, becoming grayish olive on breast and bright clear pale yellow on belly. **Similar species:** Much more common Golden-faced Tyrannulet differs in having dark eye, yellow

on face, and whiter underparts. **Habits:** Poorly known in Ecuador. Behavior similar to Golden-faced Tyrannulet, like that species seen to best advantage when it comes lower at forest edge and in clearings. **Voice:** Song (in n. Bolivia) an accelerating and slightly descending series of clear notes, "teeuw tew-tew-te-te-te-te-te-te-te" (B. Hennessey recording fide P. Coopmans) or (in s. Peru) a fast series of clear notes, the last two emphasized, "tirtetetetete-whét-whét."

Ornithion Tyrannulets
Small, inconspicuous, and superficially dissimilar tyrannulets found in humid forest canopy and borders, one species on either side of the Andes. Both have characteristic voices.

White-lored Tyrannulet, *Ornithion inerme*
Tiranolete Alipunteado   Plate 67(15)

8.5 cm (3½"). Canopy and borders of humid forest and woodland in *lowlands of east*. Thick bill black. Olive above with slaty crown; *prominent short superciliary and narrow eye-ring white (producing spectacled look)*; wings and tail duskier, wings with *two rows of large yellowish white spots on wing-coverts*, forming "white-spotted wing-bars."

Mostly below 600 m

Throat grayish white, becoming pale yellowish olive on breast and clear yellow on belly. **Similar species:** Numerous other tyrannulets have wing-bars, but this tiny species is unique in having "bars" that are made up of obviously discrete white spots. **Habits:** Found singly or in pairs, regularly accompanying mixed flocks but tending to remain high above ground and thus hard to observe; sometimes one comes lower at forest edge. Like so many other canopy-dwelling tyrannids, heard much more often than seen. **Voice:** Song a persistently repeated, rather high-pitched and wheezy "pee, dee-dee-deet" or "pee, dee-deet."

Brown-capped Tyrannulet
Ornithion brunneicapillum
Tiranolete Gorripardo   Plate 67(16)

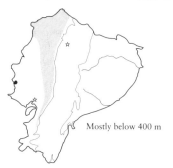

Mostly below 400 m

8 cm (3¼"). Canopy and borders of humid forest and woodland in *lowlands of west. Tiny and short-tailed.* Thick bill black. Olive above with *crown dark grayish brown* and *prominent white superciliary*; wings and tail duskier, wings with inconspicuous greenish edging (but no bars). *Bright yellow below*, with breast tinged olive. **Similar species:** Watch for combination of bold superciliary and lack of wing-bars. Cf. Sooty-headed Tyrannulet (also with plain wing, but otherwise very different). **Habits:** Found singly or in pairs, foraging by gleaning in foliage, often accompanying mixed canopy flocks. Usually remains well above ground, though sometimes coming lower at edge or in clearings. Heard far more often than seen. **Voice:** Distinctive song a fast series of high-pitched piping whistled notes, "pleee, pih-pey-peh-puh," the latter notes descending; cadence, with pause after first note, is characteristic. Sometimes just gives "pleee" note.

Southern Beardless-Tyrannulet
Camptostoma obsoletum
Tiranolete Silbador Sureño   Plate 67(13)

To 2800 m; in east mainly below 300 m, to 1600 m in Marañón drainage

9.5–10 cm (3¾–4"). *Common and widespread in a variety of semiopen habitats and forest borders in lowlands and subtropics on w. slope*, small numbers up into central and interandean valleys. *Less numerous in the east*, there mainly in canopy and borders of *várzea and riparian forest and woodland*; also occurs in Río Marañón drainage. *Usually looks distinctly bushy-crested*, and *often cocks tail*; lacks rictal bristles (hence the "beardless"). Bill rather thick, lower mandible pale at least at base. **Western birds** *pale overall, olive grayish above*, grayest on crown with whitish supraloral streak and narrow eye-ring; wings duskier with *two well-marked ochraceous to cinnamon wing-bars*. Throat and breast pale grayish, becoming yellowish white on belly. **Marañón birds** similar. **Eastern birds** notably different, somewhat smaller and *considerably darker*: upperparts grayish olive with wing-bars whitish to pale yellowish; belly clear pale yellow. **Similar species:** In the west this familiar tyrannulet is one of most frequently seen small tyrannids; here cf. especially Tumbezian Tyrannulet and Gray-and-white Tyrannulet. In the east, bushy-crested appearance is usually enough to distinguish it; cf. especially Mouse-colored and Yellow-crowned Tyrannulets. *Elaenia* are also dull-plumaged and often look crested but are much larger. **Habits:** Western birds are engaging and often confiding little birds that forage in foliage at all levels and in just about any situation. In the southwest this species and House Wren are usually the first birds to respond to playing a tape of Pacific Pygmy-Owl, both calling and fussing, likely as not gradually drawing in other species. Eastern birds are less apt to be noticed, as they generally remain high in forest and woodland canopy; they sound and act like different species (as they may be). **Voice:** Very vocal. In west most frequent calls are a slightly husky "freee?" or "weeeé?" and a more musical, descending "kleeu, klee-klee-klee." Dawn song a more complex "kleeé kee-ki-kikrrt!" (P. Coopmans). In east gives a quick high-pitched "free" followed by several fast chortling notes that distinctly drop in pitch.

Phaeomyias Tyrannulets
Drab, relatively big tyrannulets found in scrub, low woodland, and clearings, one species on either side of the Andes.

Mouse-colored Tyrannulet
Phaeomyias murina
Tiranolete Murino   Plate 67(18)

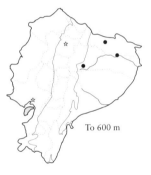

To 600 m

12 cm (4¾"). *Uncommon and local in clearings and vicinity of towns in lowlands of northeast.* Rather thick bill, pale at base of lower mandible. *Notably drab and characterless. Dull brown above* with *indistinct whitish superciliary*; wings duskier with two buffy whitish wing-bars. Throat whitish becoming dull olive grayish on breast; belly pale clear yellow. **Similar species:** Perkier-looking Southern Beardless-Tyrannulet is smaller with an expressive crest and no superciliary. Cf. also Amazonian Scrub-Flycatcher (more a forest bird) and certain *Elaenia*. Tumbesian Tyrannulet occurs only west of Andes. **Habits:** A nondescript bird found in secondary habitats; it may be increasing in Ecuador. Usually inconspicuous, gleaning for insects in dense foliage, not perching in the open for long, and apt to be overlooked until one learns its voice. **Voice:** Distinctive dry,

gravelly song a fast chattering or jumbled "jejejejejéjew" or "jejejejejéw."

Tumbesian Tyrannulet
Phaeomyias tumbezana
Tiranolete de Tumbes   Plate 67(17)

To 2300 m

12.5 cm (5"). *Desert scrub, light woodland, and gardens in arid intermontane valleys in north* (Imbabura and n. Pichincha), *and in lowlands of southwest*, in Loja ranging well up into intermontane valleys. Formerly considered conspecific with Mouse-colored Tyrannulet. *Brownish gray above* with *indistinct whitish superciliary*; wings duskier with *two buff or ochraceous wing-bars*. *Throat, breast, and flanks grayish*; belly whitish. **Similar species:** Southern Beardless-Tyrannulet is smaller and paler generally with an obvious bushy crest and usually cocked tail. Gray-and-white Tyrannulet is smaller with large amount of white always showing in crest. Mouse-colored Tyrannulet occurs only east of Andes. **Habits:** A drab bird, phlegmatic and inconspicuous, and often overlooked. General behavior similar to Mouse-colored Tyrannulet, but vocalizations very different. **Voice:** Song a sharp and squeaky "squeéky, squeey-kít!" Also gives a weird, mechanical-sounding "kit-wrzzzzzzzzzz." Probable dawn song a high-pitched, wheezy "kzeeeeet" interspersed with squeaky notes.

Gray-and-white Tyrannulet
Pseudelaenia leucospodia
Tiranolete Grisiblanco   Plate 68(18)

12.5 cm (5"). *Local in desert scrub in w. Guayas, on Isla de la Plata off Manabí, and s. Loja.* Formerly classified in genus *Phaeomyias*. Bill with pinkish base of lower mandible. *Pale grayish brown above* with

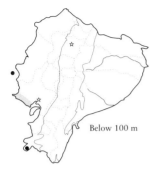

Below 100 m

considerable white nearly always exposed in crest (often spread open with bifurcated effect) and faint whitish supraloral; wings with whitish edging. *Below whitish*, tinged gray on sides and slightly creamier on belly. **Similar species:** White in the crest is normally conspicuous, and renders this otherwise obscure species easy to identify. Both Tumbesian and smaller Southern Beardless-Tyrannulets *lack* the white, and they both have buff wing-bars. Gray Elaenia occurs in totally different, humid-forest habitat. **Habits:** Favors desert washes and dry streambeds. Usually in pairs, gleaning actively in foliage of shrubs and low trees, usually perching horizontally and often cocking tail (tail can even be slowly wagged). **Voice:** Distinctive call a simple, sharp, and emphatic "chevík" or "chevík-chet."

Yellow-crowned Tyrannulet, *Tyrannulus elatus*
Tiranolete Coroniamarillo   Plate 67(14)

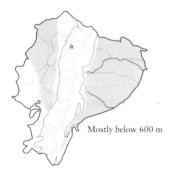

Mostly below 600 m

10.5 cm (4¼"). *Widespread* in canopy and borders of forest, secondary woodland, and clearings and gardens with scattered trees in *lowlands of east and west. Stubby black bill.* Olive above with slaty crown and *gray superciliary* above dusky line through eye, with *coronal stripe yellow* (often nearly hidden,

most evident when bird is calling or agitated); wings dusky with *two yellowish white wing-bars. Throat and sides of head pale grayish;* underparts clear yellow, clouded olive on breast. **Similar species:** This small, gray-faced tyrannulet is most often noted through its characteristic voice. Forest Elaenia is slightly larger and longer-tailed, has longer bill, and shows distinct blurry breast streaking. Cf. also Sooty-headed Tyrannulet (with plain wings) and Slender-footed Tyrannulet (with wing-*edging* only). **Habits:** A bird of canopy and densely foliaged trees in clearings, heard much more often than seen. This inconspicuous tyrannulet tends to perch vertically; it usually occurs in pairs, only rarely accompanying mixed flocks. Eats both fruit and small insects, primarily obtained in short sallies. **Voice:** Characteristic voice a clear, whistled "pray-teér," repeated at fairly long intervals, often straight through heat of day.

Myiopagis Elaenias
A *heterogeneous* group of fairly small flycatchers, some species perching fairly upright and others more horizontally; some have strong wing markings, whereas others are plain winged. One species (Gray) is unusual among this group of tyrannids in being sexually dimorphic. They inhabit forests and woodlands in the lowlands.

Gray Elaenia, *Myiopagis caniceps*
Elenita Gris   Plate 68(17)

To 600 m

12–12.5 cm (4¾–5"). Uncommon and local (under-recorded?) in *canopy and borders of humid forest in lowlands of east and north-west.* ♂ *blue-gray above* with white coronal streak (often concealed); wings black with *two bold white wing-bars and flight-feather edging. Throat and breast pale gray*, becoming grayish white on belly. **Eastern** ♀ bright olive above, grayer on head and with pale yellowish coronal streak; wings black with *two bold pale yellow wing-bars and edging on secondaries*. Throat grayish white; underparts pale greenish yellow, brightest yellow on belly. **Western** ♀ similar but with coronal patch white. **Similar species:** Gray ♂ ♂ distinctive and easily recognized, but ♀ ♀ can be more problematic (though their usually being with a ♂ generally helps). Note especially their bold, bright wing markings; those of, for instance, Forest Elaenia are less crisp and well-defined (Forest Elaenia is a duller bird overall, with blurry breast streaking). Pattern of both sexes recalls certain *Pachyramphus* becards. **Habits:** A canopy-inhabiting bird, rarely coming low even at edge. Almost always occurs in pairs, frequently accompanying mixed flocks; gleans in foliage, often holding tail partially cocked. **Voice:** ♂'s song a fast and shrill chippering that descends and fades toward end, introduced by several sharper notes, e.g., "swee swee swee wee-ee-ee-ee-ee-ee-ee-ee-ee." In e. Ecuador also gives a "tsi-si-tseeuw, tsi-tseeuw" (J. Moore recording), this not given by western birds (P. Coopmans).

Forest Elaenia, *Myiopagis gaimardii*
Elenita Selvática   Plate 68(13)

Mostly below 1000 m

12.5 cm (5"). *Canopy and borders of humid forest* (terra firme and várzea) *and secondary woodland in lowlands of east*. Head brownish gray, darker on crown with indistinct whitish supraloral and *white coronal stripe* (often concealed, most evident in vocalizing birds); olive above, wings and tail duskier, wings with *two prominent pale yellowish*

wing-bars. Throat whitish; breast pale yellow *mottled and streaked with olive*; belly pale clear yellow. **Similar species:** An obscure small elaenia, *best known through its distinctive voice*. Yellow-crowned Elaenia has a bright yellow coronal stripe, yellower wing-bars, and lacks streaky effect on breast; its general behavior and voice differ markedly. Forest Elaenia occurs regularly with several other similar, predominantly olive canopy-dwelling tyrannids. Most similar species lack Forest Elaenia's coronal stripe, except cf. ♀ Gray Elaenia; Zimmer's and Gray-crowned Flatbills both have markedly wider bills (but can look confusingly similar), and Slender-footed Tyrannulet has a pale iris and no wing-bars. **Habits:** Generally ranges well above ground, easier to see in secondary woodland and borders where it sometimes comes lower. Often forages with mixed flocks, gleaning in foliage; tends to perch horizontally, often slightly cocking tail. **Voice:** Frequently heard song a characteristic sharp, clear, and emphatic "ch-weét," usually given at long intervals; can be varied to "cheewi chi-chi."

Yellow-crowned Elaenia, *Myiopagis flavivertex*
Elenita Coroniamarilla   Plate 68(16)

Below 300 m

13 cm (5"). *Lower and middle growth inside várzea forest and woodland in lowlands of northeast*. Olive above, somewhat duskier on crown and with *bright golden yellow coronal stripe*; wings and tail duskier, wings with two prominent yellow wing-bars. *Throat and breast grayish olive*; belly pale clear yellow. **Similar species:** This species seems often to look quite disheveled, and is usually identified by combination of habitat and voice more than appearance. More widespread Forest Elaenia has white coronal

streak, whitish supraloral, and streaky effect on breast; its song differs strikingly. Cf. also ♀ Gray Elaenia. **Habits:** Found singly or in pairs, usually perching quite upright inside várzea or swampy forest. For the most part it does not accompany mixed flocks. Generally overlooked until its voice is known. **Voice:** Distinctive song an almost explosive, sharp, and very burry "jeeér-jeeer-jeeerjew" repeated at rather long intervals; can be varied to a faster "jéw-jijijijijijijew-jew."

Pacific Elaenia, *Myiopagis subplacens*
Elenita del Pacífico   Plate 68(15)

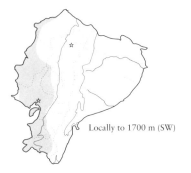

Locally to 1700 m (SW)

14 cm (5½"). Lower growth and borders of *deciduous and semihumid forest and woodland in lowlands and foothills of west; avoids humid regions.* Crown grayish brown with yellow coronal stripe (often concealed), *broad superciliary grizzled whitish and arching around blackish ear-coverts;* otherwise dull and rather pale brownish olive above; wings and tail somewhat duskier, *wings with yellowish edging* (but wing-bars obscure or lacking). Throat and breast pale grayish with blurry whitish streaking; belly pale yellow. **Similar species:** Greenish Elaenia slightly smaller, grayer on head (less brownish) with much shorter and whiter supraloral and plainer ear-coverts, and more olive breast; their calls differ strikingly. Yellow-olive Flatbill has wider bill and bolder wing markings (including wing-bars). **Habits:** A quiet and unobtrusive bird, doubtless often overlooked unless it is vocalizing; usually found singly, perching quite upright. Generally does not join mixed flocks. **Voice:** Around dawn gives an endlessly repeated "chrrr, chrrr, che-wík, chrrr, chrrr, che-wík . . ." (P. Coopmans). More frequently heard call a sharply enunciated "cheer! woorr-it" repeated at 3- to 4-second intervals.

Greenish Elaenia, *Myiopagis viridicata*
Elenita Verdosa   Plate 68(14)

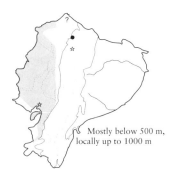

Mostly below 500 m, locally up to 1000 m

13.5 cm (5¼"). Lower growth, mid-levels, and borders of *semihumid and deciduous forest and woodland in lowlands of west.* Crown grayish with yellow coronal stripe (often hidden), *short supraloral stripe and eye-ring white;* otherwise olive above; wings and tail duskier, *wings with yellowish edging* (but wing-bars obscure or lacking). Throat pale grayish, blending into grayish olive breast; belly pale yellow. **Similar species:** Cf. Pacific Elaenia. Sooty-headed Tyrannulet markedly smaller, brighter yellow below, and lacks coronal stripe. **Habits:** Similar to Pacific Elaenia, though Greenish favors somewhat more humid situations; the two species are found sympatrically in a few locations. **Voice:** High-pitched song a strident, slurred, and burry "cheerip" or "cheeyree" (bisyllabic) or "zrreeeeer" (monosyllabic).

Elaenia Elaenias
A *very confusing* genus of midsized, mainly olive flycatchers found widely in shrubby and edge habitats (not forest). *It simply is not possible to identify every individual Elaenia,* particularly those that do not happen to be vocalizing. The White-crested/Sierran/Lesser complex is especially challenging. Elaenias tend to perch upright and have pale color on the lower mandible and bold wing-bars; many species have a crest, slight in some but very obvious in others. They occur virtually throughout Ecuador, some species only as austral migrants. Pay particular attention to the following points:

1. voice (often the best clue of all);
2. size;
3. crest (size and shape, and if any color is exposed);
4. wing-bars (a few species have 3 rather than the normal 2);
5. belly color (whitish or pale yellow); and
6. where you are (location and elevation).

Yellow-bellied Elaenia, *Elaenia flavogaster*
Elenia Penachuda   Plate 68(20)

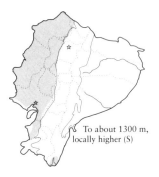

To about 1300 m, locally higher (S)

16 cm (6¼"). Fairly common in semiopen and cultivated areas as well as lighter woodland in *more humid lowlands and foothills of west*, also in Río Marañón drainage in extreme southeast. *No more "yellow-bellied" than several other elaenias.* Generally shows a *fairly conspicuous upstanding bushy crest* that usually reveals some white in center. Dull brownish olive above with indistinct whitish eye-ring, wings and tail duskier, wings with two prominent whitish wing-bars. Throat pale gray, becoming grayish olive on breast and pale yellow on belly. **Similar species:** *The only numerous elaenia in most of w. lowlands.* Lesser Elaenia is indeed smaller, and shows less of a crest; it is also somewhat darker on upperparts and throat and chest, but birds that are not vocalizing are sometimes not safely distinguished. Large Elaenia occurs only east of Andes, so overlap with Yellow-bellied possible only in Río Marañón drainage. **Habits:** Though drab in appearance, this elaenia is rather animated, excitable, and conspicuous, and especially in early morning often perches in open. Though generally seen singly or in pairs, larger numbers may gather in fruiting trees. Also catches insects in short aerial sallies. **Voice:** Very vocal. Most frequent calls, all with a hoarse or burry quality, include a "breeeyr"

and a "wreek-kreeeyuup," the latter often doubled; both members of a pair often call in a jumbled, sometimes even exuberant, manner. Dawn song a "trr-dyeéuw, trr-trreeenh-weeeuw," the two phrases alternating, or sometimes one phrase is given several times in succession.

Large Elaenia, *Elaenia spectabilis*
Elenia Tribandeada   Plate 68(21)

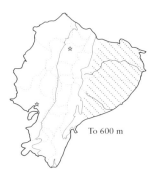

To 600 m

18 cm (7"). *A rare austral winter visitant* (late Mar.–Sep.) to shrubby clearings, riparian areas, and forest borders in *lowlands of east*. Dull brownish olive above with *only a slight crest* with but *little white in its center* (often none shows in field) and a vague whitish eye-ring; wings dusky with *three prominent whitish wing-bars.* Throat pale gray, becoming olive grayish on breast and pale yellow on belly. **Similar species:** Most resembles Yellow-bellied Elaenia (though these two species would occur together only around Zumba). Large differs in its somewhat larger size, less crested appearance with less white, and presence of 3d wing-bar on lesser wing-coverts. Mottle-backed Elaenia has very different, obvious crest and dark mottling on back. Cf. also Short-crested and Swainson's Flycatchers (*Myiarchus*). **Habits:** Similar to Yellow-bellied Elaenia, though less conspicuous; usually seen singly, often in fruiting trees together with other flycatchers (including austral migrant Small-billed Elaenias and others). **Voice:** Rather quiet in Ecuador. Occasionally gives a soft "cleeuw."

Mottle-backed Elaenia, *Elaenia gigas*
Elenia Cachudita   Plate 68(24)

18 cm (7"). *Uncommon to locally fairly common in shrubby clearings with scattered trees and on river islands in lowlands*

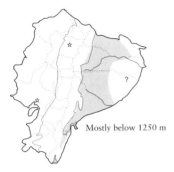

Mostly below 1250 m

and foothills of east. Nearly unmistakable because of *prominent bifurcated crest* that *protrudes straight up from forehead, exposing considerable white in center.* Olive brown above with faint whitish eye-ring and *feathers of mantle edged paler giving distinct mottled effect*; wings and tail duskier, wings with two whitish wing-bars. Throat pale grayish, becoming flammulated and clouded with olive on breast and flanks; midbelly pale clear yellow. **Similar species:** No other elaenia has such a crest. **Habits:** Similar to Yellow-bellied Elaenia. Usually found in pairs. **Voice:** Calls include a martin-like "drreet" and a shriller, loud "wor-eet!" or "wurdít," latter sometimes doubled (somewhat reminiscent of a Black-billed Thrush call; P. Coopmans). Often vocalizes from atop a shrub or low tree.

Highland Elaenia, *Elaenia obscura*
Elenia Oscura   Plate 68(27)

2150–3000 m

18 cm (7″). *Rare and local in lower growth and borders of subtropical and temperate forest and woodland in south* (Azuay and Loja). A plain, *round-headed* elaenia with *notably short bill* (often imparting a "snub-nosed" effect). Uniform dark olive above with *yellowish eye-ring* and no crest or coronal patch; wings and tail duskier, wings with two yellowish wing-bars. Throat pale yellowish, breast and flanks dull olive, midbelly clear pale yellow. **Similar species:** Sierran Elaenia markedly smaller and has somewhat crested look and white coronal patch (usually evident); its eye-ring is whitish. **Habits:** Not well known in Ecuador. Rather inconspicuous for an elaenia, tending to be more forest- or woodland-based. **Voice:** Call a fast "burrr" or "burrreep." Song (in Bolivia) consists of a plaintive first note followed by several shorter, scratchier ones, e.g., "weeeéuw-drrr-deet!" (S. Maijer recording, fide P. Coopmans).

Lesser Elaenia, *Elaenia chiriquensis*
Elenia Menor   Plate 68(25)

700–2800 m

13.5 cm (5¼″). *Apparently local in semiopen areas, clearings, and lighter woodland in foothills and subtropics of northwest* (south to n. Pichincha), also around *Zumba*; status confused by identification difficulties. *Rather dark brownish olive above* with *short crest* sometimes raised and parted to reveal white in center and vague whitish eye-ring; wings duskier with two prominent whitish wing-bars. Throat and breast dull brownish gray, belly pale yellow. **Similar species:** Smaller than Yellow-bellied Elaenia and with slighter crest; the two species generally do not occur together in Ecuador, Yellow-bellied favoring lower elevations. An even greater difficulty is posed by Sierran Elaenia, from which Lesser is very hard to distinguish; Lesser has more of a ruffled or squared-off crest and is shorter-billed; it may be slightly darker above and on breast (which is less olive), but wing-bar and belly colors seem about the same (fresh-plumaged Sierrans are more clearly yellow). **Habits:** Similar to Sierran and White-crested Elaenias. **Voice:** Apparent song a burry "bweer, wheéb, wher'r'r" (P. Coopmans recording), very different from Lesser Elaenias elsewhere (perhaps a separate species?); also a higher-pitched, clear "tseee!"

White-crested Elaenia, *Elaenia albiceps*
Elenia Crestiblanca   Plate 68(22)

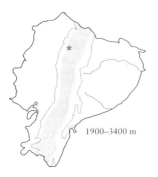

1900–3400 m

14.5 cm (5¾″). Borders of upper subtropical and temperate forest, secondary woodland, and shrubby clearings on both slopes, also on slopes above central and interandean valleys. Olive above with *narrow white coronal stripe* (usually visible, but *does not show much of a crest*) and vague whitish eye-ring; wings and tail duskier, wings with two whitish wing-bars. Throat and breast dull brownish gray, *becoming whitish on midbelly*. **Similar species:** Sierran Elaenia *very* similar but differs in having extensive yellow on belly (White-crested may have yellowish olive on flanks but never on midbelly). The two species occur together, though White-crested tends to favor drier areas, Sierran more humid ones. Cf. also Small-billed Elaenia. **Habits:** Similar to Yellow-bellied Elaenia, but generally less conspicuous. Often perches motionless for long periods, within cover and hard to see, but at other times may accompany mixed flocks; several birds may congregate at fruiting trees, where they often hover-glean for berries. Often can be located from its vocalizations. **Voice:** Calls, some very similar to Sierran Elaenia, include an abrupt "peeyr," a "wheeo," and a burry "brreeo."

Sierran Elaenia, *Elaenia pallatangae*
Elenia Serrana   Plate 68(26)
14.5 cm (5¾″). Borders of *subtropical and lower temperate* forest, secondary woodland,

1500–2800 m

and shrubby clearings on both slopes, also locally on slopes above central and interandean valleys; perhaps more numerous southward. Olive to brownish olive above with *narrow white coronal stripe* (usually visible, but *does not show much of a crest*) and vague whitish eye-ring; wings and tail duskier, wings with two whitish wing-bars. Throat and breast dull olive, *becoming pale yellow on belly*. **Similar species:** *Easily* confused with White-crested Elaenia, though that species shows no yellow on midbelly. Also closely resembles Lesser Elaenia, though that species typically shows at least some crested effect, has less white inside crest, and tends to be darker above. *Nonvocalizing birds often cannot be identified.* **Habits:** Much as in White-crested Elaenia. **Voice:** Calls include an abrupt burry "breeyp," a "wreee-yr," and a sharper "wree?" Very similar to White-crested Elaenia calls; some birds seem not to be distinguishable vocally.

Small-billed Elaenia, *Elaenia parvirostris*
Elenia Piquichica   Plate 68(23)
14.5 cm (5¾″). *An austral winter visitant* (Apr.–Oct.) to borders of humid forest and woodland, shrubby clearings, and riparian areas in *lowlands of east. Rather clean-cut for an elaenia.* Olive above with narrow white coronal stripe (usually visible, but *looks round-headed,* showing no crest) and *distinct round white eye-ring*; wings and tail duskier, wings with 2–3 whitish wing-bars (*most often 3*). *Throat and breast pale gray,* midbelly white. **Similar species:** White-crested Elaenia is not known to overlap with Small-billed (being more montane), but the two could occur together. White-crested is dingier generally (notably so on foreneck),

Below 400 m

shows a much less obvious eye-ring, and never seems to have a 3d wing-bar (which, being in fresh plumage, most Small-billeds in Ecuador do show). Small-billed's slightly stubbier bill is hardly a field character. **Habits:** Similar to Large Elaenia, though Small-billed is more numerous. **Voice:** Usually quiet in Ecuador, but occasionally gives a sharp "cheeu."

Amazonian Scrub-Flycatcher
Sublegatus obscurior
Mosquerito Breñero Amazónico   Plate 68(19)

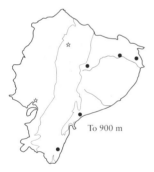

To 900 m

14 cm (5½″). *Rare and local (overlooked?) in canopy and borders of terra firme forest, secondary woodland, and adjacent pastures in lowlands and foothills of east.* Formerly considered part of Scrub Flycatcher complex (*S. arenarum*). *Bill short and black.* Olive brown above with a *narrow whitish supraloral* and incomplete eye-ring; wings and tail duskier, wings with 2–3 pale brownish wing-bars. *Throat and breast pale gray, merging into pale yellow belly.* **Similar species:** Superficially recalls a small *Elaenia*, though they all differ in their longer bills with pale lower mandibles, and none ever shows a supralo-

ral. *Myiarchus* flycatchers are larger with much longer bills, and likewise never show a supraloral stripe. Cf. also Forest Elaenia. **Habits:** Rather unobtrusive except when calling, tending to occur as sedentary pairs in forest canopy and edge; does not accompany mixed flocks. Scrub-flycatchers perch upright and sally after insects either into the air or to foliage. **Voice:** Song, given primarily around dawn, a repeated, rather sweet "chwedeé . . . chwedeé . . . chwedeé . . ." that may continue for several minutes (M. Robbins recording). Call a high-pitched, strident "zweeeeuw" (P. Coopmans).

Mecocerculus Tyrannulets
Attractively marked tyrannulets found in Andean forests, most species with *bold wing-bars* and a *conspicuous white superciliary*. All have the lower mandible pale or flesh-colored at least at its base. All but one species, the atypical White-throated, perch rather horizontally.

White-throated Tyrannulet
Mecocerculus leucophrys
Tiranillo Barbiblanco   Plate 70(21)

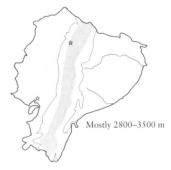

Mostly 2800–3500 m

14 cm (5½″). *Widespread in borders of temperate forest and woodland and adjacent shrubby clearings on both slopes*, often up to treeline. *A rather conspicuous, upright-perching tyrannid with distinctive puffy white throat.* Deep umber brown above with faint whitish superciliary; wings blackish with *two prominent rufous wing-bars.* *Throat white*, contrasting with olive grayish breast; belly pale yellow. **Similar species:** Other *Mecocerculus* perch horizontally, and none has a contrasting white throat; White-throated *looks quite long-tailed.* **Habits:**

Perching quite in open with tails hanging straight down, pairs or small groups of this tyrannulet frequently associate with mixed flocks. Forages both by gleaning and by making short sallies to foliage and into air. **Voice:** Infrequently heard song, given mainly around dawn, an excited-sounding "ch'd'dik, ch'd'dik, ch'd'dik, chéw," with variations (sometimes accented note is first, or sharp "kee-keek" notes are interspersed). Foraging birds often give a "pit" or "pif" contact note, sometimes in a brief fast series.

White-banded Tyrannulet
Mecocerculus stictopterus
Tiranillo Albibandeado   Plate 70(23)

Mostly 2400–3500 m

12.5 cm (5″). *Widespread in canopy and borders of temperate forest and woodland on both slopes.* Brownish olive above with gray head and *long broad white superciliary;* wings blackish with *two broad white wing-bars* and buffy yellowish flight-feather edging. Throat and breast pale gray, becoming yellowish white on belly. **Similar species:** An attractive, boldly patterned tyrannulet, liable to be confused only with White-tailed Tyrannulet. Latter is considerably smaller and shorter-tailed and has distinctly yellower wing-bars and a less prominent superciliary; it ranges mainly at lower (subtropical) elevations, though there is some overlap. **Habits:** Usually in pairs, perching horizontally and foraging actively; a frequent member of mixed flocks. Gleans in foliage, especially on outer branches, and easy to observe. **Voice:** Distinctive call an oft-given, somewhat raspy or hissing and inflected "squeeyh?," sometimes repeated 3–5 times in succession.

This can be lengthened to a "squeeee-ee-eeeyh? squeh-d'd'd'd'd'd'd'd," the first note high pitched and succeeding ones slurred into a descending trill. Dawn song consists of calls interspersed with sharper notes (P. Coopmans).

White-tailed Tyrannulet
Mecocerculus poecilocercus
Tiranillo Coliblanco   Plate 70(22)

1500–2500 m

11 cm (4¼″). *Numerous in canopy and borders of subtropical and lower temperate forest on both slopes.* Olive above with gray crown and white superciliary; *rump and uppertail-coverts pale greenish yellow,* this often quite conspicuous, even in flight; wings blackish with two prominent buffy yellowish wing-bars and yellowish flight-feather edging; tail dusky, *outer two pairs of feathers mostly white* (conspicuous from below and in flight). Throat and breast pale gray, yellowish white on belly. **Similar species:** White-banded Tyrannulet notably larger and longer-tailed, with bolder white superciliary and pure white wing-bars; it lacks white in tail and the pale area on rump; it occurs at higher elevations, with only limited overlap. Because of White-tailed's small size, it can be confused with a migrant warbler (especially Blackburnian). Cf. also Rufous-winged Tyrannulet. **Habits:** Similar to White-banded Tyrannulet. Often feeds in tree ferns. **Voice:** Call a frequently heard series of 3–4 (occasionally more) high-pitched minor-keyed notes that distinctly drop in pitch, "psi-psee-pseh." Another call is a single note of comparable quality; also gives a "ts-lik" call (P. Coopmans).

Rufous-winged Tyrannulet
Mecocerculus calopterus
Tiranillo Alirrufo   Plate 70(24)

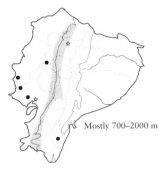

Mostly 700–2000 m

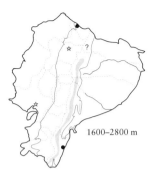

1600–2800 m

11 cm (4¼″). Seemingly local (but increasing?) in canopy and borders of *foothill and subtropical forest, woodland, and nearby clearings and plantations on w. slope*, and *on e. slope in Zamora-Chinchipe*, also locally on coastal cordillera. Unusual among tyrannulets is this distinctive species with *unique rufous edging on flight feathers, forming a conspicuous patch*. Olive above with dark gray crown and ear-coverts and long white superciliary; wings blackish with two prominent pale buff wing-bars in addition to the rufous; tail with *outer two pairs of feathers white*. Throat and breast pale gray, whitish on belly. **Similar species:** Pattern of this pretty little tyrannulet bears some resemblance to ♂ Rufous-winged Antwren. Cf. also White-tailed Tyrannulet (with which Rufous-winged is sympatric at a few sites). **Habits:** Much as in White-banded and White-tailed Tyrannulets, though Rufous-winged seems more apt to forage lower and away from actual forest. **Voice:** Call a slightly husky "pur-cheé, chi-chichu" (B. Walker recording). Also gives a fast series of emphatic notes, mainly descending, "kuw-ki-ke-ke-ku-ku" (N. Krabbe recording, fide P. Coopmans).

Sulphur-bellied Tyrannulet
Mecocerculus minor
Tiranillo Ventriazufrado   Plate 67(6)

11.5 cm (4½″). *Canopy and borders of subtropical and lower temperate forest and woodland on e. slope*, also one record from w. slope in far north. Dark olive above with gray crown and *white superciliary*, lower face grizzled gray and white; wings blackish with *two broad buff wing-bars. Mostly yellow below* with whitish chin, breast somewhat clouded olive. **Similar species:** Unique among *Mecocerculus* in having *yellow* underparts. Variegated Bristle-Tyrant similar in plumage but perches vertically and has prominent dark ear-crescent and orange-yellow lower mandible. Cf. also Plumbeous-crowned Tyrannulet. **Habits:** Forages singly or in pairs, often accompanying mixed flocks; generally stays well above ground, though sometimes coming lower at forest borders. **Voice:** Calls include a sharp and fast "chew-chew-chew" (sometimes several more notes) and a squeakier, more nasal "skwi-skwe-skwu-skwu" (M. Lysinger recording).

Serpophaga Tyrannulets
Two *very dissimilar* tyrannulets, a cute gray species closely associated with Andean streams and a plain brownish one found locally in scrub on river islands in Amazonia.

River Tyrannulet, *Serpophaga hypoleuca*
Tiranolete Ribereño   Plate 69(24)

11 cm (4¼″). *Scarce and local in early-succession growth and shrubbery on Ríos Napo and Pastaza islands in lowlands of east. Uniform grayish brown above, elongated crown feathers blackish* and with white coronal patch; plain wings and tail somewhat duskier. Below white, washed with gray across breast. **Similar species:** Drab Water-Tyrant markedly larger and grayer overall, and behaves differently. Torrent Tyrannulet occurs only along Andean streams. **Habits:**

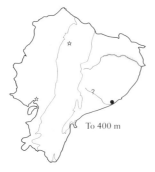

To 400 m

Usually found in pairs, like most other island birds generally not foraging in mixed flocks. Gleans actively in foliage, often in isolated bushes and small trees, but often seems restless, seldom remaining long in one area. **Voice:** Gives a variety of rather spritely chippered notes, often in an excited-sounding series. Also has a drier, more rattled, upslurred "d-d-d-r-r-ree-eet?" (J. Moore recording). Dawn song a slower and clearer "wheeeet? wee-eeeéuw," repeated slowly (P. Coopmans).

Torrent Tyrannulet, *Serpophaga cinerea*
Tiranolete Guardarríos   Plate 69(25)

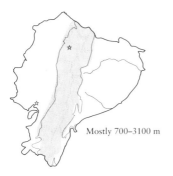

Mostly 700–3100 m

11.5 cm (4½"). *Widespread along fast-flowing rocky streams and rivers in Andes*, in both forested and open terrain. *Mostly gray*, slightly paler below and whitest on throat and lower belly. *Crown and sides of head black*, with usually concealed white coronal patch; wings and tail also black, wing-coverts with indistinct whitish edging. **Juvenile** browner. **Similar species:** This attractive, perky tyrannulet is unique and nearly unmistakable in its restricted habitat. **Habits:** Occurs in sedentary pairs, generally remain-

ing close to water (occasionally venturing out onto grassy pastures) and often perching on rocks out in stream or river, periodically wagging or elevating tail. Also feeds on wet dirt or gravel roads. Sallies for insects, sometimes a short distance into air but more often to vegetation on sides of rocks and along banks. **Voice:** Not very vocal, but gives a sharp "seep," sometimes by both members of pair in sequence.

Lesser Wagtail-Tyrant, *Stigmatura napensis*
Rabicano Menor   Plate 69(23)

Below 300 m

13 cm (5"). *Local in early-succession growth and shrubbery* (mainly *Tessaria*) *on Ríos Napo and Aguarico islands in lowlands of northeast*. A distinctive slender flycatcher with *long graduated tail*. Grayish olive above with *yellow superciliary*; wings and tail dusky, *wings with broad longitudinal patch of yellowish white, tail feathers broadly tipped and edged yellowish white*. Below yellow, tinged olive on chest. **Similar species:** Nearly unmistakable in its restricted habitat. **Habits:** Lively and attractive, usually in pairs that move incessantly through dense lower growth, sometimes coming to edge; not too difficult to observe. Tail usually held partially cocked, often with feathers fanned exposing pale tips (but it never is really wagged). **Voice:** Has various calls, including a querulous "kweeurt?" or "kweeurt? kwee," sometimes then ending in a jumble of notes, these often with a distinctive rollicking cadence, e.g., "kwi-kwu-kwrr, kwi-kwu-kwrr. . . ." Usually both members of a pair sing in syncopation.

Anairetes Tit-Tyrants
Small flycatchers with *unmistakable long and bifurcated crests* found in montane scrub and light woodland.

Tufted Tit-Tyrant, *Anairetes parulus*
Cachudito Torito   Plate 69(20)

11 cm (4¼"). *Shrubby clearings and temperate forest borders on both slopes,* locally ranging up into shrubby paramo. *Tiny* and *conspicuously crested. Iris pale yellow.* Head blackish with *long, wispy, recurved crest* (usually parted into two-horned effect), *supraloral and postocular stripe white.* Above dull grayish brown; wings and tail duskier, wings with two narrow whitish wing-bars, outer tail feathers with whitish outer webs. *Throat and breast whitish conspicuously streaked with black,* becoming pale yellow on belly. **Similar species:** The bold streaking on this very small tyrannid is usually distinctive. Larger and longer-tailed Agile Tit-Tyrant has flatter crown with no long recurved crest. Cf. range-restricted Black-crested Tit-Tyrant. **Habits:** Usually in pairs, foraging actively and restlessly in foliage of dense shrubs, sometimes with mixed flocks but usually not. Often flutters wings; gleans in foliage, sometimes also hover-gleaning or even making short sallies into air. **Voice:** Song a fairly loud, high-pitched, and fast "chuit-chuit-chuit-chuit-chuit-chidi-didi"; sometimes "chuit" or "skuit" is given independently in a slower-paced series. Also often heard is a fairly long, weak trill.

Black-crested Tit-Tyrant
Anairetes nigrocristatus
Cachudito Crestinegro   Plate 69(21)

13 cm (5"). *Very local in humid montane scrub and woodland borders in s. Loja* (Utuana). Sometimes called Marañón Tit-Tyrant, or considered conspecific with Pied-crested Tit-Tyrant (*A. reguloides*) of w. Peru.

Lower mandible mostly reddish. *Very long and recurved crest mainly black, usually parted to reveal extensive white in crown and nape. Mostly black above,* back streaked with white; wings with two white wing-bars, outer tail feathers broadly tipped white. *Throat and chest black* with indistinct white streaking; underparts whitish with black streaking on sides and flanks. **Similar species:** Truly spectacular, this tit-tyrant should not be confused in its very limited range and habitat. Tufted Tit-Tyrant much smaller, not so black, pale-eyed, etc. **Habits:** Similar to Tufted Tit-Tyrant, though Black-crested seems more prone to remain hidden inside foliage, and is thus harder to see well. **Voice:** Song an abrupt, fairly harsh chippering lasting 3–4 seconds.

Agile Tit-Tyrant, *Uromyias agilis*
Cachudito Agil   Plate 69(22)

13.5 cm (5¼"). Lower growth and borders of *temperate forest on both slopes* south to n. Loja (east) and Cotopaxi (west). Most numerous just below treeline, and *favors stands of Chusquea bamboo.* Base of lower mandible pale, orange-yellow to horn. *Long*

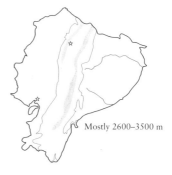

flat crest blackish, usually protruding slightly to rear, and bordered below by a *long narrow white superciliary*. Brown above, streaked whitish on nape and blackish on back; wings and tail dusky. Below yellowish white *narrowly streaked with brown on throat, breast, and flanks*; belly pale yellow. **Similar species:** Tufted Tit-Tyrant is markedly smaller and shorter-tailed, and it sports an obvious recurved and bifurcated crest; it has wing-bars (*wings plain* in Agile). **Habits:** Usually in small groups that frequently accompany mixed flocks, foraging actively by gleaning in foliage and on twigs, often in outer part of shrubs and low trees and thus not too hard to see. **Voice:** Call a brief soft trill; various other contact notes are given while foraging. Song an excited-sounding, jumbled series of "treerrr" trills and "tseeyk," "tsi-dik," or "tseee" notes (P. Coopmans).

Subtropical Doradito
Pseudocolopteryx acutipennis
Doradito Subtropical   Plate 67(19)

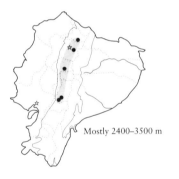

Mostly 2400–3500 m

11.5 cm (4½″). Now *rare and local in reedbeds, moist sedgy pastures, and adjacent shrubby areas in central valley from Imbabura to Chimborazo*. Uniform bright olive green above with duskier cheeks; wing-coverts obscurely edged grayish olive. *Below entirely bright yellow*. **Similar species:** Nothing really similar in Ecuador. Could carelessly be confused with a ♀ yellowthroat or ♀ Mourning Warbler, though none of those is known to occur in the limited range of doradito. **Habits:** Generally inconspicuous and occurring only in a few favored haunts, likely to be seen only if specifically sought out. On calm early mornings occasionally seen perched in open atop a shrub or reed, but otherwise generally remains

within cover. **Voice:** Song a "tzit-tzit-tzit t-konk" followed by a wing-whirr, apparently often given in a brief display flight (B. Whitney *in* Fjeldså and Krabbe 1990). Gives a "tzit" call while foraging.

Tawny-crowned Pygmy-Tyrant
Euscarthmus meloryphus
Tirano Enano Frentileonado   Plate 69(15)

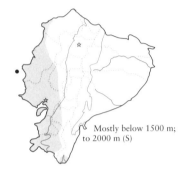

Mostly below 1500 m; to 2000 m (S)

10 cm (4″). *Common in arid scrub, shrubby clearings, and undergrowth of deciduous woodland and forest in lowlands of west*, ranging up into subtropics in Azuay and Loja; also in Río Marañón drainage around Zumba. *Forecrown rufous* and *facial area conspicuously buff*; otherwise olive above with rufous coronal patch; wings and tail duskier, *wings with two prominent buff wing-bars*. Throat white, breast pale grayish olive, belly pale yellow. **Similar species:** No other similar small tyrannid has comparable buff and rufous on face. Cf. Scale-crested Pygmy-Tyrant (with rufous scaling on crown, streaking on foreneck, etc.; it favors *more humid* areas). **Habits:** An inconspicuous small tyrannid; heard much more often than seen, though once located not particularly shy. Hops singly and in pairs through dense undergrowth, generally not with mixed flocks. **Voice:** Characteristic call an oft-repeated, fast, and explosive "plee-tirik" or "plee-ti-re-tik." Song a repeated, fast "re-tr-tr-tr-tr-tr-trreétrrt. . . ."

Mionectes Flycatchers
Very plain, slender flycatchers with narrow bills found in lower growth of humid lowland and montane forest and woodland. All three are numerous, though rather inconspicuous, birds.

Streak-necked Flycatcher
Mionectes striaticollis
Mosquerito Cuellilistado   Plate 68(2)

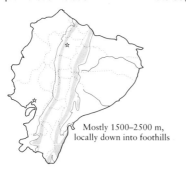

Mostly 1500–2500 m, locally down into foothills

To 2000 m, in east not below 400 m

13–13.5 cm (5–5¼″). Fairly common but inconspicuous in lower growth and borders of *subtropical and lower temperate forest on both slopes*. Mainly occurs *above* range of Olive-striped Flycatcher. Lower mandible at least basally pale. **East-slope birds** have *head and neck gray* with *small but prominent white spot behind eye*; otherwise rather bright olive above, wings and tail duskier, wings with yellowish olive edging. Throat and chest olive gray finely streaked white; *breast and belly rather bright clear yellow*, breast and flanks finely streaked olive. **West-slope birds** similar but hood more grayish olive. **Similar species:** Very similar Olive-striped Flycatcher differs in lacking any gray on hood, and its yellow on underparts is duller and streaking on belly more extensive. Its bill is typically all black. **Habits:** Usually found singly, perching vertically and at times leaning forward and bowing head; occasionally lifts a wing up over back. Sometimes joins mixed flocks, or joins aggregations of tanagers and other birds at a fruiting tree, there frequently hover-gleaning. Small groups of ♂♂ gather to display in leks. **Voice:** Rarely vocal away from leks, where ♂ gives a series of rhythmic, squeaky notes with quality of a hummingbird though individual notes vary more and some are doubled (P. Coopmans recording). Singing birds may sway head from side to side, the bill wide open exposing orange gape.

Olive-striped Flycatcher, *Mionectes olivaceus*
Mosquerito Olivirrayado   Plate 68(3)

13–13.5 cm (5–5¼″). Fairly common but inconspicuous in lower growth and borders of humid forest in *lowlands of west, and in foothill and subtropical forest on both slopes*. Mainly occurs *below* range of Streak-necked Flycatcher. Uniform olive above with *small but prominent white spot behind eye*; wings and tail duskier, wings with yellowish olive edging. *Underparts pale yellow extensively streaked with olive*. **Similar species:** Streak-necked Flycatcher confusingly similar, especially on w. slope where it shows less gray on head and neck (and thus is not dissimilar from Olive-striped). Streak-necked's post-ocular spot is slightly less conspicuous, and its yellow below is brighter, with markedly less extensive olive streaking; belly in particular is brighter, *unstreaked* yellow. Its lower mandible is mostly or all pale; bill all black in Olive-striped. **Habits:** Similar to Streak-necked Flycatcher. In a few lower subtropical sites both species are found sympatrically. **Voice:** Similar to Streak-necked Flycatcher, and equally quiet, but calls of lekking ♂♂ faster and higher pitched. Call a descending "seeeu."

Ochre-bellied Flycatcher
Mionectes oleagineus
Mosquerito Ventriocráceo   Plate 68(1)

13 cm (5″). Widespread in lower growth of humid forest and secondary woodland in *lowlands of east and west*. Lower mandible flesh-colored at least basally. *Olive above*, wings and tail dusky, wings with two indistinct ochraceous wing-bars and flight-feather edging (especially conspicuous on tertials). Throat olive grayish, breast ochraceous olive *becoming ochraceous on belly*. **Eastern birds** more richly colored below. **Similar species:** A slender, plain flycatcher, shaped much like Streak-necked and Olive-striped but *lacking*

Mostly below 1000 m

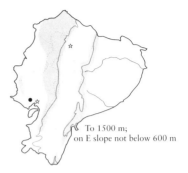

To 1500 m;
on E slope not below 600 m

any streaking. Ruddy-tailed Flycatcher smaller and more compact. **Habits:** Unobtrusive and quiet, with quick darting movements, generally found singly inside forest and woodland, less often at edge. Sometimes joins mixed flocks, or more often joins aggregations of other birds at fruiting trees; also consumes many insects. Frequently flashes a wing up over back, alternating one side after the other; also ruffles crown feathers. **Voice:** Usually quiet, but ♂♂ on their display perches can be very vocal, giving a variety of chirping notes, some fast and sharp, others nasal, with the most distinctive phrase being a "cheea-cheea-cheea."

Leptopogon **Flycatchers**
Slender and rather long-tailed flycatchers with narrow bills that are found in the lower growth of humid lowland and montane forest, where they perch vertically and are frequent flock members. Each species has a *"grizzled" face* and *dark auricular patch*; in this and their frequent wing-lifting they resemble the smaller *Pogonotriccus* bristle-tyrants.

Slaty-capped Flycatcher
Leptopogon superciliaris
Mosquerito Gorripizarro   Plate 68(4)

13.5 cm (5¼"). *Common in lower growth of foothill and lower subtropical forest on both slopes*, also locally in more humid lowlands of west and on coastal cordillera. *Bill all black. Crown slaty gray with facial area whitish grizzled gray* and *dusky patch on ear-coverts.* Otherwise olive above, wings dusky with *two broad ochraceous to buff wing-bars* and yellowish flight-feather edging. Throat pale grayish, becoming olive on breast and clear yellow on belly. **Similar species:** Marble-faced Bristle-Tyrant is similarly patterned,

but differs in its smaller size and yellowish wing-bars. Variegated Bristle-Tyrant (also with ochraceous wing-bars) is likewise smaller and has an obvious orangey lower mandible. Sepia-capped Flycatcher occurs only in e. lowlands. **Habits:** Found singly or in pairs, often accompanying mixed flocks of understory birds. Perches erectly, often on open branches, and usually easy to see; sallies out to pick off insects from leaf surfaces, less often from twigs and branches. Frequently lifts a wing up over its back. **Voice:** Rather vocal; e.-slope birds give a distinctive sharp "skeeéy, deeer," w.-slope birds a less nasal "tse-tsrrrr."

Sepia-capped Flycatcher
Leptopogon amaurocephalus
Mosquerito Gorrisepia   Plate 68(5)

To 450 m

13.5 cm (5¼"). *Scarce and local in lower growth of humid forest in lowlands of east. Crown dark brown, facial area dull buff grizzled dusky,* and *dusky patch on ear-coverts.* Otherwise olive above, tail more brownish; wings dusky *with two broad buff wing-bars* and yellowish flight-feather edging. Throat pale grayish becoming dull olive on breast and pale yellow on belly. **Similar species:** *Montane* Slaty-capped Flycatcher (no known overlap) has gray crown and whitish facial area. Though obscure, there really is nothing else much like Sepia-capped in e. lowlands. **Habits:** Similar to Slaty-capped Flycatcher, though Sepia-capped tends to be more unobtrusive and less often comes to forest edge. It frequently lifts a wing up over its back. **Voice:** Call a fast, sputtering chatter that trails off toward end, e.g., "dre- d'd'd'd'd'd'dew," sometimes introduced by a sharper, more emphasized note.

Rufous-breasted Flycatcher
Leptopogon rufipectus
Mosquerito Pechirrufo   Plate 68(6)

13 cm (5¼"). Uncommon, inconspicuous, and local in lower growth of *subtropical and lower temperate forest on e. slope. Crown dark gray; facial area, sides of head, throat, and chest rufous,* ear-coverts with obscure grizzling and a dusky patch. Otherwise olive above, tail decidedly brownish; wings dusky with two broad buff wing-bars. Lower breast olive, belly pale clear yellow. **Similar species:** Handsome Flycatcher smaller with buffier throat and chest (not such a deep rufous), shows no rufous on its facial area, and has pale lower mandible. **Habits:** Similar to Slaty-capped Flycatcher, though Rufous-breasted never seems to be as numerous or conspicuous. **Voice:** Frequently gives a loud and emphatic "skwee!" (like squeezing a baby's bath toy), sometimes run together into a very fast series of shrill sputtered notes.

Phylloscartes Tyrannulets
Now that the *Pogonotriccus* bristle-tyrants have once again been separated out, *Phyl-*

loscartes becomes a well defined genus of rather slender, arboreal tyrannulets whose long tails are usually held cocked. Both Ecuadorian species are scarce *arboreal* birds of *east-slope subtropical forests.*

Ecuadorian Tyrannulet
Phylloscartes gualaquizae
Tiranolete Ecuatoriano   Plate 67(4)

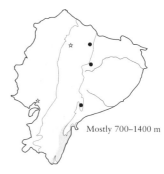

Mostly 700–1400 m

11.5 cm (4½"). Canopy and borders of *foothill and lower subtropical forest on e. slope.* Formerly placed in genus *Pogonotriccus* and then called Ecuadorian Bristle-Tyrant. *Crown gray, indistinct superciliary and eye-ring white, ear-coverts whitish indistinctly outlined with blackish.* Otherwise olive above, wings and tail dusky, wings with two pale yellow wing-bars. Throat whitish, breast mottled olive and pale yellow, belly clear yellow. **Similar species:** Closely resembles Plumbeous-crowned Tyrannulet, which is found mainly at higher elevations; that species is larger and has a stubbier bill and a pale area behind its dark ear-crescent. White-fronted Tyrannulet is also closely similar (and can be sympatric); it has a slightly heavier bill with lower mandible at least basally pale, and has white across forehead and a more prominent superciliary. Spectacled Bristle-Tyrant is a bristle-tyrant (thus perching upright) but in plumage is quite similar, differing in its pale lower mandible, bolder eye-ring, and yellower underparts. **Habits:** Forages singly or in pairs, often accompanying mixed flocks of canopy birds and generally remaining well above ground except at edge. Perches horizontally, usually holding its rather long tail partially cocked; sometimes flicks a wing up over back. **Voice:** Calls include a thin "feeee" and a spitting, almost rattled trill, "sp-i-i-i-ii-i," that at first descends, then ascends, then descends again.

Rufous-browed Tyrannulet
Phylloscartes superciliaris
Tiranolete Cejirrufo   Plate 67(5)

1300–1700 m

1200–2100 m

11.5 cm (4½"). *Local in canopy of lower subtropical forest on e. slope in s. Ecuador*, thus far *only on outlying ridges* (Cordilleras de Cutucú and del Cóndor). Crown and nape slaty with *narrow rufous frontal band and superciliary*; spot at base of bill and *ear-coverts white, latter narrowly encircled by black*. Otherwise olive above, wings and tail duskier with prominent yellowish green edging. *Throat and breast pale grayish*, becoming white on belly. **Similar species:** Striking facial pattern and lack of yellow on underparts should preclude confusion of this scarce tyrannulet though, as it usually remains well above ground, colors and pattern are often hard to discern. **Habits:** Similar to Ecuadorian Tyrannulet. **Voice:** Song a spritely "spee-ee-ee-ee-ee, spee-didi-dee."

Pogonotriccus Bristle-Tyrants
Small tyrannids with dark auricular patches found inside lower growth of *subtropical and foothill forest. They tend to perch upright* and to wing-lift frequently. The genus was briefly merged into *Phylloscartes*, though it seems surely distinct.

Marble-faced Bristle-Tyrant
Pogonotriccus ophthalmicus
Orejerito Carijaspeado   Plate 67(1)

11.5 cm (4½"). Lower and middle growth of *subtropical forest and forest borders on both*

slopes (south to Pichincha in west). Lower mandible pale at base. Crown gray, *facial area grizzled gray and white*, with *white-bordered blackish crescent on ear-coverts*. Otherwise olive above, wings and tail duskier, *wings with two yellowish wing-bars*. Upper throat grayish white, becoming yellowish olive on lower throat and breast and bright clear yellow on belly. **Similar species:** Variegated Bristle-Tyrant (e. slope only) has obviously bicolored bill and cinnamon wing-bars. Ashy-headed Tyrannulet has more bluish gray crown, no flight feather edging, and streaky (not mottled) effect on chest. Plumbeous-crowned Tyrannulet (also e. slope only) is very similar though less grizzled on face and its all-dark bill is stubbier; it perches more horizontally. Slaty-capped Flycatcher is larger with a proportionately longer bill and has ochraceous wing-bars. **Habits:** Found mainly singly or in pairs, usually accompanying mixed flocks of understory birds, generally foraging a little higher than the Slaty-capped Flycatchers that are sometimes with the same flock. Rather active, tending to perch vertically on open branches, sallying out short distances to snap up prey from leaves and twigs. Periodically a wing is flicked up over back. **Voice:** Two-parted song a fast "psee-ee-ee-ee-u, tsi-tsi-tsi," the first part descending, then ending with several higher-pitched emphatic notes. Call a doubled "ts-rt" (P. Coopmans).

Variegated Bristle-Tyrant
Pogonotriccus poecilotis
Orejerito Variegado   Plate 67(2)

11.5 cm (4½"). *Scarce in lower and middle growth of subtropical forest on e. slope. Lower mandible yellow to orange-yellow.*

1500–2000 m

700–1400 m

Crown gray, *facial area and indistinct superciliary grizzled gray and white*, with *white-bordered blackish crescent on ear-coverts*. Otherwise olive above, wings and tail duskier, *wings with two broad cinnamon wing-bars* and greenish yellow flight-feather edging. Upper throat grayish white, becoming yellowish olive on lower throat and breast and bright clear yellow on belly. **Similar species:** Marble-faced Bristle-Tyrant lacks such a strongly bicolored effect to bill, and its wing-bars are yellowish. Slaty-capped Flycatcher is larger with larger and all-black bill. Sulphur-bellied Tyrannulet shows a distinct superciliary and no crescent on ear-coverts; its horizontal posture and overall behavior are very different. **Habits:** Similar to Marble-faced Bristle-Tyrant; occasionally the two species forage in same flock. **Voice:** Calls include a tanager-like "tsit" often repeated several times, sometimes extended into a "tsit-tsit-tsit-ts-ts-ts-tseweeeét."

Spectacled Bristle-Tyrant
Pogonotriccus orbitalis
Orejerito de Anteojos   Plate 67(3)

11 cm (4¼"). *Scarce* in lower and middle growth of *foothill and lower subtropical forest on e. slope*. Lower mandible flesh. *Crown gray* contrasting with otherwise olive upperparts; *prominent eye-ring yellowish white, facial area mottled yellowish* with indistinct dusky crescent on ear-coverts; wings and tail duskier, wings with two bold pale yellowish wing-bars. Below rather bright yellow, though clouded olive on throat and breast. **Similar species:** This species' eye-ring is more conspicuous than on other bristle-tyrants, but its ear-crescent is less so. Similarly plumaged Ecuadorian Tyrannulet

differs in its all-dark bill and horizontal posture; it forages mainly in canopy. **Habits:** Similar to Marble-faced Bristle-Tyrant. **Voice:** Call a fast, high-pitched, chippered trill, at first descending a bit, then ending with 2–3 emphasized and sharper notes.

Yellow Tyrannulet, *Capsiempis flaveola*
Tiranolete Amarillo   Plate 67(20)

To 1500 m

11.5 cm (4½"). Lower and middle growth of *more humid woodland and forest borders in lowlands and foothills of west* (Pichincha to Guayas and El Oro), and *locally in foothills of northeast, favoring bamboo stands*. Slender, long-tailed, and mainly yellow. Yellowish olive above with *bold yellow superciliary*, wings and tail duskier, wings with *two broad yellow wing-bars. Below all yellow.* **Similar species:** Subtropical Doradito lacks superciliary and wings-bars and occurs in an entirely different habitat. **Habits:** Forages mainly in pairs, gleaning actively in foliage, most often perching more or less horizontally with tail held somewhat cocked; also sometimes perches vertically, however. **Voice:** Rather vocal, members of a pair staying in contact through a variety of soft calls, e.g., "pwit"; also gives a short dry trill, "tr-r-r-r-r." Frequently given song a pleasant and rollicking series of notes that often seem to lack much pattern, usually starting slowly but then quickly speeding up; it vaguely recalls song of Sooty-headed Tyrannulet.

Pseudotriccus Pygmy-Tyrants

Two small and inconspicuous flycatchers found in montane forest undergrowth, where their presence is sometimes made known by what are apparently mechanical sounds.

Bronze-olive Pygmy-Tyrant
Pseudotriccus pelzelni
Tirano Enano Bronceado   Plate 69(18)

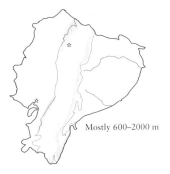

Mostly 600–2000 m

11–11.5 cm (4¼–4½"). *Fairly common but inconspicuous in undergrowth of foothill and subtropical forest on both slopes.* Iris reddish brown to dark red. *Dark and uniform.* **East-slope birds** uniform dark olive above. Throat whitish, breast and flanks olive, midbelly dull creamy yellow. **West-slope birds** browner above (especially on wings and tail), more ochraceous below (especially across breast). **Similar species:** A rather nondescript and confusing little tyrannid. Coloration vaguely recalls a *Myiobius* flycatcher though Bronze-olive is differently shaped and lacks their obvious yellow rump; behavior also markedly different. E.-slope birds also resemble certain ♀ manakins, though pygmy-tyrant is less plump and round in shape. **Habits:** Quiet and easy to overlook; single individuals are sometimes encountered in shady forest undergrowth as they hop and flutter in foliage, often jumping upward to snap insects off the underside of leaves. Usually does not accompany flocks. Wings whirr audibly as bird flies, and it also often

makes a sharp rattling sound with bill (or possibly wings?). **Voice:** Infrequently heard call a shrill and high-pitched "preeeeeeee," sometimes with a separate higher note at end. Also gives a drier descending trill.

Rufous-headed Pygmy-Tyrant
Pseudotriccus ruficeps
Tirano Enano Cabecirrufo   Plate 69(19)

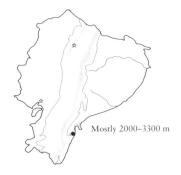

Mostly 2000–3300 m

11 cm (4¼"). Inconspicuous in undergrowth of *upper subtropical and temperate forest on both slopes* (south to Cotopaxi in west). A cute, nearly unmistakable little tyrannid, with *contrasting bright rufous head and throat*; otherwise dark olive above, with *contrasting chestnut wings and tail.* Breast and flanks olive, midbelly pale yellow. **Young birds** gradually acquire rufous and chestnut, and younger individuals may show very little, but generally enough to reveal their identity. **Similar species:** Cf. Rufous-crowned Tody-Flycatcher (which really is quite different). **Habits:** Similar to Bronze-olive Pygmy-Tyrant, which Rufous-headed appears to replace at higher elevations. **Voice:** Call a sharp and drawn-out, rattled "tzrrrrrrrrrrrr" with decided descending effect. Song a protracted and very high-pitched trill, at first descending, then ascending, "tsi-i-i-i-i-i-e-e-e-u-e-e-e-i-i-i-i?" Also makes bill (?) snaps as in Bronze-olive Pygmy-Tyrant.

Ringed Antpipit, *Corythopis torquata*
Coritopis Fajeado   Plate 67(25)

14 cm (5½"). *Uncommon on ground inside terra firme forest in lowlands of east.* Lower mandible flesh-colored; legs grayish flesh. *Distinctive pipit-like shape; walks* on ground. Dark olive brown above, somewhat grayer on crown, often a little whitish behind eye.

Mostly below 600 m

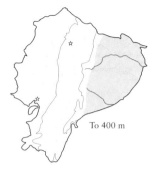

To 400 m

Throat white, *breast with broad band of bold black streaks (often coalescing into an almost solid band)*, belly whitish, grayer on lower flanks and crissum. **Immature** has breast streaking browner. **Similar species:** Nearly unmistakable, but cf. Spot-backed and Banded Antbirds. **Habits:** Walks on ground with a mincing gait, often nodding head and pumping tail up and down; also regularly perches on fallen logs and sometimes flies up to low branches. Forages by making short sallies up from ground, snatching insects off underside of leaves. Generally solitary, less often ranging in pairs, but does not associate with mixed flocks. Often first noticed as a result of its frequent and loud and emphatic bill snapping. **Voice:** Song a distinctive shrill whistled "peeur, peeur-peépit" or "preeur-preeyúr," with variations.

Myiornis **Pygmy-Tyrants**
A pair of closely related *tiny*, round-looking tyrannids that look *virtually tail-less*, one species occurring in humid lowland forests on either side of the Andes. They are among the world's smallest birds.

Short-tailed Pygmy-Tyrant, *Myiornis ecaudatus*
Tirano Enano Colicorto   Plate 69(16)

6.5 cm (2½"). Local (just overlooked?) at *borders of humid forest in lowlands of east.* Tiny and *virtually tail-less. Head gray with prominent white supraloral and eye-ring* (giving distinct spectacled look); bright olive above, wings duskier with bright yellowish flight-feather edging but only vague wing-bars. *Below white, tinged yellow on crissum.* **Similar species:** Black-capped Pygmy-Tyrant occurs only *west* of Andes. Otherwise this minute flycatcher is unlikely to be confused;

cf. Yellow-browed Tody-Flycatcher (in same habitat). **Habits:** Usually in pairs, and quite vocal and unlikely to be seen until voice is recognized. Seems sedentary, and only infrequently accompanies mixed flocks. Favors mid-level viny tangles and borders where it tends to perch motionless for long periods, then darting off suddenly to pick an insect from a leaf, zipping on to a new perch. Motions are so fast and abrupt, almost cicada-like, that they are very hard to follow. **Voice:** Most frequent song a high-pitched, insect- or frog-like "crreek" or "tsrreep" with rising inflection, usually given alone but sometimes in a series of shorter notes of similar quality.

Black-capped Pygmy-Tyrant
Myiornis atricapillus
Tirano Enano Gorrinegro   Plate 69(17)

To 800 m

6.5 cm (2½"). *Locally quite common at borders of humid forest in lowlands and foothills in northwest.* Sometimes considered conspecific with Short-tailed Pygmy-Tyrant, which it resembles. ♂ differs in having an *obvious black crown;* both sexes differ in having belly pale yellow. **Similar species:**

Short-tailed Pygmy-Tyrant occurs only east of Andes. Otherwise not likely confused; cf. Black-headed Tody-Flycatcher (in same habitat). **Habits and Voice:** Similar to Short-tailed Pygmy-Tyrant.

Lophotriccus **Pygmy-Tyrants**
Small and inconspicuous tyrannids found in forest and woodland lower growth; they are drab aside from their *wide and distinctively marked crests.*

Scale-crested Pygmy-Tyrant
Lophotriccus pileatus
Cimerillo Crestiescamado   Plate 69(13)

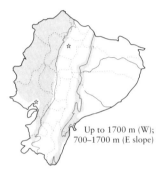

Up to 1700 m (W);
700–1700 m (E slope)

10 cm (4″). *Common in lower growth and borders of humid forest and woodland in lowlands of west, ranging up into foothills and lower subtropics*; on e. slope *only* in foothills and lower subtropics. *Favors bamboo, especially in east.* Iris yellow. Fore-crown and facial area brownish, *feathers of crown black with broad rufous edging* and *sometimes erected into a broad transverse crest* (but more often laid flat over nape); otherwise olive above, wings and tail duskier, wings with two yellowish wing-bars. Below whitish with *blurry dusky streaking on throat and breast,* flanks tinged pale olive. **Similar species:** Double-banded Pygmy-Tyrant occurs only in e. *lowlands,* with no known overlap; in any case, its crest feathers are edged gray. Otherwise this cute little flycatcher is not likely confused; cf. ♀ Black-and-white Tody-Tyrant (also with rufous crown). **Habits:** Usually found singly, less often in pairs, and generally not associating with mixed flocks. Perches motionless, often as not in open but hard to spot, suddenly darting out to pick an insect off a leaf surface, then flying off a short

distance. Heard much more often than seen, ♂♂ often continuing to call at intervals through the day, sometimes in close proximity to each other. **Voice:** Has a variety of calls, most of them strident and arresting. Often gives a short inflected trill, "trreít?" Western birds give a very fast series of short notes, "tr-tr-tr-tr-tr-tr-tr-tr," sometimes moving into some higher-pitched notes, then some lower-pitched ones, resulting in characteristic rolling sequence. E.-slope birds give a doubled or tripled trill, e.g., "trre trru," and a more drawn-out, sometimes hesitant trill, "trrrrrreét" (P. Coopmans and N. Krabbe).

Double-banded Pygmy-Tyrant
Lophotriccus vitiosus
Cimerillo Doblebandeado   Plate 69(14)

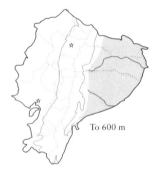

To 600 m

10 cm (4″). *Lower growth and borders of humid forest and woodland in lowlands of east.* Iris yellow. Forecrown and facial area olive, *feathers of crown black with gray edging,* occasionally erected into a transverse crest (but less often than in Scale-crested, and usually laid flat over nape); otherwise olive above, wings and tail duskier, wings with two yellowish wing-bars. Below pale yellowish with *blurry dusky-olive streaking on throat and breast.* **Similar species:** The more montane Scale-crested Pygmy-Tyrant has rufous edging on crown feathers. Cf. also White-eyed Tody-Tyrant, which is somewhat similar especially when Double-banded's crest shape and coloration are not evident. **Habits:** Similar to Scale-crested Pygmy-Tyrant, though Double-banded never seems to be as numerous and is not associated with bamboo. **Voice:** Song a distinctive short harsh trill that descends in pitch, "turrrrrrew," not

as loud or forceful as in Scale-crested; it can recall a cicada (P. Coopmans).

Hemitriccus Tody-Tyrants

A diverse group of *obscure* small flycatchers with fairly broad and somewhat flattened short bills. Three of the *Hemitriccus* occurring in Ecuador are rare or local, and even the other two are not seen all that often. They range in humid lowland and montane forest lower and middle growth and usually do not accompany mixed flocks. Unlike *Todirostrum* and *Poecilotriccus*, *Hemitriccus* tend to perch upright. All were formerly in genus *Idioptilon*.

White-eyed Tody-Tyrant
Hemitriccus zosterops
Tirano Todi Ojiblanco   Plate 69(10)

11 cm (4¼″). *Local in lower and middle growth inside hilly terra firme forest in lowlands and foothills of east* (apparently only south of Río Napo). *Iris pale gray*; lower mandible pinkish at base. *Olive above* with whitish supraloral, wings and tail duskier, wings with *two fairly prominent yellowish wing-bars*. Throat streaked grayish and whitish; breast and flanks clouded with olive, becoming pale yellow on belly. **Similar species:** A *drab* small tyrannid of tall forest, essentially olive with few distinctive markings. Double-banded Pygmy-Tyrant has lengthened, gray-edged crest feathers and is more of an edge bird. **Habits:** Inconspicuous, usually perching at mid-levels where apt to be overlooked until ♂'s endlessly repeated song is recognized. Usually solitary or in pairs, not joining mixed flocks. **Voice:** ♂'s most frequent song a simple staccato "pik, pik-pik-pik-pik," sometimes accelerated into "pik-pik-pik-pikpikpikpik," easily passed over as an insect.

Johannes's Tody-Tyrant, *Hemitriccus iohannis*
Tirano Todi de Johannes   Plate 96(11)

11 cm (4¼″). *Riparian woodland around certain oxbow lakes in lowlands of far southeast* (Kapawi). Formerly considered conspecific with Stripe-necked Tody-Tyrant (*H. striaticollis*), found mainly in s. Amazonia. Iris creamy whitish. *Olive above*, crown tinged grayish brown with *dull pale brownish ocular area and lores*, wings with yellowish edging and two faint wing-bars. Throat whitish *with fine dusky streaking, breast yellowish with blurry grayish olive streaking, belly yellow.* **Similar species:** Somewhat similar White-eyed Tody-Tyrant inhabits terra firme forest, a very different habitat from where Johannes's occurs; White-eyed has more prominent wing-bars and is less yellow below. Spotted Tody-Flycatcher differs most notably in its gray crown and crisper (not so blurry) throat and breast streaking; it occupies a different microhabitat. **Habits:** Favors viny tangles, usually near water, where it remains hard to see unless vocalizing. Generally in pairs, not associating with mixed flocks. **Voice:** Most frequent call a simple, fast, and semimusical "trrrrrrrrrrree?" (somewhat woodcreeper-like), sometimes interspersed with one or more "kew" notes, often going upscale in a series.

Black-throated Tody-Tyrant
Hemitriccus granadensis
Tirano Todi Golinegro   Plate 69(9)

10.5 cm (4″). *Local in borders of subtropical and temperate forest on e. slope* (w. Sucumbíos to w. Napo, and from Morona-Santiago southward); on w. slope only in far north. **Southern birds** olive above with *prominent*

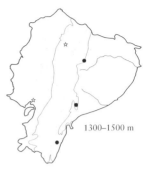

buff lores and ocular area, wings and tail duskier, wings with olive flight-feather edging (but no bars). *Throat blackish* (with almost a gorgeted effect), *contrasting with grayish breast*, becoming white on belly, flanks and crissum tinged yellow. **Northern birds** similar but with *lores and ocular area whitish*. **Similar species:** Both forms are strikingly patterned, easy to recognize in their montane habitat. **Habits:** Found singly or in pairs and, though often quiet, usually not too difficult to see as it often forages in the semi-open, not too high above ground. Makes short abrupt flights between perches, with whirr of wings often audible. Sometimes accompanies mixed flocks, but also forages alone. **Voice:** Most frequent call of southern birds a fast "whididik," with a sharper "wheék-wheék-wheék-wheék" given when bird is agitated. Northern birds give short rattling trill, "ti-ti-t-r-r-r-r-r" (P. Coopmans and N. Krabbe).

Buff-throated Tody-Tyrant
Hemitriccus rufigularis
Tirano Todi Golianteado   Plate 69(11)

12 cm (4¾"). Scarce and local in *lower and middle growth of subtropical forest on e. slope, mainly on ridges isolated to east of Andes*. Iris pale yellow; lower mandible grayish flesh. Olive above, grayer on crown; *ocular area, sides of head and neck, and breast pale dull buff*, upper throat buffy whitish streaked with gray; *belly whitish*, mottled with gray on flanks. *Wings plain*, flight feathers narrowly edged olive. **Similar species:** Even more range-restricted Cinnamon-breasted Tody-Tyrant is smaller, much brighter and richer cinnamon on face and breast, and has a yellow belly. It occurs at

higher elevations. **Habits:** Not well known. Found singly or in pairs, favoring relatively low stature and open forests on ridges or where soil is nutrient deficient. **Voice:** Calling males give a series of 4–10 (sometimes more) inflected "kyek" or "kwdíp" notes from perches 5–10 m above ground, sometimes higher.

Cinnamon-breasted Tody-Tyrant
Hemitriccus cinnamomeipectus
Tirano Todi Pechicanelo   Plate 69(12)

10 cm (4"). Lower growth of montane forest and woodland at higher elevations on *remote Cordillera del Cóndor in extreme se. Zamora-Chinchipe*. Uniform dark olive above, somewhat browner on crown, with *broad pale yellowish edging on tertials*. Ocular area, cheeks, throat, and breast bright *cinnamon*; belly pale clear yellow. **Similar species:** Buff-throated Tody-Tyrant is larger with a duller buff face and foreneck and whitish belly; it *lacks* tertial striping. **Habits:** Hardly known in life, most records being of birds captured in mist-nets. Birds seen have been alone in dense mossy undergrowth; one accompanied a small understory flock.

Voice: Call in n. Perm a fast, harsh rattle, "d-d-d-rt."

Poecilotriccus Tody-Flycatchers

Four dissimilar small flycatchers, all of them inconspicuous in dense undergrowth; one species (Rufous-crowned) is montane, whereas the others inhabit the eastern lowlands to varying degrees. Each species is most often located from its vocalizations.

Rufous-crowned Tody-Flycatcher
Poecilotriccus ruficeps
Tirano Todi Coronirrufo   Plate 69(8)

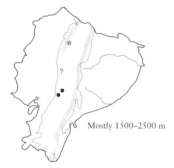

Mostly 1500–2500 m

9.5 cm (3¾"). *Shrubby lower growth at borders of subtropical forest and adjacent regenerating clearings on both slopes*; not inside forest. Sometimes called Rufous-crowned Tody-Tyrant. *Crown bright rufous* bordered behind by black line and gray nape, *cheeks buff*; bright olive above, wings black with two pale yellowish wing-bars. *Throat and upper chest white to buffy whitish*, usually bordered by some black in malar area, and separated from bright yellow of lower underparts by a diffuse blackish band across breast. **Southeastern birds** similar but with a *conspicuous black malar stripe* and *variable amount of black around and back from eye*. **Similar species:** An attractive and distinctive little tyrannid, not likely confused. Cf. the quite different Rufous-headed Pygmy-Tyrant (which inhabits forest undergrowth). **Habits:** This colorful but inconspicuous little flycatcher forages in dense lower growth; it is usually in pairs, and rarely accompanies mixed flocks. **Voice:** Soft calls include a gravelly stuttered "tttrew," "pít-tttrew," or "tttrew-pít," sometimes given as a duet.

Black-and-white Tody-Flycatcher
Poecilotriccus capitalis
Tirano Todi Negriblanco   Plate 69(7)

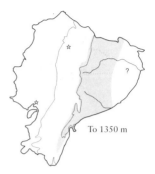

To 1350 m

9.5 cm (3¾"). *Scarce and local in tangled viny thickets in lower growth and borders of humid lowland forest, and in bamboo-dominated understory and borders of foothill and lower subtropical forest on e. slope.* Bill mostly orange-yellow, culmen darker. Sometimes called Black-and-white Tody-Tyrant. ♂ *glossy black above* with small white loral spot; *tertials broadly edged pale yellow*, bend of wing also yellow. *White below*, with black protruding onto sides of throat and chest, flanks and crissum tinged yellow. ♀ olive above with gray head and neck and *chestnut crown*; wings and tail blackish, flight feathers narrowly edged olive and with *broad yellow tertial edging*. Throat whitish, breast grayish, belly whitish tinged yellow on flanks and crissum. **Similar species:** This striking, *sexually dimorphic* tody-flycatcher is unlikely to be confused; it usually occurs in pairs. Cf. Scale-crested Pygmy-Tyrant. **Habits:** Forages singly and in pairs, appearing quite sedentary. Often quite confiding and, considering the dense nature of its preferred habitat, not too hard to observe; hops from branch to branch, occasionally making short sallies to underside of leaves. **Voice:** Call a fast, sharp "tik, t-r-r-r-r-r-ew." Agitated birds give a more explosive "tk, tk, tk, whey-whey-whey-whuh."

Golden-winged Tody-Flycatcher
Poecilotriccus calopterus
Tirano Todi Alidorado   Plate 69(4)

9.5 cm (3¾"). *Undergrowth at borders of humid lowland and foothill forest, secondary woodland, and regenerating clearings along e.*

To 1300 m

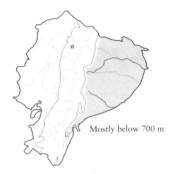

Mostly below 700 m

base of Andes (locally in e. lowlands). Formerly placed in genus *Todirostrum. Head and neck black, contrasting with bright olive back*; wings black with *conspicuous golden yellow band on greater-coverts, maroon-chestnut shoulders*, and pale yellow edging on tertials. Throat white; underparts bright yellow. **Similar species:** More numerous Common Tody-Flycatcher is pale-eyed, gray-backed, lacks Golden-winged's striking patterning on wings, and is entirely yellow below. **Habits:** Usually in pairs that remain within a few meters of ground in dense growth where, despite their bright colors, they are usually hard to see (especially without benefit of tape playback). Does not accompany mixed flocks. **Voice:** Distinctive call a dry, gravelly, almost sputtering "dre'd'd'd'deu" or "p-drrrew," often repeated several times in quick succession and sometimes given as a duet.

Rusty-fronted Tody-Flycatcher
Poecilotriccus latirostris
Tirano Todi Frentirrojizo   Plate 69(1)

9.5 cm (3¾"). *Dense undergrowth of shrubby clearings, humid forest and woodland borders, and river islands in lowlands of east.* Formerly placed in genus *Todirostrum.* Crown and neck gray with *prominent buffy ochraceous forehead and facial area*; otherwise olive above; wings and tail dusky, wings with *two ochraceous wing-bars* and yellow at bend of wing. Below dull grayish white. **Similar species:** Very unlike other Ecuadorian tody-flycatchers. Cf. Double-banded Pygmy-Tyrant. **Habits:** Inconspicuous, and hardly ever recorded except through its distinctive voice. Usually in pairs, staying low in its often almost impenetrable regenerating habitat. Does not accompany mixed flocks.

Voice: Call a sharp, low-pitched, rattled "tik, trrrr" or "tik, trrrr, trrrr," sometimes the "tik" alone.

Todirostrum Tody-Flycatchers
Small, rather colorful flycatchers that are basically arboreal in lowland forests and borders, *Todirostrum* have *wide and flat, rather long bills.* They perch more or less horizontally, and sometimes even cock their tails. Two species formerly in *Todirostrum* (Golden-winged and Rusty-fronted) have now been transferred to *Poecilotriccus.*

Black-headed Tody-Flycatcher
Todirostrum nigriceps
Espatulilla Cabecinegra   Plate 69(3)

To 900 m

8.5 cm (3¼"). Fairly common (but inconspicuous) in canopy and borders of humid forest and secondary woodland in *lowlands and foothills of west. Head glossy black, contrasting sharply with bright olive-yellow back*; wings and tail black, wings with two yellow wing-bars. *Throat white; underparts bright yellow.* **Similar species:** Yellow-browed Tody-Flycatcher occurs only east of Andes. Common Tody-Flycatcher favors more open habitats (and is never in forest canopy); it is larger and longer-tailed, and its iris is pale and upperparts mostly grayish *without* contrast on head. **Habits:** An attractively patterned but tiny bird that remains high in leafy forest canopy where hard to see, only occasionally coming lower at forest borders. Found singly or in pairs, only rarely joining mixed flocks. Heard much more often than seen. **Voice:** Far-carrying song an oft-heard, measured but slightly accelerating series of high-pitched and emphatic "tsip" notes, generally 5–8 per series.

Yellow-browed Tody-Flycatcher
Todirostrum chrysocrotaphum
Espatulilla Cejiamarilla   Plate 69(2)

To 600 m

9 cm (3½″). Locally fairly common (but inconspicuous) in canopy and borders of humid forest and secondary woodland in *lowlands of east*. *Head glossy black* with white supraloral spot and *prominent golden yellow postocular stripe*, contrasting with bright olive back; wings and tail black, wings with two yellow wing-bars. Below bright yellow, with *black streaks on malar area and across breast*. **Similar species:** Black-headed Tody-Flycatcher occurs only west of Andes. Spotted Tody-Flycatcher lacks black head and the golden brow; it never ranges in the high forest canopy that Yellow-browed favors. **Habits:** Similar to Black-headed Tody-Flycatcher, and generally equally hard to see. Likewise heard much more often than seen. **Voice:** Far-carrying song similar to Black-headed's, a series of sharp emphatic "tsip" notes, but series usually somewhat longer (averaging 8–12 notes).

Common Tody-Flycatcher
Todirostrum cinereum
Espatulilla Común   Plate 69(5)

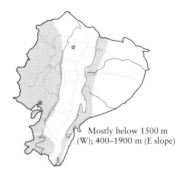

Mostly below 1500 m
(W); 400–1900 m (E slope)

9.5 cm (3¾″). *Generally numerous and conspicuous* in *semiopen areas and woodland borders* in lowlands of west and east, ranging up into foothills and lower subtropics on both slopes. More common in the west, where present in both humid and arid regions; in the east, not found too far away from Andes. *Iris whitish to pale straw.* **Western birds** have *forecrown and face black*, *shading to slaty on nape and gray on back*; wings blackish conspicuously edged yellow; rather long and graduated tail black with outer feathers whitish. Throat whitish, underparts yellow. **Eastern birds** similar but with all-yellow underparts. **Similar species:** *By far the most frequently seen tody-flycatcher in Ecuador.* Cf. Spotted Tody-Flycatcher (which occurs only on river islands in east). **Habits:** A cute and often familiar little bird, fluttering and hopping actively in vegetation at all levels but typically not too high above ground. Sometimes stands high on its legs, and often holds the rather long tail partially cocked, or even flips it from side to side; displaying birds regularly sidle along on a branch. Usually in pairs and generally not with mixed flocks. **Voice:** Both sexes often give brief trills, rather cricket-like; also frequent are various "tik" calls.

Spotted Tody-Flycatcher
Todirostrum maculatum
Espatulilla Moteada   Plate 69(6)

10 cm (4″). *Local in riparian woodland and shrubby areas on river islands in lowlands of east.* *Iris orange-yellow.* Head gray, crown

Below 250 m

with some blackish flecking; otherwise olive above; wings and tail dusky, wings with narrow yellow wing-bars. Throat whitish, underparts yellow, brightening on belly; *most of underparts* (not midbelly) *with narrow blackish streaking.* Similar species: Cf. range-restricted Johannes's Tody-Tyrant. Otherwise likely confused only with Common Tody-Flycatcher, which does not occur on river islands in e. lowlands and in any case shows no streaking below. **Habits:** Similar to Common Tody-Flycatcher, though seems more arboreal and less apt to forage close to ground. **Voice:** Most frequent song a short series of sharp, loud "peek" notes, sometimes given as a syncopated duet by both members of a pair, thus "pik-peek, pik-peek, pik-peek. . . ." These become more run together when birds are excited, such as after tape playback.

Brownish Twistwing, *Cnipodectes subbrunneus*
Alitorcido Pardo   Plate 71(13)
♂ 18 cm (7″); ♀ 15.5 cm (6″). *Tangled lower growth of humid and deciduous forest and woodland in lowlands of west, and in* humid forest in *lowlands of east.* Formerly called Brownish Flycatcher. Fairly wide bill flesh to

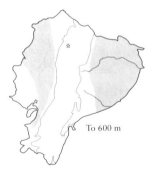

To 600 m

whitish below; iris pale brown to orangey. *Mostly dull brown, more rufous on rump and rather long tail*; wings duskier *with two dull rufescent wing-bars and flight-feather edging.* Throat pale brownish, becoming brown on breast and dingy yellowish white on belly. Adult ♂ has stiffened and twisted outer primaries with thick shafts (hard to see in field). **Similar species:** Amazonian Royal-Flycatcher is of comparable size and similarly colored but has spots on wing-coverts and a uniquely shaped head. Cf. also Thrush-like Schiffornis. **Habits:** Found singly, and very sedentary in dense and tangled viny lower growth; does not accompany mixed flocks. Frequently raises a wing up over back, slowly and almost seeming to stretch it upward (rather different from the quicker motions of *Mionectes, Leptopogon,* etc.). The use to which ♂'s uniquely twisted primaries is put remains unknown; presumably it has to do with display. **Voice:** Heard more often than seen. Displaying ♂'s distinctive song a sharp and emphatic "keeéuw-keeéuw," sometimes only a single "keeéuw" or a "keeéuw-keeéuw-kuw," often preceded by bill snapping and accompanied by wing-lifting. This is given at intervals throughout day. Call, given by both sexes, an arresting and more nasal "kuuuuwít!, kuuuuwít!" (a bit reminiscent of one of Blue-backed Manakin's calls).

Ramphotrigon **Flatbills**
Inconspicuous, forest-interior flycatchers found in the *lowlands of the east,* one species also ranging up into foothills; all are best known from their *distinctive vocalizations.* They have fairly wide bills—though not so extreme as in *Tolmomyias* or, in particular, *Rhynchocyclus*—and *wide ochraceous wing-bars.* Nests are placed in tree holes and cavities, thus very different from the *Rhynchocyclus* flatbills, to which the *Ramphotrigon* are probably not closely related.

Rufous-tailed Flatbill, *Ramphotrigon ruficauda*
Picoplano Colirrufo   Plate 70(19)
16 cm (6¼″). *Rare and local in lower and middle growth inside terra firme forest in lowlands of east.* Above dull olive green with narrow yellowish supraloral and eye-ring; wings dusky with *two broad rufous wing-bars and wide edging on flight feathers; tail*

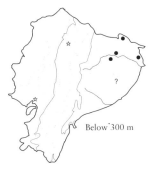

Below 300 m

bright rufous. Throat whitish with narrow olive streaking, breast and flanks olive with blurry yellowish streaking, belly clear yellow. **Similar species:** Among the myriad of similar-looking flycatchers found in Amazonian forests is this distinctive species, with its uniquely conspicuous rufous tail and rufous in wings. **Habits:** Found singly or in pairs, usually in areas with a relatively open understory; this, combined with its habit of often perching on open branches or lianas, makes this otherwise unobtrusive and not very active species relatively easy to observe. Generally does not move with mixed flocks. **Voice:** Mournful call, given at fairly long intervals, a distinctive "preeyeé-yoú," first a drawn-out mournful note, then a shorter, more abrupt one, as if in reply. Vocalizes at intervals throughout day.

Dusky-tailed Flatbill
Ramphotrigon fuscicauda
Picoplano Colinegruzco   Plate 70(18)

15.5 cm (6"). *Very rare and local in tangled lower growth (locally where there is a Guadua bamboo understory) of terra firme forest and secondary woodland in lowlands*

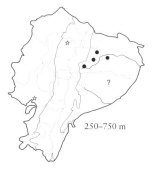

250–750 m

of northeast (w. Napo). Brownish olive above, crown somewhat darker, with a narrow broken whitish eye-ring; wings and *tail dusky, wings with two cinnamon wing-bars* and cinnamon-buff flight-feather edging, tail feathers edged cinnamon-rufous. *Below dark olive coarsely streaked with yellow,* midbelly unstreaked yellow. **Similar species:** Large-headed Flatbill is smaller, has a prominent pale supraloral as well as an eye-ring, and lacks streaking below. Olivaceous Flatbill is more uniform olive overall and lacks wing-bars. **Habits:** Poorly known in Ecuador; this is an inconspicuous and phlegmatic bird throughout its limited range. It occurs singly and in pairs, and is recorded almost exclusively through tape playback of its distinctive song. **Voice:** Song a distinctive mellow and melancholy "peeeeu, tr'r'r, treey-treey-treey-treey." Also gives a lazy "peeeeow-whooów . . . peeeeow-whooów . . ." (P. Coopmans).

Large-headed Flatbill
Ramphotrigon megacephala
Picoplano de Bambú   Plate 70(20)

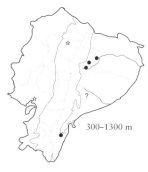

300–1300 m

13 cm (5"). *Uncommon and local in stands of bamboo in foothills and adjacent lowlands on e. slope.* Dull olive above with *prominent yellowish supraloral and eye-ring* that contrasts with dusky lores; wings and tail duskier, wings with *two prominent ochraceous wing-bars.* Throat yellowish, breast ochraceous olive vaguely flammulated paler; belly pale clear yellow. **Similar species:** Strictly confined to bamboo thickets, and often can be identified on that basis alone. The even rarer Dusky-tailed Flatbill (which in Ecuador seems *not* to be found in bamboo, unlike in some other parts of its range) is

larger, lacks supraloral, and is darker overall. Cf. also *Tolmomyias* flatbills. **Habits:** A retiring and inconspicuous flycatcher that perches upright in relatively dense cover, and is rarely seen except through tracking it down from its vocalizations. Usually found singly, and rarely accompanies mixed flocks. **Voice:** Heard more often than seen. Characteristic call a mournful "whoo-whou," second note a semitone lower in pitch; this is easily paraphrased (and readily remembered) as "bam-bü." Typically there is a very long interval, 5–10 seconds or even more, between each time it calls. Dawn song a slow "tee-tu-twít."

Rhynchocyclus Flatbills

Dull-plumaged, stolid flycatchers found in the lower growth of humid lowland and subtropical forests; so far as known, all species are entirely allopatric. They have *notably wide and flat bills* and look large-headed. Nests are purse-shaped and have a downward-projecting entrance; they are often suspended over streams or trails.

Pacific Flatbill, *Rhynchocyclus pacificus*
Picoplano del Pacífico   Plate 70(16)

To 800 m

15 cm (6"). Lower growth of humid forest in *lowlands and foothills of northwest*. Formerly considered conspecific with Eye-ringed Flatbill (*R. brevirostris*) of Middle America. *Very wide flat bill*, lower mandible flesh to whitish. Dark olive above with indistinct grayish eye-ring; wings duskier, wing-coverts with ochraceous edging, olive on flight feathers. *Throat and chest olive*, breast flammulated olive and yellow, belly clear yellow with some olive streaking on flanks. **Similar species:** Fulvous-breasted Flatbill replaces

this species at slightly higher elevations; it differs mainly in having throat and chest tawny-fulvous (not olive), but this distinction can be hard to discern in the dim light of forest interior. Broad-billed Sapayoa is much rarer (and essentially confined to Esmeraldas), and its bill is nowhere near as wide; it also has a plain wing (with no edging) and no flammulations below. **Habits:** Found singly or in pairs, often accompanying mixed understory flocks with *Myrmotherula* antwrens, antshrikes, and furnariids. Perches erectly, often on a fairly open branch or liana, peering around with rather a dazed expression, then abruptly swooping out to snatch an insect from the underside of a leaf, continuing on to another perch. **Voice:** Call a hissing "schweeeuw" (O. Jahn recording). Song a fast descending series of either clear or burry notes, "tchwee-tee-tee-te-tu-tu-tu" (O. Jahn and N. Krabbe recordings).

Fulvous-breasted Flatbill
Rhynchocyclus fulvipectus
Picoplano Pechifulvo   Plate 70(17)

900–1800 m

15 cm (6"). Lower growth of *foothill and subtropical forest on both slopes. Very wide flat bill*, lower mandible flesh to whitish. Dark olive above with indistinct grayish eye-ring; wings duskier, feathers with ochraceous edging; tail brownish. *Throat and chest tawny-fulvous*; lower underparts clear yellow with some olive streaking on flanks. **Similar species:** Pacific and Olivaceous Flatbills occur in *lowlands*, as does Brownish Twistwing. Pacific is the more similar of the two flatbills, with a similar grayish eye-ring, but it differs in foreneck color (olive, not tawny-fulvous) and more olive tail. **Habits:** Similar to Pacific

Flatbill. **Voice:** Call an infrequent wheezy and upslurred "zhreeyp."

Olivaceous Flatbill, *Rhynchocyclus olivaceus*
Picoplano Oliváceo   Plate 70(15)

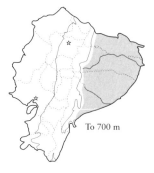

To 700 m

15 cm (6"). Lower growth of *humid forest in lowlands of east* (mainly terra firme). *Very wide flat bill*, lower mandible flesh to whitish. Dark olive above with indistinct whitish eyering; wings duskier, feathers with yellowish edging and coverts with two vague pale ochraceous wing-bars. Throat pale grayish, breast and flanks flammulated grayish olive and yellowish, belly pale clear yellow. **Similar species:** No other *Rhynchocyclus* occurs in the e. lowlands. *Ramphotrigon* flatbills are smaller and slenderer, and show bold wing-bars. *Tolmomyias* flatbills are considerably smaller, more arboreal, and not as stolid (not tending to perch vertically, etc.). **Habits:** Similar to Pacific Flatbill. **Voice:** Like other *Rhynchocyclus* rather quiet, but occasionally gives a harsh and abrupt "tshret" call, surprisingly loud. Presumed song an ascending "tuu tee tee ti ti?" (P. Coopmans).

Tolmomyias **Flatbills**
Among the most confusing and difficult of all Neotropical flycatcher genera, the *Tolmomyias* flatbills are rather small, mainly olive tyrannids that are generally best differentiated by voice. For a time they were called "flycatchers," but we revert to using "flatbill" for the genus, for in fact the bill is quite broad and flat, though not quite as much so as in their closest relatives, the *Rhynchocyclus* flatbills. Their taxonomy is in a state of flux, some species having already been split, others poised on the brink; one was only recently described. Nests are much as in *Rhynchocyclus*, though *Tolmomyias* nests are smaller.

Yellow-olive Flatbill
Tolmomyias sulphurescens
Picoancho Azufrado   Plate 68(7)

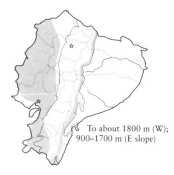

To about 1800 m (W);
900–1700 m (E slope)

13.5–14 cm (5¼–5½"). *Lower and middle growth of deciduous and semihumid forest and woodland in lowlands of west*, ranging up into subtropics in El Oro and Loja; *foothill and lower subtropical forest and borders on e. slope. Iris grayish to brownish (but normally looks rather pale)*; lower mandible pale (whitish to very pale grayish). **West-slope birds** olive above with *gray crown and nape*, whitish supraloral and narrow eyering, and suggestion of a dusky patch on ear-coverts; wings and tail duskier, wings with two yellowish wing-bars and prominent flight-feather edging. Throat pale grayish, becoming pale olive on breast and flanks, pale yellow on belly. **East-slope birds** differ in being brighter generally, and the patch on ear-coverts is blacker and more distinct. **Similar species:** For the most part—and unlike the situation elsewhere in its range—in Ecuador the Yellow-olive Flatbill does not occur sympatrically with any of its congeners. In west, confusion is possible with Yellow-margined Flatbill, though that species occurs primarily in northwest. Yellow-margined's iris is dark, its gray crown and nape contrast more with olive back, and it shows only yellow edging on wing-coverts (no wing-bars); the two differ in voice. Cf. also Greenish (especially) and Pacific Elaenias. In east, *Yellow-olive occurs only on Andean slopes, above* the range of other *Tolmomyias* (though marginally overlapping with Olive-faced). **Habits:** Found singly or in pairs, usually perching quite upright and generally not hard to observe; sometimes accompanies mixed flocks. Tends to range in lower strata than other *Tolmomyias*. Makes short sallies to leaves for insects. **Voice:** Song west of Andes a thin and well-enunciated series of quick notes, "psee-pset-pset-pset." East of Andes notes are a little longer, e.g., "swit-swit-swit-swit" (P. Coopmans). Olive-faced Flatbill's song is similar but lower pitched.

Orange-eyed Flatbill, *Tolmomyias traylori*
Picoancho Ojinaranja   Plate 68(12)

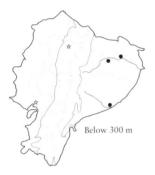

Below 300 m

13.5 cm (5¼"). *Rare and local in canopy and borders of várzea and riparian forest and woodland in lowlands of east.* A recently described species. *Iris pale orange*; lower mandible mostly pale. Olive above, crown somewhat grayer; wings and tail duskier, wings with two yellowish wing-bars and edging on flight feathers. *Supraloral area, ear-coverts, throat, and chest dull buff*; lower underparts pale yellow, tinged olive on flanks. **Similar species:** An unusually distinctive and easily identified *Tolmomyias*: no other member of genus has either an orangey eye or the buff wash on foreneck. **Habits:** Similar to Olive-faced Flatbill. **Voice:** Most frequent call a distinctive two-parted and buzzy "wheeeeezzz-birrt" or "psi-trrrrrrrr," given at rather long intervals and sometimes with a few other buzzy notes appended. Song a series of up to 5–7 well-enunciated "zhreee" notes, fairly similar to Olive-faced but notes somewhat longer and wheezier.

Zimmer's Flatbill, *Tolmomyias assimilis*
Picoancho de Zimmer   Plate 68(8)

13.5 cm (5¼"). Mid-levels and subcanopy of humid forest in *lowlands of east.* Does not include Yellow-margined Flatbill, formerly

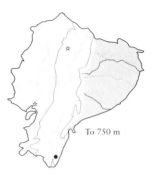

To 750 m

considered conspecific, found west of Andes. Iris brown (*normally looks dark*); *lower mandible mostly pale* (whitish to very pale grayish). Olive above, grayer on crown and nape with a narrow whitish eye-ring; wings and tail duskier, wings with two yellowish wing-bars and *pale speculum at base of outer primaries* and yellowish flight-feather edging (but wing-bars not very evident). Throat pale grayish, becoming pale olive grayish on breast and flanks, pale yellow on belly. **Similar species:** Closely resembles somewhat smaller Gray-crowned Flycatcher; Gray-crowned also shows more prominent wing-bars but lacks primary speculum (this hard to see in field, though) and also has nearly all-dark bill and pale irides. Yellow-olive Flatbill is more boldly patterned generally; its iris looks paler, its gray crown and nape stand out more, it usually shows a dark auricular patch (latter never shown by Zimmer's) and more marked wing-bars. Yellow-olive and Zimmer's generally do not occur together. **Habits:** Found singly or in pairs, often accompanying mixed canopy flocks; often forages well above ground, but sometimes comes lower at edge. Tends to perch rather horizontally, often holding tail partially cocked. **Voice:** Distinctive song a leisurely series of 3 whistled notes, each slightly higher-pitched and shriller, e.g., "weeeuw . . . weeeu . . . weee?"; this has been aptly paraphrased as "one . . . two . . . three" (J. Moore). Sometimes simply gives a "weeeée!" (P. Coopmans).

Yellow-margined Flatbill
Tolmomyias flavotectus
Picoancho Alimarginado   Plate 68(9)

13.5 cm (5¼"). Mid-level and subcanopy of humid forest and secondary woodland in *lowlands of northwest.* Formerly considered

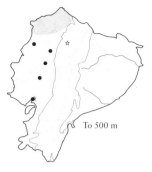

To 500 m

conspecific with the complex of "Yellow-margined" Flatbills found in Amazonia, a species that is now called Zimmer's Flatbill. Closely resembles Zimmer's, differing in having *broad yellow edging on greater wing-coverts* but no wing-bars. **Similar species:** Cf. less clean-cut Yellow-olive Flatbill; these two species appear to replace each other ecologically, with Yellow-olive in less humid areas. With its strong yellow edging, Yellow-margined's wing pattern recalls that of much smaller and otherwise rather different Golden-faced Tyrannulet. **Habits:** Similar to Zimmer's Flatbill. **Voice:** Song a harsh and very emphatic series of short notes, "zhweyk, zhwek-zhwek-zhwek-zhwek," with characteristic slight pause after slightly lower-pitched first note.

Gray-crowned Flatbill
Tolmomyias poliocephalus
Picoancho Coroniplomizo   Plate 68(10)

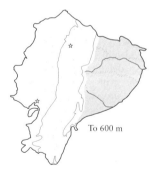

To 600 m

12 cm (4³/₄″). *Mid-levels and subcanopy of humid forest in lowlands of east.* Iris yellowish to pale brown; *bill mainly black,* lower mandible pale basally. Olive above with gray crown (somewhat contrasting) and whitish supraloral and partial narrow eye-

ring; wings and tail dusky, wings with two yellowish wing-bars and flight-feather edging. Throat pale grayish yellow, becoming grayish olive on breast and flanks, pale yellow on belly. **Similar species:** Closely resembles Zimmer's Flatbill, though that species is somewhat larger and dark-eyed, has a mainly pale lower mandible, more prominent wing-bars, a pale speculum at base of primaries (faint or lacking in Gray-crowned), and (despite the English name) somewhat more contrasting gray crown. **Habits:** Similar to Zimmer's Flatbill, and sometimes foraging with it in same canopy flock; Gray-crowned tends to stay higher above ground, though it sometimes comes lower at edge. **Voice:** Song a repeated, inflected, somewhat wheezy "fiwee?," sometimes given with an interval of 1–2 seconds, at other times in a short series, then a pause.

Olive-faced Flatbill, *Tolmomyias viridiceps*
Picoancho Cabecioliváceo   Plate 68(11)

Mostly below 800 m

12 cm (4³/₄″). *Common in lighter and riparian woodland, clearings and plantations with scattered trees, and humid forest borders (especially várzea) in lowlands of east.* Formerly considered conspecific with Ochre-lored Flatbill (*T. flaviventris*) of n. and e. South America; the enlarged species used to be called Yellow-breasted Flycatcher. Iris brown; *bill dark,* base of lower mandible pinkish. *Uniform olive above*; wings and tail dusky, wings with two yellow wing-bars. *Below yellow,* clouded olive on breast and flanks. **Similar species:** Other *Tolmomyias* have at least some gray on crown and are less plainfaced, showing more pattern. Cf. ♀ euphonias (with very different bills, etc.). **Habits:** Found singly or in pairs, sometimes

accompanying mixed flocks but at least as often foraging independent of them. More often out in clearings than other *Tolmomyias*. **Voice:** Song a series of 2–5 sharp and shrill notes that gradually become louder.

Platyrinchus Spadebills

Small, *stub-tailed* flycatchers that are inconspicuous in undergrowth of humid forest, a few species ranging up into the subtropics. Their *broad flat bills* are proportionately wider than in any other tyrannid group. Nests are small cups placed in the fork of a sapling inside forest.

White-throated Spadebill
Platyrinchus mystaceus
Picochato Goliblanco   Plate 70(11)

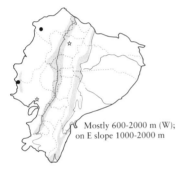

Mostly 600-2000 m (W);
on E slope 1000-2000 m

9.5 cm (3³/₄″). *Widespread in undergrowth of foothill and subtropical forest and woodland on both slopes, in west locally down into lowlands* and on coastal cordillera. *Wide flat bill* blackish, tip of lower mandible pale. Olive brown above with yellow coronal streak (usually mostly concealed; smaller or absent in ♀♀) and *buffy yellowish supraloral, eye-ring, postocular stripe, and patch on ear-coverts. Throat white*, contrasting with brownish breast and flanks; midbelly pale yellow. **Similar species:** Other than the very different Yellow-throated, this is the *only spadebill found in montane areas.* Golden-crowned Spade-bill possibly overlaps with White-throated in nw. lowlands; it has an orange-rufous crown patch (more conspicuous than White-throated's yellow) and *lacks* the contrasting white throat. **Habits:** Tends to remain in dense undergrowth where hard to see, often remaining motionless for protracted periods, then suddenly darting off like

a manakin. Usually forages singly, and rarely with mixed flocks; makes short sallies to undersides of leaves. **Voice:** Usual call an abrupt, sharp "squik!," sometimes doubled. Song a rattled trill, ascending at least in east, that increases in volume and lasts 1.5–2 seconds. Singing ♂♂ sometimes expose yellow in crest.

Golden-crowned Spadebill
Platyrinchus coronatus
Picochato Coronidorado   Plate 70(12)

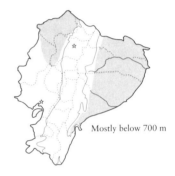

Mostly below 700 m

9 cm (3¹/₂″). Undergrowth of humid forest in *lowlands of east and northwest. Wide flat bill* black above, pale grayish below. Brownish olive above with *black-bordered rufous crown* (♂ also has yellow coronal streak, usually partially concealed) and *buffy yellowish lores, arching postocular stripe, and patch on ear-coverts.* Dull yellowish below, washed with olive on breast and flanks. **Similar species:** White-throated Spadebill has similar facial pattern but lacks black-bordered crown and has an obviously contrasting white throat. Cf. rare Cinnamon-crested Spadebill. **Habits:** Similar to White-throated Spadebill, though Golden-crowned favors areas with more open understory. **Voice:** Song an extended but rather weak, colorless, and high-pitched (but rising and falling) trill, easily passed over as coming from an insect.

Cinnamon-crested Spadebill
Mystaceus saturatus
Picochato Cresticanelo   Plate 70(14)

9 cm (3¹/₂″). *Very rare and local in undergrowth of terra firme forest in lowlands of far northeast* (Tigre Playa). *Wide flat bill* blackish, dark grayish below with pale tip.

200 m

Dark rufous brown above with whitish lores and inconspicuous eye-ring, and orange-rufous coronal streak (usually mostly concealed; vestigial in ♀♀); wings edged rufescent. Midthroat silky white; underparts whitish, sides of breast washed brown, belly pale yellow. **Similar species:** Rather plain, with less facial pattern than White-throated and Golden-crowned Spadebills; Cinnamon-crested only occurs with latter. White-crested Spadebill is considerably larger, with gray on head, white in crest, and brighter underparts. **Habits:** Poorly known in Ecuador, where the only record involves a mist-netted bird. Elsewhere behavior similar to Golden-crowned Spadebill, though perhaps accompanies mixed flocks more often. **Voice:** Calls (in Guyana) include a simple sharp "kwip," sometimes doubled to a "kwi-dip" or lengthened to a "kwip, kwi-di-dip."

Yellow-throated Spadebill
Platyrinchus flavigularis
Picochato Goliamarillo   Plate 70(13)

9.5 cm (3¾″). *Scarce and inconspicuous in undergrowth of foothill and subtropical forest on e. slope. Very wide flat bill black*

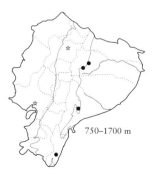

750–1700 m

above, pale grayish flesh below. *Head rufous with large white coronal patch (usually mostly concealed); otherwise olive above, duskier on wings and tail. Below pale yellow, brightest on throat,* with diffuse olive band across breast. **Similar species:** A distinctive "yellow" spadebill. More numerous and widespread White-throated Spadebill has, as its name implies, an obviously white throat; its facial pattern is much more complex, and it lacks rufous on head. **Habits:** Similar to other spadebills, and equally hard to see. Seems to favor areas with relatively open understory, especially on ridges. Often perches in the open, but remains motionless for protracted periods and thus hard to spot. **Voice:** Call a sharp "peeeyr!" repeated at long intervals, typically 4–5 seconds.

White-crested Spadebill
Platyrinchus platyrhynchos
Picochato Crestiblanco   Plate 70(10)

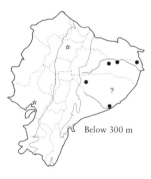

Below 300 m

11 cm (4¼″). *Rare and local in undergrowth of terra firme forest in lowlands of east. Very wide flat bill* black above, whitish below. *Crown dark gray, somewhat paler gray on rest of head,* with large white coronal patch (usually mostly concealed) and whitish loral spot; otherwise ochraceous brown above, wings and tail duskier. Throat white, *otherwise uniform bright ochraceous below.* **Similar species:** *The largest spadebill in Ecuador.* Cf. very localized Cinnamon-crested Spadebill. Ruddy-tailed Flycatcher and Cinnamon Neopipo are substantially smaller with slighter bills. **Habits:** Similar to other spadebills, though more often perching a little higher above ground. **Voice:** Most frequent call a loud and explosive "skeep!" or "skeeuw!" given every 1–2 seconds. Song,

heard less often, a sharp and burry trill that gradually rises in pitch and becomes louder before falling toward end. Singing birds also have a flight display in which they angle down steeply before recovering to another perch with a manakin-like wing-whirr.

Onychorhynchus Royal-Flycatchers

Remarkable flycatchers with *unique and colorful crests* that, sadly, are not often expanded to their full glory. They are found in lowland forest undergrowth on either side of the Andes and are notable for their *unusually long rictal bristles* and short legs. Nests are very long and loose structures with a side entrance, and they are usually suspended over a stream.

Amazonian Royal-Flycatcher
Onychorhynchus coronatus
Mosquero Real Amazónico   Plate 71(14)

To 400 m

15 cm (6"). Scarce in lower growth of humid forest in *lowlands of east*, mostly near water. *Spectacular crest* is only rarely seen fully open. Long flat bill; legs brownish yellow. Dull brown above with tiny buff dots on wing-coverts; *rump cinnamon-rufous, becoming rufous on tail* (darker toward tip). Throat whitish; underparts ochraceous-buff, breast narrowly scaled brown. When fully expanded, crest—*a large semicircular fan of shiny scarlet feathers (orange in ♀) with scattered black spots and broad shiny steel-blue tips*—is held perpendicular to axis of body. Normally, however, it is held closed, with lengthened feathers protruding to rear (some color may show through), imparting a *unique hammerheaded effect*. **Similar species:** Pacific Royal-Flycatcher occurs only west of Andes. Otherwise not likely to be confused; cf.

Brownish Twistwing. **Habits:** Generally inconspicuous, foraging quietly in undergrowth in pairs or (more often) alone; usually perches upright, with tail hanging downward. Usually does not accompany mixed flocks. Sallies quickly after fairly large flying insects (e.g., butterflies, dragonflies, wasps), often beating them against a branch to remove wings (and stingers) before swallowing. As noted above, the crest is usually held closed in a point on nape; preening birds sometimes open it, as do birds around their nest. Mist-netted birds invariably open it upon being removed from net, and they then rhythmically twist and contort head from side to side, all the while slowly opening and closing bill—an amazing performance! **Voice:** Not terribly vocal, but foraging birds sometimes give a whistled "preeé-o" or "keee-you," sometimes in an excited series, recalling a *Manacus* manakin or *Galbula* jacamar.

Pacific Royal-Flycatcher
Onychorhynchus occidentalis
Mosquero Real del Pacífico   Plate 71(15)

Mostly below 600 m

16.5 cm (6½"). Now scarce and local in lower growth of deciduous and semihumid forest and woodland in *lowlands of west*. In general form resembles Amazonian Royal-Flycatcher (found only east of Andes), with which formerly considered conspecific. Pacific differs in being larger, and is brighter and paler generally: *upperparts cinnamon-brown, rump and tail cinnamon*, and *underparts orange-ochraceous* with no breast barring. **Similar species:** Hard to confuse, but cf. Ochraceous Attila (with same overall coloration). **Habits and Voice:** Similar to Amazonian Royal-Flycatcher, though unlike that species the Pacific seems to show no tendency to occur near water.

Ornate Flycatcher, *Myiotriccus ornatus*
Mosquerito Adornado   Plate 70(7)

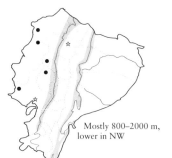

Mostly 800–2000 m,
lower in NW

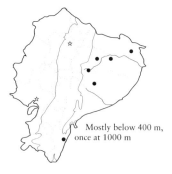

Mostly below 400 m,
once at 1000 m

12 cm (4³/₄″). *Common and conspicuous at borders of foothill and subtropical forest on both slopes*, in northwest also ranging out locally into more humid lowlands. This *cute, small* flycatcher is so colorful as to be essentially unmistakable. *Head and throat gray,* blacker on face and crown with *conspicuous white preocular patch* and semiconcealed yellow coronal stripe; back dark olive, *rump bright yellow*; wings dusky; *tail all rufous* (**east slope**) *or dusky with rufous at base* (**west slope**). Breast dark olive, belly bright yellow. **Habits:** Usually in pairs that often perch close together, sitting upright at low to middle heights; does not accompany flocks, and seems notably sedentary. Makes sudden short sallies into air, most often continuing on to another nearby branch. **Voice:** Call a sharp, high-pitched, and emphatic "wheep!" or "peeyp!," often with a short chipper appended.

Cinnamon Neopipo, *Neopipo cinnamomea*
Neopipo Canelo   Plate 78(17)

9.5 cm (3³/₄″). *Very rare and local (overlooked?) in lower growth of terra firme forest in lowlands of east*. Formerly called Cinnamon Manakin or Cinnamon Tyrant-Manakin; recent research has demonstrated it is a tyrant flycatcher. *Legs bluish gray.* Head and upper back gray with usually concealed yellow coronal patch (somewhat smaller and more orange-rufous in ♀); back brown, *rump and tail cinnamon-rufous*;

wings dusky with *two blurry rufous wingbars* and edging on inner flight feathers. Throat whitish, *underparts uniform cinnamon*. **Similar species:** Closely resembles much more numerous Ruddy-tailed Flycatcher, so much so that it is doubtless often passed over as that species. Slightly larger Ruddy-tailed has shorter yellowish legs, wider bill, and long rictal bristles (lacking in Cinnamon Tyrant; these are so long in Ruddy-tailed as to be readily visible); it lacks coronal patch. Also cf. considerably larger White-crested Spadebill. **Habits:** Not well known. Apparently solitary inside forest, sometimes accompanying mixed flocks. **Voice:** Most frequent call a thin, high-pitched "pseeeu" repeated steadily at long (typically 5 to 8-second) intervals. Apparent song a series of notes of similar quality that at first goes upscale steadily, then drops and fades away, e.g., "psee-psii-psii-psii-psii-pse-pse-psu," entire series lasting about 4–5 seconds.

Ruddy-tailed Flycatcher
Terenotriccus erythrurus
Mosquerito Colirrojizo   Plate 70(2)

10 cm (4″). Fairly common in lower and middle growth of humid forest and woodland in *lowlands of east and west*. Legs pale yellowish. *Head and neck olive gray*, becoming browner on back, cinnamon on rump, and *rufous on tail*; wings dusky, *edged cinnamon-rufous. Below uniform cinnamon-buff*, whiter on throat. **Similar species:** Cf. much rarer Cinnamon Tyrant. Otherwise this cute, large-eyed flycatcher with unusually long rictal bristles is not likely confused; Ochre-bellied Flycatcher is most similar, but it is olive above (including tail), etc. Cf. also

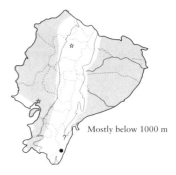

White-crested Spadebill. **Habits:** Found singly, perching erectly on an open branch from which it abruptly sallies out to capture small insects from foliage, less often to air; eats no fruit. Sometimes accompanies mixed flocks, but at least as often moves about alone. Occasionally twitches wings up over back, often both together. **Voice:** Most frequent call a weak thin "pseeoo-pseé," the second note sharper and more emphatic. More musical song a leisurely "see-tuuuwsee, tuuuw, see-tuuuw . . ." (O. Jahn recording, fide P. Coopmans).

Myiobius Flycatchers

Attractive small *wide-eyed* flycatchers with *black tails* and *unique yellow rump patches* found in undergrowth of humid lowland and foothill forest and woodland. Their bills are fairly wide and rictal bristles notably long. They are rather quiet. Nests are pearshaped with a low side entrance, suspended from the tip of a drooping branch, often over a stream.

Black-tailed Flycatcher, *Myiobius atricaudus*
Mosquerito Colinegro   Plate 70(6)

12.5 cm (5"). Lower growth of *secondary woodland and humid forest borders* in lowlands and foothills of east and west. Above olive with yellow coronal patch (usually concealed); *conspicuous sulphur yellow rump* and rather rounded black tail. *Throat and breast dull buff*; belly pale yellow. **Similar species:** East of Andes, Whiskered Flycatcher is quite similar, though its throat and breast are drabber grayish olive (with no buff tone). West of Andes, Sulphur-rumped Flycatcher is strikingly different, being bright tawny and yellow below (not just buff). **Habits:** Usually

found singly, less often in pairs, frequently accompanying understory flocks. Forages very actively, often fanning tail and drooping wings as if to show off the bright yellow rump, pivoting and pirouetting animatedly, dashing after flushed insects and also sallying to pluck them from a leaf surface; entirely insectivorous. **Voice:** Foraging birds give a weak "whit."

Whiskered Flycatcher, *Myiobius barbatus*
Mosquerito Bigotillo   Plate 70(5)

12.5 cm (5"). Uncommon and local in lower growth of *terra firme forest in lowlands of east*. Often considered conspecific with Sulphur-rumped Flycatcher, found west of Andes. Above olive with yellow coronal patch (usually concealed); *conspicuous sulphur yellow rump* and rather rounded black tail. *Throat and breast grayish olive*; belly pale yellow. **Similar species:** Black-tailed Flycatcher is dull buff on throat and breast (not grayish olive); it tends to occur in more secondary habitats. **Habits:** Similar to Black-tailed Flycatcher, which it replaces in heavier forest. **Voice:** Foraging birds occasionally give a sharp "psik."

Sulphur-rumped Flycatcher
Myiobius sulphureipygius
Mosquerito Lomiazufrado   Plate 70(4)

Mostly below 1000 m

12.5 cm (5″). Lower growth of humid forest in *lowlands and foothills of west*. Often considered conspecific with Whiskered Flycatcher, found east of Andes. Above olive with yellow coronal patch (usually concealed); *conspicuous sulphur yellow rump* and rather rounded black tail. Throat whitish, *breast bright tawny*, with belly bright yellow. **Similar species:** Black-tailed Flycatcher is dull buff on throat and breast, strikingly different from this species' bright tawny. In foothills, also cf. larger Tawny-breasted Flycatcher; it is more uniformly brown below, with much less yellow apparent on belly. **Habits:** Similar to Black-tailed Flycatcher. **Voice:** Foraging birds occasionally give a sharp "psik."

Tawny-breasted Flycatcher, *Myiobius villosus*
Mosquerito Pechileonado   Plate 70(3)

14 cm (5½″). Lower and middle growth of *foothill and lower subtropical* forest and woodland on both slopes, *occurring above the ranges of its congeners. Dark* brownish

Mostly 1000–1700 m, lower in Esmeraldas

olive above, brownest on head, ♂ with usually concealed yellow coronal patch (in ♀ cinnamon or lacking); *conspicuous sulphur yellow rump* and rather rounded black tail. Throat whitish; *breast tawny brown, the brown extending broadly down flanks and onto crissum*, with only midbelly pale yellow. **Similar species:** Often confused with Sulphur-rumped Flycatcher of w. lowlands; that species smaller and markedly paler and entirely brighter below, with bright tawny breast (not tawny-*brown*) and entirely bright yellow belly and crissum. **Habits:** Much as in Black-tailed Flycatcher, though this larger *Myiobius* seems less active and agile, and it more often forages higher above ground.

Myiophobus Flycatchers
A *rather diverse* group of small flycatchers united by their coronal patches and bold wing-bars (usually some shade of buff). The first three species inhabit forest undergrowth at varying elevations in the Andes, the next two favor shrubby growth in clearings, and the final two are more boldly patterned arboreal species of the Andes. Nests are cups placed low in the fork of a shrub or low tree.

Flavescent Flycatcher, *Myiophobus flavicans*
Mosquerito Flavecente   Plate 71(16)

1300–2500 m

12 cm (4¾″). Inconspicuous in lower and middle growth of *subtropical and lower temperate forest on both slopes*. Bill all black. Olive above with *prominent yellow supraloral and partial eye-ring* (broken in front and behind) and semiconcealed yellow coronal patch (absent in ♀♀, orange in a few ♂♂); wings and tail duskier, *wings with two ochraceous wing-bars* (lower one often more

prominent) *and flight-feather edging.* Below yellow, brightest on belly, breast flammulated or washed with olive. **Similar species:** Orange-crested Flycatcher is slightly smaller and darker above with an obvious pale lower mandible; it has a *complete* eye-ring (but no supraloral) and shows little or no flight-feather edging. Orange-crested's center of distribution is at lower elevations than Flavescent. Cf. also Roraiman Flycatcher. **Habits:** Found singly or in pairs, perching erectly inside forest or (less often) at edge, generally not accompanying mixed flocks. Makes short sallies both to foliage and into air; seems entirely insectivorous. **Voice:** Not terribly vocal. Infrequently heard song (given mainly at dawn?) a fast rhythmic series of about 5–8 "kawhik" notes (P. Coopmans recording). Call a sharp "chiyp."

Orange-crested Flycatcher
Myiophobus phoenicomitra
Mosquerito Crestinaranja   Plate 71(17)

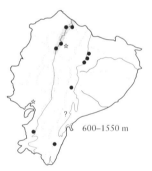

11.5 cm (4½"). Inconspicuous and local (overlooked?) in lower growth of *foothill and lower subtropical forest on both slopes.* Bill black above, *mostly fleshy yellow below.* Dark olive above with *narrow yellow eye-ring* and semiconcealed orange-rufous coronal patch (absent in ♀♀, occasionally yellow in ♂♂); wings blackish with two ochraceous wing-bars but *little flight-feather edging.* Below pale yellow, brightest on belly, breast extensively washed with olive. **Similar species:** Flavescent Flycatcher has all-black bill, yellow supraloral and more prominent (though broken) eye-ring, and much more extensive flight-feather edging; it tends to occur above range of Orange-crested. Note that color of crown patch is of little or no use in distinguishing the two species. **Habits:** Similar to Flavescent Flycatcher. **Voice:** Song a weak, thin, high-pitched "tsut-tseép-tsu."

Roraiman Flycatcher, *Myiophobus roraimae*
Mosquerito Roraimeño   Plate 71(22)

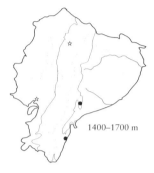

13.5 cm (5¼"). *Rare and local (overlooked?) in lower and middle growth of subtropical forest on outlying ridges in the southeast* (Cordilleras de Cutucú and del Cóndor). *Lower mandible yellow-orange.* Brown above with narrow pale yellowish eye-ring and semiconcealed orange-rufous coronal patch (small or lacking in ♀♀); wings and tail blackish, *wings with two bold cinnamon-rufous wing-bars and extensive flight-feather edging.* Throat yellowish white, becoming pale grayish olive on breast and flanks, pale yellow on midbelly. **Similar species:** Considerably larger than Flavescent Flycatcher, and much browner above with much more extensive rufous in wing. Euler's Flycatcher has no coronal patch and never shows such extensive rufous in wings. **Habits:** Poorly known in Ecuador, but behavior seems to differ little from Flavescent's. **Voice:** Unknown.

Bran-colored Flycatcher, *Myiophobus fasciatus*
Mosquerito Pechirrayado   Plate 71(19)

12–12.5 cm (4¾–5"). *Fairly common in shrubby clearings, gardens, and lighter woodland in lowlands and lower subtropical zone on w. slope;* rare in comparable habitats in lowlands of east (only close to base of Andes). **West-slope birds** *dull grayish brown above* with faint whitish supraloral and semiconcealed orange-rufous coronal patch (vestigial or absent in ♀♀); wings and tail dusky,

Mostly below 1500 m
(W); 300–1100 m (E)

Mostly 400–1400 m

wings with two rufous-buff wing-bars (paler in worn plumage). Whitish below, *breast and sides with grayish brown streaking*. East-slope birds differ in being *much more rufescent above* with yellow coronal stripe in ♂ ♂; streaking below is browner. **Similar species:** West of Andes nothing very similar, but cf. Gray-breasted Flycatcher (much more a forest bird) and ♀ Vermilion Flycatcher. East of Andes, Bran-colored overlaps with similar Olive-chested Flycatcher, though that differs in being duller and grayer above and in having a distinctly yellower belly. **Habits:** Found singly or in pairs, perching low and upright and, though sometimes in open, generally not conspicuous. Makes short sallies in pursuit of insects, both into air and to foliage. Usually not with mixed flocks. **Voice:** Calls of western birds include a rather subdued, wheezy "whis? whee-yee" and a fast "whee-yee-yee-yee-yee." Dawn song a leisurely and hesitating "weé, wu-du . . . weé, wu-du . . ." (P. Coopmans).

Olive-chested Flycatcher
Myiophobus cryptoxanthus
Mosquerito Pechioliváceo   Plate 71(18)

12 cm (4³/₄″). *Numerous in shrubby clearings and pastures as well as lighter secondary woodland in foothills and lower subtropics on east slope, also ranging out into adjacent lowlands. Apparently increasing. Above dull grayish brown* with faint whitish supraloral and semiconcealed yellow coronal patch (smaller in ♀ ♀); wings and tail dusky, wings with two pale buff wing-bars. Throat whitish, *breast and flanks with blurry grayish olive streaking, belly pale yellow.* **Similar species:** Bran-colored Flycatcher sometimes occurs with Olive-chested in e. Ecuador

(though Olive-chested is much more numerous); there the Bran-colored is markedly more rufescent above, and its breast streaking is browner and belly decidedly whiter. Olive-chested is not known to occur with duller w.-slope Bran-colored. Cf. also Euler's Flycatcher. **Habits:** Similar to Bran-colored Flycatcher. **Voice:** Calls include a spritely "weee d'd'd'd'd'd?" Dawn song an endlessly repeated "chwee . . . chwee . . . chwee . . ." (P. Coopmans).

Handsome Flycatcher, *Myiophobus pulcher*
Mosquerito Hermoso   Plate 71(20)

1500–2400 m

10.5–11 cm (4–4¹/₄″). *Uncommon in canopy and borders of subtropical forest on both slopes mainly in north* (south to Pichincha and w. Napo). Lower mandible usually flesh-yellow. **West-slope birds** have crown olive gray with whitish loral spot and narrow broken eye-ring, and semiconcealed orange-rufous coronal patch (reduced in ♀); above olive, wings and tail dusky with *two bold pale ochraceous wing-bars and prominent flight-feather edging. Throat and breast dull ochraceous* contrasting with clear yellow belly. **East-slope birds** slightly larger with *deeper ochraceous wing-bars.* **Similar species:** Orange-banded Flycatcher overlaps marginally if at all with Handsome. It differs in being larger and considerably longer-tailed and in lacking buff below. Rufous-breasted Flycatcher is larger and proportionately longer-tailed, and rufous extends up onto face. **Habits:** Unlike previous *Myiophobus* flycatchers, Handsome is an arboreal bird that forages with mixed flocks in canopy and borders. It tends to perch more horizontally than they do, and to forage more actively, making short sallies to foliage. It sometimes occurs in small (family?) groups. **Voice:** Song a rather sharp and clear "tsi-tsi-tsi."

Orange-banded Flycatcher, *Myiophobus lintoni*
Mosquerito Franjinaranja   Plate 71(21)

Mostly 2250–3200 m

13 cm (5"). *Local in canopy and borders of temperate forest and woodland on e. slope in south* (north to nw. Morona-Santiago). Lower mandible mostly dull orange. Dark brownish olive above with semiconcealed ochraceous orange coronal patch (reduced or lacking in ♀♀); wings and tail dusky, wings with *two bold pale cinnamon wing-bars* and narrow flight-feather edging. *Mostly yellow below*, throat more whitish and tinged olive on chest. **Similar species:** This fairly large and long-tailed tyrannulet is quite distinctive in its limited range, where there really are no other very similar tyrannids. Handsome Flycatcher (not known to occur with Orange-banded, though not inconceivable) is smaller and notably shorter-tailed, and has ochraceous on breast. **Habits:** Similar to Handsome Flycatcher, likewise sometimes in small groups. Orange-banded has characteristic habit of perching atop large leaves, from there making short sallies, both to foliage and into air. **Voice:** Call a sharp and arresting

"peeyk," given repeatedly as it forages. Dawn song a simple and monotonous series of "tsin" notes (P. Coopmans).

Cinnamon Flycatcher
Pyrrhomyias cinnamomea
Mosquerito Canelo   Plate 70(8)

1200–3000 m

13 cm (5"). *Generally numerous, widespread, and conspicuous at shrubby borders of foothill, subtropical, and temperate forest and woodland on both slopes.* Olive brown above with semiconcealed yellow coronal patch and narrow cinnamon rump band (usually hidden); wings and tail blackish, *wings with two broad cinnamon-rufous wing-bars and broad edging on secondaries (forming a large patch).* Below rich *cinnamon-rufous*, belly slightly paler. **Similar species:** This attractive small tyrannid is nearly unmistakable in its montane habitat, where no other is so rufescent overall. **Habits:** Usually found in pairs that perch erectly atop a shrub or small tree, often along roads or trailsides, peering around alertly; at times remarkably confiding. Makes short sallies into air after flying insects, often repeatedly returning to same perch. Pairs may remain in same limited area for long periods. **Voice:** Distinctive and often-heard call a low-pitched dry rattling, "tr-r-r-r-r-r" or "dr-r-r-r-r-r." Somewhat resembles call of White-sided Flowerpiercer.

Northern Tufted-Flycatcher
Mitrephanes phaeocercus
Mosquerito Moñudo Norteño   Plate 70(1)

12 cm (4¾"). *Borders of humid lowland and lower foothill forest in northwest.* Formerly called Common Tufted-Flycatcher or simply Tufted Flycatcher. *Fairly conspicuous pointed crest.* Lower mandible yellow. Olive above

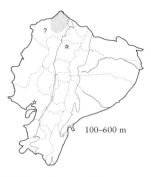

100–600 m

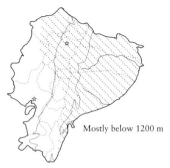

Mostly below 1200 m

with whitish loral spot and inconspicuous eye-ring; wings and tail dusky, wings with two narrow grayish wing-bars. *Throat and breast buffy olive, belly yellow.* **Similar species:** Though vaguely pewee-like, no other similarly colored flycatcher (with yellow on underparts) shows such a prominent crest. **Habits:** Perky and attractive, with quite pewee-like behavior. Found singly and in pairs, perching upright on open perches, generally not too high above ground; does not follow flocks. Sallies into air in pursuit of insects, often returning over and over to the same perch, sometimes making several short sallies in very quick succession. Usually quivers tail upon realighting. **Voice:** Call an often-heard fast series of "pee" or "pik" notes. Song a repeated fast phrase of high, thin notes, e.g., " tsu-tsu-tseét," with softer notes sometimes interspersed between phrases (P. Coopmans).

Contopus Pewees

Fairly small to midsized flycatchers, the pewees are *drab* but conspicuous tyrannids that perch erectly at forest edge and in clearings, making long sallies into the air. All are *some shade of gray*, very dark in Blackish and Smoke-colored, paler in the others. Nests are broad shallow cups placed in the fork of a tree, often quite high. Three species (Olive-sided and the wood-pewees) are migratory from North America, the others resident. Identification can present a challenge, with *voice* often being helpful.

Eastern Wood-Pewee, *Contopus virens*
Pibí Oriental   Plate 71(3)

14.5 cm (5¾"). A *locally common boreal migrant* (mostly Oct.–Apr.) to humid forest borders and clearings in *lowlands and foothills of east and west*, more numerous in

east; transients occur in the Andes. Lower mandible yellowish, sometimes tipped dusky. *Slightly crested.* Dark grayish olive, wings and tail duskier, wings with two pale gray to whitish wing-bars. Throat white; breast and flanks olive grayish, whitish to pale yellowish on midbelly and crissum. **Juvenile** has buffier wing-bars and is yellower below. **Similar species:** *Drab and easily confused*, with *behavior* and *voice* often best characters (see below); fortunately it vocalizes frequently. Cf. very similar Western Wood-Pewee; silent wood-pewees often cannot be distinguished to species. Tumbes Pewee occurs only in w. lowlands, mainly in arid regions. Willow and Alder Flycatchers are also similar but differ subtly in shape (being less crested and having shorter wings with less primary projection, but longer legs) and are less gray overall (tending to brown and olive) with bolder wing-bars. Olive-sided Flycatcher is considerably larger (though shorter-tailed) and has a different "vested" pattern below. **Habits:** Usually solitary, perching at low and middle heights, often on a branch or snag fully in open; sallies out after aerial insects, sometimes pursuing them for long distances. Often returns to same perch over and over. **Voice:** Calls frequently, apparently thereby setting up and defending wintering territories. Most often heard is a sweet and plaintive "pee-wee?," given at intervals throughout day. This main call can be interspersed with burrier and downslurred "pee-ur." ♂'s full song, "pee-a-wee," is, except on northward passage, given much less often.

Western Wood-Pewee, *Contopus sordidulus*
Pibí Occidental   Plate 71(4)

14.5 cm (5¾"). A *boreal migrant* (mostly Sep.–Apr.) to *foothill and lower subtropical*

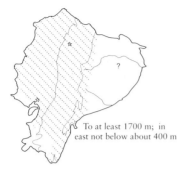

To at least 1700 m; in
east not below about 400 m

forest and clearings on both slopes, a few
also in lowlands of west. *Virtually identical
to Eastern Wood-Pewee*; often only vocalizing individuals can be safely identified to
species. *Bill usually all or mostly dark*,
but juveniles have lower mandible at least
partially yellowish to horn. Western tends to
be *darker below*, but some Easterns are
similar. **Habits:** As in Eastern Wood-Pewee;
occasionally Westerns and Easterns can be
found together, especially on migration.
Voice: Calls frequently, a melancholy and
burry "preeer" or "freeer," typically single-
noted. Song—much less often heard—a burry
"preé-ur," either repeated or with "pur-didi"
interspersed.

Tumbes Pewee, *Contopus punensis*
Pibí de Tumbes   Plate 71(5)

Mostly below 1500 m

14 cm (5½"). *Borders of deciduous and
semihumid woodland and forest and adjacent clearings in lowlands and foothills of
southwest.* Formerly considered a race of
wide-ranging Tropical Pewee (*C. cinereus*).
Lower mandible yellowish. Slightly crested.
Closely resembles Eastern Wood-Pewee,
differing in its slightly smaller size and

whitish lores (sometimes indistinct) *and in
voice* (see below). **Similar species:** Gray-
breasted Flycatcher is smaller and shows
obvious (though broken) eye-ring and
supraloral, as well as bolder wing-bars; it
inhabits forest and woodland undergrowth.
Habits: Similar to Eastern Wood-Pewee,
but—unlike Eastern—has characteristic habit
of shivering tail upon alighting on a branch.
Voice: Call a clear "peee pir" or "peee,
pidit," with quality reminiscent of Southern
Beardless-Tyrannulet.

Blackish Pewee, *Contopus nigrescens*
Pibí Negruzco   Plate 71(6)

400–900 m

13 cm (5"). *Local and scarce in canopy and
borders of humid forest in foothills and adjacent lowlands on e. slope.* Lower mandible
mostly yellow. Slightly crested. *Uniform dark
gray*, blackest on crown, wings, and tail.
Similar species: Despite the implication of
its English name, Blackish Pewee is *identical*
in coloration to the much more numerous
Smoke-colored Pewee. Aside from its
markedly larger size, Smoke-colored can be
known by its distinct bushy crest, much more
noticeable than in Blackish; it is much more
likely to perch close to ground than Blackish.
Habits: Almost invariably perches very high
in tall trees, where doubtless it often goes
unnoticed. Favors forest edge and openings,
often along or overlooking streams. Pairs of
Blackish Pewees seem quite sedentary, often
being found in same area—even the same
tree—day after day. Forages by making long
sallies into the air, often time and again
returning to same perch, usually shivering tail
as it alights. **Voice:** ♂'s song a snappy but
somewhat burry "chí-bew" repeated at 3 to
4-second intervals. Both sexes often give a

repeated sharp "pip" or "peep" call, sometimes in an irregular series (but typically *not* tripled, unlike Smoke-colored, whose call is lower pitched).

Smoke-colored Pewee, *Contopus fumigatus*
Pibí Ahumado   Plate 71(7)

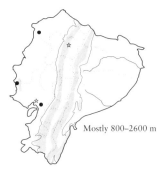

Mostly 800–2600 m

17 cm (6¾"). *Fairly common and widespread in borders of foothill, subtropical, and temperate forest and in adjacent clearings on both slopes*, also on coastal cordillera. Formerly often called Greater Pewee. Lower mandible orange-yellow. *Bushy crest usually prominent. Uniform dark gray.* **Juvenile** less crested and somewhat paler, especially below. **Similar species:** Much rarer Blackish Pewee is far smaller (smaller than even wood-pewees). Smoke-colored also can be confused with Olive-sided Flycatcher, which it resembles in behavior. Other pewees are markedly smaller, less gray, and show less crest. **Habits:** Usually perches in open, sometimes atop tall snags but also at times much lower; sallies into air, often flying out remarkably long distances, and frequently returning to original perch. Generally solitary. **Voice:** Frequently heard call a loud "pip-pip-pip," typically tripled (or even quadrupled) and often persistently repeated. Rather different song, given primarily at dawn, a rather rapid series of variable "wu-didit, weeu" or "weeeuw, wu-didit!" phrases.

Olive-sided Flycatcher, *Contopus cooperi*
Pibí Boreal   Plate 71(2)

18 cm (7"). *A boreal migrant to borders of foothill and lower subtropical forest and adjacent clearings on both slopes.* Formerly named *C. borealis*, and/or placed in genus *Nuttallornis*. *Rather bull-headed and distinctly short-tailed.* Lower mandible yellow-

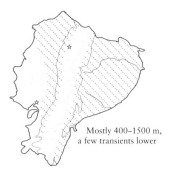

Mostly 400–1500 m, a few transients lower

ish. Dark grayish olive above; wings and tail dusky, wings with two indistinct pale grayish wing-bars. Throat and median underparts whitish to yellowish white, *contrasting with olive grayish sides and flanks*, sometimes looking mottled, *almost extending all the way across breast* (suggesting a dark, unbuttoned vest); *a tuft of white sometimes protrudes from behind wing onto sides of rump*. **Similar species:** Pewees are smaller with proportionately longer tails, and they never give the "vested" impression nor do they show white tuft on lowermost flanks. Longer-tailed and "point"-crested Smoke-colored Pewee is much more evenly dark gray below. **Habits:** A conspicuous bird, though always occurring at low densities. Perches on high snags or branches, launching out for long distances after aerial insects, frequently returning to the same branch over and over. As with the wood-pewees, individual birds presumably defend a wintering territory. **Voice:** Gives a loud, typically tripled "pip-pip-pip" call (similar to Smoke-colored's but given less persistently). True song heard even less often, mainly on northward passage, a far-carrying "hic, three-beers."

Empidonax Flycatchers
Drab migratory flycatchers from North America, all of them very similar; *identification of nonvocalizing birds is problematic.*

Acadian Flycatcher, *Empidonax virescens*
Mosquerito Verdoso   Plate 71(8)

14 cm (5½"). *A local boreal migrant* (Oct.–Mar.) *to lower growth of humid and semihumid forest, woodland, and plantations in lowlands and lower subtropics of west.* Lower mandible yellowish flesh. *Olive above*

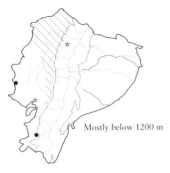

Mostly below 1200 m

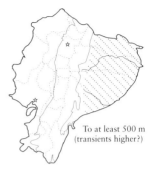

To at least 500 m
(transients higher?)

with whitish lores and *yellowish white eye-ring*; wings and tail dusky, wings with two bold whitish wing-bars. Throat grayish white becoming pale olive gray on breast, pale yellowish on flanks and crissum and whitish on midbelly. **Juvenile** has buffier wing-bars and is usually yellower below, especially on belly. **Similar species:** Closely resembles Willow/Alder Flycatcher pair, and sometimes not distinguishable in field; in Ecuador they are not known to occur together, but they could do so. Acadian tends to be more olive above and more yellowish below, and to have more prominent eye-ring. Willow/Alders tend to occur in more open habitats, and therefore are more conspicuous. **Habits:** Usually found singly in shady lower growth, perching upright and sallying to foliage. Often quite vocal on its wintering grounds. **Voice:** Frequent call a rather sharp and inflected "wheeyk" given at several-second intervals, sometimes for long periods, often revealing the presence of an otherwise unseen bird. The species' song, an explosive "ka-zéép!", is only rarely heard on its wintering grounds.

Alder Flycatcher, *Empidonax alnorum*
Mosquerito de Alisos   Plate 71(9)

14 cm (5½"). An uncommon boreal migrant (Sep.–Apr.) to *shrubby clearings, overgrown pastures, river islands, and woodland borders in lowlands of east.* Lower mandible yellowish flesh. Brownish to grayish olive with inconspicuous whitish eye-ring (often lacking) and sometimes some whitish on lores; wings and tail dusky, wings with two bold whitish wing-bars. Throat whitish, breast pale grayish to brownish olive, belly yellowish white. **Juvenile** browner above

with buffier wing-bars, belly more strongly tinged yellow. **Similar species:** Not only is it essentially impossible to separate this species from Willow Flycatcher with total confidence (unless vocalizing), but wood-pewees too can look surprisingly similar to Alder/Willow Flycatchers on their wintering grounds. Wood-pewees have more of a crested appearance, their wing-bars are weaker, and they never show any eye-ring at all; their wings are longer, legs shorter. **Habits:** Favors semiopen areas, often where damp. Usually seen singly, especially early in the day often perching atop a bush and sallying to foliage or into air. Numbers may be greatest during passage periods, for some individuals winter to Ecuador's south. **Voice:** Call a flat "peep" or "tip," not always easy to distinguish from Willow's. ♂'s song, heard reasonably often (especially during midwinter months and northward passage), a burry "free-breéo," with accent on *second* syllable.

Willow Flycatcher, *Empidonax traillii*
Mosquerito de Sauces   Plate 71(9)

14 cm (5½"). A *rare boreal migrant* (Oct.–Apr.) to *shrubby clearings, overgrown pastures, and woodland borders in lowlands*

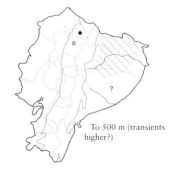

To 500 m (transients higher?)

of northeast. Nonvocalizing birds are indistinguishable from Alder Flycatcher; the relative status of both is thus hard to establish, but *Alder is much more numerous.* **Habits:** Similar to Alder Flycatcher. **Voice:** Call a short dry "whit." Sometimes heard is ♂'s song, a sharp "fítz-bew," with accent on *first* syllable.

Lathrotriccus Flycatchers

Rather dull flycatchers found in lower growth of forest, one species on either side of the Andes. Nests are soft cups placed in a fork of a shrub or low tree. The genus was recently erected for two South American flycatchers formerly placed in *Empidonax.*

Euler's Flycatcher, *Lathrotriccus euleri*
Mosquerito de Euler   Plate 71(10)

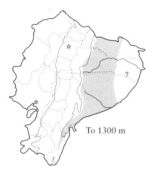

To 1300 m

13 cm (5″). Scarce and local in lower growth of humid forest and woodland in lowlands and foothills of east. *Notably drab, lacking obvious field marks.* Lower mandible yellowish flesh. *Brownish olive above* with narrow whitish eye-ring and *only a vague supraloral;* wings dusky with *two dull buff wing-bars* and flight-feather edging; tail olive brown. Throat grayish white, becoming brownish olive on breast and pale yellow on belly. **Similar species:** Willow/Alder Flycatchers are never as brown above, wing-bars are never as buff, and they are never as pale below; Euler's is much more of a forest and woodland bird. Fuscous Flycatcher is in Ecuador found exclusively on river islands and, though similar to the smaller Euler's, it differs in having all-black bill and well-marked whitish superciliary. **Habits:** Not well known in Ecuador. An inconspicuous bird

that remains in forest and woodland undergrowth, perching upright and sallying to foliage; usually not with mixed flocks. Overall comportment reminiscent of an *Empidonax.* **Voice:** Song a slightly descending series of burry notes, "zhwee-zhwe-zhwe-zhwe," similar in quality to Gray-breasted Flycatcher; also gives a simpler "zhwee-buu." Dawn song a less burry "cheeuw . . . chiu-ít" (N. Krabbe recording).

Gray-breasted Flycatcher
Lathrotriccus griseipectus
Mosquerito Pechigris   Plate 71(11)

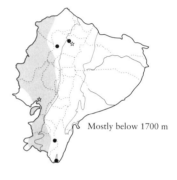

Mostly below 1700 m

13 cm (5″). *Now local in lower growth of humid and deciduous forest and woodland in lowlands of west,* ranging up into subtropics in El Oro and Loja; also in Río Marañón drainage near Zumba. Lower mandible whitish. Grayish olive above, grayer on crown, with *supraloral and broken eye-ring white;* wings dusky with *two bold white wing-bars.* Throat pale grayish, *breast gray* contrasting with yellowish white belly. **Juvenile** has buffier wing-bars and yellower belly. **Similar species:** Looks rather gray in field and this, combined with fairly prominent eye-ring and supraloral, should preclude confusion. Tumbes Pewee is somewhat larger and lacks this species' spectacles and prominent wing-bars; its behavior differs, as it usually takes prominent perches at borders (not remaining inside). **Habits:** Much as in Euler's Flycatcher, which this species seems to replace in w. Ecuador. Gray-breasted tolerates considerably less humid areas; it especially favors viny tangles. Like Euler's it is most apt to be noted when vocalizing. **Voice:** Song a burry

"zhweéur zhweer-zhwer-zhwer." Most vocal during rainy season.

Fuscous Flycatcher, *Cnemotriccus fuscatus*
Mosquerito Fusco   Plate 71(12)

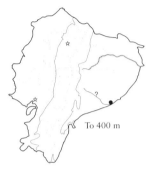

To 400 m

14 cm (5½"). *Inconspicuous but not uncommon in lower growth of riparian woodland and shrubby areas on river islands in lowlands of east.* Bill all black. Dull brown above with *fairly conspicuous whitish superciliary*; wings dusky with *two tawny-buff wingbars*. Throat whitish, *breast extensively dingy olive brown*, belly yellowish white. **Similar species:** In its limited range and habitat this flycatcher, though admittedly drab, should be readily recognizable. Euler's Flycatcher is not known to occur on river islands; it has a pale lower mandible and lacks the superciliary. Cf. also Mouse-colored Tyrannulet. **Habits:** Favors shady undergrowth, rarely coming to edge and never much in open; usually perches not far above ground with upright posture much like an *Empidonax* or *Lathrotriccus*. Generally in pairs. **Voice:** Most frequent call a low-pitched and gravelly "wor, jeér-jeér-jeér-jeér-jeér-jew" (number of "jeér" notes varying), lasting about 1–2 seconds. Also gives a more piercing "wheeéeu" at rather leisurely intervals of 6–8 seconds (J. Moore recording).

Black Phoebe, *Sayornis nigricans*
Febe Guardarríos   Plate 72(22)

17.5 cm (6¾"). Fairly common, widespread, and conspicuous *along streams and rivers* in foothills, subtropics, and lower temperate zone on both slopes, also locally in central and interandean valleys. *Favors semiopen areas, but also occurs in mainly forested*

Mostly 500–2800 m

regions, the prerequisite being the proximity of running water. Unmistakable. *Sooty black* with middle of lower belly white. *Wings with two indistinct white wing-bars, wing-coverts and flight feathers narrowly edged white*; outer web of outer pair of tail feathers white. **Habits:** Usually in pairs, often confiding and frequent around buildings and bridges (whose ledges provide ideal nesting sites). Perches in the open, generally not too high above ground, sometimes on rocks out in water; tail is periodically jerked upward. Feeds by sallying into air after flying insects. **Voice:** Not very vocal. ♂'s song a rather shrill "zhrreeee, pseekiyu," with quality somewhat reminiscent of Tropical Kingbird.

Vermilion Flycatcher, *Pyrocephalus rubinus*
Mosquero Bermellón   Plate 72(10)

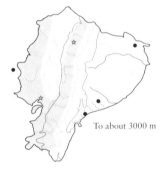

To about 3000 m

14.5–15 cm (5¾–6"). *Common and conspicuous* in semiopen areas with scattered bushes and trees, not infrequently around houses and farm buildings, in *more arid lowlands of west*, and in *arid highlands*. A few austral migrants occur in lowlands of east (Jul.–Aug.). Slightly bushy-crested. *Dazzling* ♂ unmistakable: *crown, lower face, and underparts brilliant scarlet*, contrasting with sooty blackish upperparts and mask through eyes. **West-slope** ♀ ashy brown above, paler on forehead and sootier on wings and tail; *wings virtually plain*. Throat and breast white, *breast with dusky streaking*, becoming *pink to reddish pink on belly and crissum*. A few ♀ ♀ have yellow (not red) tinge to lower underparts. **East-slope** ♀ shows little or no red below, and its dusky streaking below is more extensive. **Similar species:** Bran-colored Flycatcher is browner above and has wing-bars; it never shows any red. **Habits:** Often found in pairs, perching in open and usually at no great height above ground on shrubs, low trees, fences, and wires; austral migrants sometimes perch higher. Sallies for insects, most often to ground, also into air and to foliage. Tail is often pumped downward, with feathers spread. Often very confiding. Breeding ♂ ♂ engage in a spectacular display flight. **Voice:** Displaying ♂ mounts into air with crest puffed out, wings flapping rapidly but "weakly," slowing gaining height and then hovering before gradually descending, all the while repeating an attractive musical phrase, e.g., "pi-d'd'd'reeít." Displaying ♂ ♂ perform in both predawn darkness and broiling midday sun. Austral migrants seem silent.

Ochthoeca Chat-Tyrants

An attractive group of midsized flycatchers found in the Andes, mainly at quite high elevations. Most species have a *bold superciliary*, and more than half the Ecuadorian species have *prominent rufous wing-bars*. Although all *Ochthoeca* perch erectly, some species are inconspicuous inside forest whereas others are found much more in the open. Nests are mossy cups placed in a crevice or on a ledge of a bank or rock.

Brown-backed Chat-Tyrant
Ochthoeca fumicolor
Pitajo Dorsipardo   Plate 72(15)

14.5 cm (5¾"). *Common in shrubby areas near treeline on both slopes*, extending downslope in more open areas and up into shrubby paramo. Brown above, more rufescent on lower back and rump with *long broad buffy whitish superciliary and frontal area*; wings and tail black, with *two conspic-*

2800–4200 m

uous rufous wing-bars. Throat and lower face grayish; *underparts cinnamon-rufous* (slightly duller in ♀). **Similar species:** The only Ecuadorian chat-tyrant with both a long "brow" and rufescent underparts. **Habits:** Found singly or in pairs, often perching conspicuously atop a bush, small tree, or *Espletia* spike, sallying short distances into air or (more often) to ground. Generally confiding, flicking tail in alarm. **Voice:** Generally rather quiet, but occasionally gives a soft "pseeu" call. Dawn song a fast chattered "keé-ke-de keé-ke-de keé-kedu-keékeé-ke-du-keé" (P. Coopmans).

White-browed Chat-Tyrant
Ochthoeca leucophrys
Pitajo Cejiblanco   Plate 72(16)

2200–2800 m

14.5 cm (5¾"). *Rare and local in montane scrub, woodland patches, and hedgerows in agricultural regions in highlands of Azuay and n. Loja.* Above brownish gray with *long broad white superciliary and frontal area*; wings and tail dusky, *wings with at most faint rufescent wing-bars (usually nothing shows)*, tail with outer web of outer pair of feathers white. *Below uniform pale gray*. **Similar species:** Jelski's Chat-Tyrant considerably smaller and shows yellow in frontal area and prominent rufous wing-bars; it is more rufescent on back and rump and darker gray below. **Habits:** Not well known in Ecuador, where it seems to be distinctly scarcer than it is southward in the heart of its range. In Peru found singly or in pairs, perching upright and in the open, often on fences or phone wires or atop shrubs or low trees, sallying short distances into air or dropping to ground after insects. Often flicks wings and tail. **Voice:** Most frequent call a sharp "queeuw."

Rufous-breasted Chat-Tyrant
Ochthoeca rufipectoralis
Pitajo Pechirrufo   Plate 72(17)

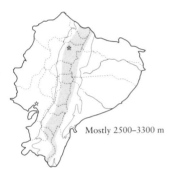

Mostly 2500–3300 m

13.5 cm (5¼"). *Borders of temperate forest and woodland on both slopes*. Brown above, more blackish on head and with *long broad white superciliary*; wings and tail blackish, *wings with a single broad rufous wing-bar*, outer web of outer pair of feathers white. Upper throat grayish, *lower throat and chest orange-rufous*; lower underparts whitish. **Similar species:** No other chat-tyrant has conspicuous rufous across chest. **Habits:** More arboreal than other chat-tyrants, usually perching at mid-levels to subcanopy in trees, often in the semiopen and straightforward to observe. Makes short sallies into air and to foliage. Sometimes accompanies mixed flocks, but at least as often away from them. **Voice:** Often quiet, but both sexes give a loud and harsh chatter, "ch-brrr, ch-brrr, ch-brrr . . . ," characteristically doubled. Dawn song a "tirip, weé-eeuw, tirip, weé-eeuw . . ." (N. Krabbe recording).

Slaty-backed Chat-Tyrant
Ochthoeca cinnamomeiventris
Pitajo Dorsipizarro   Plate 72(18)

Mostly 1700–2800 m

12 cm (4¾"). Lower growth and borders of upper subtropical and temperate forest and woodland, *almost invariably near water*, on both slopes (in west, south to Cotopaxi). *Entirely blackish above* aside from white supraloral stripe. Throat and upper chest blackish; *breast and belly chestnut*, crissum blackish. **Similar species:** A *small*, relatively chunky (short-tailed), and *very dark* chat-tyrant, essentially confined to the vicinity of rushing mountain streams; not likely confused. **Habits:** Usually in pairs, perching upright and low just inside shady forest, sometimes right at edge but never emerging far into cleared areas. Notably sedentary, and does not follow flocks. Makes short sallies into air and to foliage. **Voice:** Drawn-out call a high-pitched, sharp, and surprisingly loud "dzweeéyeeuw," often tirelessly repeated. Dawn song consists of that same note followed by 3–4 "tseét" notes.

Crowned Chat-Tyrant, *Ochthoeca frontalis*
Pitajo Coronado   Plate 72(19)
12.5 cm (5"). Uncommon in undergrowth of *temperate forest and woodland on both slopes up to treeline*. Mostly dark brown above, blackish on head and grayer on upper back, with *bright yellow frontal area* and *long white superciliary*; wings and tail dusky. Below uniform gray with dull buff crissum (latter more extensive in ♀). **Similar species:** Jelski's Chat-Tyrant is not known to overlap with this species, occurring at lower elevations and *only in Loja*. It is similar overall

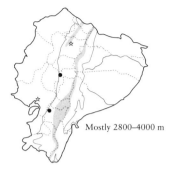

Mostly 2800–4000 m

pitched and sharp "tseeeee!" lasting about a second, sometimes—especially when excited—varied to a "tseee-krrrr" or "tse-tsirrekerrr" (P. Coopmans).

Yellow-bellied Chat-Tyrant
Ochthoeca diadema
Pitajo Ventriamarillo   Plate 72(21)

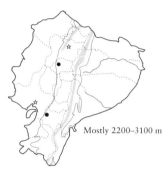

Mostly 2200–3100 m

(including yellow front) but has prominent rufous wing-bars. **Habits:** Inconspicuous, perching low in undergrowth; usually found singly, occasionally accompanying mixed flocks. **Voice:** Song a drawn-out rather high-pitched but descending trill, "sesr-rrrrrrrrrrrrrrrrrrrrrrrrrrrrrrrr," lasting several seconds (P. Coopmans).

Jelski's Chat-Tyrant, *Ochthoeca jelskii*
Pitajo de Jelski   Plate 72(20)

2200–2800 m

12.5 cm (5″). Uncommon and local in undergrowth of *upper subtropical and lower temperate forest and woodland in Loja*. Mostly brown above, blackish on head and grayer on upper back, with *bright yellow frontal area* and *long white superciliary*; wings and tail dusky, *wings with two bold rufous wing-bars*. Below uniform gray with dull buff crissum (latter more extensive in ♀). **Similar species:** In s. Ecuador the Crowned Chat-Tyrant ranges mainly on e. slope, in Loja just spilling over Continental Divide; they are not known to actually occur together. It differs principally in having plain wings, and is somewhat darker overall. **Habits:** Similar to Crowned Chat-Tyrant. **Voice:** Song a high-

12.5 cm (5″). Undergrowth of *upper subtropical and temperate forest on both slopes*. Brownish olive, blacker on crown, with *yellow frontal area and long broad superciliary*; wings and tail duskier, wings with two rufescent wing-bars. *Yellowish below*, clouded olive across breast and down flanks. **Similar species:** Much more extensively yellow than any other chat-tyrant. Cf. Flavescent Flycatcher (which lacks rufous in wings and has no superciliary). Color pattern recalls that of Citrine Warbler (with very different behavior, no rufous in wings). **Habits:** Another inconspicuous chat-tyrant, found singly or in pairs low in dense undergrowth. Usually unwary, but even so only infrequently observed. Sometimes accompanies mixed flocks. **Voice:** Most frequently heard song a very dry trill, slightly inflected at start, e.g., "tsueéurrrrrr." Dawn song a shorter "psi-uw" repeated at several-second intervals.

Drab Water-Tyrant, *Ochthornis littoralis*
Guardarríos Arenisco   Plate 72(25)

13.5 cm (5¼″). A *nondescript, dun-colored* little flycatcher, *fairly common and conspicuous along larger rivers in lowlands of east*. Sometimes placed in genus *Ochthoeca*. *Mostly pale sandy brown*, paler on rump and underparts and with *short white superciliary*;

To 400 m

2850–4100 m

wings and tail plain dusky brown. **Similar species:** Much rarer Little Ground-Tyrant has more slender bill with pale area at base, no whitish superciliary, shows vague wing-bars, and has white on outer tail; note that Drab Water-Tyrant also rests and hops on sandbars, though this is more typical of the ground-tyrant. Cf. also Fuscous Flycatcher. **Habits:** Invariably near water, favoring areas where a strong current has eroded and under-cut banks exposing protruding roots and branches where it loves to perch. Also sometimes on river islands, there favoring piles of accumulated driftwood. Most often in pairs that perch and flit within a meter of the water, sometimes repeatedly flushing ahead of an approaching boat; rather confiding. **Voice:** Rather quiet, but gives an occasional soft "free." Displaying birds, sometimes pairs, posture with wings outstretched while giving a fast and excited "weet-weedidee, weet-weedidee . . ." repeated several (sometimes many) times.

Red-rumped Bush-Tyrant
Cnemarchus erythropygius
Alinaranja Lomirrojiza   Plate 72(13)

23 cm (9"). A sleek and attractive *large* fly-catcher found at *low densities* in *paramo and semiopen areas with scattered shrubs and woodland patches in upper temperate zone on both slopes*. Formerly often placed in genus *Myiotheretes*. Unmistakable. *Fore-crown whitish becoming pale gray on hind-crown and nape*; otherwise dark brownish gray above with *contrasting rufous rump*. Wings dusky with *white patch on tertials* (especially conspicuous in flight) and cinna-mon underwing-coverts; central tail feathers blackish, *others rufous with terminal third black*. Throat streaked gray and white,

becoming gray on breast and *contrastingly rufous on belly*. **Habits:** Found singly or in pairs, almost always fully in open, perching on boulders, bushes, wires, or fences; usually drops to ground after prey, less often sallying into air. Generally quite wary, not allowing a close approach. **Voice:** Usually quiet. Birds occasionally give a shrill "kyeee" and a higher-pitched "skyeik" (N. Krabbe recordings); in Peru has been heard to give a high-pitched plaintive whistle, "wheeeu" (P. Coopmans).

Myiotheretes Bush-Tyrants
Large flycatchers found in *temperate forest and borders in the Andes*. They superficially look very different but are united by their *extensive cinnamon-rufous in the wing*.

Streak-throated Bush-Tyrant
Myiotheretes striaticollis
Alinaranja Golilistada   Plate 72(11)

23 cm (9"). *Semiopen shrubby or grassy areas and borders of forest and woodland in temperate zone on both slopes*. Brown above with vague whitish supraloral. Wings black-ish with cinnamon-rufous edging, *cinnamon*

Mostly 2400–3200 m

underwing-coverts and *wide cinnamon-rufous band along base of flight feathers* (conspicuous in flight); tail dusky from above, but *from below cinnamon with outer third blackish. Throat and upper chest white boldly streaked blackish*, underparts cinnamon-rufous. **Similar species:** Cliff Flycatcher has somewhat similar wing and tail pattern but is markedly smaller and has darker rufous-chestnut underparts with no streaking; it occurs at lower elevations. Overall aspect somewhat thrush-like. **Habits:** Forages singly or in pairs, perching in the open (often very high above ground, even on high-tension wires), sallying out after aerial insects; frequently in quite disturbed terrain, sometimes even in *Eucalyptus* woodlands. **Voice:** Fairly quiet, but has a loud clear rising whistled note with rather humanlike quality, e.g., "weeeeeuw," or a more inflected "weeeí." Infrequently heard song a "tsi-seeeé-rit" or "tsi-si-seé-rit," bearing a strong resemblance to Tropical Kingbird (P. Coopmans).

Smoky Bush-Tyrant, *Myiotheretes fumigatus*
Alinaranja Ahumada   Plate 72(12)

2000–3200 m

20.5 cm (8″). A *dark*, vaguely thrush-like flycatcher found in mid-levels and subcanopy *in upper subtropical and temperate forest and woodland on both slopes. Uniform sooty brown* with vague and short whitish superciliary and some whitish streaking on throat. Wings and tail blackish, wing-coverts narrowly edged buffyish and with *cinnamon underwing-coverts and broad band along base of flight feathers* (latter conspicuous in flight). **Similar species:** Drab and nondescript at rest, with only a hint of an eye-stripe, but the cinnamon in wing flashes out prominently in flight. **Habits:** Found singly or in

pairs, generally remaining inside forest but not that hard to observe; regularly accompanies mixed flocks. Sallies into air for insects, also hover-gleans at foliage; rarely drops to ground. **Voice:** Often quiet but both sexes give a soft "pü-pü-pü" (sometimes more "pü" notes). Dawn song a repeated "peeéu . . . peeeu . . . pu . . . peeé-pu . . ." with several-second intervals between notes (J. Moore recording).

Cliff Flycatcher, *Hirundinea ferruginea*
Tirano de Riscos   Plate 72(14)

900–1700 m

18.5 cm (7¼″). *Local around steep rocky roadcuts* (also natural cliffs) *in foothills and subtropics on e. slope. Dark brown above* with *whitish grizzling on forecrown and face.* Wings blackish with *most of flight feathers extensively rufous* (conspicuous in flight, and showing as a large patch on closed wing); tail blackish from above, but *from below cinnamon-rufous* with outer third dusky (also conspicuous in flight). Upper throat whitish, *underparts uniform rufous-chestnut.* **Similar species:** Not likely confused, especially given its strict association with roadcut/cliff habitat. Cf. larger Streak-throated Bush-Tyrant (with prominent streaking on foreneck). **Habits:** Cliff Flycatchers may have been present in Ecuador in bygone decades, but if so they went unrecorded. The species appears still to be increasing, and with ongoing road construction it doubtless will continue to do so. It is very localized and sedentary, found in pairs or small family groups, usually perching on rock faces; can be inconspicuous until it flies. Often appears oblivious to roar of traffic or close presence of people. **Voice:** Sometimes keeps up a near-constant chatter of high-pitched chattering calls, including a "wheeeyp!" and a "whee, dee-dee-ee-ee-ee" or "wheeuw-d'd'd'r!," also a continued "wha-deép, wha-deép. . . ."

Agriornis Shrike-Tyrants

Large and robust tyrannids with *heavy hooked bills*, the shrike-tyrants are among the largest of their family and are easily recognized by their *extensive white in the tail*. They inhabit *open areas at high elevations* in the Andes, with one species (White-tailed) now very rare and local. Nests are placed in crevices of walls, sometimes buildings.

Black-billed Shrike-Tyrant, *Agriornis montana*
Arriero Piquinegro   Plate 72(1)

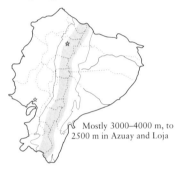

Mostly 3000–4000 m, to 2500 m in Azuay and Loja

24 cm (9½"). Wide-ranging but never especially numerous in *open grassy and agricultural areas with scattered bushes and trees in upper temperate zone and paramo*. *Hooked bill black*; iris yellowish to ivory. Dark grayish brown above with indistinct whitish supraloral stripe. Wings with some pale edging on inner flight feathers; *tail mostly white* (most conspicuous in flight), central pair of feathers blackish. *Throat and cheeks white streaked with dark brown*; breast and flanks ashy brown, becoming whitish on midbelly. **Similar species:** Likely only confused with the much rarer (and larger) White-tailed Shrike-Tyrant, which see. Cf. also Paramo Ground-Tyrant. Somewhat thrush-like at rest. **Habits:** Usually found singly, perching conspicuously on a rock, bush, or low tree, dropping to ground to capture prey; hunting birds move from perch to perch, hovering briefly with white tail flashing before pouncing. Also runs freely on ground. At times remarkably unwary, but once one is flushed, it may fly off a long distance. **Voice:** Not very vocal, but occasionally gives a loud, ringing "wheee, wheeeu" or just "wheeeu."

White-tailed Shrike-Tyrant, *Agriornis andicola*
Arriero Coliblanco   Plate 72(2)

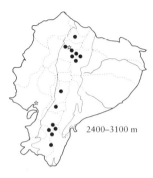

2400–3100 m

28 cm (11"). Now *very rare and local in open, sparsely vegetated shrubby areas in temperate zone and paramo*. Formerly called *A. albicauda*. Often confused with the much more numerous Black-billed Shrike-Tyrant; *despite its name, White-tailed's tail pattern is virtually identical*. White-tailed differs in its *markedly larger size* and "bulkier" shape, *heavier bill* whose *lower mandible may be basally yellowish* (but is always paler; bill never all black as in Black-billed), *dark iris*, and *much bolder and sharper blackish throat streaking*. White-tailed is somewhat paler overall, and its belly can be buff-tinged. **Habits:** Not well known, but appears to differ little if at all from Black-billed Shrike-Tyrant. **Voice:** Call a loud and surprising melodic "teeu, tcheeu-tcheeu-tcheeuw" with many variations (F. Sornoza).

Muscisaxicola Ground-Tyrants

Slim, elegant *terrestrial* flycatchers found primarily in *open terrain at high elevations*. They have *slender, rather short bills* and *long black legs*. Ground-tyrants are predominantly gray or brownish and white with contrasting blackish tails showing white on the outer web; *details of the head pattern* as well as overall size and dorsal coloration are the key identification features. Nests are placed in holes and crevices of banks and stone walls.

Paramo Ground-Tyrant
Muscisaxicola alpina
Dormilona del Páramo   Plate 72(6)

19 cm (7½"). *Fairly common in open paramo south to Azuay*; favors arid regions, avoiding areas with bushes. Now considered a species separate from *M. grisea* (Plain-capped Ground-Tyrant) of Peru and w. Bolivia.

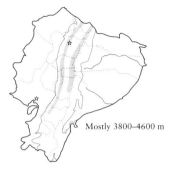

Mostly 3800–4600 m

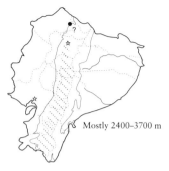

Mostly 2400–3700 m

Brownish gray above, crown tinged sepia, with *prominent but short white supraloral*; wings duskier with some pale edging on coverts; tail black, outer web of outer pair of feathers whitish. Below grayish white. **Similar species:** White-browed Ground-Tyrant differs in its longer but decidedly narrower white superciliary (despite its name, usually *less* prominent than Paramo's) with some rufous showing on hindcrown (often not evident under normal field conditions). Dorsal coloration of the two species similar. Spot-billed Ground-Tyrant much smaller and decidedly buffier below. Black-billed Shrike-Tyrant much larger and more robust, with stouter bill and far more white in tail. **Habits:** Found in pairs or (when not nesting) small loose groups, hopping and running on ground with body held low and horizontal, then abruptly pausing and looking about with erect stance. Often perches on a slightly elevated site such as a rock or wall, and frequently droops wings and flicks tail open and shut. Pursues insects both on ground and in short sallies into the air. Flight swift, direct, and graceful on slim and notably pointed wings. Displaying ♂ ♂ hover in place, then stall and drop a bit, then recover; sequence can be repeated many times. **Voice:** Generally quiet, though occasionally gives a soft "tik" note.

White-browed Ground-Tyrant
Muscisaxicola albilora
Dormilona Cejiblanca   Plate 72(5)

17 cm (6³/₄"). An *uncommon austral winter visitant to paramo and open areas in temperate zone*. Brownish gray above, *browner on crown which gradually blends into more rufous hindcrown*, and with *long but narrow* (not very conspicuous) *white superciliary*; wings duskier with some pale edging on coverts; tail black, outer web of outer pair of

feathers whitish. Below grayish white. **Similar species:** Paramo Ground-Tyrant is somewhat larger and has a bolder white supraloral; it lacks any rufous on hindcrown, though its forecrown is darker brown than White-browed's. **Habits:** Similar to Paramo Ground-Tyrant, though White-browed, being a migrant, sometimes occurs at lower elevations (even on fields in agricultural areas) and in areas where more bushes are present.

Spot-billed Ground-Tyrant
Muscisaxicola maculirostris
Dormilona Piquipinta   Plate 72(8)

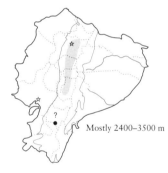

Mostly 2400–3500 m

14 cm (5¹/₂"). *Barren open places and agricultural areas with sparse vegetation in temperate zone mainly from Pichincha to Chimborazo, favoring arid regions. The smallest ground-tyrant in the highlands. Base of lower mandible yellowish to orange-yellow*, forming the inconspicuous "spot." Pale sandy brown above with *short white supraloral*; wings duskier, *feathers edged cinnamon-buff*; tail black, outer web of outer pair of feathers whitish. Throat buffy whitish, *underparts uniform pale cinnamon-buff*. **Similar species:** Little Ground-Tyrant is not known to overlap with this species; it lacks

supraloral and has a distinctly whiter belly. Paramo and White-browed Ground-Tyrants are larger, not so brown above, and lack any tint of buff below. **Habits:** Much as in Paramo Ground-Tyrant, though rarely or never in flocks and less conspicuous than other ground-tyrants; seems not to stand as erect. Prefers sparsely vegetated slopes and ravines, often perching on banks or walls. **Voice:** Has an aerial display—much as in other ground-tyrants—in which it gives a repeated "cleeoo" (Fjeldså and Krabbe 1990).

Little Ground-Tyrant, *Muscisaxicola fluviatilis*
Dormilona Chica   Plate 72(7)

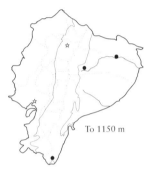

To 1150 m

13.5 cm (5¼"). A *casual wanderer* to sandbars along Río Napo, one other record (a vagrant?) from subtropics in s. Zamora-Chinchipe. Resembles only slightly larger Spot-billed Ground-Tyrant; has *similar pale area on lower mandible*. Differs in being slightly grayer above with no white supraloral, and in having *pale grayish buff breast contrasting with white belly*. **Similar species:** The only ground-tyrant likely to occur at low elevations on e. slope. Much more numerous Drab Water-Tyrant has rather prominent whitish supraloral, whitish rump, no white on tail, and whiter belly. **Habits:** Hardly known in Ecuador, where it has been found on sandbars and once on a road through an agricultural region. Elsewhere found singly or in pairs in open habitats, typically along rivers but also in open areas on e. slope of Andes.

[Dark-faced Ground-Tyrant
Muscisaxicola macloviana
Dormilona Carinegruzca]   Plate 72(9)

16.5 cm (6½"). An *accidental vagrant to open areas near s. El Oro coast*. Brownish gray

above, dull chestnut-brown on crown and with *black foreface*; wings duskier, tail black with outer web of outer pair of feathers white. *Pale grayish below*, whiter on lower belly and crissum. **Similar species:** A distinctive ground-tyrant, quite different from the species normally occurring in Ecuador (none of which has ever been seen anywhere near the coast). **Habits:** Favors open areas with short grass and plowed fields on winter quarters in coastal Peru, frequently near water; often then in loose flocks.

Short-tailed Field-Tyrant
Muscigralla brevicauda
Tiranito Colicorto   Plate 72(3)

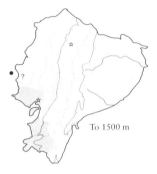

To 1500 m

11 cm (4¼"). An unmistakable *terrestrial* flycatcher, *very long-legged and very short-tailed*, found in open barren areas with at most scattered bushes and low trees in *more arid lowlands of southwest*, in sw. Azuay and Loja up into interior valleys. *Legs yellowish flesh*. Pale brownish gray above with short white supraloral and semiconcealed yellow coronal patch; *rump band pinkish buff, uppertail-coverts rufous-chestnut*. Wings dusky with two whitish wing-bars; tail black

narrowly tipped rufous-buff. Creamy whitish below, belly somewhat yellower. **Habits:** Behavior similar to the ground-tyrants, hopping and running on ground but also perches freely in bushes and low trees; pursues insects on ground and in short flutters, and often flicks wings and tail. Found singly and in pairs. **Voice:** Song a weak, sibilant "tizztízzz," sometimes preceded by a few "tik" notes; this is usually given from a low perch, but sometimes bird may mount 10–20 m up while singing.

Knipolegus Tyrants and Black-Tyrants

A diverse trio of tyrannids: a dull, monomorphic species ranges on Andean slopes, while two sexually dimorphic species are found very locally in lowlands of the northeast. Males of the two lowland species are among the only entirely black flycatchers. All are notably quiet.

Rufous-tailed Tyrant, *Knipolegus poecilurus*

Viudita Colicolorada   Plate 71(1)

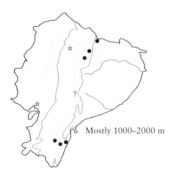

Mostly 1000–2000 m

14.5 cm (5¾"). Scarce and local at borders of *foothill and subtropical forest and adjacent shrubby clearings on e. slope*. **Sexes alike.** *Iris red.* Grayish above; wings duskier with two dull buffyish wing-bars; tail dusky *with inner webs mostly rufous* (more evident in flight). *Mostly cinnamon-buff below*, washed with gray across breast. **Similar species:** Rather nondescript and confusing. Superficially pewee-like (size, shape, attitude) but much buffier below, and no pewee has a red eye. **Habits:** Usually found singly or in pairs, most often perching erectly in semiopen, sallying into air in pursuit of insects. Does not seem to associate with mixed flocks. Often raises tail, then slowly lowers it. **Voice:** Occasion-

ally gives several high-pitched, raspy "tzreeet" notes followed by some jumbled notes (P. Coopmans).

Riverside Tyrant, *Knipolegus orenocensis*

Viudita Ribereña   Plate 96(13)

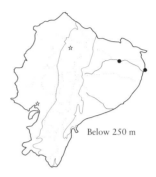

Below 250 m

15 cm (6"). *Rare and local in early-succession shrubby growth on Río Napo islands in lowlands of northeast*. Bill blue-gray tipped blackish. ♂ *uniform dull black*. ♀ *dull olive-grayish above*, wings and tail duskier. Below whitish with buffer throat and coarse blurry olive grayish streaking on breast and flanks. **Juvenile** like ♀ but with pale edging on wing-coverts and rufous edging on tail. **Similar species:** Easily confused with Amazonian Black-Tyrant, though that species occupies a different, more wooded "backwater" microhabitat (not river islands) and is smaller. ♂ Amazonian is glossier blue-black. ♀ Amazonian is browner (less gray) above with white on lores, definite wing-bars (wings essentially plain in Riverside), whiter throat (less buff), and rufous on uppertail-coverts. Cf. also ♀ Vermilion Flycatcher. **Habits:** Usually in pairs that sometimes (especially in early morning) take prominent perches atop a shrub, but for much of the day remain under cover. Often sallies to ground for prey. **Voice:** Displaying ♂♂ mount a few meters into air, then quickly drop back down to their perch, the latter accompanied by a (mechanical?) snap. Both sexes give a soft "tuk" note, and ♂♂ may accelerate this into a sputter.

Amazonian Black-Tyrant
Knipolegus poecilocercus

Viudita Negra Amazónica   Plate 96(12)

13.5 cm (5¼"). *Rare and local in undergrowth and thickets of seasonally flooded*

200 m

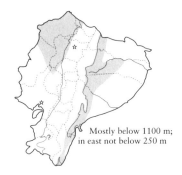

Mostly below 1100 m;
in east not below 250 m

várzea woodland in lowlands of far north-east (Río Lagarto); formerly placed in genus *Phaeotriccus*. Bill blue (♂) or dusky (♀). ♂ *entirely glossy blue-black*. ♀ olive brown above, *lores and narrow eye-ring whitish*, rufescent on uppertail-coverts; wings and tail dusky, wings with *two pale buff wing-bars*, *tail feathers edged cinnamon-rufous*. Whitish below with *heavy olive brown streaking across breast*, tinged pale yellow on belly. **Similar species:** Resembles Riverside Tyrant of river islands; for distinctions, see that species. Black-tyrant's sudden movements recall a manakin, though nothing similar is found in its restricted microhabitat. Cf. ♂ Cocha Antshrike (also black). **Habits:** A quiet and inconspicuous bird, favoring seasonally inundated areas; known in Ecuador only from a blackwater drainage. Found singly or in pairs, perching near ground or (more often) water, making short sallies to foliage or to water's surface. **Voice:** ♂ in presumed display abruptly jumps upward a meter or so and quickly returns to original perch, this action sometimes accompanied by a soft snapping sound (mechanical?).

Long-tailed Tyrant, *Colonia colonus*
Tirano Colilargo   Plate 72(4)

♂ 23–25 cm (9–10″); ♀ 18–20 cm (7–8″). *Fairly common and conspicuous at borders of humid forest and in adjacent clearings in lowlands and foothills of east and northwest*, in east not ranging too far from Andes. An unmistakable, *mainly black* flycatcher with *greatly lengthened central tail feathers* (in ♂♂ up to 12 cm [5″] longer than others). Bill very short. *Mostly black with white fore-crown and superciliary* becoming ashy gray on crown and nape; rump patch white. **Western birds** have irregular whitish area on midback. ♀ has shorter protruding tail feathers and is paler and grayer on belly. **Habits:** Usually in pairs, less often small groups, that perch on open branches and (especially) snags at forest edge and out in clearings, sallying long distances into air after small insects. Seems very sedentary. Nests are placed inside an old woodpecker hole or natural cavity. **Voice:** Most frequent call a distinctive soft, smoothly rising "sweee?," sometimes given 2–3 times in quick succession.

Fluvicola Water-Tyrants
Attractive, *black and white* flycatchers found in *open areas near water*, one on either side of the Andes (but Pied is only a vagrant). *Sexes alike.*

Masked Water-Tyrant, *Fluvicola nengeta*
Tirano de Agua Enmascarado   Plate 72(23)

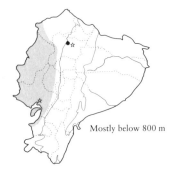

Mostly below 800 m

14.5 cm (5¾″). *Semiopen shrubby areas near freshwater (especially in marshy areas, also around rice fields) in lowlands of west.* Unmistakable. *Mostly white* with *contrasting*

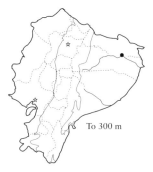

To 300 m

black stripe through eye onto ear-coverts and *black wings and tail*, latter broadly tipped white; back tinged brownish gray. **Habits:** Forages singly or in pairs mainly on or near ground, sometimes moving out onto floating vegetation; often cocks and fans tail. Quite tame and always conspicuous. Displaying birds bow up and down while facing each other with tails spread and raised. **Voice:** Call a distinctive sharp "kirt!," sometimes doubled and often given in flight. Pairs sometimes chatter together.

[Pied Water-Tyrant, *Fluvicola pica*
Tirano de Agua Pinto]   Plate 72(24)

350 m

13 cm (5"). An *accidental vagrant* to lowlands of northeast. *Head and underparts white, contrasting with black hindcrown, nape, back, wings, and tail*; scapulars, rump, and narrow tail-tip also white; some white mottling on back. **Similar species:** ♀ White-headed Marsh-Tyrant, though vaguely similar, is nowhere near as sharply black and white as this species, being essentially pale ashy brown above. **Habits:** Similar to Masked Water-Tyrant; equally conspicuous.

[White-headed Marsh-Tyrant
Arundinicola leucocephala
Tirano de Ciénega Cabecialbo]   Plate 70(9)

13 cm (5"). A *casual vagrant* to grassy areas on river islands in lowlands of northeast. Lower mandible yellow basally. ♂ unmistakable: *black* with *sharply contrasting white head and throat*. ♀ *plain ashy brown above* with white forecrown and blackish tail, wings duskier. Whitish below, washed with ashy brown on sides and flanks. **Similar**

species: ♀ is potentially confusable with even rarer Pied Water-Tyrant, which see. **Habits:** Conspicuous, perching erectly on grass stems or on a shrub or low tree, sallying for short distances into air. Only rarely drops to the ground, and does not fan or cock tail.

Attila **Attilas**
A distinctive, homogeneous group of fairly large, *bull-headed* tyrannids with *heavy and prominently hooked bills* and relatively plain patterns, *some shade of rufous predominating* in most species. Attilas are *inconspicuous* birds of lowland forest and woodland, most occurring east of the Andes; they do draw attention through their *loud and frequent vocalizing*. Nests are bulky cups placed in a niche or crevice, sometimes in a hole, usually not high above ground.

Bright-rumped Attila, *Attila spadiceus*
Atila Polimorfo   Plate 73(1)

19 cm (7½"). *Widespread in subcanopy and borders of humid forest in lowlands and foothills of east and northwest*, in east mainly in terra firme and relatively scarce. Iris

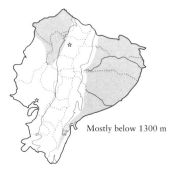

Mostly below 1300 m

reddish brown to hazel; bill basally pinkish. *Polymorphic*, with intermediates also occurring. **Olive morph** (most frequent) olive above with a vague yellowish brow and *contrasting yellow rump* (but often hidden; it can be tinged buff); wings and tail duskier, *wings with pale grayish to rufescent wing-bars*. *Throat and breast olive streaked yellow*, becoming whiter and unstreaked on belly; crissum pale yellow, or buff-tinged. Scarce **gray morph** differs in its *solid gray head and neck*, and gray throat and breast indistinctly streaked whitish. Equally scarce **rufous morph** *mainly rufous above* except for ochraceous yellow rump, and *rufous throat and breast* indistinctly streaked whitish. **Similar species:** No other attila is ever predominantly olive, as nearly three-quarters of Ecuadorian Bright-rumpeds are; further, no other attila has such prominent wing-bars, nor does any show streaking below. Note that several other attilas have equally bright yellow rumps. Cf. especially Citron-bellied Attila. **Habits:** Stolid and inconspicuous (except by voice), perching erectly at varying levels though typically quite high. Forages by sallying for insects and some fruit; sometimes accompanies mixed flocks but usually solitary. Often wags or jerks tail downward, especially when agitated. Heard far more often than seen. **Voice:** Far-carrying song, somewhat higher-pitched in western birds, a forceful and ascending series of spirited whistled doubled notes, e.g., "whup, whip, wheédip, wheédip, wheédip, wheédip, wheeeyr" with distinctive slur at end (number of "wheedip" notes variable). A frequent call is a fast laughing "weer-weer-weer-weer-weer-wheerpo" (with a variable number of "weer" notes); also gives individual staccato calls, especially in flight.

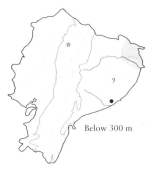

Below 300 m

morph of Bright-rumped Attila (infrequent) lacks gray on head, has brighter rump and whitish belly, etc. **Habits:** A "high-forest" attila, infrequently seen and, at least in Ecuador, not even heard all that often. Inactive behavior much like Bright-rumped Attila, though even less likely to come to forest edge. **Voice:** Song a fast and often tirelessly repeated "whee? whee? whee? whee? wheé? bu," ascending until last note. Overall quality similar to Bright-rumped Attila though most notes in that species' song are doubled.

[White-eyed Attila, *Attila bolivianus*
Atila Ojiblanco]   Plate 73(5)

250 m

19 cm (7½"). Status uncertain; known from *only one report* in *várzea forest* in lowlands of northeast (Sacha). Formerly called Dull-capped Attila. *The only attila with pale yellowish white eyes*. Bill mainly horn. *Rufous brown above*, somewhat grayer on crown, becoming bright cinnamon-rufous on rump and tail; primaries and greater wing-coverts mainly blackish. *Below cinnamon-rufous*, paler on belly. **Similar species:** Whitish eyes are conspicuous enough to preclude confu-

Citron-bellied Attila, *Attila citriniventris*
Atila Ventricitrino   Plate 73(2)

18.5 cm (7¼"). *Rare and seemingly local in subcanopy of terra firme forest in lowlands of east.* Lower mandible pale horn to pinkish. *Head gray*, back rufous brown *becoming paler cinnamon-rufous on rump* and rufous on tail; wings plain dusky. Upper throat pale grayish; *underparts bright ochraceous*, yellower on belly, and with obscure dusky streaking on chest. **Similar species:** Rufous

sion. Much more numerous and similarly colored Cinnamon Attila has dark eyes and black bill. **Habits:** More conspicuous than previous two attilas, primarily because it occurs in more open and lower-stature habitat. Found singly or in pairs. **Voice:** Song a rather leisurely and ascending series of whistled notes, almost halting at first, e.g., "whup; whup, wheep, wheep, wheep, wheeyp, wheeyp, wheebit, wheeeur," last note lower in pitch and strength.

Cinnamon Attila, *Attila cinnamomeus*
Atila Canelo   Plate 73(4)

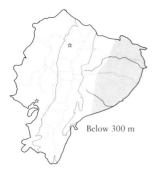

Below 300 m

19.5 cm (7³⁄₄"). *Fairly common in várzea forest and woodland, swampy places, and margins of lakes and streams in lowlands of east. Bill black. Mostly cinnamon-rufous,* somewhat paler below than above; primaries and greater wing-coverts mainly blackish. **Similar species:** This striking attila is most likely to be confused with the similarly colored Várzea Schiffornis which, however, differs markedly in shape and behavior. Citron-bellied Attila inhabits terra firme canopy and never occurs in Cinnamon's habitat; it has gray head, pale lower mandible, etc. Cf. also Chestnut-crowned Becard and very rare White-eyed Attila. **Habits:** Found singly or in pairs, regularly ranging at forest (or water's) edge and not as hard to see as many other attilas. Often agitatedly pounds tail downward. **Voice:** Has two distinctly different vocalizations, both with the same loud ringing quality, most distinctive being a slurred, almost hawk-eagle-like "tuu-eeeeur." Full song is a leisurely series more reminiscent of other attilas' though shorter, e.g., "whoor, wheer wheeér-wher."

Ochraceous Attila, *Attila torridus*
Atila Ocráceo   Plate 73(3)

Mostly below 1500 m, but higher in Loja

20.5 cm (8"). *Now uncommon and local in mid-levels and subcanopy of humid and semihumid forest, secondary woodland, borders, and adjacent clearings and plantations in lowlands and foothills of west.* Bill black. *Mostly cinnamon above,* yellower on rump, with contrasting blackish wings. *Below ochraceous yellow,* yellowest on belly. **Similar species:** Nothing really similar in range. West of Andes the only other attila is the very different Bright-rumped. Rufous Mourner and Rufous Piha are truly rufous. Very differently shaped Pacific Royal-Flycatcher has much the same overall color. **Habits:** Like other attilas, seen singly and in pairs, and generally inconspicuous. Often its presence is first made known by its far-carrying calls. **Voice:** Most frequent call a strikingly hawk-eagle-like "whoeeeer" (rather like one of related Cinnamon Attila's calls); this can be extended into a "whoeeeer, wheéu, whit-whit." Also gives a sharp "wheek!" or "keek" call. Song a mainly rising series of whistled notes, "wuuu-wuuu-weee-weee-weeé-weeé-wuyeép!," with cadence of Bright-rumped Attila though with most notes single rather than doubled (P. Coopmans).

Rhytipterna Mourners
Superficially dissimilar *Myiarchus*-like tyrannids, one grayish and the other rufous, one species in lowland forest on either side of the Andes. Note the similarity of each to a sympatric species of *Laniocera* mourner and *Lipaugus* piha (two cotingid genera). Remarkably, *Rhytipterna* nests remain unknown.

Grayish Mourner, *Rhytipterna simplex*
Copetón Plañidero Grisáceo   Plate 73(8)

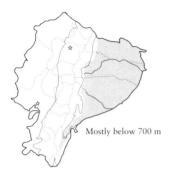

Mostly below 700 m

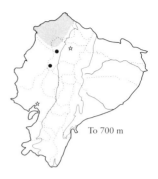

To 700 m

20.5 cm (8"). Mid-levels and subcanopy of humid forest in *lowlands of east*. Iris reddish. *Uniform plain gray*, underparts slightly paler and with slight yellowish cast, especially on belly and crissum. **Juvenile** has fulvous edging on wings and tail. **Similar species:** Screaming Piha (a cotinga) often occurs with this mourner. The larger piha has a more grayish eye, is purer gray (slightly darker above, and lacking mourner's yellowish tone below), and is shaped differently with rounder head. Their very different voices are helpful, as is fact that piha rarely or never accompanies flocks (which mourner does frequently). Cinereous Mourner (likewise a cotinga, also round-headed) differs especially in its prominent rufous wing-spotting. **Habits:** Usually found singly or in pairs, perching erectly and quietly, often on open branches, peering around in search of its large insect prey, then suddenly sallying out to snatch it. Also eats some fruit. One or two regularly accompany mixed flocks. **Voice:** Distinctive call a fast "r-t-t-t-t-t-tchéw!," explosive at end and often sounding like a sneeze, sometimes with more extended rising series of preliminary notes. At other times the "tchéw!" may be given two or even three times, or the entire phrase is repeated rapidly. Also can give a rising series of notes that slows toward end, "tu-tu-te-te tee tee teeuw teeuw?" (P. Coopmans).

Rufous Mourner, *Rhytipterna holerythra*
Copetón Plañidero Rufo   Plate 73(9)

20.5 cm (8"). *Mid-levels and subcanopy of humid forest in lowlands and foothills of northwest*. Lower mandible flesh toward base. *Uniform rich rufous*, somewhat paler

below; wings slightly duskier. **Similar species:** Easily confused with Rufous Piha (a cotinga). The larger (but proportionately shorter-tailed) piha differs subtly in having a stouter bill, paler throat, and vague pale eye-ring; the last, together with its rounder head, gives piha a softer, more dove-like expression. Voice is often the best clue of all. Speckled Mourner (likewise a cotinga, also round-headed) differs especially in its dusky wing-coverts with prominent rufous tips. Cf. also ♀ One-colored Becard. **Habits:** Similar to Grayish Mourner. **Voice:** Frequently heard wolf-whistled call a slow and drawled "wheeeip, wheeeur," first note slurred up, second slurred down; somewhat recalls song of Barred Puffbird. Song a somewhat snappier series of notes, e.g., "wheee-per, wheeéur."

Sirystes Sirystes
Distinctive gray, black, and white flycatchers that recall Myiarchus except in color. They range in forest canopy on either side of the Andes and were formerly considered conspecific.

Eastern Sirystes, *Sirystes sibilator*
Siristes Oriental   Plate 74(2)

18.5 cm (7¼"). Uncommon in canopy and borders of humid forest (especially *várzea and floodplain*) in *lowlands of east*. Does not include Western Sirystes. *Crown black*, shading to slaty on sides of head, contrasting with *mottled gray back* and *white rump*; wings and tail blackish, wing-coverts and inner flight feathers edged pale grayish. *Throat and breast pale gray, belly white*. **Similar species:** *Myiarchus*-like in shape and behavior, but with very different black, gray, and white pattern; against the light they can

To 400 m

look similar. Western Sirystes occurs only west of Andes. **Habits:** Found singly or in pairs, often accompanying mixed flocks. Often leans forward alertly, nodding head and ruffling its crown feathers when it can look bushy-crested (and in silhouette quite like a *Myiarchus* flycatcher). **Voice:** Rather vocal, with loud calls often drawing attention, including a "wheeer-péw" or "wheeer-péwpu," sometimes extended in an excited series, "wheeer-pe-pe-pew-pew-péw" or "wheeer-péw-péw-péw."

Western Sirystes, *Sirystes albogriseus*
Siristes Occidental   Plate 74(1)

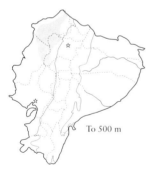

To 500 m

18.5 cm (7¹/₄″). *Uncommon and local in canopy and borders of humid forest in lowlands and lower foothills of northwest.* Formerly considered conspecific with Eastern Sirystes, found east of Andes. *Crown black*, shading to slaty on sides of head, contrasting with *gray back* and *white rump*; wings and tail blackish, *wing-coverts and inner flight feathers broadly and conspicuously edged white*, tail narrowly tipped white. *Throat and breast pale gray, belly white*. **Similar species:** Like Eastern Sirystes

(which occurs only east of Andes), this species recalls a *Myiarchus* flycatcher, though it is colored very differently. **Habits:** Much as in Eastern Sirystes. **Voice:** Most frequent call a husky "chup-chip-chip" or "prup-prip-prip-prip." Excited birds give a much faster "che-che-che-che-che-che-chut" (P. Coopmans).

Myiarchus Flycatchers
A distinctive and homogeneous group of midsized flycatchers with *somewhat expressive bushy crests* and *very similar overall patterns* with gray on the throat and breast contrasting with a yellow belly. Details of bill color, crown pattern and color, and tail pattern are crucial for identification, *usually in conjunction with their voice and distribution* (often the most important of all). All have the characteristic habit of leaning forward on their perch, often nodding or pumping their head. Nests are shallow cups placed inside tree cavities and often lined with pieces of snakeskin (sometimes fur or even insect wings).

Dusky-capped Flycatcher
Myiarchus tuberculifer
Copetón Crestioscuro   Plate 73(19)

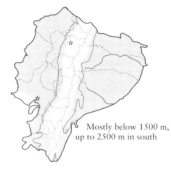

Mostly below 1500 m, up to 2500 m in south

16–17 cm (6¹/₄–6³/₄″). *Widespread* in canopy and borders of humid and deciduous forest and woodland and clearings in *lowlands of west*, in *foothill and subtropical forest and borders in south*, and in humid forest (both terra firme and várzea) in *lowlands of east*. *Except in the south, a relatively small Myiarchus*. **Western birds** have *sooty black crown* contrasting with dark olive back; wings and tail dusky, wings with two grayish to buff wing-bars and some rufous primary edging. Throat and breast pale gray, contrasting with yellow belly. **Juvenile** has more rufescent wing-edging. **Southern birds** similar (equally black-crowned) but larger. **Eastern birds** are the same size as western birds but have *crown dark sepia brown*. **Similar species:** Except in s. highlands, Dusky-capped is smaller than other *Myiarchus*, reducing likelihood of confusion. In southwest, cf. especially Sooty-crowned; in east, cf. especially Short-crested. Pale-edged Flycatcher—which also ranges in s. highlands—lacks black on crown. **Habits:** Usually found singly or in pairs, perching at varying levels (higher in continuous forest, lower at borders; rarely actually inside forest); often fluffs crown and throat feathers. Makes short sallies in pursuit of insects, sometimes even dropping to the ground; also eats considerable fruit. Often accompanies mixed flocks, but at least as often solitary. **Voice:** Frequently heard call a plaintive whistle, "wheeeuw" or "fueeerrr," given at times throughout day (often even when other birds are quiet). Sometimes this clear whistle is followed, a few seconds later, by a burry and more trilled "d'd'tírrr" (P. Coopmans).

Swainson's Flycatcher, *Myiarchus swainsoni*
Copetón de Swainson   Plate 73(16)

Below 400 m

18 cm (7"). A *scarce austral migrant* (Apr.–Sep.) to shrubby clearings, river and lake margins, and river islands in *lowlands of east. Lower mandible pale brown to pinkish* (sometimes only at base). *Rather pale grayish olive above*, one race with *contrastingly darker ear-coverts*; wings duskier with two vague whitish wing-bars and edging; tail blackish with pale outer web. Throat and breast pale gray, belly pale yellow. **Similar species:** A pale and "faded" looking *Myiarchus* that usually shows a distinctly pale lower mandible. Other *Myiarchus* occurring in e. lowlands (Short-crested and Dusky-capped) have all-black bills. Cf. also Large Elaenia. **Habits:** Usually found singly, with behavior much as in Short-crested Flycatcher. **Voice:** Seems quiet on its Ecuadorian wintering grounds.

Short-crested Flycatcher, *Myiarchus ferox*
Copetón Cresticorto   Plate 73(15)

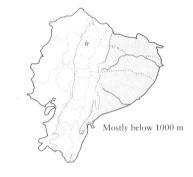

Mostly below 1000 m

18 cm (7"). Fairly common at borders of humid forest and woodland and in shrubby clearings in *lowlands and foothills of east. Bill all black. Rather dark olivaceous brown above*, sootiest on head; wings dusky with two pale grayish wing-bars and edging; tail uniform dusky. Throat and breast gray, belly clear yellow. **Juvenile** has more rufescent wing edging. **Similar species:** Swainson's Flycatcher is paler generally, and the pale color on its lower mandible is normally evident (vs. Short-crested's all-black bill). **Habits:** Found singly or in pairs, usually foraging in semiopen close to the ground, and regularly near water. By far the most frequently encountered *Myiarchus* in the e. lowlands. **Voice:** Frequently heard call a distinctive soft rolling "prrrt" or "dr'r'r'ru."

Pale-edged Flycatcher, *Myiarchus cephalotes*
Copetón Filipálido   Plate 73(17)

18 cm (7"). Canopy and borders of *subtropical forest, woodland, and adjacent clearings on e. slope*. Bill black. *Above uniform brownish olive* (with no contrasting color on crown); wings with two pale grayish wing-

Mostly 1000–2200 m

and breast pale gray, belly clear yellow. **Similar species:** Dusky-capped Flycatcher is smaller, and differs further in having fully blackish crown, brighter yellow belly, and some rufous edging in primaries. **Habits:** Similar to other *Myiarchus*. **Voice:** Most frequent call a querulous "freeee?" or "whreee?" Song combines this whistled note with low burry "tr-ret" notes; also has a descending "wheeé-deee-deee-de-du-du" (P. Coopmans).

Great Crested Flycatcher, *Myiarchus crinitus*
Copetón Viajero   Plate 73(20)

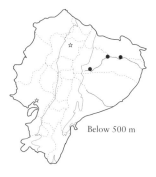

Below 500 m

bars and edging; tail blackish with *distinctly pale outer web on outermost pair of feathers.* Throat and breast pale gray, belly clear yellow. **Similar species:** Short-crested Flycatcher, which marginally overlaps with Pale-edged in lower subtropics, *lacks* pale outer edge to tail but otherwise is quite similar. Cf. also Sierran Elaenia. **Habits:** Similar to other *Myiarchus*; though forest-based, Pale-edged often forages quite low in clearings. **Voice:** Song a fast "piyp! peeyur" followed by several "peer" notes; call a loud, clear "pip" or "piup" repeated over and over (W. Lanyon).

Sooty-crowned Flycatcher
Myiarchus phaeocephalus
Copetón Coronitiznado   Plate 73(18)

To 1100 m

18 cm (7″). *Deciduous woodland, arid scrub, and clearings in lowlands and foothills of west,* also in Río Marañón drainage around Zumba. Bill black. *Forecrown ashy gray, becoming blackish on hindcrown,* latter contrasting with grayish olive back; wings dusky with two pale grayish wing-bars and edging; tail blackish *with pale tip and outer web of outermost pair of feathers.* Throat

20 cm (8″). A *casual boreal migrant* (Feb.–Mar.) to canopy and borders of humid forest, secondary woodland, and clearings in lowlands of east. Lower mandible horn-colored at least at base. Olivaceous brown above; wings with two whitish wing-bars and *rufous primary edging; tail feathers with inner webs rufous* (resulting in an almost solidly rufous underside to tail). Throat and breast gray, belly yellow. **Similar species:** This large *Myiarchus* should be readily recognized by its quite conspicuous rufous in wings and tail, not shared by any congener in Ecuador. Its calls (see below) are also diagnostic. **Habits:** Similar to other *Myiarchus*, though this arboreal species seems to remain inside forest and woodland more than the others. **Voice:** Distinctive call a loud and frequently given "whreeep?" with decided upward inflection.

Great Kiskadee, *Pitangus sulphuratus*
Bienteveo Grande   Plate 74(23)

21 cm (8¼″). Fairly common along margins of lakes and rivers and in clearings and gardens in *lowlands and foothills of east.*

To about 1000 m

Mostly below 500 m

Black bill quite heavy and straight. Head black with semiconcealed yellow coronal patch and a long broad white superciliary; *wing and tail feathers conspicuously margined rufous.* Throat white, underparts bright yellow. **Similar species:** Boat-billed Flycatcher has markedly more massive bill with arched culmen, is more olive above with less rufous wing and tail edging; its arboreal behavior differs, and its vocalizations are entirely different. Lesser Kiskadee is a less robust bird very closely tied to water; its bill is decidedly long and slender. **Habits:** A noisy and familiar bird, though in fact not as "dominant" in Ecuador as it is many other parts of its wide range. Kiskadees often perch low and fully in the open, and can be very unwary, even brazen and pugnacious; they regularly range around houses. They consume a variety of food, mostly insects and fruit, but they also plunge into water after fish and pursue small vertebrates such as lizards and even snakes, and sometimes even rob nests of other birds. **Voice:** Often very noisy, Great Kiskadees give a variety of loud calls of which the best known and most frequent is a boisterous "kis-ka-dee!," reflected in English name. This can be varied to a "geép geép ga-reér" or simply a shrill, raptor-like "keeeer."

Lesser Kiskadee, *Philohydor lictor*
Bienteveo Menor   Plate 74(24)

17 cm (6¼"). *Along margins of lakes and sluggish streams and rivers,* also in marshy shrubby pastures, in *lowlands of east.* Formerly placed in genus *Pitangus. Bill long and slender. Pattern and coloration virtually identical to Great Kiskadee,* with which Lesser regularly occurs. Lesser differs in its

markedly smaller size, very different bill shape, and *strikingly different vocalizations.* **Similar species:** Also resembles, and is often with, the similarly patterned Social Flycatcher; Social differs most notably in its short stubby bill, and in vocalizations. **Habits:** Usually in pairs, invariably near water and most often not foraging more than a few meters above water's surface (Great Kiskadee will sometimes perch high, but Lesser never does). Forages by sallying for insects to foliage and water's surface. **Voice:** Nasal, raspy calls are distinctive but decidedly subdued compared to Great's. Most frequent is a "dzreeéy, dzwee" or "dzreeéy, dzwee-dzwee-dzwee."

Boat-billed Flycatcher, *Megarynchus pitangua*
Mosquero Picudo   Plate 74(22)

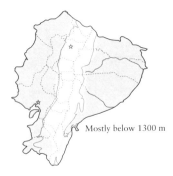

Mostly below 1300 m

23 cm (9"). *Widespread* in canopy and borders of humid and deciduous forest and woodland and clearings with large trees in *lowlands of east and west. Black bill very heavy and broad,* with arched culmen. Crown blackish with semiconcealed yellow coronal patch (more tawny-orange in **western birds**), long broad white superciliary,

and black sides of head; otherwise brownish olive above, wings and tail dusky with *only a little* rufous edging on both. Throat white, underparts bright yellow. **Similar species:** Similarly patterned and colored Great Kiskadee has a differently shaped bill (not as wide, and with straight culmen); it is browner above and shows more rufous wing and tail edging, but the two species are usually first differentiated by their very different vocalizations. **Habits:** Though noisy, Boat-billed is not nearly as conspicuous as Great Kiskadee, being more arboreal and less apt to perch low and in the open (though occasionally one will do just that). Ranges in pairs through treetops, sometimes with mixed flocks but usually solitary. Eats mainly large insects such as cicadas, often loudly beating prey against a branch before swallowing it; also consumes some fruit, but is nowhere near as omnivorous as the kiskadee. **Voice:** Most frequent call in east a strident, nasal "kryeeeh-nyeh-nyeh-nyeh," sometimes given as it pumps head. In the west gives a fast "kreh-kreh-kreh-kreh-kreh-kreeeenh" and a series of "kirrr-wick" calls.

Myiozetetes Flycatchers

Midsized, *boldly patterned* (all but one species) flycatchers that are *widespread, conspicuous, and often common in cleared areas and forest borders in the lowlands.* Unlike other flycatchers with comparable patterns and colors, *bills are short and stubby.* Nests are fairly large and untidy roofed structures with a wide side entrance, often placed near a wasp nest.

Social Flycatcher, *Myiozetetes similis*
Mosquero Social   Plate 74(26)

17 cm (6¾"). *Common and widespread* in shrubby clearings and plantations, humid forest and woodland borders, and around houses in *lowlands and foothills of east and west.* Short black bill. *Crown dark gray with semiconcealed red to orange-red coronal patch, long broad white superciliary,* and blackish sides of head; otherwise olive above; wings and tail dusky, wings with narrow pale grayish to pale buffyish edging. Throat white, underparts bright yellow. **Juvenile** may show some rufous edging in wings. **Similar species:** West of Andes, Social must be separated from

Mostly below 1400 m

Rusty-margined Flycatcher (which is not definitely known to occur east of Andes); for discussion, see that species. Gray-capped Flycatcher lacks long white brow. East of Andes also must be distinguished from similarly colored Lesser Kiskadee; that species has much longer and more slender bill. **Habits:** A conspicuous and noisy bird, omnipresent in semiopen, cutover terrain and also frequent around towns and farm buildings. Perches, sometimes partially cocking its tail, everywhere from ground to canopy of tall trees (though infrequent or lacking in canopy of more continuous forest), and is especially numerous near water. Sallies to foliage for insects (less often into air), but also eats a good deal of fruit, which is both plucked while perched and snatched while hovering. **Voice:** Gives a variety of calls, most of them quite harsh, including a frequent "kreeoouw." East of Andes has a chattered "ti-ti-ti-tíchew, chew" (also gives single "chew" or "chek" calls); west of Andes a chattered "kree-kree-kree."

Rusty-margined Flycatcher
Myiozetetes cayanensis
Mosquero Alicastaño   Plate 74(25)

17 cm (6¾"). Fairly common—*especially near water*—in shrubby clearings and plantations, and humid forest and woodland borders in *lowlands and foothills of west*; no confirmed records from east. Resembles Social Flycatcher, and regularly found together with it; *often the two are best distinguished by voice.* Rusty-margined's coronal patch is yellow-orange, not that different from Social's patch (which is often not truly red). Rusty-margined differs further in its blacker crown and sides of head, lack of pale

Mostly below 1000 m

edging on wing-coverts, and *obvious rufous primary edging* (but beware juvenile Socials which may show this too; *these will also show obvious pale edging on coverts*). **Habits:** Similar to Social Flycatcher. **Voice:** Most frequent and distinctive call a whining and almost plaintive, nearly evenly pitched "freeeea" or "wheeeeea," not very loud, somewhat recalling Dusky-capped Flycatcher. Also gives other faster, excited calls (sometimes in a duet) that recall the Social, including a "cheepcheeree-chew" and a fast repeated "keewít."

Gray-capped Flycatcher
Myiozetetes granadensis
Mosquero Cabecigris   Plate 74(27)

Mostly below 1000 m

17 cm (6¾"). Common and noisy in borders of humid forest and woodland and in shrubby clearings, often near water, in *lowlands and foothills of east and northwest*. Iris pale brownish gray. *Head gray with semi-concealed orange-red coronal patch and only a short and narrow white superciliary* (extending back only to just over eye); otherwise olive above; wings and tail duskier,

wings with narrow pale olive edging. Throat white, underparts bright yellow. ♀ has crown patch reduced or lacking. **Juvenile** has olive tinge to crown, some buff edging on wings and tail. **Similar species:** Social and Rusty-margined Flycatchers have much more striking facial patterns with a bold white brow; in a few places in the northwest, all three species occur together. The considerably larger Tropical Kingbird has an olive chest, notched tail, and longer bill; it lacks Gray-capped's pale brow. In east cf. rarer Dusky-chested Flycatcher. **Habits:** Similar to Social Flycatcher, though more tied to forest and more often ranging in actual forest canopy. Like the Social, eats both insects and fruit. **Voice:** Most calls are sharper than Social's—some rival Great Kiskadee's in strength and intensity—and include a "kip!" often repeated in a long series and "kip, keer, k-beer" or "kip, keer, kew-kew." Dawn song of western birds a "kip, kip, kip, keeuw-kreh" phrase lasting 2–3 seconds (O. Jahn recording), of eastern birds a faster "kip, kip, kip, kip, kip, kip, ke-ke-kree-yí" phrase lasting 1–2 seconds (P. Coopmans recording).

Dusky-chested Flycatcher
Myiozetetes luteiventris
Mosquero Pechioscuro   Plate 74(10)

To 600 m

14.5 cm (5¾"). *Scarce* in canopy and borders of terra firme forest in *lowlands of east*. Formerly sometimes placed in genus *Tyrannopsis*. *Uniform dark olive brown above* with semiconcealed yellow-orange coronal patch. Throat whitish vaguely streaked dusky; underparts bright yellow, *flammulated with olive on breast*. **Similar species:** Smaller than other *Myiozetetes*, from which it also differs in its *unmarked* head and breast streaking. Gray-capped, because it too lacks a broad white brow, is the most similar. Also cf. larger Sulphury Flycatcher, and Piratic Flycatcher. **Habits:** Much less often encountered than other *Myiozetetes*, doubtless in part because of its habit of almost always remaining in forest canopy. Other than that, behaves (and sounds) much like other *Myiozetetes*. Does not accompany mixed flocks, though a pair sometimes congregates with other birds at fruiting trees. **Voice:** Has excited-sounding calls that recall Gray-capped's and include a fast nasal "nyeeuw-nyeeuw-keep-kít," sometimes given as a jumbled duet, also a repeated "nyeeuw."

Conopias Flycatchers

Myiozetetes-like flycatchers that differ from that genus in their *longer and more slender bills*, the four *Conopias* in Ecuador occur mainly in the canopy of lowland humid forest, one species (Lemon-browed) in the subtropics.

Lemon-browed Flycatcher
Conopias cinchoneti
Mosquero Cejilimón   Plate 74(17)

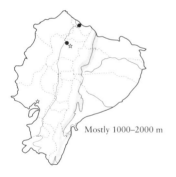

Mostly 1000–2000 m

16 cm (6¼"). *Uncommon in borders of subtropical forest and adjacent clearings on e. slope and on w. slope in far north*. Above olive with *long broad pale yellow superciliary extending back from forehead nearly to nape*; wings and tail dusky. Below bright yellow, somewhat clouded olive on sides. **Similar species:** No other similar flycatcher has a *yellow* brow; if a brow is present, it is *white*. **Habits:** Found in well-separated pairs or family groups; they seem to have large home ranges, and often seem restless, rarely

remaining for long in one place. Lemon-broweds often perch fully in open on leaves or bare branches, calling frequently and drawing attention to themselves. Eat both insects and fruit, both usually obtained in flight. Pairs apparently nest in old, disused oropendola and cacique nests. **Voice:** Distinctive, far-carrying call a series of shrill notes, e.g., "pi-dee!" or "di-d'reeee," often rapidly repeated. Calling birds often vigorously pump their head.

White-ringed Flycatcher, *Conopias albovittata*
Mosquero Aureola   Plate 74(15)

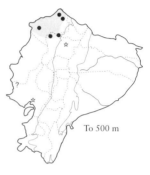

To 500 m

16.5 cm (6½"). *Canopy and borders of humid forest in lowlands and lower foothills in far northwest*. Does not include Yellow-throated Flycatcher, found east of Andes, with which formerly sometimes considered conspecific; sometimes placed in genus *Coryphotriccus*. Head black with semiconcealed yellow coronal patch and *long broad white superciliary extending back from forehead to encircle nape*; otherwise dark olive above, wings and tail duskier. Throat white; underparts bright yellow. **Similar species:** Social and Rusty-margined Flycatchers have stubbier bills and a white superciliary that does not "wrap around" nape; they differ markedly in vocalizations. **Habits:** Usually in pairs or family groups that remain well above ground, rarely coming lower even at borders. White-ringeds often perch on top of leaves, scanning nearby foliage and sallying out to snatch insects from upper surface of leaves; they regularly accompany mixed flocks. **Voice:** Distinctive call a dry, fast, whirring or rattling trill, "tree-r-r-r-r, tree-r-r-r-r . . . ," that commences with a longer note.

Yellow-throated Flycatcher, *Conopias parva*
Mosquero Goliamarillo   Plate 74(14)

16.5 cm (6½″). Status uncertain; known from *only a few records* in canopy of terra firme forest in *lowlands of far east*. Formerly sometimes considered conspecific with White-ringed Flycatcher, found west of Andes. Resembles that species, differing in its *entirely yellow underparts* (including throat). Similar species: Equally rare and local Three-striped Flycatcher is smaller, paler olive on back, and lacks a coronal patch (Yellow-throated's admittedly hard to see in field); it is best told by its different calls (below). Habits: Similar to White-ringed Flycatcher. Voice: Distinctive call a loud, ringing, rhythmic "kluyuyu kluyuyu kluyuyu . . . ," sometimes continued for long periods.

Three-striped Flycatcher, *Conopias trivirgata*
Mosquero Trirrayado   Plate 74(16)

14 cm (5½″). *Rare and local in canopy and borders of várzea forest in lowlands of far northeast.* Head blackish with long broad white superciliary (but no coronal patch); otherwise *rather pale olive above, wings and*

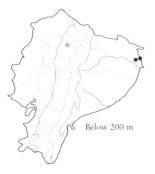

tail contrastingly duskier. Below bright yellow. Similar species: Social Flycatcher is larger and has stubbier bill, white throat, and usually prominent pale edging on wing feathers (wings much less marked in Three-striped, also contrasting more with olive back). Cf. also Yellow-throated Flycatcher. Habits: Not well known in Ecuador. Similar to White-ringed Flycatcher, remaining high in forest canopy and—unless vocalizing—easy to overlook. Voice: Distinctive call a harsh, grating "jew" or "jeeuw," often repeated rapidly.

Myiodynastes Flycatchers
Large, heavy-bodied flycatchers with heavy bills, *Myiodynastes* is a rather heterogeneous genus, two species with prominently streaked plumage. All are noisy and conspicuous. Nests are placed in the holes of trees and crevices.

Streaked Flycatcher, *Myiodynastes maculatus*
Mosquero Rayado   Plate 74(19)

20.5 cm (8″). A *large* and *boldly streaked* flycatcher, *widespread* in canopy and borders of humid forest and woodland and adjacent clearings in lowlands and foothills of east and west. In the east mainly in várzea and riparian habitats (both residents and austral migrants, the latter Apr.–Aug.); in the west also in more deciduous habitats. Lower mandible flesh-colored at base. Resident birds *brown above streaked with dusky*, with semiconcealed yellow coronal patch, *whitish superciliary*, broad blackish area across face and ear-coverts, whitish lower cheeks, and prominent dusky malar streak. Wings dusky with narrow rufous to buff edging; *rump and tail mainly rufous*. Throat white, underparts whitish to pale yellowish *broadly streaked dusky especially across breast and down flanks and on crissum.* **Austral migrants** (only in east) are markedly darker above with *broad blackish streaking,* and have *bolder and more extensive streaking below,* whitish edging on wing-coverts and inner flight feathers, and a *mainly blackish tail* with only narrow rufous edging. **Similar species:** Cf. Sulphur-bellied Flycatcher. Variegated Flycatcher smaller with stubbier bill, blackish crown; it is less obviously streaked. **Habits:** Found singly or in pairs, and usually noisy and conspicuous (though austral migrants seem less vocal). Especially in the west, sometimes around houses. Pursues a variety of insects, some captured in aerial sallies, others in sallies to foliage; also eats considerable fruit. **Voice:** Has a variety of loud and harsh vocalizations, most frequent being a "kip!," also a "chup" or "eechup," all sometimes repeated interminably. More musical song, given at dawn and dusk (even when nearly dark), is a fast and rhythmic "wheeé-cheederee-wheé" (sometimes without final "wheé"); it can also be given repeatedly.

Sulphur-bellied Flycatcher
Myiodynastes luteiventris
Mosquero Ventriazufrado   Plate 74(18)

Below 400 m

20.5 cm (8″). A *boreal winter visitant* (mostly Oct.–Apr.) to canopy and borders of humid forest and woodland, riparian areas, and shrubby clearings in *lowlands of east.* Resembles better-known Streaked Flycatcher. Differs from resident races of that species as follows: *broad dusky malar stripe joined across chin* (forming a "chin strap"), little or no rufous edging on primaries, and *ground color of lower underparts usually distinctly clear*

sulphur yellow with unstreaked crissum. **Habits:** Similar to Streaked Flycatcher. **Voice:** Often quiet, but may give a loud and forceful "squeez!-ya" or just a repeated "squeez!"

Baird's Flycatcher, *Myiodynastes bairdii*
Mosquero de Baird   Plate 74(20)

To 1000 m

23 cm (9″). An impressive-looking, *large* flycatcher of *deciduous woodland, arid scrub, and towns in lowlands of southwest.* Heavy, mainly blackish bill. *Broad black mask from forehead back through eyes onto ear-coverts,* surmounted by sandy brown crown (palest above mask) with semiconcealed yellow coronal patch; back olive brown, becoming rufous on rump. Wings dusky, *feathers very broadly edged rufous; tail mostly rufous,* outer feathers edged dusky. Throat whitish, becoming ochraceous on breast, both obscurely streaked with grayish; belly pale yellow. **Similar species:** Nothing really similar. Golden-crowned Flycatcher occurs only in montane areas. **Habits:** Usually found in pairs and often conspicuous, perching in the open at varying levels on branches, fences, and wires. Forages mainly for large insects, sallying mainly to foliage, also dropping to the ground; also eats much fruit. **Voice:** Call, given mainly in early morning (also at dusk), a rather infrequently heard "wrrr-yeeít . . . wrrr-yeeít . . . ," steadily repeated at 2 to 4-second intervals. Sometimes several of these phrases are followed by an ascending jumbled phrase (P. Coopmans).

Golden-crowned Flycatcher
Myiodynastes chrysocephalus
Mosquero Coronidorado   Plate 74(21)

20.5 cm (8″). *Borders of foothill and subtropical forest and woodland and adjacent*

Mostly 1000–2200 m

Mostly below 800 m

clearings on both slopes. Crown brownish gray with semiconcealed yellow coronal patch, long broad white superciliary, and broad dusky area across face onto ear-coverts; otherwise olive above. Wings and tail dusky with fairly prominent rufous edging. *Lower cheeks and throat pale buff, separated by dusky malar stripe;* underparts yellow, *breast clouded and flammulated with olive.* **Similar species:** In general form reminiscent of Great Kiskadee or Boat-billed Flycatcher, neither of which occurs in *montane* areas inhabited by this large flycatcher; in any case, they show neither malar stripe nor breast streaking. Streaked Flycatcher is basically a lowland bird, and much more generally streaked. Cf. also Baird's Flycatcher. **Habits:** Found singly or in pairs, perching at varying levels though most often not very high; favors areas along rushing mountain streams. Sometimes joins mixed flocks, but usually solitary. Eats both insects and fruit. **Voice:** A rather noisy bird, with loud raucous calls including a squealing "skweé-ah!" or "squeeé-yu," both repeated insistently. Dawn song a repeated "squeeé-yu-d'r'r" (P. Coopmans).

Piratic Flycatcher, *Legatus leucophaius*
Mosquero Pirata   Plate 74(11)

14.5 cm (5¾"). Borders of humid forest and woodland and *especially tall trees in adjacent clearings in lowlands of east and west.* *Persistently vocal when breeding,* otherwise inconspicuous. *Stubby black bill. Uniform dark olive brown above* with semiconcealed yellow coronal patch, *long whitish superciliary,* blackish face, *whitish malar area,* and dusky submalar streak. Wings plain and dusky, tail blackish. Throat and breast

whitish, breast with blurry dusky-brown streaking, becoming pale yellow on lower belly and crissum. **Similar species:** Variegated Flycatcher (austral migrant to east) has a similar pattern but is larger with a longer bill, more mottled back, much more pale edging on wings, and rufous on uppertail-coverts and tail edging. **Habits:** Inconspicuous except when singing, remaining high in trees and usually hard to see well. Eats mainly small fruits. Pairs usurp nests of various other birds, especially those of oropendolas and caciques but also many others, incessantly harassing its rightful owners until they give it up. **Voice:** ♂ sings tirelessly when breeding, repeating a whining querulous "weé-yee," sometimes followed by a fast "pi-ri-ri-ri-ri"; it may continue through heat of day. Also gives an endlessly continued "pee-pee-pee-pee-pee . . ." (J. Moore recording).

Variegated Flycatcher, *Empidonomus varius*
Mosquero Variegado   Plate 74(12)

18.5 cm (7¼"). An *uncommon austral migrant* (Mar.–Sep.) to riparian growth, shrubby clearings, and forest and woodland borders in *lowlands of east.* Head blackish

To 500 m

with semiconcealed yellow crown patch, long whitish superciliary, whitish malar area, and dusky submalar streak; *back dusky brown mottled and streaked whitish*, uppertail-coverts rufous. Wings dusky, *feathers prominently edged whitish*; tail blackish, feathers edged rufous. Throat whitish; underparts yellowish white with profuse dusky-brown streaking. **Similar species:** Piratic Flycatcher much smaller with stubbier bill and plain brown back; it lacks pale wing-edging and rufous on tail. Streaked Flycatcher considerably larger with longer and heavier bill, and more coarsely streaked below. **Habits:** Usually seen singly on its wintering grounds, though sometimes several congregate with other tyrannids in a fruiting tree. **Voice:** Generally quiet, but occasionally a bird will voice a high-pitched and thin "pseee."

Crowned Slaty Flycatcher
Griseotyrannus aurantioatrocristatus
Mosquero Coronado   Plate 74(13)

Mostly below 1100 m

18 cm (7″). A *fairly common austral migrant* (mostly Mar.–Sep.) to clearings with scattered trees and forest borders and canopy in *lowlands of east*. Formerly placed in genus *Empidonomus*. *Brownish gray above* with *contrasting black crown*, semiconcealed yellow coronal patch, gray superciliary, and dusky ear-coverts. *Uniform smoky gray below*, paler and tinged yellowish on belly. **Similar species:** This conspicuous flycatcher appears very uniform and often looks distinctively *flat-crowned* as well. **Habits:** Usually solitary, almost always perching fully in the open, frequently in the crown of trees or on snags. Often sallies repeatedly into the air, like a pewee or kingbird often returning to same branch over and over. Also

eats some fruit (but less than Variegated). **Voice:** Seems very quiet on its wintering grounds.

Sulphury Flycatcher, *Tyrannopsis sulphurea*
Mosquero Azufrado   Plate 74(9)

Below 400 m

19 cm (7½″). Scarce and local, primarily around groves of *Mauritia* palms, in *lowlands of east*. Recalls a chunky, short-tailed *Tropical Kingbird*. Head gray, somewhat darker and duskier on face, with semiconcealed yellow coronal patch; back dull brownish olive, *becoming brownish dusky on wings and rather short squared tail*. *Midthroat and upper chest white with some gray streaking*, grayer on sides of throat and olive on sides of chest; breast and belly bright yellow. **Similar species:** Much more common Tropical Kingbird is larger and has a longer and distinctly notched tail; though also olive on chest, it shows no streaking and its throat is not as contrastingly white. Dusky-chested Flycatcher is much smaller with stubbier bill and browner upperparts. **Habits:** Almost always in pairs that tend to be inconspicuous as they perch high on palm fronds and often are quiet for long periods, then may burst into a frenzy of activity with much calling. Feeds mainly on aerial insects, often sallying long distances; also eats some fruit. **Voice:** Calls varied, but all are high-pitched and piercing, sometimes with harsh quality, sometimes squeaky; they include a fast "jee-peet! jee-peeteet, jeepeet!" and a "squeezrr-squeezrr-prrr."

Tyrannus Flycatchers and Kingbirds
The genus *Tyrannus* includes one of Ecuador's most numerous and conspicuous birds, the Tropical Kingbird, but the other

members of the genus are considerably less numerous here, with two species (White-throated and Gray) being no more than casual wanderers. They inhabit open or semi-open terrain, and most are migratory, some strongly so. Nests are shallow cups placed in forks in trees, sometimes in the semiopen.

Tropical Kingbird, *Tyrannus melancholicus*
Tirano Tropical   Plate 74(5)

Mostly below 1800 m

21.5 cm (8½″). *Very common and conspicuous in open and semiopen areas, including built-up areas and towns, in lowlands and foothills of east and west*; in such regions one of most frequently seen birds. Less numerous in extensively forested regions and desert-like areas. *Head gray* with *somewhat contrasting darker mask through eyes* and semiconcealed orange coronal patch; otherwise grayish olive above. Wings and tail brownish dusky, wing feathers narrowly edged paler, *rather long tail slightly forked*. Throat pale grayish becoming grayish olive on chest; underparts bright yellow. **Similar species:** Because it so soon becomes familiar, use Tropical Kingbird as basis of comparison with scarcer kingbirds and various other flycatchers. Cf. especially White-throated and Snowy-throated Kingbirds, and Gray-capped and Sulphury Flycatchers. **Habits:** Seen singly or in pairs (though flocks of possible austral migrants have been noted in east), usually perching fully in the open on exposed branches and wires and often remaining active through hot midday periods, one of few birds habitually to do so. Eats mainly insects captured during long and sometimes intricate sallies, also consumes considerable fruit. **Voice:** Has a variety of high-pitched twittering calls, e.g., "pee, ee-ee-ee-ee". ♂'s dawn song a short series of

"pip" or "pee" notes followed by a rising twitter, "piririree?" (often 2–3 of these rising twitters); this is frequently one of first bird sounds to greet the new dawn, sometimes given before first light.

White-throated Kingbird, *Tyrannus albogularis*
Tirano Goliblanco   Plate 74(6)

Below 300 m

21 cm (8¼″). A *very rare austral migrant* (Jul.–Aug.) to forest borders and riparian areas in *lowlands of east*. Resembles much more numerous Tropical Kingbird. Differs in its *notably paler gray head*, which therefore *contrasts more with dark mask*; paler and brighter olive back; *pure white throat* which contrasts with bright yellow underparts, with *only a faint tinge of olive on chest* (much less than in Tropical Kingbird). **Similar species:** In strong midday light Tropical Kingbirds can look quite pale-headed and white-throated, but they never show such a contrasting "mask." Snowy-throated Kingbird occurs only west of Andes. **Habits:** Similar to Tropical Kingbird. In Ecuador all birds seen have been solitary individuals, sometimes consorting with Tropicals. **Voice:** Appears to be essentially silent on its wintering grounds.

Snowy-throated Kingbird
Tyrannus niveigularis
Tirano Goliníveo   Plate 74(8)

19 cm (7½″). *Breeds in desert scrub, shrubby areas, and woodland borders in lowlands of southwest*, migrating north during non-breeding season (Jun.–Nov.). Crown gray with blackish mask through eyes and semi-concealed yellow coronal patch; *back pale olivaceous gray*. Wings dusky, *coverts and inner flight feathers edged whitish*; tail blackish, nearly square. *Throat white* becoming

Mostly below 500 m

pale gray on breast and clear pale yellow on belly. **Similar species:** Tropical Kingbird is larger, darker and more olive on back, and has less pallid underparts (grayer on throat, more olive on chest, brighter yellow on belly); its tail is distinctly notched. White-throated Kingbird occurs only east of Andes. **Habits:** Much as in Tropical Kingbird; it and the attractive Snowy-throated sometimes breed in the same areas though the latter favors more arid regions; when not breeding the two species also routinely occur together. **Voice:** Shorter and drier than comparable calls of Tropical Kingbird, including a sharp "kip!" that can be extended into a "kip! kr-r-ee-ee-ee." Dawn song a fast and jumbled "ki-ki-ki-kr-reé-it!," not as shrill as Tropical's (P. Coopmans).

[Gray Kingbird, *Tyrannus dominicensis*
Tirano Gris]   Plate 74(7)

21.5 cm (8½"). An *accidental vagrant* to El Oro coast. *Rather heavy bill. Gray above* with *dusky mask through eyes* and semiconcealed orange coronal patch; wings dusky, coverts and inner flight feathers edged whitish; tail dusky and *slightly forked. White*

below, tinged gray especially across breast. **Similar species:** Snowy-throated Kingbird is somewhat smaller with a pale yellow belly and nearly squared-off tail. In strong light Tropical Kingbird can look very washed out and pale below. **Habits:** Much as in other kingbirds. The El Oro bird was at edge of mangroves.

Eastern Kingbird, *Tyrannus tyrannus*
Tirano Norteño   Plate 74(4)

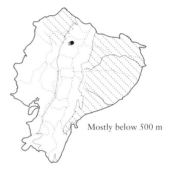

Mostly below 500 m

20.5 cm (8"). A *boreal migrant* (Oct.–Apr.) to humid forest borders and clearings in *lowlands of east*, most numerous as a transient (Oct.–Nov. and Mar.–Apr.); stragglers elsewhere. Bill relatively small. *Slaty above, blackest on head* with semiconcealed coronal patch yellow-orange. Wings duskier, wing-coverts and inner flight feathers edged whitish; squared tail black with *white tip. Whitish below*, clouded with gray on breast. Adults in worn plumage can look faded, and may show little or no white in tail. **Similar species:** Juvenile and heavily worn adult Fork-tailed Flycatchers may lack tail streamers, in which case they can look surprisingly similar to this kingbird, though almost invariably a tail cleft is apparent. Fork-taileds further differ in their more distinctly black-capped look, paler gray back and purer white underparts, and they never show any white tail-tipping. **Habits:** Often in flocks, sometimes quite large, and frequently seen migrating by day in compact groups low over forest canopy, pausing at forest edge and along lakeshores and rivers. During passage may consort with Fork-tailed Flycatchers, less often with Tropical Kingbirds and other tyrannids. Eastern Kingbirds are primarily frugivorous in Ecuador, but especially during northward passage they commence sallying after aerial insects like other kingbirds. **Voice:** On its wintering grounds eerily—to those familiar with its boisterous behavior when breeding—silent; a few soft chatters are sometimes given by resting or roosting birds.

Fork-tailed Flycatcher, *Tyrannus savana*
Tijereta Sabanera   Plate 74(3)

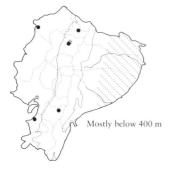

Mostly below 400 m

♂ 38–40 cm (15–16″), ♀ 28–30 cm (11–12″), including *very long, deeply forked tail* (shorter in ♀♀, immatures, and molting birds). Irregular austral winter visitant (mostly Mar.–Sep.), but often numerous during passage periods, to humid forest borders and clearings in *lowlands of east*; stragglers elsewhere. Formerly named *Muscivora tyrannus*. *Head and nape black* with semiconcealed yellow coronal patch, contrasting with *pearly gray back*. Wings dusky, tail black with outer web of outer pair of feathers (the long pair) basally white (this can be prominent from the side, even on "short-tailed" individuals). *Below pure white.* **Juvenile** has a more brownish cap and lacks extremely long tail streamers (though its outer tail feathers are almost always markedly longer than the others). **Similar species:** Should not be confused, no other Ecuadorian bird having a comparable tail; but cf. Eastern Kingbird (with which Fork-tailed sometimes consorts). **Habits:** In Ecuador seen mainly in small, migrating flocks that sometimes alight in situations improbable for this savanna-loving bird, even sometimes in forest canopy (this especially when migrants are forced down by heavy rains). Like the Eastern Kingbirds with which they often consort, Fork-taileds consume a good deal of fruit when not breeding, this usually taken while hovering on wing. They

also sally after insects, when their long and flexible outer tail feathers apparently assist in maneuverability. **Voice:** Seems to be silent in Ecuador.

Pachyramphus Becards
Attractively patterned and *large-headed* tyrannids, the *Pachyramphus* becards are relatively sluggish and inconspicuous arboreal birds found in forest and borders, mainly in the lowlands though a few species are montane. Sexually dimorphic, *males tend to gray and black with white accenting, females rufous and buff*; two species lack dimorphism. Their large and often conspicuous nests are globular with a side entrance, and are suspended from a fork, often well above the ground and near an active bee or wasp nest.

Yellow-cheeked Becard
Pachyramphus xanthogenys
Cabezón Cachetiamarillo   Plate 75(1)

650–1700 m

14.5 cm (5³/₄″). Locally fairly common in clearings with tall trees and humid forest and woodland borders in *foothills and lower subtropics on e. slope*; a nonforest becard. Formerly often considered conspecific with Green-backed Becard (*P. viridis*) of e. South America. ♂ has *crown glossy black* with white lores; *upperparts contrasting bright olive*, tail dusky-olive; wings black, coverts and inner flight feathers broadly edged pale olive. *Cheeks, sides of neck, throat, and chest bright yellow*, becoming yellowish olive on breast and whitish on belly. ♀ has forecrown blackish with *remainder of head, nape, and throat gray*; otherwise olive above, wings and tail as in ♂ but *lesser wing-coverts rufous-chestnut*. Breast pale olive, belly whitish. **Similar species:** This attractive becard is unlikely to be confused in its foothill/sub-tropical range. The smaller Barred Becard occurs at higher elevations, and though ♂'s barring may be hard to see, its extensive white in wing is not; ♀ is much less gray about head and has more rufous on wing. **Habits:** Usually in pairs, foraging in foliage at varying heights though mainly well above ground where it remains inconspicuous unless ♂ is singing. Generally does not associate with mixed flocks. **Voice:** ♂'s pretty song, given at relatively long intervals, a subdued series of soft whistled notes, "du, du-de-de-de-dididididididi?," lasting 2–3 seconds; it is often preceded by one or more upslurred "te-wik?" notes.

Barred Becard, *Pachyramphus versicolor*
Cabezón Barreteado   Plate 75(2)

Mostly 1500–2600 m

13 cm (5"). *Canopy and borders of subtropical and lower temperate forest and woodland on both slopes.* A chunky and small becard. *♂ glossy black above* with gray rump; *scapulars, wing-coverts, and inner flight feathers boldly edged white.* Lores, eye-ring, sides of head and neck, and throat greenish yellow, fading to whitish below, *sides of head and neck and entire underparts with light dusky barring.* ♀ has *slaty crown* contrasting with olive upperparts; eye-ring yellow. *Wing-coverts mostly rufous-chestnut* and with rufous to buff edging on flight feathers; tail dusky. Below pale yellow, fading on belly, with *light dusky barring throughout.* **Similar species:** Though the barring may be inconspicuous at any distance, both sexes can readily be known in their montane habitat by their, round-headed shape and somewhat lethargic behavior; ♂'s white, and ♀'s rufous, in wing are prominent. **Habits:** Found

singly or in pairs, often accompanying mixed canopy flocks of tanagers and other birds. Gleans in foliage. **Voice:** ♂'s pretty song a rather fast, clear, and musical "tree, tree-dee-dee-dee-dee" with distinctive pause after the first note (sometimes up to 10 notes).

Slaty Becard, *Pachyramphus spodiurus*
Cabezón Pizarroso   Plate 75(3)

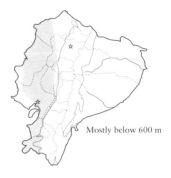

Mostly below 600 m

14 cm (5½"). *Scarce and local* in semihumid and deciduous woodland, and in clearings and plantations with scattered trees in *lowlands of west.* ♂ has crown black with *pale grayish lores*; otherwise slaty gray above, variably mixed with black. Wings and tail blackish *with whitish edging on wing-coverts and flight feathers.* Below uniform gray. ♀ bright cinnamon-rufous above, slightly darker on crown with pale grayish lores; black greater primary-coverts, inner webs to primaries, and tips to flight feathers. *Uniform pale buff below.* **Similar species:** *Often confused with* the *very similar One-colored Becard,* which is much more numerous than the nearly endemic Slaty. One-colored is markedly larger, though this can be hard to judge unless direct size comparison is possible. ♂ ♂ are somewhat easier, for ♂ One-colored *lacks* Slaty's pale lores and edging on wing feathers. ♀ ♀, however, are so closely similar (aside from size) that distinguishing them can be very difficult, and is often best affected by seeing a pair. Most ♀ ♀ One-coloreds show a dusky smudge around eye lacking in Slaties, but otherwise their overall coloration is essentially identical; some ♀ ♀ One-coloreds even have black on greater wing-coverts. Cinnamon Becard is also closely similar though it has buffy whitish supraloral lacking in ♀ Slaty. **Habits:** Often

in pairs, and regularly foraging fairly close to ground, in part because so many trees in its range are themselves relatively short. **Voice:** ♂'s song a short fast series of musical notes that start slowly and then quickly accelerate and rise in pitch and become a little louder, "tu, tu, tee-tee-titititititrí." Also gives a 2-second-long, slurred trill, starting lower, then evenly pitched (P. Coopmans).

[Cinereous Becard, *Pachyramphus rufus*
Cabezón Cinéreo]   Plate 75(4)

14 cm (5½"). Uncertain; known only from several old specimens from *e. base of Andes in Zamora-Chinchipe*. ♂ *pearly gray above* with *contrasting black crown* and *white supraloral and frontlet*. Wings blackish, feathers edged with white; tail dusky-gray. Below grayish white, palest on throat and midbelly. ♀ *bright cinnamon-rufous above*, crown slightly darker and with whitish lores; black greater primary-coverts, inner webs to primaries, and tips to flight feathers. *Below whitish*, tinged buff across breast. **Similar species:** ♂ Black-and-white Becard larger and darker gray generally, and has broad white tips to tail. ♀ in its range could only be confused with Chestnut-crowned Becard, which has distinctive gray nape band. **Habits:** Unknown in Ecuador. Elsewhere in its range favors clearings and secondary woodland, not undisturbed forest, with arboreal behavior like other becards. **Voice:** Similar to Slaty Becard.

Chestnut-crowned Becard
Pachyramphus castaneus
Cabezón Nuquigris   Plate 75(5)

14 cm (5½"). Borders of humid forest and adjacent clearings in *lowlands and lower foothills of east*. **Sexes alike.** *Cinnamon-*

Locally to 1000 m

rufous above, darker and more chestnut on crown, with dusky lores and buffy whitish supraloral turning into a *gray stripe that extends back from eye and encircles nape*; blackish greater primary-coverts, inner webs to primaries, and tips to flight feathers. *Pale cinnamon-buff below*, whitest on throat and midbelly. **Similar species:** The only mainly "rufous" becard east of Andes. Cinnamon Becard occurs west of Andes. Cf. ♀ of very rare Cinereous Becard. **Habits:** Usually in pairs, generally not accompanying mixed flocks; often easy to overlook as they tend to remain well above ground in tall, leafy trees. **Voice:** ♂'s soft and musical song a whistled "teeeuw-teeu-teeu" (sometimes only 1, or up to 5, "teeeu"s) delivered in a leisurely fashion.

Cinnamon Becard
Pachyramphus cinnamomeus
Cabezón Canelo   Plate 75(6)

Mostly below 800 m

14 cm (5½"). Common in borders of humid forest, secondary woodland, and adjacent clearings in *more humid lowlands and foothills of west*. **Sexes alike.** *Uniform bright cinnamon-rufous above* with *dusky lores and a buffy whitish supraloral*; *lacks* black on

greater primary-coverts. *Pale cinnamon-buff below*, whitest on throat and midbelly. **Similar species:** ♀ of rarer Slaty Becard lacks Cinnamon's pale supraloral and has (often prominent) black greater primary-coverts. ♀ One-colored Becard is distinctly larger and also lacks pale supraloral; it usually shows considerable dusky around eye, lacking in Cinnamon (except on lores). Chestnut-crowned Becard occurs only east of Andes. **Habits:** Similar to Chestnut-crowned Becard, though Cinnamon tends more often to occur closer to ground and out in clearings and plantations. **Voice:** ♂'s song similar to Chestnut-crowned Becard's, but usually a little more spritely (not descending) and with more terminal "teeu" notes.

White-winged Becard
Pachyramphus polychopterus
Cabezón Aliblanco   Plate 75(7)

To 900 m (E);
600–1500 m (W)

15 cm (6"). *Secondary and riparian woodland, borders of humid forest, and adjacent clearings in lowlands of east*; also in *secondary and edge habitats in foothills and lower subtropics of northwest*. **Eastern** ♂ *mainly black*: black above, *glossier on crown*. *Wings with two bold white wing-bars*, upper one broader; outer tail feathers broadly tipped white. Below sooty black. **Western** ♂ very different: sides of neck, nuchal collar, and rump gray; in addition to white wing-bars, has *white edging on scapulars and inner flight feathers. Below entirely gray.* ♀♀ throughout olive brown above, *more grayish brown on crown* and with whitish supraloral and partial eye-ring. Wings dusky with *prominent cinnamon-buff on scapulars, wing-bars, and flight-feather edging*; outer tail feathers broadly tipped cinnamon-buff. Below dull olive yellowish, clearest yellow on

belly. **Similar species:** Eastern ♂, being so black in conjunction with prominent white in wing, distinctive. ♀ resembles ♀ of Black-capped and Black-and-white Becards; Black-capped's crown is rufous-chestnut (not dull grayish brown), whereas Black-and-white's bright chestnut crown is prominently outlined in black. W.-slope ♂♂ are easily confused with ♂ of more numerous Black-and-white Becard, but latter differs in its obvious pale gray lores, pure gray back (no black intermixed), and lack of white on scapulars. **Habits:** Usually in pairs, foraging lethargically in leafy canopy and edges of trees; however, because White-winged favors secondary growth, it often comes closer to the ground and tends to be easier to observe than other becards. **Voice:** Eastern ♂'s fairly fast song a pretty and melodic series of mellow notes, e.g., "teu, teu, tu-tu-tu-tu-tu-tu" (sometimes more "tu" notes) but always with more slowly delivered introductory notes. Western ♂'s song delivered more slowly, resulting in a different effect, e.g., "teu, teu, teu, teu, ti-teu, teu" or "teeu, tew-tew, teeu." Dawn song of western ♂ a rather slow "teu, tew-tew-tew" (P. Coopmans).

Black-capped Becard
Pachyramphus marginatus
Cabezón Gorrinegro   Plate 75(9)

To 700 m

14 cm (5½"). *Canopy and borders of humid forest (mainly terra firme) in lowlands of east.* ♂ has crown glossy black with pale gray lores, *back mixed black and gray*, rump pure gray. Wings black with *white scapulars, two wing-bars, and edging on inner flight feathers*; tail black, outer feathers broadly tipped white. *Underparts pale gray.* ♀ like ♀ of larger White-winged Becard, differing in its *rufescent crown*. **Similar species:** ♂ of sym-

patric White-winged Becard much blacker, both above and below; further, it is a species of second-growth, rarely or never occurring in the forest canopy where Black-capped takes over. Both sexes of Black-and-white Becard are rather similar, but that species *does not occur in e. lowlands*. **Habits:** An arboreal becard that often accompanyes mixed canopy flocks; generally remains well above ground in tall forest, thus hard to see well (except from canopy observation platforms). **Voice:** ♂'s pretty song a short series of clear, musical notes with varying pattern, e.g., "teeu, whee-do-weét" (often repeated several times in fast succession); one frequent phrase can be transcribed as "fleur-de-lis," also often repeated quickly. Sometimes also gives an accelerating series of more evenly pitched notes, e.g., "teeu, tee-tee-tee-te-ti" (P. Coopmans).

Black-and-white Becard
Pachyramphus albogriseus
Cabezón Blanquinegro   Plate 75(8)

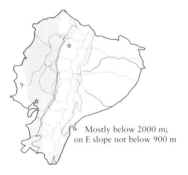

Mostly below 2000 m; on E slope not below 900 m

14.5 cm (5¾″). *Uncommon in canopy and borders of foothill and subtropical forest on both slopes*; *in west also occurs in lowlands*, here also in more deciduous habitats and in secondary growth. ♂ has crown glossy black with *pale gray lores, back and rump plain gray*. Wings black with *two white wing-bars and edging on inner flight feathers* (but none on scapulars); tail black, outer feathers broadly tipped white. *Underparts pale gray*. ♀ much as in slightly larger White-winged Becard but has *crown rufous-chestnut broadly margined with black*, and white supraloral extending back as broken eye-ring. **Similar species:** ♂ most apt to be confused with ♂ of w.-slope White-winged Becard, both being gray below, but White-

winged lacks pale lores and always has considerable black on back. Black-capped Becard occurs only in e. lowlands. **Habits:** Similar to Black-capped Becard, replacing it in montane forests. **Voice:** Recalls Black-capped Becard. Western ♂ has pleasant "tu-tu-dwít?" song, repeated three times, then a pause, then the three phrases again. Eastern ♂ gives a more leisurely and longer phrase with the last note strongly inflected, e.g., "twe, twe, tweu, tu-wít?" (P. Coopmans).

Platypsaris Becards
A trio of larger and heavier-billed becards with rather plain patterns and whose *crown feathers are often raised into a bushy crest*. Nests are typically placed near the tip of a branch. The genus is sometimes merged into *Pachyramphus*.

One-colored Becard, *Platypsaris homochrous*
Cabezón Unicolor   Plate 75(10)

Below 1500 m

16.5 cm (6½″). Widespread and locally fairly common in canopy and borders of deciduous and humid forest and woodland, locally even in secondary scrub, in *lowlands and foothills of west*. ♂ *slaty black above*, blackest on crown, wings, and tail. *Below uniform gray*. A few (older?) ♂♂ show a little pink on throat. ♀ *uniform rufous above* with *dusky lores* and *often some dusky around eye*; primaries dusky, and usually some blackish on greater wing-coverts. *Uniform cinnamon-buff below*, palest on throat. **Young ♂♂** at first resemble ♀; they gradually acquire adult's black and gray, commencing with the crown and then the back, ending with wings and tail. Thus one can see all-rufous-and-buff individuals with black crown and back, and all-black individuals with rufous wings and tail, both very striking. **Similar species:** Neither sex is really "one-colored," both being paler below. ♂ of much smaller (and scarcer) Slaty Becard differs in its prominent pale edging on wing feathers. ♀ One-colored is plainer than other "rufous" becards, lacks any paler area on or above lores, and dusky around eyes is not shown by any other species. Cf. range-restricted Crested Becard. **Habits:** Often in pairs, foraging much like other becards though seems more active. Regularly raises crown feathers into a rounded bushy crest, pumping head alertly. Sometimes with flocks, but at least as often solitary. **Voice:** ♂'s song a loud, sharp, sputtering "stet-ee-ee-teet-tsit-tsitts-tsít," rather variable but completely lacking the melodic quality of *Pachyramphus* becards. Oft-given call a rather high-pitched and squeaky "tweíuuw" (P. Coopmans).

Pink-throated Becard, *Platypsaris minor*
Cabezón Golirrosado   Plate 75(12)

17 cm (6¾"). *Scarce in canopy and borders of terra firme forest in lowlands of east.* ♂ *black above* with a little white on bend of wing. *Blackish gray below* with *patch of rosy pink on lower throat and upper chest* (often surprisingly inconspicuous). ♀ has *slaty gray crown and back contrasting with rufous wings and tail*, often some rufous on upper-tail-coverts. Below uniform buff. Some (younger?) ♀♀ have crown and back more olivaceous gray. **Similar species:** ♂ distinctive in range, despite the fact that its pink is often hard to see; ♂ of sympatric White-winged Becard, also blackish, has obvious white in wings and tail. ♀, with contrasting dark crown and back, really does not resemble other becards; Chestnut-crowned is the most

similar. **Habits:** Usually in pairs, often accompanying mixed canopy flocks; probably often overlooked as it tends to remain well above ground, and for a becard seems relatively quiet. **Voice:** ♂'s song a clear, melodic "teeuuuweeet" often followed by twittering notes.

Crested Becard, *Platypsaris validus*
Cabezón Crestado   Plate 75(11)

2550–2600 m

18.5 cm (7¼"). Status uncertain; known from only one record in *canopy and borders of temperate forest on e. slope in s. Zamora Chinchipe* (*Tapichalaca*). Heavy bill. ♂ *black above*, glossiest on crown and slatier on wings and tail. *Below uniform olivaceous gray.* ♀ has *sooty crown contrasting sharply with rufous of remaining upperparts*; lores buffyish; primaries dusky. Below uniform cinnamon-buff. **Similar species:** The largest becard, and not known to range with any other. The smaller One-colored comes closest, but it only occurs at much lower elevations and in drier terrain; ♂ One-colored is more uniformly slaty and black, ♀ more uniformly rufous and buff. **Habits:** Hardly known in Ecuador. One bird seen was accompanying a large mixed flock dominated by various tanagers. **Voice:** Unknown in Ecuador. Elsewhere seems not especially vocal, occasionally giving various squeaky or twittery notes, also a series of clearer notes "sui-sui-sui . . . (up to 6 or so).

Tityra Tityras
Distinctive *chunky and short-tailed* birds with *white or pearly gray and black plumage*. Tityras are conspicuous in lowland forest canopy and borders, nesting in holes (often in tall snags).

Black-tailed Tityra, *Tityra cayana*
Titira Colinegra   Plate 75(13)

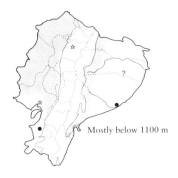

To 500 m

Mostly below 1100 m

21.5 cm (8½″). Fairly common in canopy and borders of humid forest in *lowlands of east. Wide orbital area and most of bill rosy red,* bill tipped black. ♂ has *head black* contrasting with *pale pearly gray upperparts* and *white underparts.* Wings (except for tertials) and tail also contrastingly black. ♀ has much the same pattern but grayer above with *variable amount of coarse black streaking* (often prominent), *especially on back; breast also has black streaking,* narrower but still prominent. **Similar species:** ♀ is only tityra with streaking. ♂ differs from ♂ Masked Tityra in having a fully black head (white of back extends to hindcrown in Masked) and an all-black tail (tail grayish white with only a black subterminal band in Masked). Black-crowned Tityra lacks red on bill and face. **Habits:** Often found in pairs and regularly perching on high exposed branches, with a special fondness for tall snags on which it may rest or hop for long periods. Flies strongly and directly, often sweeping for long distances in the open, its white and black plumage flashing conspicuously. Eats much fruit, also large insects, latter usually snatched on wing. **Voice:** Frequently given and unusual call a brief nasal croak or grunt, "urt," sometimes doubled in which case sometimes second note is slightly higher-pitched (given by ♀?). Often calls in flight.

Masked Tityra, *Tityra semifasciata*
Titira Enmascarada   Plate 75(14)

21 cm (8¼″). Fairly common in canopy and borders of humid forest and woodland in *lowlands and foothills of west,* and *in east mainly near Andes. Wide orbital area and*

most of bill rosy red, bill tipped black. ♂ has *forecrown, face, and upper chin black* contrasting with *very pale pearly gray upperparts* and *white underparts.* Wings (except for tertials) black, *tail grayish white* with broad black subterminal band. ♀ like ♂ but with head dusky brownish, back gray, and underparts pale gray. **Similar species:** Both sexes of Black-tailed Tityra have all-black tails; ♂ has more extensive black on head, ♀ shows conspicuous streaking on back and breast. Both sexes of Black-crowned Tityra lack red on bill and face. **Habits and Voice:** Similar to Black-tailed Tityra. The two species occur together locally along e. base of Andes.

Black-crowned Tityra, *Tityra inquisitor*
Titira Coroninegra   Plate 75(15)

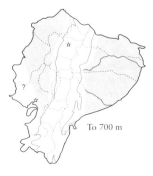

To 700 m

18 cm (7″). Uncommon in canopy and borders of humid forest and woodland in lowlands of east and west. Both sexes have *bill black above, gray below* (with *no red*). ♂ has *crown and face black;* otherwise pale pearly gray above and white below. Wings (except for tertials) black; tail white with black subterminal band (**west slope**) or all black (**east slope**). ♀♀ much like their

respective ♂ ♂, but with *buff frontlet and prominent rufous-chestnut sides of head*; back duller and slightly darker gray, sometimes with brown streaking. **Similar species:** Both sexes of the other two tityras have conspicuous rosy red on bill and face; however, beware ♀ Black-crowneds whose cheeks, especially in strong afternoon light, can look reddish. **Habits:** Similar to Black-tailed and Masked Tityras. **Voice:** Calls are similar to other tityras', and likewise often doubled, but tend to be drier (less "grunty") and are usually weaker, e.g., "zik-zik" or "chet-chet."

Cotingas: Cotingidae (33)

Cotingas are exclusively Neotropical birds closely related to both the Manakins (Pipridae) and the Tyrant Flycatchers (Tyrannidae); they have even all been combined into the same huge family. Included are two groups formerly considered separate families, Oxyruncidae (Sharpbill) and Rupicolidae (Cocks-of-the-rock). Cotingas are found exclusively in humid forests, both in lowland and montane areas; none ranges in open terrain. They are exceptionally diverse in both size and form, and generalizations are difficult. The family includes some of the largest and most spectacular passerines, the umbrellabirds and certain fruitcrows. Many cotingas, including some of the best known, exhibit strong sexual dimorphism, the males often beautifully colored or bizarrely ornamented (the cock-of-the-rock is both!); but in others the sexes are alike, and colors subdued. Many cotingas are essentially mute, whereas others—such as some of the pihas—are very vocal indeed. Some males display in spectacular leks, whereas in others not only is there no display, but no permanent pair bond is formed, females alone caring for the young. In a few genera, such as *Ampelion* and *Pipreola*, permanent pairs are formed and both sexes care for the young. Most cotingas are frugivorous, though in some species this diet is varied with some insects, and certain larger cotingas are exclusively insectivorous. Nests are typically flimsy stick platforms.

[Sharpbill, *Oxyruncus cristatus*
Picoagudo]   Plate 96(14)

17 cm (6¾"). Canopy and borders of *foothill forest on lower slopes of remote*

Cordillera del Cóndor in se. Zamora-Chinchipe (Miazi). *Sharply pointed bill*; iris reddish to orange. **Sexes much alike.** Olive above with yellowish edging on wings; *head and neck whitish with prominent blackish scaling*; sides of crown black with semiconcealed red crest (orange in ♀). *Throat whitish scaled blackish; underparts pale yellowish profusely spotted with black.* **Similar species:** Not likely confused, but cf. Scaled Fruiteater, Swainson's Thrush, and Spotted Tanager (none of them really very similar). **Habits:** Unknown in Ecuador. Elsewhere typically seen as single individuals that glean along branches and among leaves, sometimes even hanging upside-down, probing into moss and curled-up leaves; also eats some fruit. Often rather stolid, perching quietly for long periods, but sometimes accompanies mixed flocks. **Voice:** ♂'s unmistakable and far-carrying song a drawn-out somewhat shrill and buzzy trill that gradually drops in pitch and fades in intensity, "zheeeeeeeeu-uuu'u'u'u'u'ur."

Ampelion Cotingas

Sluggish cotingas found in Andean forests and borders, notable for their striking nuchal crests, sometimes expanded but more often laid flat and not very noticeable. **Sexes usually alike.** Nests are shallow cups; both sexes help raise the young.

Red-crested Cotinga, *Ampelion rubrocristatus*
Cotinga Crestirroja   Plate 76(2)

21 cm (8¼"). *Borders of temperate forest and woodland and in woodland patches above treeline on both slopes*, and above central and interandean valleys. *Bill chalky white to pale gray with black tip*; iris red. *Mostly gray*, blacker on head, wings, and tail; *semicon-*

Mostly 2500–3500 m

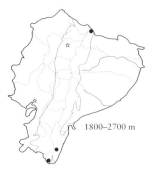

1800–2700 m

cealed nuchal crest of long maroon feathers, usually laid flat with only a little color protruding, sometimes flared spectacularly. Some white streaking on rump and belly, crissum white boldly streaked black; *broad white band across tail* visible mainly in flight and from below. **Juvenile** browner with no nuchal crest, whitish streaking on rump, and *whitish underparts with coarse dark streaking*. **Similar species:** Though vaguely thrush-like, given a decent view this gray cotinga really should not be confused. Juveniles somewhat recall more colorful Chestnut-crested Cotinga. **Habits:** Conspicuous though rarely very numerous; seen singly or in pairs, most often perching motionless and upright atop a shrub or low tree. Seems sluggish, and sometimes quite tame. Does not accompany mixed flocks. Eats much fruit, especially mistletoe, but also sallies for insects. Displaying birds fan crests and bow at each other with tails spread. **Voice:** Usually quiet. Sometimes gives a low and guttural "rrreh," in full song extended into a frog-like "k-k-k-k-k-rrrréh."

Chestnut-crested Cotinga, *Ampelion rufaxilla*
Cotinga Cresticastaña   Plate 76(18)

20.5 cm (8″). A *colorful and boldly patterned* cotinga, *rare and local* in canopy and borders of *upper subtropical and lower temperate forest on e. slope*. Unmistakable. Bill grayish blue with black tip; iris red. Crown blackish with *ample nuchal crest of long bright chestnut feathers* (usually apparent, and sometimes flared widely); *sides of head and neck, and throat cinnamon-rufous*; otherwise olivaceous gray above with some dusky streaking. Wings and tail blackish with patch of bright chestnut on shoulders.

Chest gray, *breast and belly pale yellow boldly streaked blackish*. **Habits:** Much like Red-crested Cotinga, though Chestnut-crested never seems as numerous, certainly not in Ecuador, where in fact this fine cotinga seems inexplicably scarce. Usually perches in tall trees well above ground. **Voice:** Most frequent call a dry, raspy, and nasal stuttered "reh, r-r-r-r-r-réh," longer than Red-crested's comparable call. This may be given with crest fully exposed.

Chestnut-bellied Cotinga, *Doliornis remseni*
Cotinga Ventricastaña   Plate 76(17)

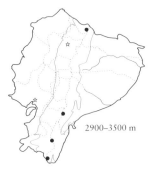

2900–3500 m

21 cm (8¼″). *Rare and local in treeline woodland on e. slope of Andes*. A recently described species. Bill slaty gray; iris dark red. ♂ has *crown and nape black with semi-concealed maroon-chestnut nuchal crest*; otherwise dark grayish brown above, more blackish on wings and tail. Throat and sides of head dark gray becoming grayish brown on breast; *belly and crissum rich rufous-chestnut*. ♀ similar but lacking black crown. **Similar species:** Could only be confused with Red-crested Cotinga, but Red-crested is notably paler gray with conspicuous white on

bill and in tail. **Habits:** Similar to Red-crested Cotinga, though Chestnut-bellied is strictly confined to treeline, and is never as numerous as Red-crested can be. At some sites it has been observed feeding on fruits of *Escallonia* trees, sometimes together with Red-crested Cotingas. **Voice:** Unknown.

Pipreola Fruiteaters

Attractive *plump and short-tailed* cotingas found *inside Andean forests* where they tend to remain inconspicuous and elusive. Although all fruiteaters are *predominantly moss green*, there otherwise is marked sexual dimorphism, with males usually having some black on the head and/or orange or red on the chest. The bill is red or orange in males, often duller in females. They are relatively infrequently seen, despite having distinctive though high-pitched vocalizations that reveal their presence. Nests are shallow cups of moss, and both sexes assist in raising the young.

Barred Fruiteater, *Pipreola arcuata*
Frutero Barreteado   Plate 76(14)

Mostly 2500–3300 m, locally down to 2250 m

23 cm (9″). Lower and mid-levels of *temperate forest* on both slopes; occurs *at higher elevations than other fruiteaters*, though overlapping with Green-and-black. Iris grayish olive (northward perhaps reddish); bill and legs coral red. ♂ has *head, throat, and chest glossy black*; otherwise bright olive above. Wings with large pale yellowish spots on wing-coverts and tertials; tail with broad black terminal band and narrow white tipping. *Breast and belly evenly barred black and pale yellow.* ♀ lacks black on head and bib; its *entire underparts are evenly barred black and pale yellow.* **Similar species:** The largest fruiteater, and the only one with barring on underparts. **Habits:** Found singly or in pairs, and often even more sluggish and unsuspicious than other fruiteaters, at times sitting motionless for long periods. Sometimes accompanies mixed flocks, but more often solitary; several may assemble at a fruiting tree. **Voice:** ♂'s call a thin and very high-pitched "seeeeeeeeeh" that lasts some 2–3 seconds.

Green-and-black Fruiteater, *Pipreola riefferii*
Frutero Verdinegro   Plate 76(9)

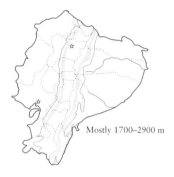

Mostly 1700–2900 m

18 cm (7″). Lower and middle growth and borders of *subtropical and lower temperate forest on both slopes*; *generally the most numerous fruiteater*. Bill and legs reddish orange. ♂ has *entire head, throat, and chest black suffused* (especially on throat and chest) *with green, margined on neck and around bib with narrow yellow border*; otherwise bright moss green above, *tertials narrowly tipped whitish.* Underparts yellow more or less mottled or streaked with green (midbelly unmarked yellow in **west-slope birds**). ♀ like ♂ but black of hood replaced by green, and bib has no yellow border; lower underparts entirely solidly streaked and mottled with green. **Similar species:** ♀ Black-chested (e. slope) and Orange-breasted (w. slope) Fruiteaters have pale (not dark) irides and grayish (not reddish orange) legs, and they lack pale tertial tipping. **Habits:** Found singly or in pairs, occasionally in small groups; like other fruiteaters, often perches quietly and motionless for long periods, but also sometimes follows mixed flocks and then can be a little more active. Eats fruit, plucked while hovering or sometimes while perched. **Voice:** ♂'s call a very high-

pitched and sibilant "ts-s-s-s-s-s-s-s-s," slowing a little toward end and lasting 2–3 seconds; sometimes fades off at end, e.g., "ts-s-s-s-s-se-eeeeeeeuuw." Also gives a single high-pitched whistle, first ascending and then descending; Barred's single-note whistle descends, Black-chested's ascends. Also gives various sharper "tsip" contact calls, sometimes in series.

Black-chested Fruiteater, *Pipreola lubomirskii*
Frutero Pechinegro   Plate 76(10)

1500–2100 m

18 cm (7"). *Uncommon in mid-levels of subtropical forest on e. slope. Iris yellow*; bill coral red; *legs olive-gray.* ♂ has *head, throat, and midchest glossy black* contrasting with bright green upperparts and sides of chest. Underparts pale yellow with green mottling on flanks. ♀ uniform bright green above and on throat and chest; underparts streaked green and pale yellow. **Similar species:** Both sexes of Green-and-black Fruiteater differ in their dark eye and red legs, and in having tertial tipping; ♂ differs further in having yellow border to bib. **Habits:** Similar to Green-and-black Fruiteater, but less numerous and even more stolid; seems more arboreal. **Voice:** ♂'s very thin and high-pitched song a drawn-out and ascending "pseeeeeeeét," becoming stronger toward end. Also gives a "pseeet" call.

Orange-breasted Fruiteater, *Pipreola jucunda*
Frutero Pechinaranja   Plate 76(11)

18 cm (7"). *Uncommon in lower and middle growth of foothill and subtropical forest on w. slope. Iris yellow*; bill coral red; *legs olive-gray.* Unmistakable ♂ has *head and throat glossy black*; otherwise bright green above.

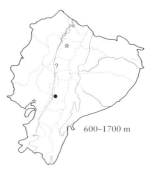

600–1700 m

Chest bright fiery orange connected to orange-yellow band that arches up onto sides of neck, chest margined blackish; underparts pale yellow with green mottling on flanks. ♀ uniform bright green above and on throat and chest; underparts streaked green and pale yellow. **Similar species:** In its elevation range, where no other fruiteater occurs (marginal overlap at most with Green-and-black), not likely confused. **Habits:** As in Green-and-black Fruiteater, though less conspicuous and less apt to follow mixed flocks. **Voice:** ♂'s song a thin and very high-pitched "pseeeeeeeeét," drawn out and ascending much as in the related Black-chested.

Scarlet-breasted Fruiteater, *Pipreola frontalis*
Frutero Pechiescarlata   Plate 76(12)

1000–1700 m

15.5 cm (6"). *Mid-levels and subcanopy of foothill and subtropical forest on e. slope. Iris yellow*; bill and legs orange (♂) or more dusky (♀). ♂ has *crown dark shiny bluish green*; otherwise bright green above, tertials narrowly tipped yellowish. Upper throat yellow, *lower throat and chest shiny fiery red; underparts bright yellow*, with bright green on flanks. ♀ bright green above with narrow tertial tipping as in ♂. Throat yellowish sparsely scaled green; underparts yellow, breast and flanks densely scaled green. **Similar species:** Fiery-throated Fruiteater is notably smaller. Besides this, ♂ differs notably in being much greener below (with virtually no yellow); ♀♀ are more similar, but ♀ Fiery-throated's green barring below is so dense that very little yellow shows. **Habits:** Similar to Green-and-black Fruiteater, though Scarlet-breasted tends to be more arboreal. **Voice:** ♂'s song an infrequently heard, sharp and piercing "psii."

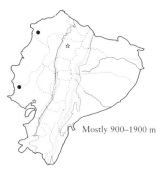

Mostly 900–1900 m

Fiery-throated Fruiteater
Pipreola chlorolepidota
Frutero Golifuego   Plate 76(13)

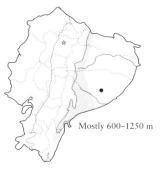

Mostly 600–1250 m

13 cm (5″). Scarce (overlooked?) in lower and middle growth of foothill forest on e. slope, locally out into adjacent lowlands as well. *By far the smallest fruiteater and occurs at lower elevations than any other Pipreola.* Iris pale grayish; bill salmon tipped dusky; legs orange. ♂ bright green above with tertials broadly tipped whitish. *Throat and chest scarlet, contrasting with green on remaining underparts,* midbelly somewhat yellowish. ♀ like ♂ above. *Below rather uniformly barred green and yellowish,* most densely green on breast. **Similar species:** Most likely confused with larger Scarlet-breasted Fruiteater, with which Fiery-throated overlaps; for distinctions, see that species. **Habits:** Infrequently encountered, apparently everywhere occurring at low densities. Has been seen accompanying mixed flocks. **Voice:** Call a very short and high-pitched "tsi" (P. Coopmans).

Scaled Fruiteater, *Ampelioides tschudii*
Frutero Escamado   Plate 76(15)
19 cm (7½″). Scarce in *mid-levels and subcanopy of foothill and subtropical forest on*

both slopes, also locally on coastal cordillera. A *plump, arboreal* fruiteater with *short tail;* nearly unmistakable. Iris yellow, lower madible bluish gray. ♂ has crown and sides of head black, *yellowish white lores and moustachial stripe,* and *pale yellow nuchal collar; above otherwise bright* olive, *centers of feathers black imparting a distinctly scaly look,* uppertail-coverts somewhat scaled black. Wings mostly black, greater coverts olive forming a wide band; tail black, outer feathers white-tipped. Throat whitish; underparts yellow, *feathers broadly edged olive imparting scalloped effect.* ♀ has similar overall pattern but differs in its olive head (with no black), and *feathers of underparts are broadly edged black* (thus even more striking). **Habits:** Inconspicuous and often quite stolid, seen singly or in pairs, most often when accompanying mixed flocks. Hops along larger horizontal limbs looking for insects, and also eats considerable fruit. **Voice:** ♂'s characteristic song a loud whistle, "wheeeeééééeeur," fading away and dropping in pitch toward end, repeated at 3- to 6-second intervals.

White-browed Purpletuft, *Iodopleura isabellae*
Yodopleura Cejiblanca   Plate 76(16)
11.5 cm (4½″). Scarce in *canopy and borders* of humid forest in *lowlands of east,* sometimes out into isolated trees in adjacent clearings. Nearly unmistakable, a *small* cotinga with *short tail* and proportionately long wings. **Sexes alike,** aside from ♂'s purple flank tufts (inconspicuous and often hidden), tufts white in ♀. Brownish black above with *bold white loral spot, postocular stripe, and malar streak,* and white rump band. *Throat and median underparts white,*

Mostly below 500 m

sides and flanks mottled and barred dusky-brown. **Habits:** Usually perches high above ground where easily overlooked unless on an exposed dead branch. Often in pairs; does not associate with other birds. Makes long, flycatcher-like sallies after aerial insects; also eats considerable amount of fruit. **Voice:** Often quiet, but sometimes gives a soft plaintive "wheee," occasionally doubled or tripled.

Andean Laniisoma, *Laniisoma buckleyi*
Laniisoma Andino   Plate 76(8)

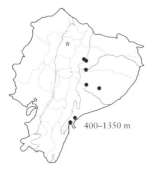

400–1350 m

17.5 cm (6¾"). *Rare and local inside foothill forest on e. slope of Andes*, ranging locally out into adjacent lowlands and up into lower subtropics. Formerly considered conspecific with *L. elegans* (Brazilian Laniisoma) and then called Elegant Laniisoma or Mourner, or Shrike-like Cotinga. Bill blackish above, pale greenish below. ♂ has *black crown* with narrow pale greenish eye-ring; otherwise contrastingly olive green above. *Bright yellow below with variable amount of coarse black scaling across breast, down flanks, and on crissum*. ♀ similar but crown dusky and with *entire* underparts scaled black. **Immature** like

respective ♂ and ♀ but *with a few large rufous spots on tips of wing-coverts*. **Similar species:** No fruiteater is as scaled with black below; cf. especially Scaled Fruiteater. Cf. also even rarer and range-restricted Sharpbill. **Habits:** Poorly known. Usually found singly inside tall forest, often near streams, ranging at various levels above ground. **Voice:** ♂'s persistently given song a thin and very high-pitched "psiiiiiiueeeé," reminiscent of Black-streaked Puffbird.

Laniocera Mourners
Rather plain cotingas found inside lowland forests on either side of the Andes. Their systematic position has been debated, and while now considered to be cotingas, they do superficially resemble certain flycatchers.

Cinereous Mourner, *Laniocera hypopyrra*
Plañidera Cinérea   Plate 73(6)

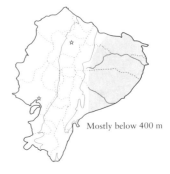

Mostly below 400 m

20 cm (8"). Scarce in lower and middle growth inside terra firme forest in *lowlands of east*. Narrow golden eye-ring. **Sexes alike.** *Ashy gray*, somewhat paler below; wings duskier *with two rows of large cinnamon-rufous spots*, tertials and tail feathers also tipped cinnamon-rufous; *pectoral tuft pale yellow or orange-rufous*, but often hidden. **Immatures** have some rufous intermixed with black spotting on breast. **Similar species:** Grayish Mourner (a flycatcher) lacks rufous wing-spotting and shows no pectoral tuft; it is flatter crowned, resulting in a "fiercer" expression (not "soft" and dove-like as in Cinereous Mourner). Cf. also Screaming Piha. **Habits:** Inconspicuous and only rarely seen. Usually solitary, sometimes accompanying understory flocks but more often independent. **Voice:** ♂'s plaintive song a tirelessly

repeated, high-pitched, and ringing "teeyr, teeoweeét, teeoweeét, teeoweeét . . ." (up to 10 "teeoweeét"s in succession, then a pause) that seems to be given from certain regularly used perches. Also gives a series of 3–4 plaintive whistles, "teeéuw, teeuw-teeuw-teeuw!" (P. Coopmans).

Speckled Mourner, *Laniocera rufescens*
Plañidera Moteada   Plate 73(7)

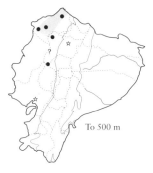

20 cm (8″). Scarce in lower and middle growth inside humid forest in *lowlands of northwest*. Narrow golden eye-ring. *Mostly rufous brown*, breast feathers often scaled with dusky (especially in immatures); *wing-coverts dusky*, feathers with *large rufous tips*. ♂ has often-hidden pale yellow pectoral tuft (usually lacking in ♀). **Similar species:** Rufous Mourner (a flycatcher) is more uniform rufous, showing none of Speckled's conspicuous pattern on wing-coverts; Speckled's head shape is rounder, imparting a "softer" expression. Cf. also Rufous Piha. **Habits:** Similar to Cinereous Mourner. **Voice:** ♂♂ tirelessly repeat a ringing and ventriloquial "tleeyr, tlee-yeeí, tlee-yeeí, tlee-yeeí . . ." with up to 12–15 "tlee-yeeí"s then a pause before starting up again; pattern and quality similar to Speckled Mourner. Sometimes several ♂♂ sing within earshot of each other.

Lathria and *Lipaugus* Pihas
Plain cotingas (like *Laniocera* they have been considered to be flycatchers) with rather stout bills, found inside humid lowland and montane forest. They are inconspicuous aside from their *loud calls*, though one species (Olivaceous) seems to be silent. **Sexes are much alike.** Nests are shallow and flimsy cups, lending credence to their being cotin-gas. Recent evidence supports the separation of the first two species into the genus *Lathria*.

Olivaceous Piha, *Lathria cryptolophus*
Piha Olivácea   Plate 73(14)

1000–1800 m

23.5 cm (9¼″). Scarce and local in lower and middle growth inside *subtropical forest on e. slope and in northwest*. ♂ olive green above, somewhat duskier on wings and tail and with semiconcealed black coronal patch; bend of wing and underwing-coverts yellow. *Throat and breast olive green, becoming yellower on belly*. ♀ lacks coronal patch. **Similar species:** Gray-tailed Piha (only on e. slope, mainly at lower elevations) is markedly grayer on tail and belly. Cf. also Olive and Ochre-breasted Tanagers. **Habits:** A lethargic and inconspicuous bird, generally solitary. Occasionally accompanies mixed flocks, and has been seen feeding both on larger insects and on fruit. **Voice:** Surprisingly, nothing seems to be on record.

Gray-tailed Piha, *Lathria subalaris*
Piha Coligris   Plate 73(13)

23.5 cm (9¼″). Scarce and local in lower and middle growth inside *foothill and lower subtropical forest on e. slope*. Narrow gray eyering. ♂ *olive green above* with semiconcealed black coronal patch and more grayish rump; bend of wing and underwing-coverts yellow and *tail pure pale gray*. Throat and breast olive green with inconspicuous, pale shaft streaks, *becoming pale gray on lower belly and crissum*. ♀ has smaller coronal patch (or it may be lacking). **Similar species:** Cf. Olivaceous Piha, *which lacks any gray*. **Habits:** Similar to Olivaceous Piha, likewise very inconspicuous, but Gray-tailed differs strik-

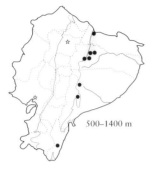

500–1400 m

mixed flocks but more often found alone. Heard much more than seen. **Voice:** This piha has one of the best known and most powerful voices of any bird occurring in Amazon basin, but nonetheless it is often a frustrating bird to see, even when one is calling right in front of you. Four to 10 ♂♂ gather in loose leks inside humid forest, perching some 5–8 m above ground, there remaining nearly motionless, even while calling hardly opening bill. The classic call a very loud—it can carry one km or more, and is deafening at close range—and ringing "weee weee-ah" (sometimes two initial "weee" notes), usually preceded by a few softer and more guttural notes; also gives a querulous and less loud "kweeeah" or series of loud "kweeeo" notes.

ingly in having a loud voice. **Voice:** ♂'s far-carrying song, given at long intervals (often a minute or more, and thus hard to track to its source), a clear and ringing "cheeeer-yeeéng!" with second syllable higher pitched than first. A softer and shorter version, "chureeee?," is also given (by ♀♀?).

Screaming Piha, *Lipaugus vociferans*
Piha Gritona   Plate 73(11)

Mostly below 500 m

24.5–25.5 cm (9½–10″). *Lower and middle growth inside humid forest* (mainly in terra firme) *in lowlands of east. Very vocal*, but *surprisingly inconspicuous. Plain gray*, a bit duskier on wings and tail and somewhat paler on belly. **Juvenile** tinged brown on wings. **Similar species:** Dusky Piha is exclusively montane. Screaming Piha is thus more apt to be confused with Grayish Mourner, which routinely occurs with it. The mourner differs in its smaller size, browner (not so gray) iris, more slender bill, and yellowish cast to belly. Piha's shape is vaguely thrush-like, but no thrush in Amazonia is so uniformly gray. **Habits:** Generally seen singly as it perches erectly, occasionally sallying after a large insect or to fruit. Sometimes with

Dusky Piha, *Lipaugus fuscocinereus*
Piha Oscura   Plate 73(10)

1700–2600 m

32.5 cm (12¾″). Scarce and local in canopy and borders of *subtropical and temperate* forest and secondary woodland on *e. slope. The only piha occurring high on Andean slopes. Large* and *rather long-tailed. Gray above*, duskier on wings and tail. *Olivaceous-tinged gray below*, somewhat paler on throat. **Similar species:** Occurs with no other piha; similar-looking, though smaller and shorter-tailed, Screaming Piha ranges only in lowlands. Dusky is unlikely to be confused, though in a quick view it can be mistaken for the much more common Great Thrush (which has an orange bill and legs and is sootier). **Habits:** Most often seen in small groups as they forage in mixed flocks with other fairly large birds such as Northern Mountain-Caciques, Turquoise Jays, and Hooded Mountain-Tanagers. **Voice:** Not terribly vocal, certainly not as much so as

Screaming Piha. ♂♂ give, perhaps in loose leks, a loud "wheeeo-wheeeeyr," sometimes repeated at 5- to 10-second intervals (but at times interval can be much longer); often just "wheeeo" is given. Seems most vocal in late afternoon.

Rufous Piha, *Lipaugus unirufus*
Piha Rojiza   Plate 73(12)

23.5 cm (9¼″). Lower and middle growth inside humid forest in *lowlands and lower foothills in northwest*, now mainly in Esmeraldas. Bill flesh or brownish at base. *Uniform cinnamon-rufous*, slightly paler below and palest on throat; brightest on wings and tail. May show a vague paler eye-ring. **Similar species:** Easily confused with Rufous Mourner, a tyrannid. The smaller, more slender, and proportionately longer-tailed mourner differs marginally in its less stout bill and is more uniform below, not somewhat paler on throat. The Piha has a rounder head, which results in a "softer," more dove-like expression. They are often best distinguished by voice. **Habits:** Generally inconspicuous, perching quietly and lethargically for long periods, then suddenly sallying after a large insect or to pluck a fruit. Sometimes occurs in small, loose groups, but rarely associates with mixed flocks. **Voice:** Unlike Screaming Piha, Rufous seems not to form true leks, ♂♂ rather giving a variety of loud and explosive whistled calls, e.g., "peeeéuw," "wheeeéo," and "chow-eeéo," sometimes in a short series. Calls sporadically and often at long intervals, sometimes in response to a sudden loud noise such as the crash of a falling branch or a shout; one such disturbance call is a descending series that ends in

a sputter, e.g., "ki-ke-kuw-k-kr-k-kr-k-kr" (O. Jahn and N. Krabbe recordings).

Purple-throated Cotinga
Porphyrolaema porphyrolaema
Cotinga Golipúrpura   Plate 76(1)

18.5 cm (7¼″). *Scarce in canopy and borders of humid forest in lowlands of east*. Unmistakable ♂ *black above*, feathers of scapulars, back, and rump fringed white, also a *single broad white wingstripe* and tertial edging. *Throat deep purple*; underparts white, with a little black barring on lower flanks. ♀ brown above, *feathers fringed buffy whitish*, *crown irregularly barred buff and blackish*. *Throat cinnamon-buff*; *underparts narrowly and evenly barred black and buff*, crissum cinnamon-buff. **Similar species:** No ♀ *Cotinga* is barred below or has rufous throat; ♀ Purple-throateds can look vaguely thrush-like. **Habits:** Much as in *Cotinga* cotingas, but much more often noted in pairs than they are. Seen infrequently, usually while perching high in forest canopy, less often at fruiting trees (when sometimes with other cotingas). **Voice:** Unlike *Cotinga*, which are virtually silent, Purple-throated has rather powerful voice, though it seems not often to be given. ♂'s song a loud "wheeeeeeeur" that lasts 1–2 seconds and recalls frequent call of Dusky-capped Flycatcher though longer and dropping more in pitch.

Cotinga Cotingas
Arboreal cotingas found in lowland forests, the males *famous for their intense blue plumage*, with its tone varying between species. Females are browner and much plainer, though they can be recognized by their *distinctive plump silhouette with small,*

rounded, dove-like head. They are apparently entirely frugivorous. Nests are flimsy stick platforms placed high above the ground; females alone care for the young.

Blue Cotinga, *Cotinga nattererii*
Cotinga Azul   Plate 76(5)

Mostly below 300 m

18.5 cm (7¼"). Scarce in canopy and borders of humid forest in *lowlands of far northwest*, where the only *Cotinga*. ♂ *mostly bright shining blue* with black around eye; most of wing (except lesser-coverts) and tail also black. *Contrasting patch on throat and upper chest purplish black* and *band down median lower underparts dark purple.* ♀ dusky brown above, feathers scaled whitish and often showing vague pale eye-ring. Below dull buff, more cinnamon-buff on belly, *breast (especially) and belly feathers dark-centered resulting in bold scaly effect.* **Similar species:** Cf. ♀ Black-tipped Cotinga and ♂ Swallow Tanager. **Habits:** Usually seen singly though occasionally several will gather in a fruiting tree. Solitary birds sometimes perch high on exposed branches, especially in early morning and during sunny late afternoons. Flight swooping, fast, and direct; flying ♂♂ produce a twittering or rattled sound, apparently with wings. **Voice:** ♂ not known to produce any vocal sound; agitated ♀♀ may utter loud shrieks at nest.

Plum-throated Cotinga, *Cotinga maynana*
Cotinga Golimorada   Plate 76(6)

19.5 cm (7¾"). Canopy and borders of humid forest and adjacent clearings in *lowlands of east. Iris yellow,* but more grayish in juveniles (and some ♀♀?). ♂ *bright shining turquoise blue* with scattered pink feather

Mostly below 700 m

bases showing through and *contrasting small throat patch shining plum purple;* flight feathers and tail mainly black. ♀ grayish brown above, feathers narrowly and inconspicuously scaled whitish or pale buff; *underwing-coverts cinnamon-buff* (quite evident in flight). Below slightly paler grayish brown, *becoming more ochraceous on belly;* feathers of breast and (to a lesser extent) belly dark-centered imparting a somewhat scaly look. **Similar species:** Regularly occurs with Spangled Cotinga, which is slightly larger. ♂ Spangled is slightly paler blue, and considerably more black from its feather bases shows through (resulting in a more dappled effect; Plum-throated's blue looks "smoother"); in addition Spangled has more extensively black wings and a larger purple throat patch. ♀♀ of the two species can be hard to distinguish, but ♀ Spangled is slightly darker and more ashy grayish overall, shows less ochraceous on belly, and its underwing-coverts are markedly duller buff. **Habits and Voice:** Much as described for Blue Cotinga. Plum-throated often occurs with Spangled Cotinga, the two sometimes even feeding together in the same fruiting tree.

Spangled Cotinga, *Cotinga cayana*
Cotinga Lentejuelada   Plate 76(7)

20 cm (8"). Canopy and borders of humid forest (mainly terra firme) in *lowlands of east.* ♂ *bright pale shining turquoise blue* with *black bases of many feathers showing through* (especially on head, back, and breast), resulting in a dappled (or "spangled") effect; *contrasting large patch on throat and upper chest bright magenta purple; wings and tail mostly black,* wing-coverts edged with pale blue. ♀ *rather dark*

Mostly below 400 m

grayish brown above and on throat and breast, darkest on wings, with feathers narrowly scaled whitish; underwing-coverts dull pale buff. Lower underparts dull pale buff, flank feathers dark-centered. **Similar species:** Resembles Plum-throated Cotinga (especially ♀♀); for distinctions, see that species. **Habits and Voice:** Much as described for Blue Cotinga.

Pompadour Cotinga, *Xipholena punicea*
Cotinga Púrpura   Plate 76(3)

Mostly below 700 m

19.5 cm (7³/₄"). *Very rare in canopy of terra firme forest in lowlands of far southeast*; still known in Ecuador only from a 1964 specimen. Iris creamy white to pale yellow. Stunning ♂ *shining crimson purple with mainly white wings* (latter contrasting conspicuously); some purple scapular feathers are stiff, pointed, and elongated, extending down over white flight feathers. ♀ *uniform ashy gray*, darker above (especially on wings) and palest on belly, a few birds with some pink on crissum; *wing-coverts and inner flight feathers conspicuously edged white.* **Similar species:** ♂ unmistakable; even at great distances its unique snowy white wings flash

out. ♀ with pale eye, overall gray plumage, and white wing-edging distinctive in range; the larger Black-tipped Cotinga occurs only west of Andes. **Habits:** Not known in Ecuador. Elsewhere general behavior resembles that of *Cotinga* cotingas, also regularly perching on high snags (especially in early morning) and coming to fruiting trees. Small groups of displaying ♂♂ fly at each other with unusually slow flight, the flying bird displacing a perched bird, this process being repeated numerous times. ♀♀ may perch nearby. **Voice:** Essentially silent. A hollow rattle has been heard (D. Stotz).

Black-tipped Cotinga, *Carpodectes hopkei*
Cotinga Blanca   Plate 76(4)

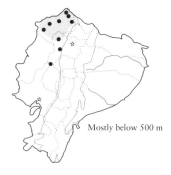

Mostly below 500 m

♂ 25 cm (9³/₄"); ♀ 24 cm (9¹/₂"). *Canopy and borders of humid forest in lowlands and foothills of northwest.* Sometimes called White Cotinga. Iris orange. Unmistakable ♂ *pure snowy white*, with outer primaries and central tail feathers minutely tipped black (but black hard to see in the field). Slightly smaller ♀ *ashy gray above*, blacker on wings and tail with *wing-coverts and inner flight feathers conspicuously edged with white.* Throat and breast somewhat paler gray, belly white. **Similar species:** Snowy white ♂ unmistakable at any distance; flying ♂♂ tityras can also look mainly white. ♀ resembles ♀ Pompadour Cotinga, found only east of Andes, though Black-tipped is markedly larger. **Habits:** ♂♂ very conspicuous, regularly perching on high dead snags where they can be spotted from great distances. ♀♀ seen much less often, usually at fruiting trees where several may gather at once. ♂♂ engage in what are apparently display flights in which they slowly flap from tree to tree; at other times their flight is faster and more direct. Even when not at fruiting trees, this cotinga sometimes ranges in small groups comprising up to 5–6 birds of both sexes. **Voice:** Nothing seems known, but its congeners (in s. Central America) vocalize, so this species may too.

Bare-necked Fruitcrow, *Gymnoderus foetidus*
Cuervo- Higuero Cuellopelado   Plate 77(7)

Mostly below 300 m

♂ 38 cm (15″); ♀ 33 cm (13″). Conspicuous (especially as it so often flies in the open) at borders of humid forest, sometimes also in forest canopy, in *lowlands of east*. Bill mostly bluish gray. ♂ *mainly black* with *contrasting silvery gray wings*; feathers of head short and plushlike; *sides of neck and throat unfeathered and pale blue, skin folded*. Smaller ♀ slatier generally, wings concolor with back, and sides of neck with bare skin less extensive. **Juvenile** like ♀ but scaled with whitish below. **Similar species:** Virtually unmistakable, especially the bizarre-looking ♂ ♂. ♀ vaguely recalls ♀ Amazonian Umbrellabird, especially in distant flight, and the two are often found in same areas; fruitcrow's silhouette is of a small head and slender neck, very different from umbrellabird. **Habits:** Ranges both singly and in small groups, and apparently prone to wander. Unlike other large cotingas, often flies high above forest canopy, flapping with distinctive deep, rowing wingstrokes, the silvery on ♂'s wings flashing conspicuously. Perched birds hop from branch to branch like a toucan or umbrellabird. Eats both fruit and large insects. **Voice:** Apparently mute.

Purple-throated Fruitcrow, *Querula purpurata*
Querula Golipúrpura   Plate 77(1)

Mostly below 500 m

♂ 28 cm (11″); ♀ 25.5 cm (10″). Widespread in mid-levels and subcanopy of humid forest in *lowlands of east and northwest*. Bill leaden blue. *Entirely black*, ♂ with *large throat patch shiny reddish purple*. **Similar species:** No other similar bird shares ♂'s purple throat patch, though in poor light this color can be hard to discern. When it cannot be seen, the fruitcrow can be confused with various mainly black caciques or even a ♀ umbrellabird; note fruitcrow's chunky and short-tailed shape. In flight note also fruitcrow's broad rounded wings. **Habits:** Ranges through forest in noisy bands of 3–6 birds in which purple-throated (adult) ♂ ♂ are normally in minority. Often they accompany mixed flocks of other fairly large birds such as caciques or nunbirds, but they also troop about independently. Flight swooping, often punctuated by long glides. Eats both fruit and large insects. **Voice:** Gives a variety of loud and mellow calls, including a drawn-out "ooo-waáh" or "kwih-oo, ooo-waáh"; in flight often gives a "wah-wah-wheéawoo." Calling birds often flick or spread tail. Flocks can be lured in by imitating these calls; they may approach quite closely, leaning forward and peering around, ♂ ♂ flaring and ruffling their gorgets. Nests are flimsy stick platforms; several birds may attend young.

Red-ruffed Fruitcrow, *Pyroderus scutatus*
Cuervo Higuero Golirrojo   Plate 77(2)

♂ 38–40.5 cm (15–16″); ♀ 35.5–38 cm (14–15″). A *large* and spectacular fruitcrow, *very rare*—inexplicably so—*inside montane forest in foothills and subtropics of north-*

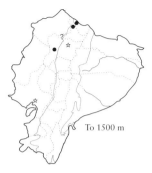

To 1500 m

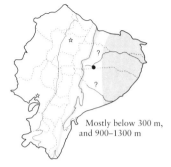

Mostly below 300 m,
and 900–1300 m

west; few records. Bill bluish gray (♂)
or dusky (♀). **Sexes alike** (aside from size
difference). Black above. Chin black with
*large and shiny flame-red bib on throat and
chest* (with somewhat crinkled effect); *lower
underparts mostly rufous-chestnut*, lower
belly and crissum black. **Similar species:** Virtually unmistakable, but cf. Long-wattled
Umbrellabird (which has no red). **Habits:**
Essentially unknown in Ecuador. Elsewhere
mainly solitary, ranging inside forest at
varying heights and at times seeming almost
curious. **Voice:** ♂♂ gather in leks where they
display from branches fairly close to ground,
leaning forward on their perches and extending red foreneck feathers, which hang away
from body like a ruff; they then emit a very
deep booming call, "ooom-ooom-ooom."
For the most part silent away from leks, but
rarely a single "ooom" may be given.

Cephalopterus Umbrellabirds
Bizarre large cotingas with *"umbrella
shaped"* crests and *long pendent chest
wattles* that range locally in humid forests,
one species on either side of the Andes.

Amazonian Umbrellabird
Cephalopterus ornatus
Pájaro Paraguas Amazónico   Plate 77(5)

♂ 48–49.5 cm (19–19½″); ♀ 41–42 cm
(16–16½″). Occurs in *two distinctly different
habitats*, but scarce and local in both: in
canopy and borders of *várzea and riparian
forest in lowlands of east*, and canopy and
borders of *foothill and lower subtropical
forest on e. slope*. Iris whitish; bill mostly
pale bluish gray. ♂ glossy black with *unmistakable large "umbrella-shaped" crest* (sometimes recurved forward over bill, almost

obscuring it, but more often held upright,
spike-like) with *white shafts of frontal
feathers* usually prominent. Also has *wide,
pendent wattle* (8–10 cm [3–4″] long) that
hangs from lower throat (but often is partly
retracted, making it less conspicuous). ♀
smaller and not as glossy, with crest smaller
(*but still very evident*, though showing no
white feather shafts), and *short* wattle.
Similar species: Unlikely to be confused;
Long-wattled Umbrellabird occurs only west
of Andes. Flying birds look vaguely
woodpecker-like as they have much the same
undulating flight. **Habits:** Usually seen singly,
less often in small groups; perches stolidly
in trees, generally remaining obscured by
foliage. Hops somewhat awkwardly from
branch to branch, toucan-like; seems quite
wary, especially in lowlands. Apparently
subsists almost entirely on large insects,
consuming fruit rarely if at all. In lowlands favors stands of *Cecropia* and other
trees, particularly on islands. **Voice:** Small
groups of displaying ♂♂ gather in leks at
certain regularly used sites, perching at
varying heights but usually quite high.
At intervals they lean forward with crest
expanded and wattle enlarged and hanging
downward and emit a low-pitched moaning
"boom" that has been likened to a bull's bel-
lowing. Otherwise essentially silent.

Long-wattled Umbrellabird
Cephalopterus penduliger
Pájaro Paraguas Longuipéndulo   Plate 77(4)

♂ 40–42 cm (15¾–16½″); ♀ 35.5–37 cm
(14–14½″). *Rare and local in canopy and
borders of foothill and lower subtropical
forest on w. slope*, mainly in north. Resembles
respective sexes of Amazonian Umbrellabird

Mostly 200–1100 m

(found only on *e. slope* of Andes). Long-wattled is smaller with proportionately shorter tail, and both sexes have dark brown iris. ♂ has shafts of crest feathers black (*not white*), and *wattle much longer* (20–30 cm; 8–10″). **Similar species:** In its range could only be confused with even rarer Red-ruffed Fruitcrow. **Habits:** Similar to montane population of Amazonian Umbrellabird. Though usually quite wary, at times birds are much bolder, even seeming indifferent to observer's presence (or almost curious). **Voice:** Up to 5–10 ♂♂ gather at traditionally used, dispersed leks inside remote montane forest. There they periodically give very low-pitched and far-carrying "boooh" or "wooom" calls, preceded by the bird's leaning forward on its perch and greatly lengthening wattle (O. Jahn et al.). Grunting calls are also given by groups of ♂♂, often when they are chasing each other.

Black-necked Red-Cotinga
Phoenicircus nigricollis
Cotinga Roja Cuellinegra   Plate 77(3)

♂ 23 cm (9″); ♀ 24 cm (9½″). Now *rare and local inside humid forest (mainly in terra firme) in lowlands of east*. Bill brownish; legs

To 400 m

pale greenish or yellowish gray. *Stunning* ♂ has *brilliant scarlet crown* contrasting sharply with *deep black back*; *rump and most of tail scarlet*, tail tipped black. Wings dusky brown, outer primaries narrowed and curved. Throat black, *contrasting with scarlet underparts*. ♀ has reddish crown; *otherwise bronzy olive above*, duskier on wings; tail dull carmine red, narrowly tipped blackish. Throat brown, *remaining underparts red*. **Similar species:** ♂ is one of Ecuador's most beautiful birds, and the thrill of seeing one is compounded by its relative rarity and the difficulty in finding it; it cannot be confused. ♀ has enough of ♂'s pattern that it too can be readily recognized; no similar bird occurs in e. lowland forests. **Habits and Voice:** An elusive and shy denizen of remote forests, now eliminated from most areas near human settlement. Usually seen singly at low and middle heights inside terra firme; eats fruit. ♂♂ gather in leks, perching on branches 6–10 m above ground with red rump feathers fluffed out, periodically uttering an explosive "skeéyh!," sometimes in series. Other ♂♂ follow suit, producing a burst of calling that continues 1–2 minutes before they gradually fall silent. Foraging birds (both sexes) occasionally give the same call.

Andean Cock-of-the-rock, *Rupicola peruviana*
Gallo de la Peña Andino   Plate 77(6)

Mainly 900–2100 m

30–30.5 cm (11¾–12″). A well known, chunky cotinga found *locally in and near forested gorges and ravines in foothills and subtropics on e. slope and in northwest*. ♂'s iris yellow (e. slope) or mainly red (w. slope), ♀'s always bluish white; bill and legs yellow (♂) or dusky (♀). Spectacular ♂ has *bushy* and laterally compressed frontal crest that mostly conceals bill. On **east slope** *mostly bright reddish orange*; wings and tail black, *innermost flight feathers wide and contrastingly pearly gray*. On **west slope** *mostly intense blood-red*. ♀ has smaller frontal crest. On **east slope** *mostly orangey brown*; wings and tail browner, inner flight feathers widened like ♂'s. On **west slope** *mostly brownish carmine*. **Similar species:** Unmistakable, even the comparatively dull-colored ♀♀ readily known by distinctive shape and orangey or reddish plumage. **Habits and Voice:** Found mainly inside forest, less often at edge, favoring the vicinity of streams; often seen swiftly flying across clearings or gorges. Foraging birds are mainly solitary, though several may gather at fruiting trees; in most areas quite shy. Seen to best advantage at leks, where as many as 12 or more ♂♂ may gather to display, usually on branches and lianas 2–6 m above ground; ♀♀ often nest nearby on wet ledges and hollows. Here ♂♂ bow, strut, and jump about, often flapping wings and snapping bills. Displaying ♂♂ give a variety of loud squawking and grunting calls (some recalling squeals of a pig), raised to a cacaphony by a ♀'s approach. Foraging birds of both sexes give loud and querulous "uaankk?" or "kwaannk?" calls, especially in flight or when nervous.

Manakins: Pipridae (20)

The manakins are a strictly Neotropical family that attains its highest diversity in Amazonian forests; some species occur on lower Andean slopes and west of the Andes. "Classic" manakins are small, plump birds with short tails that exhibit striking sexual dimorphism, *males typically being black with some bright colors*, *females much duller and basically olive*. The family includes several genera that are likely not "true" manakins at all; these are dull-plumaged, and they show no sexual dimorphism and do not display. Displays of many true manakins are among the most fabled Neotropical avian sights: in many they are very elaborate with stereotyped behaviors, sometimes coordinated with other males, and an array of vocalizations, some mechanical, is given. Manakins feed mainly on small fruits obtained in brief hovering flights. Nests are small shallow cups; only females attend the young.

Pipra, Dixiphia, and *Lepidothrix* Manakins

Ranging in lowland and foothill forests, *males are strikingly patterned and colored*, females much duller and more olive. Some older females apparently develop traces of male plumage. Males of some species gather in leks, whereas in others they display more or less alone; a variety of vocalizations is produced. *Dixiphia* and *Lepidothrix* are generic names recently reintroduced for certain species formerly included in *Pipra*.

Golden-headed Manakin, *Pipra erythrocephala*
Saltarín Capuchidorado   Plate 78(1)

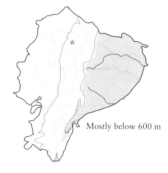

Mostly below 600 m

9 cm (3½″). Fairly common in lower growth of humid forest (mainly terra firme) and secondary woodland in *lowlands of east*. Iris white (♂) or grayish (♀); maxilla dusky, *mandible pinkish white*; legs flesh-colored. Unmistakable ♂ glossy black with *head shining golden yellow*; thighs red and white (hard to see except in display). ♀ dull olive above; paler and more grayish olive below, becoming more yellowish on belly. **Similar species:** ♀ is drab, but can be known by its partially pale bill; bills of similar sympatric ♀ manakins (Blue-crowned, White-crowned) are all dark. ♀ Blue-crowned is brighter green above (not so olive), ♀ White-crowned has a grayer head and obvious red eye. Red-capped Manakin occurs only west of Andes. **Habits and Voice:** ♀♀ and ♂♂ that are not displaying are inconspicuous and most likely to be seen when coming to fruiting trees (often with other manakins). Mist-netting reveals them to be more numerous than one would expect. Displaying ♂♂ gather in loose groups of up to 10–12 birds, perching on

favored branches 5–10 m above ground where they engage in stereotyped postures and movements including darting to-and-fro flights (often so fast they are hard to follow), sidling along a branch, and "about-faces"; in full display they stand high, exposing thigh colors. Displaying ♂♂ are noisy and attract attention; they emit a variety of sharp chips, buzzes, and trills, the most distinctive being a "jeet-jeet jeje-e-e-e-e-e jeet" or "jeet-jeet jeje-rrrrrrr-jeet" and "whir-whír-whíyt! tzeeét," sometimes given in flight while approaching display branch. Common call a simple "peeu." ♀♀ appear to be mainly silent.

Red-capped Manakin, *Pipra mentalis*
Saltarín Cabecirrojo   Plate 78(2)

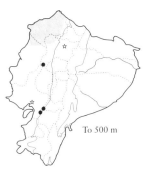

To 500 m

9.5 cm (3¾"). Fairly common in lower growth of humid forest and secondary woodland in *lowlands of northwest*. Iris white (♂) or brown (♀); maxilla blackish, mandible whitish; legs grayish brown. Unmistakable ♂ glossy black with *head brilliant scarlet*; thighs (seen mainly in display) and underwing-coverts yellow, also some yellow around gape. ♀ dull olive above; paler and more grayish olive below, more yellowish on belly. Similar species: *Note this species' w.-slope range*, where there are few other manakins with which to confuse it. ♀ Blue-crowned is most likely candidate, but it is brighter green above and has all-dark bill. The scarce Broad-billed Sapayoa is larger, etc. Cf. also ♀ White-bearded Manakin (with orangey legs). **Habits and Voice:** Similar to Golden-headed Manakin. Displaying ♂♂ at leks are noisy and have a variety of loud and sharp calls, including a protracted "tzik-tzik-tzeeeeeeeeuw-tzík!" given as they fly between display branches, the final sharp "tzík!" as they land. This can be varied to a "tzik-tsik-tzeee"; most vocalizations resemble Golden-headed's.

Wire-tailed Manakin, *Pipra filicauda*
Saltarín Cola de Alambre   Plate 78(6)

Mostly below 500 m

11.5 cm (4½"), but tail filaments add 4 cm (1½") to ♂, 2.5 cm (1") to ♀. Undergrowth inside humid forest, mainly near water, in *lowlands of east*. Formerly placed in genus *Teleonema. Iris white in both sexes.* Unmistakable ♂ has *crown, nape, and upper back bright red* contrasting with black of remaining upperparts; white on inner flight feathers shows mainly in flight; *shafts of tail feathers project as long wire-like filaments that curve downward and inward. Forehead, face, and underparts bright golden yellow.* ♀ olive above and somewhat paler olive below, becoming pale yellow on belly; *tail filaments as in* ♂ (but not quite so long). **Similar species:** ♀ readily recognized from obvious pale eye and tail filaments (quite apparent in field). **Habits and Voice:** Like most manakins, Wire-taileds—even the spectacular ♂♂—are quite inconspicuous, most likely seen either at fruiting trees or when displaying. ♂♂ display either singly or with a partner, with short flights (some with slow wingbeats) and a "swoop-in." Most amazing is that a ♂ may actually "tickle" either a ♀ or its display partner with its tail filaments. Most frequent vocalization distinctive, a drawn-out, nasal, and descending "eeeeuw." Also gives an upslurred "sweeee" call reminiscent of Blue-crowned though longer.

White-crowned Manakin, *Dixiphia pipra*
Saltarín Coroniblanco   Plate 78(3)

Mostly 500–1500 m

To 900 m

9.5 cm (3¾"). Lower growth of humid and montane forest in *foothills and lower subtropics on e. slope, also out into adjacent lowlands. Iris red. ♂ entirely deep black* with *contrasting white crown and nape.* ♀ has *crown and sides of head gray*; otherwise dark olive above. Below paler yellowish olive. **Juvenile** ♂ like ♀ but grayer below. **Similar species:** ♂ of smaller Blue-rumped Manakin has pale blue rump. Other similar ♀ ♀ manakins are more uniform olive, lacking this species' gray on head and reddish eye. **Habits and Voice:** Similar to other small manakins, and like them inconspicuous except when at fruiting trees and during display. Displaying ♂ ♂ gather in small groups in lower growth, perching 3–6 m above ground and engaging in ritualized flights between branches, often with the white of crown spread and flattened; a markedly slow and butterfly-like flight is given when a ♀ is nearby. Displaying ♂ ♂ frequently give a loud and buzzy "dzzzzzeuw."

Blue-crowned Manakin, *Lepidothrix coronata*
Saltarín Coroniazul   Plate 78(5)

8.5 cm (3¼"). *Numerous in undergrowth inside humid forest in lowlands of east and northwest.* ♂ *sooty black* with *crown bright azure blue.* ♀ *viridian to bluish green above*; throat pale greenish yellow, breast greenish, belly pale clear yellow. **Similar species:** ♂ is only Ecuadorian manakin with a blue crown; note, however, that this color can be surprisingly hard to see in dim light of forest interior. ♀ Blue-crowned is brighter green

above than other small manakins except Blue-rumped, which inhabits forests at higher elevations (possibly with some overlap; they certainly come very close). **Habits and Voice:** Similar to other small manakins, likewise inconspicuous and seen mainly at fruiting trees and when ♂ ♂ are displaying. ♂ ♂ perch on slender horizontal branches 2–5 m above ground, usually several birds within earshot of each other. Aside from vocalizations, display consists solely of simple back and forth flights, often with blue crown feathers flattened and spread laterally. Displaying ♂ ♂ emit a soft "chi-werr" every few seconds (recalling the more enunciated song of Dwarf Tyrant-Manankin), often preceded by a faint, high-pitched "sweeee?," sometimes repeated several times. Also gives a brief soft trill.

Blue-rumped Manakin, *Lepidothrix isidorei*
Saltarín Lomiazul   Plate 78(4)

7.5 cm (3"). Local in undergrowth of *foothill and lower subtropical forest on e. slope.* ♂ black with *shiny white crown and nape* and *pale azure blue rump and uppertail-coverts.* ♀ viridian green above, *more yellowish on*

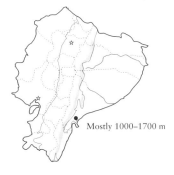

Mostly 1000–1700 m

crown and *paler and brighter on rump and uppertail-coverts*, latter contrasting with dusky tail. Below paler and duller green, midbelly pale yellowish. **Similar species:** Exquisite ♂ unmistakable aside from possible confusion with ♂ White-crowned Manakin which lacks blue rump and is notably larger. ♀ Blue-crowned Manakin is more uniform green above, lacking Blue-rumped's yellowish tone to crown and contrastingly paler rump. **Habits and Voice:** Similar to Blue-crowned Manakin, but as Blue-rumped never seems to be as numerous (and may vocalize less?), it is seen less frequently. Display similar to Blue-crowned's. Displaying ♂'s song an upslurred "koooit" repeated at 2- to 5- second intervals (L. Navarrete recording).

Blue-backed Manakin, *Chiroxiphia pareola*
Saltarín Dorsiazul   Plate 78(7)

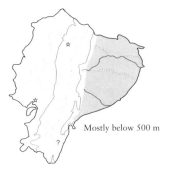

Mostly below 500 m

12.5 cm (5"). Undergrowth in *terra firme forest in lowlands of east*. Legs orange (♂) or *orange-yellow* (♀). Unmistakable ♂ black with *patch of deep red on crown* and *pale azure blue mantle*. ♀ olive above with indistinct paler eye-ring, wings somewhat duskier. Paler olive below, belly more yellowish. **Similar species:** ♀ White-bearded Manakin is smaller and shorter-tailed; legs typically are brighter orange than in this species. The two species occupy different habitats, White-bearded being restricted to secondary woodland and borders. Green Manakin resembles ♀ Blue-backed but has dark legs. **Habits and Voice:** Inconspicuous like so many other manakins, this deep forest species is generally seen even less often than the others are. Displays of the beautiful ♂♂ are mesmerizing, but birds are often shy and easily

disturbed. They usually perform in pairs on low branches, giving a rich throaty "che-wurrr" or "te-turrr" (sometimes doubled or varied). This may continue for long periods, but it changes dramatically if a ♀ arrives. ♂♂ then go into a frenzy of activity, rapidly jumping over each other and sidling on their perches ("cartwheeling"), giving a more nasal "wr-r-r-aang, wr-r-r-aang . . ." ever faster until one bird signals an end to it all with a sharp and loud "swee-ee-eék!" From then on only that ♂ (the "ringleader") displays, crouching and making circular flights, and a copulation may ensue. Other calls given in different contexts include a *Schiffornis*-like whistled "tooo-eee," often doubled, a "tooo-eee, tooo-eee, cheh," and a "weeooeét?"

Golden-winged Manakin, *Masius chrysopterus*
Saltarín Alidorado   Plate 78(8)

Mostly 800–2000 m, locally lower in west

11 cm (4¼"). Lower growth of *foothill and subtropical forest on both slopes*, also locally on coastal cordillera. Bill pale flesh; legs brownish flesh to purplish. Unmistakable **east-slope ♂** black with *bright golden yellow forecrown (feathers curling forward over bill)* becoming *flame orange on nape*, feathers on sides of crown elongated and forming short "horns"; *patch on throat yellow; inner webs of flight feathers pale yellow (flashing conspicuously in flight)*. West-slope ♂ similar but with *nape feathers reddish brown*. ♀ olive, somewhat paler below, yellowish on belly and with *distinctive pale yellow patch on midthroat and upper chest*. **Similar species:** ♀♀ of this montane manakin are drab, but yellow on foreneck is usually quite evident, as is the pinkish bill. **Habits and Voice:** Inconspicuous and doubtless often overlooked; occasionally one may accompany an under-

story flock, or rise up into mid-levels. ♂♂ display in small groups, their activities focused on a mossy log or buttressed root. They approach the log slowly, and upon landing crouch with crest raised and "horns" flared, bowing from side to side. A frog-like "nurrt" call is uttered periodically, and also is given elsewhere, but in general this is a quiet manakin. One displaying ♂ gave a "tseeeuuuw, tsi-si-k-tzík", latter notes sputtering and perhaps mechanical (N. Krabbe recording).

White-bearded Manakin, *Manacus manacus*
Saltarín Barbiblanco   Plate 78(9)

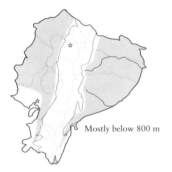

Mostly below 800 m

11 cm (4¹/₄″). Undergrowth of *secondary woodland and forest borders in lowlands of east and west. Legs bright orange.* ♂ basically *black and white*: black above with gray rump. *Throat—which displaying birds often puff out into a "beard"—and nuchal collar white*, becoming grayish on underparts. ♀ olive above, paler and more grayish olive below, yellower on belly. **Similar species:** Handsome ♂ nearly unmistakable, and ♀ can be known by its orange legs, brighter than legs of any other ♀ manakin. Cf. especially ♀ Blue-backed Manakin (larger with longer tail, paler and yellower legs). **Habits and Voice:** As with other manakins, inconspicuous away from its leks, where ♂♂ are very noisy and attract attention. Foraging birds are mainly solitary, feeding on small fruits; several may gather in a productive tree, often with other manakins. Such birds (both sexes) occasionally give an occasional "chee-pu" call, but they really come into their own at their leks in dense undergrowth, where 12 or more ♂♂ may gather to display. Each ♂ has its own "court," a small area

from which leaves and other debris are cleared; other ♂♂ are usually close by. Displaying ♂♂ fly back and forth very rapidly between two saplings (almost appearing to bounce back and forth) and also sidle up and down. All the while a variety of sounds is produced, including whistled "peeoo" or "peeur" calls, but by far the most striking is a very loud, firecracker-like snap, apparently produced mechanically by the wings and often given in a fast series.

Machaeropterus Manakins
Very small manakins found in forest on opposite sides of the Andes. Males are strikingly colored and have *modified inner flight feathers*, much more extreme in the Club-winged Manakin.

Striped Manakin, *Machaeropterus regulus*
Saltarín Rayado   Plate 78(10)

Mostly below 700 m, to 1100 m (S)

9 cm (3¹/₂″). Lower growth *inside terra firme forest in lowlands and foothills of east.* Iris dark red; legs purplish. Unmistakable ♂ has *shiny red crown and nape*; otherwise olive above. Throat whitish; *underparts streaked reddish chestnut and white.* ♀ olive above; dingy whitish below with *vague brownish chest band* and *indistinct reddish streaking on belly, most pronounced on flanks.* **Similar species:** No other ♀ manakin shows any streaking below. **Habits and Voice:** Similar to other forest-inhabiting manakins, likewise inconspicuous and seen mainly at fruiting trees or when ♂♂ are displaying. ♂♂ have display perches from which they vocalize, usually alone but often within earshot of another individual. Singing ♂♂ give soft, clear, whistled "who-cheéuw" repeated at 10 to 15-second intervals. When this attracts

attention of a ♀, ♂ switches to making sharp buzzy sounds (presumably with wings) as it literally revolves around a slender branch; in Brazil ♂♂ have even been observed hanging upside-down.

Club-winged Manakin
Machaeropterus deliciosus
Saltarín Alitorcido   Plate 78(11)

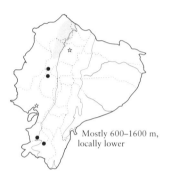

Mostly 600–1600 m, locally lower

9.5 cm (3¾″). Local in *lower growth inside foothill and lower subtropical forest on w. slope*. Formerly placed in genus *Allocopterus*. Legs purplish. Unmistakable ♂ with *scarlet crown* but otherwise *mostly rufous-chestnut*, paler on head and darker on belly; wings and tail black, *inner flight feathers partially white and peculiarly thickened, stiffened, and twisted*, bend of wing yellow and underwing-coverts white. ♀ olive above with *some cinnamon-rufous on face*; *inner secondaries white on inner webs*, underwing as in ♂. Throat whitish, breast and flanks olive, mid-belly pale yellow. **Similar species:** No other ♀ manakin shows rufous on face or white on wings. **Habits and Voice:** General behavior much as in Striped Manakin, though Club-winged is more apt to come to forest edge, at least when feeding. ♂'s display quite different, however. Single birds perch within earshot of each other 3–5 m above ground and give an odd ringing and metallic "kip, kip, buuuuuw" (sometimes only one "kip"). With each "kip" the wings are fluttered, exposing white, and then with each "beeuww" they are held upward for 1–2 seconds almost meeting over back, as bird leans forward on perch. Both sounds are thought to be mechanical, produced by the highly modified secondaries.

Chloropipo Manakins
Inconspicuous, fairly long-tailed manakins found in lower growth of forest, especially on *lower Andean slopes*. They are *decidedly unvocal*; no display has been described.

Green Manakin, *Chloropipo holochlora*
Saltarín Verde   Plate 78(13)

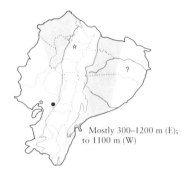

Mostly 300–1200 m (E); to 1100 m (W)

12 cm (4¾″). Undergrowth *inside humid forest in foothills and adjacent lowlands on both slopes*, in west now mainly in Esmeraldas. *Legs grayish.* **Sexes alike. Eastern birds** *uniform moss green above* with an indistinct pale eye-ring. Throat, breast, and flanks olive, with *pale yellow midbelly*. **Western birds** markedly duller: more olive above and darker olive below (with yellow midbelly thus contrasting more). **Similar species:** A dull and confusing manakin, apt to be mistaken for a ♀ *Pipra* or *Dixiphia* but larger and longer-tailed; Blue-crowned is perhaps the most similar. Eastern birds differ from ♀ Blue-backed Manakin in leg color (grayish vs. Blue-backed's orangey yellow); cf. also Jet Manakin. In northwest, cf. also Broad-billed Sapayoa. **Habits:** Solitary, quiet, and infrequently seen; however, often captured in mist-nets, so not really a rare bird. One is occasionally seen accompanying a mixed flock, and also sometimes comes to feed at fruiting trees. **Voice:** Very quiet. A harsh, growling "arrrn" has been heard during agonistic encounters at fruiting trees (R. Prum), and soft sputtering calls have been recorded in the northwest (O. Jahn).

Jet Manakin, *Chloropipo unicolor*
Saltarín Azabache   Plate 78(12)

12 cm (4¾″). Local in *undergrowth inside subtropical forest on e. slope.* ♂ *glossy blue-*

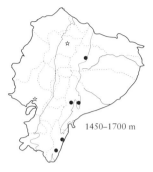

1450–1700 m

black above, duller black below; underwing-coverts white. ♀ *uniform dark olive* with vague paler eye-ring, somewhat grayer on throat and belly; underwing-coverts white. **Similar species:** ♂ distinctive in its limited range. ♀ could readily be confused with Green Manakin, though latter mainly occurs at lower elevations (limited overlap with Jet); Green differs in being less *sooty* olive than ♀ Jet, and it has yellowish midbelly and dark (not white) underwing-coverts. **Habits:** Hardly known in life. Virtually all Ecuadorian records are of mist-netted birds. **Voice:** Call a rough, downslurred whistle, "peeeeer" (T. J. Davis).

Yellow-headed Manakin
Chloropipo flavicapilla
Saltarín Cabeciamarillo   Plate 78(14)

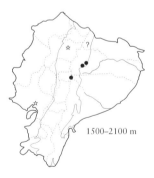

1500–2100 m

12 cm (4³⁄4″). *Very rare* in *undergrowth of subtropical forest on east slope in n. Ecuador. Iris orange to red.* ♂ has *crown and hindneck bright golden yellow*; otherwise bright olive above; underwing-coverts white. Cheeks and throat yellowish olive; *otherwise mostly bright yellow below.* ♀ similarly patterned though not as brightly colored; *crown*

and nape still yellower than back. **Similar species:** ♂ nearly unmistakable. ♀ is so much yellower on crown and paler olive on back than Green Manakin that confusion seems unlikely; Green Manakin mainly occurs at lower elevations (limited overlap with Yellow-headed). ♀ Jet Manakin is much darker generally. **Habits:** Barely known in Ecuador. Like the Green Manakin, Yellow-headed at least occasionally accompanies mixed flocks of tanagers and other birds; it may come more to forest edges than other *Chloropipo*. **Voice:** Unknown.

Orange-crested Manakin
Heterocercus aurantiivertex
Saltarín Crestinaranja   Plate 78(15)

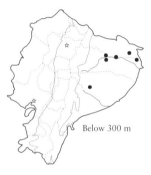

Below 300 m

14 cm (5¹⁄2″). *Scarce and local in lower growth of várzea forest and woodland in lowlands of east*; largely confined to *blackwater drainages.* Formerly called Orange-crowned Manakin. ♂ has *grayish head* with *orange coronal stripe* (usually hidden); otherwise dull olive above. *Throat grayish white; underparts dull cinnamon-buff*, more olive across chest and down sides. ♀ similar, but lacking crown stripe (some ♂♂, likely younger birds, also seem to lack this). **Similar species:** A dull manakin, not nearly as flashy as its two congeners (found elsewhere in tropical South America). Overall shape and posture vaguely thrush-like; cf. also White-crested Spadebill (a terra firme bird). **Habits:** Usually seen singly, often as it perches quietly and motionless in understory; feeds at fruiting trees, sometimes along streams. ♂♂ seem to have regularly used perches where they spend a good deal of time, singing very occasionally. In ne. Peru an aerial display has been observed (fide J. Alvarez J.). **Voice:** At long

intervals ♂ gives a penetrating trill, typically first descending and then ascending (J. Moore recording). Also gives a high-pitched sibilant "wsiii."

Dwarf Tyrant-Manakin
Tyranneutes stolzmanni
Saltarincillo Enano   Plate 78(16)

Mostly below 500 m

7.5 cm (3"). A *tiny, drab* manakin found in *lower and mid-levels of humid forest (mainly terra firme) in lowlands of east*; fairly common, at least by voice. *Iris pale* (whitish, hazel, or pale grayish). **Sexes alike.** Uniform olive above; throat and breast pale grayish olive, belly pale yellow. **Similar species:** ♀ Golden-headed Manakin, though small, is considerably larger than this well-named, truly minute species. Tyrant-manakin is usually recognized, however, on the basis of its distinctive song (see below). **Habits:** Unless vocalizing, a very inconspicuous little bird. On rare occasions one will be noticed as it comes to a fruiting tree, sometimes even in canopy. **Voice:** ♂'s song, given at 4- to 5-second intervals throughout much of day (usually not in early morning, however), is a well-enunciated "jew-pit" or "ur-jit," slightly recalling softer song of Blue-crowned Manakin. Singing birds usually perch on an unobstructed branch 5–10 m above ground, but because they don't move much and are so small, they can be difficult to spot. Birds in the canopy also give a very different call, a more melodic "tuee-tuee-tuee-tuee" (number of "tuee" notes varying); this call may be given by both sexes.

Wing-barred Piprites, *Piprites chloris*
Piprites Alibandeado   Plate 78(18)
12.5 cm (5"). *Mid-levels and subcanopy of terra firme forest, woodland, and borders in*

Mostly below 1100 m

lowlands and foothills of east. Formerly called Wing-barred Manakin. Looks large-headed and "wide-eyed." **Sexes alike.** Bright olive above with *yellow lores and eye-ring* and *gray nape and sides of neck*; wings with two broad yellowish wing-bars and tertial tipping; tail tipped whitish. *Pale yellow below*, clouded olive across breast. **Similar species:** Does not really look like any other manakin, more resembling certain becards in overall shape and color pattern. **Habits:** Seen singly or in pairs, often accompanying mixed flocks, gleaning for insects in foliage, much like a becard. Most often recorded through its very distinctive voice. **Voice:** Far-carrying song a loud and rhythmic phrase with unmistakable hesitant cadence, "whip, pip-pip, pididip, whip, whip?"

Schiffornis Schiffornises
Plainly patterned, retiring birds of the forest understory, the two Schiffornises are *heard many times over for each time they are seen.* Their taxonomic affinities have been much disputed, and are still not resolved, but it is clear these are not "true" manakins. Pairs are evidently not formed, and the nest is a bulky cup placed atop a stump or in dense vegetation near a trunk.

Thrush-like Schiffornis, *Schiffornis turdinus*
Chifornis Pardo   Plate 78(21)
15.5 cm (6"). *Undergrowth of humid forest in lowlands, foothills, and lower subtropics of west*; in *foothills and lower subtropics on e. slope*; and *locally in lowlands of east.* Formerly called Thrush-like Manakin or Thrush-like Mourner. **Sexes alike.** **East-slope** and **western birds** similar: *essentially uniform dull brownish olive*, wings somewhat more rufescent, only very slightly paler below. **Eastern**

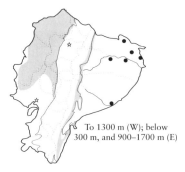

To 1300 m (W); below
300 m, and 900–1700 m (E)

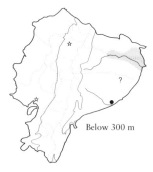

Below 300 m

lowland birds are *paler generally*, with *markedly grayer underparts* and a more rufescent crown. **Similar species:** Dull and featureless, this schiffornis will usually be known from its distinctive song; note its round-headed shape and prominent, large dark eyes set off by vaguely paler eye-ring. In far northwest, cf. Broad-billed Sapayoa; it is much purer olive and behaves differently. Cf. also Várzea Schiffornis. **Habits:** Forages unobtrusively in lower growth, often clinging to vertical stems like an antbird; only rarely joins mixed flocks. Feeds mainly on insects, captured in short sallies to foliage and stems. Heard far more often than seen. **Voice:** Song phrases show distinct geographic variation, though all have similar clear whistled quality; in all likelihood more than a single species is involved. In west gives a very slow, rising "teeeeu . . . weee-tí?" On e. slope gives a faster and more melancholy and rhythmic "teeeu, wheeu-wheé-tu-tu." In e. lowlands reverts to a slow "teeeeu, weee, tu-weeé." Often responds to tape playback, and will sometimes decoy in to a whistled imitation.

Várzea Schiffornis, *Schiffornis major*
Chifornis de Várzea   Plate 78(20)

15 cm (6″). *Local in undergrowth of várzea forest and woodland in lowlands of east.* Formerly called Greater Manakin or Várzea Mourner. **Sexes alike.** *More or less uniform bright cinnamon-rufous,* paler below (especially on belly) and on rump, wings duskier; *shows variable amount of gray on face,* in some extending to crown. **Similar species:** Thrush-like Schiffornis inhabits terra firme forest and is much darker and duller generally. Coloration of Várzea Schiffornis recalls that of Cinnamon Attila (and the two are

often together), but latter's different hooked bill, larger size, vertical posture, and behavior should preclude confusion; its calls are very different too. **Habits:** Much as in Thrush-like Schiffornis, and likewise heard much more often than seen. **Voice:** Song has same distinctive quality of Thrush-like Schiffornis; typically a slow "tee, towee-tee, towee?" or "teeoo, teewee? . . . teeoo . . . teeoo, teeweet." Excited birds often give a rattle, "chrrrrrrrt."

Broad-billed Sapayoa, *Sapayoa aenigma*
Sapayoa   Plate 78(19)

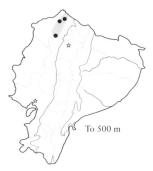

To 500 m

15 cm (6″). *Lower growth of humid forest in lowlands of far northwest.* Formerly called Broad-billed Manakin; sometimes called simply Sapayoa. Rather broad, flat bill; tail fairly long. *Uniform olive,* duskier on wings and tail and somewhat yellower on throat and midbelly. **Sexes alike,** aside from ♂'s semiconcealed yellow coronal patch. **Similar species:** About the same color as various ♀ manakins, Broad-billed Sapayoa is larger and longer-tailed, and behaves differently. Green Manakin is the most similarly sized and shaped though it too is smaller; it shows a vague yellowish eye-ring as well as more

yellow on belly. Pacific Flatbill has even wider bill and shows prominent yellowish wing-edging and bars (wings are plain in the sapayoa). **Habits:** Usually seen singly, less often in pairs, regularly accompanying mixed understory flocks with *Myrmotherula* antwrens, etc. Generally quiet and inconspicuous. Tends to perch upright, scanning nearby foliage in a manner reminiscent of a *Rhychocyclus* flatbill, sallying abruptly. **Voice:** Gives a soft trill, also a slightly louder "chipp, ch-ch-ch."

Crows, Jays, and Magpies: Corvidae (6)

A nearly cosmopolitan family of midsized to quite large birds; only jays are found in South America, where they do not form a major element in the avifauna. Jays are attractive, boldly patterned and colored birds, blue predominating in all Ecuadorian species but one. They are social and very noisy, attracting attention wherever they occur. **Sexes are alike.** Jays are omnivorous, and they build bulky cup nests of twigs that, despite their size, are so well hidden they are hard to find.

Cyanolyca Jays

Beautiful sleek jays found in *montane forests*, only one species numerous in Ecuador. All three are *predominantly blue* and have *black masks* and dark soft-part colors.

Black-collared Jay, *Cyanolyca armillata*
Urraca Negricollareja   Plate 49(11)

33 cm (13″). *Very rare and apparently local in temperate forest and borders on e. slope south to w. Napo*; few records. Formerly considered conspecific with White-collared Jay (*C. viridicyana*) of Peruvian and Bolivian Andes; expanded species was called Collared

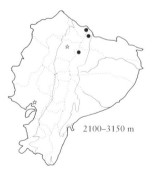

2100–3150 m

Jay. Ultramarine blue above, *only somewhat paler on crown*, with contrasting black mask. *Throat ultramarine blue*, outlined by wide black collar; remaining underparts dark greenish blue. **Similar species:** *Often confused with much more numerous and similar Turquoise Jay*. Black-collared differs in having a longer tail, and is less greenish blue generally; it lacks Turquoise's contrastingly pale milky area on forecrown, and its darker throat contrasts less with underparts. **Habits:** Similar to Turquoise Jay's. **Voice:** Has a wide vocal repertoire, giving a variety of short calls, most frequent being a rising "shrwee?" lacking Turquoise's hoarse quality.

Turquoise Jay, *Cyanolyca turcosa*
Urraca Turquesa   Plate 49(12)

Mostly 2000–3000 m

32 cm (12½″). *Fairly common in upper subtropical and temperate forest, woodland, and borders on both slopes*, also locally above interandean valleys; relatively tolerant of disturbed conditions. *Mostly turquoise blue with black mask and narrow black collar outlining milky turquoise blue throat; contrasting crown also milky turquoise blue*, whitest on forecrown just to rear of the black frontlet. **Similar species:** Beautiful Jay of northwest is much darker overall with contrasting white crown and no collar. In northeast cf. much rarer Black-collared Jay. **Habits:** Bold, sometimes even inquisitive, Turquoise Jays travel in small groups, foraging at all levels, mainly searching for insects though also eating some fruit. Rarely, however, do they perch for long in open. Often accompany various other larger birds such as Hooded Mountain-Tanagers and Northern Mountain-Caciques. **Voice:** Most frequent of a variety of calls is a loud, arrest-

ing "jeeyr" with a hissing quality, often given in a short series.

Beautiful Jay, *Cyanolyca pulchra*
Urraca Hermosa   Plate 49(13)

1300–2000 m

27 cm (10½"). A *scarce* jay of subtropical forests and borders on *w. slope south to Pichincha*. *Dark* overall, mostly violet-blue with *crown contrastingly milky bluish white*, becoming violet-blue on upper back; both mantle and breast often suffused (sometimes strongly) with dusky brown; mask black. **Similar species:** Much more numerous and more often encountered Turquoise Jay is larger, and markedly paler overall with obvious black collar lacking in Beautiful. **Habits:** Considerably shyer and more reclusive than Turquoise Jay, with which Beautiful never seems to travel. Tends to forage more in pairs (at most in small groups), and more often to stay frustratingly hidden in cover. **Voice:** Though often quiet, has a varied vocal repertoire including a "chee" and a more emphatic "chewp" or "tjik," often doubled, both calls most often repeated 3–5 times; also various clicking sounds. Effect is clearer and more staccato than in Turquoise Jay.

Cyanocorax Jays
Heavier bodied than *Cyanolyca*, *Cyanocorax* jays range primarily in the *lowlands*, though one is montane. All have *black extending from the face down over the throat, forming a bib*; most are otherwise patterned (often boldly) in blue, white, and black.

Violaceous Jay, *Cyanocorax violaceus*
Urraca Violácea   Plate 49(14)

37 cm (14½"). A *common, noisy, and conspicuous* jay of humid forest borders, sec-

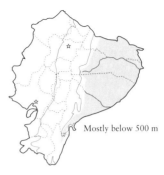

Mostly below 500 m

ondary woodland, and clearings in *lowlands of east*, where *the only jay present* and thus nearly unmistakable. *Mostly dull violet-blue*, somewhat brighter on wings and tail, with contrasting *milky bluish white nape*; head, throat, and chest black. This jay's whitish nape stands out like a beacon, even when bird is in poor light and no color can be discerned; rearcrown feathers are often raised or ruffled, imparting a characteristic bushy-crested effect. **Habits:** Troops about in small groups, regularly perching in open, and often seen flying along edge of rivers or (if not too wide) actually crossing them. Though mainly an edge bird, it sometimes ranges through canopy of more or less continuous terra firme; rarely, however, does it drop to the ground. Often travels with other larger birds such as toucans, or joins them at fruiting trees. **Voice:** Has a variety of calls, most frequent and characteristic being a loud raucous "jeeyr!" often repeated interminably.

White-tailed Jay, *Cyanocorax mystacalis*
Urraca Coliblanca   Plate 49(16)

32.5 cm (12¾"). Generally uncommon in deciduous woodland and scrub in *southwest*,

Mostly below 1200 m, in Loja locally to 2000 m

where *the only jay present*. Iris pale yellow. Unmistakable *bold blue and white pattern*; *tail mainly white* (especially obvious in flight), as are *hindneck, upper back, and underparts*; *head and bib black with conspicuous white facial patches*. **Habits:** Forages in small groups (rarely more than 3–5 together), generally remaining rather close to ground; when feeding often drops to the ground itself. Usually quite shy, foraging in cover and seen mainly as it briefly flies in open. **Voice:** For a jay, White-tailed has relatively limited vocal repertoire, with a fast metallic "cho-cho" or "tjuk-tjuk" call being most frequent.

Inca Jay, *Cyanocorax yncas*
Urraca Inca   Plate 49(15)

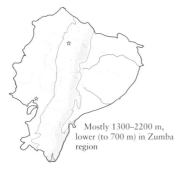

Mostly 1300–2200 m, lower (to 700 m) in Zumba region

29.5–30.5 cm (11½–12″). Fairly common at borders of *subtropical forest and in secondary woodland on e. slope*. Formerly considered conspecific with Green Jay (*C. luxuosus*) of n. Middle America. Iris pale yellow. Unmistakable and unique, the only jay with *mainly green upperparts and bright yellow underparts*; *crown and nape bluish white* with *frontal crest blue*; *outer tail feathers yellow* (very conspicuous in flight). **Habits:** Moves about, often in a follow-the-leader fashion, in groups of up to 6–8 birds; forages at all levels in trees, tending to move independently of other birds. Turquoise Jays replace Incas at higher elevations. Though conspicuous, Inca Jays are often quite shy, rarely perching for long in the open and quickly retreating at observer's approach. **Voice:** Vocalizations are varied, many of them bizarre and un-birdlike. A typically trebled "nyaa-nyaa-nyaa" or "djeng-djeng-djeng" is most frequent and distinctive; also

gives a "tshhh-tshhh-tshhh," long bubbly trills, and a single clicking note. Readily attracted by imitations.

Vireos, Peppershrikes, and Shrike-Vireos: Vireonidae (12)

Rather plain arboreal birds, exclusively American in distribution, the vireos are found mainly in the canopy and borders of humid forest; a few species are more montane, or occur in lower growth or more deciduous situations. Olive predominates in all species; **sexes are alike**. All (aside from the few migrants) are very vocal, their frequently given songs and calls drawing attention to what otherwise are *very obscure* birds.

Cyclarhis Peppershrikes

Fairly large vireos with *notably stout and prominently hooked bills*. Both species are arboreal and inconspicuous, and would be rarely seen were it not for their tirelessly repeated, melodic songs.

Rufous-browed Peppershrike
Cyclarhis gujanensis
Vireón Cejirrufo   Plate 81(9)

Mostly below 1500 m, locally to 2500 m (W); 900–1900 m (E slope)

15 cm (6″). *Widespread in deciduous woodland, scrub, and clearings and gardens in lowlands of west, southward up into subtropics*; also in canopy and borders of subtropical forest and woodland on *e. slope north to Morona-Santiago. Bill massive and strongly hooked pale horn*; iris hazel, *legs pinkish*. **Western birds** yellowish olive above with *obvious chestnut superciliary*; *broad band across breast bright yellow* (sometimes extending up over throat), belly whitish.

East-slope birds have *entire crown chestnut*, intermixed with a little olive in some; throat and breast olive, belly gray. Similar species: Western birds unlikely to be confused. E.-slope birds resemble Black-billed Peppershrike (no known overlap, Black-billed occurring farther north), but Black-billed has blackish (not horn-colored) bill, bluish gray (not pink) legs, and olive crown (not mainly or entirely chestnut). Habits: Gleans sluggishly in foliage at varying heights above ground, and often (especially on east slope, where trees are much taller) hard to see as it tends to remain inside cover. Usually in pairs, sometimes accompanying mixed flocks. Voice: Very vocal, often singing through heat of day; song a short but melodious phrase that may be tirelessly repeated for several minutes before it switches to a new phrase. Call a descending series of 3–7 slurred notes (first usually loudest), e.g., "dreeu, dreeu, dreeu."

Black-billed Peppershrike
Cyclarhis nigrirostris
Vireón Piquinegro   Plate 81(10)

650–2300 m

15 cm (6″). Generally scarce in canopy and borders of *foothill and subtropical* forest and woodland on both slopes, *primarily in n. Ecuador. Bill blackish*; iris greenish or grayish yellow, *legs bluish gray*. Olive above (*including crown*) with *forehead and short narrow superciliary chestnut*; *mostly gray below*, with some olive across breast. Similar species: Cf. much better known Rufous-browed Peppershrike. Black-billed especially resembles e.-slope race of Rufous-browed (latter is almost equally gray below) but differs in its soft-part coloration, olive (not

mainly chestnut) crown, and narrow dark brow. Habits and Voice: Song and call similar to Rufous-browed Peppershrike's. Because of its tall forest habitat, Black-billed tends to be seen less often, though it vocalizes equally persistently.

Slaty-capped Shrike-Vireo
Vireolanius leucotis
Vireón Coroniplomizo   Plate 81(11)

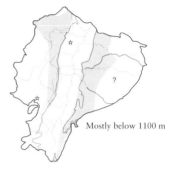

Mostly below 1100 m

14 cm (5½″). An attractive vireo with *striking facial pattern* found *high in canopy and borders of humid forest in lowlands and foothills in east and west. Heavy hooked bill*; iris lime green. *Head gray* with *broad bright yellow superciliary and spot below eye*; underparts also bright yellow. Birds east of Andes also have *white cheek stripe*; birds west of Andes have pink (not grayish) legs. Similar species: Unique face pattern should preclude confusion. Habits: Usually found singly or in pairs, foraging well above ground where it gleans deliberately in foliage and regularly accompanies mixed flocks of canopy-based tanagers. Heard much more often than seen. Voice: Song a repeated single penetrating "tyeer" note, given at a rate of about one note/second. In the west the "tyeer" note is more drawn out and evenly pitched, in the east it is shorter with a descending effect (P. Coopmans).

Vireo Vireos
Plain arboreal birds with slightly hooked bills, mainly olive upperparts, and whitish to yellowish underparts. Vireos are larger, longer-tailed, and flatter-crowned than are greenlets, and their behavior is generally more sluggish.

Red-eyed Vireo, *Vireo olivaceus*
Vireo Ojirrojo   Plate 81(12)

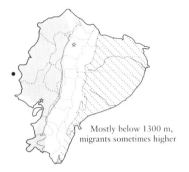

Mostly below 1300 m,
migrants sometimes higher

14.5 cm (5³/₄″). *Widespread and often numerous* in a variety of wooded and forested habitats in lowlands of both east and west, also regularly out into clearings and gardens. *Complex local status*, with *both* boreal and austral migrants occurring (primarily in east); breeding populations are found in the west and probably also around Zumba and in woodland on Río Napo islands. Iris reddish, in some birds (especially boreal migrants) quite bright but often not conspicuous. *Crown gray* with *prominent white superciliary bordered above and below by a thin black line*; otherwise olive above and mainly whitish below. **Western breeders** have *quite extensive greenish yellow on flanks and crissum* (but this is nearly duplicated by immatures of other races). **Similar species:** Yellow-green Vireo frequently occurs with Red-eyed in e. lowlands and must be distinguished from Red-eyed with care, especially from younger birds. Yellow-green has less crisp facial pattern, more olive (less pure gray) crown, and yellowish (not greenish) edging on flight feathers. Also cf. more montane Brown-capped Vireo. **Habits:** Essentially arboreal, gleaning in foliage and also (especially migrant populations?) consuming much fruit; frequently with mixed flocks, migrants regularly occurring in small groups. **Voice:** Western breeding birds have an often-heard song consisting of a series of short, somewhat musical phrases, e.g., "tche-wit . . . tche-wut . . ." that may continue for protracted periods, even in heat of day, during the rainy season. Birds found on Napo islands give shorter, more repetitive song that recalls Dusky-capped Greenlet. Call a descending,

rather nasal "jeeeyr." Migrants appear not to sing, or do so very little.

Yellow-green Vireo, *Vireo flavoviridis*
Vireo Verdiamarillo   Plate 81(13)

Below 400 m

14.5 cm (5³/₄″). A boreal winter resident (Sep.–Apr.) to borders of humid forest, secondary woodland, and clearings mainly in *lowlands of east*. Resembles Red-eyed Vireo, and often occurs with it; less often in forest canopy. Differs in its more olive grayish crown, *more washed-out facial pattern* (black lines outlining superciliary being obscure or lacking), brighter olive upperparts with yellowish flight-feather edging, and *brighter and more extensive lemon yellow on sides, flanks, and crissum*. **Similar species:** Note that young migrant Red-eyed Vireos may have comparable yellow below (though it is usually paler and less extensive). Resident Red-eyeds of west also have similar yellow below, but Yellow-green is almost unrecorded from there. **Habits:** Similar to Red-eyed Vireo, and equally frugivorous. **Voice:** Even though not a breeder in Ecuador, Yellow-greens seem to sing considerably more than do nonbreeding Red-eyeds; they frequently give short snatches of their jerky, clipped song (e.g., "ch-ree, chree, swee, chr-ee . . ."), even while feeding.

Brown-capped Vireo, *Vireo leucophrys*
Vireo Gorripardo   Plate 81(14)

12.5 cm (5″). *A relatively drab and plain vireo, widespread and often numerous* in canopy and borders of *subtropical* forest, secondary woodland (sometimes even in small degraded patches), and adjacent clearings on both slopes. Formerly often considered conspecific with Warbling Vireo (*V. gilvus*) of

Mostly 1300–2600 m,
down to 600 m (SW)

900–1400 m

North America. *Crown distinctly brownish, superciliary whitish; lower underparts extensively pale yellowish.* **Similar species:** No other *Vireo* shows brown on crown. Several greenlets do have brown crowns, but these always *lack* an eye-stripe; cf. especially Rufous-naped Greenlet. Other generally similar-appearing birds that often occur with this species (e.g., various tyrannulets) show wing-bars. **Habits:** Arboreal, foraging deliberately at varying levels, usually remaining high but more often low at edge; often fully in open and quite easy to see. Pairs regularly accompany mixed flocks of montane tanagers, etc. **Voice:** Song a short fast musical warble, given much less persistently than is Red-eyed's song. Also often gives a rising burry "zhreee" call note, frequently doubled.

Hylophilus Greenlets

Smaller than vireos with finer and more pointed bills that often are pale (most often flesh colored), at least on the lower mandible. Some species also have strikingly pale irides, but otherwise these predominantly olive birds are relatively featureless, often best known from their characteristic songs and calls. Greenlets forage more actively than vireos.

Rufous-naped Greenlet
Hylophilus semibrunneus
Verdillo Nuquirrufo   Plate 81(15)

12.5 cm (5″). A *rather large*, dark-eyed greenlet found locally in canopy, mid-levels, and borders of *foothill forest on e. slope in w. Napo. Crown and nape rich rufous, with rufous patch on sides of chest as well; face and most of underparts whitish.* **Similar species:** Only sympatric greenlets in its limited range are the very different Oliva-

ceous and Tawny-crowned; latter is pale-eyed with rufous only on forecrown and is a bird of forest undergrowth (not subcanopy). Brown-capped Vines has a prominent superciliary, yellow on underparts. **Habits:** Much like better-known Dusky-capped Greenlet of e. lowlands (the two do not seem to have been found together). Pairs or small groups are usually encountered while foraging with mixed flocks of tanagers, etc. **Voice:** Frequently given song a repeated, fast "cheedodoweédidideét," similar to Dusky-capped's song but slightly longer and faster.

Dusky-capped Greenlet
Hylophilus hypoxanthus
Verdillo Ventriamarillo   Plate 81(16)

Mostly below 400 m

11.5 cm (4½″). An *obscure* greenlet of canopy and borders of humid forest (mainly in terra firme) and borders in *lowlands of east. Iris dark;* lower mandible pinkish. *Crown brown* (despite its English name!), becoming *bronzy brownish olive on back; mostly pale yellow below.* **Similar species:** Only other greenlet in forest canopy is the much rarer and more local Lemon-chested, which has a pale iris, whitish underparts with yellow breast band, and very different voice. Also apt to be confused with various ♀ ♀ antwrens (with some of which it may occur, even in same flock), though none of these is as unpatterned as the greenlet. **Habits:** Easily overlooked as it usually ranges well above ground with mixed flocks of tanagers; often in pairs, foraging actively by gleaning in foliage, sometimes hanging upside-down or clinging acrobatically. **Voice:** Attention is often drawn to it by its distinctive and frequently heard "itsochoweét" song.

Lesser Greenlet, *Hylophilus decurtatus*
Verdillo Menor   Plate 81(19)

Mostly below 1100 m

10 cm (4″). Often numerous in canopy and borders of humid and deciduous forest and secondary woodland in *lowlands and foothills of west, where the only arboreal greenlet. Plump, puffy-headed, and short-tailed. Very plain*, essentially olive above and *whitish below; narrow whitish eye-ring*. **Similar species:** Cf. rare Tennessee Warbler (with a finer bill, superciliary rather than eye-ring, rather different behavior). Brown-capped Vireo is larger with brown crown, whitish superciliary, and yellowish underparts. **Habits:** Forages actively, fluttering and sometimes even hanging upside-down, at times in small groups; frequently accompanies mixed flocks. More often seen closer to ground than previous two greenlets. **Voice:** Most frequent vocalization an often endlessly repeated "wichee-cheeu," similar to but shorter than Dusky-capped Greenlet's song. Also gives a variety of nasal scolding calls, sometimes repeated (e.g., "nyah-nyah-nyah").

Olivaceous Greenlet, *Hylophilus olivaceus*
Verdillo Oliváceo   Plate 81(18)

600–1450 m

12 cm (4¾″). A *dull-plumaged, featureless* greenlet found in *shrubby clearings and forest and woodland borders* mainly in foothills along *e. base of Andes. Bill dull pinkish; iris whitish*. Dull olive above, more yellowish on forehead; *below uniform yellowish olive*, yellowest on belly. **Similar species:** This species' plain olivaceous appearance can cause confusion, especially on nonsinging birds, but soft-part coloration is normally distinctive. Cf. Tawny-crowned Greenlet (found in undergrowth *inside* forest). **Habits:** Forages singly or in pairs, generally unobtrusive and remaining in cover. Usually not with mixed flocks. **Voice:** Most often recorded from its distinctive and loud song, a fast series of up to 10–12 musical "suwee" or "peer" notes.

Lemon-chested Greenlet
Hylophilus thoracicus
Verdillo Pechilimón   Plate 81(17)

12 cm (4¾″). *Rare and seemingly local* (probably overlooked at least to some extent) in

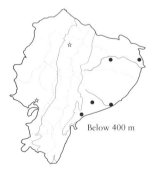

Below 400 m

canopy and borders of terra firme forest in *lowlands of east. Iris whitish*; bill dull pinkish. Bright olive above with gray on rearcrown; *grayish white below* with *prominent broad olive-yellow band across breast.* **Similar species:** Liable to be confused only with Dusky-capped Greenlet (which occurs with it and *is far more common*), but Dusky-capped is really quite dissimilar with yellow lower underparts, dark iris, etc. **Habits:** Like Dusky-capped, Lemon-chested tends to forage well above ground and is hard to see well; it is most apt to be found with mixed flocks. **Voice:** Most often recorded from its simple rhythmic song, a fast "peedit-peedit-peedit-peedit-peedit" or "twee, deedit-deedit-deedit."

Tawny-crowned Greenlet
Hylophilus ochraceiceps
Verdillo Coronileonado   Plate 81(20)

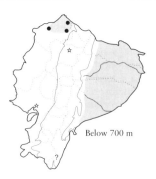

Below 700 m

11.5 cm (4½"). *Lower growth inside humid forest* in lowlands of east and northwest (principally Esmeraldas). *Iris obviously pale. Crown conspicuously tawny*; otherwise rather nondescript. **Eastern birds** more grayish below, **northwestern birds** more olive below. **Similar species:** Somewhat resembles ♀ Plain Antvireo, but that has a dark iris, more extensive rufous on crown, etc.; they are not known to occur together in Ecuador. Cf. also various ♀ *Myrmotherula* antwrens. **Habits:** Forages mainly as pairs, accompanying mixed understory flocks of antbirds and other species. **Voice:** Song a distinctive plaintive and descending "teeeeuw," sometimes repeated at intervals for long periods. Also often heard is nasal scolding "nyahh" call, often repeated several times.

Thrushes: Turdidae (22)
A large and nearly cosmopolitan group of birds that reaches its maximum diversity in the Old World, but is also well represented in Ecuador. Although a few species are bold and familiar birds of semiopen areas, most thrushes are shy and reclusive, inhabiting either montane or lowland forests. They are plain and relatively sombre in plumage, though their bills and legs are often brightly colored, as are eye-rings. Some are superb songsters, among the finest in Ecuador. Thrushes eat both insects and fruit. Nests are cup-shaped, reinforced with mud in certain *Turdus*; they are usually placed in a shrub or tree, but solitaires and *Catharus* nest on or near the ground.

Andean Solitaire, *Myadestes ralloides*
Solitario Andino   Plate 82(1)

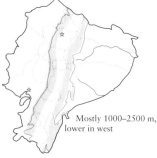

Mostly 1000–2500 m, lower in west

18 cm (7"). *Widespread and often common* (though inconspicuous, and heard more often than seen) in lower and middle growth of *foothill and subtropical* forest, secondary woodland, and borders on both slopes. *Base of bill and legs yellow.* **Sexes alike.** *Warm rufescent brown above*, shading into *gray on forecrown, face, and underparts*; *band at base of inner web of primaries* and *outer tail feathers silvery gray*, both flashing conspicuously in flight. Often-seen **immature** mostly rufous brown (including below) *heavily spotted with buff.* **Habits:** Shy and unobtrusive, sometimes perching quietly and motionless for protracted periods, then suddenly flying off. **Voice:** Most often recorded from its far-carrying and lovely—but ventriloquial—songs, which differ on either side of Andes. On w. slope this is a series of clear, liquid, flute-like notes, sometimes interspersed

with more guttural or gurgling notes, delivered at a leisurely pace, "tleee . . . leedlelee . . . lulee . . . turdelee . . . treelee . . . teeulteeul. . . ." Sometimes the effect is similar to a nightingale-thrush's song, though solitaire's is generally less repetitive. On e. slope shriller and less flute-like, the phrases sometimes more jumbled and intervals longer.

Rufous-brown Solitaire, *Cichlopsis leucogenys*
Solitario Rufimoreno   Plate 82(2)

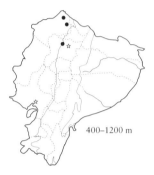

400–1200 m

20.5 cm (8″). *Scarce and very local* in lower and middle growth inside *foothill forest of northwest* (especially *El Placer in Esmeraldas*). Formerly sometimes placed in genus *Myadestes*. Bill *longer* than Andean Solitaire's and *yellow-orange below*; inconspicuous narrow yellow eye-ring. **Sexes alike.** *Mainly rufous brown* with *throat and supraloral rich reddish chestnut* and *crissum bright orange ochraceous*. **Similar species:** Many *Turdus* thrushes are also brown, but none is as rufescent as this solitaire, and none has a bicolored bill. **Habits:** Inconspicuous, usually occurring singly within forest and apt to be overlooked unless singing (which fortunately it often is). **Voice:** Song dissimilar from Andean's, a series of complex, variable, and rapidly uttered phrases, mainly quite musical though some chattering or even twittering notes can be interspersed; usually each phrase differs from the preceding one. Singing birds flutter wings, making them a little easier to spot than the usually motionless singing *Turdus* thrushes.

Black Solitaire, *Entomodestes coracinus*
Solitario Negro   Plate 82(3)

23 cm (9″). *Scarce and local in foothill and subtropical forest and borders in northwest.*

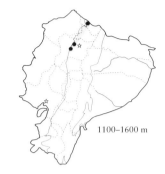

1100–1600 m

Unmistakable. **Sexes alike.** Iris red. *Glossy jet black* aside from *conspicuous diagonal white slash on face*, white pectoral patch (usually hidden by wing), *white band at base of primaries*, and *white outer tail feathers* (latter two flashing prominently in flight). **Habits:** Usually solitary, though several may gather at fruiting trees in favorable locales. Surprisingly inconspicuous given its striking plumage pattern, and most often noted in swift flight across openings or at forest edge. **Voice:** Weird song a weak but surprisingly far-carrying long "wreeeeeeeenh" (lasting a little over a second) with a ringing but at the same time almost nasal quality; it seems not to be heard very often. Call a much weaker "tseeu" (P. Coopmans recording).

Catharus Nightingale-Thrushes and Thrushes
Shy and inconspicuous, relatively small thrushes found inside humid or montane forest. The first two species are resident on Andean slopes and are notable for their *beautiful songs* and *distinctive bright soft-part colors*. The second pair are boreal migrants with much duller plumage. **Sexes alike.**

Slaty-backed Nightingale-Thrush
Catharus fuscater
Zorzal Sombrío   Plate 82(5)

18 cm (7″). Undergrowth of *subtropical and lower temperate* forest on both slopes (more numerous in west), generally at *higher* elevations than Spotted Nightingale-Thrush. *Bill, legs, and narrow eye-ring orange; iris white to pale grayish. Above dark slaty gray; below olivaceous gray*, whitish on midbelly. **Similar species:** Never shows the prominent spotting below of Spotted Nightingale-Thrush, and is

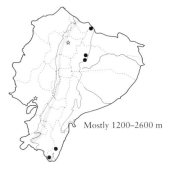

Mostly 1200–2600 m

darker above (slaty rather than olive). Other *Catharus* thrushes are brown-backed and have dark soft-part colors. **Habits:** Inconspicuous, hopping about on or near ground, often in heavy cover. **Voice:** Much more often heard than seen. Melodious and leisurely song a series of simple phrases, e.g., "toh-toh-tee . . . tee-toh" or "tlee-to-tleedelee . . . to wee-tlee?" Call a distinctive querulous "wrrenh?"

Spotted Nightingale-Thrush, *Catharus dryas*
Zorzal Moteado   Plate 82(4)

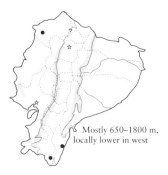

Mostly 650–1800 m,
locally lower in west

17 cm (6¾"). A *beautiful* thrush found in undergrowth of *foothill and lower subtropical* forest on both slopes (more numerous in west) and locally on coastal cordillera. Generally found at *lower* elevations than Slaty-backed Nightingale-Thrush. *Bill, legs, and narrow eye-ring bright orange. Head black* contrasting with *olive remaining upperparts; below apricot yellow with conspicuous dusky spotting.* **Similar species:** Slaty-backed Nightingale-Thrush lacks spotting, and is darker above though its head is *concolor* with rest of upperparts (thus black head does

not contrast). Other *Catharus* thrushes are brown-backed, have dark soft-part colors, and lack warm yellow underparts. **Habits:** Much like Slaty-backed and in general equally reclusive and hard to see, though occasionally (especially early in day) coming out onto forest trails to feed. Occasionally attends swarms of army ants, when observation can be easier. **Voice:** Much more often heard than seen. Song a beautiful series of short musical phrases that proceed with relatively brief pauses, e.g., "tru-lee? . . . cheelolee . . . troloweé . . . cheetrelelee . . . troloweé. . . ." It is slightly lower pitched than Slaty-backed's song, and notes often have a burrier quality.

Gray-cheeked Thrush, *Catharus minimus*
Zorzal Carigris   Plate 82(6)

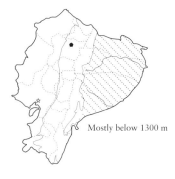

Mostly below 1300 m

18 cm (7"). An inconspicuous and usually scarce boreal winter resident (Oct.–Apr.) in lower growth inside humid forest (especially terra firme) in *lowlands and foothills of east. Drab and relatively unpatterned.* Above dull olive brown with *grayish lores and cheeks* and usually a narrow whitish eye-ring; below whitish, breast spotted with dusky. **Similar species:** More numerous Swainson's Thrush is similar but differing in its normally obvious buff lores and eye-ring, buffyish cheeks, and stronger buff wash on breast. **Habits:** Generally found alone inside forest, tending to remain in dense cover and less often coming to edge than Swainson's. **Voice:** Call a nasal "vreer." Species' true song, a complex jumble of somewhat nasal notes that clearly descends in pitch, is only rarely heard in Ecuador.

Swainson's Thrush, *Catharus ustulatus*
Zorzal de Swainson   Plate 82(7)

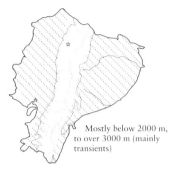

Mostly below 2000 m,
to over 3000 m (mainly
transients)

Mostly 1000–2000 m

18 cm (7″). An *often common* transient (especially) and boreal winter resident (Oct.–Apr.) in lower growth and borders of humid and montane forest and woodland, *principally in lowlands and foothills and particularly numerous in east. Above olive brown* with *lores and bold eye-ring buff* (imparting a distinct *spectacled look*) and *buffyish cheeks*; below whitish, breast spotted with dusky and variably tinged buff. **Similar species:** Cf. scarcer Gray-cheeked Thrush. **Habits:** Most often solitary, hopping on ground or feeding at fruiting trees; during migration, however, sometimes in loose flocks. Shy and flighty—though less so than the Gray-cheeked—and much more apt to be seen at edge and in secondary growth. **Voice:** A distinctive short liquid "whit" call is often heard; also gives a nasal "wrreeenh." Song, a lovely series of upslurred melodic phrases, is given occasionally, especially on northward passage.

Pale-eyed Thrush, *Platycichla leucops*
Mirlo Ojipálido   Plate 82(8)

21.5 cm (8½″). Scarce and seemingly local (and erratic?) in *foothill and subtropical* forest and borders on both slopes. Distinctive ♂ *entirely lustrous black* with *conspicuous bluish white iris* (but no eye-ring); bill and legs bright yellow. ♀ more obscure, mostly dark brown with *lower underparts somewhat paler and more mottled fulvous or grayish*; iris pale brown or grayish (but no eye-ring), bill blackish, legs dull yellowish. **Similar species:** ♀ Glossy-black Thrush is similar but more uniform and darker below, and has an eye-

ring. **Habits:** An arboreal thrush, generally inconspicuous and not often encountered except when ♂ ♂ are singing. **Voice:** Song a series of variable but most often short phrases that usually have a squeaky or tinny quality (sometimes more musical), delivered with long intervening pauses. ♂ ♂ may mount to top of a tall tree and continue to sing for long periods, bill often wide open.

Turdus Thrushes
Large thrushes found in a variety of habitats from montane and lowland forests to semi-open areas in the highlands (one, the Great, even at the edge of paramo). The species favoring open areas are familiar birds, but numerous other thrushes are shy and only infrequently encountered; many of the latter are recorded mainly from their often attractive songs. Identification sometimes is not easy, though soft-part colors often provide an important clue.

Chiguanco Thrush, *Turdus chiguanco*
Mirlo Chiguanco   Plate 82(9)

27.5 cm (10¾″). Semiopen and agricultural terrain and gardens in *arid parts of central valley and interandean slopes from Cotopaxi south*, more numerous southward. Bill and legs yellow to yellow-orange; *lacks* any eye-ring. **Sexes alike.** *Essentially uniform pale ashy brown*, slightly paler below. **Similar species:** Most likely confused with Great Thrush which, as its name implies, is indeed larger (at least in Ecuador) and longer-tailed. Greats here are substantially darker and ♂ ♂ have a bright yellow eye-ring; confusion is most likely in s. Ecuador, where Greats are slightly paler than they are northward. **Habits:** Generally a familiar and conspicuous

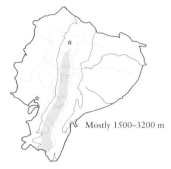

Mostly 1500–3200 m

thrush, often around houses. Frequently hops on ground, feeding in fields and on lawns, also in fruiting trees. **Voice:** Song a rather simple melodic phrase repeated over and over, usually terminating in a jumble or twitter; sings mainly around dawn or dusk.

Great Thrush, *Turdus fuscater*
Mirlo Grande   Plate 82(10)

Mostly 2500–4000 m, locally lower in Loja

33 cm (13″). A *very common and conspicuous, large* and *long-tailed* thrush of clearings, agricultural areas, gardens, montane scrub and secondary woodland, and borders of temperate-zone montane forest on both slopes (ranging up to treeline), also occurring widely across central valley in n. Ecuador and in interandean valleys southward. *Bill orange, legs orange-yellow, eye-ring bright yellow* (but eye-ring lacking in ♀♀). *Essentially uniform sooty*, slightly paler below. **Birds from Azuay south** are slightly paler. **Similar species:** Cf. Glossy-black Thrush (which occurs somewhat lower on Andean slopes, and is more forest-based), and in drier interandean areas cf. paler Chiguanco Thrush. Great Thrush is substantially larger than either. In a brief view this atypically large

thrush can look surprisingly like a variety of other birds (even, for example, a small raptor). **Habits:** Familiar, often perching in the open and seen in swift flight across roads and other open areas. Numerous in Quito, and one of most frequently seen birds in many montane areas. **Voice:** Loud and arresting calls are frequent: a sharp "keeyert!," a "kurt-kurt!," and an incessant "kweep?" Song, though melodic, is surprisingly weak, and given mostly in darkness of predawn.

Glossy-black Thrush, *Turdus serranus*
Mirlo Negribrilloso   Plate 82(11)

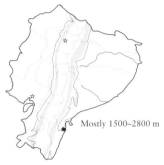

Mostly 1500–2800 m

25 cm (9¾″). Middle and upper levels of *subtropical and temperate forest and borders* on both slopes. ♂ *lustrous black* with *yellow-orange bill and legs, orange eye-ring.* ♀ *uniform dark brown* with yellowish brown bill and legs, narrow orange-yellow eye-ring. **Similar species:** ♂ most likely confused with the more common and substantially larger Great Thrush, which is much less a true forest bird (though the two can occur together). Great is not so deep black as ♂ Glossy-black. ♀ Glossy-black is more uniform, particularly below, than other montane thrushes with which it might be confused (cf. especially ♀ Pale-eyed). **Habits:** A basically arboreal thrush, rarely leaving forest cover and seldom dropping to ground. **Voice:** ♂'s song is (for a *Turdus*) uninspired, a short and tirelessly repeated phrase that rises toward end, e.g., "tee-do-do-eét?" It is often delivered as bird sits on an exposed perch in the canopy.

Chestnut-bellied Thrush, *Turdus fulviventris*
Mirlo Ventricastaño   Plate 82(14)

24 cm (9½″). *Generally scarce and local in subtropical forest and borders on e. slope;*

Mostly 1500–2500 m

seems most numerous on outlying ridges. Bill yellow; eye-ring orange. A handsome thrush, unmistakable as *the only one in Ecuador with rufous belly*. Head black contrasting with dark gray upperparts. Throat black lightly streaked with gray; breast gray; *belly bright rufous*. ♀ has head slightly duskier. **Habits:** Essentially an arboreal thrush, generally shy and infrequently encountered though occasionally one is found hopping boldly on a moist trail or roadside. **Voice:** ♂'s song, a rather fast series of clipped phrases, is mediocre for a *Turdus*, and not often heard.

Plumbeous-backed Thrush, *Turdus reevei*
Mirlo Dorsiplomizo   Plate 82(13)

Mostly below 1600 m

23 cm (9″). A distinctive thrush found locally in deciduous and semihumid forest, woodland, and adjacent clearings in *lowlands of southwest*, in Loja locally up into lower subtropics (especially when not not breeding?); apparently seasonal in some areas. *Iris bluish white* (a conspicuous feature, and unique among Ecuadorian *Turdus*). **Sexes alike.** *Above blue-gray*, slightly duller and grayer

on head. Throat white sharply streaked blackish; breast grayish white with *broad area on sides and flanks creamy buff*. **Immatures** with buff spotting above and dark spotting below are frequently seen. **Habits:** Mostly arboreal, and not particularly shy or hard to see; substantial aggregations sometimes assemble at fruiting trees. Nests during rainy season. **Voice:** Call an abrupt and piercing, descending "pseeeu" that recalls one of Scrub Blackbird's vocalizations but is more drawn out. It can be varied to be more evenly pitched or even ascending. Song, apparently given for only a brief period when breeding, a fairly fast, typical *Turdus* caroling (P. Coopmans).

Marañón Thrush, *Turdus maranonicus*
Mirlo del Marañón   Plate 82(15)

650–1600 m

21.5 cm (8½″). A distinctive thrush, relatively numerous and conspicuous *in Río Marañón drainage of extreme southeast, mainly around Zumba*. Favors secondary woodland, scrub, and gardens. **Sexes alike.** *Uniform dark brown above; white below with bold and profuse brown spotting and scaling*. **Similar species:** No other *Turdus* is as heavily marked below. Various immature thrushes may show some spotting on underparts but are never as profusely marked as in Marañón. **Habits:** Much like other *Turdus*; Marañón is sometimes quite conspicuous, hopping boldly on ploughed fields and grassy areas, but at other times seems mainly to remain inside cover. **Voice:** Song a pleasant, leisurely, and typical *Turdus* caroling, slower than Black-billed Thrush's song and with more slurred notes (P. Coopmans).

Black-billed Thrush, *Turdus ignobilis*
Mirlo Piquinegro   Plate 82(16)

To 1200 m

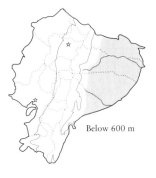

Below 600 m

22.5 cm (8¾"). A *dingy* thrush of *semiopen*
habitats in *lowlands of east*, favoring clearings and early-succession habitats. *Bill blackish*. **Sexes alike.** Dark *olive* brown above;
throat white streaked brown, with *fairly
extensive white patch across upper chest*;
lower underparts dull grayish, whiter on
median belly. **Similar species:** Other thrushes
found in e. lowlands are more forest-based.
Hauxwell's and Lawrence's Thrushes are
browner generally; White-necked shows a
yellow eye-ring and darker upperparts.
Habits: Though basically arboreal, also feeds
on ground and in places quite tame. The tail
is often quivered upon alighting. **Voice:** Song
a series of pleasant musical phrases, often
quite subdued and sometimes heard in darkness of predawn. Distinctive call an upslurred
"we-eét?" (somewhat reminiscent of a
Mottle-backed Elaenia call); also a more
evenly pitched "kweet."

Lawrence's Thrush, *Turdus lawrencii*
Mirlo Mímico   Plate 82(17)

23 cm (9"). Inconspicuous in canopy of
humid forest (terra firme and várzea, especially the former) in *lowlands of east*. *Best
known from ♂'s extraordinary song*. ♂ has
*bill and prominent eye-ring bright orange-
yellow*; ♀ has blackish bill and *narrower
yellow eye-ring*. Above dark brown; throat
whitish streaked with blackish, otherwise
fairly warm brown below. **Similar species:** ♂
distinctive, but ♀ with duller soft-parts is
easily confused with Hauxwell's Thrush.
Hauxwell's is paler and more rufescent

brown generally and never shows any yellow
on eye-ring. **Habits:** Basically arboreal and
apparently feeding primarily in fruiting trees;
also occasionally drops to ground to forage,
especially in moist situations. Generally hard
to see; even singing ♂ ♂ rarely perch in the
open and are almost always frustrating to
locate. **Voice:** Song a long-continued series
of near-perfect imitations of usually short
portions of songs and calls of a wide variety
of other syntopic bird species; single ♂ ♂
may have a repertoire that includes dozens
of other species. A few phrases of its own
are sometimes integrated into the song, and
it sometimes initiates a song bout by repeating a phrase that sounds strikingly solitaire-
like (e.g., "tu, telee-ti?"). Call a distinctive
ascending "ku, kup, kit?" or "kup-kip?"

Pale-vented Thrush, *Turdus obsoletus*
Mirlo Ventripálido   Plate 82(21)

23 cm (9"). Scarce and local in *foothill and
lower subtropical forest on w. slope*. Bill dark
gray to brown; no eye-ring. **Sexes alike.**
Essentially uniform dark brown with a *contrasting white crissum* (sometimes extending

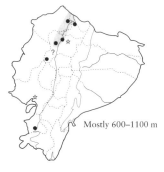

Mostly 600–1100 m

up onto midbelly). **Similar species:** Despite being drab and relatively uniform, the Pale-vented Thrush should be readily recognized in its *limited range*. Ecuadorian Thrush is generally paler and more olivaceous brown, and favors semiopen areas, generally in less wet regions. Hauxwell's Thrush occurs only east of Andes. **Habits:** An arboreal thrush that remains inside forest, where usually shy and hard to see. **Voice:** Song a fairly fast and melodic caroling delivered from a usually hidden perch in subcanopy or mid-levels; pace considerably faster than Dagua Thrush's. Calls include a "zhweek" and "wuk."

Hauxwell's Thrush, *Turdus hauxwelli*
Mirlo de Hauxwell   Plate 82(18)

Mostly below 300 m

23 cm (9″). Scarce in humid forest and wood-land (especially várzea or at least near water) in *lowlands of east*. Bill dark gray to brown; no eye-ring. **Sexes alike.** *Essentially warm brown* with *median belly and crissum white* (usually in sharp contrast, but sometimes washed with buff in which case contrast is less). **Similar species:** ♀ Lawrence's Thrush is quite similar though darker brown above (not so warm or rufescent) and showing some yellow on eye-ring (♂ ♂, with obvious yellow bill and eye-ring, are easy). **Habits:** Generally an inconspicuous thrush, tending to remain inside forest; seen most readily when singing or feeding at a fruiting tree. **Voice:** Song a leisurely series of simple but melodic phrases that can continue for protracted periods; cadence recalls song of White-necked Thrush. Some individuals apparently incorporate imitations of other birds (fide T. Parker) but never with the frequency or fidelity of Lawrence's Thrush. Calls include an ascend-ing "drree?" and a querulous upslurred "kweeeow?" (J. Moore recordings).

Ecuadorian Thrush, *Turdus maculirostris*
Mirlo Ecuatoriano   Plate 82(22)

Mostly below 1900 m

23 cm (9″). A *dull* thrush of mainly lightly forested and wooded habitats and adjacent gardens in *lowlands and subtropics of west*, where the most numerous and widespread *Turdus*. Formerly considered a disjunct race of Bare-eyed Thrush (*T. nudigenis*) of n. South America. *Bill olive-yellow*; dull orange-yellow eye-ring. **Sexes alike.** Basically an *unpatterned, uniform dull olivaceous brown*; throat lightly streaked and somewhat paler on midbelly and crissum. **Similar species:** Paler and more uniform than any other sympatric thrush. Cf. especially Dagua Thrush (with white chest crescent, dark bill, etc.). **Habits:** Mainly an arboreal thrush and rather shy. **Voice:** Song a musical caroling. Most frequent call a distinctive cat-like and querulous "queeoww," also a "chuk."

White-necked Thrush, *Turdus albicollis*
Mirlo Cuelliblanco   Plate 82(20)

21.5 cm (8½″). *Lower growth inside humid forest* (primarily terra firme) and mature sec-ondary woodland in *lowlands and foothills of east*. Bill blackish; narrow yellow eye-ring. **Sexes alike.** Above deep brown. *Throat white thickly streaked with dark brown* and bor-dered below by a *conspicuous white crescent*; *underparts pale gray*, whiter on midbelly and crissum. **Similar species:** White crescent on upper chest conspicuous, even in the subdued light of forest interior this relatively reclusive thrush favors. Cf. especially Black-billed Thrush, which also has white on upper chest

To 1100 m

but lacks yellow eye-ring and is duller above. **Habits:** Rarely emerges from forest interior, then mainly to feed at fruiting trees. Sometimes attends swarms of army ants. **Voice:** Heard far more often than seen. Subdued and very leisurely song a rather monotonous series of short slurred musical phrases that often continues for protracted periods, even through heat of day. Hauxwell's Thrush's song is similar but delivered at a brisker pace. Song is somewhat ventriloquial and hard to track to its source. Oft-heard call a distinctive "wuk."

Dagua Thrush, *Turdus daguae*
Mirlo Dagua   Plate 82(19)

?

To 600 m

21.5 cm (8½"). Uncommon and decidedly local in humid forest and secondary woodland in *lowlands and foothills of northwest*, in recent years mainly in *Esmeraldas*. Formerly considered a race of White-throated Thrush (*T. assimilis*) of Middle America. Bill mostly dark; *eye-ring yellow*. **Sexes alike.** Above deep brown. *Throat white thickly streaked with dark brown* and bordered below by a *conspicuous white crescent*; *underparts dull brown*, midbelly and crissum white. **Similar**

species: *West of Andes no other thrush has a white crescent on chest*. Ecuadorian Thrush (which sometimes occurs with it) is paler overall and lacks white chest crescent. The dark and uniform Pale-vented Thrush also lacks white crescent. **Habits:** More arboreal than similar-looking White-necked Thrush (found east of Andes); otherwise similar. **Voice:** Song a long-continued musical caroling with somewhat monotonous effect similar to White-necked Thrush's but pace a little faster (very different from White-throated Thrush). A common call is an excited-sounding, repeated "queeyrp?" (O. Jahn and K. Berg recordings); also gives a "krrup" call.

Andean Slaty-Thrush, *Turdus nigriceps*
Mirlo Pizarroso Andino   Plate 82(12)

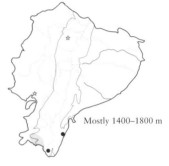

Mostly 1400–1800 m

21.5 cm (8½"). Uncommon and local in *subtropical forest and woodland in south*, primarily in s. *Loja* where apparently present only Jan.–May, when it breeds; also a few records of presumed nonbreeders (austral migrants? trans-Andean migrants?) in lowlands of southeast (Jun.–Jul.). Sometimes called Slaty Thrush. *Bill, legs, and eye-ring yellow in* ♂; ♀'s bill dark and legs more brownish, but still with *yellow eye-ring*. Distinctive ♂ *mostly dark gray above* becoming blacker on crown; *somewhat paler gray below* with throat white sharply streaked black. ♀ more difficult, being *brown* where ♂ is gray, though retaining some gray on sides and flanks. **Similar species:** Predominantly gray ♂ distinctive; ♀ can be more problematic. On its breeding grounds, most apt to be confused with Ecuadorian Thrush (paler brown overall, with olive bill, and weaker throat streaking). East of Andes cf. White-necked and Black-billed Thrushes. **Habits:** An arboreal thrush, shy and hard to see (even when singing). **Voice:** Song a series of jumbled phrases of high-pitched, sometimes even shrill or burry, notes. Singing birds perch within cover.

Mockingbirds and Thrashers: Mimidae (2)

Superficially thrush-like, slender birds with long tails, some well known for their singing ability. The family ranges mainly in North and Middle America and the West Indies, and only mockingbirds occur in South America. **Sexes are alike.**

Long-tailed Mockingbird
Mimus longicaudatus
Sinsonte Colilargo   Plate 81(1)

Mostly below 1500 m, to 1900 m in Loja

29.5 cm (11½"). Common in desert and coastal scrub, around houses, and agricultural areas in *lowlands of southwest*; strongly favors *arid regions*. Unmistakable in range, with *very long tail carried loosely* (almost like an ani's) with *obvious white tail corners*; also shows white on wings. Essentially *brownish gray above* with *prominent white superciliary* and *considerable black on ear-coverts*. Below white, breast feathers scaled darker. **Habits:** Conspicuous, often perching tamely atop a shrub or hopping on ground with long tail held elevated. Sometimes remains active through heat of day. **Voice:** Song a long-continued series of chuckling or chortling notes, sometimes subdued but at times fairly loud, often continued for protracted periods. May sing even when it is hot and windy and other birds are silent.

Tropical Mockingbird, *Mimus gilvus*
Sinsonte Tropical   Plate 81(2)

24 cm (9"). *Very local in agricultural terrain in highlands of Imbabura*, also a w. Napo

1900–2600 m

record. *Pale gray above* with dusky eye-patch surmounted by *white superciliary*; wings and tail mainly blackish, *tail with large white corners*. Below whitish. **Similar species:** Not likely confused; larger and more mottled-looking Long-tailed Mockingbird occurs only in arid southwest. **Habits:** Usually in pairs or family groups; conspicuous and easy to see. Hops on ground (favoring lawns and pastures) with tail held partially cocked, often lifting and partially spreading wings. Only recently first found in Ecuador; may increase? **Voice:** Song an often rambling series of usually musical phrases, each repeated several times and sometimes interspersed with various clucking or wheezy notes.

Dippers: Cinclidae (1)

Distinctive, short-tailed birds that range exclusively along rushing streams, dippers are found on all continents except Australia. Nests are large, dome-shaped mossy structures with a side entrance placed in a crevice above water, often under a bridge or even under a waterfall. **Sexes are alike.**

White-capped Dipper, *Cinclus leucocephalus*
Cinclo Gorriblanco   Plate 81(22)

15.5 cm (6"). An unmistakable *chunky*, short-tailed, *blackish and white* bird, *strictly confined to swift-flowing rocky streams and rivers in Andes. Above brownish black* with *contrasting white crown* and less conspicuous white patch on back. *Mostly white below*, blackish on sides of chest and on lower belly. **Habits:** Occurs in both forested and semiopen areas, the requirement being a suitable watercourse. Found singly or in pairs, most often spotted perched atop a boulder

Mostly 700–3800 m

out in the rushing torrent, often bobbing up and down and flicking wings. Usually the tail is held up jauntily. Feeds mainly (entirely?) by picking at objects along water's edge; though characteristic of dippers elsewhere, actually plunging into water seems not to occur in this species. Typical flight is low over water on furiously beating wings. **Voice:** Infrequently heard song a loud trill, often nearly drowned out by noise of rushing water. Much more frequent is a sharp "dzeet" call that often announces approach of a flying bird.

Swallows and Martins: Hirundinidae (17)

Familiar and nearly cosmopolitan, swallows are aerial birds with long pointed wings that differ most notably from the superficially similar swifts in their more maneuverable flight and ability—despite their feet being small—to perch "nomally" on branches and wires. Most species are countershaded, dark above and pale below (though a few are all dark), and most have notched or forked tails. Swallows and martins—martins are simply large swallows—are conspicuous and often gregarious birds found primarily in open country, many species especially near water; some species are highly migratory. Virtually all of their food is insects, captured in fast graceful flight; their mouths are small but open wide. Nesting is often colonial, most species placing nests in a hole or burrow, others constructing their own cavity out of mud and placing it on a human-made structure.

Progne Martins

Large swallows found in the lowlands, the martins can pose serious identification difficulties unless they are seen well (which fortunately is often possible). Wings are relatively broad and somewhat triangular. Sexual dimorphism is marked in some species (the only swallows in which this is the case).

Brown-chested Martin, *Progne tapera*
Martín Pechipardo   Plate 79(1)

Below 600 m

18 cm (7"). A distinctive *brown-backed* martin, in the east ranging principally along rivers (nesting in banks), in the west in fairly humid regions from Los Ríos southward. Sometimes separated in genus *Phaeoprogne*. **Sexes alike.** *Brown above* and mainly white below with *prominent breast band brownish*. **Austral migrants** (especially) have brown spots extending down midbreast as a point. **Similar species:** Other martins, even when young, are always blue-black above. Sand Martin is similarly colored but much smaller with different flight style. **Habits:** Conspicuous but generally not very numerous, favoring open and semiopen terrain in lowlands. Austral migrants are so far recorded only from east, but seem possible elsewhere, perhaps even in highlands. Perches on fences or wires, often together with other swallows. Flight typically martin-like, powerful and swooping; often glides on characteristically *bowed wings*, then exposing *silky white on sides of tail*, almost recalling Solitary Sandpiper. **Voice:** Calls much like other martins' but often seem to descend in pitch.

Gray-breasted Martin, *Progne chalybea*
Martín Pechigris   Plate 79(2)

18 cm (7"). *By far Ecuador's most common martin*, widespread in semiopen and open areas especially around towns and other

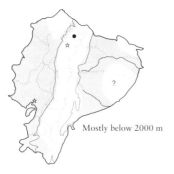

Mostly below 2000 m

inhabited areas, mainly in lowlands; most numerous in southwest. **Sexes nearly alike.** *Steely blue above*, glossier in ♂♂; *belly white*, sometimes with a little dusky streaking. Tail fairly long and forked. **Similar species:** Cf. the other two blue-backed martins, both of them much rarer. Brownchested Martin is obviously *brown*-backed. **Habits:** A conspicuous swallow, perching on wires and buildings and often nesting in colonies under eaves (where these are not available, in dead snags). Roosts can be very large during the nonbreeding season. Regularly flies well above ground, unlike Brownchested. **Voice:** Song a lovely liquid chortling or gurgling, "chrrrrrt," given especially when nesting. Calls include a rather loud "churr" or "chreet," often given in flight.

[Purple Martin, *Progne subis*
Martín Purpúreo]   Plate 79(3)

18.5 cm (7¼″). A *very rare* transient or boreal winter visitor (Dec.–Apr.) to semiopen areas, so far only in highlands (especially near water) but seems possible elsewhere, especially in lowlands of east. ♂ *entirely glossy blue-black*; tail fairly long and forked (much

like Gray-breasted's). ♀ resembles Graybreasted Martin but usually shows a *pale grayish or whitish forecrown* and *whitish nuchal collar* (neither ever present in Graybreasted). **Similar species:** Cf. equally rare Southern Martin. **Habits:** The few Ecuadorian reports involve single birds or very small groups associating with other swallows; its principal migratory routes lie to east.

[Southern Martin, *Progne elegans*
Martín Sureño]   Plate 79(4)

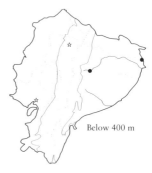

Below 400 m

19.5 cm (7¼″). A *casual* transient or austral winter visitor (only two Apr. reports) to semiopen areas in lowlands of east; perhaps overlooked. Sometimes named *P. modesta* (when Galápagos and w.-Peruvian birds are considered conspecific). ♂ virtually identical to ♂ Purple Martin but with slightly longer and more deeply forked tail (not a field character). ♀ somewhat easier, with *essentially uniform dusky brownish underparts* (belly at most slightly paler). **Similar species:** Gray-breasted Martin is somewhat smaller and always shows obvious contrasting white on belly. The similar Southern and Purple Martins would not be expected to occur simultaneously in Ecuador, breeding as they do at opposite seasons. **Habits:** The few Southern Martins that have been seen in Ecuador have been associating with Graybreasted Martins.

Tachycineta **Swallows**
Fairly small *bicolored* swallows with notched tails, glossy blue-green upperparts and white or whitish underparts, with *white rumps*. Only one species ranges widely in Ecuador. **Sexes are alike,** or nearly so.

White-winged Swallow, *Tachycineta albiventer*
Golondrina Aliblanca   Plate 79(8)

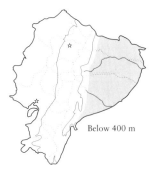

13.5 cm (5¼"). Generally numerous and conspicuous in open areas near water in lowlands of east. *The only swallow with white on upperwing.* An attractive swallow with *mainly glossy blue-green upperparts, white rump,* immaculate white underparts, and a *large white patch on inner flight feathers and upper wing-coverts* (the last usually obvious, but in worn plumage it may be abraded and not so conspicuous). **Juvenile** browner above. **Similar species:** Blue-and-white Swallow lacks white on wings and rump, is bluer above, and has black crissum. **Habits:** Most numerous around lakes and larger rivers, perching on snags or rocks protruding from water and flying gracefully low over the surface; usually does not fly very high. Often with White-banded Swallow, though that species favors narrower and more forested watercourses. **Voice:** Most frequent call a rather pretty "wrreeeet." Nesting birds give a pretty but soft gurgling.

Tumbes Swallow, *Tachycineta stolzmanni*
Golondrina de Tumbes   Plate 79(9)
11.5–12 cm (4½–4¾"). Nests (Apr.; probably not resident) in overgrazed arid scrub *near Zapotillo in lowlands of sw. Loja.* Formerly considered conspecific with Mangrove Swallow (*T. albilinea*) of Middle America. *Small* and *rather drab. Bluish green above* with *whitish rump showing dusky shaft streaking;* grayish white below with *some dusky shaft streaking.* **Similar species:** Blue-and-white Swallow is far more clean-cut, lacks pale rump. **Habits:** Perches on wires and snags, sometimes in small groups; appar-

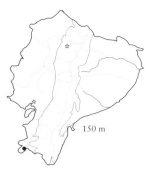

ently nests in holes in dead trees. Shows little or no association with water. **Voice:** A simple buzzy "dzeet" call has been heard around nests (M. B. Robbins et al.).

[Tree Swallow, *Tachycineta bicolor*
Golondrina Bicolor]   Plate 96(10)

13.5 cm (5¼"). A *casual austral winter visitant* to semiopen areas in lowlands of n. Esmeraldas. **Sexes alike,** ♀ duller. *Glossy dark greenish blue above;* wings blacker, often with some whitish tertial edging. *Pure white below.* **Immature** more dusky brown above and not so pure white below, often showing smudgy brownish breast band. **Similar species:** The only *Tachycineta* without a white rump; no other member of the genus occurs in nw. Ecuador. More likely to be confused with smaller Blue-and-white Swallow, though lacking that species' black crissum. Compare immature to smaller Sand Martin. **Habits:** Similar to other migratory swallows; occurs irregularly at the southern edge of its wintering range, but sometimes in quite large milling flocks.

Notiochelidon Swallows

A trio of swallows found primarily in the *Andes*, all species with glossy blue-black upperparts and all three with foot color nearly the same flesh-pink. **Sexes are alike.**

Brown-bellied Swallow, *Notiochelidon murina*
Golondrina Ventricafé   Plate 79(5)

Mostly 2500–4000 m

13.5 cm (5¼″). A *slim, dark* swallow of semi-open areas (including paramo) that is widespread in *highlands. Dark steely bluish green above; uniform smoky grayish brown below. Tail quite deeply forked.* **Similar species:** In general an upper-elevation replacement of the Blue-and-white Swallow, the two species sometimes flying together in the zone of overlap (which includes Quito). The smaller Blue-and-white has less deeply forked tail, white underparts, etc. **Habits:** Favors cliffs and roadcuts, especially near woodland and forest, but also regular around houses. Flight swooping and graceful, usually not too high above ground. Perches on wires less often than Blue-and-white. **Voice:** Flight call a rather scratchy "tjrrrp."

Blue-and-white Swallow
Notiochelidon cyanoleuca
Golondrina Azuliblanca   Plate 79(6)

12–12.5 cm (4¾–5″). *Common and widespread* in open and semiopen areas in *highlands* (but not in paramo); a few occur down into lowlands, in east only as an austral migrant (Apr.–Sep.). *The most frequently seen swallow in built-up and agricultural areas in highlands. Entirely glossy steel blue above* and white below with *obvious black crissum.* **Juvenile** browner above, sometimes some dusky spotting on chest. **Austral**

To 3000 m

migrants have black on crissum restricted to its sides. **Similar species:** Cf. much scarcer Pale-footed Swallow. Dull-plumaged juveniles can easily be passed off as another species of brown-backed swallow, but even they show black on crissum. **Habits:** A familiar, tame, and conspicuous swallow, often seen perching on wires and fences. Nests, regularly in small colonies, in holes in banks and buildings. **Voice:** Most frequent call a drawn-out, scratchy, and rising "tree-ee-ee-ee" or "dzzzrheee?," sometimes starting with a sputter. Also gives a thinner "tseet," especially in flight.

Pale-footed Swallow, *Notiochelidon flavipes*
Golondrina Nuboselvática   Plate 79(7)

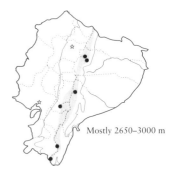

Mostly 2650–3000 m

11.5 cm (4½″). Scarce and local (overlooked?) at edge of *temperate-zone forest and woodland on e. slope.* Much outnumbered by the similar Blue-and-white Swallow. Pale-footed differs in its slightly smaller size, *pinkish buff throat and chest,* and *sooty brown sides and flanks.* Both species have equally "pale" pinkish feet. **Similar species:** Pale-footed and the far more numerous Blue-and-white Swallow sometimes fly together, and then are hard to separate, especially against a back-lit sky. Pale-footed's actual throat color is often hard to discern, but it does usually look a little darker than rest of underparts (Blue-and-white's throat is always snowy white). **Habits:** Graceful flight style much like Blue-and-white Swallow's. Unlike Blue-and-white, only rarely is the Pale-footed seen perched, then usually on snags. **Voice:** Flight call a "d-d-d-dreet" or "dzreet," drier and more broken than Blue-and-white's comparable call (though similar, it can be picked out with practice).

White-banded Swallow, *Atticora fasciata*
Golondrina Fajiblanca   Plate 79(10)

Mostly below 900 m

14.5 cm (5³⁄₄″). *Common along forest-bordered rivers and larger streams in lowlands of east*, ascending major rivers up to base of Andes. An unmistakable, beautiful swallow with a *long, deeply forked tail*. **Sexes alike.** *Dark steel blue with a conspicuous white band across breast.* **Habits:** Generally in small groups that perch on rocks or (especially) snags protruding from water. Groups flush together—almost like the bats that sometimes roost nearby–and then swoop about gracefully low over the water before gradually reassembling. Almost never ranges far from water, but sometimes flies quite high. **Voice:** Frequently heard call, often given in flight, a distinctive, fast "trrrdt," often drawn out or repeated several times.

White-thighed Swallow, *Neochelidon tibialis*
Golondrina Musliblanca   Plate 79(11)

10.5–11.5 cm (4¹⁄₄–4¹⁄₂″). *Local and generally scarce* at edge of humid and foothill forest, in west especially in Esmeraldas, in east mainly

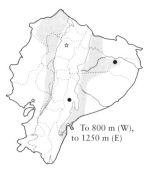

To 800 m (W),
to 1250 m (E)

near Andes. **Sexes alike.** A *small, basically uniform dark brown* swallow; white thighs hard to see but can sometimes be discerned on perched birds. **Eastern birds** larger and longer-tailed, less dark overall, and have distinctly paler rump. **Similar species:** Southern Rough-winged Swallow is larger (even than eastern White-thigheds) and paler below with a cinnamon throat. **Habits:** Usually ranges in small monospecific groups, often perching together on dead snags. Flight fast and erratic, often low over forest canopy less tied to water than the Rough-wing. **Voice:** Calls include a thin, high-pitched "tsee-tit" and a "chit-it, chee-dee-dit?," somewhat reminiscent of Blue-and-white Swallow.

Southern Rough-winged Swallow
Stelgidopteryx ruficollis
Golondrina Alirrasposa Sureña   Plate 79(12)

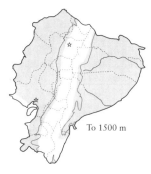

To 1500 m

13 cm (5″). *Widespread* in semiopen areas in humid lowlands and lower subtropical zone; *more numerous in west.* Before *S. Serripennis* of North and Middle America was specifically separated, known simply as Rough-winged Swallow. **Sexes alike.** Dull grayish brown above; *throat cinnamon-buff*, breast and

flanks pale grayish brown with pale yellowish midbelly and crissum. **Western birds** have *contrasting whitish rump*; in **eastern birds** rump concolor. **Similar species:** White-thighed Swallow is smaller and more uniformly dark below, showing no color on throat. Cf. also Sand Martin and immature (brownish-backed) Blue-and-white Swallow. **Habits:** Regularly in small groups, often nesting in riverbanks or roadcuts, perching on protruding branches. Frequently feeds low over water, often with other swallows; swooping flight rather strong, appearing long-winged. **Voice:** Most common call a distinctive rough, upslurred "djreeet."

Sand Martin, *Riparia riparia*
Martín Arenero   Plate 79(13)

To 2500 m

12 cm (4³/₄"). An uncommon transient (especially Sep.–Nov. and Mar.–Apr.) and boreal winter visitant to open areas, mainly in lowlands. In America often called Bank Swallow. **Sexes alike.** A *small* swallow, *uniform brown above* and white below with *brown band crossing chest*, usually extending down as a "spike" on midbreast. **Similar species:** Brown-chested Martin is similarly colored but much larger, with a different, more languid flight style. Southern Rough-winged Swallow is larger with buff (not white) throat. **Habits:** Occurs most often in groups, frequently accompanying transient Barn or Cliff Swallows; regularly feeds over water. Flight fast and "fluttery." **Voice:** Usually quiet though sometimes gives a quick rattled "brrt."

Barn Swallow, *Hirundo rustica*
Golondrina Tijereta   Plate 79(16)

14–16.5 cm (5¹/₂–6¹/₂"), depending on length of tail streamers. A *common and wide-*

To 3500 m

spread transient (especially Sep.–Nov. and Feb.–Apr., when sometimes in large numbers) and boreal winter visitor to open areas, especially in lowlands but can occur almost anywhere when migrating; most numerous in southwest. *Tail long and deeply forked* (shorter in juveniles and molting adults, but some fork always evident) with *white spots on inner webs.* Steely blue above; *mostly cinnamon-buff to buffy whitish below*, throat more richly colored and at least partially outlined by blackish blue. **Breeding-plumage ♂♂** most deeply colored; **juveniles** and **worn adults** duller above and paler below. **Similar species:** No similar swallow has the deeply forked tail. Beware molting or worn Barns in which tail streamers may not be so evident; at least a slight fork is, however, always present. **Habits:** Feeds over open terrain, often around or over water and regularly with other swallows (especially other migrants); passage birds fly purposefully low over ground, sometimes in endless streams. Often perches on wires, and may roost in large numbers in sugarcane fields. **Voice:** Some soft twitters are given, but nonbreeders are usually quiet.

Petrochelidon Swallows
A pair of swallows with steely blue upperparts and essentially square tails. The genus is sometimes merged into *Hirundo*. **Sexes are alike.**

Cliff Swallow, *Petrochelidon pyrrhonota*
Golondrina de Riscos   Plate 79(15)

13–13.5 cm (5–5¹/₄"). An uncommon transient (especially Sep.–Oct. and Mar.–Apr.) and boreal winter visitor to open areas. *Tail essentially square.* Mostly dull steely blue-black above with *buffy whitish forehead,*

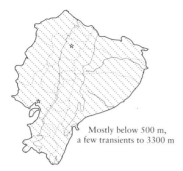

Mostly below 500 m,
a few transients to 3300 m

grayish nuchal collar, whitish back streaking, and *prominent cinnamon-rufous rump*; *sides of head and throat dark chestnut.* Grayish white below. **Similar species:** In southwest cf. Chestnut-collared Swallow. Otherwise most likely confused with similarly colored Barn Swallow; however, even immature and worn-plumaged adult Barns, which often lack long tail streamers, do not show the Cliff's contrasting pale rump. **Habits:** Behavior like Barn Swallow's, and often noted flying with much larger numbers of that species (much less often with Chestnut-collared). **Voice:** Usually quiet when not breeding.

Chestnut-collared Swallow
Petrochelidon rufocollaris
Golondrina Ruficollareja   Plate 79(14)

To about 2000 m

12 cm (4¾″). Locally numerous around towns and in agricultural terrain in *southwest*, southward ranging up into subtropics. Formerly considered conspecific with Cave Swallow (*P. fulva*) of sw. United States, Mexico, and West Indies. *Tail essentially square.* Overall form and *prominent rufous rump* much as in larger Cliff Swallow (though

rump is *darker*), but Chestnut-collared differs in having a *conspicuous rufous nuchal collar connected to breast band*; *cheeks and throat contrastingly white.* In addition, Chestnut-collared's chestnut forehead is so dark as to be inconspicuous in the field (very different from Cliff's prominent pale forehead). **Habits:** Nests colonially under eaves of buildings, feeding over adjacent agricultural terrain. **Voice:** Frequently heard call (often given in flight) a gravelly "chrrt."

Wrens: Troglodytidae (26)
Almost exclusively American (one species extends to the Palearctic), the wrens reach their highest diversity in Middle America and northwestern South America. Most are small and compact birds with slender bills; *colors are subdued*—brown, rufous, and white predominate—with *dark barring on the wings and tail prominent in many.* **Sexes are alike.** Ranging mainly in pairs, most wrens skulk in forest and woodland undergrowth; a few are arboreal, however, and some (e.g., *Campylorhynchus* and *Cyphorhinus*) are more social. Many wrens have loud and often complex songs, in some given antiphonally by members of a pair; the songs of certain species are among the most beautiful in Ecuador. Nests are large, sometimes untidy, ball-shaped or domed structures with a side entrance; they may be placed inside a hole or crevice.

Black-capped Donacobius
Donacobius atricapillus
Donacobio   Plate 81(3)
22 cm (8″). Common and conspicuous in *grassy and marshy vegetation* around lakes (especially) and along rivers in *lowlands of east*, smaller numbers in wet pastures with tall

Mostly below 600 m

grass, a few also now ranging up in cleared areas on east slope. Formerly called Black-capped Mockingthrush. Virtually unmistakable. *Iris bright yellow. Head black*, upper-parts mainly rich brown, tawnier on rump; *underparts buff. Broad white tail-tipping* obvious in usually weak fluttery flight. **Habits:** Occurs mainly as sedentary pairs (less often small family groups) that often perch conspicuously atop bushes or in grass. They feed mainly on the ground, especially while hopping at water's edge. **Voice:** Very vocal, with large repertoire of calls, the most frequent being a loud "quoit-quoit-quoit-quoit" and a harsh "jeeyah" (sometimes repeated). Displaying pairs perch side by side, bobbing heads, wagging fanned tails, and exposing an orange sac on sides of neck, all the while calling antiphonally, one giving a continued "chrrr," the other a loud "kweea."

Campylorhynchus Wrens

The *largest* wrens, *boldly patterned with contrasting spotting and barring*. Despite their size, *Campylorhynchus* are surprisingly furtive, sneaking around in dense vegetation, with their presence usually first revealed by their *loud, rhythmic, often scratchy vocalizations*.

Thrush-like Wren, *Campylorhynchus turdinus*
Soterrey Mirlo   Plate 80(1)

Mostly below 1100 m

20.5 cm (8"). Generally common (*but heard much more often than seen*) in canopy and borders of humid forest and woodland in *lowlands and foothills of east*, though less numerous in extensively forested regions. Nearly unmistakable. A *large* wren—by far the largest in Amazonia—but really not very

"thrush-like." Mostly dull grayish brown above with somewhat scaly effect; *white below profusely spotted with grayish brown*. **Habits:** Ranges mainly in pairs, less often small groups, that forage mostly well above ground, clambering about in epiphytes and viny tangles and among palm fronds. Generally inconspicuous. **Voice:** Mostly recorded from its unmistakable and powerful voice, one of the most characteristic and memorable sounds of Amazonia. Pairs suddenly burst into a duet with complex and variable phrasing, common phrases being a "chookadadoh, choh, choh" and "chooka-chook-chook." Its quality is markedly more musical than that of Ecuador's other two *Campylorhynchus*.

Band-backed Wren, *Campylorhynchus zonatus*
Soterrey Dorsibandeado   Plate 80(3)

To 800 m

18.5 cm (7¼"). Borders of humid forest and woodland and adjacent clearings with scattered tall trees in *lowlands and foothills of northwest. Above boldly banded black and buffy whitish* with grayish crown; *below whitish boldly spotted with black*, becoming *ochraceous on belly* with dark flank barring. **Similar species:** Replaced southward by Fasciated Wren, which favors *more arid* habitats. Fasciated is similarly patterned but lacks ochraceous on belly. **Habits:** Pairs and small groups creep about in dense foliage, mainly at borders and in clearings, showing a special fondness for the base of palm fronds (where nests are often placed) and vine tangles. Usually quite inconspicuous. **Voice:** Song loud and rhythmic, being a repetition of a harsh, scratchy phrase; also gives several "chak" calls.

Fasciated Wren, *Campylorhynchus fasciatus*
Soterrey Ondeado   Plate 80(2)

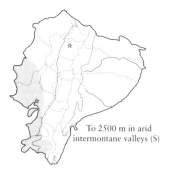

To 2500 m in arid intermontane valleys (S)

19 cm (7½″). *Common in arid scrub, deciduous woodland, hedgerows, and around houses in lowlands of southwest,* locally infiltrating more humid regions. Resembles Band-backed Wren. *Equally boldly banded and spotted,* but grayer overall (not so brown). Fasciated differs most notably in having no ochraceous on belly. **Habits:** In part because of the more open nature of its habitat, Fasciated is a more conspicuous bird than Band-backed Wren, and ranges more often in larger the groups (regularly up to 6–8 birds together) that frequently drop to the ground as they feed, hopping around with their tails held high. **Voice:** Similar to Band-backed Wren.

Gray-mantled Wren, *Odontorchilus branickii*
Soterrey Dorsigris   Plate 80(25)

1100–1900 m (E slope); below 500 m (NW)

12 cm (4¾″). An inconspicuous *gnatcatcher-like* wren found *high in canopy and borders of foothill and lower subtropical forest on e. slope; rare in lower foothills of far northwest. Mostly gray above,* crown browner and more streaked; *long narrow tail boldly banded gray and black;* below whitish. **Western birds** show less banding on upper tail. **Similar species:** No other wren really resembles it, *or forages in similar way.* On e. slope, cf. Equatorial Graytail. **Habits:** Found singly or in pairs that often accompany mixed canopy flocks, foraging by hopping along epiphyte-laden larger branches and leaning out from side to side to peer underneath or pausing to inspect clumps of vegetation. The long slender tail is often cocked high. **Voice:** Infrequently heard song a fairly short dry trill. Also gives a "swe-swe-swe-swe-swe . . ." (P. Coopmans).

Cinnycerthia Wrens
Uniform-looking, chunky *rufous or brown* wrens found in the *undergrowth of Andean forests,* replacing each other altitudinally. Their songs are exceptionally melodious.

Rufous Wren, *Cinnycerthia unirufa*
Soterrey Rufo   Plate 80(4)

2200–3400 m

16.5 cm (6½″). Locally common in *undergrowth of temperate forest on both slopes. Uniform deep rufous brown* with *contrasting black lores;* barring on wings and tail *extremely faint* (barely noticeable in field). **Similar species:** Sepia-brown Wren replaces Rufous at lower elevations and is duller (less rufous) brown with more prominent wing and tail barring. The similar Rufous Spinetail occurs in comparable situations though it differs in behavior and voice; spinetail lacks barring on wings and tail, has longer and more graduated tail with pointed rectrices. **Habits:** Keeps to dense cover as it creeps about in groups of up to 6–10 birds, sometimes fast moving; favors areas with much bamboo. **Voice:** Musical song often given by several birds as a duet, and usually consists of a repeated simple note or short phrase overlaying a trill. Repeated notes or phrases tend to be shorter than in Sepia-brown.

Sepia-brown Wren, *Cinnycerthia olivascens*
Soterrey Caferrojizo   Plate 80(5)

Mostly 1500–2500 m

16 cm (6¼″). *Undergrowth of subtropical forest on both slopes.* Formerly named *C. peruana*; has been called Sharpe's Wren. *Dull rufescent brown*, some birds have variable amount of grayish on face and throat and/or white on forehead; *wings and tail narrowly but distinctly barred with black.* **Similar species:** The brighter Rufous Wren ranges at higher elevations (little or no overlap); it shows minimal or no wing and tail barring. Western Hemispingus can look vaguely similar. **Habits:** Similar to Rufous Wren, though Sepia-brown tends to travel in smaller groups (often only a pair is present) and more often accompanies mixed understory flocks. **Voice:** Complex song consists of a series of variable, musical phrases and trills, with changing emphasis. Repeated phrases tend to be longer than in Rufous.

Grass Wren, *Cistothorus platensis*
Soterrey Sabanero   Plate 80(16)

10–10.5 cm (4–4¼″). A *small* wren, not uncommon (but secretive) in *moist grassy and sedgy situations in paramo*, also in clearings and agricultural areas in the temperate zone and locally in central and interandean valleys. In North America (conspecific?) called Sedge Wren. *Buffy brown above* with *back prominently streaked black and buffy*

Mostly 2800–4000 m

whitish; crown vaguely streaked, and wings and tail prominently banded with dusky. *Mostly buffyish below.* **Similar species:** House Wren is much more uniform, with no streaking on back, etc. Cf. also Streak-backed and Many-striped Canasteros. **Habits:** Creeps about mouse-like on or near the ground in dense vegetation, only rarely emerging from cover. Most apt to be noted when singing or calling, which fortunately it does frequently. **Voice:** Nasal call a distinctive insistent "meur-meur-meur. . . ." Song, often delivered from an exposed position on a shrub or rock, a much prettier series of musical phrases and trills that can sound quite canary-like.

Thryothorus Wrens
Small to midsized wrens that skulk in dense undergrowth of woodland and forest borders. Like most wrens, *Thryothorus* are heard far more often than seen; their songs are loud, varied, and vigorous, and they often are given as a duet by members of a pair. *Thryothorus* are brown or rufous above, paler below (whitish to rufescent, often with some barring); many have streaked cheeks and a white brow, and most have barring on tail (sometimes wings as well).

Bay Wren, *Thryothorus nigricapillus*
Soterrey Cabecipinto   Plate 80(6)

14.5 cm (5¾″). A pretty wren of dense lower growth at edge of humid forest and woodland in *lowlands and foothills of west*, south of Pichincha only along humid base of Andes. *Head and neck black* with *large white patch on cheeks*; otherwise bright rufous brown above, wings and tail boldly barred black. Throat and midchest white, *underparts elsewhere boldly barred black and white*, with

Mostly below 900 m,
to 1300 m around Mindo

flanks washed rufous. **Northern Esmeraldas birds** are even more extensively black-barred below. **Similar species:** Almost unmistakable; no other *Thryothorus* shows mainly black head and extensively barred underparts. **Habits:** Among the usually sneaky *Thryothorus*, the handsome Bay is comparatively easy to see: it is prone to bursting from cover (at least briefly), and also creeps around in well-vegetated gardens (e.g., those at Tinalandia). Like its congeners, Bay usually occurs in pairs, which tend to be very sedentary. **Voice:** Very noisy. Vigorous loud song consists of a series of complex musical phrases that are repeated several times before moving on to next; has a sharp staccato quality. Also chirrs frequently and has other calls, a "heetowíp!" being frequent.

Plain-tailed Wren, *Thryothorus euophrys*
Soterrey Colillano   Plate 80(7)

Mostly 2200–3200 m

16–16.5 cm (6¼–6½″). Undergrowth of *temperate forest, woodland, and borders on both slopes*, and locally above central and inter-andean valleys. Strongly favors *Chusquea* bamboo. A large *Thryothorus* with *bright rufous upperparts* (wings and *tail unbarred*), grayish to brownish crown, and *bold facial*

pattern (superciliary, malar and submalar streaks). **West-slope birds** are *prominently spotted on breast*, whereas in **east-slope birds** spotting is *never as profuse*, and it decreases southward to where birds near Peruvian border are merely plain grayish below. **Similar species:** Whiskered Wren of w. lowlands never occurs so high in Andes; it shows no spotting below and has barred tail. **Habits:** Ranges in pairs, hopping and creeping about in often nearly impenetrable undergrowth. Sometimes accompanies mixed flocks, but in general not often seen except after tape playback. **Voice:** Mostly recorded from its fast musical song, often given as a rollicking duet by members of a pair; neighboring pairs often answer. Also has a loud and rather dry alarm call, "tjek-tje-tje-tjek."

Whiskered Wren, *Thryothorus mystacalis*
Soterrey Bigotillo   Plate 80(8)

To 1500 m

16 cm (6¼″). Undergrowth and viny tangles in humid forest borders and secondary woodland in *west* from *more humid lowlands up into lower subtropics*. Formerly considered conspecific with Moustached Wren (*T. genibarbis*) of s.-cen. South America. A *large* wren with *bold facial pattern* (white superciliary, strongly streaked cheeks, and *white malar and black submalar streaks*) and *rufous-chestnut mantle contrasting with grayish upper back*; tail barred but *wings unbarred*; underparts dingy and plain. **Similar species:** In its range likely confused only with Bay Wren, which has mainly black head and extensive barring below. Plain-tailed Wren occurs at higher elevations, has breast spotting, etc. **Habits:** An exceptionally skulking wren, creeping about in pairs in

dense thickets and viny tangles. May ascend up to 10–12 m above ground, higher than most of congeners. **Voice:** Most often recorded from its exceptionally rich and musical song which has a liquid gurgling quality and often long pauses between phrases. Call an almost frog-like "kwi," sometimes given in series of 3–4.

Coraya Wren, *Thryothorus coraya*
Soterrey Coraya   Plate 80(9)

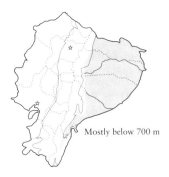

Mostly below 700 m

14.5 cm (5¾"). Often numerous at borders of humid forest and secondary woodland in *lowlands of east*. *Sides of head blackish with some white streaking*, becoming *solidly blackish on malar area*; otherwise mainly rufous brown above with boldly barred tail; below mainly dingy grayish buff. **Similar species:** The only other *Thryothorus* in e. lowlands is Buff-breasted, which can sound somewhat like Coraya but looks quite different (extensive white on cheeks, bright buff on underparts). **Habits:** Pairs forage more often with mixed understory flocks than do most other *Thryothorus*, and they then may creep around in tangles well above ground. **Voice:** Song a variable series of repeated musical phrases but less rich than in many of its congeners (and less staccato than Buff-breasted); phrases often start with a drawn-out note and then repeat a short note, and may include a "jeeyr-jeeyr" or "choh-choh-choh." One call is a rhythmic "tu-dk tu-choow, tu-dk tu-choow. . . ."

Buff-breasted Wren, *Thryothorus leucotis*
Soterrey Pechianteado   Plate 80(11)

14 cm (5½"). Rather uncommon in thickets around lakes and along rivers and in under-

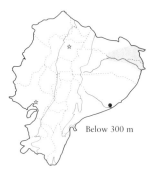

Below 300 m

growth of várzea forest borders and woodland in *lowlands of east*. *Uniform brown above* with *white superciliary and cheek streaking* and *black barring on wings* and tail; throat white, becoming *pale buff on breast and deeper buff to cinnamon-buff on flanks*. **Similar species:** Coraya Wren differs in having black on face, no barring on wings. **Habits:** Behavior much like other *Thryothorus*: usually in pairs, most often not with flocks, with presence strongly tied to presence of water. Despite often being numerous elsewhere, not frequently encountered in Ecuador. **Voice:** Song a loud vigorous series of very fast staccato phrases repeated rapidly several times before switching to next. Call a frequently heard staccato note, usually repeated twice, e.g., "totok totok!"

Superciliated Wren, *Thryothorus superciliaris*
Soterrey Cejón   Plate 80(12)

Mostly below 1500 m

14.5 cm (5¾"). The western "equivalent" of Buff-breasted Wren, found in *dry scrub and thickets in lowlands of southwest*, locally ranging into more humid regions in woodland undergrowth. *Essentially bright rufous above* with bold black wing and tail barring; *superciliary, face, and most of underparts pure white*, with only a trace of buff on flanks. **Similar species:** Easy to recognize in its range. The only other *Thryothorus* in more arid parts of w. Ecuador is the dissimilar Speckle-breasted, which has conspicuous spotting below, plain wings, etc.; Speckle-breasted favors woodland. **Habits:** Usually in pairs that skulk in heavy cover, occasionally emerging to edge to feed (sometimes on ground) or to sing. **Voice:** Song similar to Buff-breasted's but phrases usually not as fast or rollicking; has a more staccato quality than Speckle-breasted. Also has several churring calls.

Speckle-breasted Wren, *Thryothorus sclateri*
Soterrey Pechijaspeado   Plate 80(10)

To about 1600 m

13.5–14 cm (5¼–5½"). A relatively small *Thryothorus* of deciduous and semihumid woodland undergrowth and borders in *lowlands and foothills of southwest*, and in Río Marañón drainage of extreme southeast. Sometimes considered conspecific with Spot-breasted Wren (*T. maculipectus*) of Middle America. Plain brown above with black barring on tail but *none on wings*; *ear-coverts streaked or speckled black and white*, surmounted by thin white superciliary; below mostly whitish with *breast prominently speckled with black*, flanks rufescent. **Marañón birds** are slightly larger and *more boldly and extensively speckled black below*. **Similar species:** There are few other *Thryothorus* in its range or habitat. Stripe-throated Wren has similar facial pattern but has barred wings and tail and shows no spotting below; it occurs in *humid* forest. Cf. also larger and brighter Superciliated Wren. **Habits:** Usually in pairs, often inquisitive and

regularly joining small mixed flocks in understory, sometimes moving higher in dense tangles. **Voice:** Variable song more or less typical of genus, though less staccato than Superciliated. Frequently given call a distinctive rising sound similar to rubbing one's fingers against tines of a comb.

Stripe-throated Wren, *Thryothorus leucopogon*
Soterrey Golirrayado   Plate 80(13)

To 750 m

12 cm (4¾"). A scarce and local wren found in humid forest, secondary woodland, and borders in *lowlands and foothills of northwest*, most common in n. Esmeraldas. Iris dull yellowish to hazel. A *small*, rather *dull* wren. Olive brown above with *black barring on wings* and tail; *sides of head and throat prominently streaked black and white*, surmounted by a narrow white superciliary. Below dull brown. **Similar species:** Cf. larger Speckle-breasted Wren (it and Stripe-throated are not known to actually occur together); Speckle-breasted's spotting below can be obscure, but it always shows *plain* wings. **Habits:** Favors viny tangles, and often accompanies small understory flocks with *Myrmotherula* antwrens and other species. **Voice:** Frequently heard call a distinctive "chu, ch-chu," with song apparently a run-together version of this. Also gives a level series of well-spaced whistles, "teeee . . . teeee . . . teeee . . . teeee . . ." (P. Coopmans).

Troglodytes Wrens
Small brownish wrens showing *relatively little pattern*, both Ecuadorian *Troglodytes* are pert little birds with *short tails usually held cocked*.

House Wren, *Troglodytes aedon*
Soterrey Criollo   Plate 80(14)

To 3300 m

Mostly 1500–3200 m, much lower on coastal cordillera

11.5 cm (4½″). *Widespread and generally common*, occurring in a variety of semi-open habitats, *especially around houses* (its English name highly appropriate) and agricultural regions. Scarcer in lowlands of east. A *small, plain* wren with *no obvious features. Tail often held cocked*. Essentially grayish brown above and buffy whitish below, with *weak* pale superciliary and *indistinct* dusky barring on wings and tail. On El Oro coast (elsewhere?) a more or less sooty morph (?) occurs. **Similar species:** The generally similar Mountain Wren also often cocks its even shorter tail, but it is much more associated with wooded and forested habitats and is more rufescent above with a bolder and buffier eye-stripe. Grass Wren has prominently streaked back and very different, inconspicuous behavior. **Habits:** A familiar bird, often tame, hopping about in shrubbery and usually undisturbed even by a close approach, though often scolding interminably. **Voice:** Pleasant gurgling, warbled song should quickly become known, and may be delivered from an exposed perch. Also has a distinctive nasal "jeeyáh" call.

Mountain Wren, *Troglodytes solstitialis*
Soterrey Montañés   Plate 80(15)

11 cm (4¼″). *Widespread and generally numerous in subtropical and temperate forest and woodland*. A *short-tailed, rufescent* wren with *bold and contrastingly buff superciliary*. Basically *rufous brown above* and *pale buff below*, with *quite bold* blackish wing and tail barring. **Similar species:** House Wren is paler, duller, and longer tailed; it inhabits semiopen

terrain. **Habits:** Usually found singly or in pairs, often moving with mixed flocks, ranging at varying levels from undergrowth to subcanopy and often noted hopping on moss-covered limbs and trunks. Favors borders and openings. **Voice:** Fast song a short, fairly musical series of tinkling notes, often uttered as it forages. Call an often-heard brief trill, "tchr-r-r."

Henicorhina Wood-Wrens
Small wrens with *very short tails* that are usually held *cocked*. Wood-wrens hop around in pairs close to the ground in humid or montane forest, and their rollicking songs are often heard.

White-breasted Wood-Wren
Henicorhina leucosticta
Soterrey Montés Pechiblanco   Plate 80(17)

Mostly below 900–1000 m

11 cm (4¼″). Often numerous (especially by voice) on or near ground in *humid forest in lowlands of east and northwest*, smaller numbers up into foothills. *Very short tail. Throat and breast white*, "cleaner" in **eastern** birds; *sides of head and neck boldly streaked*. **Eastern birds** have *crown contrastingly*

black, whereas **northwestern birds** have crown rufous brown, nearly concolor with back. **Similar species:** Gray-breasted Wood-Wren ranges at *higher* elevations (with local overlap, at least in northwest); though generally similar, it is clearly *gray*-breasted. **Habits:** Pert and attractive, ranging in pairs near forest floor, favoring dense growth around treefalls and other openings. Though certainly heard far more often than seen, not an especially shy bird. **Voice:** Phrased song somewhat variable, but always with rich quality; individual phrases tend to be short and are usually repeated several (up to 4–6) times. A frequent phrase is "churry-churry-cheer." Northwestern birds sound quite different, giving a very liquid "weee-wyí-tee-tuuw" (P. Coopmans). Call throughout a reiterated gravelly "chrrr."

Gray-breasted Wood-Wren
Henicorhina leucophrys
Soterrey Montés Pechigris   Plate 80(18)

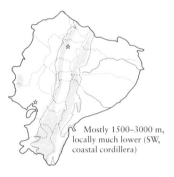

Mostly 1500–3000 m, locally much lower (SW, coastal cordillera)

11 cm (4¼″). Common—but heard much more often than seen—in undergrowth of *subtropical and temperate forest, woodland, and borders on both slopes*, also on coastal cordillera. *Tail very short*, though slightly less so than in White-breasted, which Gray-breasted resembles. *Throat and (especially) breast gray*, but this paler in **southwestern race**, which occurs both in Andes and on coastal cordillera. Has *equally boldly streaked sides of head and neck* as White-breasted Wood-Wren. **Similar species:** On remote Cordillera del Cóndor, cf. Bar-winged Wood-Wren. **Habits:** Usually in pairs that creep about in tangles and dense undergrowth where often hard to see well; actually, however, not especially shy and indeed often

inquisitive. **Voice:** Frequently heard song a series of relatively long and complex phrases (often uttered by a duetting pair), each usually repeated a few times before going on to next; usually more staccato than White-breasted. Chirring call is similar to White-breasted's.

Bar-winged Wood-Wren
Henicorhina leucoptera
Soterrey Montés Alibandeado   Plate 80(19)

1700–1950 m

11 cm (4¼″). Montane forest undergrowth and borders at *higher elevations* on remote *Cordillera del Cóndor in extreme se. Zamora-Chinchipe*. Resembles much more widespread Gray-breasted Wood-Wren, but has *two conspicuous white wing-bars* and is somewhat whiter below than sympatric race of Gray-breasted. **Habits:** As in Gray-breasted Wood-Wren. Bar-winged can occur with Gray-breasted and replaces it entirely above 1700–1800 m. **Voice:** Much as in Gray-breasted—the two sometimes respond to each others' voices—but somewhat more melodious and less staccato.

Cyphorhinus Wrens
Heavily built wrens found in family groups *on or near the ground inside humid or montane forest*. Their bills are thick with a high, ridged culmen. *Cyphorhinus* are best known for their *beautiful songs*, among the loveliest in the world.

Chestnut-breasted Wren
Cyphorhinus thoracicus
Soterrey Pechicastaño   Plate 80(20)

15 cm (6″). Scarce inside *subtropical forest on e. slope*, occurring at *higher elevations* than other *Cyphorhinus*. *Throat and breast*

1100–2000 m

orange-rufous extending up onto sides of neck; *upperparts dark brown, crown duskier,* and *wings and tail unbarred.* **Similar species:** Musician Wren occurs mainly at lower elevations, though apparently there is limited overlap. It differs in its smaller size, orange-rufous forecrown, and barred wings and tail. **Habits:** Usually occurs in pairs that skulk in dense undergrowth, sometimes near streams; generally does not accompany mixed flocks. **Voice:** Recorded most often through its simple but lovely and almost ethereal song, a repetition of the same minor-key note or pair of notes, the second a half-tone higher or lower than the first. Repetitions may continue for up to several minutes without pause. Chestnut-breasted's song lacks the interspersed "churr" notes so typical of its congeners.

Musician Wren, *Cyphorhinus arada*
Soterrey Virtuoso   Plate 80(21)

Mostly below 1000 m

13 cm (5″). Uncommon inside humid forest (principally terra firme) in *lowlands and foothills of east.* Forecrown, superciliary and face, throat, and breast dark orange-rufous; otherwise dull brown, wings and tail barred black. Unlike Song Wren, Musician has only a small bare bluish area around eye. **Similar species:** Song Wren is found only west of Andes. Chestnut-breasted Wren of Andean slopes is larger with a solidly dark crown (no rufous) and unbarred wings and tail. Beware confusion with certain ♀ antbirds, e.g., Spot-winged. **Habits:** Behavior similar to Song Wren's, though Musician tends to be shyer and is less often encountered. **Voice:** Musician's marvelous song consists of a series of complex musical phrases interspersed with churring and piping notes. It tends to be more complex and modulated than Song Wren's.

Song Wren, *Cyphorhinus phaeocephalus*
Soterrey Canoro   Plate 80(22)

To 900 m

13 cm (5″). Inside humid forest and secondary woodland in *lowlands and foothills of west.* Extensive bare ocular area conspicuously pale blue. Mostly dull brown, *wings and tail barred black; sides of head, throat, and chest deep rufous.* **Similar species:** Several antbirds (e.g., Chestnut-backed) show a comparable pale blue ocular area, but none of these have barring on wings. In Ecuador the Chestnut-breasted Wren does not occur on w. slope of Andes. Musician Wren ranges only east of Andes. **Habits:** Found in pairs or small family groups, hopping about on or near ground, most often away from mixed flocks. Forages mainly by flicking leaves with bill, often a good way to spot it. **Voice:** Though often revealed by its near-constant chirring, far more memorable is this species' lovely song, a series of beautiful and sometimes complex musical phrases with churrs and tremolos interspersed, each phrase repeated over and over before going

on to next; it resembles Musician Wren's song but is somewhat simpler.

Microcerculus Wrens
Small, dark wrens of the forest floor whose *beautiful far-carrying songs* are heard far more often than the birds are seen. *Bills are long and slender, legs notably long,* and tails short.

Southern Nightingale-Wren
Microcerculus marginatus
Soterrey Ruiseñor Sureño   Plate 80(23)

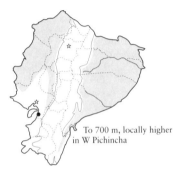

To 700 m, locally higher in W Pichincha

11 cm (4¼″). An *obscure* but distinctive *dark* wren found on floor of wet and humid forest in *lowlands of east and west*, small numbers ranging up into foothills; now local in most of west. Formerly called simply Nightingale Wren, or sometimes (inaccurately) Scaly-breasted Wren. *Bill long and slender*, legs very long. *Tail very stubby.* Uniform dark brown above; in **east and far northwest** *underparts mostly white*, with sides, flanks, and lower belly solid to mottled or scaled brown. In **most of west** dramatically different, with *even and dense dusky-brown scaling* except on mainly whitish throat. **Juvenile** scaled with dusky. **Similar species:** East of Andes cf. much more local Wing-banded Wren. Somewhat recalls a *Scytalopus* tapaculo though these are all longer tailed, etc. **Habits:** Furtive and inconspicuous, walking and hopping about in damp places, favoring ravines with fallen logs and dense vegetation; teeters its hindquarters, both when standing and while walking. Does not accompany flocks. **Voice:** *Heard much more often than seen.* Song unmistakable: after a fast and irregular opening, gives an extended, descending series of long sibilant notes delivered at ever-longer intervals (toward the end, pause may last 10 or more seconds).

Wing-banded Wren, *Microcerculus bambla*
Soterrey Alifranjeado   Plate 80(24)

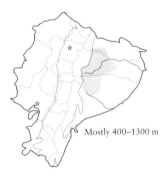

Mostly 400–1300 m

11.5 cm (4½″). Local in undergrowth of humid and foothill forest and secondary woodland in *foothills and lowlands near base of Andes in northeast.* Dark brown above, wings blacker and *crossed by conspicuous single white band; throat and breast gray,* becoming dark brown on belly. *Juveniles* are scalier generally but already show the wingband. **Similar species:** Resembles more widespread Southern Nightingale-Wren, but the white wing-band stands out like a beacon and renders this otherwise obscure bird nearly unmistakable. Cf. Banded Antbird. **Habits:** Much like Southern Nightingale-Wren's, equally reclusive and heard much more often than seen. **Voice:** Beautiful song a slightly descending series of clear notes that gradually accelerate into a crescendo, then a long pause before another series commences; sometimes the phrase slows down rather than accelerating.

Gnatcatchers and Gnatwrens:
Polioptilidae (5)
Warbler-like birds found in forest and woodland; the gnatwrens range in undergrowth, whereas the gnatcatchers are more arboreal. They were formerly often considered American representatives of the vast, primarily Old World warbler assemblage (the Sylviidae).

Microbates and *Ramphocaenus*

Gnatwrens

Small, superficially wren-like birds of forest and woodland undergrowth, united by their long bills. **Sexes are alike.**

Tawny-faced Gnatwren
Microbates cinereiventris
Soterillo Carileonado   Plate 81(7)

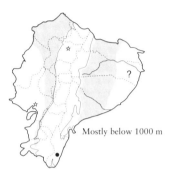

Mostly below 1000 m

10.5 cm (4"). Humid forest and secondary woodland undergrowth in *lowlands and foothills of east and west*, in east not ranging too far from Andes. Formerly sometimes called Half-collared Gnatwren. *Short stubby tail, usually held cocked and often moved around.* **Eastern birds** have *sides of head and neck bright tawny* contrasting with dark brown upperparts. Throat white bordered by black malar streak and *partial collar of black streaks across chest*; *underparts mainly gray*. **Western birds** have blackish postocular streak on tawny face. **Similar species:** Much rarer Collared Gnatwren (*northeast only*) is similarly shaped but very differently patterned below. Long-billed Gnatwren is notably longer-tailed and paler below with no streaking. Cf. ♀ *Myrmotherula* antwrens. **Habits:** Usually in pairs, hopping restlessly through often tangled growth, constantly wagging usually cocked tail. Does not range far above ground, and regularly is with understory flocks. Often quite tame, though not easy to see in its dense habitat. **Voice:** Song a plaintive, clear "teeeéuw" repeated every few seconds (P. Coopmans). Foraging birds frequently give a nasal scold, "nyaaah," sometimes repeated; also a "tsek-tsek-tsek," sometimes accelerated into a chattering "chrichrichrichrichri."

Collared Gnatwren, *Microbates collaris*
Soterillo Collarejo   Plate 81(8)

Below 250 m

10.5 cm (4"). Rare and local in understory of humid forest in *lowlands of far northeast. Short stubby tail, usually held cocked.* Uniform brown above but with *complex facial pattern incorporating a white superciliary and face crossed by a black postocular line and bordered below by a broad black malar stripe. White below* with *broad black pectoral band* and some gray and brown on flanks. **Similar species:** Not likely confused when the head pattern can be seen, but cf. Tawny-faced Gnatwren (much darker below, etc.). **Habits:** Similar to Tawny-faced Gnatwren's, but reported to attend antswarms (which Tawny-faced at most does rarely). **Voice:** Has scolding notes similar to Tawny-faced's. A true song has been reported from the Guianas, a series of soft thin notes repeated steadily at 3 to 4-second intervals.

Long-billed Gnatwren
Ramphocaenus melanurus
Soterillo Piquilargo   Plate 81(6)

12 cm (4¾"). Widespread but inconspicuous in lower growth of humid forest and wood-

Below 600 m (E),
to 1300 m in west

land in *lowlands of east and west*, in west also in foothills; *favors viny tangles. Long slender bill; long slim tail often cocked*, feathers *tipped white*. Brown above, face more rufescent. Whitish to pale buff below. **Western birds** have grayer back, tail feathers more broadly tipped white, and underparts more cinnamon-buff. **Similar species:** Tawny-faced and Collared Gnatwrens have much stubbier tails and shorter bills; they tend to remain closer to the ground. Also superficially resembles various wrens (e.g., certain *Thryothorus*), but these are much shorter-billed and most show conspicuous barring on wings and tail. **Habits:** Active and attractive little birds that range in pairs, hopping nimbly through dense growth up to 10 m above ground, *often wagging or animatedly flipping their tails around*. Less often with mixed flocks than *Microbates* gnatwrens. **Voice:** Song a distinctive clear trill or at times a harsher rattle, often rising and becoming louder but with substantial individual (geographic?) variation. In west tends to be more musical and variable in pitch (usually rising at first), in east more evenly pitched.

Polioptila Gnatcatchers

Distinctive slender, *predominantly gray*, *long-tailed* arboreal birds found in lowlands.

Tropical Gnatcatcher, *Polioptila plumbea*

Perlita Tropical   Plate 81(4)

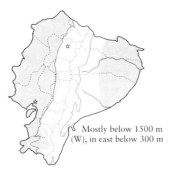

Mostly below 1500 m
(W), in east below 300 m

11 cm (4¼″). A *slender* and *long-tailed* little bird, *widespread and common in lowlands of west* where it occurs in a variety of forested and wooded habitats, even in arid scrub; in southwest, also well up into arid subtropics. In east, scarcer and essentially confined to humid forest canopy. ♂ *bluish gray above*

with *sharply contrasting glossy black crown*; wings blackish, inner flight feathers edged white; tail black with *outer feathers conspicuously white*. Below white. In **western birds**, *white extends up onto face*. ♀ similar but crown gray like back; face patterns as in ♂ ♂. **Similar species:** In most of its Ecuadorian range nearly unmistakable as the only gnatcatcher present. In northwest, cf. Slate-throated; here the two gnatcatchers can occur together, though Tropical is more widespread; note that there *both* species range in humid forest canopy. **Habits:** Gleans actively at various levels from forest canopy to near ground. Much more familiar in the west than the east, where it is inconspicuous, tending to remain high above ground. *The long tail is usually held cocked at a jaunty angle* and is often twitched from side to side. Regular with mixed flocks. **Voice:** A nasal "nyaah" call is frequently given. Songs differ geographically. Western birds have a simple descending series of high thin "weet" or "swee" notes that fade toward end or terminate in a twitter. Eastern birds give a very different, evenly pitched, much stronger, and faster "chichichichichichichichi."

Slate-throated Gnatcatcher
Polioptila schistaceigula

Perlita Pechipizarrosa   Plate 81(5)

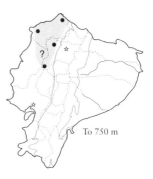

To 750 m

11 cm (4¼″). Rare to locally uncommon in canopy and borders of humid forest in *lowlands and foothills of northwest*. **Sexes alike.** *Mostly slaty gray* with *contrasting white lower breast and belly* and narrow white eye-ring; tail black with *outer feathers only very narrowly fringed white*. **Similar species:** Much darker than Tropical Gnatcatcher, both sexes of which are *entirely white below*.

Tropicals also have much more white in tail. **Habits:** Much as in Tropical Gnatcatcher, but Slate-throated almost always forages in canopy well above ground, only occasionally coming lower (at edge); it ranges in pairs, regularly accompanying mixed flocks. **Voice:** Most frequent vocalization a short, rather faint, and slightly ascending trill, "trrrrrrrt?" Less often given is song, a weak but longer and higher-pitched trill, noticeably descending in pitch (P. Coopmans).

Pipits and Wagtails: Motacillidae (1)
Slender, brown, streaky birds found mainly in grasslands around the world; wagtails are basically Old World in distribution. Only a few pipit species occur in South America, and only one in Ecuador.

Paramo Pipit, *Anthus bogotensis*
Bisbita del Páramo   Plate 81(21)

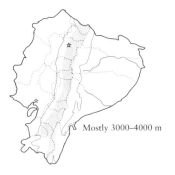

Mostly 3000–4000 m

15 cm (6″). A slim, superficially finch-like bird of *Andean grasslands and paramo*. **Sexes alike.** *Bill slender; tail distinctly notched, with outer feathers whitish* (latter most apparent in flight). *Rather long pinkish legs.* Above boldly streaked buffy ochraceous and blackish. *Uniform dull buff below* (paler and grayer in worn plumage) with band of sparse dusky streaking across chest. **Similar species:** ♀♀ of various finches potentially found with this pipit all have heavier and more conical bills; most show more extensive streaking below. All hop and *do not walk*, as pipit often does. **Habits:** Found singly or in pairs (often well-separated) that parade about in grassy areas but tend to be inconspicuous except where grass is short. Rarely associates with other birds. **Voice:** Pleasant song a variable series of musical notes and phrases, often with slurred first note. It is delivered mainly from a perch such as a rock or fence post, sometimes also during a skylarking flight display in which ♂ mounts up and then slowly glides back to earth.

New World Warblers: Parulidae (31)
A varied group of attractive small birds, the New World Warblers are most diverse in North America, from which most species migrate during the winter. Only a small subset of these migrants reach Ecuador, where they are much less evident than in tropical countries to the north; only the Blackburnian, Blackpoll, and Canada Warblers are at all numerous. Although the migrants are often colorful when in breeding garb, most of Ecuador's resident species are comparatively plain birds, with olive and yellow predominating. They inhabit forested or wooded areas, where some species (especially the migrants) are arboreal, others favoring lower growth; most species occur in the Andes, relatively few in the lowlands. Although residents have often attractive and melodic songs, the boreal migrants sing rarely or not at all in their winter quarters (and their voices are thus not described here). Warblers are chiefly insectivorous, but some (mainly the migrants) also eat fruit and consume nectar. Nests of resident species are either cup-shaped (the yellowthroats) or domed or partially domed structures, well hidden on or near the ground.

Vermivora Warblers
Small, arboreal warblers with fine bills, similar to *Dendroica* but with less complex plumage patterns.

Golden-winged Warbler
Vermivora chrysoptera
Reinita Alidorada   Plate 83(13)

12 cm (4³/₄″). A *very rare* boreal winter visitant (so far only Jan.–Mar.) to borders of subtropical forest and secondary woodland in *north*, especially in Mindo area. Bill slender. Beautiful ♂ unmistakable, with *conspicuous black ear-coverts and throat* and *bright golden yellow forecrown and large patch on wing-coverts*; otherwise gray above and pale grayish below. ♀ **and immatures**

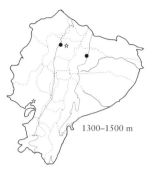

1300–1500 m

echo ♂'s pattern, with *dusky to gray throat and ear-coverts*; young birds in particular are otherwise duller and less contrasty. **Similar species:** Even Golden-wingeds with relatively dull face patterns are easily known by extensive yellow on wings, which is always obvious. **Habits:** Seen singly, usually with mixed flocks of arboreal birds. Often probes into suspended dead leaves, sometimes clinging upside-down while doing so.

Tennessee Warbler, *Vermivora peregrina*
Reinita Verdilla   Plate 83(3)

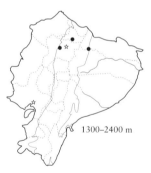

1300–2400 m

12 cm (4¾"). A *very rare* boreal winter visitant (late Oct.–early Mar.) to borders of montane forest, secondary woodland, and adjacent clearings in *n. Ecuador*, especially in the Mindo area. *Very plain*, with *slender bill.* Olive above with *thin whitish to pale yellowish superciliary* and often a *single narrow pale wing-bar; pale yellowish below* with (often quite obvious) *white crissum.* **Breeding plumage ♂♂** (which have not been seen in Ecuador) have crown and nape gray and underparts all white. **Similar species:** Cf. various greenlets (especially Lesser) and Yellow Warbler (some plumages of which can

be similar overall, *though Yellows never show a superciliary*). **Habits:** Tennessee Warblers have usually been found singly in Ecuador, though in their primary wintering range small groups are regularly noted. They often associate with mixed flocks, usually foraging rather high. In other areas Tennessees can be notably nectarivorous, congregating in flowering trees in gardens and residential areas; this could occur in Ecuador as well, but seems not to have been reported.

Tropical Parula, *Parula pitiayumi*
Parula Tropical   Plate 83(4)

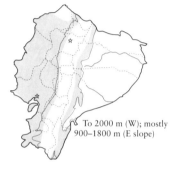

To 2000 m (W); mostly 900–1800 m (E slope)

11 cm (4¼"). *Common and widespread* in a variety of forest and wooded habitats ranging from montane forest in the subtropical zone on both slopes to deciduous forest, woodland, and even scrub in lowlands of west. Avoids the very wet lowlands of northwest. Essentially unmistakable. *Dull blue to bluish gray above* with *black foreface, olive green back patch*, and *white wing-bars. Throat and breast orange ochraceous*, becoming yellow on belly and white on crissum. **Sexes nearly alike,** ♀ slightly duller. **Habits:** This beautiful warbler is basically arboreal, often occurring in pairs and associating with mixed flocks; it tends to remain rather high above ground in tall forest, but regularly approaches ground in scrubbier habitats. **Voice:** ♂'s distinctive song, given persistently (even at midday when other birds are often silent), an accelerating and rising buzzy trill that most often is preceded by several thin or chipping notes, e.g., "tzip-tzip-tzip-tzip-tzrrrrrrrip."

Dendroica Warblers
The "classic" warblers of North America, where the vast majority breed, most of these

retreating to the Neotropics during the northern winter. All *Dendroica* are essentially arboreal birds that forage actively at various levels in woodland and forest borders, regularly joining mixed flocks. Sexual dimorphism is marked, and many have distinctly different breeding and nonbreeding plumages; these complexities can cause identification problems.

Yellow Warbler, *Dendroica aestiva*
Reinita Amarilla   Plate 83(6)

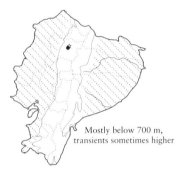

Mostly below 700 m, transients sometimes higher

12.5 cm (5"). A scarce boreal winter resident (Sep.–Apr.) in semiopen and shrubby areas and lighter woodland in lowlands of both east and west, mainly in n. Ecuador. Mangrove Warbler is here considered a separate species. *Mainly bright yellow* ♂ resembles ♂ Mangrove Warbler but *lacks any rufous on crown*, and *rufous streaking on breast and flanks usually prominent*. ♀ tends to be brighter and yellower than ♀ Mangrove, often looking *essentially pale yellow with little pattern or contrast*. **Similar species:** ♂ with yellow overall appearance and rufous breast streaking is readily recognized, but the plainer ♀ can be somewhat confusing; note its slender, pointed bill shape. In east, cf. Orange-fronted Plushcrown. **Habits:** Active and conspicuous, foraging primarily in shrubbery, favoring areas near water. **Voice:** Frequently gives a sharp "chip" note.

Mangrove Warbler, *Dendroica petechia*
Reinita Manglera   Plate 83(5)

12.5 cm (5"). Locally common in *mangroves along coast*. Sometimes considered conspecific with the migratory Yellow Warbler. ♂ *mostly bright yellow* (more yellowish olive

above) with *rufous-chestnut crown*; usually shows some faint rufous streaking on underparts. ♀ much duller and less yellow, often more grayish above and whitish below; as in ♂, wings are *edged yellowish* and *tail has yellowish inner webs*. **Similar species:** Cf. Yellow Warbler (which in Ecuador seems not to have been found in mangroves, though elsewhere it does occur in them). **Habits:** Found *mainly in mangroves*, on a few islands also in scrub. Mainly arboreal, though at low tide often dropping to ground to forage on exposed mud and mangrove roots. **Voice:** ♂'s lively and fast song somewhat variable but typically a short series of "swee" notes ending with warble or sharp "chip" note. Both sexes give an often incessant chipping.

Cerulean Warbler, *Dendroica cerulea*
Reinita Cerúlea   Plate 83(7)

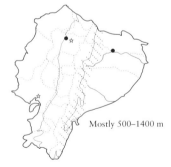

Mostly 500–1400 m

12 cm (4¾"). A scarce boreal winter resident (Oct.–Apr.) in canopy and borders in *foothill and lower subtropical forest and taller woodland on e. slope*, only a few reports (mainly transients?) from elsewhere. ♂ *azure blue above* with *bold white wing-bars*; white below with *narrow but conspicuous black band*

across chest and black streaking down flanks. ♀ *more greenish blue above* with *narrow pale yellowish superciliary*; below more yellowish with streaking blurrier and chest band faint or even absent. **Immature** ♀ more olive above and even yellower below. **Similar species:** Nonbreeding-plumage Blackpoll Warbler is larger with obvious back streaking, olive upperparts (no blue tone), and no superciliary. **Habits:** Tends to forage in trees high above ground, descending only at borders, and therefore often overlooked. Generally found singly, often while accompanying mixed flocks of tanagers and other warblers.

Blackpoll Warbler, *Dendroica striata*
Reinita Estriada   Plate 83(10)

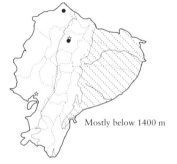

Mostly below 1400 m

13 cm (5″). A fairly common boreal winter visitant (Oct.–Apr.) to canopy and borders of humid forest, woodland, and clearings in *lowlands of east*, smaller numbers on e. slope. **Nonbreeding birds** very drab, essentially olive above with *blackish back streaking* and *bold white wing-bars*; *yellowish below with fine dusky streaking across breast and down flanks*, and with *white crissum*. Older ♂♂ brighter yellowish on throat and breast. **Breeding plumage** of ♂ gradually assumed during Mar.–Apr., with *striking black crown and snowy white cheeks*, *black malar stripe continuing down as streaks on sides*. **Breeding** ♀ much duller, resembling nonbreeding birds but more grayish above and whitish below. **Similar species:** Cf. nonbreeding Bay-breasted Warbler (much rarer in Ecuador than the Blackpoll). ♀ and nonbreeding Cerulean Warbler are smaller, more bluish above with a distinct superciliary. **Habits:** Often occurs in small groups, perhaps especially when actually on migration, feeding at all levels though most often

not very high. Forages rather deliberately. **Voice:** ♂♂ on northward passage occasionally give faint versions of their very high-pitched, sibilant song.

Bay-breasted Warbler, *Dendroica castanea*
Reinta Pechicastaña   Plate 83(8)

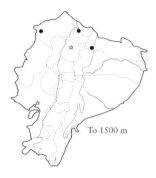

To 1500 m

13 cm (5″). A *casual* boreal winter visitant (Jan.–Feb.) to canopy and borders of humid lowland and subtropical forest and woodland in n. Ecuador. **Nonbreeding birds** very drab, essentially olive above with blackish back streaking and bold white wing-bars; *below uniform pale buffyish to whitish*, often with *at least a trace of chestnut on flanks* but with *no streaking*. **Breeding plumage** ♂ much more striking, with *crown, throat, chest, and sides chestnut* and *large pale buff patch on sides of neck*. ♀ similarly patterned, but notably duller. **Similar species:** Nonbreeding-plumage Blackpoll Warbler similar but tends to be yellower below with at least some streaking; never showing any color on flanks and with white crissum. Its legs are pale whereas Bay-breasted's tend to be dark. **Habits:** Much like Blackpoll Warbler.

Blackburnian Warbler, *Dendroica fusca*
Reinita Pechinaranja   Plate 83(9)

12.5 cm (5″). A *common* boreal winter visitant (Oct.–Apr.) to canopy and borders of *subtropical and temperate* forest and woodland on both slopes, more numerous in east. **Adult** ♂ *basically black above* with *very wide white wing-bars* (often almost forming a patch) and *fiery orange superciliary and neck patch* outlining black cheeks; *throat and chest fiery orange* becoming white on belly,

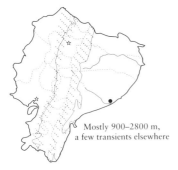

Mostly 900–2800 m,
a few transients elsewhere

with considerable black flank streaking. ♀ and immature *patterned like ♂ but much duller, more grayish olive above and with yellow replacing orange on face pattern, throat, and chest.* **Similar species:** *By far the most numerous migrant warbler in the highlands.* Nonbreeding Blackpoll Warbler is duller than even the dullest immature ♀ Blackburnian, with a much less strongly marked facial pattern, etc. **Habits:** Arboreal, foraging at varying heights above ground but most frequent in younger growth. Can at times occur in astonishing numbers, dozens moving together with tanager flocks, this perhaps mainly on migration.

[Black-throated Green Warbler
Dendroica virens
Reinita Cariamarilla]   Plate 96(15)

1400–2500 m

12.5 cm (5″). An *acidental* boreal winter visitor to montane forest borders and adjacent clearings (Mindo). *Contrasting yellow face in all plumages.* **Adult** ♂ bright olive above with *sides of head mostly bright yellow* (auriculars outlined with olive); wings and

tail blackish with two bold white wing-bars. *Throat and chest black,* extending down on sides as black streaking; underparts whitish, crissum tinged yellowish. ♀ similarly patterned but not as bright generally, and with less extensive black on throat. **Immature** even duller, especially ♀♀, with little or no black on throat and reduced streaking on sides. **Similar species:** Adults' combination of black throat and yellow face distinctive. Immatures can be confused with ♀ of much more numerous Blackburnian Warbler, but that species never looks "yellow-faced" and shows back streaking (back is plain olive in Black-throated Green, regardless of plumage). **Habits:** Much like Blackburnian Warbler.

[Chestnut-sided Warbler
Dendroica pensylvanica
Reinita Flanquicastaña]   Plate 83(11)

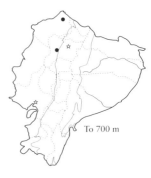

To 700 m

12.5 cm (5″). An *accidental* boreal winter visitant to nw. Ecuador; favors secondary woodland and humid forest borders. **Nonbreeding plumage** *bright yellowish olive above* with *narrow white eye-ring; grayish white below,* usually with *at least some chestnut on flanks.* **Breeding plumage** very different with complex pattern dominated by *bright yellow crown* and *extensive chestnut on flanks;* ♀ similar to but duller than ♂. **Similar species:** Nonbreeding Bay-breasted Warbler is larger and duller overall, with streaked back but no eye-ring, buffier underparts. **Habits:** Arboreal, foraging actively in foliage; characteristically *cocks tail* and droops wings.

Black-and-white Warbler, *Mniotilta varia*
Reinita Blanquinegra   Plate 83(1)

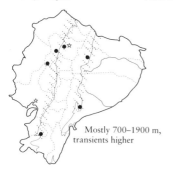

Mostly 700–1900 m,
transients higher

12.5 cm (5″). A rather rare boreal winter
visitant (Sep.–Apr.) to foothill and subtropical forest and woodland, mainly in n.
Ecuador. An unmistakable *black-and-white-
striped* warbler that *creeps about on tree
trunks and larger limbs. Head, back, and
most of underparts striped black and white.*
♀ and **immatures** whiter below with less
black streaking; **older** ♂♂ show more black
on throat and cheeks. **Habits:** Found singly,
most often while accompanying a mixed
flock, probing bark for insects. Typically does
not forage too high above ground.

American Redstart, *Setophaga ruticilla*
Candelita Norteña   Plate 83(15)

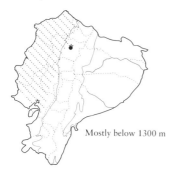

Mostly below 1300 m

12.5 cm (5″). A scarce boreal winter resident
(Oct.–Mar.) to humid forest borders, secondary woodland, adjacent clearings, and
mangroves in lowlands of west and on both
Andean slopes. **Adult** ♂ unmistakable,
mostly black with *large orange patches on
wings, base of tail, and sides*; belly white.
Adult ♀ **and immature** similarly patterned

but *yellow replaces orange*; they are grayish
olive above and white below, with adult ♀♀
grayer on head and older immature ♂♂
irregularly splotched with black. **Similar
species:** *Myioborus* whitestarts have similar
animated behavior, but their plumage patterns are very different. **Habits:** Forages very
actively, tail often fanned and wings drooped,
pirouetting and sallying for short distances,
never remaining motionless for long. Usually
found singly, and regularly accompanies
mixed flocks.

Prothonotary Warbler, *Protonotaria citrea*
Reinita Protonotaria   Plate 83(2)

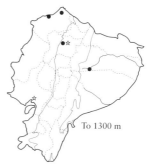

To 1300 m

13.5 cm (5¼″). A *casual* boreal winter visitant (Oct.–Mar.) to woodland and nearby
clearings (probably also mangroves) in lowlands on both slopes; only in *n. Ecuador.*
Nearly unmistakable. Beautiful ♂ has *head
and most of underparts bright rich golden
yellow* with *wings and tail contrasting blue-
gray*; extensive white flashes in outer tail
feathers. ♀ similarly patterned but with
duller yellow head and underparts; best field
mark is often the *unmarked blue-gray wings.*
Similar species: Yellow Warbler is smaller,
but birds of migratory population also look
mainly golden yellow, though they are more
uniform, never showing gray wings. **Habits:**
Forages in lower growth, where often quite
bold. Elsewhere *occurs mainly near water*
(both fresh and salt), though this seems not
to have been reported in Ecuador.

Seiurus Waterthrushes and Ovenbird
Mainly terrestrial, vaguely thrush-like
warblers. Both species are olive brown above
and *prominently streaked* below. **Sexes are
alike.**

Northern Waterthrush, *Seiurus noveboracensis*
Reinita Aquática Norteña   Plate 83(16)

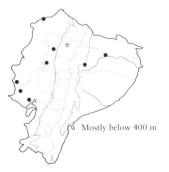

Mostly below 400 m

14 cm (5½″). A scarce boreal winter resident (Oct.–Apr.) *on or near ground* in shrubby areas and woodland (including mangroves) in lowlands on both slopes; *almost invariably near water. Olive brown above* with *narrow but prominent yellowish buff superciliary.* Buffy whitish below with *bold dark brown streaking.* **Similar species:** Likely confused only with rarer Ovenbird (which see). **Habits:** A distinctive warbler that is often seen *walking sedately on muddy ground,* usually *bobbing rearparts up and down.* Most often found singly. **Voice:** Call, a distinctive loud metallic "tchink," often draws attention.

Ovenbird, *Seiurus aurocapillus*
Reinita Hornera   Plate 83(17)

700–1000 m

14.5 cm (5¾″). An *accidental* boreal winter visitant to lower growth of humid forest in foothills at base of Andes on both slopes. *Olive above* with *white eye-ring* and *dull orange coronal streak bordered with black.* White below *prominently streaked with black on breast and down flanks.* **Similar**

species: Northern Waterthrush has a superciliary but no head striping or eye-ring; it is much more tied to water. **Habits:** Shy and unobtrusive on its wintering grounds, walking sedately on ground, often slowly teetering rearparts up and down. Usually solitary. Both Ecuador records involve mist-netted birds.

Geothlypis **Yellowthroats**
Relatively skulking warblers that are resident in shrubby and grassy areas of western and southern Ecuador. Males have distinctive *black facial areas*; females are duller and less patterned.

Olive-crowned Yellowthroat
Geothlypis semiflava
Antifacito Coronioliva   Plate 83(20)

Mostly below 1200 m

13.5 cm (5¼″). *Rank tall grass in pastures and in dense shrubbery* in *humid* lowlands and lower subtropics of west. ♂ has *broad black mask extending from forecrown back over cheeks to sides of neck*; otherwise plain olive above. Entirely bright yellow below. ♀ much like ♂ but *lacking mask*; thus essentially plain olive above and bright yellow below. **Similar species:** ♂ Black-lored Yellowthroat's mask is much smaller and it has gray on crown; ♀♀ of the two species are quite similar, but ♀ Black-lored shows some gray on crown, and it has small yellow supraloral and eye-ring (both totally lacking in the *plainer-faced* Olive-crowned). **Habits:** Tends to skulk in heavy cover and except for singing ♂♂ hard to see. **Voice:** Song longer and more complex than Black-lored's, a rich and musical series of phrases that usually ends in a jumble. Call a harsh and nasal "chreeuw."

Black-lored Yellowthroat
Geothlypis auricularis
Antifacito Lorinegro   Plate 83(21)

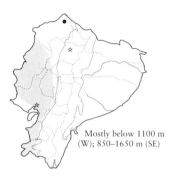

Mostly below 1100 m
(W); 850–1650 m (SE)

13–14 cm (5–5½″). Shrubby clearings and
borders of lighter woodland in lowlands and
foothills of southwest, and in Río Marañón
drainage of far southeast. Formerly considered conspecific with Masked Yellowthroat
(*G. aequinoctialis*). ♂ has *small area of black
on lores and around eye*, with *gray crown*;
otherwise olive above and quite bright yellow
below. ♀ has *yellow supraloral and narrow
eye-ring* and *gray on crown and ear-coverts*;
otherwise olive above and yellow below.
Marañón birds slightly larger but otherwise
similar. **Similar species:** Olive-crowned Yellowthroat favors more humid regions. Its ♂
has a much larger black mask but shows no
gray on crown; similar ♀ has plainer face
with no gray. **Habits:** Most often in pairs that
skulk in thick cover, emerging occasionally
to forage at borders; much more in evidence
during rainy season, when it breeds and ♂♂
are often seen singing from prominent
perches. **Voice:** Song of southwestern birds
a short vigorous series of clear notes
ending in a warble, "swee-swee-swee-swee-
chuchuchcu," with almost a House Wren-like
quality; sometimes given in a brief display
flight. Song of southeastern birds a pleasant
warble becoming a faster descending series
of shorter notes, "weche-chewi-chechi-we-
titititittititi" (P. Coopmans).

Oporornis **Warblers**
Skulking migratory warblers found in dense
lower growth, neither species numerous in
Ecuador.

Mourning Warbler, *Oporornis philadelphia*
Reinita Plañidera   Plate 83(12)

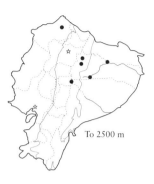

To 2500 m

13 cm (5″). A *rare* boreal winter resident
(Nov.–Feb.) in undergrowth of dense shrubby
woodland and humid forest borders, most
often near water, in lowlands and subtropics
mainly in *northeast*. ♂ with *extensive gray
hood* that becomes *black on chest* (latter
sometimes scaled paler); otherwise plain olive
above and uniform bright yellow below. ♀
and immature similarly patterned but duller,
with no black and often showing a *broken
white eye-ring*; immatures in particular show
more brownish hood that is *most pronounced on its sides*. **Similar species:** ♀ ♀
and immatures can be confused with ♀ ♀
yellowthroats, though neither yellowthroat
occurs in Mourning's known range, and none
ever looks "hooded". **Habits:** Forages singly
on or near ground; does not accompany
mixed flocks.

Connecticut Warbler, *Oporornis agilis*
Reinita Ojianillada   Plate 96(16)

14 cm (5½″). An *accidental* boreal winter visitant to far northwest. In all plumages shows

50 m

conspicuous, complete white or buffy whitish eye-ring. **Adult** ♂ olive above with *gray hood* (palest on throat). Below yellow. **Adult** ♀ similar but *hood more grayish brown or even brownish buff.* **Immature** (especially ♀) like ♀ but hood even browner. **Similar species:** Resembles somewhat smaller Mourning Warbler, ♀ of which differs in its *broken* eye-ring (never complete); note also that Connecticut has *longer undertail-coverts* (extending more than half-way down tail, often imparting a short-tailed appearance). **Habits:** Much as in Mourning Warbler, though even more skulking. Connecticut sometimes walks on ground or along limbs (like Ovenbird). The Ecuador bird was mist-netted.

Canada Warbler, *Wilsonia canadensis*
Reinita Collareja   Plate 83(14)

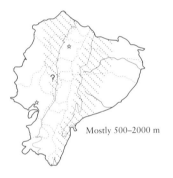

Mostly 500–2000 m

13 cm (5″). A fairly common boreal winter resident (Oct.–Apr.) in *foothill and subtropical forest, secondary woodland, and borders on e. slope* (rarer on w. slope), in lowlands of east as a transient. Readily recognized by *"necklace" of blackish streaks across chest,* dark and well marked in ♂♂, fainter but still evident in ♀♀ and immatures. ♂ *bluish gray above* with *yellow supraloral and eye-ring forming "spectacles"* and black foreface. Bright yellow below, becoming white on crissum. ♀ and **immature** duller, grayer (less blue) above. **Similar species:** ♀♀ and immatures can be confused with ♀♀ yellowthroats, though none of these is gray above or ever looks "spectacled." **Habits:** Forages quite actively, often partially cocking tail and flipping it around. Regularly joins mixed flocks of understory birds. **Voice:** Unlike other migrant wood-

warblers, ♂♂ sing regularly on northward passage, and may give a snatch of their jumbled warbled song even at other times.

Myioborus Whitestarts
Common and attractive warblers resident in montane forests, where they are conspicuous flock members, the Spectacled replacing the Slate-throated higher. **Sexes are alike.** They were formerly usually called "redstarts."

Slate-throated Whitestart, *Myioborus miniatus*
Candelita Goliplomiza   Plate 83(18)

Mostly 800–2400 m, lower in west

13.5 cm (5¼″). *Common,* widespread, and conspicuous in *foothill and subtropical* forest, woodland, and borders on both slopes, also on coastal cordillera. Occurs at *lower elevations* than Spectacled Whitestart. *Uniform slaty gray above and on throat,* with small rufous crown patch; underparts contrastingly yellow; *outer tail feathers white,* exposed when tail is fanned (which it frequently is). **Similar species:** Spectacled Whitestart has bold yellow spectacles and its yellow extends up onto throat. **Habits:** Forages very actively, usually not too far above ground, often drooping wings and flaring tail feathers as if to expose the white. Pairs regularly accompany mixed flocks, sometimes even seeming to lead them. **Voice:** Song an accelerating series of weak "chi" notes that slightly rise or remain on same pitch.

Spectacled Whitestart
Myioborus melanocephalus
Candelita de Anteojos   Plate 83(19)

13.5 cm (5¼″). *Common* and conspicuous in *temperate* forest, woodland, and borders on both slopes. Replaces Slate-throated Whites-

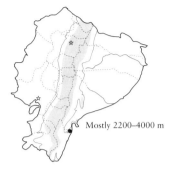

Mostly 2200–4000 m

Mostly 2000–3500 m

tart at *higher elevations*. Gray above with black face and *conspicuous yellow lores and eye-ring* and rufous crown patch; *underparts entirely yellow (including throat)*; *outer tail feathers white*, exposed when tail is fanned (which it frequently is). Some birds found near treeline on e. slope near Colombian border have *more extensive yellow on foreface*. **Similar species:** Slate-throated Whitestart has face and throat all *dark*. **Habits:** Much as in Slate-throated Whitestart, equally lively and animated, and likewise often so tame as to be almost oblivious of the observer. **Voice:** Pleasant song a variable, high-pitched series of twittering notes and phrases with little discernible pattern, sometimes long-continued and at first more subdued, gradually becoming more forceful.

Basileuterus Warblers
Dull-plumaged warblers that are resident mainly in montane forest and woodland undergrowth where they forage actively and often accompany mixed flocks. Olive and yellow predominate, with most species showing a characteristic pattern on the crown or face. **Sexes are alike.** Their songs are usually loud and melodic, and serve not only to draw attention to them but also assist in identification.

Black-crested Warbler
Basileuterus nigrocristatus
Reinita Crestinegra   Plate 83(22)

13.5 cm (5¼″). *Common* in undergrowth of *subtropical and temperate* forest borders, secondary woodland, and regenerating scrubby clearings and even hedgerows on both slopes, and on slopes above central and interandean valleys. *Conspicuous black crown stripe* bor-

dered below by *broad bright yellow superciliary*; *lores also black*. Otherwise olive above, bright yellow below. **Similar species:** At higher elevations generally the most frequently encountered *Basileuterus*; easy to recognize by its contrasty face pattern. The duller Citrine Warbler has no black on face, and its brow is characteristically shorter. **Habits:** Usually occurs in pairs which move about nervously through the dense low cover; one of few birds habitually to frequent bracken ferns. Though it is not particularly shy, the dense nature of its favored habitat often precludes getting a leisurely look at it. Sometimes joins mixed flocks, but also often forages alone. **Voice:** Frequently heard song starts slowly with several "chit" notes, then accelerates into a musical phrase that ends with series of insistent "chew" notes.

Citrine Warbler, *Basileuterus luteoviridis*
Reinita Citrina   Plate 83(23)

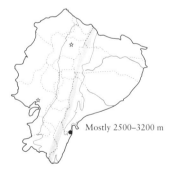

Mostly 2500–3200 m

14 cm (5½″). Lower growth of *temperate* forest and borders on *e. slope*. A rather dull *Basileuterus*, olive above with *short yellow superciliary* (broadest in front of eye and only barely extending behind it) and dusky lores.

Dull yellow below, washed with olive on sides and flanks. **Similar species:** Superciliaried Hemispingus has a longer and narrower white superciliary as well as gray on crown and cheeks. Oleaginous Hemispingus is more olive and uniform, showing little yellow below and almost no superciliary. Also cf. the brighter Black-crested Warbler. **Habits:** Found in pairs and small groups that forage very actively through lower growth (but most often *not* near ground, unlike Black-crested). Regularly accompanies mixed flocks, and often quite bold. **Voice:** Song a long series of rapidly uttered high-pitched notes that rise and fall in pitch in almost random fashion, sometimes accelerating into a terminal trill; sometimes given by several birds at once.

Chocó Warbler, *Basileuterus chlorophrys*
Reinita del Chocó   Plate 83(25)

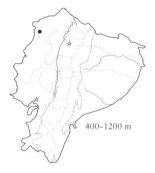

400–1200 m

13 cm (5″). Locally common in lower and middle growth of montane forest and secondary woodland in *foothills on w. slope south to Chimborazo.* Formerly considered conspecific with Golden-bellied or Cuzco Warbler (*B. chrysogaster*) of se. Peru. *Olive overall* with a *relatively dull head pattern* showing dull orange coronal streak, blackish lateral crown stripe, and *mainly olive superciliary* (yellow in front of eye). Otherwise olive above; median underparts yellow, sides and flanks broadly olive. **Similar species:** Three-striped Warbler has a different head pattern (pale superciliary much bolder and ear-coverts mainly black) and dull buffy yellowish (not olive and yellow) underparts. **Habits:** Forages in pairs or small groups, regularly accompanying mixed flocks; often moves about higher above ground than other

Basileuterus, thus easier to observe. **Voice:** Frequently heard and distinctive song a very thin, wiry, and buzzy "t-t-t-t-tzzzzzzzzzzzz."

Three-striped Warbler, *Basileuterus tristriatus*
Reinita Cabecilistada   Plate 83(24)

Mostly 1000–2000 m

13 cm (5″). Often common in undergrowth of *subtropical and foothill* forest and woodland on both slopes. *Color of underparts varies geographically*, but always has a *distinctive bold facial pattern* of *yellowish buff coronal streak and superciliary* and *black lateral crown stripe and blackish cheeks*; otherwise olive above. On **west slope** basically dull buffy yellowish below; on **east slope** considerably yellower below (especially to south). **Similar species:** On w. slope, cf. Chocó Warbler (northward) and Three-banded Warbler (southward). On e. slope, because of distinctive facial pattern there really is nothing very similar. **Habits:** Much like other forest-based *Basileuterus*, foraging actively in pairs or small groups, often accompanying understory flocks. **Voice:** Song a fast, jumbled series of high-pitched notes that gradually accelerate into a crescendo and rise in pitch.

Three-banded Warbler
Basileuterus trifasciatus
Reinita Tribandeada   Plate 83(26)

12.5 cm (5″). Lower growth of foothill and subtropical forest, secondary woodland, and borders on *west slope in El Oro and Loja.* *Coronal streak and superciliary pale ashy gray* with black lateral crown stripe and eyeline; otherwise olive above. *Throat and chest pale grayish*, underparts yellow. **Similar species:** A spritely warbler, not likely confused in its limited range. Three-striped

Mostly 800–2400 m

color of underparts, no other *Basileuterus* combines extensive gray face and conspicuous rufous on crown. **Habits:** Usually in pairs, most often accompanying mixed flocks and remaining inside forest and woodland, less often at edge. **Voice:** Attractive and musical song, often given antiphonally, varies individually but usually is a rapidly delivered phrase that rises and seems to end with a query, then is followed by similar (but often descending) reply from mate. A series of chattering notes often precedes song.

Warbler (occurring just to the north on west slope; overlap possible?) has no gray on face, blackish cheeks, and duller more buffyish underparts (not so bright yellow). **Habits:** Forages restlessly, often holding tail partially cocked; regularly accompanies small mixed flocks. Often bold, frequently coming to edge. **Voice:** Song a fast series of high-pitched notes, similar to Three-striped Warbler.

Russet-crowned Warbler
Basileuterus coronatus
Reinita Coronirrojiza   Plate 83(27)

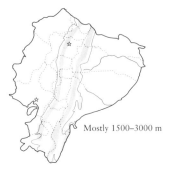

Mostly 1500–3000 m

14 cm (5½"). Widespread in undergrowth of subtropical and temperate forest, secondary woodland, and borders on both slopes, and locally on slopes above interandean valleys. *Color of lower underparts varies racially*, but always has *distinctive gray face and sides of neck* with black eyeline and lateral crown stripe as well as an *obvious orange-rufous crown*; upperparts otherwise olive; throat and chest very pale gray. On **most of west slope** lower underparts yellow; on **most of east slope** whitish on breast and pale yellow on belly. In **Azuay, El Oro,** and **Loja** grayish white below. **Similar species:** Regardless of

Gray-and-gold Warbler, *Basileuterus fraseri*
Reinita Grisidorada   Plate 83(28)

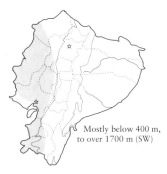

Mostly below 400 m, to over 1700 m (SW)

14 cm (5½"). A pretty warbler, *often common*, found in undergrowth of deciduous and humid woodland, scrub, and sometimes forest borders in *lowlands and foothills of southwest. Bluish gray above* with diffused olive midback patch, *white supraloral*, and black lateral crown stripe; coronal streak yellow northward, ochraceous orange southward. *Bright yellow below.* **Similar species:** Other *Basileuterus* are more olive (not gray) above, and none occurring with it is as brightly colored. **Habits:** Forages actively, usually on or near ground, less often with mixed flocks than many of its congeners. **Voice:** Characteristic song hesitates at first, then becomes a short rising series of musical notes, e.g., "titu, titu, tituyuteeteechee?"; overall quality reminiscent of Russet-crowned.

Buff-rumped Warbler, *Basileuterus fulvicauda*
Reinita Lomianteada   Plate 83(29)

13.5 cm (5¼"). *On or near ground along streams and rivers* in lowlands and foothills of east and west. Formerly considered con-

To about 1000 m

specific with *B. rivularis* (Riverside, or River, Warbler), and sometimes placed in genus *Phaeothlypis*. Easily recognized by its unique and obvious *buff rump and basal half of tail*, conspicuous in flight and often apparent even on perched birds as tail feathers are often partially spread. Otherwise rather dull, essentially brownish olive above with a buff superciliary, buffy whitish below. **Habits:** Found singly or in pairs, hopping at water's edge or perching on rocks, frequently switching fanned tail from side to side, as if to display the buff. **Voice:** Vigorous song an accelerating crescendo of loud "tew" notes that end with a series of emphasized fast "tchéw" notes.

Tanagers, Honeycreepers, Bananaquit, and Plushcap: Thraupidae (143)

A large and varied family of birds found only in the Americas, the vast majority of them in the Neotropics; only a few migrants range north to North America. It now includes two single species formerly considered separate families, the Tersinidae (Swallow Tanager) and Catamblyrhynchidae (Plushcap). The tanagers are sometimes combined with other groups (including the wood warblers and icterids) into one huge family of 9-primaried oscine birds, the Emberizidae. Many tanagers are very attractive, colorful birds though others are much duller, being mainly dull olive, brown, or grayish. Bills vary as well, from slender and decurved in the honeycreeper group (which also was formerly considered a separate family, the Coerebidae) to quite stout and hooked. Some tanager species show strong sexual dimorphism in plumage, but a majority do not, or show very little. Some are good singers, but again, most species are not. A majority are arboreal in forest and woodland, both in the lowlands and the Andes; a smaller number of species occurs in forest lower growth and in semiopen areas. They are about equally frugivorous and insectivorous, with the honeycreepers also taking much nectar. Nests are typically cup-shaped, but certain groups are exceptions, notably the Bananaquit and the euphonias with their ball-shaped nests with side entrances.

Bananaquit, *Coereba flaveola*
Mielero Flavo   Plate 84(1)

Mostly below 1100 m, locally to 1800 m (S)

10.5–11 cm (4–4¼"). Widespread in secondary woodland, forest borders, clearings, and gardens in lowlands and foothills of east and west; *more numerous in west*, in east ranging mainly near base of Andes and scarce or absent in extensive forest. **Sexes alike.** *Short, decurved bill*; short tail. Above dusky with *blackish crown and sides of head*, *striking long white superciliary*, white wing speculum, and yellow on rump. *Throat gray* contrasting with *yellow underparts*. **Habits:** An active, seemingly nervous little bird that in Ecuador is rarely or never as familiar as it can become elsewhere. Forages at all levels, mainly by probing for nectar into flowers of many species; also eats some fruit. It regularly congregates with other birds (e.g., various tanagers and hummingbirds) at flowering or fruiting trees. **Voice:** A short, shrill, often buzzy or even hissing song, which can be repeated interminably, is frequently heard.

Cyanerpes Honeycreepers
Small tanagers of humid forests that have *decurved bills*, *brightly colored legs*, and *short tails* (though Red-legged's is longer). They are strongly dimorphic, the pretty males

being some shade of purple or blue, females green and streakier.

Short-billed Honeycreeper, *Cyanerpes nitidus*
Mielero Piquicorto   Plate 84(19)

Below 400 m

Mostly below 1200 m

9.5 cm (3³⁄₄″). *Rare and local* in canopy and borders of humid forest (principally terra firme) in *lowlands of east. Short decurved bill; legs pale pink to orange flesh.* ♂ *mostly bright deep blue* with *large black throat patch extending down over chest*; wings and tail, as well as lores, also black. ♀ green above with dusky lores; streaked underparts much like ♀ of far more numerous Purple Honeycreeper but *lacking blue malar stripe.* **Similar species:** Purple Honeycreeper has a decidedly *longer and more obviously decurved* bill, and differs in leg color (bright yellow in ♂, dull yellowish in ♀); ♂ Purple is less blue (and more purple) than ♂ Short-billed, and it has a smaller black bib. ♀ ♀ of the two are so similar that at the heights above ground where they are usually found they are generally best identified by the company they keep. Apart from plumage differences, Red-legged Honeycreeper (*also rare in east*) is markedly longer billed and also longer tailed. **Habits:** Much as in Purple Honeycreeper, but—at least in Ecuador—primarily seen foraging high above ground, usually as pairs accompanying mixed flocks.

Purple Honeycreeper, *Cyanerpes caeruleus*
Mielero Purpúreo   Plate 84(17)

11 cm (4¹⁄₄″). Often common in canopy and borders of humid forest and secondary woodland and adjacent clearings in *lowlands and (smaller numbers) foothills of east and west. Bill long, slender, and decurved*; legs

bright yellow in ♂ (yellow appearing painted on), duller yellow in ♀. Beautiful ♂ *mostly deep purplish blue* with lores, throat patch, wings, and tail contrastingly black. ♀ green above with *buffyish lores, throat, and face* (face streaked) and *blue malar streak.* Underparts streaked green and yellowish. **Similar species:** Red-legged Honeycreeper is somewhat larger and longer-tailed with red (♂) or reddish (♀) legs; ♂ has conspicuous pale blue crown, whereas more uniform ♀ has a vague whitish brow and *no buff on face or throat.* Cf. also rare Short-billed Honeycreeper. **Habits:** Often in small groups, regularly accompanying mixed tanager flocks and joining in feeding aggregations at fruiting or flowering trees; also gleans for insects. Though usually ranging high above ground, sometimes comes lower, especially in clearings. **Voice:** Often gives a "zhree" call, sometimes repeated, less often a "tsik," but does not appear to have any real song.

Red-legged Honeycreeper, *Cyanerpes cyaneus*
Mielero Patirrojo   Plate 84(18)

11.5–12 cm (4¹⁄₂–4³⁄₄″). *Uncommon and local (surprisingly so)* in canopy and borders of humid forest and woodland and adjacent clearings in lowlands of northwest and east. *Bill long, slender, and decurved*; legs bright red in ♂, reddish in ♀. Beautiful ♂ *bright purplish blue* with *contrasting pale turquoise crown*; lores, patch on back, wings, and comparatively long tail black. ♀ olive green above with *vague whitish superciliary.* Dull pale yellowish below with *blurry olive streaking on breast.* Both sexes have *yellow underwing-coverts* that flash conspicuously in flight. **Nonbreeding** ♂ ♂ assume eclipse plumage in which they resemble ♀ ♀ except

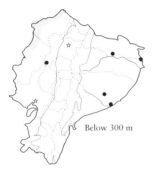

Below 300 m

for retaining black wings and tail. **Similar species:** Purple Honeycreeper is smaller and shorter-tailed and has bright yellow (♂) or yellowish (♀) legs and no yellow under wing. ♂ Purples have black on throat but none on back, lack Red-legged's striking pale crown; ♀ Purples have buff on face and throat and a blue malar streak. ♀ Green Honeycreeper has a heavier bill showing yellow, is brighter (not so olive), and lacks streaking. Cf. also rare Short-billed Honeycreeper. **Habits:** Much like Purple Honeycreeper though—at least elsewhere—favoring more open situations and less tied to tall forest. Likewise often in small groups that may travel substantial distances, pause to feed, then move on. **Voice:** Calls include a frequent "tsip" note (sometimes repeated, and given in flight) and an ascending "zhreee?"

Green Honeycreeper, *Chlorophanes spiza*
Mielero Verde   Plate 84(21)

Mostly below 800 m

14 cm (5½″). Widespread in canopy and borders of humid forest and secondary woodland in *lowlands and foothills of east and west*. Bill stouter and less decurved than in *Cyanerpes* honeycreepers, *yellow* with dark culmen (♂) or *yellowish* (♀); iris dark red. ♂ *lustrous green to bluish green* with *contrasting black head*. ♀ *quite uniform bright green*, somewhat paler below. **Similar species:** Bright ♂ virtually unmistakable. ♀ is plainer and can be confused with juveniles of certain *Tangara* tanagers (some of which, e.g., Bay-headed, are equally uniform green), but note honeycreeper's stouter bill showing at least some yellow. ♀ Blue Dacnis has a straighter and more pointed bill, blue on head. **Habits:** Arboreal like other honeycreepers, but usually in pairs and not so often in small groups. Frequently accompanies mixed flocks comprising other tanagers. **Voice:** Has various "tsip" or "chip" calls.

Golden-collared Honeycreeper
Iridophanes pulcherrima
Mielero Collarejo   Plate 84(20)

1100–2000 m (E slope), to 650 m in NW

12 cm (4¾″). Uncommon in canopy and borders of subtropical forest on east *slope*, ♂ colorful and strongly patterned; also a few records from *foothills in northwest. Bill fairly long* (more so than in the *Tangara* tanagers with which it so often associates) with *mandible mostly yellow*; iris dark red. ♂ has *black hood, upper back, and scapulars contrasting with orange-yellow nuchal collar and pale opalescent yellowish underparts*; opalescent straw lower back and rump; *wings mostly ultramarine blue*. ♀ much duller, dull olive above but *usually showing at least an echo of* ♂'s *golden collar; wing feathers edged dull bluish green*. Mostly dull yellowish buff below. **Similar species:** Colorful ♂ unmistakable, but drab ♀ can be confusing, her identity often being made known by accompanying ♂. Note ♀'s bill shape (not as thick or stout as in *Tangara*), collar (though

faint, usually evident), and wing edging. **Habits:** Usually occurs in pairs, often at edge of forest or woodland and then not difficult to observe. Generally accompanies mixed flocks of *Tangara* and other tanagers, and seems to eat mainly various fruits (frequently *Cecropia* catkins) with relatively few insects being consumed.

Dacnis Dacnises
Small warbler-like tanagers with *short, sharply pointed bills*. All are sexually dimorphic, males being *colorful and boldly patterned*, females considerably duller (and often more difficult to identify). Their voices are undistinguished.

Blue Dacnis, *Dacnis cayana*
Dacnis Azul   Plate 85(1)

Mostly below 1000 m

12.5 cm (5″). *Common and widespread* in canopy and borders of humid forest and secondary woodland and adjacent clearings in lowlands and foothills of east and west, *most numerous in northwest*. Bill quite long and pointed with pinkish base; iris red; *legs pinkish*. ♂ *mostly blue* (darker and more ultramarine in *west*, paler and more turquoise in *east*) with *black throat patch and back*; wings and tail black, feathers edged blue. ♀ *bright green* with *head contrastingly bluish (especially in west)* and throat grayish. **Similar species:** All honeycreepers have obviously decurved bills. No other dacnis is as predominantly blue as ♂, whereas ♀'s contrasting bluish head is also unique in genus. **Habits:** Usually in pairs or small groups, foraging at all levels (lower at edge) and frequently accompanying mixed flocks. Feeds both at fruiting trees and by gleaning (often acrobatically) insects from foliage and

branches. **Voice:** Not very vocal; occasionally gives a "tsit" call note.

Black-faced Dacnis, *Dacnis lineata*
Dacnis Carinegro   Plate 85(3)

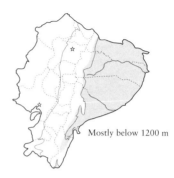

Mostly below 1200 m

11.5 cm (4½″). Canopy and borders of humid forest in *lowlands and foothills of east. Iris bright yellow*. Pretty ♂ *boldly patterned in turquoise and black* (essentially black above and turquoise below and on crown) with *contrasting white midbelly and crissum*. ♀ much drabber and more confusing: dull brownish olive above, somewhat grayer on head; dull pale grayish below, whiter on midbelly and more olive on flanks. **Similar species:** ♂ nearly unmistakable in range. Nondescript ♀ presents more of a problem, but her obvious pale eye distinguishes it from many similar species (♀ of more brownish Yellow-bellied Dacnis, with which Black-faced regularly occurs, has red eye). Cf. much rarer White-bellied Dacnis. **Habits:** Much as in Blue Dacnis, with Black-faced also most often seen accompanying mixed-species tanager flocks or congregating at fruiting tree at forest edge. **Voice:** Gives a "tsleyp" call (N. Krabbe recording).

Yellow-tufted Dacnis, *Dacnis egregia*
Dacnis Pechiamarillo   Plate 85(2)

11.5 cm (4½″). Widespread in secondary woodland, borders of humid and deciduous forest, and adjacent clearings in *lowlands of west*. Less tied to forest than is its e.-slope replacement, Black-faced Dacnis, with which formerly considered conspecific. *Iris bright yellow*. ♂'s pattern similar to ♂ Black-faced Dacnis but turquoise of a slightly greener hue and *midbelly and crissum bright yellow*; also

To 900 m

has *bright yellow pectoral tuft protruding in front of wing.* ♀ likewise similar to ♀ Black-faced, but like ♂ has *yellow midbelly* and *yellow tuft in front of wing.* **Similar species:** ♂ unmistakable in range. ♀ can be difficult, though in range there are few similarly sized and shaped birds with pale irides that are quite so drab. **Habits:** Behavior much like Blue Dacnis. Yellow-tufted is, however, more apt to be found in less humid regions, and seems to have adapted relatively well to widespread deforestation, occurring regularly in plantations and other partially cleared areas. ♂♂ especially may perch on high exposed branches for protracted periods. **Voice:** Gives a thin, high-pitched "tsrrip" call (O. Jahn recording).

Yellow-bellied Dacnis, *Dacnis flaviventer*
Dacnis Ventriamarillo   Plate 85(4)

Mostly below 500 m

12.5 cm (5"). Canopy and borders of humid forest in *lowlands of east*, often (but not always) near water. *Iris bright red.* Unmistakable ♂ *boldly patterned in bright yellow and black* with *contrasting olive green crown.* Upperparts black with yellow scapulars and rump; underparts yellow with black

midthroat and breast mottling. ♀ much duller, olive brown above and pale brownish buff below with *obscure brownish mottling on throat, breast, and flanks.* **Similar species:** ♀ Black-faced Dacnis is slightly smaller and more olive (less brown) overall; it has yellow (not red) eye, and lacks such extensive mottling below (though it may show a little). **Habits:** Much like other dacnises, though Yellow-bellied forages more often apart from mixed flocks, and usually occurs only in pairs. **Voice:** Seldom heard (or perhaps just seldom noticed) song a sharp and fairly high-pitched "whuh-zeeé" (J. Moore recording).

Scarlet-thighed Dacnis, *Dacnis venusta*
Dacnis Musliescarleta   Plate 85(5)

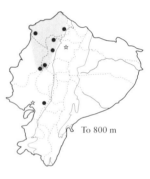

To 800 m

12 cm (4¾"). *Scarce* in canopy and borders of humid forest and adjacent clearings in *lowlands and (especially) foothills of northwest.* Iris dark red. Beautiful ♂ nearly unmistakable, and only dacnis with *black underparts. Above mostly bright cornflower blue* with black forehead and lores, sides of back, and wings and tail. *Scarlet thighs* diagnostic but often hard to see. ♀ much duller, with dull bluish green upperparts and *dingy buffy grayish underparts.* **Similar species:** ♂ might carelessly be mistaken for Blue-necked Tanager. Drab ♀ can be confusing; ♀ Blue Dacnis is green below, ♀ of pale-eyed Yellow-tufted Dacnis is olive and yellow below. **Habits:** Often forages in small groups, as often apart from mixed flocks as with them; sometimes ranges high above ground in forest canopy but easier to see when it comes lower, at edge and in clearings.

Scarlet-breasted Dacnis, *Dacnis berlepschi*
Dacnis Pechiescarleta   Plate 84(22)

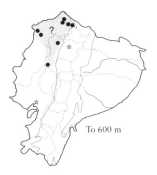

12 cm (4³/₄″). *Rare to uncommon and local in canopy and borders of humid forest and secondary woodland in lowlands and (especially) foothills of northwest. Iris yellow.* Beautiful ♂ unmistakable, *shining blue above and down onto throat and chest with opalescent streaking on mantle; wide breast band flame scarlet,* fading to orange-buff on belly. ♀ *distinctly browner than other vaguely similar dacnises or tanagers:* essentially brown above, paler and buffier brown below, with *red band across breast* (narrower than ♂'s, and not so bright). **Similar species:** Cf. ♀ or juvenile ♂ Crimson-breasted Finch (a species normally not found in this dacnis's humid forest habitat, but not inconceivable as a nonbreeding wanderer). **Habits:** Not well known. Usually in pairs, often associating with mixed flocks. Generally remains well above ground. **Voice:** Song a very fast, high, and evenly pitched series of thin notes, "tsit-sitsitsitsitsitsitsiti" (O. Jahn recording).

White-bellied Dacnis, *Dacnis albiventris*
Dacnis Ventriblanco   Plate 84(23)

11.5 cm (4¹/₂″). *Very rare* in canopy and borders of humid forest in *lowlands of east. Golden yellow iris.* ♂ *mostly bright cobalt blue* with *black mask* and some black mottling on back; wings and tail mainly black. *Belly contrastingly white.* ♀ much duller and not easy to identify: green above and *mostly greenish yellow below* (yellowest on mid-belly), throat more grayish. **Similar species:** ♂ likely confused only with certain *Tangara* tanagers (e.g., Masked, with which it can occur), but none of these has similar overall

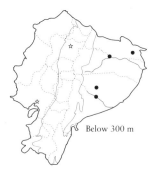

pattern and none is pale-eyed. ♀ closely resembles ♀ of far commoner (and syntopic) Black-faced Dacnis, but latter is more olive (not as bright) green above and not so yellow below. **Habits:** Not well known, and inexplicably rare throughout its range. Has been found singly or in pairs in association with mixed flocks of other tanagers.

Conirostrum Conebills
Small, warbler-like tanagers with *sharply pointed bills* and *predominantly blue-gray plumage.*

Chestnut-vented Conebill
Conirostrum speciosum
Picocono Culicastaño   Plate 84(3)

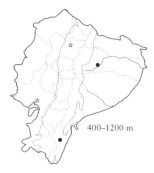

11 cm (4¹/₄″). *Rare and very local* in canopy and borders of humid forest and secondary woodland *along e. base of Andes* (especially around Zamora). ♂ *rather dark and uniform bluish gray,* only slightly paler above than below, with *contrasting chestnut crissum* (usually quite conspicuous); sometimes shows small white wing-speculum. ♀ has pale lores and *bluish gray crown and nape* that contrast with *rather bright olive upper-*

parts. Grayish white below, sometimes with some buff on crissum. **Similar species:** ♀ can be confusing, looking superficially warbler-like; cf. especially Tennessee Warbler. Also looks vaguely greenlet-like. **Habits:** Not well known in Ecuador, where it has usually been seen in flowering trees (often *Erythrina*), often with Bananaquits and other tanagers. Also feeds by gleaning, warbler-like, for insects in foliage. Elsewhere it regularly accompanies mixed flocks of canopy birds. **Voice:** Not known in Ecuador.

[Bicolored Conebill, *Conirostrum bicolor*
Picocono Bicolor]   Plate 84(2)

300 m

11.5 cm (4½″). A *dingy* conebill known from only *one report* from a *Río Napo island*. *Iris reddish brown; legs dusky pink*. Sexes alike. *Above pale grayish blue; below dingy grayish buff*. Immatures yellowish tinged below. **Similar species:** Should be distinctive in its restricted habitat. ♀ of smaller Chestnut-vented Conebill is brighter olive across back (not bluish) with gray restricted to head and nape; at least in Ecuador, Chestnut-vented has not been found on river islands. **Habits:** Elsewhere favors stands of *Cecropia* and (sometimes) also earlier successional stages of woodland; occurrence strictly tied to river islands, and *rarely or never seen off them*. Warbler-like in its foraging. Often quite tame.

Cinereous Conebill, *Conirostrum cinereum*
Picocono Cinéreo   Plate 84(4)

12.5 cm (5″). A *nonforest* conebill, *widespread mainly in drier regions* and often numerous in gardens and a variety of

Mostly 2500–3500 m

shrubby and lightly wooded habitats in the *highlands*. Sexes alike. Olivaceous brown above with darker brown crown and *buff superciliary*; wings blackish with *conspicuous L-shaped white wing-patch* (formed by wing-bar and speculum). Below dull ochraceous buff. **Similar species:** No vaguely similar bird has a wing-patch similar to this species'; it and the superciliary are lacking in ♀ Rusty Flowerpiercer (regularly found with conebill). **Habits:** Usually in pairs or small groups, sometimes with mixed flocks but at least as often independent of them. Forages actively, often quite low, mainly by gleaning for insects in foliage, at times clinging upside-down as it inspects the underside of leaves. **Voice:** Song a fast jumble of twittering notes and phrases, sometimes given while bird continues to feed.

Blue-backed Conebill, *Conirostrum sitticolor*
Picocono Dorsiazul   Plate 84(5)

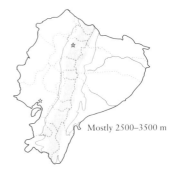

Mostly 2500–3500 m

13 cm (5″). A pretty and boldly patterned conebill of *temperate forest and woodland on both slopes*, conspicuous and often quite numerous. **Sexes alike.** Head, neck, and chest

black contrasting with *mainly blue mantle* and *rich rufous underparts*; wings and tail mainly blackish. **Similar species:** General pattern recalls certain flowerpiercers' (and they and the conebill often range together), but their bills are hooked at tip and none has bicolored underparts. **Habits:** Usually in pairs or small groups, almost invariably encountered accompanying a mixed flock of other montane tanagers. Forages actively for insects, especially in outer foliage and often clinging upside-down while inspecting the underside of leaves. Tail is sometimes wagged. **Voice:** Song a complex series of sputtering, sibilant notes.

Capped Conebill, *Conirostrum albifrons*
Picocono Coronado   Plate 84(6)

Mostly 2000–2800 m

13 cm (5″). A *sexually dimorphic* conebill of *upper subtropical and temperate forest on both slopes*, more numerous in east. ♂ *black* with *dark glossy blue crown*; lesser wing-coverts, scapulars, lower back and rump, and crissum suffused with dark blue. In extreme north on e. slope, *crown white* (very contrasting). ♀ has *grayish blue crown*, bluish gray sides of head and neck, and *mainly bright olive upperparts*; *throat and chest bluish gray*, lower underparts yellowish olive. **Similar species:** A relatively inconspicuous conebill, tending to remain high in trees and often not seen well. *Often most easily recognized by its near-constant tail-wagging.* ♂'s blue is dark and especially in dull light can look blackish. Gray-hooded Bush-Tanager resembles ♀ conebill (both species tail-wag), but the tanager is larger, pink-billed, grayer (not so bluish) on head, and brighter yellow below. **Habits:** Tends to range in taller forest than Blue-backed Conebill,

and usually at somewhat lower elevations. Forages in pairs or small groups, often with mixed flocks; usually remains well above ground. **Voice:** Infrequently heard song a high-pitched and penetrating "tsu-tseeu, tsu-tseeu, tsu-tseeu" usually preceded by a jumbled "tsududuit."

Giant Conebill, *Oreomanes fraseri*
Picocono Gigante   Plate 84(7)

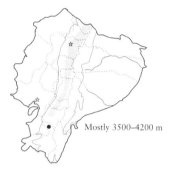

Mostly 3500–4200 m

15 cm (6″). A *fancy, large* conebill found locally and in small numbers *high in Andes* in *Polylepis* groves, *at and above true tree-line*. Sexes alike. *Bill quite long and very sharply pointed. Mostly gray above* with *contrasting white cheeks* and thin chestnut eyeline. *Below chestnut.* **Similar species:** Not likely confused, but cf. much smaller Blue-backed Conebill (with vaguely similar color pattern). Behavior somewhat recalls the differently patterned Pearled Treerunner (sometimes with it). **Habits:** Generally scarce, Giant Conebills are typically found in widely dispersed pairs; they sometimes accompany mixed flocks. One can sometimes be located by listening or watching for a bird scaling off pieces off a *Polylepis* tree's flaky bark. Foraging birds frequently hitch along trunks and larger limbs like a *Sitta* nuthatch of North America/Eurasia, less often moving out to smaller terminal branches. **Voice:** Generally not very vocal, but has a fairly musical, twittering song, e.g., "cheet, cheeveét, cheeveét."

Tit-like Dacnis, *Xenodacnis parina*
Xenodacnis   Plate 84(8)

14 cm (5½″). *Very local* in semiopen, shrubby *Gynoxys*-dominated woodland mainly on *Las Cajas plateau in Azuay. Stubby pointed*

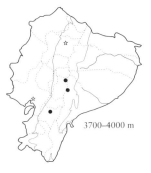

3700–4000 m

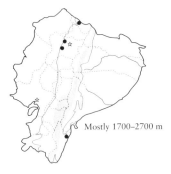

Mostly 1700–2700 m

bill. Striking ♂ *deep blue narrowly streaked with glistening paler blue*, especially above. Pretty ♀ has *blue forecrown and ocular area*; grayish brown upperparts with blue edging on wings and tail. *Cinnamon-buff below*, paling on midbelly. **Similar species:** Not likely confused, bill shape distinguishing it even when colors are obscured in poor light. Cf. various *Diglossa* flowerpiercers. **Habits:** Usually in pairs or small noisy groups, sometimes accompanying mixed flocks; generally remains quite low. Forages very actively, especially gleaning aphids and their sugary secretions from the underside of leaves of *Gynoxys* shrubs. **Voice:** Quite vocal, with various calls, usually loud. Song notably loud for size of bird, a fast and variable series of penetrating whistled notes, e.g., "zwit-zwit-zwit-zwit-zhweet-zhweet-zhweet," often interspersed with high-pitched or scratchy notes. This is sometimes given antiphonally by members of a pair, ♂ giving the first parts.

Diglossa and *Diglossopis* Flowerpiercers

Distinctive small tanagers found in the Andes, mostly in forested or wooded habitats. Most have the *bill obviously upturned and sharply hooked at the tip*, this used to pierce the corolla (base) of flowers in order to get at nectar. **Sexes are usually alike** (exceptions being White-sided and Rusty), with blues, blacks, and grays predominating. Several species were recently separated in the genus *Diglossopis*.

Bluish Flowerpiercer
Diglossopis caerulescens
Pinchaflor Azulado   Plate 84(9)

13.5 cm (5¼"). A *uniform-looking flowerpiercer* found locally in *subtropical and lower*

temperate forest, woodland, and scrub, *mainly on e. slope* but also in northwest. *Bill relatively "normally" shaped* (not especially upturned and showing little hook at tip); *iris reddish to orange.* Grayish blue, somewhat paler below, especially on belly; foreface blackish. **Similar species:** The more numerous and widespread Masked Flowerpiercer (which sometimes occurs with Bluish, though more often ranging at higher elevations) has more a hooked and upturned bill and is brighter and deeper blue generally with a red eye and better-defined and more contrasting black mask; beware especially duller juvenile Maskeds. **Habits:** Sometimes ranges high in canopy of tall montane forest, but also regular in windswept elfin woodland; regularly accompanies mixed flocks of tanagers and other birds. Though probing flowers like other flowerpiercers, Bluish forages much more by gleaning for insects in foliage; it also eats some small fruits. **Voice:** Song a descending series of high-pitched and squeaky twittering notes. Characteristic call a sharp and high-pitched "tsin" (P. Coopmans).

Masked Flowerpiercer, *Diglossopis cyanea*
Pinchaflor Enmascarado   Plate 84(10)

14.5 cm (5¾"). A beautiful flowerpiercer, common and widespread on both slopes in temperate forest and woodland, borders, and adjacent clearings and gardens. *Iris bright red.* ♂ *rich ultramarine blue* with *contrasting large black mask.* ♀ somewhat duller. **Similar species:** Cf. usually scarcer Bluish Flowerpiercer and (in northwest) the much more local Indigo Flowerpiercer. Blue-and-black Tanager, though colored much the same and often occurring with this species, differs in having a dark eye, normally shaped

Mostly 2400–3500 m

bill, and contrasting black wings and tail. **Habits:** Often occurs in small (occasionally even large) groups, forming a prominent element in the bird faunas of many basically forested upper-elevation locales. Regularly forages with mixed flocks, equally probing flowers and eating small fruits. **Voice:** Song a series of thin "seet" notes ending with twitter, but sometimes entirely jumbled.

Golden-eyed Flowerpiercer
Diglossopis glauca
Pinchaflor Ojidorado   Plate 84(16)

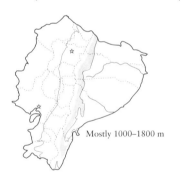

Mostly 1000–1800 m

12 cm (4¾″). A *strikingly yellow-eyed* flower-piercer found in canopy and borders of *foothill and subtropical forest on e. slope.* Formerly called Deep-blue Flowerpiercer. *Iris bright golden yellow. Uniform deep blue*; lores black. **Similar species:** The only flower-piercer with yellow eyes, a conspicuous feature in the field, making it easy to recognize. **Habits:** Usually in pairs or small groups, most often foraging high above ground in tall forest though sometimes lower at edge; frequently accompanies mixed flocks. Forages by gleaning for insects, often in bromeliads, only infrequently probing flowers.

Voice: Song a fast, high-pitched but descending series of thin notes, jumbled toward end; notably higher pitched than song of Bluish.

Indigo Flowerpiercer, *Diglossopis indigotica*
Pinchaflor Indigo   Plate 84(15)

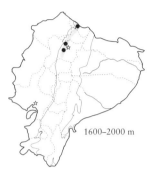

1600–2000 m

11.5 cm (4½″). Very *rare and local* in *mossy subtropical forest on w. slope. Iris bright red. Uniform bright deep blue*; lores black. **Similar species:** Equally red-eyed Masked Flowerpiercer generally occurs at higher elevations (though unrecorded, some overlap is possible) and differs in being considerably larger with an obvious large black mask. **Habits:** Not well known in Ecuador. In general seems to be a western counterpart of e. slope's Golden-eyed Flowerpiercer, with similar overall behavior. **Voice:** Call a high-pitched thin note reminiscent of Bluish Flowerpiercer (P. Coopmans).

Glossy Flowerpiercer, *Diglossa lafresnayii*
Pinchaflor Satinado   Plate 84(11)

14.5 cm (5¾″). Temperate forest and borders on both slopes, *most numerous just below*

Mostly 2700–3500 m

treeline. Glossy black with *obvious bluish gray shoulders.* **Similar species:** Smaller Black Flowerpiercer is equally black (though not so glossy) but *lacks bluish shoulders*; it is less of a forest-based bird. **Habits:** Usually found singly or in pairs, often remaining inside cover, moving rather deliberately in foliage and at times hard to see. Generally forages independently of mixed flocks, piercing the corolla of flowers; also gleans for insects. **Voice:** Long-continued song a series of semi-musical twittering and jumbled notes, often delivered while perched atop a low tree or shrub.

Black Flowerpiercer, *Diglossa humeralis*
Pinchaflor Negro   Plate 84(12)

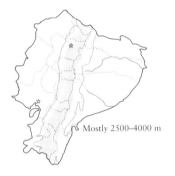

Mostly 2500–4000 m

13.5 cm (5¼″). *Widespread and generally numerous* in shrubby areas, gardens, and lighter woodland (even *Polylepis*) in the high-lands; *a nonforest bird. Uniform dull black.* **Similar species:** The larger Glossy Flower-piercer is often confused with this usually more numerous *Diglossa*, but Glossy differs in having bluish shoulders (normally not diffi-cult to see). Glossy favors montane forest and borders, only rarely moving out into gardens even when these are close by. **Habits:** Nervous and flighty, foraging singly or in pairs, usually rather low; almost always remains indepen-dent of mixed flocks. Forages mostly at flowers, both by piercing corollas or by direct probing. **Voice:** Song a brief fast twittering, recalling song of Cinereous Conebill.

White-sided Flowerpiercer, *Diglossa albilatera*
Pinchaflor Flanquiblanco   Plate 84(14)

12 cm (4¾″). *Widespread in upper subtro-pical and temperate forest, woodland, and*

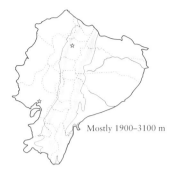

Mostly 1900–3100 m

borders on both slopes, sometimes in gardens nearby. ♂ *dark slaty* with *partially concealed (but usually protruding) white tuft on sides;* underwing-linings also white. ♀ has *white tufts similar to* ♂*'s* (but somewhat smaller); otherwise olive brown above, paler buffy brown below. **Immature** like ♀ but vaguely streaked below. **Similar species:** The distinc-tive white is almost always in evidence because of nervous mannerisms of this little *Diglossa,* which *almost always is flicking its wings,* exposing white. When white is hidden, ♀♀ or immatures might be mistaken for ♀ Slaty Finch (though their bill shapes differ dramatically). Black Flowerpiercer is obvi-ously black (but ♂ White-sided's gray can look decidedly dark in some lights, causing potential confusion); cf. also ♀ Rusty Flow-erpiercer. **Habits:** Usually in pairs, foraging restlessly at varying levels but generally low and at edge of forest or woodland. Often accompanies mixed flocks of other tanagers, moving quickly between flowers. Also gleans for insects. **Voice:** Distinctive song a short, dry, unmusical trill, often trailing off at end; Cinnamon Flycatcher's similar call is harsher.

Rusty Flowerpiercer, *Diglossa sittoides*
Pinchaflor Pechicanelo   Plate 84(13)

11.5 cm (4½″). *Local* (surprisingly so) in shrubby clearings, gardens, and forest and woodland borders, *mainly in subtropics;* a *nonforest* bird, occurring in both humid and arid regions. ♂ *bicolored:* basically *bluish gray above* and *cinnamon-buff below,* with face somewhat blackish. Dull ♀ brownish olive above, dingy yellowish buff below with *blurry dusky streaking on throat and chest.* **Similar species:** ♂ distinctive (though cf. Blue-backed and Cinereous Conebills). ♀ is

Mostly 1700–2800 m

obscure but lacks white at sides shown by ♀ White-sided Flowerpiercer; no other *Diglossa* shows any streaking below. **Habits:** Usually noted singly or in pairs, sometimes feeding at flowers with Black or White-sided Flowerpiercers but generally not with mixed flocks. Most often seen in gardens and other disturbed situations. Active, and often acrobatically hanging upside-down when piercing and probing flowers. **Voice:** Song variable, either a short thin twitter or a fast series of high-pitched notes followed by a lower-pitched burry note.

Hemithraupis Tanagers
Small, *warbler-like* tanagers with pointed bills found in the lowlands. Males are *strongly patterned and readily recognized*, but females are similar and tricky to separate.

Guira Tanager, *Hemithraupis guira*
Tangara Guira   Plate 86(18)

To 1100 m

13 cm (5″). A pretty, small tanager of borders of humid forest, secondary woodland, and adjacent plantations in *lowlands and foothills of west and east*; scarce or absent well east of Andes. Bill yellowish to dull

orange with blackish culmen. ♂ *boldly patterned*, with *black face and throat outlined by yellow and bordered below by orange-rufous breast*. Otherwise bright olive above with lower back and rump orange-rufous and yellow; pale yellowish below. **Western birds** have a more ochraceous superciliary. ♀ much duller, essentially olive above with vague pale yellow superciliary and eye-ring; pale dull yellowish below with grayish olive flanks. **Similar species:** ♂ unlikely to be confused, but warbler-like ♀ can cause difficulties; it most resembles ♀ Yellow-backed Tanager (found only in east), but latter is brighter and more uniform yellow below and lacks yellow brow and around eye. ♀ can even be confused with ♀♀ of various euphonias (though it is a bit larger and longer-tailed than any, and with a finer and more pointed bill). Cf. also Orange-fronted Plushcrown. **Habits:** An arboreal tanager, usually in pairs and regularly accompanying mixed flocks, gleaning actively in foliage, most often on outside branches so not hard to observe. Generally avoids continuous forest. **Voice:** Song an unmusical series of high-pitched squeaky notes.

Yellow-backed Tanager
Hemithraupis flavicollis
Tangara Lomiamarilla   Plate 86(17)

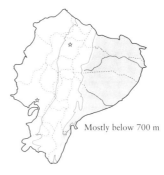

Mostly below 700 m

13 cm (5″). *Canopy of terra firme forest in lowlands and foothills of east*. ♂♂ *strikingly black, white, and yellow*, ♀♀ obscure. Bill yellowish with blackish ridge. ♂ *black above* with *bright yellow lower back and rump* and a small white wing speculum and yellow on lesser wing-coverts. *Throat also bright yellow*, contrasting with white underparts, mottled black on breast and sides, crissum

also yellow. ♀ *dark* olive above, wings duskier *broadly edged yellowish. Below uniform yellowish.* **Similar species:** ♂ distinctive in reasonable light, but ♀ can cause problems (especially as the species generally remains so high above ground). ♀ Guira Tanager is paler olive above and shows a narrow yellowish superciliary lacking in ♀ Yellow-backed; its underparts are less uniform yellow, showing some olive on flanks. **Habits:** Usually in pairs, almost always foraging well above ground, and as a result can be hard to see clearly. Usually found accompanying mixed flocks comprised of tanagers and other birds.

Scarlet-and-white Tanager
Erythrothlypis salmoni
Tangara Escarlatiblanca   Plate 86(19)

To 700 m

13 cm (5″). Local in canopy and borders of humid forest and secondary woodland in *lowlands and foothills of far northwest.* Sometimes placed in genus *Chrysothlypis.* ♂ ♂ *stunningly red and white,* ♀ ♀ *bronzy brown and whitish.* Rather long bill. ♂ *vibrant glistening scarlet above and on throat, chest, and median stripe on underparts;* breast and belly otherwise white. ♀ *bronzy* olive above and dull yellowish buff below, with *sides and flanks broadly whitish* (with pattern reminiscent of ♂'s). **Similar species:** ♂ unmistakable at any distance (and despite small size, can sometimes be picked out from far away). ♀ usually identified by the company she keeps (species generally occurs in small groups, so this is easy); it is browner above than other generally similar species (e.g., ♀ Guira Tanager), most of which have some yellow below; its contrastingly pale flanks are distinctive. **Habits:** Behavior much

like Guira Tanager, though Scarlet-and-white more apt to occur in small groups; like the Guira, seems to favor edge and semiopen situations, and thus often easy to observe. Forages actively, mainly by gleaning in outer foliage, but also hovers; also eats much small fruit. Regularly with mixed flocks. **Voice:** Often-heard and distinctive call a fast, brief, descending series of fairly high-pitched notes, e.g., "tsi-tsi-tse-tsu-tu" (P. Coopmans).

Thlypopsis Tanagers
Small, warbler-like tanagers with short bills that favor shrubby secondary growth. Simply patterned, all three Ecuadorian species have *prominent orange-rufous or yellow-orange.*

Orange-headed Tanager, *Thlypopsis sordida*
Tangara Cabecinaranja   Plate 90(7)

To 500 m

13.5 cm (5¼″). An *orange-headed* tanager found mainly in *early-succession riparian growth and river islands* (also locally in clearings) in *lowlands of east.* **Sexes alike.** *Hood yellow-orange* (yellower on throat) contrasting with *gray upperparts.* Below dingy grayish. **Immature** has olive head, yellow on throat and chest. **Similar species:** This simply patterned but pretty tanager is not likely to be confused in its *lowland* range. **Habits:** Usually in pairs, gleaning actively in foliage at all levels, generally in semiopen and not difficult to observe; sometimes with mixed flocks. **Voice:** Song a high-pitched stuttering series usually preceded by several longer notes.

Rufous-chested Tanager, *Thlypopsis ornata*
Tangara Pechicanela   Plate 90(6)

12.5 cm (5″). Scarce in montane forest and woodland borders in the *highlands,* more numerous southward. **Sexes alike.** *Entire head and underparts orange-rufous* contrast-

Mostly 1800–3000 m

ing with *white median belly*; otherwise olivaceous gray above. **Similar species:** Not likely confused in its *Andean range.* Rufous-crested Tanager has gray on head and no white on belly; it is a forest bird. Cf. Buff-bellied Tanager (no range overlap). **Habits:** Usually in pairs, generally in semiopen and often found some distance from forest, locally even in relatively arid regions. Forages actively at all levels, sometimes associating at least loosely with mixed flocks. **Voice:** Occasionally gives a somewhat metallic and jumbled "see-sje-se-seek-sje-se-seek-se-sjuk" (P. Coopmans).

Buff-bellied Tanager, *Thlypopsis inornata*
Tangara Ventrianteada   Plate 96(18)

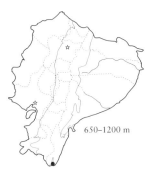

650–1200 m

12.5 cm (5"). Shrubby woodland and forest borders in *Río Marañón drainage around Zumba.* ♂ with *crown and nape orange-rufous*, becoming *buff on face and entire underparts*; upperparts contrastingly olivaceous gray. ♀ has crown and nape more olivaceous (hardly contrasting with back) and paler underparts. **Similar species:** Rufous-chested Tanager (which does not occur around Zumba) has underparts extensively

orange-rufous, not merely buff. **Habits:** Much like Rufous-chested Tanager, though less arboreal, mainly foraging close to the ground, sometimes even in tall grass. In addition to gleaning warblerlike in foliage, it also probes into flowers. **Voice:** Unknown.

Fawn-breasted Tanager
Pipraeidea melanonota
Tangara Pechianteada   Plate 87(1)

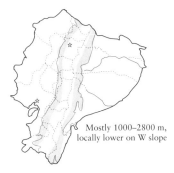

Mostly 1000–2800 m,
locally lower on W slope

14 cm (5½"). A *pretty blue and buff tanager of the Andes*, widespread and conspicuous—but never that numerous—in clearings, agricultural areas, and secondary woodland; absent or nearly so from extensively forested regions. *Iris bright red.* ♂ with *crown and nape bright blue* and *contrasting black mask.* Otherwise dusky-blue above, *uniform fawn-buff below.* ♀ similar but duller. **Similar species:** Superficially resembles ♂ Golden-rumped Euphonia (and the two are sometimes found together), especially because of the similar pale blue on crown, but the smaller and dark-eyed euphonia differs in its black throat and yellow rump. Cf. also Rufous-crested Tanager and ♀ Blue-and-yellow Tanager. **Habits:** Usually found in pairs, foraging quietly in semiopen, often perching for protracted periods on exposed dead branches, peering around. Sometimes with mixed flocks, but at least as often moves independently. **Voice:** A quiet bird, but does give a fast series of simple, high-pitched "see" notes; also gives a more jumbled, euphonia-like song and a high-pitched trill.

Chlorophonia Chlorophonias
Beautiful, *predominantly bright emerald green* tanagers found on Andean slopes. In shape they recall the euphonias but are *even*

plumper. Males in full plumage are often a distinct minority, evidently more than one year being required to attain adult plumage.

Blue-naped Chlorophonia
Chlorophonia cyanea
Clorofonia Nuquiazul   Plate 85(7)

Mostly 800–2000 m

11.5 cm (4½″). Scarce in *canopy and borders of foothill and lower subtropical forest on e. slope*. Beautiful ♂ has *entire head, throat, and chest bright grass green* contrasting with *bright blue nape, back, and rump*; eye-ring pale blue, wings and tail green. Underparts contrastingly bright yellow. ♀ similar and only slightly duller green above, with *bright blue restricted to nape*; yellow on underparts somewhat clouded with green, but *still contrasting* with green throat and chest. **Similar species:** Both sexes of Chestnut-breasted Chlorophonia have blue crown, lacking in Blue-naped; Chestnut-breasted favors somewhat higher elevations. Cf. also ♀ Yellow-collared Chlorophonia (which essentially replaces Blue-naped on w. slope). **Habits:** Regularly in small groups that usually remain high above ground; usually not with mixed flocks. Generally inconspicuous, tending to remain in cover and often remaining motionless for some time, like so many small parrots; then (also recalling parrots) they may burst from cover and fly off. They eat much mistletoe. **Voice:** Call, sometimes given at rest (also in flight), a plaintive soft "peeeng" or "teeuw."

Yellow-collared Chlorophonia
Chlorophonia flavirostris
Clorofonia Cuellidorada   Plate 85(8)

10 cm (4″). A *gaudy* chlorophonia, scarce and perhaps seasonal or erratic in *canopy and*

Mostly 400–1500 m

borders of foothill and lower subtropical forest in northwest. Bill and legs salmon; iris white, eye-ring yellow. Stunning ♂ unmistakable, *mostly bright emerald green* with *bright yellow nuchal collar, rump, border to green chest, and median lower underparts*. ♀ *mainly green* (a bit duller than in ♂), with yellow restricted to eye-ring and median lower underparts. **Similar species:** Soft-part colors of both sexes unique. Even the uniformly bright green ♀♀ are unlikely to be confused in their limited range; only possible confusion is with larger Blue-naped Chlorophonia (no confirmed overlap). **Habits:** Much like Blue-naped Chlorophonia, though at least occasionally Yellow-collared has been seen in considerably larger flocks. **Voice:** Distinctive nasal and plaintive call, often given in flight, a drawn-out "peeeeeeee," sometimes interspersed with short, clear "winh" calls.

Chestnut-breasted Chlorophonia
Chlorophonia pyrrhophrys
Clorofonia Pechicastaña   Plate 85(6)

11.5 cm (4½″). Canopy and borders of *subtropical and temperate* forest, *mostly on e. slope* but also in northwest, at *higher eleva-*

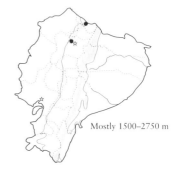

Mostly 1500–2750 m

tions than other chlorophonias. *Multicolored* ♂ nearly unmistakable, with *deep cobalt blue crown outlined with black, bright pale green face, throat, and chest* separated from bright yellow underparts by black line, and with *chestnut stripe down median underparts to crissum.* Above otherwise deep green with yellow rump. ♀ echoes ♂'s pattern and *retains blue crown* but is somewhat duller, especially below, and lacks yellow on rump; *outline to crown chestnut.* **Similar species:** ♀ might carelessly be confused with ♀ of smaller Golden-rumped Euphonia; euphonia's blue crown is more extensive and paler (thus more noticeable) and *lacks any contrast below.* **Habits:** Much like other chlorophonias, though tending more to range in pairs or very small groups (rarely more than 3–5 together), not in flocks. **Voice:** Call a clear "teeeu" that drops at end; also gives a higher-pitched "peeeee."

Euphonia Euphonias

Distinctive small, *short-tailed* tanagers with *stubby bills.* Euphonias are wide-ranging, arboreal birds found primarily in the lowlands, with diversity being greatest in humid forest; many eat mistletoe berries. There is strong sexual dimorphism in most species, males typically being *steely blue above and yellow below, usually with a yellow crown patch and a dark throat,* females mainly olive and yellow *often with rufous or gray below.* Identification is often tricky, and the duller females can be confused with males of various manakins (which have a somewhat similar shape). Males often have a white wingstripe and white tail spots, visible especially in flight. Songs of several species are notably variable, and some even imitate other birds.

Thick-billed Euphonia, *Euphonia laniirostris*
Eufonia Piquigruesa   Plate 85(14)

11.5 cm (4½"). *Widespread in lowlands* in a variety of wooded and forested habitats and in clearings in lowlands of east (where less numerous) and west (where in both humid and arid regions). *Bill slightly thicker* than in other euphonias, but this hard to see in field. ♂ glossy steel blue above with *relatively large yellow patch on forecrown. Entirely* yellow below. **Western birds** have (often hidden) white tail spots lacking in **eastern birds.** ♀

Mostly below 1500 m

olive above; yellow below, clouded with olive across breast and down sides. **Immature** ♂♂ resemble ♀♀ but early on acquire yellow forecrown and blue-black face. **Similar species:** ♀ readily confused with other ♀♀ euphonias, though it is slightly larger and thicker-billed; it is plainer and more uniform than most, being devoid of obvious markings. Cf. especially ♀ Orange-crowned. **Habits:** Usually in pairs or small groups, often with other tanagers including other euphonias, regularly congregating at fruiting trees. Forages at all levels, though rarely inside forest. **Voice:** Rather vocal. Both sexes often give a musical "chweet" call. ♂'s song a variable series of musical and chattering notes and phrases that can continue interminably; it often includes brief renditions of calls and songs of other bird species.

Golden-rumped Euphonia
Euphonia cyanocephala
Eufonia Lomidorada   Plate 85(9)

11 cm (4¼"). A pretty, *blue-crowned, non-forest* euphonia; uncommon in semiopen areas and montane forest borders in *highlands,* a few ranging down into foothills. Formerly called Blue-hooded Euphonia

Mostly 1200–2800 m

(*E. musica*). Both sexes have an unmistakable *bright turquoise blue crown and nape*. Colorful ♂ glossy purplish black above with *bright yellow rump*. Sides of head and throat black (with yellow frontlet from Azuay to Loja); underparts rich orange-yellow. ♀ olive above with tawny frontlet; yellowish below. **Similar species:** Cf. ♀ of larger Chestnut-breasted Chlorophonia (also blue-crowned). **Habits:** Usually in pairs or small groups, generally perching high in trees out in partially cleared areas, sometimes even in parks or gardens. Generally does not associate with mixed flocks. Seems inordinately fond of mistletoe berries, even more so than other euphonias. **Voice:** Not especially vocal, but calls include a low "tueer" and a "chit" or "chuk." Song an often long-continued jumble of semimusical notes and twitters.

crowned Euphonia has a larger crown patch and is more orange-ochraceous below. ♀ closest to ♀ Rufous-bellied Euphonia, but that differs in having a yellowish (not ochraceous) forecrown and grayer (not so buffy) underparts, with tawny (not yellowish) crissum. **Habits:** Usually in pairs or small groups, foraging at all levels from high in forest canopy to near ground; this is the only euphonia found regularly near the ground inside forest, where it often accompanies understory flocks. As a consequence, it is also more often mist-netted than others. **Voice:** Variable. Calls include a clear "ding-ding-ding," a "chee!," an upslurred "kueé," and a more gravelly "cheeur-cheeur." Song a variable, almost random-sounding, series of semimusical phrases given in a leisurely manner.

Orange-bellied Euphonia
Euphonia xanthogaster
Eufonia Ventrinaranja   Plate 85(10)

Mostly below 2000 m

White-vented Euphonia, *Euphonia minuta*
Eufonia Ventriblanca   Plate 85(11)

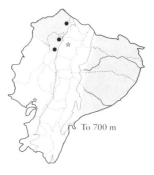

To 700 m

11 cm (4¼"). *The most widespread Ecuadorian euphonia in humid regions*, occurring in forest and woodland from *lowlands in both west and east up into subtropics on both slopes*. ♂ mostly steel blue above (face and nape more purplish) with *forecrown ochraceous-tinged yellow*. Throat black tinged purple; *underparts ochraceous-tinged yellow*. ♀ olive above with *tawny-ochraceous patch on forecrown* and *gray nape*. *Buffy grayish below*, buffiest on belly, with sides and flanks yellowish olive. **Similar species:** As it will be seen so often, this is a good euphonia to learn to recognize quickly. Unfortunately, it is poorly named, not being very "orange" below. Cf. Purple-throated Euphonia (only around Zumba). ♂ Orange-

9.5 cm (3¾"). *Generally scarce* in *canopy and borders of humid forest and secondary woodland* in lowlands of east and northwest. Both sexes have *lower median belly and crissum white (♂) or whitish (♀)*. The *smallest* Ecuadorian euphonia. ♂ steely blue-black above with *only forehead yellow*. Throat black glossed purplish; underparts bright yellow with *midbelly and crissum white*. ♀ olive above. Throat grayish white; breast, sides, and flanks yellowish; *midbelly and crissum whitish*. **Similar species:** No other euphonia has white on crissum and lower midbelly (sometimes hard to see). ♂'s yellow crown patch is notably *restricted*, reaching back only to just before eye. Several other ♀♀ euphonias also have yellowish flanks, but in none does this color also extend broadly across the breast. **Habits:** Usually found singly or in pairs, generally remaining high in trees where easily overlooked; often associates with other euphonias, and regularly accompanies mixed flocks. **Voice:** Call a simple "beem" or "seeu;" infrequently heard song a variable and jumbled warbling with interspersed chipping notes.

Purple-throated Euphonia, *Euphonia chlorotica*
Eufonia Golipúrpura   Plate 85(18)

To 1400 m

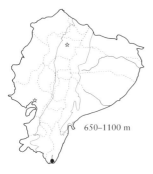

650–1100 m

10 cm (4"). Forest borders, woodland, and adjacent clearings in *Río Marañón drainage around Zumba*. ♂ steely blue-black above, purpler on head; forecrown yellow. Throat black glossed purple; underparts (*including crissum*) bright yellow. ♀ olive above with yellow on forecrown. *Mostly grayish white below*, with sides, flanks, and crissum yellowish. **Similar species:** Orange-bellied Euphonia is slightly larger; ♂ ♂ are otherwise similar, though Orange-bellied is slightly more ochraceous below and on forecrown; Purple-throated's forecrown patch is also considerably smaller. ♀ Orange-bellied differs in having a grayer nape and is more noticeably ochraceous on forecrown and belly. **Habits:** Arboreal behavior typical of other euphonias; in its limited Ecuadorian range often with Thick-billeds. **Voice:** Frequently given call a far-carrying, clear "beem-beem."

Orange-crowned Euphonia, *Euphonia saturata*
Eufonia Coroninaranja   Plate 85(13)

10 cm (4"). A *nonforest* euphonia of deciduous woodland, humid forest borders, and cleared areas with scattered trees in *lowlands and foothills of west*. Handsome ♂ richly

colored, with *entire crown deep yellow-orange*, upperparts and throat glossy dark violaceous. *Underparts deep orange-ochraceous*. ♀ *very plain*: olive above and yellowish below, shaded with olive on sides, flanks, and crissum. **Similar species:** ♂ Orange-bellied Euphonia has crown patch smaller and yellow (not so orange), and (despite its name) yellower underparts than ♂ Orange-crowned. ♀ Orange-crowned resembles ♀ Thick-billed Euphonia (and the two are often together, with Thick-billed generally outnumbering it) but is somewhat smaller and has a less heavy bill; unless seen well, however, go by accompanying (and very different) ♂ ♂. **Habits:** Arboreal behavior similar to other euphonias. **Voice:** Call a simple "beem-beem." Song a leisurely series of "tsit" notes, nasal "tcheeur" notes, and fast "tididit" phrases (P. Coopmans).

Fulvous-vented Euphonia, *Euphonia fulvicrissa*
Eufonia Ventrileonada   Plate 85(12)

10 cm (4"). Humid forest, secondary woodland, and (especially) borders in *lowlands and foothills of northwest*. Both sexes have

To 500 m

fulvous on lower underparts. ♂ steely blue above and on throat, with yellow patch on forecrown. Yellow below with *midbelly and crissum tawny-fulvous.* ♀ olive above with *rufous forecrown* and bluish gray tinge to nape. Olive yellowish below with *midbelly and crissum tawny.* **Similar species:** No other euphonia in range has the contrasting (and easy to see) tawny-fulvous on lower underparts. **Habits:** Usually in pairs or small groups, ranging more often in understory than most euphonias (though it also frequents canopy), and sometimes with Orange-bellied Euphonias in such situations; regularly accompanies mixed flocks. **Voice:** Frequently heard call a distinctive gravelly "trrrt-trrrt," very different from Orange-bellied. Song a fast jumbled series of high-pitched notes interspersed with lower-pitched trills (O. Jahn recording).

Rufous-bellied Euphonia, *Euphonia rufiventris*
Eufonia Ventrirrufa   Plate 85(15)

Mostly below 500 m

11.5 cm (4½"). Canopy and borders of humid forest in *lowlands of east.* ♂ entirely glossy steel-blue above and on throat and chest *(with no crown patch).* Underparts rich *tawny*, with golden pectoral patch sometimes protruding from under bend of wing. ♀ olive above with *yellowish forehead* and *bluish gray nape. Below pale gray* with contrasting olive-yellow sides and flanks and *tawny crissum.* **Similar species:** Other ♂ ♂ euphonias (except White-lored) in range of this species have conspicuous yellow forecrown patch; its lack often results in Rufous-bellied's not at first even being recognized as a euphonia. ♀ Orange-bellied Euphonia closely resembles ♀ Rufous-bellied, differing

in its more ochraceous forehead and dingier underparts (with no tawny). ♀ White-lored Euphonia is also quite similar but it has a whitish loral area and yellow (not tawny) crissum. **Habits:** An arboreal euphonia, usually occurring in pairs and tending to remain well above ground though sometimes coming lower at edge when feeding in a fruiting tree. Often accompanies mixed flocks. **Voice:** Call frequently heard and distinctive, a fast gravelly "drrt-drrt-drrt-drrt."

Bronze-green Euphonia, *Euphonia mesochrysa*
Eufonia Verdibronceada   Plate 85(17)

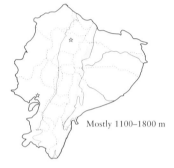

Mostly 1100–1800 m

10 cm (4"). Canopy and borders of *foothill and subtropical forest on e. slope.* ♂ *comparatively dull,* steely olive with *prominent yellow forehead* and grayish crown and nape. Throat, chest, and sides yellowish olive, with *rich ochraceous yellow midbreast and belly.* ♀ much like ♂ but *lacking* yellow forehead. Mostly yellowish olive below with midbreast and belly pale gray. **Similar species:** ♀ ♀, which lack ♂ ♂'s obvious and distinctive yellow frontlet, are often confused or passed over. ♀ Orange-bellied Euphonia (often together) is more dull buffyish below and has only a dull yellowish forecrown. ♂ White-lored Euphonia resembles ♂ Bronze-green but has white on foreface and no yellow on forecrown; ♀ White-lored is much more extensively gray below than ♀ Bronze-green. In any case, the White-lored is found in e. lowlands below Bronze-green's range (no known overlap). Immature ♂ Thick-billed Euphonia can look superficially like ♂ Bronze-green because it may acquire yellow forecrown when still retaining mainly olive plumage. **Habits:** An inconspicuous and not often encountered euphonia that tends to

remain high in tall forest where observation is usually difficult. Regularly accompanies mixed flocks with other tanagers. **Voice:** Call a distinctive, gravelly "treeuh, treeuh." Song consists of 2 clear notes followed by a musical trill, "tee-teeu-trrrrrt."

White-lored Euphonia, *Euphonia chrysopasta*
Eufonia Loriblanca   Plate 85(16)

Mostly below 600 m

11 cm (4¼"). Canopy and borders of humid forest in *lowlands of east*. Formerly called Golden-bellied Euphonia. *Distinctive white loral area in both sexes.* ♂ glossy olive above with grayish hindcrown and nape; *white on lores extends down over chin. Bright golden yellow below with extensive but vague olive mottling.* ♀ like ♂ above. *Below mainly pale gray* with *lower flanks and crissum (only) yellow.* **Similar species:** No other euphonia has white on foreface. ♀ Rufous-bellied Euphonia is also extensively pale gray below, but aside from lacking white lores it has a tawny (not yellow) crissum. **Habits:** Arboreal behavior much like that of several other euphonias. Like the Rufous-bellied (with which it regularly occurs), White-lored generally remains well above ground, only occasionally coming lower, then primarily at edge. Often in pairs, sometimes with mixed flocks. **Voice:** Frequently heard calls include a repeated "wheet" and an explosive "pitz-week" or "pitzaweek;" ♂'s song a long-continued series of sputtering notes and phrases with little discernible pattern.

Chlorochrysa Tanagers
Mainly bright green tanagers found in subtropical forest, one on either slope. Compared to *Tangara*, *Chlorochrysa* are smaller, less plump, and more agile.

Orange-eared Tanager
Chlorochrysa calliparaea
Tangara Orejinaranja   Plate 87(2)

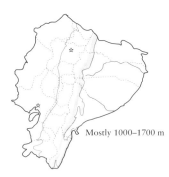

Mostly 1000–1700 m

12.5 cm (5"). A *colorful* tanager with complex pattern, often common in canopy and borders of *foothill and subtropical forest on e. slope*. ♂ mostly bright shining emerald green; small orange spot on midcrown, and an *orange rump band* (often conspicuous in flight). *Throat black*, connecting to *orange-red patch on sides of neck*. ♀ duller than ♂, mainly green with diffused pattern and brownish gray throat but retaining the orange rump. **Similar species:** No other tanager on Andes' e. slope is predominantly such a bright green. **Habits:** Usually found in pairs or small groups, frequently as they accompany mixed flocks with other tanagers. Forages actively in foliage, often moving rapidly and quickly proceeding from tree to tree, acrobatically clinging to leaves or briefly hovering. Seems to eat mainly insects. **Voice:** Foraging birds give an occasional "zeep" or "tsip."

Glistening-green Tanager
Chlorochrysa phoenicotis
Tangara Verde Reluciente   Plate 87(3)

12.5 cm (5"). *Uncommon and local in foothill and lower subtropical forest and secondary woodland, especially where wet and mossy, on w. slope.* ♂ almost entirely bright glistening emerald green, with small glistening gray patches behind and below eye, and another on shoulders. ♀ slightly duller. **Similar species:** Cf. ♀ Green Honeycreeper (also all green, though nowhere near as intensely colored). Emerald Tanager (which occurs sympatrically with Glistening-green) is also

600–1700 m

Mostly 600–1400 m

bright green but shows a strong black pattern on face and back. Various immature *Tangara* can also be mainly dull green. **Habits:** Much like Orange-eared Tanager. **Voice:** Gives various high-pitched "tseet" notes, sometimes in a short descending series, e.g., "tsi-tsi-tseeuw-tseeuw-tseeuw."

Tangara Tanagers

The quintessential tanagers: colorful, boldly patterned, and *conspicuous, Tangara* tanagers will always be birders' favorites, and some rank among the more beautiful Neotropical birds. It is far from easy to generalize about the genus, though most species range primarily in montane or humid forests. *Diversity is highest in the Andean foothills and subtropics*, where their mixed-species flocks are a notable avian feature and up to 8 to 10 species can range together. Plumage patterns can be very complex; despite the diversity of species, generally identification does not pose any difficulties. Many species are not particularly vocal, and their calls are often not very distinctive; these are not mentioned below.

Rufous-throated Tanager, *Tangara rufigula*
Tangara Golirrufa   Plate 87(4)

12 cm (4¾"). An unmistakable *black-speckled* tanager found locally in *foothill and lower subtropical forest and secondary woodland on w. slope*, favoring mossy cloud forest conditions. **Sexes alike.** *Head black with contrasting rufous throat. Otherwise black above*, feathers edged golden green *with pronounced scaly effect*. Pale opalescent below, feathers centered black resulting in *pronounced spotted effect*. **Similar species:** Beryl-spangled Tanager also gives a generally spangled or spotted effect. **Habits:** Usually occurs in pairs or small groups, regularly accompanying mixed flocks with other tanagers. Forages mostly by gleaning for insects from foliage, but also eats much fruit. **Voice:** Song a high-pitched stuttered chatter.

Gray-and-gold Tanager, *Tangara palmeri*
Tangara Doradigris   Plate 86(14)

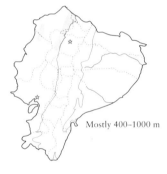

Mostly 400–1000 m

14.5 cm (5¾"). A *rather large, predominantly pale gray Tangara* of *foothill forest and borders in northwest*, also on coastal cordillera in the northwest. **Sexes alike.** *Pale gray above* with small black mask, black scapulars, and more opalescent back. *Whitish below* with *sprinkling of black spots on sides of neck and chest*, and opalescent gold tinge across foreneck. **Similar species:** Not likely confused, but cf. Golden-hooded Tanager. **Habits:** Usually in pairs or small groups, often with mixed flocks of other tanagers. Conspicuous birds, they often rest on exposed high branches for protracted periods, then may fly long distances, sometimes with a flock straggling along behind. Mainly frugivorous. **Voice:** Rather noisy for a *Tangara*, giving a variety of sharp or semimusical calls, the most frequent being a far-carrying and distinctive "chi-chup swee?"

Golden Tanager, *Tangara arthus*
Tangara Dorada   Plate 87(5)

Mostly 900–2000 m

13.5–14 cm (5¼–5½"). *Common and wide-spread in canopy and borders of foothill and subtropical forest and woodland on both slopes. The only predominantly rich golden Tangara.* Sexes alike. **West-slope birds** *mostly rich golden to ochraceous yellow with contrasting large black patch on ear-coverts;* back prominently streaked black, wings and tail black with yellow edging. **East-slope** birds slightly larger and with rufous wash on throat and breast. **Similar species:** Confusion unlikely, but in w. foothills cf. Silver-throated Tanager. **Habits:** Almost invariably seen in pairs or small groups, usually accompanying mixed flocks with other tanagers; generally one of the more numerous *Tangara* at lower elevations in the Andes. In addition to eating fruit (often congregating with other tanagers at fruiting trees), also forages for insects a good deal, typically by sidling along mossy branches and peering underneath. **Voice:** Calls include a smacking "chup."

Emerald Tanager, *Tangara florida*
Tangara Esmeralda   Plate 86(6)

13 cm (5"). A *mainly bright emerald green Tangara* of *canopy and borders of foothill forest and secondary woodland in northwest*, also on coastal cordillera in w. Esmeraldas. Sexes alike. *Mostly bright emerald green with bright yellow crown and contrasting large black patch on ear-coverts;* back prominently streaked black, wings and tail black with green edging. **Similar species:** A beautiful

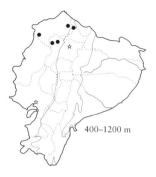

400–1200 m

tanager, not likely confused in its limited range. Glistening-green Tanager is even more intensely shining green, and shows none of Emerald's black. Golden Tanager has a similar pattern but is (obviously) yellow, not green. **Habits and Voice:** Much like Golden Tanager.

Silver-throated Tanager, *Tangara icterocephala*
Tangara Goliplata   Plate 87(6)

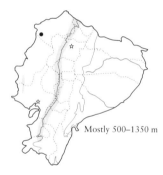

Mostly 500–1350 m

13.5 cm (5¼"). A *mainly golden yellow Tangara* of canopy and borders of *foothill forest and woodland on w. slope*, also on coastal cordillera. ♂ *mainly bright golden yellow with large silvery greenish white throat patch* bordered above by a black malar stripe; back boldly streaked black, wings and tail black with green edging. ♀ somewhat duller, often with a streakier crown and grayish throat. **Similar species:** Could only be confused with really rather different Golden Tanager. **Habits:** Often occurs in quite large groups (up to 10–12 birds), regularly accompanying mixed flocks with other tanagers. Eats primarily fruit, often congregating with other tanagers at fruiting trees; forages for insects mainly by searching along mossy limbs. **Voice:** Call, often given in flight, a characteristic buzzy "bzeet," harsher than calls of congeners.

Saffron-crowned Tanager
Tangara xanthocephala
Tangara Coroniazafrán   Plate 87(7)

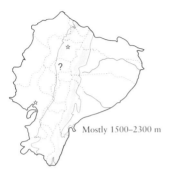

Mostly 1500–2300 m

13.5 cm (5¼″). Canopy and borders of *subtropical forest and woodland on e. slope*; *scarce on w. slope*, and only in northwest. Sexes alike. *Most of head saffron yellow* with *small mask, nuchal band, and throat patch black*. Otherwise opalescent bluish green, with midbelly and crissum cinnamon-buff; *back streaked black*, and wings and tail black with bluish green edging. Similar species: Flame-faced Tanager is slightly larger and has a *solid black back* (with no streaking), large opalescent area on wing-coverts, etc. Golden-eared Tanager has black on crown and nape, but no black on throat (which is opalescent green). Habits: Most often in pairs or small groups, foraging at varying levels and often accompanying mixed flocks with other tanagers. Eats much fruit; when searching for insects tends to glean in outer foliage and on smaller branches.

Golden-eared Tanager, *Tangara chrysotis*
Tangara Orejidorada   Plate 87(8)

14 cm (5½″). A beautiful *Tangara*, uncommon in canopy and borders of *subtropical forest on east slope*. Sexes alike. *Crown, nape, and malar streak black surrounding long opalescent green superciliary and coppery gold ear-coverts*. Otherwise mostly opalescent green, *mantle boldly black-streaked*, wings and tail black edged opalescent green; *midbreast, midbelly, and crissum cinnamon-rufous*. Similar species: Saffron-

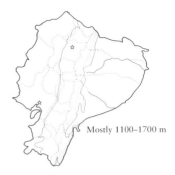

Mostly 1100–1700 m

crowned Tanager has head, *including ear-coverts*, yellow (black only on mask and nape band), paler median lower underparts, etc. Metallic-green Tanager is duller, with unstreaked back but black on scapulars, merely greenish ear-coverts, paler median lower underparts. Habits: Even in range generally one of less numerous *Tangara*, usually found in pairs while accompanying a mixed flock of other tanagers. Forages for insects mainly by hopping along mossy limbs, inspecting their undersides; also eats much fruit.

Flame-faced Tanager, *Tangara parzudakii*
Tangara Cariflama   Plate 87(9)

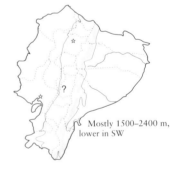

Mostly 1500–2400 m, lower in SW

14–14.5 cm (5½–5¾″). A spectacular large *Tangara*, not uncommon in canopy and borders of subtropical forest and woodland on both slopes. Sexes alike. East-slope birds especially colorful, with *scarlet forecrown and cheeks* merging into *bright golden yellow on hindcrown and sides of neck*, and contrasting with *small black mask, throat patch, and bar encircling ear-coverts*. *Back solidly black*, rump opalescent; wings and tail mainly black but with *large and contrasting opalescent area on wing-coverts.* Below silvery greenish opalescent, buffier on lower belly and crissum. **West-slope birds** are slightly smaller with *orange face* and yellow lower cheeks. **Similar species:** Not likely confused, but on w. slope cf. Saffron-crowned Tanager (which is rare there; it has black-streaked back, no opalescent wing-coverts patch, etc.). **Habits:** Much like Golden Tanager's, and like that species foraging for insects mainly by sidling along larger moss- and lichen-covered limbs, pausing from time to time to peer underneath. Rather lethargic and methodical in its movements.

Golden-naped Tanager, *Tangara ruficervix*
Tangara Nuquidorada   Plate 87(12)

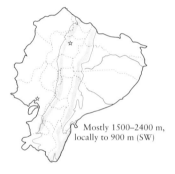

Mostly 1500–2400 m, locally to 900 m (SW)

13 cm (5″). Canopy and borders of *subtropical forest and woodland on both slopes.* **Sexes alike.** *Mostly turquoise blue* with *band across hindcrown golden buff* bordered by black and violet-blue; forehead, ocular area, and chin black. Wings and tail black, feathers edged turquoise blue; midbelly and crissum pale buffyish. **Similar species:** No other *Tangara* combines mostly turquoise plumage with golden on nape. Latter can be hard to see, in which case this species can be confused with Metallic-green Tanager and even ♂ Swallow Tanager. Cf. also ♂ Black-capped Tanager (with vaguely similar pattern, especially in poor light). **Habits:** A widely distributed but usually not terribly numerous *Tangara.* Occurs in pairs and small groups, most often with mixed flocks but sometimes apart. Forages for insects by peering under larger limbs and gleaning in foliage, and makes short sallies more often

than other *Tangara*; also consumes much fruit.

Blue-browed Tanager, *Tangara cyanotis*
Tangara Cejiazul   Plate 87(10)

1400–1900 m

12 cm (4¾″). A *scarce* and *relatively small Tangara* found in canopy and borders of *subtropical forest on e. slope.* **Sexes alike.** *Mostly black above* with *prominent superciliary, rump, and lesser wing-coverts turquoise blue*; wing and tail feathers edged turquoise blue. Median lower underparts buff. **Similar species:** Metallic-green Tanager is duller and greener with opalescent (not black) back, less contrasting brow, etc. Cf. also similarly colored ♂ of smaller Black-faced Dacnis. **Habits:** Similar to many other *Tangara*, and like them usually seen in pairs (small groups are less frequent) as they accompany mixed flocks. Forages for insects mainly by inspecting smaller terminal branches and outer foliage.

Metallic-green Tanager, *Tangara labradorides*
Tangara Verdimetálica   Plate 87(11)

13 cm (5″). Canopy and borders of subtropical forest and woodland and adjacent clearings on *w. slope south to Pichincha*, and on *e. slope from Morona-Santiago southward.* **Sexes alike.** *Mostly subdued opalescent bluish green* (in **northwest**; **southeastern** birds more opalescent *green*, especially on foreneck and lesser wing-coverts). *Small mask, midcrown and nape, and scapulars black*; wings and tail black edged bluish green; midbelly and crissum dull buff. **Similar species:** ♂ Black-capped Tanager is relatively unpatterned and gray with an entirely black crown; ♀ Black-capped is basically greenish

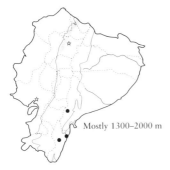

Mostly 1300–2000 m

much like many of congeners, Beryl-spangled often being one of the more numerous members of mixed *Tangara* flocks that are such a prominent feature of Ecuador's montane forests. Forages for insects mainly by gleaning in outer foliage and on twigs and smaller branches.

Blue-and-black Tanager, *Tangara vassorii*
Tangara Azulinegra   Plate 87(15)

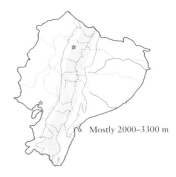

Mostly 2000–3300 m

with no black (crown only dusky). Golden-naped Tanager is much more generally turquoise blue (not as green-hued). On e. slope cf. also Blue-browed Tanager. **Habits:** Usually in pairs or small groups, often accompanying mixed flocks of other tanagers; somewhat less of a forest-based tanager than many other *Tangara*. Forages for insects chiefly by gleaning in outer foliage and on smaller terminal branches.

Beryl-spangled Tanager, *Tangara nigroviridis*
Tangara Lentejuelada   Plate 87(14)

1400–2500 m

13.5 cm (5¼″). A *boldly spangled Tangara*, common and widespread in canopy and borders of *subtropical forest and woodland on both slopes*. **Sexes alike.** East-slope birds have *crown, nape, and rump opalescent green* with black bases of feathers showing through in places; small mask and back black; wings and tail black with greenish blue edging. *Below black heavily spangled with opalescent green.* Spangling of **west-slope birds** bluer. **Similar species:** No other *Tangara* shows the conspicuously spangled effect of this handsome species. Cf. Metallic-green and Black-capped Tanagers. **Habits:** Behavior

13 cm (5″). A *mainly blue Tangara* of canopy and borders of *temperate* forest and woodland on both slopes, ranging at *higher elevations* in Andes than congeners, often up to treeline. ♂ *mostly deep shining cobalt blue* with small mask and wings and tail black; lesser wing-coverts and wing-bar also cobalt blue. ♀ slightly duller. **Similar species:** Not apt to be confused, but cf. Masked Flowerpiercer (much the same blue, but has a very different hooked bill, red eye, and not so much black on wings and tail). **Habits:** Usually in small groups, often with flocks of other tanagers such as mountain-tanagers (usually not with other *Tangara*, however). Forages for insects very actively, gleaning in foliage, usually remaining inside and often restless, quickly moving from one tree to the next, not remaining long in the open.

Black-capped Tanager, *Tangara heinei*
Tangara Gorrinegra   Plate 87(16)

13 cm (5″). Uncommon in borders of *subtropical* forest, secondary woodland, and adjacent clearings (basically a nonforest *Tangara*) on both slopes, but only in n. Ecuador. ♂ has *black crown* contrasting with *uniform shining silvery bluish gray remaining upperparts. Throat, sides of neck, and chest*

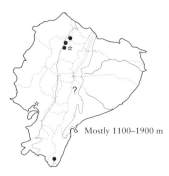

Mostly 1100–1900 m

opalescent green with streaky effect, especially on chest; silvery bluish gray below. ♀ duller, with *dusky crown* (feathers edged green) *contrasting with shining green upperparts. Throat, sides of neck, and chest streaky opalescent green* becoming gray on midbelly, with flanks green. **Similar species:** Silverbacked Tanager replaces this species southward; its ♀ is patterned much like ♀ Black-capped, though Silver-backed has coppery throat, etc. Cf. also Beryl-spangled Tanager (with opalescent crown, extensively spangled underparts). **Habits:** Much like other montane *Tangara*, though more often foraging in clearings and outside actual forest, and more often foraging as pairs independent of mixed flocks.

Silver-backed Tanager, *Tangara viridicollis*
Tangara Dorsiplateada   Plate 87(17)

Mostly 1300–2300 m

13 cm (5″). Subtropical forest borders and secondary woodland in *s. El Oro, Loja, and s. Zamora-Chinchipe*. Formerly called Silvery Tanager. Both sexes have *coppery throat*. Striking ♂ has *crown, nape, and most of underparts black* (flanks broadly gray) contrasting with *shining coppery throat and*

cheeks and *opalescent gray mantle*. ♀ much duller, with dusky-brown crown and mainly shining green upperparts. *Throat and cheeks dull coppery*; chest greenish, with lower underparts mostly grayish. **Similar species:** Likely confused only with the very rare Strawbacked Tanager, which see. Black-capped Tanager occurs farther north. **Habits:** Much like numerous other montane *Tangara*, though seems less tied to extensive forest than do many other species, and found in many areas that now support only low secondary woodland. Usually in pairs or small groups, often with mixed flocks of various tanagers and other birds, frequently foraging quite low.

Straw-backed Tanager, *Tangara argyrofenges*
Tangara Dorsipajiza   Plate 96(19)

1350–1600 m

13 cm (5″). Canopy and borders of *lower subtropical forest on e. slope in remote se. Zamora-Chinchipe* (Panguri). Formerly called Green-throated Tanager. Pattern of both sexes *resembles Silver-backed Tanager*, with which sympatric at its sole known Ecuadorian locality. Spectacular ♂ differs in having *shining opalescent straw mantle* (not gray), opalescent green throat and cheeks (not coppery), and black wings and tail. ♀ has yellower mantle and *somewhat streaky shining silvery green throat, cheeks, and chest* (not coppery). **Habits:** Much like Silverbacked Tanager. At Panguri, Straw-backed was (like Silver-backed) rare and strictly inhabited subtropical forest, not entering secondary growth.

Scrub Tanager, *Tangara vitriolina*
Tangara Matorralera   Plate 87(13)

14 cm (5½″). Fairly common in scrub, gardens, light woodland in *intermontane*

800–2500 m

valleys of n. Ecuador (south to Quito), *mainly in arid regions*; apparently spreading southward. ♂ has *crown rufous* contrasting with *black mask*; otherwise dull silvery greenish above, wings and tail black with greenish edging. Below somewhat paler silvery grayish. ♀ somewhat duller and more greenish. **Similar species:** Not an especially colorful tanager, the often overlooked Scrub occurs in a region where few other tanagers occur (and no other *Tangara*). **Habits:** Usually in pairs, generally in semiopen. Most often forages independently of other birds.

Blue-necked Tanager, *Tangara cyanicollis*
Tangara Capuchiazul   Plate 86(10)

To 1400 m (W);
500–1800 m (E slope)

13cm (5″). A *lovely* tanager, *common and conspicuous in forest borders and adjacent clearings and gardens* in *subtropics on both slopes*, also in *more humid lowlands of west*. Sexes alike. **West-slope birds** have *hood mostly bright turquoise blue*, contrasting sharply with *black back and underparts*, lower belly more violet. *Rump turquoise blue; large area on wing-coverts glistening greenish coppery*. **East-slope birds** similar, but *rump glistening straw* and *wing-coverts glistening*

coppery. **Similar species:** Arguably one of the more stunning members in a wonderful genus, the beautiful Blue-necked is unlikely to be confused, though its pattern recalls that of the more subdued Masked (e. slope) and Golden-hooded (w. slope) Tanagers. **Habits:** Essentially a nonforest tanager, most often in small groups and frequently seen in many areas; regularly occurs with mixed flocks, but also forages independently.

Masked Tanager, *Tangara nigrocincta*
Tangara Enmascarada   Plate 86(11)

Mostly below 600 m

13cm (5″). Canopy and borders of humid forest, secondary woodland, and adjacent clearings in *lowlands of east*. ♂ has *hood mostly pale lavender blue* (with small black mask and pale greenish cheeks), *contrasting with black back and broad pectoral band*; rump blue; wings and tail black with broad greenish blue edging and blue shoulders. *Midbelly white*, flanks blue. ♀ duller, with pectoral band dusky. **Similar species:** Similarly-patterned Blue-necked Tanager is mainly found at somewhat higher elevations, and has hood much more intense blue together with extensive coppery on wing-coverts and all-dark underparts. Cf. also ♂ of very rare White-bellied Dacnis. **Habits:** Usually occurs in pairs, less often small family groups, generally in association with mixed flocks of tanagers and other birds. In forest tends to forage high, so easier to see when it comes lower at edge and in clearings. **Voice:** Often gives a dry chatter.

Golden-hooded Tanager, *Tangara larvata*
Tangara Capuchidorada   Plate 86(12)

13cm (5″). Canopy and borders of humid forest, secondary woodland, and adjacent

To 800 m

clearings in *lowlands of northwest*. Formerly called Golden-masked Tanager. **Sexes alike.** *Hood mostly golden-buff* (with small black mask surrounded by violet-blue), *contrasting with black back and broad pectoral band*; wings and tail black with narrow blue edging and pale blue shoulders; rump opalescent blue. Midbelly white, flanks bluish. **Similar species:** Nearly unique in range. Similarly patterned Blue-necked Tanager has hood intense blue, all-dark underparts, large coppery area on wing-coverts. **Habits:** Behavior much like Masked Tanager's though seems more numerous and is less forest-based. More frugivorous than many *Tangara*, when foraging for insects mainly gleaning in outer foliage. **Voice:** Often gives a dry chatter, similar to Masked's.

Turquoise Tanager, *Tangara mexicana*
Tangara Turquesa   Plate 86(13)

Mostly below 600 m

13.5 cm (5¼″). Often common in canopy and borders of humid forest, secondary woodland, and clearings in *lowlands of east*. **Sexes alike.** *Above mostly black*; *below mainly cobalt blue, extending up over entire face*, black feather bases showing through irregu-

larly, especially on flanks. *Midbreast, belly, and crissum contrastingly bright yellow.* **Similar species:** Given reasonable light, not likely confused. Turquoise Tanagers can look surprisingly dark (it certainly is not "turquoise"), though the yellow usually shows up well. Opal-rumped and Opal-crowned Tanagers also look dark, but they have no yellow on belly or opalescence on rump. **Habits:** Almost invariably in groups of 3–6 birds which mainly move independently of other birds; usually remain quite high above ground. Forages in cleared areas more often than many *Tangara*, but also ranges in the canopy of continuous forest (though harder to see there). Searches for insects by inspecting branches, often on dead limbs.

Opal-rumped Tanager, *Tangara velia*
Tangara Lomiopalina   Plate 86(2)

Mostly below 600 m

14.5 cm (5¾″). Uncommon in canopy and borders of humid forest in *lowlands of east*. **Sexes alike.** Mainly black above with *opalescent straw lower back and rump*; forehead, face, and throat deep blue; wings and tail black with blue edging. *Below mainly purplish blue* with *rufous-chestnut midbelly and crissum*. **Similar species:** Opal-crowned Tanager (which is often with Opal-rumped, even in the same flock, and also has an opalescent rump) has an obvious opalescent forecrown and brow, and lacks rufous on belly. **Habits:** Much like many other forest-based *Tangara*, usually in pairs or small groups and nearly always accompanying mixed flocks of other canopy birds, including various tanagers. Feeds mainly on fruit, searching for insects mainly by inspecting epiphytes and smaller terminal limbs.

Opal-crowned Tanager, *Tangara callophrys*
Tangara Cejiopalina   Plate 86(3)

Mostly below 600 m

14.5 cm (5³/₄″). Canopy and borders of humid forest in *lowlands of east*; generally more numerous than Opal-rumped Tanager. **Sexes alike.** *Forecrown and broad superciliary opalescent straw*, contrasting with black hindcrown and back, and then with *opalescent straw lower back and rump*; wings and tail black with broad blue edging. *Below entirely shining deep blue.* **Similar species:** Opal-rumped Tanager has head entirely black and blue (with no opalescence) and rufous-chestnut on lower underparts. **Habits:** Much as in Opal-rumped Tanager, with which Opal-crowned is often found; searches for insects more on larger limbs, peering around to their underside.

Paradise Tanager, *Tangara chilensis*
Tangara Paraíso   Plate 86(4)

Mostly below 1200 m

14 cm (5¹/₂″). *Unmistakable*, with *multicolored and gaudy pattern*; *often common* in canopy and borders of forest in *lowlands and foothills of east*. **Sexes alike.** Head *bright yellowish apple green* contrasting with black

nape and back and *bright scarlet lower back and rump* (latter conspicuous in flight, but at rest usually hidden); wing-coverts bright blue, wings and tail black. *Below mostly bright turquoise blue*, black on midbelly, more violet on throat. **Habits:** This famous, stunning tanager often troops about in rather large groups (up to 10–12 birds) that generally move independently, though sometimes mixed flocks seem to form around them. A lively and active *Tangara*, usually remaining well above the ground; on occasion a group may come lower, usually at edge or in a clearing (almost never inside forest), most often when lured down by a productive fruiting tree. **Voice:** Dawn song a steadily repeated high-pitched and upslurred "sweee?" interspersed with lower-pitched "tsut" notes (P. Coopmans).

Green-and-gold Tanager, *Tangara schrankii*
Tangara Verdidorada   Plate 86(5)

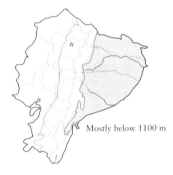

Mostly below 1100 m

13.5 cm (5¹/₄″). *Common and widespread* in humid forest, secondary woodland, and adjacent clearings in *lowlands of east*. ♂ *mostly bright green* with *bright yellow crown, median underparts, and rump*, and *broad black mask and forehead*. Back boldly streaked black; wings and tail black with greenish blue edging. ♀ duller, with greener crown and yellow on rump not so bright. **Similar species:** A colorful tanager, most apt to be confused with smaller Yellow-bellied Tanager though that *lacks* mask and has prominent black spotting below. **Habits:** Behavior much like other *Tangara*, and regularly with them, foraging at all levels. However, Green-and-gold also frequently accompanies understory flocks *inside* forest, something the others rarely or never do.

Blue-whiskered Tanager, *Tangara johannae*
Tangara Bigotiazul   Plate 86(7)

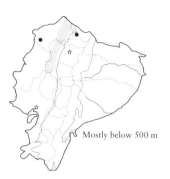

Mostly below 500 m

13.5 cm (5¼″). *Rare and local* in canopy and borders of humid forest and secondary woodland in *lowlands and foothills of northwest.* Sexes alike. *Mostly bright emerald green* with *black face and throat* and *small but conspicuous blue malar streak* (the "whisker"). Back boldly black-streaked, rump yellow; wings and tail black with blue edging. **Similar species:** In its range likely confused only with Emerald Tanager (not found in lowlands, though the two do occur together in foothills of nw. Pichincha); Emerald has bright yellow crown and a large black patch on ear-coverts (but none on throat), lacks the blue whisker. **Habits:** Behavior much like numerous other *Tangara*, tending to forage high in trees, only occasionally coming lower. Usually occurs in pairs.

Spotted Tanager, *Tangara punctata*
Tangara Punteada   Plate 86(9)

13 cm (5″). A *conspicuously black-spotted Tangara* of canopy and borders in *foothill and lower subtropical forest and woodland on e.*

Mostly 900–1500 m

slope. **Sexes alike.** Bright green above, *feathers centered black imparting a scaly look*; wings and tail black with broad yellowish green edging. *Face, throat, and breast bluish white with profuse black spotting* (especially on breast), becoming *white on midbelly*; flanks yellowish green. **Similar species:** Yellow-bellied Tanager is slightly smaller, and its ground color below is basically green (not whitish) with midbelly bright yellow; though ranging locally with Spotted in foothills, it primarily is a *lowland* bird. **Habits:** Behavior much like many other *Tangara*, most frequently found with other tanagers in mixed flocks. Usually remains well above ground, coming lower mainly where attracted by a fruiting tree. Often in small groups.

Yellow-bellied Tanager, *Tangara xanthogastra*
Tangara Ventriamarilla   Plate 86(8)

Mostly below 1100 m

12 cm (4¾″). A *mostly bright green Tangara* of canopy and borders of humid forest and secondary woodland in *lowlands and foothills of east.* **Sexes alike.** Mostly bright emerald green, *feathers of head, back, throat, and breast black-centered imparting spotted effect*; rump plain green, wings and tail black with broad greenish blue edging. *Midbelly plain bright yellow*, flanks plain green. **Similar species:** Spotted Tanager lacks yellow below (its midbelly is white) and it has a bluish white ground color to face and foreneck (not green). Green-and-gold Tanager has conspicuous black mask and lacks spotting below. **Habits:** Much like many other forest-based *Tangara* though Yellow-bellied seems more restricted to forested or wooded habitats, rarely venturing far into cleared areas.

Bay-headed Tanager, *Tangara gyrola*
Tangara Cabecibaya   Plate 86(15)

13.5 cm (5¼"). *Widespread* in canopy and borders of humid forest, secondary woodland, and adjacent clearings from *lowlands up into subtropics on both slopes; more numerous in west*. **West-slope birds** have *head brick red*; otherwise bright green above, bluer on uppertail-coverts. *Below mostly bright turquoise blue*, becoming green on lower flanks and crissum. **East-slope birds** differ in having a striking golden yellow nuchal band and shoulders (absent or faintly indicated in western birds). ♀♀ duller than ♂♂. **Juvenile** more or less uniform green, even to showing little reddish on head. **Similar species:** A lovely tanager, most individuals easily distinguished by reddish heads. In far northwest, cf. Rufous-winged Tanager. **Habits:** Usually in pairs or small groups, frequently with mixed flocks of other tanagers where often one of more numerous species. Feeds primarily on fruit, foraging for insects mainly by hopping along larger branches and peering around to their underside.

Rufous-winged Tanager, *Tangara lavinia*
Tangara Alirrufa   Plate 86(16)

13 cm (5"). Canopy and borders of humid forest in *lowlands and foothills of far northwest*. Stunning ♂ unmistakable, with *head and most of wing bright brick red*. Otherwise mostly bright green, with *nape and back bright golden yellow* and blue on midthroat and median belly. ♀ much duller, *essentially plain green* with no yellow on back and nape, little or no rufous on head, and often little rufous in wings (though *usually a patch on at least flight feathers shows*). **Similar species:**

Bay-headed Tanager never shows any rufous in wing and is mainly blue below; the two species have never actually been found together in Ecuador. **Habits:** Much like Bay-headed Tanager.

Iridosornis Tanagers
Midsized, very attractive (*blue predominating*) but quite inconspicuous tanagers of *montane forest undergrowth*. **Sexes are alike.**

Purplish-mantled Tanager
Iridosornis porphyrocephala
Tangara Dorsipurpurina   Plate 88(2)

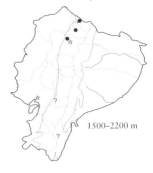

16 cm (6¼"). *Very rare and local* in lower growth of *subtropical* forest on *northwest*. Nearly unmistakable in range: *mostly rich purplish blue* (deepest on head and chest, blackish on mask) with *contrasting bright yellow throat patch*; midbelly buff, crissum dull chestnut. **Similar species:** Similar Yellow-throated Tanager found only on e. slope. Golden-chested Tanager found at *lower* elevations and has yellow *chest* (not throat patch). **Habits:** An inconspicuous tanager that tends to hop quietly and sluggishly

through undergrowth, sometimes perching stolidly for long periods, occasionally on an open limb. **Voice:** Song (in Colombia) a very high-pitched phrase, e.g., "ts-ts-tseéuit tseeuwee" (P. Coopmans recording).

Yellow-throated Tanager, *Iridosornis analis*
Tangara Goliamarilla   Plate 88(1)

1400–2300 m

16 cm (6¼"). Scarce, local, and inconspicuous in lower growth and borders of *subtropical forest on e. slope*, more numerous southward. Nearly unmistakable in range: *dull blue above*, more purplish on crown and nape, more greenish on back and rump; mask blackish. *Bright yellow throat patch* contrasts with *dull buffy ochraceous underparts*; crissum dull chestnut. **Similar species:** Purplish-mantled Tanager found only in *northwest*. **Habits:** Much like Purplish-mantled Tanager, though Yellow-throated seems more often to trail after mixed flocks, and may more often range out of forest into edge habitats and even adjacent clearings. **Voice:** Quiet, though foraging birds infrequently give a high-pitched but downslurred "tseeeur."

Golden-crowned Tanager
Iridosornis rufivertex
Tangara Coronidorada   Plate 88(3)

16.5 cm (6½"). A *stunningly beautiful* tanager, fairly common from *treeline down into temperate forest and woodland on e. slope and in northwest. Mainly bright deep purplish blue with contrasting rich golden yellow patch on crown* (like a skullcap). Hood otherwise black; lower belly and crissum chestnut. **Similar species:** In marginal

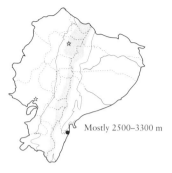

Mostly 2500–3300 m

light this lovely tanager can look very dark aside from its golden crown patch; it then might quickly be confused with Plushcap (and the two species are often together). **Habits:** Typically in pairs, frequently accompanying mixed flocks of other tanagers, brush-finches, etc. Usually forages close to ground, remaining under cover; soon after dawn a bird will sometimes perch atop a bush or low tree, surveying its domain. **Voice:** Generally quiet, but foraging birds infrequently give a weak "tsit."

Anisognathus Mountain-Tanagers
Boldly patterned and quite large tanagers of Andean forests at varying elevations (depending on species, from foothills to treeline). They are more conspicuous and gregarious than *Iridosornis*, often moving with flocks. Sexes are alike.

Scarlet-bellied Mountain-Tanager
Anisognathus igniventris
Tangara Montana Ventriescarlata   Plate 88(4)

18.5 cm (7¼"). A *showy* tanager, *relatively numerous and widespread* in *temperate* woodland, forest borders, even in hedgerows

Mostly 1500–3500 m

in agricultural regions on both slopes, above the central and interandean valleys, and *up to treeline*. Unmistakable. Mostly black with *scarlet auricular patch*; *shoulders and rump bright blue* (rump color most evident in flight). *Underparts vivid scarlet.* **Immature** more orange below. **Habits:** Moves about in pairs or small groups (occasionally up to 10–12 birds together) that, despite their brilliant colors, are often frustratingly hard to see well; they tend to remain inside cover, and all too often are just seen flying from tree to tree. Sometimes with mixed flocks, but also often moves independently. **Voice:** Song a distinctive and pretty series of cascading bell-like tinkling notes, not sounding very much like a tanager; it too is most often given from concealment.

Lacrimose Mountain-Tanager
Anisognathus lacrymosus
Tangara Montana Lagrimosa   Plate 88(5)

Mostly 2300–3200 m

18 cm (7″). *Common in temperate forest, borders, and woodland on e. slope,* locally to w. slope in Azuay and El Oro. *Unique yellow spots on face, a small one below eye (the "teardrop") and a larger one on ear-coverts.* Otherwise dusky bluish slate above with blue wing and tail edging; *entirely mustard yellow below.* **Similar species:** Blue-winged Mountain-Tanager is more lemon yellow below, has brighter blue on wing, has yellow on crown (but no facial spots). **Habits:** A conspicuous tanager, usually foraging in small groups and regularly moving with mixed flocks of other tanagers, etc.; often feeds in open, frequently at edge and rather low. **Voice:** Song an infrequently heard (given mainly soon after dawn) jumbled and complex series of high-pitched notes.

Blue-winged Mountain-Tanager
Anisognathus somptuosus
Tangara Montana Aliazul   Plate 88(6)

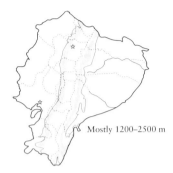

Mostly 1200–2500 m

18 cm (7″). *Generally common and widespread in canopy and borders of subtropical and lower temperate forest and woodland on both slopes;* tolerant of some habitat disturbance. Black above with *broad yellow crown stripe*; wings with *cobalt blue shoulders* and *bright turquoise blue edging on flight feathers (forming a large patch)*; tail also edged blue. *Entirely bright yellow below.* On **east slope** (south to Morona-Santiago) *back moss green* (not black). On **west slope** (south to Chimborazo) shoulders are the same turquoise blue as flight-feather edging. **Similar species:** On w. slope, cf. scarcer Black-chinned Mountain-Tanager. ♂♂ of many euphonias are similarly patterned, but they are much smaller, etc. **Habits:** One of the finest tanagers, gratifyingly numerous and conspicuous in most of its Ecuadorian range, though it seems scarcer in the southwest. Typically moves in groups of up to 8–10 birds, often with mixed flocks, at times even appearing to lead them. Regularly forages in the open, often coming quite low at forest edge and in clearings. Sometimes rests on high exposed branches for long periods. **Voice:** Song a rather long, jumbled, and patternless series of high-pitched phrases and notes. Dawn song a simpler and more rhythmic series of high-pitched wheezy notes (P. Coopmans).

Black-chinned Mountain-Tanager
Anisognathus notabilis
Tangara Montana Barbinegra   Plate 88(7)

18 cm (7″). Canopy and borders of *foothill and subtropical forest on w. slope.* Head and nape black with *only a small stripe of yellow*

Mostly 1400–2200 m, but lower in El Oro

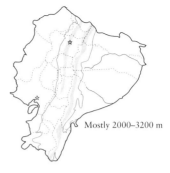

Mostly 2000–3200 m

on midcrown; back and rump shiny yellow-olive; wings and tail black with blue edging not very prominent. *Below rich orange-yellow.* **Similar species:** Blue-winged Mountain-Tanagers occurring with the Black-chinned on w. slope have black backs, more lemon yellow underparts, and much more conspicuous blue on wing. **Habits:** Much like Blue-winged Mountain-Tanager, though Black-chinned more often occurs as pairs (at most in small groups) and is usually not as bold or conspicuous; the two species sometimes move together in same flock, though Black-chinned's center of distribution is lower. **Voice:** Song a series of high-pitched notes, repeated over and over, e.g., "tsit-tsit-tseeéu-tsit-tsit-tseeu-tsit" (J. Moore recording).

Buthraupis Mountain-Tanagers

A diverse group of *large* and *colorful* tanagers of high-elevation Andean forests and woodlands. Behaviorally they differ markedly from each other. **Sexes are alike.**

Hooded Mountain-Tanager
Buthraupis montana
Tangara Montana Encapuchada   Plate 88(8)

22.5 cm (8¾"). A beautiful *large* mountain-tanager of *upper subtropical and temperate forest and borders on both slopes* (though not in southwest). Virtually unmistakable. *Iris bright red. Head and throat black* contrasting with *deep vibrant blue upperparts,* wings and tail black edged with same blue. *Bright yellow below* with lower flanks blue and *black thighs* (surprisingly obvious). **Habits:** Very different from other *Buthraupis,* this showy tanager generally occurs in conspicuous and noisy groups of up to 4–8 birds

that troop through canopy, regularly perching on prominent branches and often flying long distances in the open, high across a valley or downslope. They sometimes accompany other fairly large birds such as caciques and jays, but usually are not with mixed tanager flocks. **Voice:** Flying birds frequently give a repeated loud "tee-tee-tee-tee" call that is sure to draw attention. Loud choruses of "weeek!" or "to-weeek!" calls are given by several birds together, usually soon after dawn but also during day in response to disturbance. Also gives a repeated "tsee-tsee-tseét?" (P. Coopmans).

Masked Mountain-Tanager
Buthraupis wetmorei
Tangara Montana Enmascarada   Plate 88(9)

2950–3600 m

20.5 cm (8"). *Scarce and local in woodland undergrowth near treeline on e. slope. Crown and nape yellowish olive,* becoming olive on back and *bright yellow on rump* (rump color conspicuous in flight); wing-coverts tipped blue. *Face and upper throat black* (the "mask") *conspicuously outlined with bright yellow.* Mainly yellow below, some dusky flecking on sides and flanks. **Similar species:**

Not likely confused, especially in its very limited range and habitat, with a unique facial pattern and showing less blue than other mountain-tanagers. **Habits:** Occurs singly or in pairs, often accompanying mixed flocks of timberline birds (various other tanagers, Pale-naped Brush-Finch, etc.). In general surprisingly inconspicuous, tending to remain within cover close to the ground, emerging most often under foggy conditions. Often first glimpsed as it flies from one patch of cover to next, the yellow rump flashing prominently. **Voice:** Seems very quiet. Infrequently heard song a fairly long-continued series of high-pitched "tsee" notes of variable intensity, almost hummingbird-like and surprisingly weak for the size of the bird.

Black-chested Mountain-Tanager
Buthraupis eximia
Tangara Montana Pechinegra   Plate 88(10)

Mostly 2750–3300 m

21 cm (8¼″). *Generally scarce in temperate* forest and woodland, *especially at and not far below treeline*, on both slopes. *Crown and nape deep blue*; upperparts otherwise *moss green*, wings and tail edged the same green and with blue lesser wing-coverts. *Sides of head, throat, and chest black*; underparts yellow. **Similar species:** Very different behaving and even larger Hooded Mountain-Tanager has an all-black head (with no blue) and all-blue upperparts (no green). Cf. Masked Mountain-Tanager. **Habits:** Nowhere is this species as bold and conspicuous as the much more frequently encountered Hooded Mountain-Tanager, the Black-chested tends to occur in pairs or at most small groups, generally remaining independent of mixed flocks. Only infrequently does it perch in the open. **Voice:** Dawn song

a simple series of 2 alternating notes, the first lower-pitched, e.g., "tchew syéeuw, tchew syéeuw, tchew syéeuw ..." (N. Krabbe recording).

Bangsia and *Wetmorethraupis* Tanagers
Similarly shaped, *plump* and *rather short-tailed* tanagers found locally in lower growth of wet foothills, the two *Bangsia* in the northwest, the Orange-throated very locally in the southeast. Plumage patterns are simple but attractive. **Sexes are alike.**

Golden-chested Tanager, *Bangsia rothschildi*
Tangara Pechidorada   Plate 88(11)

100–600 m

16 cm (6¼″). Scarce and perhaps local in mid-levels of humid forest in *lower foothills of far northwest*. Simply patterned: *mostly dark navy blue* with *very contrasting large yellow patch on chest*; crissum also yellow. **Similar species:** Moss-backed Tanager has similar yellow chest patch but upperparts are green, etc.; it occurs at slightly higher elevations. Purplish-mantled Tanager (also predominantly bright blue) has an obvious yellow *throat*. **Habits:** Rather stolid, often perching quietly for protracted periods, then hopping barbet-like and somewhat clumsily along larger limbs; usually not hard to see. Found singly or in pairs, sometimes trailing after tanager flocks. **Voice:** Infrequently heard song a buzzy, insectlike "tiz-ez-ez-ez-ez-ez-ez."

Moss-backed Tanager, *Bangsia edwardsi*
Tangara Dorsimusgosa   Plate 88(12)

16 cm (6¼″). Locally common in mid-levels and borders of montane forest in *foothills of northwest*. Lower mandible flesh-yellow.

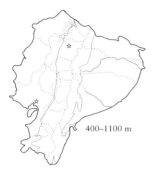

400–1100 m

Large round area on sides of head dull blue enclosed by black; back and underparts moss green (a bit duller below) with *large patch on midchest yellow*. **Similar species:** Not likely confused: combination of blue face, yellow on chest, and mainly green plumage virtually unmistakable. Chunky shape, overall green coloration, and even sluggish behavior recall a fruiteater. **Habits:** Rather stolid, often perching for long periods without moving much, but generally remaining in the open so not too difficult to observe. Overall form recalls a barbet. Sometimes one will allow exceptionally close approach. Generally found in pairs, often accompanying mixed flocks of tanagers and other birds. **Voice:** Though normally quiet, breeding birds may mount to top of a tree, usually soon after dawn, there giving their un-tanager-like song, a series of simple unmusical chippered trills that go up and down in pitch.

Orange-throated Tanager
Wetmorethraupis sterrhopteron
Tangara Golinaranja   Plate 96(20)

18 cm (7″). A spectacular tanager known only from *foothill forest canopy and borders*

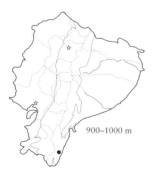

900–1000 m

on remote s. slopes of the Cordillera del Cóndor in se. Zamora-Chinchipe. Unmistakable, with *unique bright orange throat. Black above* with wing-coverts and inner flight feathers extensively blue. *Throat and chest bright orange*, contrasting with *mainly yellowish buff underparts*. **Habits:** Conspicuous where it occurs, found in small groups of up to about 6 birds that often are seen hopping along larger limbs and probing into moss and epiphytes. Most often they move independently of mixed flocks. **Voice:** Dawn song (in Peru) a steadily repeated 3-noted phrase delivered from a high perch, e.g., "we-tsí-tsoo . . ." (P. Coopmans).

Buff-breasted Mountain-Tanager
Dubusia taeniata
Tangara Montana Pechianteada   Plate 88(13)

2250–3500 m

19 cm (7½″). Widespread but never especially numerous or conspicuous in borders and lower growth of *temperate forest, secondary woodland, and adjacent shrubby clearings and scrub on both slopes*. **Sexes alike.** Mostly dark blue above with *head, neck, and throat black* and *long arched superciliary of "frosted" pale blue streaks. Chest band buff* (often not conspicuous); underparts yellow, crissum also buff. **Similar species:** Though overall pattern is similar to that of several other mountain-tanager's, Buff-breasted's streaky, pale blue superciliary is unique. **Habits:** Usually slow-moving and not easy to see. Tends to hop deliberately through dense lower growth, in some areas favoring stands of *Chusquea* bamboo. Though sometimes accompanying mixed flocks, at least as often it seems to forage independently of them. **Voice:** Most often noted from its frequently

given and distinctive song, a loud and far-carrying clear and sweet "feeee-buuu."

Grass-green Tanager, *Chlorornis riefferii*
Tangara Carirroja   Plate 88(18)

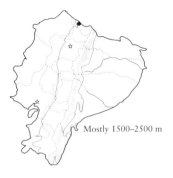

20.5 cm (8"). An unmistakable, *fairly large, bright green* tanager of *upper subtropical and temperate* forest and woodland on both slopes. Sexes alike. *Bill and legs salmon red. Mostly vivid green* with *mask, chin, and crissum contrastingly chestnut-red.* Similar species: Other bright green Andean tanagers (e.g., Glistening-green) are nowhere near as large as this stocky, mountain-tanager-sized species. Habits: Usually occurs in small groups of up to 6–8 birds, regularly accompanying mixed flocks of other tanagers and often conspicuous, foraging in semiopen; can be quite tame. Voice: Frequently heard call a distinctive dry and nasal "eck," sometimes given in a short series and then sounding like a rattle. Less often heard song a fast complex series of harsh nasal notes, usually given at and soon after dawn.

Rufous-crested Tanager, *Creurgops verticalis*
Tangara Crestirrufa   Plate 87(18)

16 cm (6¼"). A *simply patterned* tanager found locally in *canopy and borders of upper subtropical and temperate forest on e. slope;* on w. slope in extreme north. *Heavy bill.* ♂ *gray above* and *cinnamon-rufous below;* inconspicuous coronal patch cinnamon-rufous outlined with black. ♀ very similar, but lacking coronal patch and somewhat paler below. Similar species: No similarly colored and patterned bird occurs in this species' subtropical forest canopy habitat. Black-eared Hemispingus is a lower-growth

bird, shows a black mask, etc.; ♂ Rusty Flowerpiercer favors edge and is smaller with a very different hooked bill. Habits: Usually found singly or in pairs, gleaning for insects on mossy limbs and in foliage, sometimes even flycatching; usually remains well above ground. Eats relatively little fruit. Often accompanies mixed flocks of other tanagers. Voice: Seems very quiet.

Swallow Tanager, *Tersina viridis*
Tersina   Plate 86(1)

15 cm (6"). *Conspicuous in semiopen areas and humid forest and woodland borders in foothills and adjacent lowlands of east and west,* favoring hilly areas. Widespread, but *seasonal or erratic in most areas;* can be common. *Bill broad and flat.* ♂ unmistakable, *bright turquoise blue* with *contrasting black face and throat,* wings and tail black with broad blue edging. Midbelly white, with *black barring on flanks.* ♀ *bright green* but mottled grayish on foreface, wings and tail black with green edging. *Breast and belly pale yellow* with *conspicuous dusky-olive barring on flanks.* Immature ♂♂ frequent, resembling ♀ but with irregular patches of

blue. **Similar species:** ♂'s brilliant blue color can be surprisingly difficult to discern in some lights, in which case its distinctive chunky shape and unique (and more evident) black flank barring are often better field marks. ♀'s flank barring is distinctive among other vaguely similar greenish tanagers. **Habits:** A notably gregarious tanager with unusual behavior. Occurs in groups (sometimes large) virtually throughout year, even when breeding tending to aggregate in loose colonies where conditions are favorable; nests are in holes, usually burrows dug into banks. Often perches in the open, even on dead limbs (cotinga-like). Eats considerable fruit, but also sallies out gracefully in pursuit of passing insects. Tends to remain independent of other birds. **Voice:** Often-heard and distinctive call a sharp and unmusical "dzeep;" it is sometimes given in flight. Also gives a short jumbled phrase of squeaky notes, *Thraupis*-like (J. Moore recording).

Thraupis Tanagers

Usually numerous tanagers of *semiopen habitats*, Blue-grays and Palms occurring in the lowlands where they are *among the more familiar birds in settled areas*, the other two in the highlands. Subdued coloration varies; only the Blue-and-yellow is sexually dimorphic.

Blue-gray Tanager, *Thraupis episcopus*
Tangara Azuleja   Plate 89(1)

Mostly below 1500 m, locally higher

16.5 cm (6½"). A *widespread, familiar,* and (especially in *west*) often *common* tanager in lowlands and foothills. Most numerous in settled areas, clearings, and gardens (even occurring in the middle of towns and cities),

also ranging in borders and even canopy of forest and woodland. **Sexes alike.** *Mostly pale grayish blue,* darkest on back; flight feathers broadly edged bright blue. Wing-coverts vary: **west** of Andes bright blue, in **east** *mostly white.* In **Marañón drainage** most birds show white on wing-coverts, but some do not. **Similar species:** Though relatively unpatterned (especially in west), this common tanager is unlikely to be confused, though in poor light the (olive) Palm Tanager can look somewhat similar. **Habits:** Well known and conspicuous, Blue-gray Tanagers will quickly become familiar though actually they are not all that common in primarily forested areas. Nervous and active, they forage—mainly for fruit, but also for insects (sometimes even flycatching)—in many situations, frequently coming low in clearings. Often in groups, regularly accompanying other birds. **Voice:** Song an often-heard jumble of fast, squeaky notes; calls are of a similar quality and include a rising "suweee?"

Palm Tanager, *Thraupis palmarum*
Tangara Palmera   Plate 89(2)

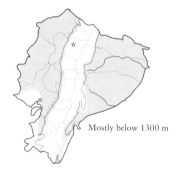

Mostly below 1300 m

17 cm (6¾"). *Common* in settled, semiopen areas in lowlands and foothills, ranging in smaller numbers into borders and even canopy of humid forest and secondary woodland. **Sexes alike.** *Mostly grayish olive,* with (especially in west) a glossy sheen on back and underparts; palest on yellowish olive forecrown. Olive wing-coverts *contrast with mainly black flight feathers* (so that *wing looks bicolored*). **Similar species:** A dull-plumaged tanager that in poor light can be confusing, though two-toned wing usually is evident. **Habits:** A conspicuous bird,

the Palm Tanager is nonetheless generally not as familiar as the Blue-gray, with which it regularly is found. Shows a real predilection for palms of various species, often foraging for insects along the fronds, even hanging acrobatically upside-down from their tips. **Voice:** Much as in Blue-gray Tanager.

Blue-capped Tanager, *Thraupis cyanocephala*
Tangara Gorriazul   Plate 89(3)

Mostly 1800–1900 m

18 cm (7″). *Upper subtropical and temperate* forest borders, secondary woodland, and adjacent shrubby clearings on both slopes and above central and interandean valleys, *favoring more humid regions*. **Sexes alike.** *Crown and nape bright shiny blue* with small blackish mask; *upperparts otherwise bright olive. Below bluish gray* with *lower flanks, crissum, and thighs olive yellow*; underwing-coverts also yellow. **Similar species:** This simply patterned but attractive tanager is not likely to be confused; in poor light conditions the yellow often stands out the most. ♀ Blue-and-yellow Tanager is much duller. **Habits:** Usually conspicuous, remaining more or less in the open, often most numerous in areas not supporting extensive forest. Forages in pairs or small groups, sometimes with mixed flocks but also regularly apart from them. **Voice:** Song a series of sharp and high-pitched squeaky notes or phrases, somewhat reminiscent of Lacrimose Mountain-Tanager. Calls are single notes of comparable quality.

Blue-and-yellow Tanager
Thraupis bonariensis
Tangara Azuliamarilla   Plate 89(4)

16.5 cm (6½″). *Lighter woodland, scrub, and gardens in more arid parts of central and*

Mostly 1800–3000 m

interandean valleys. Sexes differ markedly. ♂ very colorful: *head and throat blue* with orbital area black; back olive, and *rump bright orange-yellow* (prominent in flight). *Breast also bright orange-yellow*, belly paler yellow; some olive on sides. ♀ much duller: *grayish brown above, head more bluish; dingy buff below*, more grayish on throat. **Similar species:** ♂ unmistakable, but nondescript ♀ can be confusing if seen alone (fortunately, the species usually moves about in pairs). Bluish on head in conjunction with size and drab plumage will usually identify ♀; cf. ♀ or immature Scrub Tanager and ♀ Fawn-breasted Tanager. **Habits:** Less conspicuous than its congeners. May forage unconcernedly at close range, though usually remains within cover; one of the few tanagers found in settled, semiopen terrain of arid highlands. **Voice:** ♂'s song a series of 4–6 sweet, doubled notes, e.g., "purseé, purseé, purseé, purseé," totally lacking the squeaky quality of congeners' songs.

Ramphocelus Tanagers
Common and conspicuous tanagers found in semiopen shrubby habitats in the lowlands, all species having *silvery on the lower mandible* (especially gleaming and obvious in males).

Silver-beaked Tanager, *Ramphocelus carbo*
Tangara Concha de Vino   Plate 89(6)

18 cm (7″). *Common and conspicuous* in shrubby and edge habitats of various kinds, usually most numerous near water, in *lowlands and foothills of east*. ♂'s *swollen mandible gleaming silvery white*, maxilla blackish; ♀'s mandible duller grayish silvery. ♂ *rich velvety blackish maroon*, with *redder*

Mostly below 1100 m

To 600 m

throat and dark crimson chest. ♀ dark reddish brown above and on throat; rump and underparts paler dull reddish. **Similar species:** ♂'s lush colors are evident only in good light (it then looks stunning); at other times it can appear blackish. ♀ markedly duller, but dark throat is unique among comparable reddish tanagers. Masked Crimson Tanager is brighter and more boldly patterned. Cf. also ♂ Red-crowned Ant-Tanager (much more a forest bird). **Habits:** One of the most frequently seen birds in settled areas and in shrubby habitat around lake and river margins. Silver-beaks troop about in small noisy groups of 4–6 birds, usually only one or two being fully adult ♂♂. They forage actively at all levels, but typically do not range high above ground. Though often moving in monospecific groups, they also sometimes accompany mixed flocks, or aggregate with other tanagers at fruiting trees. **Voice:** A loud "tchink" call, often doubled, is the most frequent vocalization, given by both sexes throughout day, often in flight. Less often heard is ♂'s rather monotonous song, a repetitive series of short, simple, semimusical phrases, e.g., "tchu-wee tchu-wee chyeét."

Masked Crimson Tanager
Ramphocelus nigrogularis
Tangara Enmascarada   Plate 89(5)

18.5 cm (7¼"). A beautiful and unmistakable red and black tanager of shrubby forest borders, especially near water, in lowlands of east. ♂'s swollen mandible gleaming silvery white, maxilla blackish; ♀'s mandible duller grayish silvery. Head, neck, and underparts intense bright crimson with black foreface and median belly; otherwise black above, but rump also crimson. Otherwise black. ♀

somewhat duller than ♂. **Habits:** More a forest-based bird than the Silver-beaked Tanager, though the two species do often range together. Masked Crimsons typically troop about in ebullient, flashy groups of up to 10–12 birds, enlivening the scene wherever they go. General behavior much as in Silver-beaked, though Masked Crimsons forage higher more often. **Voice:** Common and most distinctive call a metallic "tchink," often given in flight; somewhat higher-pitched than Silver-beaked's comparable call. Song a spritely series of musical whistled phrases, recalling song of Red-capped Cardinal.

Lemon-rumped Tanager
Ramphocelus icteronotus
Tangara Lomilimón   Plate 89(7)

Mostly below 1600 m

18.5 cm (7¼"). Common and conspicuous in forest and woodland borders, shrubby clearings, and gardens in more humid lowlands and foothills of west. Sometimes called Yellow-rumped Tanager; has been considered conspecific with Flame-rumped Tanager (R. flammigerus) of w. Colombia. Unmistakable. Both sexes have bill mostly silvery bluish with black tip and bright lemon yellow lower back and rump (especially conspicuous in flight, but clearly evident even on perched birds, when it is often puffed up). ♂ otherwise *entirely velvety black*. ♀ otherwise grayish brown above, duskier on wings and tail; *mostly clear yellow below*, whitish on throat. **Habits:** Found in pairs or small groups that are hard to miss wherever they occur, often perching in the open or flying across roads or clearings; seems most numerous in settled areas, and often occurs with Blue-gray and Palm Tanagers. Adult ♂ ♂ are usually in the minority, though being exceptionally bold and conspicuous they are also frequently seen. **Voice:** Both sexes give a variety of harsh call notes. ♂ has a more musical but simple and repetitious dawn song.

Vermilion Tanager, *Calochaetes coccineus*
Tangara Bermellón   Plate 88(14)

Mostly 1100–1800 m

18 cm (7″). A beautiful, *essentially scarlet* tanager of canopy and borders of *subtropical forest on e. slope*. **Sexes alike.** Bill blackish with base of mandible silvery gray. *Shiny scarlet* with *black bib from ocular area down over throat*; *wings and tail also black*. **Similar species:** Masked Crimson Tanager has similar overall color pattern (though its back and midbelly are black), but it occurs only in e. *lowlands*. Breeding ♂ Scarlet Tanager lacks black bib. **Habits:** Usually occurs in small groups of 3–5 birds that accompany mixed flocks of other tanagers, most often various *Tangara*. Mainly forages well above ground, actively hopping along horizontal branches (both large and small), searching for insects in moss and among leaves. Seems not to come to fruiting trees as often as many other tanagers with which it associates. **Voice:** Generally silent, but foraging birds give sharp "chip" notes.

Piranga Tanagers
Fairly heavy tanagers with thick, usually pale bills, arboreal in montane forest and borders. Summer and Scarlet are the only boreal migrant tanagers in Ecuador. Most species show strong sexual dimorphism, *males predominantly some shade of red, females olive or yellow*.

Highland Hepatic-Tanager, *Piranga lutea*
Tangara Bermeja Montañero   Plate 89(16)

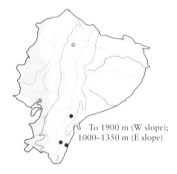

To 1900 m (W slope); 1000–1350 m (E slope)

18 cm (7″). Woodland, forest, and adjacent clearings in *more arid lowlands of west*, ranging up into subtropics on w. slope (especially in Loja); also a few records from southeast. Formerly all hepatic-tanagers were considered conspecific, under the name *P. flava* (Hepatic Tanager). Bill dusky above, horn below. ♂ *uniform carmine red* with *dusky lores* and somewhat duskier wings and tail. ♀ *olive above* with *dusky lores*; *yellow below*, tinged with olive especially on sides and flanks (belly clear bright yellow). **Similar species:** Both sexes of Summer Tanager are similar. ♂ Summer is a paler, more rosy red (*especially below*) than ♂ Highland Hepatic; ♀ Summer may show an orangey tinge below, never seen in Highland Hepatic. Both sexes of Summer lack Highland Hepatic's dusky lores (but these often hard to see in Highland Hepatic, too). Summer's bill, though typically pale when breeding, is darker on its wintering grounds, so this character is of less value here. Hepatic's bill is comparatively stout, Summer's bill slightly longer. **Habits:** An arboreal tanager, foraging at all levels though most often quite high, gleaning methodically in foliage; also eats much fruit. Usually in pairs, often accompanying mixed flocks. **Voice:** Call

a distinctive abrupt "chúp-chitup," sometimes shortened to just "chúp." Song a fast
series of rich burry phrases, recalling a
Turdus thrush.

Summer Tanager, *Piranga rubra*
Piranga Roja   Plate 89(15)

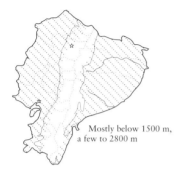

Mostly below 1500 m,
a few to 2800 m

18 cm (7"). A boreal winter resident
(Oct.–Apr.) in humid forest and woodland
borders and clearings in lowlands of east and
west, a few up into highlands; favors nonforest situations. Bill usually dusky horn,
sometimes paler. ♂ *rosy red, somewhat paler
below*; wings and tail somewhat duskier. ♀
olive above, somewhat duskier on wings and
tail. Yellow below, washed olive especially on
sides and flanks; often *orange tinged*. Immature ♂ ♂ develop patches of pale red as they
molt. Similar species: Both sexes *closely*
resemble Highland Hepatic-Tanager, which
see for distinctions. Cf. also Scarlet Tanager.
Habits: Much as in Highland Hepatic-
Tanager, though more apt to occur in gardens
and semiopen. Voice: Frequently heard staccato call a distinctive, well-enunciated "pi-ti-
chuk" or just "pi-tuk." Does not sing in
Ecuador.

Scarlet Tanager, *Piranga olivacea*
Piranga Escarlata   Plate 89(14)

17 cm (6¾"). A boreal winter resident
(Oct.–Apr.) in canopy and borders of humid
forest, secondary woodland, and adjacent
clearings in lowlands, *much more numerous
in east*; a few on Andean slopes as well. Bill
horn. **Nonbreeding** ♂ olive above with *contrasting blackish wings and tail*; olive yellow
below. Molts into **breeding plumage** while in
Ecuador, gradually acquiring splotches of red

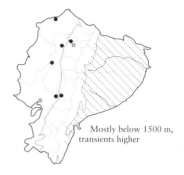

Mostly below 1500 m,
transients higher

until becoming an unmistakable *vivid scarlet*
with *jet black wings and tail*; younger ♂ ♂
paler and more orangey, and may even show
indistinct red or yellowish wing-bars. ♀ like
nonbreeding ♂ but wings only dusky, not
so contrasting. Similar species: ♀ Summer
Tanager's wings are never as dusky or blackish as Scarlet's always are, and they tend to
be more orange or ochraceous tinged below.
Habits: Similar to Highland Hepatic- and
Summer Tanagers, but tending to remain
more in forest canopy, less often ranging low
in clearings or early-succession growth.
Voice: Call a throaty, well-enunciated "chip-
burr," sometimes just the "chip." Does not
sing in Ecuador.

White-winged Tanager, *Piranga leucoptera*
Piranga Aliblanca   Plate 88(16)

Mostly 800–1800 m

14 cm (5½"). Canopy and borders of *foothill
and lower subtropical forest on both slopes*.
Unmistakable; both sexes have *bold white
wing-bars*, unique among comparable tanagers. ♂ *scarlet* with *black lores, wings, and
tail*. ♀ with similar pattern, but *olive above*
and *yellow below*. Habits: An arboreal
tanager, usually in pairs that glean deliberately in foliage and on outer branches, pri-

marily well above ground though sometimes lower at edge. Often accompanies mixed flocks of other tanagers, and indeed White-winged's characteristic calls often herald the imminent approach of such flocks. **Voice:** Call a distinctive sharp "tsupeét" or "wheet, tsupeét." Infrequently heard song a 4- to 5-noted phrase of similar quality, e.g., "tsee-tsee-tsu-tsu."

Red-hooded Tanager, *Piranga rubriceps*
Piranga Capuchirroja   Plate 88(15)

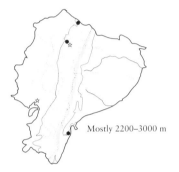

Mostly 2200–3000 m

18.5 cm (7¼"). *Scarce in canopy and borders of temperate forest on e. slope,* on w. slope a few in northwest. Unmistakable. ♂ has *entire head, throat, and breast bright scarlet* contrasting with olive upperparts (yellower on rump) and bright yellow underparts; wings mainly black with yellow lesser wing-coverts. ♀ similar, but with scarlet extending down only over throat. **Similar species:** Molting ♂ Scarlet or Summer Tanagers could conceivably develop a red hood reminiscent of this species' pattern. **Habits:** Occurs at low densities, thus not often encountered, but conspicuous. Forages in pairs or small groups, hopping sluggishly through canopy and often perching in the open for protracted periods. Sometimes with mixed flocks. **Voice:** Song a combination of thin trills, e.g., "titititi," interspersed with sweeter, more musical phrases such as "tswe, weéteetseet-see." Also gives sharper, more piercing "tsee-ee-ee-ee."

Chlorothraupis Tanagers
Drab, stocky, and *heavy-billed* tanagers found in undergrowth of lower-elevation Andean forests where small groups often accompany mixed flocks.

Lemon-spectacled Tanager
Chlorothraupis olivacea
Tangara Ojeralimón   Plate 89(10)

To 450 m

17 cm (6¾"). Lower growth inside very humid forest in *lowlands of far northwest.* Formerly called Lemon-browed Tanager. Heavy black bill. ♂ mostly dark olive with *contrasting bright yellow lores and eye-ring* (forming the "spectacles") and *yellow throat.* ♀ very similar, not quite so dark olive. **Similar species:** Ochre-breasted Tanager lacks facial pattern and is more ochraceous below (with no yellow); it is more of a foothill bird, replacing this species at slightly higher elevations. Juvenile Lemon-spectacleds lack "spectacles" and could especially be confused with Ochre-breasted, though Lemon-spectacleds are much more intense olive. Olive Tanager occurs only on e. slope. Cf. also very rare Yellow-green Bush-Tanager. **Habits:** Forages actively in small groups of 2–4 birds, often accompanying (or even leading) mixed understory flocks. **Voice:** Feeding birds often give incessant excited-sounding, chattering calls in a rapid series, "treu-treu-treu-treu." Also gives a more nasal "nyaah-nyaah-nyaah-nyaah-nyaah!" (P. Coopmans). Elaborate and musical song similar to Olive Tanager's.

Olive Tanager, *Chlorothraupis frenata*
Tangara Oliva   Plate 96(21)

17 cm (6¾"). *Very local* in lower and middle growth of *foothill forest on e. slope* (mostly n. Sucumbíos). Sometimes considered conspecific with Carmiol's Tanager (*C. carmioli*) of s. Central America. *Heavy black bill,* some yellow on lower mandible in younger ♀♀. ♂ *uniform olive,* somewhat paler below and

600–1100 m

yellower on olive-streaked throat. ♀ similar, but lores yellowish and with *clearer yellow throat* showing no streaking. **Similar species:** Yellow-throated Bush-Tanager is markedly smaller with gray underparts, etc. **Habits:** Forages in active and noisy small groups that often accompany (and may even lead) understory flocks. **Voice:** Harsh chattering calls are given intermittently by foraging birds. More notable is its lovely song, given mainly at dawn and not heard very often, a series of loud ringing melodic notes, each repeated several times before continuing on to next, with initial phrase that in pattern and strength recalls Buff-rumped Warbler.

Ochre-breasted Tanager
Chlorothraupis stolzmanni
Tangara Pechiocrácea   Plate 89(9)

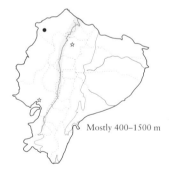

Mostly 400–1500 m

18 cm (7″). Lower growth and borders of *foothill and lower subtropical forest on w. slope,* also on coastal cordillera in w. Esmeraldas. *Notably drab. Bill heavy,* often showing pinkish gape; *iris bluish gray.* **Sexes alike.** Dull olive above, *mainly dull ochraceous buff below,* palest on throat and tinged olive on sides and flanks. Esmeraldas birds

have crown more grayish. **Similar species:** This heavily built, nondescript tanager is often best recognized by its *lack* of obvious field characters. Cf. Lemon-spectacled and Dusky-faced Tanagers. **Habits:** Forages in noisy groups of up to 10–15 birds that move rapidly though lower growth (sometimes straying up into mid-levels), as often as not independent of other birds. **Voice:** Rough chattering calls are given more or less incessantly by foraging birds. Song is given around dawn and consists of an endless series of loud harsh notes, rather high-pitched, sometimes given by several birds at once resulting in an unpleasant cacophony; also gives a long-continued repetition of a single loud and lower-pitched "wheeu" note (often doubled) interspersed with jumbles. Regularly incorporates imitations of other species (P. Coopmans).

Red-crowned Ant-Tanager, *Habia rubica*
Tangara Hormiguera Coronirroja   Plate 89(17)

Below 700 m

17–17.5 cm (6³/₄–7″). *Uncommon in lower growth inside terra firme forest in lowlands of east.* ♂ *mostly dull brownish red,* paler and redder below (especially on throat) with flanks gray; *crown patch red* bordered by thin black line. ♀ brown above with *tawny-yellow crown patch;* dingy ochraceous below, *palest on throat.* **Similar species:** ♀ Silver-beaked Tanager somewhat resembles ♂ ant-tanager, but former is redder on belly (ant-tanager reddest on throat, which is very dark in Silver-beaked), has pale lower mandible, and lacks crown patch. Cf. ♀ Fulvous-crested Tanager. ♀ ant-tanager also superficially resembles several *Automolus* foliage-gleaners. **Habits:** Usually in pairs or (less often) small groups, foraging actively with understory flocks; moves rapidly and seems quite shy, thus not often seen well for long. **Voice:** Foraging birds of both sexes frequently give a gravelly "chrrr" or "chiup" scold, sometimes repeated. Simple, somewhat burry song a somewhat thrush-like melodic phrase given at leisurely pace, e.g., "pur-peeyr-pur-cheéyr."

Gray-headed Tanager, *Eucometis penicillata*
Tangara Cabecigris   Plate 89(11)

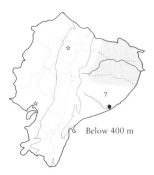

Below 400 m

18 cm (7″). Local in lower growth of *várzea and swampy forest* in lowlands of *east*. Sexes alike. *Head gray* with *short bushy crest* (sometimes laid flat, but often flared up, at which time white feather bases can be conspicuous); above otherwise bright olive. *Throat grayish white*; *underparts rich yellow*. **Similar species:** ♀ White-shouldered Tanager has similar color pattern but is much smaller and lacks any crest; further, it is arboreal, rarely or never found in undergrowth. **Habits:** An active and excitable bird with an expressive crest that is raised conspicuously when agitated (as so often this species seems to be). Usually forages in pairs, sometimes with mixed flocks but more often moving independently. **Voice:** A chattering call can be given almost incessantly. Song a jumbled series of high-pitched sputtering notes.

Dusky-faced Tanager, *Mitrospingus cassinii*
Tangara Carinegruzca   Plate 89(18)

18 cm (7″). *Dense shrubby borders of humid forest and woodland in lowlands and foothills of west*. Sexes alike. *Iris grayish white*, standing out against *blackish face and throat*. *Above uniform slaty gray* with *contrasting "oily" yellowish olive crown*. Underparts the

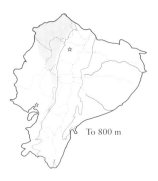

To 800 m

same oily yellowish olive. **Similar species:** This dark, vaguely antbird-like tanager is unlikely to be confused with any other tanager: the pale eye is conspicuous and the slaty and olive color combination distinctive. *Chlorothraupis* tanagers are more uniform and *dark*-eyed. **Habits:** Usually in small, noisy, monospecific groups that tend to remain in dense cover, rarely emerging into the open for very long; favors areas near streams. Only occasionally accompanies other understories birds, then most often Tawny-crested Tanagers. Very nervous and excitable, nearly constantly twitching wings and jerking tail. **Voice:** Foraging birds call almost incessantly, a repeated gravelly "chrt-chrt-chrt. . . ." Infrequently heard dawn song a jumbled series of squeaky notes with elements reminiscent of a *Chlorothraupis* tanager and Orange-billed Sparrow (P. Coopmans).

Tachyphonus Tanagers
Midsized tanagers found mainly in lowland forests, some species in lower growth, others mainly in canopy and edge. Males are *primarily black*, relieved by yellow, buff, or white areas in the crown, on the throat or flanks, or on the wings; females are *duller and less patterned*, more or less brownish or olive. All have *pale bluish on at least the lower mandible*. Most members of the genus are not very vocal.

White-lined Tanager, *Tachyphonus rufus*
Tangara Filiblanca   Plate 90(5)

18.5 cm (7¼″). *Local in shrubby clearings and light secondary woodland in lowlands and foothills of northwest and along e. base of Andes*. Lower mandible pale bluish gray toward base. ♂ entirely glossy black with

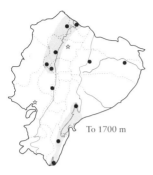

To 1700 m

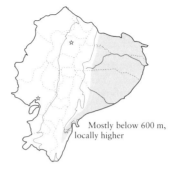

Mostly below 600 m, locally higher

white at bend of wing, *white underwing-coverts* (flashing conspicuously in flight), and some white on scapulars (often hidden). ♀ *uniform rufous*, slightly paler below. **Similar species:** ♂ White-shouldered Tanager shows much more white on closed wing. Neither ♂ Shiny Cowbird (which has a more purplish gloss) nor Scrub Blackbird (which has longer and more pointed bill) has any white in plumage. ♀'s rufous color resembles that of Rufous Mourner and several becards, but they behave very differently and none ever shows bluish on bill. **Habits:** Usually in pairs and—despite being found primarily in semiopen, settled terrain—not very conspicuous, tending to forage within cover and not perching very often in the open. Frequently seen in quick flight across a road or opening, and then often best identified by the two such radically differently colored birds being associated together. Generally not with flocks. **Voice:** Not terribly vocal. ♂'s song typically involves a repetition of a simple semimusical phrase, e.g., "cheép-chooi . . . cheép-chooi. . . ."

Flame-crested Tanager, *Tachyphonus cristatus*
Tangara Crestiflama   Plate 90(4)

15.5–16 cm (6–6¼"). *Canopy and borders of humid forest in lowlands of east.* ♂ glossy black with *broad flat crest flame-orange, golden-buff rump,* and *ochraceous patch on center of throat* (last often not very conspicuous). ♀ rufescent brown above; *throat whitish, underparts rather rich ochraceous.* **Similar species:** ♂ Fulvous-crested Tanager is superficially similar but has a less prominent crest and no throat patch at all; further, it *does* have white and rufous patches on flanks. Fulvous-crested is more a lower

growth bird, not arboreal like Flame-crested. ♀ Flame-crested is most likely confused with ♀ of similarly patterned and colored, but considerably larger, Fulvous Shrike-Tanager; these two species often range together, even in same flock. **Habits:** An arboreal tanager, usually in pairs, foraging well above the ground though sometimes coming lower at edge; generally seen accompanying mixed flocks, sometimes large ones. Forages mostly by gleaning for insects in foliage, less often coming to fruiting trees.

Fulvous-crested Tanager
Tachyphonus surinamus
Tangara Crestifulva   Plate 90(3)

To 900 m

15.5–16 cm (6–6¼"). *Lower growth and borders of humid forest in lowlands and foothills of east.* ♂ glossy black with *rufous patch in crown* (often concealed), *whitish pectoral tuft,* and *small rufous area on flanks* (tuft and flank patch sometimes partially hidden by wing); rump pale rufous. ♀ olive above with *gray head* and *broken but conspicuous yellowish eye-ring.* Below dingy buff, palest on throat and yellowest on belly. **Similar species:** ♀ Fulvous-crested Tanager can be confusing until one realizes—usually from its behavior and the presence of its mate—that it's a tanager. Flame-crested Tanager is more of a canopy bird; ♂ Flame-crested has a throat patch but lacks color on flanks, whereas ♀ Flame-crested is considerably browner above without the distinctly gray head and no eye-ring. **Habits:** Usually in pairs or small groups, foraging in lower and middle growth, often accompanying mixed flocks. Can be quite unsuspicious.

White-shouldered Tanager
Tachyphonus luctuosus
Tangara Hombriblanca   Plate 90(1)

Mostly below 800 m, locally higher in NW

13.5 cm (5¼"). *Fairly common in canopy and borders of humid and deciduous forest and woodland in lowlands and foothills of west*; notably less numerous in lowlands of east. ♂ glossy black with *conspicuous large white patch on wing-coverts* (underwing-coverts also white). ♀ olive above with *contrasting gray head*. Throat grayish white, *underparts bright yellow*. **Similar species:** In east, beware confusion of ♂ with superficially similar (and equally black) ♂ White-winged Becard. ♂ White-lined Tanager shows much less white on closed wing, and is not an arboreal, forest-based bird. ♀ recalls a miniature Gray-headed Tanager (which in Ecuador occurs only in east), but Gray-headed is found in undergrowth and its bushy crest is usually evident. ♀ Fulvous-crested Tanager has yellowish eye-ring and is dull buff (not bright yellow) below. In west, cf. Ashy-throated Bush-Tanager (with no yellow on belly, etc.). **Habits:** Forages actively in foliage, usually in pairs or small groups and often with mixed flocks. Usually easy to see, tending to glean

in outer foliage and often coming relatively low at edge and in clearings.

Tawny-crested Tanager, *Tachyphonus delatrii*
Tangara Crestinaranja   Plate 90(2)

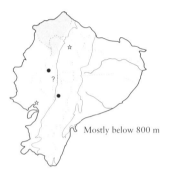

Mostly below 800 m

14.5 cm (5¾"). Shrubby borders and lower growth of humid forest and secondary woodland in *lowlands and foothills of northwest*. ♂ black with *conspicuous golden tawny crest*. ♀ *uniform dark olive brown*. Immature ♂ brown like ♀ but may already show adult's tawny crest. **Similar species:** ♂ essentially unmistakable in range. Uniform ♀ is darker than any sympatric tanager, superficially more resembling certain finches (e.g., ♀ Lesser Seed-Finch), grosbeaks (e.g., Blueblack), or even suboscines (e.g., Ruddy Foliage-gleaner), though bill shapes and behavior of all of these differ. **Habits:** Very active and conspicuous, foraging at varying heights; may join mixed flocks but more often forms large and often monospecific flocks that sweep through forest so quickly you often can't get a good look at one before they are gone. **Voice:** Feeding birds frequently give a loud "chint" call.

Fulvous Shrike-Tanager, *Lanio fulvus*
Tangara Fulva   Plate 89(13)

17.5 cm (7"). *Mid-levels and subcanopy of terra firme forest in lowlands and foothills of east*. Fairly heavy hooked bill. Striking ♂ has *black hood, wings, and tail* contrasting with *ochraceous yellow back*, rump more fulvous; some white on scapulars (often hidden). *Chestnut wash across chest*, with *underparts tawny-ochraceous*. ♀ much duller: olivaceous brown above, more rufescent on rump and duskier on crown. Throat

Mostly below 1100 m

pale grayish buff, becoming ochraceous olive on breast, brighter ochraceous on flanks, yellower on midbelly. **Similar species:** ♂ difficult to confuse, but ♀ closely resembles ♀ of smaller Flame-crested Tanager; aside from size, ♀ shrike-tanager is more rufescent on rump and lower underparts. **Habits:** Usually occurs in pairs, frequently with mixed flocks, and with its loud insistently repeated calls often apparently acts as a flock leader; more often inside forest than are *Tachyphonus*. **Voice:** Frequently given call a sharp "tseeuw" or "tcheuw," often doubled or tripled.

Scarlet-browed Tanager
Heterospingus xanthopygius
Tangara Cejiescarlata   Plate 89(12)

?

To 800 m

18 cm (7"). Canopy and borders of humid forest and tall secondary woodland in *lowlands and foothills of northwest*. Heavy slightly hooked bill. Unmistakable ♂ *mostly black* with *scarlet postocular tuft*, *bright yellow rump*, and *white pectoral tuft usually protruding from under wing*. ♀ grayer (*slaty above*, *ashy below*) and without fancy head markings, but retaining *bright yellow rump* and *white pectoral tuft*. **Similar species:** Even

duller ♀ is unlikely to be confused, especially in its habitat and range; from below can be confused with ♂ Yellow-rumped Tanager. **Habits:** Generally found in pairs, less often small groups, that forage high above ground in tall trees, mainly gleaning in foliage but sometimes coming to fruiting trees. Often accompanies mixed flocks. Sometimes one perches on an exposed branch, fully in the open, for a protracted period. **Voice:** Call a far-carrying "dzeet" or "dzip." Song an infrequently heard squeaky twitter "cheero-bitty, cheero-bitty, cheero-pit-sup."

Chlorospingus Bush-Tanagers
Fairly small, chunky tanagers found in Andean forests and woodlands, some species in canopy and edge, others in lower growth. Most are *relatively numerous*, and many are *quite gregarious* as well. Coloration is dull, with olive typically predominating. **Sexes are alike.**

Common Bush-Tanager
Chlorospingus ophthalmicus
Clorospingo Común   Plate 90(9)

1500–2500 m (E slope);
700–1450 m (SW)

14–14.5 cm (5½–5¾"). A *dingy* bush-tanager of canopy and borders of *subtropical forest and woodland on e. slope* and on w. slope in *El Oro and w. Loja*. Iris whitish to dull pale orange. Olive above with grayish head. *Throat pale buffy whitish with vague dusky speckling, pectoral band greenish yellow;* underparts pale gray, some olive on flanks. **Similar species:** Ashy-throated Bush-Tanager is similar but has a crisper pattern and a dark eye; on east slope it also has an obvious white postocular. **Habits:** Forages actively at all levels, though generally not actually inside forest except at small openings; often in quite large groups (up to 10–12 birds together), and regularly joining mixed flocks. Gleans for insects mainly in outer foliage, also consuming much fruit. **Voice:** A variety of undistinctive "chip" or "tsit" notes, some quite strong, is frequently given, and sometimes are accelerated into a sputtering series of notes of comparable quality. Dawn song a monotonous series of steadily repeated "tsit" notes, sometimes ending in a chatter.

Ashy-throated Bush-Tanager
Chlorospingus canigularis
Clorospingo Golicinéreo   Plate 90(12)

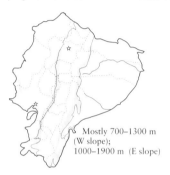

Mostly 700–1300 m (W slope); 1000–1900 m (E slope)

13.5 cm (5¼"). Canopy and borders of *foothill and lower subtropical forest and woodland on both slopes*, also locally on coastal cordillera. **West-slope birds** bright olive above with *contrasting gray head*. Below grayish white, *chest crossed by bright yellow pectoral band*, flanks olive. **East-slope birds** differ in having a *small white postocular stripe* and dark ear-coverts. **Similar species:** Common Bush-Tanager also has yellow on chest, though it is duller and more diffused (not so bright and contrasting); Common further differs from Ashy-throated in its pale eye and generally drabber plumage. In west, cf. also ♀ White-shouldered Tanager. **Habits:** Much as in Common Bush-Tanager (the two species sometimes move in same flock), though Ashy-throated is more arboreal and rarely or never occurs in the large groups typical of Common.

Dusky Bush-Tanager
Chlorospingus semifuscus
Clorospingo Oscuro   Plate 90(13)

14.5 cm (5¾"). *A drab, dark bush-tanager of foothill and subtropical forest on w. slope*

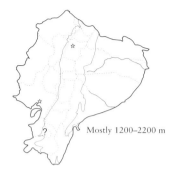

Mostly 1200–2200 m

south to w. Cotopaxi. Formerly called Dusky-bellied Bush-Tanager. *Iris pale reddish brown. Head and neck dark gray;* otherwise olive above. *Below brownish gray,* palest on mid-belly and olive on flanks and crissum. **Similar species:** Even though it too is drab on the w. slope, Yellow-throated Bush-Tanager's yellow throat is always obvious. Ochre-breasted Tanager is markedly larger with a heavier bill and ochraceous underparts. **Habits:** Often forages in quite large groups, sometimes up to 10–20 birds together; frequently accompany mixed flocks. Duskies forage more in lower strata than do Common and Ashy-throated Bush-Tanagers, in this more resembling other Ecuadorian bush-tanagers. **Voice:** Song a series of almost hummingbird-like, high-pitched notes that gradually speed up and gain strength, becoming quite "spanking" before ending in a dry sputter. Heard at dawn, also sometimes in later afternoon just before birds go to roost.

Yellow-green Bush-Tanager
Chlorospingus flavovirens
Clorospingo Verdiamarillo   Plate 90(14)

14.5 cm (5¾"). *Very rare and local in foothill forest and borders in northwest. Very*

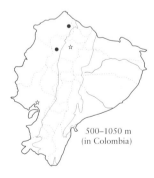

500–1050 m (in Colombia)

uniform. Dull olive above, somewhat duskier on lores and ear-coverts. *Olive yellow below*, brightest on throat and midbelly. **Similar species:** In its limited range the only other bush-tanager is the Yellow-throated, whose underparts are brownish gray. Cf. larger Ochre-breasted Tanager. Olive Tanager occurs only on e. slope. ♀ Tawny-crested Tanager is much darker and browner. **Habits:** One of the least well known Ecuadorian birds, with the only recent reports being a few from El Placer. In Colombia forages in pairs or small groups that often associate with mixed flocks, most often moving in middle strata and subcanopy (thus typically higher than Yellow-throated). **Voice:** Call a loud husky "chut" (S. Hilty).

Yellow-throated Bush-Tanager
Chlorospingus flavigularis
Clorospingo Goliamarillo   Plate 90(10)

Mostly 700–1800 m

15 cm (6"). *Common in lower growth and borders of foothill and subtropical forest on both slopes*, also locally on coastal cordillera. *Favors ravines and the vicinity of streams. Iris hazel to brownish orange.* Olive above with *distinctly gray lores. Throat bright yellow* (on **west slope** more pronounced on *sides of throat*) contrasting with *gray (east slope)* or *brownish gray (west slope) under-parts*. **Similar species:** Yellow-whiskered Bush-Tanager occurs only on e. slope, there mainly at higher elevations but with some overlap. Yellow-whiskered differs in its grayish eyes, concolor olive lores, obviously "flaring" yellow on sides of throat, and much less pure gray underparts. **Habits:** Often forages in quite large and noisy groups of up to 10–15 birds, sometimes with mixed

flocks but at least as often moving independently. Usually easy to observe, sometimes quite tame. **Voice:** Foraging birds give a near-constant "chit" contact note. Dawn songs differ on either side of the Andes: in the west a monotonous series of high-pitched "tsit" notes at rate of about 2/second, with rather a hermit-like quality; in the east a steady series of 2 alternating notes, "tsuw-tseét, tsuw-tseét. . . ."

Yellow-whiskered Bush-Tanager
Chlorospingus parvirostris
Clorospingo Bigotudo   Plate 90(11)

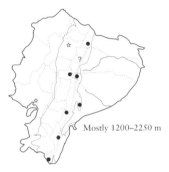

Mostly 1200–2250 m

14.5 cm (5¾"). Lower and middle growth of *subtropical forest on e. slope.* Formerly called Short-billed Bush-Tanager. *Iris whitish to pale gray.* Olive above. *Sides of throat mustard yellow* (the flaring "whiskers"); underparts dingy brownish gray. **Similar species:** Cf. Yellow-throated Bush-Tanager. On e. slope that species has purer gray under-parts with a neat and uniform lower edge to yellow throat; its eyes are distinctly browner (though still pale) and lores contrastingly gray. **Habits:** Similar to Yellow-throated Bush-Tanager (and locally even traveling with it in the same flock), but Yellow-whiskered seems never to be as numerous or to travel in such large groups, nor does it seem to have any special preference for the vicinity of streams. **Voice:** Foraging birds frequently give a "tsrreet" note.

Gray-hooded Bush-Tanager
Cnemoscopus rubrirostris
Tangara Montés Capuchigris   Plate 90(15)

15 cm (6"). Canopy and borders of *upper subtropical and temperate forest and wood-land on e. slope,* also locally in *northwest.*

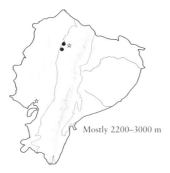

Mostly 2200–3000 m

3200–4000 m

Sexes alike. *Bill and legs conspicuously pinkish. Entire head, throat, and chest plain gray,* throat and chest slightly paler. Otherwise olive above, yellow below. **Similar species:** Can often be recognized by *near-constant tail-wagging,* a common behavior also of Capped Conebill; despite color dissimilarities, in poor light these two species thus can be confused. No *Chlorospingus* bush-tanager is as bright below, and none has pink bill and legs. All *Hemispingus* show at least some head pattern. **Habits:** Arboreal, especially numerous in stands of alders; often accompanies mixed flocks. Forages mainly by gleaning for insects, wagging tail all the while (sometimes the bird's entire rearparts seem to be moving), methodically inspecting outer foliage and larger horizontal branches. **Voice:** Foraging birds give "tsit" and sharper "tsik" call notes. Dawn song a simple, high-pitched, and endlessly repeated "tswee-tsur" (P. Coopmans), sometimes varied to a "sweee swee tsur" (N. Krabbe recording).

Black-backed Bush-Tanager
Urothraupis stolzmanni
Quinero Dorsinegro   Plate 90(16)

15 cm (6"). *Local in treeline shrubbery and woodland (sometimes in Polylepis) on e. slope* south to Morona-Santiago. **Sexes alike.** Nearly unmistakable, with *black upperparts* and *contrasting white throat* (sometimes puffed out); breast white flecked and scaled with gray, remaining underparts gray mottled with white, grayest on flanks and crissum. **Similar species:** Vaguely recalls an *Atlapetes* brush-finch, with Slaty being the most similar (though it has a chestnut crown, white wing-patch, etc.). Cf. also Black-headed Hemispingus. **Habits:** Usually in groups of up to 6

birds that often accompany small flocks. Gleans unobtrusively in foliage, frequently remaining in outer part of trees so not difficult to observe. **Voice:** Foraging birds give a soft "tsit" call.

Hemispingus Hemispinguses

Plain, simply patterned tanagers found in *lower growth and borders of Andean forests,* especially at *higher elevations.* Certain species rather strongly resemble *Basileuterus* warblers, and members of the two genera regularly forage together. *Olive and gray predominate,* often with black or yellow accenting. **Sexes are alike.**

Black-capped Hemispingus
Hemispingus atropileus
Hemispingo Coroninegro   Plate 90(17)

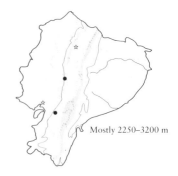

Mostly 2250–3200 m

18 cm (7"). Fairly common in *lower growth of temperate forest on both slopes. Head black with long narrow buffy whitish superciliary;* otherwise olive above, olive yellow below, more ochraceous on foreneck. **Similar species:** Superciliaried Hemispingus is markedly smaller, brighter yellow below, and has shorter brow with no black on head. Cf.

also much rarer Tanager Finch (very local in *northwest only*). **Habits:** Forages deliberately, often while accompanying mixed flocks of other montane species. Frequently moves in small groups, and generally not a hard bird to observe. Often most numerous where there is extensive *Chusquea* bamboo. **Voice:** Contact calls include a "tsit" and other high-pitched calls and chatters. Less often heard song a fast series of high-pitched sputtering notes, rather undistinctive but not as explosive as some other hemispinguses.

Superciliaried Hemispingus
Hemispingus superciliaris
Hemispingo Superciliado   Plate 90(18)

Mostly 2400–3200 m

14 cm (5½"). *Canopy and (especially) borders of temperate forest and secondary woodland on both slopes*, locally occurring up to treeline. A rather *warbler-like* hemispingus, basically olive above with *crown and cheeks dusky to blackish* (darkest in front of eye) and *long narrow white superciliary*; *bright yellow below*. **Southern birds** (Azuay, El Oro, and Loja) differ in having *crown and cheeks considerably paler grayish olive*. **Similar species:** Somewhat resembles Black-capped Hemispingus (especially in north), and often with it, but Black-capped is notably larger with mainly black head (no gray), and is much more suffused with olive below. Citrine Warbler is also somewhat similar, differing in its shorter and more yellowish superciliary and entirely olive crown and cheeks (no trace of gray). **Habits:** Occurs mostly in small groups, foraging actively in outer foliage, often accompanying mixed flocks. **Voice:** Call a harsh chatter whose pitch often drops in middle, then recovers. Song an accelerating and rather loud series

of jumbled notes, sometimes given by several birds at once.

Oleaginous Hemispingus
Hemispingus frontalis
Hemispingo Oleaginoso   Plate 90(19)

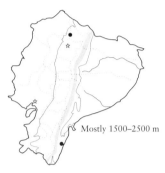

Mostly 1500–2500 m

14.5 cm (5¾"). *Scarce in lower growth and mid-levels of subtropical forest and borders on e. slope*. A *drab* hemispingus, simply *olive above* and *yellowish olive below*; a dull yellowish superciliary is vague and indistinct, sometimes not evident at all. **Similar species:** *Essentially devoid of field marks*, generally best recognized on that basis. Black-capped Hemispingus has an obvious superciliary and black on head; Superciliaried Hemispingus is much yellower below and also has conspicuous superciliary. Rare and local Yellow-green Bush-Tanager is confined to nw. foothills, and is considerably larger with yellower throat, etc. **Habits:** Usually found in pairs foraging in undergrowth, often accompanying mixed flocks, frequently with *Basileuterus* warblers (e.g., Three-striped). Generally quite inconspicuous. **Voice:** Explosive song a jumbled and accelerating series of high-pitched squeaky notes, similar to Black-eared Hemispingus.

Black-eared Hemispingus
Hemispingus melanotis
Hemispingo Orejinegro   Plate 90(20)

14.5 cm (5¾"). Rare to uncommon and local in lower growth and borders of *upper subtropical and lower temperate forest and secondary woodland on e. slope*. *Crown and nape gray* and *face black*, these *separated by a pale grayish line*; otherwise uniform brownish gray above. *Uniform cinnamon-buff*

Mostly 1800–2700 m

below. **Similar species:** So distinctively patterned that confusion is unlikely, but cf. vaguely similar Rufous-crested and Fawn-breasted Tanagers. **Habits:** Usually in pairs, less often in small groups, regularly accompanying mixed flocks, tending to remain in cover and often hard to see clearly. Shows a decided predilection for *Chusquea* bamboo. **Voice:** Song an explosive and jumbled series of high-pitched sputtering notes, similar to Oleaginous Hemispingus.

Western Hemispingus
Hemispingus ochraceus
Hemispingo Occidental   Plate 90(21)

1600–2200 m

14.5 cm (5¼″). Rare and local in undergrowth of *subtropical forest and woodland on w. slope*. Formerly considered conspecific with Black-eared Hemispingus. *Much duller and more uniform* than Black-eared Hemispingus, with *face only dusky* (hence showing little contrast) and *underparts drab buffy olivaceous*, crissum buffier. **Similar species:** This species looks so dull that it doubtless often goes unidentified, being passed over as immature of some commoner tanager, or even a Sepia-brown Wren. **Habits:** An incon-

spicuous bird, foraging in undergrowth and—unlike Black-eared and Piura Hemispinguses—not seeming to favor areas with an extensive bamboo understory. Usually in pairs or small groups, regularly with understory flocks. **Voice:** Song similar to Black-eared Hemispingus.

Piura Hemispingus, *Hemispingus piurae*
Hemispingo de Piura   Plate 90(22)

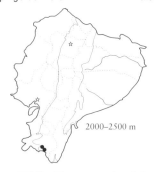

2000–2500 m

14.5 cm (5¾″). Now very local in *lower growth of lower temperate forest and woodland in s. Loja*. Formerly considered conspecific with Black-eared Hemispingus. *Entire head and throat black* with *contrasting bold white superciliary*; otherwise uniform brownish gray above. *Uniform rich cinnamonrufous underparts*. **Similar species:** This striking hemispingus is not likely to be confused in its limited range and habitat. Black-eared Hemispingus occurs only on e. slope. **Habits:** Similar to Black-eared Hemispingus. Usually in pairs, most often foraging independently of mixed flocks. **Voice:** Song similar to Black-eared Hemispingus, but delivery rate somewhat slower (P. Coopmans).

Black-headed Hemispingus
Hemispingus verticalis
Hemispingo Cabecinegro   Plate 90(23)

14 cm (5½″). Borders and canopy of temperate forest and woodland, *especially near treeline*, on *e. slope*; more numerous southward. A very distinctive, *mainly gray* hemispingus. *Contrasting straw-colored or creamy iris. Head and throat black* with narrow buffyish median crown stripe; *otherwise gray*, paler below and becoming whitish on midbelly. **Similar species:** Can only be confused with Black-backed Bush-Tanager (which has an obvious white throat, etc.) or Slaty Brush-

Mostly 2700–3400 m

Finch (with a much more complex head pattern, etc.). **Habits:** Almost invariably seen in pairs or small groups while foraging with mixed flock of other treeline birds. Gleans in foliage and often remains fully in the open for extended periods, frequently hopping and even walking atop stiff leaves. **Voice:** Song a series of rather high-pitched jumbled phrases (N. Krabbe recording).

Black-and-white Tanager
Conothraupis speculigera
Tangara Negriblanca   Plate 89(8)

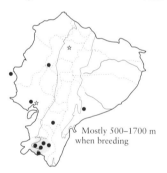

Mostly 500–1700 m when breeding

16.5 cm (6½″). A locally fairly common breeder *during rainy season* (ca. Feb.–May) in secondary scrub and lighter woodland in *foothills and subtropical zone of w. Loja*, but "disappearing" during rest of year; a scatter of records from elsewhere. Iris dark red; bill black above, bluish below with black tip. ♂ *mostly glossy blue-black* with *sharply demarcated white breast and belly*, also a *conspicuous white patch at base of primaries*; rump and flanks gray. Much duller ♀ olive above and pale yellowish below with *variable amount of olive flammulation across breast*. **Similar species:** Superficially similar ♂ Black-and-white Seedeater is much smaller and has

a more conical bill. ♀ recalls Streaked Saltator though that always shows an eyebrow. Immature Black-faced Tanager (also basically olive) differs in lacking breast streaking and in having a yellowish eye-ring. **Habits:** Breeding ♂ ♂ conspicuous, often perching in open and attracting attention through their frequent singing, though immediately after their arrival on breeding grounds they can be sneaky (P. Coopmans). At other seasons decidedly easy to overlook (as ♀ ♀ always are). **Voice:** ♂'s very distinctive song (recalls a blackbird's) a loud and ringing "chree-yóng, chree-yóng" that can be repeated up to 3–6 times; this is often given for protracted periods, even during sunny and hot midday hours.

Magpie Tanager, *Cissopis leveriana*
Tangara Urraca   Plate 89(19)

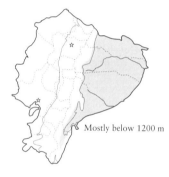

Mostly below 1200 m

25.5–26.5 cm (10–10½″). A *large, conspicuous, black-and-white tanager* of canopy and borders of humid forest, secondary woodland, and adjacent clearings in *lowlands of east*, a few up into foothills. **Sexes alike.** Unmistakable. *Tail very long and strongly graduated. Iris bright yellow. Glossy blue-black hood extends down to point on breast. Otherwise white*, with wings and tail black, *tail feathers broadly tipped white* (obvious in flight). **Habits:** Generally seen in pairs or small groups, usually not associating with mixed flocks. Often perches in open and easy to observe, though sometimes remaining quite high above ground. **Voice:** Has a variety of strong, metallic calls, the most distinctive an arresting metallic "tchenk," sometimes given in series and somewhat resembling Silver-beaked Tanager's call. Less often heard song a disjointed series of surprisingly subdued jumbled and metallic notes.

Black-faced Tanager
Schistochlamys melanopis
Tangara Carinegra   Plate 90(8)

Mostly 650–1600 m

18 cm (7"). Local in clearings and scrubby secondary woodland in *Río Marañón drainage of s. Zamora-Chinchipe* (Zumba to Valladolid, but spreading). **Sexes alike.** Bill bluish gray tipped black. **Adult** unmistakable: *mostly gray,* somewhat paler below becoming whitish on midbelly; *forehead, face, and bib contrastingly black.* **Immature** entirely different, being *olive above* with *yellowish eye-ring,* and *yellowish olive below.* Subadults develop black face and bib before they become gray. **Similar species:** Olive young birds are so different from adults they often go unrecognized; they most resemble a saltator, despite being plainer and more uniform than any. ♀ Black-and-white Tanager is also somewhat alike, though its yellower underparts show some olive breast streaking. **Habits:** Usually found singly or in pairs, regularly perching in semiopen, sometimes atop shrubs or low trees. Usually not with mixed flocks. **Voice:** Song a rich and melodic, grosbeak-like phrase.

White-capped Tanager
Sericossypha albocristata
Tangara Caretiblanca   Plate 88(17)

24 cm (9½"). A *large* and *very showy* tanager, scarce and infrequently encountered in *canopy and borders of upper subtropical and lower temperate forest on e. slope.* Unmistakable. *Black* with *conspicuous snowy white crown* (obvious even at tremendous distances). ♂ has *throat and chest crimson;* ♀ has smaller throat patch dark purple (so dark that the color is often not apparent). Young birds have no color on bib. **Habits:** Ranges

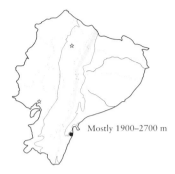

Mostly 1900–2700 m

through forest canopy in flocks, typically of 4–8 birds but occasionally up to 12 or even more; they often fly long distances and have very large home ranges. Generally do not accompany mixed flocks, tending more often to move with other large passerines such as Turquoise Jays or caciques, sometimes independently. Mannerisms quite jay-like, though they more often perch for long periods in open, even on open snags. **Voice:** Quite noisy, with far-carrying jay-like calls that often herald approach of a flock. Most frequent call an arresting "cheeeyáp!," other flock members following with one or more shrieking "cheeyp!" or "peeeyr!" calls. A flock sometimes will decoy in to tape playback, providing an unforgettable and spectacular sight.

Plushcap, *Catamblyrhynchus diadema*
Gorradiadema   Plate 96(22)

Mostly 2000–3500 m

14 cm (5½"). Lower growth of *upper subtropical and temperate forest and woodland* on both slopes, *almost always in stands of Chusquea bamboo.* Formerly called Plush-capped Finch. **Sexes alike.** Bill *thick and stubby. Forecrown bright golden yellow* (feathers short and plushlike), hindcrown

and nape black; upperparts otherwise dark gray. *Face and entire underparts rich chestnut.* Immature much duller, brownish olive above and olivaceous buff below. **Similar species:** Adults not likely confused though Golden-crowned Tanager shares yellow on the crown (though it is positioned differently, etc.). Distinctive bill shape should identify even potentially confusing dull-plumaged immatures. **Habits:** Generally an inconspicuous bird, staying inside cover and most often found while foraging with a mixed flock in lower growth. Feeds by probing into stems and nodes of *Chusquea* bamboo. **Voice:** Usually quiet, but complex song a series of nearly random chips and twitters.

Saltators, Grosbeaks, and Cardinals: Cardinalidae (15)

Mainly arboreal birds associated with the 9-primaried Emberizid assemblage, here considered a separate family following Gill (1994). They have heavy bills and eat mainly seeds and fruit. Many are excellent songsters. Nests are open cups, placed at varying levels in trees and shrubbery.

Saltator Saltators and Grosbeaks

Large arboreal grosbeaks characterized by their *quite heavy and "swollen" bills,* saltators range in a variety of forested and wooded situations, a few species even occurring out into arid scrub. Most have subdued coloration and patterning with a *bold superciliary.* **Sexes are alike.**

Buff-throated Saltator, *Saltator maximus*
Saltador Golianteado   Plate 91(1)

20.5–21 cm (8–8¼″). *Generally common and widespread* in canopy and borders of humid forest, woodland, and clearings in *lowlands of east and west,* smaller numbers up into lower subtropics. *Mostly bright olive above* with short white superciliary. Chin white, *lower throat buff, bordered by black malar stripe;* grayish below with buff crissum. **Similar species:** Grayish Saltator (east only) is gray above (not olive) with an entirely white throat. **Habits:** Arboreal, foraging at all levels though rarely or never coming low inside forest. Pairs regularly accompany mixed flocks, and often come to fruiting trees. **Voice:** Dawn song a series of short, sweet,

Mostly below 900 m

warbled phrases, phrases often repeated several times. During day often gives a shorter and sharper "ti-tueéweet."

Black-winged Saltator, *Saltator atripennis*
Saltador Alinegro   Plate 91(2)

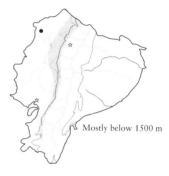

Mostly below 1500 m

20.5 cm (8″). A *boldly patterned* saltator of canopy and borders of montane and humid forest, woodland, and shrubby clearings and plantations in *foothills and lower subtropics on w. slope,* also locally in *humid lowlands of west.* Head black with *conspicuous long white superciliary and patch on ear-coverts;* above bright olive with *wings and tail contrastingly black.* Throat white; underparts pale grayish, crissum buff. **Similar species:** Unlikely to be confused because of striking black and olive pattern. **Habits:** Behavior much like Buff-throated Saltator's, sometimes even occurring with it in the same mixed flock. **Voice:** Song varies but is always given at a distinctive leisurely pace with long pauses between phrases or notes, somewhat oriole-like. Slurred phrases are melodic, and often drop or rise noticeably in pitch and are combined in various ways, e.g., "twee, twaa, toou, toweer, tweeeear" or a slow "teeyr, teeyr" followed by a jumble of sputtered notes.

Grayish Saltator, *Saltator coerulescens*
Saltador Grisáceo   Plate 91(3)

Mostly below 1300 m

21 cm (8¼"). Riparian areas, várzea forest borders, and shrubby clearings (*generally near water*) in *lowlands of east*, also following clearings up e. slope of Andes. *Uniform dark gray above* with short white superciliary. *Throat snowy white bordered by black malar stripe*; underparts pale gray, buff on lower belly and ochraceous-buff on crissum. **Similar species:** Buff-throated Saltator is olive (not gray) above with buff on throat. **Habits:** Generally a conspicuous saltator, perching freely in the open, and often in gardens around houses. Usually in pairs. **Voice:** Song loud and frequently heard, a series of clear notes, e.g., "chu-chu-chu-cheeú." Marañón drainage birds also have very different and more oriole-like song, perhaps given mainly at dawn, e.g., "tewe-chóo-weee-tcho-tchewée-tchewée!" (P. Coopmans). Call a ringing metallic "tchink"; also gives a cascading series of somewhat nasal and metallic notes, e.g., "wikewi-kewi-kewi-kewi-kewi-kewi."

Black-cowled Saltator, *Saltator nigriceps*
Saltador Capuchinegro   Plate 91(4)

22 cm (8½"). Montane woodland, forest borders, and regenerating scrub in *highlands of southwest, primarily in Loja. Bill salmon red to bright orange*. Mainly gray, with *contrasting black hood extending over head and down onto chest*; lower belly and crissum buff. **Similar species:** Nearly unmistakable in its limited range, where no similar gray bird

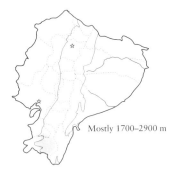

Mostly 1700–2900 m

has such a large and brightly colored bill. Slate-colored Grosbeak occurs only in lowlands. **Habits:** Most often in pairs, sometimes moving with small mixed flocks. Less conspicuous than many other saltators, tending more often to remain in cover. **Voice:** Simple and short song a ringing, explosive "kurt, sweee-it!"

Streaked Saltator, *Saltator striatipectus*
Saltador Listado   Plate 91(6)

300–2500 m (N); mostly below 1500 m in west and south

19–20.5 cm (7½–8"). Locally common in arid scrub, deciduous woodland, and gardens in *three discrete areas*: *arid intermontane valleys of n. Ecuador south to n. Pichincha*; *more arid lowlands and foothills of west*; and *Río Marañón drainage of extreme southeast*. Formerly named *S. albicollis*. *Confusing regional and age-related variation*: not all birds are "streaked." Bill black *usually tipped yellow*. In **intermontane valleys of north**, where bill *not* tipped yellow: mostly gray above with short white superciliary, olive only on wings; white below with *dusky streaking across breast*. In **west** olive above with *long and wide white superciliary*, tail duskier; *unstreaked yellowish white below*.

Immatures, however, are strikingly different (looking like a separate species), with *profuse olive streaking across breast and down flanks* and a *shorter* white superciliary. In **Marañón drainage** reverts to looking like northern intermontane birds (with *streaking below*) though upperparts olive and bill yellow-tipped. **Similar species:** The only saltator showing streaking below; unstreaked birds of w. lowlands have the distinctive *long* white brow. Cf. vaguely similar ♀ Black-and-white Tanager. **Habits:** Generally a conspicuous and familiar saltator, often in trees and shrubs around houses and in towns; frequently found feeding placidly in fruiting trees. **Voice:** Song a loud and melodic "tchew-tchew-tcheeér" (sometimes 3 "tchew" notes), with distinctive long slurred final note.

Masked Saltator, *Saltator cinctus*
Saltador Enmascarado   Plate 91(5)

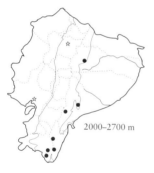

2000–2700 m

21.5 cm (8½″). Rare and apparently local (perhaps mainly overlooked) *inside subtropical and lower temperate forest on e. slope.* Bill black with *variable amount of red (mainly red in some)*; iris usually orangey. *Bluish gray above* with *black face and throat*; tail strongly graduated, *outer feathers broadly tipped white* (almost cuckoo-like). Below white with *conspicuous black chest band*, some gray on flanks. **Similar species:** Nearly unmistakable, with essentially unique color pattern. **Habits:** Relatively inconspicuous, usually found singly or in pairs, generally within cover; single birds or pairs are occasionally the seen accompanying mixed flocks. At least in south has been seen eating *Podocarpus* fruits. **Voice:** Pleasant

song a melodic "chu-chu-chu-chuwit?" (P. Coopmans recording).

Slate-colored Grosbeak, *Saltator grossus*
Picogrueso Piquirrojo   Plate 91(7)

Mostly below 1200 m

20 cm (7¾″). *Subcanopy and mid-levels inside humid forest and woodland in lowlands of east and west,* a few up into lower subtropics. Formerly placed in genus *Pitylus.* *Heavy bill coral red.* ♂ *dark bluish gray* with white upper throat and black foreface and broad margin around throat patch. ♀ similar but slightly paler and more olivaceous gray, and lacking any black on head or neck. **Similar species:** Easily recognized, especially on account of its conspicuously red bill, shared by nothing else much like it. **Habits:** Generally inconspicuous (especially when not singing), ranging in pairs and tending to stay within cover, only rarely coming low. Sometimes accompanies mixed flocks, but at least as often moves independently. **Voice:** Fine and rich song variably phrased but usually short, given at intervals throughout day; recalls a peppershrike. Calls include a sharp metallic "pink" and a nasal or whining "nyaaa."

Red-capped Cardinal, *Paroaria gularis*
Cardenal Gorrirrojo   Plate 91(9)

16.5 cm (6½″). A beautiful and unmistakable "cardinal," conspicuous and generally numerous *near water in lowlands of east*; favors *shrubbery along edge of lakes, ponds, and sluggish rivers and streams.* **Sexes alike.** Base of mandible flesh; iris orangey. *Head and chin bright crimson-red* with small black area around eye and black lower throat ending in point on chest. *Otherwise glossy blue-black above, pure white below.* **Juvenile**

Mostly below 300 m

has no red: crown and upperparts brown, face and throat buff. **Habits:** Lovely and conspicuous, often perching fully in the open and usually confiding. Seen in pairs or small groups, sometimes hopping and feeding on floating vegetation. **Voice:** Not all that vocal, but has a clear sweet song, a variable series of short phrases, often repeated for protracted periods, e.g., "chit-tweet-tu . . . chit-tweet-tu . . ." or "suwee-chu . . . suwee-chu. . . ."

Pheucticus Grosbeaks
Robust cardinalids with *very heavy bills*, especially massive in the two resident species. All three species are arboreal, favoring semiopen situations.

Southern Yellow-Grosbeak
Pheucticus chrysogaster
Picogrueso Amarillo Sureño   Plate 91(10)

To 3500 m

21 cm (8¼"). Widespread and locally common in arid scrub, lighter woodland, and agricultural terrain and gardens in highlands, also in more arid lowlands of southwest. Sometimes called simply Yellow Grosbeak, *P. chrysopeplus*, this when considered conspe-

cific with Mid. Am. forms. *Massive bill* blackish to dusky above, paler grayish or horn below. ♂ has *head, neck, rump, and entire underparts golden yellow*; back, wings, and tail black, wings with bold white patches and tail with broad white corners. **Immature** ♂♂ have upperparts variably streaked blackish, duskier wings and tail. ♀ duller generally with *coarse dusky streaking above*, rump mottled dusky-olive, wings and tail duskier with tail only narrowly tipped white, breast with a dull orange wash and some fine dusky streaking. **Similar species:** A familiar species, likely confused only with the scarcer and more localized Black-backed Grosbeak (restricted to xeric intermontane valleys); see comparison under that species. In southwest, cf. Yellow-tailed and White-edged Orioles. **Habits:** Usually found singly or in pairs, less often in small groups (especially at food concentrations). Basically arboreal, but nevertheless not especially hard to see, frequently perching in semiopen, often quite stolid and tame. **Voice:** Rich and melodious song a spirited, fast caroling usually delivered from a prominent perch. Call a metallic "pink" similar to other *Pheucticus*.

Black-backed Grosbeak
Pheucticus aureoventris
Picogrueso Dorsinegro   Plate 91(11)

Mostly 1500–3200 m

21.5 cm (8½"). *Uncommon and local in arid scrub, agricultural regions, and gardens in intermontane valleys south to Chimborazo. Massive bill* blackish to dusky above, gray below often with dark tip. ♂ has *upperparts black and extending down on sides of neck to form "hood,"* usually with some yellow speckling on back and (especially) rump. Wings and tail black, wings with bold white patches and tail with broad white corners. Bright yellow below with some black mottling on throat, chest, and down sides. **Immature** ♂♂ and ♀ dusky-brown above with vague yellowish mottling (especially on rump); ♀ with tail only narrowly tipped whitish. **Similar species:** Adult ♂♂ with solid black upperparts are easy, but ♀♀ and some immatures can be hard to separate from Southern Yellows; Black-backeds are darker above (especially on crown), this extending over sides of head and neck forming a dark hood (this area in Southern Yellow is much yellower). **Habits and Voice:** Similar to Southern Yellow-Grosbeak; occasionally the two species are together, and they have even been known to hybridize.

Rose-breasted Grosbeak
Pheucticus ludovicianus
Picogrueso Pechirrosado   Plate 91(12)

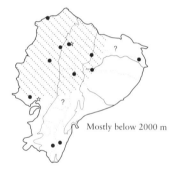

Mostly below 2000 m

18.5 cm (7¼″). A *scarce boreal migrant* (Oct.–Mar.) to canopy and borders of montane forest and woodland and in clearings, mainly in foothills and subtropics. *Heavy whitish bill*. Breeding ♂ (Feb. onward) unmistakable, with *head, throat, and upperparts black* with white wing-patches and mainly white rump. *Conspicuous rosy red breast patch*; *underparts mainly white*. Underwing-coverts rosy (often evident in flight). ♀ and **nonbreeding** ♂ more dusky-brown above with *buff to whitish superciliary and coronal stripe*. Below whitish with *narrow dusky streaking*, throat and breast tinged buff (and often a hint of rose). ♀'s underwing-coverts yellow. **Similar species:** ♀-plumaged birds almost resemble an overgrown sparrow, but their relatively large size, heavy bill, and head striping should preclude

confusion. **Habits:** Arboreal, perching at varying levels and often lethargic; in Ecuador usually found singly. **Voice:** Call a metallic "pink," very similar to other *Pheucticus*. Has not been heard to sing in Ecuador.

Blue-black Grosbeak, *Cyanocompsa cyanoides*
Picogrueso Negriazulado   Plate 91(13)

Mostly below 1000 m

16 cm (6¼″). Widespread in *lower growth of humid forest and woodland in lowlands of east and west. Heavy blackish bill*, somewhat paler at base. ♂ *uniform dark blue*. **East of Andes** *paler and brighter* blue on forehead, brow, malar area, and shoulders; but these areas are less contrasting **west of Andes**. ♀ *uniform deep rich chocolate brown*. **Similar species:** Cf. ♂ of accidental Blue Grosbeak. ♀♀ of Large-billed and Black-billed Seed-Finches are paler and more fulvous brown (not as warmly colored as in grosbeak); their bills are more massive and squared off. Though sometimes ranging into woodland undergrowth, seed-finches typically range in more open habitats. **Habits:** Usually in pairs that stay *inside* forest; shy and furtive, generally not accompanying mixed flocks. Heard much more often than seen. **Voice:** Song a series of of rich musical whistled notes that first are slow and hesitant, then become jumbled and fade away; ♀ often echoes ♂ with a soft and short version. Call also frequently heard, a metallic "chink," sometimes doubled.

Blue Grosbeak, *Guiraca caerulea*
Picogrueso Azul   Plate 96(23)

16.5 cm (6½″). An *accidental* boreal winter visitor to shrubby clearings in lowlands of northeast. *Stout bill*, paler and more bluish

200 m

gray below. ♂ *deep blue*, blacker on foreface; wings and tail dusky, *wings with two prominent cinnamon to rusty wing-bars*. Fresh-plumaged ♂ ♂ have buff tips to blue feathers, partially obscuring blue. ♀ warm brown above obscurely streaked dusky on back, rump tinged grayish blue; *wings and tail much as in* ♂. Below buffy brown. **Similar species:** Much more numerous Blue-black Grosbeak inhabits forest and woodland undergrowth (not semiopen habitats favored by this vagrant), and neither sex ever shows a trace of the wing-bars so prominent in this species. **Habits:** Favors dense lower growth, often feeding on ground. Sometimes perches in open atop a shrub or small tree, frequently spreading tail or twitching it sideways. **Voice:** Call a distinctive sharp metallic "tchink."

Yellow-shouldered Grosbeak
Parkerthraustes humeralis
Picogrueso Hombriamarillo   Plate 91(8)

Mostly below 600 m

16 cm (6¼″). *Canopy and borders of terra firme forest in lowlands of east.* **Sexes alike.** Formerly placed in genus *Caryothraustes*. *Stout bill*, mandible gray. *Crown and nape gray, broad facial mask black, malar stripe*

white, throat white scaled black. Otherwise yellowish olive above with yellow on shoulders, gray below with yellow crissum. **Similar species:** If the complex head pattern can be seen, nearly unmistakable; overall form and color pattern vaguely like Buff-throated Saltator. **Habits:** Found singly or in pairs, generally accompanying mixed flocks, usually remaining high above ground. Sometimes perches on high exposed branches for long periods. **Voice:** Not very vocal. Call a sharp, high-pitched "cheét-swit" or "suweet." Song, heard less often, a jumbled series of similar twittered notes.

**[Dickcissel, *Spiza americana*
Llanero]**   Plate 96(26)

400 m

15 cm (6″). An *accidental* boreal winter visitant to grassy areas in lowlands of northeast. **Breeding** ♂ (Mar. onward) has *mainly gray head* with *yellow superciliary and malar streak*; above otherwise pale brown, streaked blackish on back; wings with *prominent rufous shoulders*. Chin white, *bordered below by V-shaped black bib extending down over chest*; *breast yellow*, fading to pale grayish on belly. **Nonbreeding** ♂ duller, with yellow less bright but still apparent and black bib veiled. ♀ **and immatures** even duller than nonbreeding ♂, but *still with much the same pattern*; below whitish with some blackish streaking, especially across breast and down sides, and with *band of pale yellow across breast*. **Similar species:** Yellow-browed Sparrow is considerably smaller, lacks rufous on shoulders, etc. Cf. also ♀ House Sparrow. **Habits:** The Ecuador bird was consorting with a mixed flock of seedeaters. In its normal wintering range can occur in large,

dense flocks. **Voice:** Distinctive call a harsh, low-pitched "drrt."

Emberizine Finches: Emberizidae (53)

A large and diverse group, part of the 9-primaried "assemblage" that also includes the wood-warblers, tanagers, grosbeaks, and icterids; all are sometimes merged into one gigantic family, the Emberizidae, but here they are separated into family-level units. The Emberizidae typically have deep conical bills, adapted for eating seeds, and short rather rounded wings. Plumage patterns tend to be dull and simple, with brown, gray, and olive predominating, but there are numerous exceptions. Some species show sexual dimorphism, others do not. They occur in a variety of habitats ranging from undergrowth inside forest and woodland (e.g., brush-finches and *Arremon* sparrows) to open, often grassy areas (e.g., seedeaters and seed-finches). Many Emberizine finches are excellent songsters. Nests are typically cup-shaped and hidden in undergrowth near or on the ground.

Crimson-breasted Finch
Rhodospingus cruentus
Pinzón Pechicarmesí   Plate 92(27)

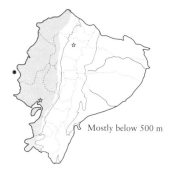

Mostly below 500 m

11 cm (4¼"). Seasonally common during rainy season (Jan.–May) in scrub and woodland in *lowlands of southwest*, moving northward and into more humid regions (even forest borders) when not breeding. Formerly called Crimson Finch. *Bill slender and sharply pointed.* ♂ unmistakable, *black above* and *scarlet below*, fading on lower belly; coronal stripe also scarlet. In fresh plumage black feathers are scaled brownish. ♀ much duller: pale brown above and *yel-lowish buff below* with browner sides. **Immature** ♂ like ♀ but often with orange wash across breast. **Similar species:** ♀-plumaged birds are plain and nondescript, resembling ♀♀ seedeaters, especially Variable (also quite buffy), but seedeater bills are shorter and more conical. **Habits:** Widespread and conspicuous when breeding during the rainy season. During the rest of the year more gregarious, with groups sometimes associating with seedeater flocks. Can then be more arboreal, even feeding in flowering trees. **Voice:** Breeding ♂'s frequently given song a buzzy "tsee-tzztzz" with quality reminiscent of Blue-black Grassquit.

Blue-black Grassquit, *Volatinia jacarina*
Semillerito Negriazulado   Plate 92(1)

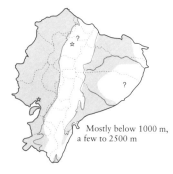

Mostly below 1000 m, a few to 2500 m

10 cm (4"). *Common and widespread in agricultural regions and grassy areas in lowlands of west*, smaller numbers up into subtropics, especially in arid intermontane valleys; less numerous and more local (but likely increasing) in lowlands and foothills of east. *Bill slender and pointed.* ♂ *glossy blue-black*, sometimes showing white at bend of wing; on **Pacific-slope birds**, wings browner. **Subadult and molting** ♂♂ mottled blackish and brown. ♀ dull brown above; whitish to pale buff below, *breast and flanks streaked dusky*. **Similar species:** *Sporophila* seedeaters (with which grassquits often consort) have more conical and less pointed bills. ♂ grassquit is more uniformly black than any seedeater, and ♀ grassquit is more streaked below. Cf. also ♀ Slaty Finch (a more montane bird found in undergrowth). **Habits:** Omnipresent and one of the most familiar and frequently seen birds in settled regions of west, regularly consorting with various seedeaters (especially

when not nesting). Feeds on grass seeds.
Voice: Breeding ♂♂ tirelessly give an explosive buzzy "dzeee-u" usually accompanied by a short vertical flutter and jump into the air.

Tiaris Grassquits

Small seedeater-like finches, differing from *Sporophila* in their *somewhat narrower and more pointed bills*; their nests are globular or dome-shaped with a side entrance. They range in grassy and open shrubby areas; both species appear to be increasing in Ecuador.

Yellow-faced Grassquit, *Tiaris olivacea*
Semillerito Cariamarillo   Plate 92(15)

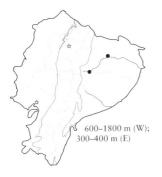

600–1800 m (W);
300–400 m (E)

10 cm (4″). *Local but evidently increasing in grassy pastures and along roads in foothills and subtropics in northwest* (also a few Napo records). ♂ olive above with *black crown, face, and breast* contrasting with *bright yellow superciliary and throat patch*; belly grayish olive. Subadults have less extensive black on breast. ♀ duller with no black, but *echoing ♂'s distinctive head pattern*. **Similar species:** ♂'s attractive face pattern renders it nearly unmistakable; ♀ is comparatively dull but enough face pattern is apparent for it to be recognized. **Habits:** A conspicuous bird that occurs in scattered pairs or small groups, at times associating with seedeaters. Feeds on grass seeds; often perches on fences and low shrubs. **Voice:** ♂'s song a weak, colorless, flat trill, "tee-ee-ee-ee."

Dull-colored Grassquit, *Tiaris obscura*
Semillerito Oscuro   Plate 92(14)

11 cm (4¼″). A well-named, *obscure* bird of shrubby clearings, gardens, and woodland and forest borders in more humid lowlands and foothills on *w. slope*, and in Río Marañón drainage of far southeast. Formerly

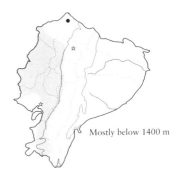

Mostly below 1400 m

often placed in genus *Sporophila*. **Sexes alike.** *Bill dusky above, yellowish below.* Grayish olive brown above; paler brownish gray below, fading to whitish on midbelly. **Similar species:** Resembles many ♀♀ seedeaters, and sometimes associates with them. Its bicolored bill differentiates it from most *Sporophila* with which it occurs. Often most easily recognized by ♂'s song, quite different from any seedeater's. **Habits:** Usually in pairs or small groups, with general behavior much like various seedeaters and other grassquits though favoring shrubbier (less grassy) habitats than many, and thus somewhat less conspicuous. May be increasing. **Voice:** ♂'s distinctive song heard when breeding, mainly during first half of year, an explosive and buzzy, e.g., "zeetig, zeezeezig" with many variants (but much less musical than the songs of most *Sporophila*).

Oryzoborus Seed-Finches

Similar to *Sporophila* seedeaters but differing in their *heavy, squared-off bills (huge in some species)*. Males are mainly black, females brown; both sexes can be somewhat confusing and hard to identify. Their taxonomy is complex and continues to be disputed.

Lesser Seed-Finch, *Oryzoborus angolensis*
Semillero Menor   Plate 92(18)

12.5 cm (5″). *Shrubby* (usually *not* grassy) *clearings and forest and woodland borders in lowlands* of east and west, in west only in more humid regions. Sometimes treated as two species, *O. funereus* (Thick-billed Seed-Finch) west of Andes and *O. angolensis* (Chestnut-bellied Seed-Finch) east of Andes. *Heavy squared-off black bill.* ♂ **west of Andes** *entirely glossy black* with small white wing speculum and underwing-coverts. **East**

Mostly below 900 m

of Andes similar but with *contrasting chest-nut breast and belly* (color so dark as to appear black in some lights). ♀♀ similar throughout range: brown above and *fulvous brown below*; underwing-coverts also white, but no speculum. **Similar species:** Ecuador's two other seed-finches are substantially larger with more massive bills; both are much rarer than Lesser. ♀♀ *Sporophila* and *Amaurospiza* seedeaters are smaller with more rounded bills. **Habits:** Generally found singly or in pairs, sometimes in association with a seedeater flock, but rarely or never forming groups of its own species. **Voice:** ♂'s pretty song, often delivered from a prominent perch, a long and often complex phrase that gradually becomes more jumbled and twittery.

Large-billed Seed-Finch
Oryzoborus crassirostris
Semillero Piquigrande   Plate 92(20)

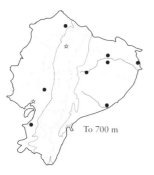

To 700 m

14.5 cm (5¾″). *Local and scarce* in damp grassy areas and shrubby margins near water in *lowlands of west* (now mainly in Esmeraldas?) *and northeast. Very heavy squared-off bill, whitish in* ♂ but blackish in ♀. ♂ *entirely glossy black* with conspicuous wing-

speculum and underwing-coverts white. ♀ brown above, fulvous brown below. **Similar species:** ♂ relatively easy throughout its Ecuadorian range, because of *white* bill. ♀♀ are more problematic: west of Andes can only be confused with ♀♀ of considerably smaller and proportionately smaller-billed Lesser Seed-Finch; east of Andes more difficult, with ♀ Black-billed Seed-Finch being similar but larger with an even more massive bill. Both species are best identified through their respective ♂♂. Cf. also ♀ Blue-black Grosbeak. **Habits:** Found singly or in pairs, occasionally in association with seedeaters and other species but more often independent. **Voice:** ♂'s song a rich and melodic warbling that starts slowly and then speeds up.

Black-billed Seed-Finch, *Oryzoborus atrirostris*
Semillero Piquinegro   Plate 92(19)

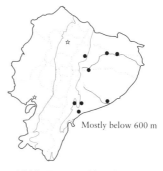

Mostly below 600 m

16.5 cm (6½″). *Rare and local* in damp grassy areas and clearings as well as shrubby lake margins in *lowlands of east*. Formerly considered conspecific with Great-billed Seed-Finch (*O. maximiliani*) of e. South America. *Bill enormously thick, black in both sexes.* ♂ *entirely glossy black* with conspicuous wing speculum and underwing-coverts white. ♀ brown above, fulvous brown below. **Similar species:** ♂ Large-billed Seed-Finch has a conspicuously white bill. ♀ Large-billed can be difficult to distinguish from ♀ Black-billed, though it is smaller with a less massive bill. So far the two species have not been found to occur at the same site, though it is not inconceivable that they could. **Habits and Voice:** Similar to Large-billed Seed-Finch so far as known.

Sporophila Seedeaters
Numerous and conspicuous small finches with *thick and stubby bills*. Seedeaters

inhabit open country, either in grassy or shrubby terrain. They forage for seeds, often reaching up or out to stems, less often picking up seeds from the ground. Males of most species are strongly patterned and easy to identify, but the much duller—basically olive or brown—females and juveniles present a much greater challenge and often are best known by their accompanying males. Breeding males are very vocal, often singing from prominent perches; nonbreeders gather in flocks, several species often together.

Slate-colored Seedeater
Sporophila schistacea
Espiguero Pizarroso   Plate 92(2)

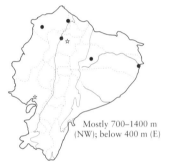

Mostly 700–1400 m
(NW); below 400 m (E)

11 cm (4¼"). *Rare and erratic in lower growth of montane and humid forest borders and adjacent, usually shrubby, clearings in foothills and lower subtropics in northwest, and in lowlands and foothills of northeast. Bill rich yellow* (♂) or dusky (♀). *♂ mostly slaty gray, usually with a small whitish patch on sides of neck*; wings blackish with white speculum and usually a single (upper) wingbar. ♀ olive brown above, paler buffy brown below becoming more creamy whitish on midbelly. **Similar species:** ♂ is only predominately gray seedeater in Ecuador, and also is the only one with a yellow bill. ♀♀, however, are probably not safely identified except when associating with ♂♂. **Habits:** Much more an arboreal, woodland bird than other Ecuadorian *Sporophila*. Though not (yet?) reported here, elsewhere it can be temporarily numerous when bamboo is seeding. Rarely or never occurs in mixed flocks with other seedeaters. **Voice:** ♂'s variable and high-pitched song a loud, fast,

and unmusical series of notes, e.g., "zit-zit-zee-zee-zee-ze-ze-z-z-z-z," rather un-*Sporophila*-like (recalling a Bananaquit); it often starts with several loud ringing notes.

Caquetá Seedeater, *Sporophila murallae*
Espiguero de Caquetá   Plate 92(4)

To 400 m

11.5 cm (4½"). Uncommon in grassy and shrubby areas at woodland borders, lake edges, and river islands in *lowlands of east*. Formerly considered part of Variable Seedeater (*S. americana*). Bill blackish. ♂ black above with rump vaguely whitish; white wing speculum and *indistinct whitish wingbars*. Below whitish, *extending up as partial nuchal collar*, and with *mottled blackish chest band*. ♀ olive brown above, paler buffy brown below. **Similar species:** ♂♂ of smaller Lined and Lesson's Seedeaters both have an obvious white malar stripe and lack any trace of a nuchal collar. ♀♀ Caquetá Seedeaters, though a bit larger than other ♀ *Sporophila* in the Oriente and *dark*-billed, are difficult to identify on their own; usually, however, a ♂ is present to simplify matters. **Habits:** Usually occurs as scattered pairs, sometimes associating with flocks of other seedeaters but at least as often on its own. **Voice:** ♂'s song a variable series of jumbled but musical notes, usually quite long and rapidly delivered.

Variable Seedeater, *Sporophila corvina*
Espiguero Variable   Plate 92(3)

11 cm (4¼"). *Common and widespread* in agricultural regions, grassy clearings, and gardens in *more humid lowlands of west*, smaller numbers up into subtropics. Formerly named *S. aurita*, and sometimes considered conspecific with *S. americana* from ne. South America. Bill blackish. ♂ *black above* with

To 1500 m

whitish rump; wing speculum white. White below, *extending up as partial nuchal collar*, and with *narrow black band across chest*. ♀ yellowish olive brown above, *paler buffy brownish below, even paler and yellower on midbelly*. **Similar species:** Attractively patterned ♂ is the only seedeater in its range with black upperparts. ♀ is yellower below than other seedeaters with which it is found. ♀ Crimson-breasted Finch (which sometimes occurs with Variables) has a longer and more pointed bill. **Habits:** Generally the most frequent *Sporophila* in the west, though less common in more arid regions. Can occur in quite large flocks when not breeding, then often associating with other seedeaters. More than other seedeaters, the Variable regularly forages quite high up, and is often attracted to flowering trees. **Voice:** ♂'s song a variable but always musical twittering, often longer than songs of its congeners. Call an oft-heard "cheeu."

Lined Seedeater, *Sporophila lineola*
Espiguero Lineado   Plate 92(8)
11 cm (4¼″). Apparently a *casual* austral migrant (Aug.–Dec.) to grassy areas in *lowlands of northeast*, but status still unclear and

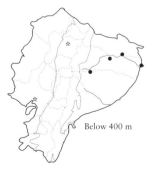

Below 400 m

perhaps more numerous than the few records would indicate (only ♂♂ can be identified). Bill blackish (♂) or *mostly yellowish* (♀). ♂ black above with *white coronal stripe* (often inconspicuous), *prominent broad white malar stripe*, and white wing speculum. *Throat black* (emphasizing the white malar area); underparts otherwise white. ♀ pale olive brown above, paler buff to yellowish buff below. **Similar species:** ♂ of (more numerous) Lesson's Seedeater is similar though it *lacks* coronal stripe (but beware Lineds on which this may be obscure or difficult to see), and often looks less "crisp" below (showing more black mottling on sides). Cf. also ♂ Caquetá Seedeater, which also is black and white, but with a notably different head pattern, black pectoral band, white in wing, etc. ♀ hard to distinguish from other ♀♀ *Sporophila* (and impossible to separate from ♀ Lesson's), though note yellowish bill; other ♀♀ seedeaters with which it occurs have black or blackish bills. **Habits:** In Ecuador usually occurs singly or in small groups in association with flocks of other seedeaters, typically in areas where tall grass is seeding. **Voice:** Not known to sing in Ecuador.

Lesson's Seedeater, *Sporophila bouvronides*
Espiguero de Lesson   Plate 92(7)

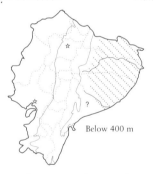

Below 400 m

11 cm (4¼″). *Rare* (but perhaps more numerous?) intratropical migrant (mostly Nov.–Apr.) to grassy areas in *lowlands of northeast*. Bill blackish (♂) or *mostly yellowish* (♀). ♂ black above with *prominent broad white malar stripe* and white wing speculum. *Throat black* (emphasizing malar area); underparts white with some blackish mottling across breast and down sides. ♀ pale olive brown above, paler buff to yellowish buff below. **Similar species:** ♂ Lined Seedeater has

a white coronal streak (sometimes hard to see) and is purer white below. ♀ ♀ of the two species cannot be distinguished, but based on relative numbers of ♂ ♂ of the two species, Lesson's is presumed considerably more numerous Cf. also ♂ Caquetá Seedeater (likewise black and white, but with notably different head pattern, black pectoral band, white in wing, etc.). **Habits:** Essentially identical to Lined Seedeater, but Lesson's—being more common—is more apt to occur in small groups. **Voice:** Not known to sing in Ecuador.

Black-and-white Seedeater
Sporophila luctuosa
Espiguero Negriblanco   Plate 92(5)

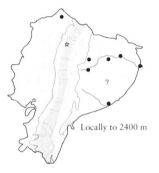

Locally to 2400 m

11 cm (4¼"). Breeds during first half of year in shrubby clearings and agricultural areas in *subtropics and temperate zone on both slopes*. At other times at least some birds *descend down into lowlands of east (especially near Andes)*, concentrating in areas with seeding tall grass. Bill bluish gray (♂) or dusky (♀). Simply patterned ♂ *black above and on throat and chest*, with a *small but conspicuous white wing speculum*. *Lower underparts white*. ♀ plain olive brown above, paler buffy brownish below becoming dull yellowish on midbelly. **Similar species:** ♂ Yellow-bellied Seedeater's overall pattern is similar, but its mantle is olive (not black) and its belly yellower (though in worn plumage this can be quite pale); it also shows at most a faint wing speculum. ♀ ♀ of these two species cannot be distinguished. **Habits:** When breeding, occurs in pairs in relatively shrubby terrain; at other times favors more open grassier areas and often in flocks (sometimes big, and mixing with other seedeaters).

Voice: ♂'s song a distinctive, quite unmusical series of 6–8 rapidly delivered harsh notes, sometimes two-parted, with almost icterid-like quality and unlike other *Sporophila*. Not known to sing when in non-breeding flocks in e. lowlands.

Yellow-bellied Seedeater
Sporophila nigricollis
Espiguero Ventriamarillo   Plate 92(6)

Locally to 2400 m

11 cm (4¼"). Fairly common in grassy areas, shrubby clearings, and roadsides in more humid lowlands and lower Andean slopes, *especially in west*. Bill pale bluish gray (♂) or dusky (♀). ♂ has *crown, face, throat, and chest black* contrasting with *pale yellow lower underparts*; upperparts olive, with pale wing speculum indistinct or even absent. **Western birds** often more deeply colored below (but there is individual variation throughout range); older ♂ ♂ often more uniformly blackish above. ♀ plain olive brown above, paler buffy brownish below becoming dull yellowish on midbelly. **Similar species:** ♂ is only seedeater with yellow on underparts (but beware pale, washed-out birds: these can look quite whitish). Cf. ♂ Black-and-white Seedeater. ♀ is difficult, though usually enough ♂ ♂ are present to preclude confusion. **Habits:** When breeding, occurs as scattered pairs; at other times often in quite large groups, sometimes mixing with other seedeaters (e.g., Variables and Chestnut-throateds). **Voice:** ♂'s song a variable but musical and short phrase (though often slightly harsher than Variable's), usually ending with two buzzier notes, e.g., "tsee-tsee-tsee-bseeooo, bzee-bzee."

Parrot-billed Seedeater, *Sporophila peruviana*
Espiguero Pico de Loro   Plate 92(9)

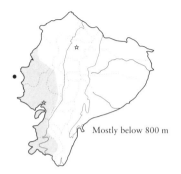

Mostly below 800 m

650–1900 m

11.5 cm (4½″). Grassy areas, agricultural regions, and scrub in *more arid lowlands of west*, locally up into arid lower subtropics in Loja. *Bill extremely large with very curved culmen, yellowish in* ♂, duller and more horn-colored in ♀. ♂ gray to brownish gray above with white wing speculum and usually two whitish wing-bars. *Throat and chest black, usually separated from gray head by a wide white malar stripe*; lower underparts whitish. Young and nonbreeding ♂♂ have a more diffuse and mottled pattern on fore-neck, and may show little or no black. ♀ pale brownish above, *wings usually with two buffyish bars*. Below buffy whitish. **Similar species:** Though often looking scruffy, both sexes should be readily recognized by the over-sized bill. Overall pattern of Chestnut-throated Seedeater (with which Parrot-billed often occurs) is similar, though its small bill is not. **Habits:** When not breeding (ca. Jul.–Dec.) regularly gathers in flocks, sometimes quite large, often associating with other seedeaters, Blue-black Grassquits, and Crimson-breasted Finches. **Voice:** Breeding ♂♂ sing persistently, a short phrase of harsh unmusical notes, e.g., "jew-jee-jew"; often just a series of well-spaced "jew" notes is given, then a couplet or triplet of "jee" notes. Singing birds often remain hidden in foliage but change perches often.

Drab Seedeater, *Sporophila simplex*
Espiguero Simple   Plate 92(11)

11 cm (4¼″). A well-named, *drab* seedeater, *local in arid scrub and adjacent agricultural*

areas in intermontane valleys of s. Azuay and Loja. Bill brownish, paler below. ♂ pale grayish brown with *two prominent white wing-bars*. Drab pale grayish below. ♀ similar, but *wing-bars dull buff*. **Similar species:** Wing-bars are *the* mark for this otherwise nondescript seedeater. ♀ Parrot-billed Seedeater is similar in overall plumage but has a much heavier bill. Cf. also Chestnut-throated Seedeater (both sexes with streaked back, etc.). Dull-colored Grassquit lacks wing-bars. **Habits:** Not well known in Ecuador, but general behavior appears to differ little from congeners. **Voice:** ♂'s song a series of short, rather harsh phrases, e.g., "tche-tzjee-tzjee-tche-tjzeee-tjzeee-tzjit."

Chestnut-throated Seedeater
Sporophila telasco
Espiguero Gorjicastaño   Plate 92(10)

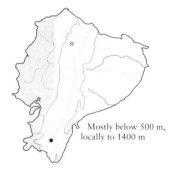

Mostly below 500 m, locally to 1400 m

10 cm (4″). *Common* in agricultural regions, grassy and shrubby areas, and settled areas in *lowlands of west*, locally (seasonally?) up into subtropics of El Oro and Loja. Bill black (♂) or pale brownish (♀). Attractive ♂ *gray above with vague dusky streaking on crown*

and mantle and *whitish on rump and base of tail* (latter an excellent field mark in flight); wings and tail blackish, wings with white speculum. *Upper throat chestnut*; underparts pure white. Throat patch of nonbreeding ♂♂ often obscure or even lacking. ♀ pale brown above with *distinctive dusky streaking on crown and mantle*; wings with white speculum. Below whitish, some brownish streaking across chest. **Similar species:** *The only seedeater showing streaking above* (this especially helpful for ♀). Cf. Parrot-billed Seedeater. **Habits:** Similar to other *Sporophila*. Chestnut-throated is especially conspicuous during the rainy season in first half of year when it breeds and when ♂♂ are often singing lustily from all around; at other seasons gathers in large flocks, often consorting with Variable Seedeaters and grassquits. **Voice:** ♂'s attractive song a short stacatto musical warbling, sometimes with a little sputter at end. Species is often kept as a cagebird.

Ruddy-breasted Seedeater, *Sporophila minuta*
Espiguero Pechirrojizo   Plate 92(12)

To 1500 m

10 cm (4″). Local in grassy areas, scrub, and roadsides in *lowlands and intermontane valleys of northwest.* Bill blackish (♂) or *mostly dull flesh-colored to orangey (♀).* ♂ *grayish brown to pure gray above* (grayer when breeding) with *rump rufous* (duller when not breeding); wings with small white speculum. *Rufous below.* ♀ buffy brown above, wings and tail duskier, wings with buffyish edging and (often) a small white speculum. Below buff to grayish buff. **Similar species:** ♂ distinctive, but ♀♀ as usual can be tricky except through associated ♂♂. ♀'s pale bill and wing speculum (if present)

helpful; cf. especially ♀ Variable. **Habits:** Not well known or especially numerous in Ecuador, but elsewhere similar to other seedeaters (generally favoring savannas and extensive human-created grasslands, habitats essentially nonexistent in Ecuador). **Voice:** Breeding ♂'s song a pleasant and musical series of warbled notes and phrases, usually starting with several couplets.

Chestnut-bellied Seedeater
Sporophila castaneiventris
Espiguero Ventricastaño   Plate 92(13)

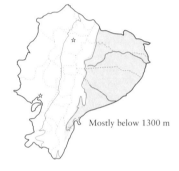

Mostly below 1300 m

10 cm (4″). *Common* in agricultural regions, grassy areas, along edges of rivers and lakes, and river islands in *lowlands of east, now spreading up into lower subtropics.* Bill blackish. Pretty ♂ *bluish gray above,* wings and tail blackish, wings with gray edging. *Throat and median underparts chestnut,* sides and flanks broadly bluish gray. ♀ closely resembles ♀ Ruddy-breasted Seedeater (no overlap) aside from bill color difference (pale in Ruddy-breasted). **Similar species:** ♂ distinctive in range. ♀ smaller and browner than other sympatric ♀♀ seedeaters. **Habits:** By far the most numerous and widespread seedeater in the Oriente, generally familiar wherever there is suitable grassy habitat, quickly following clearings into formerly forested terrain. Often in groups, seemingly even when breeding. **Voice:** ♂'s song a pleasant warbling, usually given from an exposed perch but generally not too high above ground. Call a clear "cheeu."

Blue Seedeater, *Amaurospiza concolor*
Semillero Azul   Plate 92(16)

12.5 cm (5″). *Rare and local in lower growth of foothill and subtropical forest on w. slope,*

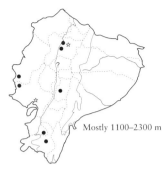

Mostly 1100–2300 m

Mostly 2600–3800 m

and locally on coastal cordillera. ♂ *uniform indigo-blue* with foreface slightly more blackish. ♀ *uniform rather bright tawny-brown*, slightly paler below. Juvenile like ♀ but more rufescent below, and sometimes shows dull buff wing-bars. **Similar species:** ♂♂ often appear quite blackish (blue apparent only in good light); ♀♀ tawnier than other ♀♀ seedeaters. Cf. especially ♂ Blue-black Grassquit and ♀ Lesser Seed-Finch; neither of these species is really a bird of woodland/forest. **Habits:** Generally inconspicuous, foraging mostly inside cover, hopping about in foliage; does not feed out in the open in grassy areas like the *Sporophila* seedeaters. **Voice:** ♂'s song a brief, fast, somewhat jumbled warbling with a sweet quality, e.g., "sweet-sweet-sweet-saweet."

Catamenia Seedeaters

Small, rather dull seedeaters found in open or shrubby terrain in *the Andes, mainly at high elevations*. Males are mainly gray, females predominantly brown and streaky; in both sexes *bills are yellow or pinkish*. *Catamenia* are not as gregarious as *Sporophila*.

Plain-colored Seedeater, *Catamenia inornata*
Semillero Sencillo   Plate 92(21)

13.5 cm (5¼"). *Fairly common and widespread in grassy areas and paramo in highlands. Bill brownish pink.* ♂ mostly rather pale gray with *blackish-streaked back*; belly tinged buff, crissum chestnut. ♀ grayish brown above with blackish streaking. Yellowish buff below *streaked with dusky on throat and breast*; crissum buff. **Immature** like ♀ but streaking coarser and more extensive. **Similar species:** Both sexes of scarcer Paramo Seedeater are darker generally,

though they have *paler* bills (varying from yellowish to pinkish, in ♂♂ sometimes almost looking white); they favor shrubbier terrain. ♀ Band-tailed Seedeater has a distinctive white tail-band (though this is visible mainly in flight). Ash-breasted Sierra-Finch has a more pointed and darker bill, is shorter-tailed. **Habits:** Forages mainly on or near ground, often in small groups; sometimes associates with other open-country montane finches such as Ash-breasted and Plumbeous Sierra-Finches. **Voice:** ♂'s song a series of (usually 3) short semimusical trills, the second higher-pitched than the first and last.

Paramo Seedeater, *Catamenia homochroa*
Semillero Paramero   Plate 92(22)

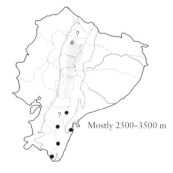

Mostly 2500–3500 m

13.5 cm (5¼"). *Scarce and local in shrubbery near treeline and at edge of temperate forest on both slopes. Bill very pale* (yellowish to pinkish, sometimes looking whitish). ♂ *uniform dark slaty gray* with *blackish foreface* and chestnut crissum. ♀ dark olive brown above streaked blackish. Olive brown below becoming more fulvous on belly and chestnut on crissum; *lacks streaking*. **Immature like ♀ but browner and more coarsely streaked above and below, ♂♂ gradually becoming grayer. **Similar species:** Both sexes of Plain-colored Seedeater are paler generally, and have somewhat darker, more obviously pinkish bills. ♂ Plain-colored lacks Paramo's blackish foreface; ♀ shows streaking on underparts. Plain-colored favors more open terrain (though the two species do occasionally occur together) and is *considerably more numerous.* **Habits:** An infrequently encountered bird, tending to remain in shrubbery; pairs or small groups sometimes accompany mixed flocks. Occasionally found feeding on the ground. **Voice:** ♂'s song a long, drawn-out, clear whistled note, sometimes given alone but more often followed by higher-pitched, shorter, and more burry whistle, e.g., "teeeeeeeee-tjeeeee?" (P. Coopmans).

Band-tailed Seedeater, *Catamenia analis*
Semillero Colifajeado   Plate 92(23)

Mostly 1500–3000 m

12.5 cm (5″). Fairly common in semiopen agricultural and settled terrain, mainly in arid regions, in highlands. *Stubby butter yellow bill in* ♂, ♀'s *duller.* Dapper ♂ *plain gray* with blackish foreface and chestnut crissum; tail blackish *with white band across its middle* (visible mainly in flight and from below). ♀ *pale* grayish brown above streaked with blackish. Buffy whitish below streaked with blackish, belly plain white and crissum buff; *tail as in* ♂. **Similar species:** Other *Catamenia* seedeaters *lack* white in tail, though this is often hard to see until birds are flushed. ♀ Band-tailed is paler than the others. Cf. also superficially similar Band-tailed Sierra-Finch (larger with a longer and more pointed bill, yellowish legs). **Habits:** A

conspicuous small seedeater, ranging in pairs and small groups, foraging mainly on the ground but also on tall grass stems. Perches freely in shrubs and low trees. **Voice:** ♂'s song a buzzy trill introduced by a sometimes faint semimusical note.

Phrygilus Sierra-Finches
Small to midsized finches that are mainly terrestrial in open, often barren habitats, primarily in the Andes though two species (Ash-breasted and Band-tailed) also range locally on the southwestern coast. *Shades of gray predominate,* with females browner and more streaked. *Phrygilus* are larger than the *Catamenia* seedeaters they sometimes accompany.

Plumbeous Sierra-Finch, *Phrygilus unicolor*
Frigilo Plomizo   Plate 92(24)

Mostly 3000–4300 m, locally to 4800 m

15 cm (6″). *Generally common in shrubbery near treeline and paramo.* ♂ *uniform leaden gray* with narrow white eye-ring. ♀ brown above and whitish below, *everywhere coarsely streaked with dusky*; indistinct whitish wing-bars. **Similar species:** Ash-breasted Sierra-Finch is notably smaller and occurs almost entirely at lower elevations than Plumbeous. ♂♂ Ash-breasteds are paler gray and have back streaking, ♀♀ less prominently streaked below and with whitish belly. **Habits:** Occurs in pairs and small groups, often allowing a close approach as they feed on ground, regularly on roadsides. Frequently perches on rocks or bushes, but rarely is very high above ground. Sometimes with other birds such as cincloides. **Voice:** Generally quiet, with infrequently heard song a brief "zhree."

Ash-breasted Sierra-Finch, *Phrygilus plebejus*
Frigilo Pechicinéreo   Plate 92(25)

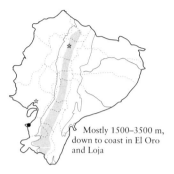

Mostly 1500–3500 m,
down to coast in El Oro
and Loja

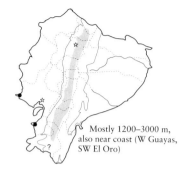

Mostly 1200–3000 m,
also near coast (W Guayas,
SW El Oro)

12 cm (4³⁄₄″). A *small and drab* finch, *common and often conspicuous* (more numerous southward) in *shrubby, often overgrazed arid terrain* in highlands and interior valleys, down to coast in El Oro. **Sexes alike.** Brownish gray above, grayest on head and rump, with *dusky streaking on back. Below paler gray*, becoming *whitish on belly.* **Juvenile** browner above and whitish below streaked dusky. **Similar species:** Plain-colored Seedeater is somewhat larger and longer-tailed; has stubbier pinkish bill. ♂♂ Plain-coloreds have chestnut crissum lacking in the sierra-finch, whereas ♀♀ are buffier below. ♂ Plumbeous Sierra-Finch is larger and more uniform, darker gray with no back streaking at all. **Habits:** Forages mainly on the ground, sometimes in quite large flocks, especially when not breeding. Sometimes associates with other finches, e.g., Band-tailed Seedeaters. **Voice:** ♂'s song a very short buzzy trill, "tzrrrt" or "tzzzzzzzzi."

Band-tailed Sierra-Finch, *Phrygilus alaudinus*
Frigilo Colifajeado   Plate 92(26)

14–14.5 cm (5¹⁄₂–5³⁄₄″). Somewhat local in *barren, arid areas with sparse vegetation* in highlands and interior valleys, also near coast in w. Guayas and El Oro. *Rather long and slender bill bright yellow; legs yellow.* ♂ gray, back browner and broadly streaked blackish; *lower breast and belly contrastingly white.* Tail black with *white band across its center* (visible mainly in flight and from below). Coastal birds are smaller and paler. ♀ brown above streaked with blackish; whitish below streaked with dusky on throat

and chest; *tail as in* ♂. **Similar species:** Both sexes of smaller Band-tailed Seedeater have a similar tail pattern, but the seedeater has a much stubbier bill and pale grayish legs. ♂ seedeater has obvious chestnut crissum, ♀ has buffier lower underparts. **Habits:** Found singly or in pairs, rarely or never in groups or flocks, in this differing from most other seed-finches and seedeaters. Forages mainly on ground, often out in the open so not hard to see, though resting in shade during heat of day. **Voice:** Breeding ♂ sings mostly during display flights, giving fairly musical series of gurgling phrases that end with long buzzy "zzhhhhhh" as it glides back to earth; occasionally one sings from the ground or an exposed perch, "dzi dzi-dzi-dzíuw."

[Cinereous Finch, *Piezorhina cinerea*
Pinzón Cinéreo]   Plate 96(25)

1100 m
(in Peru down to coast)

16.5 cm (6¹⁄₂″). A *casual* wanderer to open desertlike terrain (one sighting from sw. Loja). *Robust* and *pallid.* **Sexes alike.** *Massive yellow bill;* legs dull yellow. *Pale gray above* with blackish lores and malar spot. *Even paler gray below, with throat and midbelly whitish.* **Similar species:** So big and pale that it is unlikely to be confused. Band-tailed Sierra-Finch has a much more slender bill and white in tail, etc. Cf. also Sulphur-throated Finch (also can look pale, and has a massive bill, but is streaked above, etc.). **Habits:** In Peru ranges in small groups, foraging mainly on ground; often quite stolid and tame. Presumably only a wanderer to Ecuador. **Voice:** Dawn song a pleasant and rather slowly delivered series of loud notes and jumbled phrases, e.g., "chew, che-wét-chú, chee, che-wi-cher-chu-wít, che-weé . . . " (P. Coopmans).

Sicalis Yellow-Finches

Small to midsized finches found locally in open terrain in the Andes and western lowlands. *Yellow predominates* in two species but is much reduced in the drab Sulphur-throated. Of the three, only the familiar and attractive Saffron Finch is at all numerous in Ecuador.

Saffron Finch, *Sicalis flaveola*
Pinzón Sabanero Azafranado   Plate 91(20)

Locally to 2000 m

13.5 cm (5¼"). *Conspicuous and locally common in settled and agricultural regions in Loja and coastal El Oro, a few around Guayaquil and Zumba* (spreading?). ♂ *mostly bright yellow* becoming *orange on forecrown;* above somewhat more olive, vaguely streaked dusky on back; wings and tail somewhat duskier. ♀ similar but slightly duller. **Juvenile** *much more brownish gray,* streaked dusky on crown and mantle, with olive edging on wings and tail. Pale grayish below, more or less unstreaked, with *pale yellow pectoral band, sometimes extending up around hindneck as a nuchal collar.* **Similar species:** Adults of this attractive finch

are unlikely to be confused; streaky young birds are usually seen in association with them. Latter are readily known by the yellow across breast and around hindneck. **Habits:** Where it occurs, generally a numerous and familiar bird, often in small flocks and typically most numerous around habitations. Generally feeds on ground, often on lawns. **Voice:** ♂'s vigorous song a somewhat variable series of well-enunciated, cheery notes, e.g., "tsip, tsee-tit, tsee, tseeti, tsee, tsee, tseeti."

Grassland Yellow-Finch, *Sicalis luteola*
Pinzón Sabanero Común   Plate 91(21)

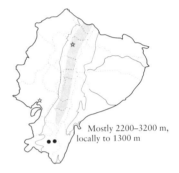

Mostly 2200–3200 m, locally to 1300 m

12 cm (4¾"). A *mainly yellowish* finch, somewhat local and erratic in *grassy areas and marshes around edges of lakes and in adjacent fields and pastures in highlands.* ♂ olive to grayish brown above streaked dusky and with *superciliary, ocular area, and malar streak yellow* and rump plain yellowish olive; flight feathers edged buffy yellow. *Below yellow,* brightest on throat and midbelly, washed grayish olive on sides and flanks. ♀ similar but browner above and paler yellow below. **Similar species:** Not likely confused in Ecuador, where it is the only yellow-finch in highlands, though this and the Saffron Finch could overlap in Loja. Might carelessly be confused with certain streaky highland seedeaters or sierra-finches (especially when facing away from you), though none of these is anywhere near so yellow. **Habits:** Notably gregarious, occurring in flocks virtually throughout year, and often seeming "semi-colonial" even when breeding. In Ecuador, however, not very well known and certainly not as numerous as it can be elsewhere. Feeds mostly on the ground, usually not with other birds; often noted only when flying past,

sometimes high above ground. **Voice:** Breed-ing ♂'s song a series of mixed buzzy and more musical trilled notes, usually given in a hovering display flight but sometimes also from a low perch (♂♂ then usually fluffing out rump feathers). Flight call a "tzi-tzit" (N. Krabbe recording).

Sulphur-throated Finch, *Sicalis taczanowskii*
Pinzón Sabanero Golisurfureo   Plate 91(22)

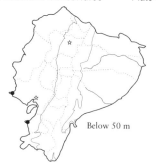

Below 50 m

12 cm (4³/₄"). A *nondescript heavy-headed* and *short-tailed* finch of *barren, desert-like areas on Santa Elena Peninsula and in sw. El Oro.* Now scarce; few if any recent records. Formerly placed in genus *Gnathospiza.* **Sexes alike.** *Very heavy horn-colored bill.* Pale grayish brown above, streaked darker on back; flight feathers edged yellowish. *Vague superciliary, narrow maler streak, and upper throat pale yellow* (but this often so faded as to not be very evident); underparts dull whitish, crissum tinged yellow. **Similar species:** A drab bird that usually lacks char-acteristic marks aside from its oversized bill; when evident, the yellow on foreface is dis-tinctive. Cf. Band-tailed Sierra-Finch. **Habits:** Notably erratic, tending to move about in compact, dense flocks of up to 50–100 birds that scatter out to feed on open ground; when flushed, may swirl away for a considerable distance. **Voice:** Not known.

Slaty Finch, *Haplospiza rustica*
Pinzón Pizarroso   Plate 92(17)

12.5 cm (5"). Erratic (*usually scarce*) in lower growth and borders of subtropical and temperate forest on both slopes, *favoring bamboo. Bill slender and sharply pointed.* ♂ *uniform dark gray,* a bit paler below. ♀ olive brown above, wing feathers edged rufescent. Dirty whitish below with *blurry dusky streak-*

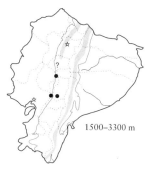

1500–3300 m

ing on throat and especially across breast. **Similar species:** ♂ recalls ♂ of larger Plumbeous Sierra-Finch, but that species is only found in paramo at much higher eleva-tions. ♀ resembles ♀ Blue-black Grassquit overall, though grassquit is smaller with *unstreaked* throat; it occurs in open grassy terrain in the lowlands. **Habits:** Though gen-erally rare and infrequently encountered, can become locally numerous when bamboos are seeding; has also been seen feeding on *Cecropia* catkins. Tends to remain in cover, sometimes emerging to feed on or near ground in grassy margins. **Voice:** ♂'s complex song a fast series of chips, buzzes, and trills, often ending with a downward raspy trill; it is some-times given in flight.

Red Pileated-Finch
Coryphospingus cucullatus
Brasita de Fuego Rojo   Plate 96(24)

1100–1400 m

13.5 cm (5¹/₄"). A *mainly reddish* finch of shrubby second-growth in *Río Marañón drainage in Zumba region.* Formerly called Red-crested Finch. ♂ *above dark vinous red* with narrow white eye-ring and *mostly black crown* that usually at least partially conceals *scarlet coronal stripe. Below dull crimson.* ♀ *lacks* black and red on crown and is browner above, but retaining *crimson rump* (often visible in flight) and *narrow white eye-ring.* Throat whitish, *underparts rosy pink.* **Similar species:** Not likely to be confused as no other finch is so uniformly reddish; duller ♀ ♀ are sometimes best known by their eye-ring, which is always evident. **Habits:** In Ecuador seems usually to occur in pairs, foraging on or near the ground, most often remaining in cover. **Voice:** ♂'s song, given mainly as part of the dawn chorus, an introductory note followed by a simple phrase that is repeated 3–6 times, e.g., "chewit, weét-chewit, weét-chewit, weét-chewit. . . ."

Atlapetes and Buarremon Brush-Finches
Midsized finches found in the undergrowth and borders of *montane forest and woodland in the Andes*, a few (e.g., White-headed and the very rare Pale-headed) in more deciduous scrub and woodland. Plumage patterns are simple, with grays and olives predominating; note in particular *whether the underparts are basically yellow or white* and the *pattern and color of the face and crown.* **Sexes are alike.** Brush-finches are active and energetic birds, often moving about in small family groups, sometimes accompanying mixed flocks. Some are more secretive, notably the White-rimmed and the two *Buarremon* species (the latter recently reseparated as a genus from *Atlapetes*). Note that the vocalizations of most of the brush-finches are similar and difficult to distinguish; they have a song (given mainly at dawn) consisting of a series of pretty clear notes (e.g, some variation of "tsi-tseee-tseee-tsi-tsi") and (fide N. Krabbe, especially) also a "cascading" call, often given by members of a pair. They also give various contact notes. In the species accounts below, vocalizations are not described unless they differ from this.

Pale-naped Brush-Finch
Atlapetes pallidinucha
Matorralero Nuquipálido   Plate 93(1)

18 cm (7″). *Shrubbery near treeline and at edge of temperate forest and woodland on e. slope.* Above plain gray with cinnamon forecrown *becoming white from midcrown back over nape* and black sides of head. Below

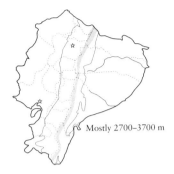

Mostly 2700–3700 m

yellow heavily clouded with olive. **Similar species:** Rufous-naped Brush-Finch has an *entirely rufous crown.* **Habits:** Usually in pairs or small family groups, actively foraging through lower growth, sometimes dropping down to the ground; often accompanies mixed flocks.

Rufous-naped Brush-Finch
Atlapetes latinuchus
Matorralero Nuquirrufo   Plate 93(2)

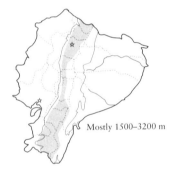

Mostly 1500–3200 m

17 cm (6¾″). *Relatively common, widespread, and conspicuous* in woodland (even where patchy) and forest borders on both slopes and above central and interandean valleys. Formerly named *A. rufinucha* (now split). Varies geographically. In **most of Ecuadorian range** gray above with *rufous crown* and black sides of head. Dull yellow below. In **southwest** similar, but with *prominent black submalar streak* and yellow lores. In **southeast** also similar, but has a *large white wing speculum.* **Similar species:** Tricolored Brush-Finch has yellower crown; it occurs at lower elevations on w. slope. Pale-naped Brush-Finch has white rearcrown and nape; it occurs mainly at and just below tree-

line on e. slope. **Habits:** A relatively bold and arboreal brush-finch, therefore often quite conspicuous; regularly hops about in the semiopen, and more often in very disturbed areas than many of congeners.

Tricolored Brush-Finch, *Atlapetes tricolor*
Matorralero Tricolor   Plate 93(3)

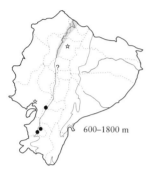

600–1800 m

18 cm (7″). Locally common in lower growth of *foothill and subtropical forest and woodland on w. slope*. Mostly dark olive above with *rich brownish gold crown* and black sides of head. Below yellow, sides and flanks broadly washed with olive. **Similar species:** Pattern recalls Rufous-naped Brush-Finch, though that species' crown is actually rufous; it occurs only at higher elevations. Overall coloration also somewhat like Dusky-faced Tanager. **Habits:** Notably more arboreal than other Ecuadorian brush-finches, routinely foraging 5–10 m above ground. Usually in pairs or small groups, sometimes moving with understory flocks. **Voice:** Song higher pitched than in Rufous-naped, and often has a wheezy quality.

Slaty Brush-Finch, *Atlapetes schistaceus*
Matorralero Pizarroso   Plate 93(5)

18 cm (7″). *Shrubby borders of temperate forest and woodland up to near treeline on e. slope south to nw. Morona-Santiago.* Mostly gray above with *chestnut crown and nape* and black sides of head; wings and tail blackish with *conspicuous white wing speculum.* Throat white bordered by *prominent black submalar and white malar streaks*; underparts gray, whiter on midbelly. **Similar species:** The only brush-finch with whitish/gray underparts on e. slope; smaller White-

Mostly 2500–3400 m

winged Brush-Finch occurs in drier, scrubbier habitats on interandean slopes (no overlap known). **Habits:** Occurs singly or in pairs, foraging in lower growth, often with mixed flocks, sometimes together with Rufous-naped Brush-Finches. Relatively arboreal, but except in early morning remains in dense cover. **Voice:** Song phrases sometimes shorter than in Northern Rufous-naped's song, e.g., "weyé-chuw," but they also can be of similar length.

White-winged Brush-Finch
Atlapetes leucopterus
Matorralero Aliblanco   Plate 93(4)

Mostly 1000–2600 m

15.5 cm (6″). *Shrubby growth and lighter woodland, sometimes even plantations and gardens, on slopes above central and interandean valleys*, mainly in *arid regions* (locally also moving onto w. slope in more humid but cleared areas). In **most of Ecuadorian range** (south at least to Chimborazo) mostly gray above with *large white wing speculum; entire crown and nape cinnamon-rufous* and sides of head black. *Whitish below*, tinged gray on flanks. In **southwest** (s. El Oro and Loja), black of face protrudes onto forecrown, and with a *variable amount of scattered white feathering on face, sometimes extensive.* **Similar species:** Slaty Brush-Finch occurs only on e. slope where White-winged is not found. In south, similarly patterned but larger Bay-crowned Brush-Finch, which overlaps with White-winged in Loja highlands, differs in having no wing speculum. White-headed Brush-Finch has no rufous on crown, its entire head being black and white. **Habits:** Usually in pairs or small groups, foraging actively in lower growth; flocks may be larger in nonbreeding season. In Loja usually found at *lower* elevations than Bay-crowned Brush-Finch, but *higher* than White-headed.

Bay-crowned Brush-Finch, *Atlapetes seebohmi*
Matorralero Coronicastaño   Plate 93(6)

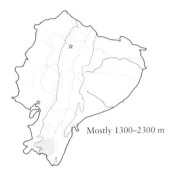

Mostly 1300–2300 m

16.5 cm (6½"). Local in lower growth of subtropical woodland, borders, and scrub in *Loja.* Mostly gray above with no white wing speculum; *crown and nape rich rufous* and sides of head black. White below with prominent black submalar streak, sides and flanks broadly gray. **Similar species:** White-winged Brush-Finch is smaller and less clean-cut (in area of overlap with Bay-crowned usually with scattered white on face) with conspicuous white wing speculum. **Habits:** Similar to White-winged Brush-Finch; generally remains within cover.

White-headed Brush-Finch, *Atlapetes albiceps*
Matorralero Cabeciblanco   Plate 93(7)

16 cm (6¼"). A striking brush-finch showing *no* rufous found in undergrowth of deciduous (often quite arid) woodland and scrub in s. *Loja,* occurring at *lower elevations* than other brush-finches. *Forecrown, face, and*

200–1100 m

throat white contrasting with *black hindcrown and nape*; otherwise pale brownish gray above, wings and tail duskier, wings with a prominent white speculum. Below whitish, chest tinged gray, flanks and crissum tinged grayish buff. **Similar species:** Cf. very rare and local Pale-headed Brush-Finch. Some White-winged Brush-Finches in Loja show so much white on their face as to superficially resemble a White-headed, but White-winged's crown is always rufous (not white and black). **Habits:** Similar to White-winged Brush-Finch.

Pale-headed Brush-Finch
Atlapetes pallidiceps
Matorralero Cabecipálido   Plate 93(8)

1500–2100 m

16 cm (6¼"). *Now very rare and local in low woodland and scrub in certain arid interandean valleys of s. Azuay, where recently relocated near Girón.* Acutely endangered. Resembles a *"faded, washed-out"* White-headed Brush-Finch. *Entire head whitish* (no black on hindcrown) with ill-defined pale brownish stripes on sides of crown and back from eye. **Similar species:** White-headed Brush-Finch is much more clean-cut, with

crisp black and white head pattern; it is not known to occur within very limited range of Pale-headed. All other vaguely similar brush-finches have rufous on crown. **Habits:** A small population of this endemic brush-finch was finally rediscovered in Nov. 1998, after the species had gone unseen for more than 30 years. Behavior similar to White-winged Brush-Finch. **Voice:** Cascade calls weaker and higher pitched than in congeners (N. Krabbe).

White-rimmed Brush-Finch, *Atlapetes leucopis*
Matorralero de Anteojos   Plate 93(9)

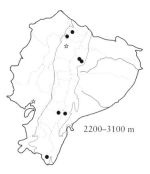

2200–3100 m

18 cm (7″). A *dark* brush-finch found very locally in *undergrowth inside upper subtropical and temperate forest on e. slope south to Azuay and Morona-Santiago*, also on *w. slope in far north*. Blackish above with *chestnut crown and nape* and *conspicuous white eye-ring and short postocular streak*. Below dark olive. **Similar species:** Olive Finch has a similar overall color pattern but lacks the spectacles; it occurs at *lower* elevations. **Habits:** Notably inconspicuous, hopping on or near ground, almost always remaining inside forest cover. Sometimes associates with flocks, but at least as often independent. **Voice:** Song a forceful series of pretty and melodic notes and phrases, often including repetitions, rather different from other *Atlapetes* (N. Krabbe recording).

Chestnut-capped Brush-Finch
Buarremon brunneinucha
Matorralero Gorricastaño   Plate 93(10)

19 cm (7½″). Widespread in *undergrowth of foothill and subtropical forest and woodland on both slopes, also on coastal cordillera*. A handsome brush-finch with *chestnut crown*

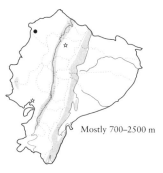

Mostly 700–2500 m

(more golden laterally) and *black forehead and sides of head*, forecrown with three small white vertical markings; otherwise dark olive above. *Throat white (often puffed out)*, bordered below by *black chest band*; underparts whitish, sides extensively olive grayish. Birds found on w. slope from s. Chimborazo to nw. Azuay, and on coastal cordillera, *lack* chest band. **Similar species:** Stripe-headed Brush-Finch shows no chestnut on crown. **Habits:** More terrestrial and often less conspicuous than *Atlapetes* brush-finches. Feeds (generally alone) by flicking aside leaves and other debris with bill, not scratching with feet. Does not usually accompany mixed flocks. **Voice:** Rather often heard, but variable, song several very high-pitched notes, the last often trilled. Call a high-pitched, penetrating "tseep."

Stripe-headed Brush-Finch
Buarremon torquatus
Matorralero Cabecilistado   Plate 93(11)

Mostly 1900–3500 m (N); 900–3000 m (S, locally even lower)

19 cm (7½″). Widespread in *undergrowth of upper subtropical and temperate forest and woodland* on both slopes, and on slopes above central and interandean valleys. Mostly olive above with *gray coronal stripe*

and superciliary on otherwise black head.
White below, broadly gray on sides and
flanks. **Similar species:** Likely to be confused
only with Chestnut-capped Brush-Finch
(though lacking chestnut on crown). The two
are not known to occur sympatrically in
Ecuador (Stripe-headed generally ranging
higher), but they may, especially in the southwest. Black-capped Sparrow is smaller with
a bold white superciliary, mainly or entirely
gray back, etc. Cf. also Black-striped
Sparrow. **Habits:** Similar to Chestnut-capped
Brush-Finch, equally shy and inconspicuous
though it can be excited by squeaking. Stripe-
headed also often puffs out its white throat.
Voice: Song a thin and high-pitched phrase,
e.g., "tsué tsu-zeét tseíuw," not quite as fast
or high pitched as in Chestnut-capped.

Olive Finch, *Lysurus castaneiceps*
Pinzón Oliváceo   Plate 93(12)

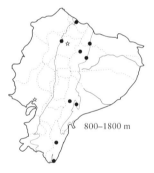

800–1800 m

15 cm (6"). A scarce and *inconspicuous*, dark
olive finch found in *undergrowth of foothill
and subtropical forest on e. slope, and on w.
slope in northwest. Sexes alike. Mostly dark
olive*, wings and tail duskier, with *crown and
nape chestnut* and *face and throat dark gray.*
Similar species: Brush-finch-like in overall
shape and comportment, but darker and
more uniform-looking than any. **Habits:**
Usually in pairs that hop through dense
undergrowth, often near water and showing
a predilection for ravines. The habitat it
favors is typically dense, so birds are hard to
see well, but once located they often do not
seem to be especially shy; sometimes respond
strongly to sqeaking. **Voice:** Song a fast series
of very high-pitched sibilant notes, e.g.,
"tsee-tsi-tsi-tititi-tsi-tsi-tsü-tsii," hard to hear
over the sound of rushing water. Call a short,

high-pitched, flat trill, "tsi-d-d-d-d-d-d-d" (P.
Coopmans).

Tanager Finch, *Oreothraupis arremonops*
Pinzón Tangara   Plate 93(13)

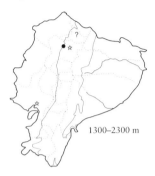

1300–2300 m

20.5 cm (8"). A *mainly rufous* finch, *very rare
and local* in *undergrowth and borders of subtropical forest on w. slope in northwest.* **Sexes
alike.** Unmistakable. *Head black with bold
whitish coronal stripe and long broad superciliary. Otherwise rufous*, browner above
and more orangey below with grayer midbelly; tail dusky. **Habits:** Overall comportment resembles a brush-finch. Forages
in pairs or small groups, hopping slowly
through thick growth, sometimes dropping
to ground where it flicks leaves with bill.
Usually not with mixed flocks. **Voice:** Song
a series of high-pitched buzzy notes interspersed with some that are slightly more
musical, e.g., "zzeee-zéee-zzeee-zi-zi-zéee";
has a characteristic cadence. Usual call—at
least in Colombia (has not been heard in
Ecuador)—a soft, frog-like "wert" repeated
at 2- to 3-second intervals (S. Hilty). Also
gives a soft "tsit" call.

Arremon Sparrows
Attractive and boldly patterned sparrows
that are inconspicuous in the *undergrowth of
lowland forest and woodland.*

Orange-billed Sparrow
Arremon aurantiirostris
Saltón Piquinaranja   Plate 93(14)

15 cm (6"). An attractive and nearly unmistakable sparrow found in *undergrowth of
humid forest and woodland in lowlands of
east and west*, smaller numbers up into
foothills. Well named, with a *conspicuous*

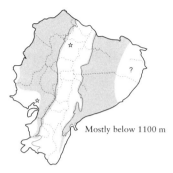

Mostly below 1100 m

bright orange bill. Head black with *conspicuous long white superciliary*; otherwise bright olive above. White below with *neat black pectoral band*. Birds **west of Andes** have shoulders yellow, this being flame-orange in birds from **east**. Sexes basically alike, but ♀ tinged buff below, especially on sides. **Similar species:** Cf. Black-capped Sparrow (with *black* bill, etc.). The two species basically separate out ecologically (Black-capped favoring drier habitats) but do occur together at a few sites. **Habits:** Generally an unobtrusive bird, hopping about on or near ground, usually remaining inside forest though sometimes emerging into semiopen at borders, especially in early morning. Usually in pairs, generally not accompanying mixed flocks. **Voice:** In the west, song a very high-pitched, fast, and jumbled series of notes, e.g., "tsu-t-t-ti-tu-ti-t-t," very short (only a second long). In the east, song a very different series of buzzy notes, e.g., "tzeeeee-zee-zee-zeeeeeet."

Black-capped Sparrow, *Arremon abeillei*
Saltón Gorrinegro   Plate 93(15)

15 cm (6"). *Undergrowth of deciduous woodland, forest, and scrub in lowlands of south-*

Mostly below 800 m, locally to 1600 m

west (locally into more humid situations); also in Río Marañón drainage around Zumba. *Bill black*. In most of range ♂ *bluish gray above* with *black head and neck* and white superciliary starting above eye; some birds show a faint whitish wing-bar. Below white with black pectoral band, gray on sides. In **Río Marañón drainage** differs in having longer white superciliary (starts on lores) and *olive back and rump*. ♀ differs only in having some buff on sides. **Similar species:** Orange-billed Sparrow has a bright orange bill and favors more humid regions (very limited overlap with Black-capped). ♂ Collared Warbling-Finch has head with black only on cheeks, and shows much white in tail. The larger Stripe-headed Brush-Finch has gray head striping, no pectoral band. **Habits:** Similar to Orange-billed Sparrow, though even less likely to emerge into open. It likewise can be excited by squeaking. **Voice:** Song of Pacific-slope birds less high-pitched and sibilant than Orange-billed's, a fast "tseeét, tsi-tsi-tsi-tseeét." Song of Marañón birds similar but delivered more slowly, e.g., "sweée, sweée, si-si-si-si-si" (P. Coopmans).

Black-striped Sparrow, *Arremonops conirostris*
Saltón Negrilistado   Plate 93(16)

To 1400 m

16.5 cm (6½"). Somewhat local in shrubby clearings, overgrown pastures, and lighter woodland in *semihumid lowlands and foothills of west*; also very locally in lowlands of east on Río Pastaza islands near Kapawi Lodge. **Sexes alike.** *Head gray with narrow but conspicuous black stripes down midcrown and through eye*; otherwise uniform bright olive with yellow on bend of wing. Below whitish, washed with pale gray on sides and flanks. **Similar species:** Both

Arremon sparrows are more boldly patterned with conspicuous white head striping and black pectoral band. Cf. also larger Stripe-headed Brush-Finch. **Habits:** Generally found singly or in pairs, feeding mainly on ground though also often hopping about in dense low vegetation; usually quite shy, and heard more often than seen. Does not typically accompany mixed flocks. **Voice:** Most frequent song of western birds an often-heard series of inflected, whistled "ho-wheet" notes. Less often gives a series of well-enunciated notes delivered deliberately at first but then accelerating, e.g., "cho; cho; cho, chocho-cho-cho-chochochochch." Call a "kluk" (P. Coopmans).

Ammodramus Sparrows

Small, plain, "streaky" sparrows with *pointed tails* found in open grassy areas. **Sexes are alike.**

Yellow-browed Sparrow
Ammodramus aurifrons
Sabanero Cejiamarillo   Plate 93(19)

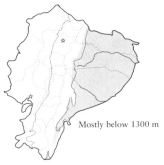

Mostly below 1300 m

13 cm (5"). *Common and widespread in grassy areas of east*, mainly in lowlands but now also spreading onto lower Andean slopes. Formerly placed in genus *Myospiza*. Brownish gray above with dusky streaking and *conspicuous yellow on face* (extent somewhat variable but usually incorporating *lores, short superciliary, eye-ring, and anterior part of cheeks*); bend of wing also yellow. Below pale grayish, whiter on throat and midbelly. **Similar species:** Though relatively drab and obscure, this frequently seen sparrow is always readily known by its facial yellow. **Habits:** A familiar bird, hopping about on the ground, often fully in open; frequently perches atop shrubs and low trees

and on fences. Generally found singly or in pairs, most often not associating with the seedeaters that share its grassy habitat. **Voice:** Often-heard song an easily recognized buzzing, "tic, tzzzz-tzzzzz," frequently repeated at intervals right through heat of day. Also gives a fast, high-pitched "tseew tseew tsee tsee tsee."

Grasshopper Sparrow
Ammodramus savannarum
Sabanero Saltamontes   Plate 93(18)

2800–2900 m

11.5 cm (4½"). A *very small, obscure* sparrow with *"spiky" short tail. Now perhaps extirpated in Ecuador*, with a few old records from the Quito area. Elsewhere inhabits *less-disturbed grasslands.* Brownish gray above with extensive blackish streaking and mottling and *narrow whitish coronal streak*; bend of wing yellow. *Throat and breast buff*, fading to whitish on belly. **Similar species:** Yellow-browed Sparrow occurs only east of Andes. Juvenile Rufous-collared Sparrow is much smaller, etc. Cf. also Grass Wren. **Habits:** Unknown in Ecuador. Elsewhere inconspicuous and shy, mostly seen while singing. Creeps about on or near ground in tall grass; when flushed, usually does not fly far, pitching back into cover and hard to relocate. **Voice:** Elsewhere song an almost hissing, insect-like trill, "pi-tuk-tzzzzzzzz"; though weak and high-pitched, it carries surprisingly well. Singing birds perch near tip of grass stem or on a low shrub. Sometimes sings at night.

Tumbes Sparrow, *Aimophila stolzmanni*
Sabanero de Tumbes   Plate 93(20)
14.5 cm (5¾"). *Arid scrub and shrubby areas with intermixed tall grass in lowlands and*

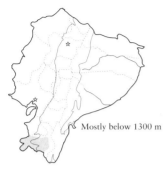

Mostly below 1300 m

Mostly 1500–3500 m, locally down to 900 m

lower *subtropical zone of Loja.* Formerly placed in genus *Rhynchospiza.* **Sexes alike.** *Bill heavy* with lower mandible grayish white. *Head gray with brown lateral crown stripe and eye-stripe;* above otherwise brown with blackish streaking, *shoulders rufous-chestnut* (often conspicuous) and bend of wing yellow (often hard to see). Throat white with *black submalar streak;* underparts grayish white, grayest across breast and down flanks. **Similar species:** Cf. really rather different Rufous-collared Sparrow (limited overlap in any case, Rufous-collared mainly at higher elevations) and ♀ Band-tailed Sierra-Finch. **Habits:** Found singly or in pairs, foraging mainly on the ground; though often remaining within cover, not especially shy and thus not particularly hard to see, and responds readily to pishing. Generally not with flocks. **Voice:** Song, generally given from a prominent perch, a simple but attractive series of 3–5 ringing metallic notes, e.g., "chew-chew-chew-chew" or "tre-tre-tre-tre-tréeeeng." Sings mainly during rainy season; at other times only "tsip" call notes are given.

Rufous-collared Sparrow, *Zonotrichia capensis*
Chingolo   Plate 93(17)

14 cm (5½"). *Widespread, common, and familiar in semiopen shrubby and grassy areas throughout highlands, often around houses,* ranging down locally into subtropics. **Sexes alike.** *Almost invariably shows a perky bushy crest. Head gray with prominent black striping,* contrasting with a *conspicuous rufous collar on hindneck.* Above rufescent brown, streaked blackish on back; wings with two whitish bars. Below mainly whitish with *black patch on sides of chest.* Frequently seen **juvenile** quite different: much duller and streakier

generally, especially below. At least a trace of the rufous collar is usually apparent. **Similar species:** One of the more numerous birds of nonforest areas in the highlands, this attractive sparrow presents no identification challenges except when still in juvenal plumage. Juveniles may be confused with certain other "streaky" sparrow-like birds, though crest and collar are generally apparent except on very young individuals. **Habits:** Tame and conspicuous, occurring in pairs or family groups (loose flocks when not breeding); often most common in settled areas. Remains numerous in gardens and urban areas through much or all of its Ecuadorian range, these fortunately not yet having been invaded by House Sparrows. Feeds mainly on the ground. **Voice:** Well known but variable song consists of 1 or 2 long slurred whistled notes followed by a trill, e.g., "tee-teeoo, tee-ee-ee-ee"; there appears to be both regional and individual variation. Call a sharp metallic "chip."

Collared Warbling-Finch
Poospiza hispaniolensis
Pinzón Gorgeador Collarejo   Plate 93(21)

13.5 cm (5¼"). *Local in arid scrub and woodland in lowlands of southwest;* most numerous on *Isla de la Plata.* Some birds show pinkish or dull orange on at least base of bill. Attractive ♂ mainly *gray above* with *conspicuous long white superciliary* and *prominent black cheeks;* back often at least tinged brown, sometimes dusky-streaked. *Inner webs of outer tail feathers white* (conspicuous from below and in flight). Below white with *patch on chest black,* sides and flanks gray. Drab ♀ more grayish brown above but with *facial pattern similar* (though much less contrasty). Below whitish with *band of dusky*

Mostly below 300 m, in Loja up to 1450 m

streaking across chest and some down flanks. **Similar species:** Black-capped Sparrow lacks white in tail, and aside from white eye-stripe its head is black. ♀'s face pattern is usually sufficient to identify it. Both sexes can be recognized in flight by white in tail, a character not shared by other sparrow-like birds in sw. Ecuador (♀ Band-tailed Sierra-Finch's white is positioned *across* tail). **Habits:** Usually in pairs or small groups, though flocking is characteristic of the Isla de la Plata population; birds in this population are also notably tame. Often arboreal, though sometimes also feeding on ground. **Voice:** ♂'s vigorous and far-carrying song a ringing, well-enunciated series of notes, e.g., "swik-swik-sweéu," sometimes given from prominent perch but more often while hidden. There is some regional and individual variation. Sings mainly late in rainy and early in dry seasons.

American Orioles and Blackbirds: Icteridae (30)

A diverse group of birds found only in the Americas, the icterids are united by their stout, long, and sharply pointed bills and strong legs and feet. Otherwise they vary. Some species are mainly or entirely black, others brightly colored. In some there is no sexual dimorphism (other than size, *males being larger in many species*), but in others it is striking. A majority of species are arboreal in forest and woodland, but a few inhabit more open grassy areas. Some icterids have attractive melodic songs, whereas others emit only loud and harsh vocalizations. Even their nests exhibit striking variation, the arboreal species constructing large and beautifully woven pendant nests, others building much simpler cup nests; the two cowbirds are brood parasites.

Cacicus Caciques
Mainly or entirely black icterids, some with *bright yellow or red on the rump*, a few with *bright yellow also on the wings*. They are smaller than oropendolas and have less yellow on the tail. As with oropendolas, bills are sharp and pointed, most often pale; males are notably larger than females. Arboreal and noisy birds that attract attention, caciques are found in humid and montane forest borders, often ranging in groups. Nesting is usually colonial.

Yellow-rumped Cacique, *Cacicus cela*
Cacique Lomiamarillo   Plate 94(1)

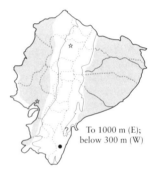

To 1000 m (E); below 300 m (W)

♂ 27–29 cm (10½–11¼"); ♀ 23–25 cm (9–9¾"). *Common and familiar in cleared areas and forest borders (especially near water) in lowlands of east*; less numerous and more local in forest and woodland borders and clearings in *lowlands of west*. Iris pale to grayish blue; bill ivory yellow (east) or light dusky (west). **Eastern** ♂ glossy black with large bright yellow patch on inner wing-coverts; *rump, crissum, and basal third of tail also bright yellow*. **Western** ♂ similar but somewhat smaller and with yellow on tail more restricted. ♀♀ resemble respective ♂♂ but black duller and sootier. **Similar species:** *The only black and yellow cacique in the Ecuadorian lowlands*. Oropendolas have yellow only on lateral tail feathers (none on rump or wing). Cf. Orange-backed Troupial. **Habits:** Gregarious and conspicuous wherever it occurs, often flying in compact or streaming groups, sometimes with other icterids mixed in. Nests in colonies, often close to houses (and in east also frequently along rivers and lakeshores); for protection, nests are usually placed close to a bee or wasp nest. Oropendolas (usually Russet-backed or Crested) may nest close by. Forages mainly on fruit but also in flowering trees, often with oropendolas and other birds. **Voice:** Has a variety of loud calls, some harsh and slashing, others more melodic. Singing ♂♂ may perform for long periods around colonies, often leaning forward and ruffling rump feathers. Eastern birds incorporate mimicry of other species into their singing, but western birds (whose songs tend to be more melodic and pleasing) are not known to do so. Western birds also give a distinctive mellow "ee-choo-kee-oong" (P. Coopmans).

Northern Mountain-Cacique
Cacicus leucoramphus
Cacique Montañes Norteño   Plate 94(2)

Mostly 2000–3100 m

♂ 29.5–30.5 cm (11¹⁄₂–12″); ♀ 24–25 cm (9¹⁄₂–9³⁄₄″). *Canopy and borders of upper subtropical and temperate forest on e. slope.* Formerly often called Mountain Cacique (*C. chrysonotus*); n. and s. populations in the Andes were then considered conspecific. Iris pale blue (brown in younger birds); bill pale bluish gray. ♂ glossy black with *bright yellow wing-coverts and rump.* ♀ similar but somewhat sootier black. **Similar species:** Yellow-rumped Cacique occurs in lowlands (no known overlap, and seems unlikely) and also has yellow on crissum and on the base of its *shorter* tail. Subtropical Cacique's red rump (like Mountain's yellow) is usually hidden on perched birds, causing potential confusion until the usually obvious yellow on Mountain's wing-coverts is seen; these two

caciques do overlap altitudinally. **Habits:** Ranges in small noisy groups, foraging at all levels though most often fairly high; regularly with other birds such as Turquoise Jays and Hooded Mountain-Tanagers. Seems to feed primarily on insects, probing into bark crevices and epiphytic growth. **Voice:** Quite vocal, with a variety of loud calls including a "wree-wree-wree-wreeuh," sometimes just a single "wree!" or "kreeuh!," and a repeated more nasal "skeeuh."

Red-rumped Cacique, *Cacicus haemorrhous*
Cacique Lomirrojo   Plate 94(3)

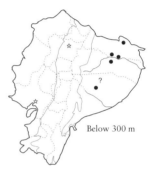

Below 300 m

♂ 27.5–28.5 cm (10³⁄₄–11¹⁄₄″); ♀ 22.5–23.5 cm (8³⁄₄–9¹⁄₄″). *Very rare in canopy and borders of terra firme in lowlands of east.* Iris blue (brown in younger birds); bill greenish yellow. **Sexes alike.** *Entirely black* (somewhat glossier above) with *scarlet lower back and rump.* **Similar species:** Resembles Subtropical Cacique; there is no known overlap between the two species, Subtropical being purely montane. Subtropical's red on rump is less extensive (basically encompassing only its rump proper) and its tail is proportionately longer. Their vocalizations differ. On perched birds the red on rump is generally hidden, potentially causing confusion with other black caciques. Scarlet-rumped Cacique occurs only west of Andes. **Habits:** In Ecuador an inexplicably rare bird, seen singly or in at most small groups, sometimes foraging with other icterids, especially oropendolas. **Voice:** Has a wide variety of harsh or guttural calls that are often interspersed with somewhat more melodic notes, including a drawn-out "zhweeeeeo." Foraging birds mainly give a harsh "zhap! zhap! zhap!"

Subtropical Cacique, *Cacicus uropygialis*
Cacique Subtropical   Plate 94(5)

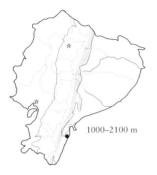

♂ 28–30.5 cm (11–12″); ♀ 25–25.5 cm (9¹/₂–9³/₄″). *Canopy and borders of subtropical forest and adjacent clearings on e. slope.* Formerly considered conspecific with Scarlet-rumped Cacique of w. lowlands. Iris pale blue (brown in younger birds); bill pale yellowish green or greenish white. **Sexes alike.** *Entirely black with scarlet rump.* **Similar species:** *The only cacique with red rump occurring in montane forests.* In plumage closely resembles Scarlet-rumped of w. lowlands, though differing in its proportionately longer tail and heavier bill; voice also differs. **Habits:** A conspicuous and noisy cacique that forages actively in upper levels, often associating with Inca Jays, various tanagers, and sometimes Russet-backed Oropendolas and mountain-caciques. Frequently hops along larger horizontal limbs, probing into bromeliads and inspecting crevices and the underside of leaves. Also eats fruit. **Voice:** Has a variety of vocalizations, the most frequent being a loud ringing jay-like "greer" often given in series, a repeated "weee-de-rit!," and a liquid "wurt-wurt-wurt-wurt" that recalls a common call of Black-capped Donacobius. Also gives a fast "chi-chi-zi-zi-zi-zi-zi-jéw" and a "keeyoow keeyoow keeyoow keeyoow" (P. Coopmans).

Scarlet-rumped Cacique
Cacicus microrhynchus
Cacique Lomiescarlata   Plate 94(4)

♂ 23–24 cm (9–9¹/₂″); ♀ 20.5–21.5 cm (8–8¹/₂″). *Fairly common in humid forest canopy and borders in lowlands of west.* Formerly considered conspecific with Subtropical Cacique of the Andes. Iris pale blue (brown in younger birds); bill greenish

yellow. **Sexes alike.** *Entirely black with scarlet rump.* **Similar species:** *The only cacique with a red rump occurring in lowlands of west*; recall that Subtropical does not occur on Andes' w. slope. Red is usually hidden except in flight, causing potential confusion with other black caciques, especially Yellow-billed (though that species has a yellow eye, etc.). **Habits:** An arboreal cacique, trooping about in noisy groups of typically 4–8 individuals, often associating with other icterids or Purple-throated Fruitcrows. Forages actively in foliage, often rummaging in palm fronds (sometimes hanging acrobatically, exposing the red) or inspecting dead leaves. **Voice:** Has a variety of vocalizations, most frequent a loud, ringing "treeo, trew!-trew!-trew!-trew!" but also several other whistled notes including a liquid "tleeo" or "kleeo," sometimes given in series, and a peculiar gurgling sound.

Ecuadorian Cacique, *Cacicus sclateri*
Cacique Ecuatoriano   Plate 94(6)

♂ 23–23.5 cm (9–9¹/₄″); ♀ 19.5–20 cm (7³/₄–8″). *Scarce and local in canopy and borders of várzea forest and woodland in lowlands of east.* Formerly called Ecuadorian Black Cacique. *Iris pale blue*; bill pale bluish

gray. **Sexes alike.** *Entirely black.* **Similar species:** Perched Red-rumped Caciques often appear all black, their red on rump usually not being evident until they fly; calls differ. Solitary Cacique is also all black, but it has a dark iris; behavior of these two species differs markedly. **Habits:** Not well known, but appears to be a typical arboreal cacique, usually seen in small groups of up to only 3–4 birds. Forages much like Scarlet-rumped Cacique. **Voice:** Has a variety of arresting calls including a repeated "cheé-ker" sometimes followed by a jay-like "k-cheeyow?," a mournful clear "kleeéur" often preceded by several soft "wop" notes, a penetrating "kweeyh-kweeyh-kweeyh-kweeyh-wonhh?," and a "wo-wo-wo-wo-whaahh?" (J. Moore recordings).

Solitary Cacique, *Cacicus solitarius*
Cacique Solitario   Plate 94(7)

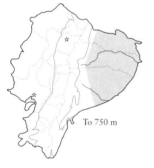

To 750 m

♂ 27 cm (10½″); ♀ 23 cm (9″). *Dense undergrowth of regenerating clearings and early-succession woodland, especially near water, in lowlands of east.* Formerly called Solitary Black Cacique. *Iris brown* (the only adult cacique with dark eyes); *bill pale greenish.* **Sexes alike.** *Entirely black.* **Similar species:** The only cacique of e. lowlands normally found *in undergrowth*; others are basically arboreal, though all occasionally come lower (and Solitary sometimes forages higher up in trees, especially where these are flowering). Especially cf. scarce Ecuadorian Cacique (also all black, but blue-eyed). Yellow-billed Cacique does not occur in e. lowlands. **Habits:** Usually in pairs that tend to skulk in dense lower growth where often hard to see until vocalizations give away their presence. Frequently probes into dead leaves and other suspended debris. **Voice:** Has a varied repertoire of loud, strident vocalizations. Perhaps

most frequent are a penetrating "keeyoh keeyoh keeyoh" or "kyoong kyoong kyoong," a loud fast "chochochochochocho," and an often-repeated "kway." Also often gives a nasal "wheeeah" or "wheeeah-ah" (similar to a donacobius), less often an extended sharp descending "skeeeeeeunh" and a loud "popp!"

Yellow-billed Cacique
Amblycercus holosericeus
Cacique Piquiamarillo   Plate 94(8)

To 1700 m (W);
1900–3100 m (E slope)

♂ 23.5 cm (9¼″); ♀ 22 cm (8½″). An *undergrowth-inhabiting* cacique found in *deciduous forest and woodland in lowlands of west,* ranging higher in Loja; and locally in *upper subtropical and temperate forest on e. slope. Bill and iris pale yellow.* **Sexes alike.** *Entirely dull black.* **Similar species:** General appearance and behavior quite like Solitary Cacique's, but these two species do not occur together; Solitary's eye is dark (unlike Yellow-billed's obvious straw color). Cf. also Subtropical Cacique (whose red rump is often concealed; its iris is obviously blue). **Habits:** Usually in pairs that skulk in dense lower growth, revealing themselves mainly as they fly across an opening or trail, sometimes accompanying mixed flocks of understory birds. In Andes favors stands of bamboo. **Voice:** Song of western-lowland birds a series of loud ringing whistled notes, e.g., "pee!-pee!-peeo-peeo-peeo . . ." (up to 10–15 "peeo"s). Also gives an often-paired "whew-whew, whew-whew . . ." that is sometimes echoed by female's single "wheee? chrrrr". Song of Andean birds also ringing, but markedly higher-pitched and shriller, "teeeee teeuw teeeee, teeeee teeuw teeeee" with ♀ chiming in with a "wheee? chrrrr" much like western birds (M. Lysinger recording). Latter song is vaguely reminiscent of Buff-breasted

Mountain-Tanager. Call a repeated and guttural "kuhkuhkuhkuhkuh."

Band-tailed Oropendola, *Ocyalus latirostris*
Oropéndola Colifajeada   Plate 94(9)

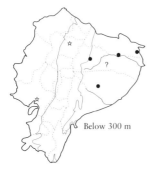

Below 300 m

♂ 32.5–33.5 cm (12³/₄–13¹/₄"); ♀ 25–26 cm (9³/₄–10¹/₄"). *Very rare in várzea forest canopy and borders in lowlands of east.* Iris blue; bill ivory whitish with small frontal shield and base of maxilla blackish. **Sexes alike.** *Mostly velvety black* with glossy bluish sheen on wings; crown, hindneck, and upper back dark chestnut (but color hard to discern in the field). Tail pattern distinctive (but also hard to see in the field): usually looks entirely dark from above, but *from below and in flight outer feathers can be seen to be primarily yellow, leaving black band at tip.* **Similar species:** Most apt to be confused with the far more common Yellow-rumped Cacique, which has a somewhat similar tail pattern (though yellow visible from above, and extends to rump). When its yellow in tail is hidden, Band-tailed can look essentially dark and then can be confused with Ecuadorian or Solitary Caciques. **Habits:** Barely known in Ecuador. In Peru moves in small groups, often accompanying larger numbers of Yellow-rumped Caciques and Russet-backed Oropendolas; birds have been seen roosting with the former in large stands of *Gynerium* cane. **Voice:** Foraging calls include some liquid chortles, a "chewop," "ke-cho!," and a "skeedelop-chop."

Chestnut-headed Oropendola
Zarhynchus wagleri
Oropéndola Cabecicastaña   Plate 94(11)

♂ 34.5–35 cm (13¹/₂–13³/₄"); ♀ 27–28 cm (10¹/₂–11"). A handsome oropendola of

To 700 m

canopy and borders of humid forest and woodland in lowlands and foothills of west. Sometimes placed in genus *Psarocolius*. Iris blue; *conspicuous swollen frontal shield* and bill greenish ivory, sometimes tipped dusky. *Head and neck rich chestnut* merging into black on back and wings, as well as on breast, and then back to chestnut on rump and belly. *Tail mostly yellow,* with central pair and outer web of outer pair of feathers blackish. Immatures similar but duller. Sexes alike, except ♂ has an inconspicuous wispy hairlike crest. **Similar species:** *The only oropendola found in the w. lowlands* and as such unlikely to be confused. Cf. Yellow-rumped Cacique (smaller, with different tail pattern, no chestnut, etc.). **Habits:** Gregarious, trooping in straggling flocks that clamber, sometimes acrobatically, in forest trees, occasionally also out into trees in adjacent clearings (usually nesting in such situations). Virtually omnivorous, consuming much fruit but also searching for large insects and even small frogs and lizards; even comes to flowering trees. **Voice:** Commonest call a deep "chok" or "kok," but both sexes also have a variety of other short loud calls including a startling "chak chak." Displaying ♂♂ have a loud gurgling song preceded by several harsh slashing notes; unlike other oropendolas they do not bow forward, merely rising up on perch and ruffling feathers.

Casqued Oropendola, *Clypicterus oseryi*
Oropéndola de Casco   Plate 94(10)

♂ 36–38 cm (14–15"); ♀ 28–29.5 cm (11–11¹/₂"). A striking but *scarce* oropendola of canopy and borders of humid forest (mainly terra firme) in *lowlands of east.* Sometimes placed in genus *Psarocolius*. Iris blue; *conspicuous frontal shield (visibly*

Below 300 m

To 1000 m

swollen in ♂ *)* and bill creamy yellow, usually tipped dusky. **Sexes alike.** *Mainly rufous-chestnut* with contrasting *olive-yellow throat and breast*; central tail feathers dusky-olive, outer feathers bright yellow. In flight shows rather broad wings. **Similar species:** Green and Olive Oropendolas lack casque and have bill and (in Olive) facial area brightly colored; both species are larger than Casqued, though ♀♀ Greens do approximate ♂♂ Casqueds in size. **Habits:** Usually in small groups, sometimes associating with other oropendolas and caciques though apparently always nesting independently; colonies are often placed in trees overhanging fairly small forested rivers. Usual flight rather undulating, quite different from the steady rowing of *Psarocolius* oropendolas. **Voice:** Has a variety of very loud, squawking calls including a "zhrak!" and a repeated "zhreeo! zhreeo! zhreeo;" ♂♂ in display give a long "squa-a-a-a-oóok!" and a ringing "ko-kooó-glee!"

Psarocolius Oropendolas

Spectacular *large* icterids (males considerably larger than females) with *distinctive mainly yellow tails* found in the canopy and borders of humid and montane forest, *all but one species only in the eastern lowlands.* Bills are long and sharply pointed, *often brightly colored.* They nest in *colonies*, with their unmistakable long pouch nests suspended from branches of a tall tree, usually isolated in a clearing or at forest edge. All have a *varied repertoire of loud, often harsh notes*, for males culminating in spectacular lunging displays.

Crested Oropendola, *Psarocolius decumanus*
Oropéndola Crestada   Plate 94(12)
♂ 46–47.7 cm (18–18½"); ♀ 36–37 cm (14–14½"). Widespread in canopy and

borders of humid forest, secondary woodland, and clearings in *lowlands of east.* Iris blue; *bill ivory to pale greenish yellow.* *Mostly black* with rump and crissum dark chestnut; tail yellow except central pair of feathers blackish. **Sexes alike,** except ♂ has inconspicuous hairlike crest. **Similar species:** *No other oropendola in its range is basically black.* Cf. various caciques (all smaller, etc.). **Habits:** Usually conspicuous, foraging in flocks of varying size and sometimes accompanying other icterids; also sometimes roosts with them (especially Russet-backeds) on river islands, but nesting colonies almost invariably are apart. In flight looks elongated and stretched out, with steady rowing wing-beats. **Voice:** Displaying ♂♂ have spectacular display, usually given near nesting colony, in which they lean far forward, audibly fluttering wings and tail, while uttering a loud gurgling and slashing song that accelerates into a crescendo. Both sexes also give other, shorter loud calls as they forage.

Russet-backed Oropendola
Psarocolius angustifrons
Oropéndola Dorsirrojiza   Plate 94(13)
♂ 44–48 cm (17¼–19"); ♀ 34.5–38 cm (13½–15"). *Variable. The only oropendola found on Andean slopes,* there inhabiting canopy and borders of foothill and subtropical forest and woodland; *also common in lowlands of east,* favoring riparian areas and várzea forest. *Bill entirely black in birds of e. lowlands and on e. slope of Andes,* but yellowish ivory on Andean slopes from s. Morona-Santiago southward; on w. slope bill orange-yellow. Iris usually brown, but pale blue in some (older?) birds. **Sexes alike. Eastern birds** *essentially dull olivaceous washed or stained with rufous,* most yellow-

To 2000 m; on W slope
not below 1000 m

Mostly below 600 m

ish on face and most rufous on rump; tail yellow with central pair of feathers dusky and outer pair at least partially dusky-olive. On **southeast Andean slopes** similar (aside from their very different bill) but face yellower. **West-slope birds** differ more, being *decidedly darker and more rufescent* with a *contrasting yellow forehead*. **Similar species:** No other oropendola is found in Andes, which simplifies things there. In e. lowlands, where other oropendolas do occur, Russet-backed is unique in its entirely black bill; it also is *notably dull-plumaged overall*. **Habits:** *The most numerous and conspicuous oropendola in e. lowlands*, often gathering in large flocks and sometimes roosting in truly huge aggregations on certain river islands. Behavior there much like Crested Oropendola, but less likely to forage in extensive terra firme (though regularly overflying it). In Andes usually scarcer, there foraging mainly with flocks of caciques, jays, and larger tanagers. **Voice:** Song of displaying ♂♂ similar throughout species' Ecuadorian range, in the east a loud and accelerating, slashing "g-g-guh-guh-gágok!," in the west a loud "g-kyoooyk!," given as bird leans forward on its perch with flapping wings and raised tail. Flying and foraging birds give a loud "chak" call.

Green Oropendola, *Psarocolius viridis*
Oropéndola Verde   Plate 94(14)

♂ 46–49 cm (18¼–19½"); ♀ 37–38 cm (14½–15"). Somewhat local, mainly in canopy and borders of terra firme forest, in *lowlands of east*. Iris blue; *frontal shield and bill pale greenish yellow to ivory, tipped orange-red*; small area of pinkish to dull orange skin around eye and at base of bill. *Mostly yellowish olive*, with rump, lower belly, and crissum chestnut; tail yellow except central pair of feathers dusky-olive. **Sexes alike** except ♂ has inconspicuous hairlike crest. **Similar species:** Duller Russet-backed Oropendola (less of a true forest bird than Green) has black bill in e. lowlands. Olive Oropendola is *brighter* generally with chestnut rearparts *including wings*; bill is black, and it shows bare pink cheeks. **Habits:** Similar to Crested Oropendola, though Green is much scarcer and more of a forest bird; sometimes, however, the two range together. Colony size usually small. **Voice:** ♂'s display at nesting colony much like Crested's, bird leaning so far forward as to seem almost to loose its balance, wings fluttering furiously; "song" more melodic and less harsh, with a rolling quality. Both sexes also give harsh contact notes, both when foraging and in flight.

Olive Oropendola, *Psarocolius yuracares*
Oropéndola Oliva   Plate 94(15)

47.5–52 cm (18¾–20½"); ♀ 41–43 cm (16–17"). A spectacular *large (especially ♂♂)* oropendola found in *lowlands of east*, mainly in canopy and borders of *terra firme forest*.

Mostly below 300 m

Sometimes considered conspecific with *P. bifasciatus* (Pará Oropendola) of e. Amaz. Brazil; both were often placed in genus *Gymnostinops*. Iris brown; *bill black with orange-red tip; conspicuous bare cheek patch bright pink. Foreparts bright yellow-olive; rearparts (including all of wings) bright chestnut;* tail yellow with central pair of feathers olive. **Sexes alike** except for ♂'s inconspicuous wispy hairlike crest. **Similar species:** Green Oropendola has mainly pale bill (but bill is tipped orange-red in both species), lacks conspicuous pink cheeks, and has olive wings. **Habits:** Similar to Crested Oropendola, though Olive is much scarcer and tends to be found in forest, though it may overfly just about anywhere (its heavy ponderous wingbeats audible from afar) and it sometimes roosts with other oropendolas on river islands. Colony size is small. **Voice:** ♂'s vocalization in display similar to that of other *Psarocolius*, being a "tek-tk-tk-k-k-k-goo-guhloóp!" Foraging birds give various harsh, sharp calls.

Shiny Cowbird, *Molothrus bonariensis*
Vaquero Brilloso   Plate 95(12)

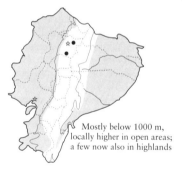

Mostly below 1000 m, locally higher in open areas; a few now also in highlands

20–21 cm (8–8¼″). *Widespread and locally common in semiopen and agricultural regions in lowlands and foothills of west,* but less numerous in east (where mainly along rivers). ♂ *glossy purplish black* with wings and tail glossed greenish blue. ♀ *more or less dingy grayish to brownish gray,* somewhat paler below; whitish postocular streak is usually evident, especially in west. In Loja notably paler below, essentially grayish white with blurry dusky streaking. **Immatures** like respective ♀♀ but more yellowish below, often showing obscure dusky streaking. **Similar species:** ♂ is more glossy purple than

other superficially similar birds such as ♂ White-lined Tanager; Scrub Blackbird lacks ♂ cowbird's purplish gloss (being just dull black) and it is shaped differently (not so "hunched"). In ne. lowlands, cf. scarce Velvet-fronted Grackle. ♀ is so drab as to be quite confusing when seen alone, though normally it is not; much more typical is to see a flock of cowbirds in which both ♂♂ and ♀♀ are present, simplifying things. **Habits:** Usually in small flocks that most often forage on open ground, often with tails characteristically held partially cocked. True to its name, sometimes associates with cattle, feeding on insects they disturb. Often flies in tight groups. The species is a brood parasite on a wide variety of smaller passerine birds. **Voice:** ♂'s song a complex musical twittering, usually given from a prominent perch (often several ♂♂ together) and accompanied by ruffling of neck feathers.

Giant Cowbird, *Molothrus oryzivorus*
Vaquero Gigante   Plate 95(15)

To 2000 m

♂ 35.5–38 cm (14–15″); ♀ 30.5–33 cm (12–13″). *Widespread in semiopen areas and forest borders in lowlands of east and west,* smaller numbers up into subtropics (especially in northwest). Formerly placed in genus *Scaphidura*. Iris orange or orange-red in ♂, yellower in ♀, brown in younger birds. ♂ *glossy purplish black* with *conspicuous ruff on neck* that *usually imparts curiously small-headed look.* ♀ notably smaller and sootier, with ruff smaller or even sometimes not apparent (*though it still looks small-headed*). **Similar species:** Characteristic small-headed silhouette is so distinctive it usually precludes confusion; even the smaller ♀ is much larger than, for instance, differently shaped Scrub Blackbird. **Habits:** Unlike Shiny Cowbirds, Giants typically forage solitarily or at most in small scattered groups, sometimes on open ground but also occasionally in trees when they may accompany oropendolas. Individuals are also often seen parading around on sandbars and riverbanks. Frequently noted in flight high overhead when its undulating flight style, alternating between several fast flaps and a brief closing of wings (causing a dip), is distinctive. This cowbird's distribution is quite closely tied to the presence of oropendolas and caciques, on which it is an obligate brood parasite, and around whose colonies ♀♀ cowbirds are often seen when these are active. **Voice:** Notably silent.

Scrub Blackbird, *Dives warszewiczi*
Negro Matorralero   Plate 95(11)

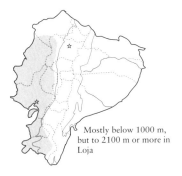

Mostly below 1000 m, but to 2100 m or more in Loja

♂ 24 cm (9½″); ♀ 23 cm (9″). A *noisy and conspicuous* blackbird found in *semiopen settled and agricultural terrain in lowlands of west* (though avoiding more arid areas). Rather heavy pointed bill. *Entirely glossy black.* ♀ slightly duller than ♂. **Similar species:** Cf. ♂ of markedly smaller and purplish-glossed Shiny Cowbird and of much larger Great-tailed Grackle (latter strictly coastal, with long creased tail, etc.). **Habits:** Usually in pairs or small monospecific groups that forage principally on the ground though often perching in shrubs and trees. Generally bold and conspicuous, hard to miss in range. **Voice:** Frequently heard song, usually delivered from a prominent perch though sometimes also from within concealment of a leafy tree, an arresting and ringing series of far-carrying but quite melodious notes, typically a variation of "wr-tzzzeeét! worgleeo, worgleeo-glezeé." Two birds may sing together, often "pumping" their foreparts up and down as they sing. Also often gives a siskin-like "clee" or "seeeuw."

Great-tailed Grackle, *Quiscalus mexicanus*
Clarinero Coligrande   Plate 95(14)

♂ 43–46 cm (17–18″); ♀ 32–34 cm (12½–13½″). *Local in and near mangroves along coast.* Formerly placed in genus *Cassidix.* ♂'s iris yellow, ♀'s yellowish to pale brown, darker in young birds; rather long and heavy bill black. Large ♂ *glossy blue-black*, wings and tail more glossed greenish blue; *tail very long and noticeably creased*, often looking keel-shaped. Much smaller ♀ dusky brown above with *buff superciliary and throat*; *underparts pale buffy brownish*, becoming duskier on belly; tail decidedly shorter with little or no crease, blackish. **Similar species:** Nearly unmistakable in its restricted range and habitat. Scrub Blackbird is much smaller, etc. **Habits:** Feeds mostly in the open on ground, often on muddy shorelines, striding along boldly and scavenging virtually anything edible. Often roosts in mangroves, sometimes in large aggregations. Elsewhere this species has spread away from its original coastal habitat, to which it is still restricted in Ecuador; whether this will continue to be the case remains to be seen. **Voice:** Noisy, both sexes (especially ♂♂) with a wide variety of loud and strident vocalizations. Both sexes frequently give a fast "trit-trit-trit" and a harsh guttural "chak" or "chuk," often in flight. ♂♂ are frequently seen displaying and singing with neck stretched and bill pointing upward; they then give a repertoire of sharp strident calls including a prolonged rising whistled "wh-eeék?" and others.

Velvet-fronted Grackle, *Lampropsar tanagrinus*
Clarinero Frentiafelpado   Plate 95(13)

Below 300 m

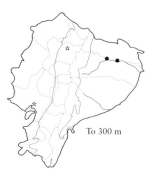

To 300 m

♂ 21.5–22 cm (8½–8¾"); ♀ 19–19.5 cm (7½–7¾"). *Uncommon and local in lower and middle growth of várzea forest and along edges of oxbow lakes and sluggish rivers and streams in lowlands of northeast.* Rather short pointed bill. Sexes alike. *Entirely black,* with virtually no gloss. Forecrown feathers dense and plushlike, but this hard to see in the field. Similar species: ♂ Shiny Cowbird is considerably glossier purple on head, neck, and underparts; its bill is also heavier. The two species can occur together, so be careful; both being gregarious, the presence of ♀-plumaged cowbirds will usually help. Habits: Usually occurs in monospecific groups of up to 10–20 birds (more often 6 or fewer), foraging at all levels, sometimes down to ground or water. Around lakes and along streams sometimes hops on floating vegetation. Voice: Quite vocal, with various chuckling calls being given by feeding birds, e.g., a fast, "ch-ch-ch-ch-ch." What seems to be song is a richer gurgling, also fast, e.g., "chuh-duh-duhree, chá-chá" or "gluk-gluk-glí-gluk."

Pale-eyed Blackbird
Agelaius xanthophthalmus
Negro Ojipálido   Plate 95(10)

20.5 cm (8"). *Rare and very local in marshy and shrubby vegetation fringing certain lakes in lowlands of northeast* (Napo); mainly known from *Limoncocha. Iris straw-colored to whitish.* Sexes alike. *Entirely black.* Immature more brownish above and broadly streaked with buffyish or yellowish below. Similar species: Conspicuous pale iris is distinctive in its limited range and habitat.

Other similarly sized all-black icterids potentially occurring with it (e.g., Velvet-fronted Grackle, ♂ Shiny Cowbird) have *dark* irides; ♀ Giant Cowbird has an orange eye but is much larger than Pale-eyed Blackbird. Habits: Most conspicuous in early morning when birds more often perch atop a shrub or forage in the open at water's edge; at other times usually remains within cover, hopping about near water level in thick marshy vegetation. Usually occurs in pairs. Voice: ♂'s song a loud ringing "tew-tew-tew-tew." Call a harsh "chrk!" (P. Coopmans).

Icterus Orioles and Troupials
Midsized, often very attractive icterids with long tails. They are *basically orange or yellow and black;* sexual dimorphism occurs in only one species, the Baltimore. Orioles and troupials are arboreal birds found mainly in forest and woodland borders in the lowlands; none is truly montane. Songs are well developed, so much so that in many other countries they are popular cagebirds (fortunately this is not the case in Ecuador).

Moriche Oriole, *Icterus chrysocephalus*
Bolsero de Morete   Plate 95(9)

20.5–21 cm (8–8¼"). A striking *black and yellow* oriole found in canopy and borders of humid forest and adjacent clearings in *lowlands of east.* Bill rather long and slightly decurved, bluish at base. Sexes alike. *Mostly black* with *crown* (aside from black forecrown), *shoulders, rump, and thighs bright yellow.* Rather *long-tailed.* Similar species: Other orioles in Ecuador are not so predominantly black. As a result the Moriche more apt to be confused with other mainly black

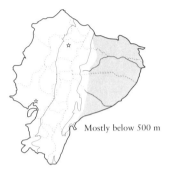

Mostly below 500 m

To 750 m

icterids (e.g., Yellow-rumped Cacique), though their shape and positioning of yellow rather different. Overhead it can even resemble a ♂ Flame-crested Tanager. **Habits:** Usually found in pairs or family groups, foraging at all levels though usually quite high (but occasionally even drops to the ground at forest edge). Sometimes follows mixed flocks but at least as often forages independently, searching for insects in foliage (regularly inspecting palm fronds, sometimes hanging upside-down) and sometimes at flowering trees. The long tail is often jerked around spasmodically, and for short periods may sometimes even held sideways. **Voice:** Gives an easily recognized, leisurely series of musical notes and phrases interspersed with distinct pauses, e.g., "sweet . . . peeyr . . . pyur . . . peeyr . . . pyur . . . kreer . . . wrrrt . . ." or "purit . . . skeeyr . . . tyi-pur-twee-twee-twee-skeey. . . ." Call a "twik? tweeu! twik? tweeeu!" (P. Coopmans).

Orange-backed Troupial, *Icterus croconotus*
Turpial Dorsinaranja   Plate 95(7)

23–23.5 cm (9–9¼"). *A beautiful, large, orange and black oriole found in riparian growth around lake and river margins, woodland borders, and shrubby, well-vegetated cleared areas in lowlands of east.* Has been called simply Troupial (*I. icterus*) or Orange-backed Oriole. Slightly decurved bill blackish with pale bluish base to lower mandible; small bare blue area behind eye, which *yellow.* **Sexes alike.** *Mostly bright orange* with black face and bib (lower margin with "shaggy" effect); wings and tail mostly black, wings with orange shoulders and *white patch on secondaries.* **Similar species:** This stunning oriole is not likely to be con-

fused in the Oriente, where no other oriole with bright orange regularly occurs. Indeed there really is no other similarly bright orange bird of any kind there (can even look scarlet in strong afternoon light); Oriole Blackbird is *rich yellow*, not orange. **Habits:** Usually found in pairs, generally moving independently of mixed flocks; forages in dense shrubby growth and often—despite its brilliant colors—not very conspicuous. Frequently spotted in flight while crossing a stream or road. Pairs sometimes appropriate the nest of a Yellow-rumped Cacique for their own use. **Voice:** Song a series of loud, rich musical phrases, each phrase typically simple and most often two-parted, e.g., "tree-tur" or "cheer-to," and repeated slowly (sometimes with long hesitations) up to 8–10 times before switching to another phrase.

Baltimore Oriole, *Icterus galbula*
Bolsero de Baltimore   Plate 95(8)

19 cm (7½"). A *casual boreal winter visitant* (Nov.–early Apr.) to borders of humid forest and woodland and clearings in lowlands and foothills, mainly west of Andes. Formerly sometimes called Northern Oriole. Slender

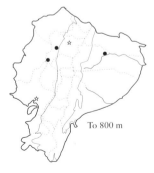

To 800 m

pointed bill, bluish at base. ♂ *mostly bright orange and black*: *entire hood*, back, and most of wings and tail *black*; wings with orange lesser-coverts and a single white bar as well as edging, outer tail feathers primarily orange. *Lower back, rump, and underparts orange.* ♀ variable, but typically somewhat mottled brownish olive to brownish gray above, grayer on back and browner (sometimes almost golden) on head and rump; wings and tail duskier, *wings with two white bars and edging*, outer tail feathers with orange edging. *Mostly yellowish orange below, brightest on breast.* **Similar species:** "Hooded" pattern of ♂ differs from that of other Ecuadorian orioles except for the considerably larger Orange-backed Troupial. ♀ needs to be compared to various tanagers, all of which have stouter bills. **Habits:** Arboreal, often attracted to flowering trees. Only single birds have been seen in Ecuador, but in its usual wintering range often occurs in groups. **Voice:** Both sexes have a chattering call, and less often give a slurred whistled note.

White-edged Oriole, *Icterus graceannae*
Bolsero Filiblanco   Plate 95(6)

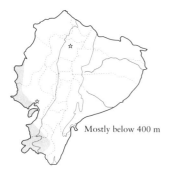

Mostly below 400 m

20.5 cm (8″). Desert scrub and deciduous woodland and forest in *more arid lowlands of southwest*, ranging up into subtropics in Loja. Base of mandible bluish gray. **Sexes alike.** *Mostly bright orange-yellow* with black facial area, bib, and back. Wings and tail mainly black, wings with yellow lesser-coverts and *conspicuous white patch on secondaries*, *outer tail feathers inconspicuously edged and tipped white*. **Similar species:** Often confused with Yellow-tailed Oriole. In Ecuador, Yellow-tailed shows white edging on flight feathers (though not the obvious solid large

patch of White-edged, which actually is named for the edging on its rectrices); the two are most easily distinguished by Yellow-tailed's extensive yellow in tail (even from above, when its tail looks mainly black, some yellow is usually evident along tail's outer edge). Yellow-tailed is more golden yellow (not so orangey) and favors more humid situations, though the two can occur together. **Habits:** Usually in pairs or small (family) groups, foraging at varying levels. **Voice:** Song consists of a series of rich musical phrases, each repeated several times before going on to the next, e.g., "chiro-chowee . . . weeeenh-weh . . . chiro-chowee . . . piro, chiro-chowee . . . weeeenh-weh . . . piro, chiro-chowee . . ." (resembling Yellow-tailed, but less musical and with characteristic nasal "weeenh-eh" notes interspersed). Call a distinctive throaty "jori-jori," characteristically doubled.

Yellow-tailed Oriole, *Icterus mesomelas*
Bolsero Coliamarillo   Plate 95(5)

Mostly below 900 m, higher in Loja

21.5 cm (8½″). Woodland and forest borders, clearings, gardens, and plantations in *more humid lowlands of west*. Base of mandible bluish gray. **Sexes alike.** *Mostly bright golden yellow* with black facial area, bib, and back. Wings and tail mainly black, wings with large yellow patch on lesser-coverts and narrow white edging on flight feathers, *tail with outer feathers mainly or entirely yellow* (with no white). **Similar species:** Cf. White-edged Oriole (more orange, with mainly black tail showing no yellow and wings with solid white patch). **Habits:** Generally more familiar than White-edged Oriole, more often in settled and agricultural regions; one of the few birds that seems to have adapted to the biologically nearly sterile banana plantations, at least their edges. Sometimes perches and even sings from roadside phone wires. **Voice:** Song a series of repeated rich musical phrases, rather similar to White-edged Oriole's but more melodious, and often with "swelling" or crescendo effect. Distinctive call a mellow "chup-cheet" or "chup-chup-cheet," sometimes a repeated "kip-chur."

Oriole Blackbird, *Gymnomystax mexicanus*
Negro Bolsero   Plate 95(4)

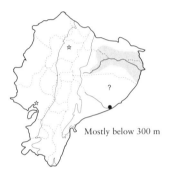

Mostly below 300 m

♂ 30.5 cm (12″); ♀ 26.5 cm (10½″). A *spectacular, large* icterid of *sandbars and islands in larger rivers of lowlands in east*. Sexes alike. *Mostly bright golden yellow* with *contrasting black back, wings, and tail*; bare ocular area and short malar streak also black. **Juvenile** similar but slightly paler yellow, and with black crown patch. **Similar species:** Nearly unmistakable; only possible confusion would be with Orange-backed Troupial though that is mainly *orange* and black. **Habits:** A conspicuous bird, usually out in the open. Generally in pairs or small loose flocks (occasionally up to 20–30 birds) that forage mostly on the ground but perch readily in shrubs and low trees, also on stumps and piles of debris. Normally does not associate with other birds. **Voice:** Infrequently heard and unmusical song a phrase of peculiar wheezy notes, phraseology variable but always with the same strange quality, e.g., "zzhhrreéo, zhreo-zhréw." Call a very different quick sharp "kring!" or "kyeeng!" with ringing quality.

Red-breasted Blackbird, *Sturnella militaris*
Pastorero Pechirrojo   Plate 95(1)

19 cm (7½″). *Local in lush moist pastures and fields in lowlands of east*; spreading and

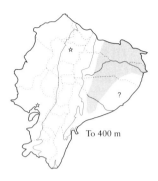

To 400 m

increasing. Formerly in genus *Leistes*. Fairly long pointed bill. ♂ *more or less uniform black above. Throat and breast bright red* with belly contrastingly black. In fresh plumage feathers edged pale brownish, obscuring the black and red. ♀ broadly streaked blackish and buff above with *long pale buff superciliary and coronal stripe*. Mostly buff below with some dusky streaking on sides and belly, *variably tinged pink on belly* (but some almost always present). **Similar species:** The larger Peruvian Meadowlark does not occur in e. lowlands. Cf. also ♀ and nonbreeding ♂ Bobolink. **Habits:** Feeds mostly on ground, but perches freely on fence posts, wires, and clumps of grass, generally not too high. Loosely colonial, even when nesting; in nonbreeding season often in small flocks. **Voice:** ♂'s song consists of several introductory notes followed by long, buzzy trilled note, and is usually given in midst of a flight display in which it mounts 5–10 m above ground. Call a simple "chirt."

Peruvian Meadowlark, *Sturnella bellicosa*
Pastorero Peruano   Plate 95(2)

20.5 cm (8″). *Common and conspicuous* in pastures, agricultural terrain, desert scrub, and shrubby areas intermixed with grass in *more arid lowlands of west*, also spreading up into more arid highlands. Formerly called Peruvian Red-breasted Meadowlark. Rather long and very pointed bill, bluish gray below. Unmistakable and handsome breeding ♂ coarsely streaked buffy brown and blackish above with *bold long superciliary whitish* (red in front of eye) and buff coronal stripe; bend of wing red and underwing-coverts white; tail blackish. Face and sides of neck black; *throat and breast bright red*, becom-

Locally to 2500 m or even higher

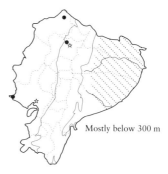

Mostly below 300 m

ing *black on belly*. In fresh plumage brown predominates above, and the black and red are obscured by pale feather edging; worn birds can look quite black above. ♀ similar to ♂ above except tail gray with blackish barring and *superciliary entirely whitish*. Below dingy grayish white with variable amount of blackish streaking and a *usually obvious red tinge on throat and breast*. **Similar species:** Not likely confused, even freshly plumaged birds showing at least some red below. Red-breasted Blackbird occurs only in east. **Habits:** Mainly terrestrial when feeding, but perches freely atop shrubs and low trees and on fences. Quite gregarious, when not breeding often forming flocks of up to 50 or more birds and even when nesting often seems semicolonial, concentrating in particularly favorable situations. **Voice:** ♂'s song a prolonged wheezy descending note preceded by several short ones, e.g., "tee-tee-zho-zhweeeeee," often given during a short display flight in which it catapults steeply into air and then glides back to earth; also sings from perches. Both sexes often give a sharp raspy "chak" call.

Bobolink, *Dolichonyx oryzivorus*
Tordo Arrocero   Plate 95(3)

17–18 cm (6¾–7"). A *scarce transient* (Oct.–Nov.; Apr.–May) to areas with *extensive tall grass*, mostly in lowlands of east. Fairly short conical bill; *tail "spiky" with feathers sharply pointed*. ♀ and **nonbreeding** ♂ buffy brown above streaked with blackish, *crown boldly striped dusky and buff. Below yellowish buff* with sparse dusky streaking down sides and flanks. **Breeding** ♂ (seen in Ecuador on northward passage) very different and unmistakable with *head and*

underparts black, golden buff nuchal area, white scapulars and large rump patch. In some birds this pattern is still obscured by buff feather-tipping. **Similar species:** ♀ Red-breasted Blackbird has similar overall pattern (and can occur in same habitats as migrating Bobolinks), but its "normal" tail shape is very different and its underparts are always at least tinged with red. **Habits:** In Ecuador occurs mainly with flocks of seedeaters, favoring areas with extensive tall grass. Usually inconspicuous in such situations, only occasionally perching high enough on a grass stem to be seen. **Voice:** Distinctive call, a metallic "ink," often given by birds both in flight and when perched. Does not seem to sing in Ecuador.

Cardueline Finches: Fringillidae (6)
Small, gregarious finches with *conical bills* and notched tails, males with *attractive bold black, yellow, and olive patterns*, females duller. Siskins are characterized by their *conspicuous yellow wing-bands*. They range in semiopen country and forest borders, mainly in the highlands, and have attractive twittering songs. Most of the family occurs in the Old World, only a few *Carduelis* ranging into South America; formerly they were placed in genus *Spinus*.

Hooded Siskin, *Carduelis magellanica*
Jilguero Encapuchado   Plate 91(17)

10–10.5 cm (4–4¼"). *Easily the most numerous siskin, ranging widely in semiopen settled and agricultural areas in highlands.* ♂ has *black hood* contrasting with *olive back* and bright olive-yellow underparts, back vaguely dusky-streaked. Wings and tail black, *wings with yellow band on greater-coverts and another across base of flight feathers*, tail

Mostly 1000–3500 m, lower in Loja

with yellow at base. **Southern** ♂♂ tend to be brighter generally with contrastingly yellow rump. ♀ much duller, with no black on head: grayish olive above with vague dusky streaking, somewhat yellower on rump; *dingy pale grayish below, somewhat whiter on belly*; wings and tail as in ♂. **Similar species:** Learn the Hooded well as a basis of comparison with other more range-restricted siskins; cf. especially Saffron and Olivaceous Siskins. **Habits:** Generally in small groups, foraging at varying levels, both well up in trees and on the ground; feeds almost exclusively on seeds. Often quite tame. Flight distinctively undulating. **Voice:** ♂'s pretty song a sometimes long-continued twittering, sometimes given simultaneously by several birds.

Saffron Siskin, *Carduelis siemiradzkii*
Jilguero Azafranado   Plate 91(19)

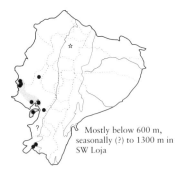

Mostly below 600 m, seasonally (?) to 1300 m in SW Loja

10–10.5 cm (4–4¼″). *Local at borders of deciduous forest and in scrub in lowlands of southwest.* ♂ resembles ♂ Hooded Siskin, differing in being brighter generally: *back more golden olive* (with no dusky streaking) and *underparts considerably brighter yellow.* ♀ likewise *yellower generally, especially*

below (♀ Hooded being much duller *grayish* below). **Similar species:** Cf. Hooded Siskin. Saffron and Hooded may overlap in Loja though in general they segregate by elevation, Saffron occurring mostly below 600 m, Hooded mostly above 1000 m; however, both can be erratic and seasonal. ♀♀ of the two are often easier to separate, Saffrons being so much yellower below than Hoodeds. **Habits and Voice:** Similar to Hooded Siskin.

Olivaceous Siskin, *Carduelis olivacea*
Jilguero Oliváceo   Plate 91(18)

Mostly 900–1700 m

10–10.5 cm (4–4¼″). Canopy and borders of *foothill and subtropical forest and adjacent clearings on e. slope.* ♂ very similar to ♂ Hooded Siskin but *slightly* darker olive on back and more olive-tinged below. ♀ more readily separated, being *essentially olive below* (not grayish), yellower on midbelly and crissum. **Similar species:** ♂ Olivaceous and Hooded Siskins are essentially indistinguishable, so best to go by their accompanying ♀♀; at least for the most part Olivaceous occurs at *lower* elevations. **Habits** and **Voice:** Similar to Hooded Siskin, though Olivaceous seems to be much more of a forest-based bird, rarely occuring any distance away from it. Unlike the Hooded, Olivaceous does not often come to the ground.

Andean Siskin, *Carduelis spinescens*
Jilguero Andino   Plate 91(16)

11 cm (4¼″). *Local and perhaps erratic in paramo and temperate forest and woodland borders on both slopes in n. Ecuador,* mainly in *Carchi.* Sexes nearly alike. *Black crown* contrasting with olive face; above otherwise

2800–3600 m

dark olive, yellower on rump, and with some dusky streaking on back. Wings and tail blackish, wings marked as in Hooded Siskin but *tail lacking any yellow*. Below uniform yellowish olive. ♀ slightly duller than ♂. **Juvenile** lacks black crown. **Similar species:** ♂ Hooded Siskin has black hood (*including throat, which contrasts with olive-yellow* underparts); ♀ Hooded, apart from lacking any black at all on head, is grayish (not olive) below. **Habits and Voice:** Similar to Hooded Siskin. This species and Hooded have been seen in mixed flocks at certain localities.

Yellow-bellied Siskin, *Carduelis xanthogastra*
Jilguero Ventriamarillo   Plate 91(15)

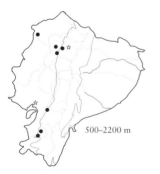

500–2200 m

11.5 cm (4½″). Scarce and local in canopy and borders of *foothill and subtropical forest* and adjacent clearings on *w. slope*, also on coastal cordillera in Esmeraldas. Distinctive ♂ *black* with *contrasting bright yellow breast and belly*; *bold bright yellow band crosses flight feathers*, and considerable yellow at base of tail. ♀ mostly dark olive above, duskier on head; wings and tail marked as in ♂. *Throat and chest dusky-*

olive, contrasting with yellow breast and upper belly; *midbelly whitish*. **Similar species:** Mainly black ♂ unlikely to be confused. ♀'s contrast on underparts (echoing ♂'s) distinctive; all other ♀♀ siskins are more uniform below. **Habits:** Generally scarce and erratic, and more associated with actual forest (even if patchy) than other siskins. Usually in pairs or at most small groups, often ranging well above the ground. **Voice:** Song a fast jumble of thin twittering notes, often long-continued. Call a high-pitched "pee."

Lesser Goldfinch, *Carduelis psaltria*
Jilguero Menor   Plate 91(14)

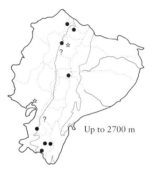

Up to 2700 m

10 cm (4″). *Very local* in borders of subtropical and temperate woodland and adjacent clearings on *w. slope*; on e. slope only in arid grassy valleys *near Baños*. Bill pale dusky-*horn* (in siskins bill notably darker). ♂ *glossy black above* and *entirely bright yellow below*. Wings with *white patch at base of primaries and edging on tertials*; tail with considerable white at base (visible mainly in flight). ♀ uniform olive above, wings brownish dusky but *marked as in* ♂, tail plain dusky. Olive yellow below, becoming clear yellow on midbelly. **Similar species:** All siskins (both sexes) have yellow (not white) wing markings. Only the ♂ Yellow-bellied is equally black above, but it shows *bicolored*, black and yellow underparts. **Habits:** In Ecuador usually seen singly or in pairs; once observed with Hooded Siskins but more typically occurs alone. Feeds on seeds at varying levels including ground. **Voice:** Song a musical but somewhat disjointed twittering, frequently long-continued. Often-heard call (regularly given in flight) a clear "kleeu."

Old World Sparrows: Passeridae (1)

The House Sparrow, originally native to Eurasia, was introduced into North America and southern South America in the 19th century. Only recently having arrived in Ecuador, unfortunately it still seems to be increasing here.

House Sparrow, *Passer domesticus*
Gorrión Europeo   Plate 93(22)

15 cm (6″). *Strictly a commensal of people*, since the 1970s *spreading in towns and cities across much of west and south*, favoring more arid regions. ♂ can be quite dapper, but often so soiled or dusty that pattern obscured: *crown gray, nape chestnut, cheeks and sides of neck white*, and *bib on throat and chest black*. Otherwise brownish above streaked black, but rump plain gray; wings with single white bar; whitish below. ♀ much more nondescript: pale grayish brown above with dusky back streaking and *whitish superciliary*, wings with whitish bar; dingy whitish below. **Similar species:** ♂ easy to recognize, and even drab ♀ can generally be known by company she keeps. Cf. Rufous-collared Sparrow. **Habits:** Usually in groups, often perching on buildings but feeding mainly on ground; generally conspicuous, with noisy and often aggressive behavior. Elsewhere Rufous-collared Sparrow has tended to disappear where House Sparrow has become established, though whether this will happen in Ecuador remains to be seen. **Voice:** Flocks keep up a near-constant chattering.

Bibliography

Blake, E. R. 1977. *Manual of Neotropical Birds*. Vol. 1. Chicago: University of Chicago Press.

Brown, L., and D. Amadon. 1968. *Hawks, Eagles, and Falcons of the World*. Feltham, Middlesex, U.K.: Country Life Books.

Chantler, P., and G. Driessens. 1995. *Swifts: A Guide to the Swifts and Treeswifts of the World*. Sussex, U.K.: Pica Press.

Chapman, F. M. 1926. The distribution of bird life in Ecuador. *Bull. AMNH* 55: 1–784.

Cleere, N., and D. Nurney. 1998. *Nightjars: A Guide to the Nightjars, Nighthawks, and Their Relatives*. New London, Conn.: Yale University Press.

Curson, J., D. Quinn, and D. Beadle. 1994. *Warblers of the Americas: An Identification Guide*. Boston: Houghton Mifflin.

del Hoyo, J. 1994. Family Cracidae (chachalacas, guans, and currasows). Pp. 310–363 *in* J. del Hoyo, A. Elliott, and J. Sargatal, eds. *Handbook of the Birds of the World*. Vol. 2. Barcelona, Spain: Lynx Edicions.

Enticott, J., and D. Tipling. 1997. *A Photographic Handbook of the Seabirds of the World*. London: New Holland Limited.

Fjeldså, J., and N. Krabbe. 1990. *Birds of the High Andes*. Copenhagen: Zoological Museum of the University of Copenhagen.

Gill, F. 1994. *Ornithology*. Rev. ed. New York: W. H. Freeman.

Haffer, J. 1974. *Avian speciation in tropical South America*. Publ. Nuttall Ornithol. Club no. 14.

Hayman, P., J. Marchant, and T. Prater. 1986. *Shorebirds: An Identification Guide to the Waders of the World*. London: Croom Helm.

Hilty, S. L., and W. L. Brown. 1986. *A Guide to the Birds of Colombia*. Princeton, N.J.: Princeton University Press.

Howell, S. N. G., and S. Webb. 1995. *A Guide to the Birds of Mexico and Northern Central America*. Oxford, U.K.: Oxford University Press.

Jaramillo, A., and P. Burke. 1999. *New World Blackbirds: The Icterids*. Princeton, N.J.: Princeton University Press.

Juniper, T., and M. Parr. 1998. *Parrots: A Guide to the Parrots of the World*. New Haven, Conn.: Yale University Press.

Krabbe, N., and T. S. Schulenberg. 1997. Species limits and natural history of *Scytalopus* tapaculos (Rhinocryptidae), with descriptions of the Ecuadorian taxa, including three new species. *Studies in Neotropical Ornithology Honoring Ted Parker*, Ornithol. Monogr. no. 48: 47–88.

Madge, S., and H. Burn. 1988. *Waterfowl: An Identification Guide to the Ducks, Geese, and Swans of the World*. Boston: Houghton Mifflin.

Meyer de Schauensee, R. 1970. *A Guide to the Birds of South America*. Wynnewood, Penn.: Livingston Publishing.

Ridgely, R. S., P. J. Greenfield, and M. Guerrero G. 1998. *Una Lista Anotada de las Aves del Ecuador Continental*. Quito: Fundación Ornitológica del Ecuador (CECIA).

Ridgely, R. S., and J. A. Gwynne. 1989. *A Guide to the Birds of Panama*. Rev. ed. Princeton, N.J.: Princeton University Press.

Ridgely, R. S., and G. Tudor. 1989. *The Birds of South America*. Vol. 1. Austin, Tex.: University of Texas Press.

Ridgely, R. S., and G. Tudor. 1994. *The Birds of South America*. Vol. 2. Austin, Tex.: University of Texas Press.

Rosair, D., and D. Cottridge. 1995. *Photographic Guide to the Shorebirds of the World*. New York: Facts on File.

Stiles, F. G., and A. Skutch. 1989. *A Guide to the Birds of Costa Rica*. Ithaca, N.Y.: Cornell University Press.

Taylor, P. B., and B. van Perlo. 1998. *Rails: A Guide to the Rails, Crakes, Gallinules, and Coots of the World*. New Haven, Conn.: Yale University Press.

Winkler, H., D. A. Christie, and D. Nurney. 1995. *Woodpeckers: A Guide to the Woodpeckers, Piculets, and Wrynecks of the World*. Sussex, U.K.: Pica Press.

Index of English Names

Index of Scientific Names